VOLUME I

Selected Material from

COLLEGE

PHYSICS

PHYS 21800 · General Physics I · IUPUI

Third Edition

Alan Giambattista
Cornell University

with additional material from

Student Solutions Manual to accompany
COLLEGE PHYSICS

Third Edition

Alan Giambattista
Cornell University

Betty McCarthy Richardson

Robert C. Richardson

D1444006

Mc Graw Hill **Learning Solutions**

Boston   Burr Ridge, IL   Dubuque, IA   New York   San Francisco   St. Louis
Bangkok   Bogotá   Caracas   Lisbon   London   Madrid
Mexico City   Milan   New Delhi   Seoul   Singapore   Sydney   Taipei   Toronto

The McGraw·Hill Companies

Selected Material from College Physics, Third Edition
Volume I
PHYS 21800 • General Physics I • IUPUI

This book is a McGraw-Hill Learning Solutions textbook and contains select material from the following sources:
College Physics, Third Edition by Alan Giambattista. Copyright © 2010 by The McGraw-Hill Companies, Inc.
Student Solutions Manual to accompany College Physics, Third Edition by Alan Giambattista, Betty McCarthy Richardson, and Robert C. Richardson. Copyright © 2010 by The McGraw-Hill Companies, Inc.
Both are reprinted with permission of the publisher. Many custom published texts are modified versions or adaptations of our best-selling textbooks. Some adaptations are printed in black and white to keep prices at a minimum, while others are in color.

1 2 3 4 5 6 7 8 9 0 DIG DIG 12 11 10

ISBN-13: 978-0-07-744108-1
ISBN-10: 0-07-744108-7

Learning Solutions Specialist: Liz Recker
Production Editor: Nina Meyer
Cover Design: Lou Civitello
Cover Photos: © Jupiterimages Corporation
Printer/Binder: Digital Impressions

About the Authors

Alan Giambattista grew up in Nutley, New Jersey. In his junior year at Brigham Young University he decided to pursue a physics major, after having explored math, music, and psychology. He did his graduate studies at Cornell University and has taught introductory college physics for over 20 years. When not found at the computer keyboard working on *College Physics*, he can often be found at the keyboard of a harpsichord or piano. He is a member of the Cayuga Chamber Orchestra and has given performances of the Bach harpsichord concerti at several regional Bach festivals. He met his wife Marion in a singing group. They live in an 1824 parsonage built for an abolitionist minister, which is now surrounded by an organic dairy farm. Besides making music and taking care of the house, gardens, and fruit trees, they love to travel together.

Betty McCarthy Richardson was born and grew up in Marblehead, Massachusetts, and tried to avoid taking any science classes after eighth grade but managed to avoid only ninth grade science. After discovering that physics tells how things work, she decided to become a physicist. She attended Wellesley College and did graduate work at Duke University. While at Duke, Betty met and married fellow graduate student Bob Richardson and had two daughters, Jennifer and Pamela. Betty began teaching physics at Cornell in 1977. Many years later, she is still teaching the same course, Physics 101/102, an algebra-based course with all teaching done one-on-one in a Learning Center. From her own early experience of math and science avoidance, Betty has empathy with students who are apprehensive about learning physics. Betty's hobbies include collecting old children's books, reading, enjoying music, travel, and dining with royalty. A highlight for Betty during the Nobel Prize festivities in 1996 was being escorted to dinner on the arm of King Carl XVI Gustav of Sweden. Currently she is spending spare time enjoying grandsons Jasper (the 1-m child in Chapter 1), Dashiell and Oliver (the twins of Chapter 12), and Quintin, the newest arrival.

Robert C. Richardson was born in Washington, D.C., attended Virginia Polytechnic Institute, spent time in the United States Army, and then returned to graduate school in physics at Duke University where his thesis work involved NMR studies of solid helium-3. In the fall of 1966 Bob began work at Cornell University in the laboratory of David M. Lee. Their research goal was to observe the nuclear magnetic phase transition in solid ^{3}He that could be predicted from Richardson's thesis work with Professor Horst Meyer at Duke. In collaboration with graduate student Douglas D. Osheroff, they worked on cooling techniques and NMR instrumentation for studying low-temperature helium liquids and solids. In the fall of 1971, they made the accidental discovery that liquid ^{3}He undergoes a pairing transition similar to that of superconductors. The three were awarded the Nobel Prize for that work in 1996. Bob is currently the F. R. Newman Professor of Physics and the Senior Science Advisor at Cornell. In his spare time he enjoys gardening and photography.

In loving memory of Dad and of my niece, Natalie

Alan

In memory of our daughter Pamela,
and for Quintin, Oliver, Dashiell, Jasper,
Jennifer, and Jim Merlis

Bob and Betty

Brief Contents

Contents

PART TWO

Thermal Physics

List of Selected Applications

Note: Within the Problems, (#) = Chapter Number; CQ = Conceptual Question; MC = Multiple-Choice Question; P = Problem; R&S = Review & Synthesis.

Biology/Life Science

Number of cells in the body, Ex. 1.9, p. 14
Tensile forces in the body, Sec. 2.8, p. 56
Can the lion catch the buffalo? Sec. 3.3, p. 90
Speed in centrifuge, Ex. 5.2, p. 150
The centrifuge, Sec. 5.7, p. 171
Energy conversion in animal jumping, Ex. 6.12, p. 210
Energy transformation in a jumping flea, Sec. 6.7, p. 210
Conditions for equilibrium in the human body, Sec. 8.5, p. 281
Flexor versus extensor muscles, Sec. 8.5, p. 281
Force to hold arm horizontal, Ex. 8.10, p. 281
Forces on the human spine during heavy lifting, Sec. 8.5, p. 283
Sphygmomanometer and blood pressure, Sec. 9.5, p. 327
Specific gravity measurements in medicine, Sec. 9.6, p. 329
Floating and sinking of fish and animals, Ex. 9.8, p. 331
Speed of blood flow, Ex. 9.9, p. 334
Plaque buildup and narrowed arteries, Sec. 9.8, p. 337
Narrowing arteries and high blood pressure, Sec. 9.9, p. 340
Arterial blockage, Ex. 9.12, p. 341
How insects can walk on the surface of a pond, Sec. 9.11, p. 343
Surface tension of alveoli in the lungs, Ex. 9.14, p. 344
Surfactant in the lungs, Sec. 9.11, p. 344
Tension and compression in bone, Ex. 10.2, p. 359
Osteoporosis, Sec. 10.3, p. 361
Size limitations on organisms, Sec. 10.3, p. 363
Comparison of walking speeds for various creatures, Ex. 10.10, p. 378
Sensitivity of the human ear, Sec. 11.1, p. 394
Sound waves from a songbird, Ex. 12.2, p. 425
Human ear, Sec. 12.6, p. 432
Echolocation of bats and dolphins, Sec. 12.10, p. 443
Ultrasound and ultrasonic imaging, Sec. 12.10, p. 444
Temperature conversion, Ex. 13.1, p. 460
Warm-blooded vs. cold-blooded animals, Ex. 13.8, Sec. 13.7, p. 476
Diffusion of O_2 into the bloodstream, Sec. 13.8, Ex. 13.9, pp. 478-479
Using ice to protect buds from freezing, Sec. 14.5, p. 500
Temperature regulation in the human body, Sec. 14.7, p. 510
Thermal radiation, Sec. 14.8, p. 515
Thermal radiation from the human body, Ex. 14.15, p. 515
Electrolocation in fish, Sec. 16.4, p. 581
Electrocardiogram and electroencephalogram, Sec. 17.2, p. 612
Neuron capacitance, Ex. 17.11, p. 624
Defibrillator, Ex. 17.12, Sec. 18.11, pp. 627, 672
RC circuits in neurons, Sec. 18.10, p. 671
Defibrillator, Sec. 18.11, p. 672
Magnetotactic bacteria, Sec. 19.1, p. 697
Medical uses of cyclotrons, Sec. 19.3, p. 705
Electromagnetic blood flowmeter, Sec. 19.5, p. 710
Magnetic resonance imaging, Sec. 19.7, p. 723
Magnetoencephalography, Sec. 20.3, p. 753
Fluorescence, Sec. 22.3, p. 818
Thermograms of the human body, Sec. 22.3, p. 818
X-rays in medicine and dentistry, CAT scans, Sec. 22.3, p. 820
Navigation of bees, Sec. 22.7, p. 837
Endoscope, Sec. 23.4, p. 863
Kingfisher looking for prey, Ex. 23.4, p. 866
Human eye, Sec. 24.3, p. 898
Correcting myopia, Sec. 24.3, Ex. 24.4, pp. 900-901
Correcting hyperopia, Ex. 24.5, p. 901
Iridescent colors in butterfly wings, Sec. 25.3, p. 934
Resolution of the human eye, Sec. 25.8, p. 950
Positron emission tomography, Sec. 27.9, p. 1021
Electron microscopes, Sec. 28.3, p. 1036
Lasers in medicine, Sec. 28.9, p. 1052
Radiocarbon dating, Sec. 29.4, p. 1082

Dating archeological sites, Ex. 29.9, p. 1083
Biological effect of radiation, Sec. 29.5, p. 1085
Radioactive tracers in medical diagnosis, Sec. 29.5, p. 1088
Gamma knife radio surgery, Sec. 29.5, p. 1089
Radiation therapy, Sec. 29.5, p. 1089
Problems (1) P: 49, 51-52, 59-60, 66, 69, 87. (2) P: 74, 112. (3) P: 36, 105. (4) P: 6, 88, 90. (5) P: 11, 53, 54, 77, 83; R&S: 4, 18. (6) P: 50, 57, 73, 103, 108. (7) CQ: 8; P: 87. (8) CQ: 9-11, 16; P: 39-46, 85, 99, 105, 107, 112-113; MCAT: 6-17. (9) CQ: 7, 12, 14; P: 8, 13, 18, 20, 22, 26, 36, 38, 42, 55, 59, 63, 70, 82, 85-88, 100, 101. (10) P: 2, 6, 8, 11, 15, 38, 76, 86-88, 91, 96. (11) CQ: 2; P: 16. (12) CQ: 4, 5, 8; P: 1, 2, 11, 19, 42, 49-52, 56-58, 60, 67, 68; R&S: 4, 15. (13) P: 31, 51, 57-58, 77, 89, 90, 102-103, 105. (14) CQ: 3; P: 14-15, 20, 41-42, 46, 53-55, 58, 63-64, 68, 70-71, 76-80, 90-91, 93, 97. (15) P: 55, 60, 67, 75. (16) P: 26, 53, 75. (17) P: 36, 60, 72, 84-85, 102, 108, 107, 111, 114. (18) CQ: 11, 17, 19; P: 24, 25, 86, 95-96, 103, 118. (19) P: 41-42, 97, 106. (20) CQ: 8. (21) P: 69. (22) P: 23. (23) CQ: 20. (24) CQ: 10, 13, 14, 17, 18; MC: 4-5; P: 22-28, 39, 72, 75, 76. (25) CQ: 16; P: 10, 54, 57, 61, 71. (26) CQ: 5. (27) CQ: 3, 21; P: 59, 62, 63. (28) P: 14-15. (29) CQ: 9, 11-12, 14; MC: 10; P: 35, 36, 41, 46-48, 69, 75, 79. (30) R&S: 10-13.

Chemistry

Collision between krypton atom and water molecule, Ex. 7.9, p. 242
Why reaction rates increase with temperature, Sec. 13.7, Ex. 13.8, p. 474
Polarization of charge in water, Sec. 16.1, p. 565
Current in neon signs and fluorescent lights, Sec. 18.1, p. 643
Spectroscopic analysis of elements, Sec. 27.6, p. 1010
Fluorescence, phosphorescence, and chemiluminescence, Sec. 27.7, p. 1018
Electronic configurations of atoms, Sec. 28.7, p. 1045
Understanding the periodic table, Sec. 28.7, p. 1046
Problems (7) P: 39. (13) CQ: 13-14; P: 27-30, 32-39, 76, 79, 86, 87. (14) P: 10. (16) P: 17, 92. (17) P: 2, 3, 49, 92. (18) MC: 1; P: 7; R&S: 11. (19) P: 28-32, 88, 96. (26) P: 43, 86. (27) P: 5, 6, 9-10, 31-44, 46-48, 51, 52, 64, 66, 68, 71-72, 74, 76, 78-79, 81-82, 85. (28) CQ: 12-18; MC: 4; P: 6, 11, 20, 30, 36, 40-41, 43-45, 47, 57, 64, 65. (29) P: 4-17, 19, 21-32, 37-40, 42, 51-57, 59-67. (30) R&S: 11-12, 16, 17, 27; MCAT: 1-2, 6-8.

Geology/Earth Science

Angular speed of Earth, Ex. 5.1, p. 149
Hidden depths of an iceberg, Ex. 9.7, p. 330
Why ocean waves approach shore nearly head on, Sec. 11.8, p. 406
Resonance and damage caused by earthquakes, Sec. 11.10, p. 411
Ocean currents and global warming, Sec. 14.7, p. 511
Global climate change, Sec. 14.8, p. 516
Second law and evolution, Sec. 15.8, p. 548
Second law and the "energy crisis", Sec. 15.8, p. 548
Electric potential energy in a thundercloud, Ex. 17.1, p. 604
Thunderclouds and lightning, Sec. 17.6, p. 624
Earth's magnetic field, Sec. 19.1, p. 696
Deflection of cosmic rays, Sec. 19.1, p. 700
Magnetic force on an ion in the air, Ex. 19.2, p. 701
Intensity of sunlight reaching the Earth, Ex. 22.6, p. 829
Colors of the sky during the day and at sunset, Sec. 22.7, p. 836
Rainbows, Sec. 23.3, p. 858
Cosmic rays, Ex. 26.2, 26.4, pp. 979-982
Radioactive dating of geologic formations, Sec. 29.4, p. 1084
Neutron activation analysis, Sec. 29.6, p. 1095
Angular momentum of hurricanes and pulsars, Sec. 8.8, p. 291
Problems (1) P: 55. (5) P: 70. (8) CQ 21. (9) CQ: 9; P: 46, 67, 80, 98-99. (11) CQ: 9; P: 61-62, 66, 68-70. (12) P: 4, 5, 46-48. (13) P: 49. (14) CQ: 4, 6; P: 89, 92, 94. (15) MCAT: 2-3. (16) P: 61, 75, 80. (17) CQ: 19; P: 66, 77, 86, 87. (18) P: 125, 126. (22) CQ: 6, 7, 15; P: 53, 54, 63. (29) CQ: 6; P: 70.

Astronomy/Space Science

Mars Climate Orbiter failure, Sec. 1.5, p. 9
Why Voyager probes keep moving, Sec. 2.4, p. 36
Orbiting satellite, Ex. 2.9, p. 42
Circular orbits, Sec. 5.4, p. 160
Speed of Hubble Telescope orbiting Earth, Ex. 5.8, p. 161
Geostationary orbits, Sec. 5.4, p. 162
Kepler's laws of planetary motion, Sec. s 5.4, 8.8, pp. 162, 292
Orbit of geostationary satellite, Ex. 5.9, p. 163
Orbiting satellites, Ex. 5.10, p. 164
Apparent weightlessness of orbiting astronauts, Sec. 5.7, p. 170
Artificial gravity and the human body, Sec. 5.7, p. 171
Elliptical orbits, Sec. 6.2, p. 191
Escape speed from Earth, Ex. 6.8, p. 204
Orbital speed of Mercury, Ex. 6.7, p. 204
Center of mass of a binary star system, Ex. 7.7, p. 239
Motion of an exploding model rocket, Ex. 7.8, p. 241
Orbital speed of Earth, Ex. 8.15, p. 292
Composition of planetary atmospheres, Sec. 13.6, p. 475
Temperature of the Sun, Ex. 14.13, p. 514
Aurorae on Earth, Jupiter, and Saturn, Sec. 19.4, p. 708
Cosmic microwave background radiation, Sec. 22.3, p. 819
Light from a supernova, Sec. 22.2, p. 822
Doppler radar and the expanding universe, Sec. 22.8, p. 839
Telescopes, Sec. 24.6, p. 907
Hubble Space Telescope, Sec. 24.6, p. 910
Radio telescopes, Sec. 24.7, p. 911
Observing active galactic nuclei, Sec. 26.2, p. 973
Aging of astronauts during space voyages, Ex. 26.1, p. 976
Nuclear fusion in stars, Sec. 29.8, p. 1097
Problems (1) P: 9, 58, 78, 85. (2) P: 45, 49-55, 57, 93-94, 115. (3) MC: 5; P: 94-95. (4) P: 33-34, 72. (5) R&S: 11, 16, 25, 36, 37. (6) P: 19, 37-38, 40-46, 81, 98. (8) CQ: 17; P: 7, 70; R&S: 14, 83, 94, 104. (9) CQ 5. (10) P: 21. (11) P: 1, 5. (13) P: 71. (14) MC: 1-3. (15) R&S: 3, 9. (16) P: 91. (19) P: 17, 102. (21) R&S: 5. (22) P: 16, 34, 36-37, 39, 40, 44, 56-57, 64, 78. (24) CQ: 5, 12; MC: 6; P: 45-50, 63, 71, 63, 73, 79. (25) CQ: 3-4; P: 52, 55, 63, 73, 79; R&S: 16, 22; MCAT: 3-6. (26) CQ: 8, 12; MC: 3-4; P: 3, 5, 8-9, 13-19, 22, 35, 40-41, 46, 61, 65-66, 68-69, 72, 74, 78-79, 82, 84. (27) CQ: 5; P: 58. (29) P: 3. (30) P: 22.

Architecture

Cantilever building construction, Sec. 8.4, p. 275
Strength of building materials, Sec. 10.3, p. 361
Vibration of bridges and buildings, Sec. 10.10, p. 381
Expansion joints in bridges and buildings, Sec. 13.3, p. 461
Heat transfer through window glass, Ex. 14.10, 14.11, pp. 508-509
Building heating systems, Sec. 14.7, p. 510
Problems (9) CQ: 4. (10) CQ: 5, 12; P: 1, 17, 89. (13) P: 12, 19, 84. (14) P: 62, 72, 81. (15) CQ: 12; R&S: 10.

Technology/Machines

Advantages of a pulley, Sec. 2.8, p. 56
Catapults and projectile motion, Ex. 4.9, p. 129
Mercury manometer, Ex. 9.5, p. 225
Products to protect the human body from injury, Ex. 7.2, p. 229
Safety features in a modern car, Sec. 7.3, p. 230
Recoil of a rifle, Sec. 7.4, p. 236
Atwood's machine, Ex. 8.2, p. 265
Angular momentum of a gyroscope, Sec. 8.9, p. 294
Hydraulic lifts, brakes, and controls, Sec. 9.3, p. 320
Hydraulic lift, Ex. 9.2, p. 321
Hot air balloons, Sec. 9.6, p. 331
Venturi meter, Ex. 9.11, p. 337
Sedimentation velocity and the centrifuge, Sec. 9.10, p. 343
Operation of sonar and radar, Sec. 12.10, p. 444
Bimetallic strip in a thermostat, Sec. 13.3, p. 462
Volume expansion in thermometers, Sec. 13.3, p. 464
Heat engines, Sec. 15.5, p. 538
Internal combustion engine, Sec. 15.5, p. 538
Refrigerators and heat pumps, Sec. 15.6, p. 540
Photocopiers and laser printers, Sec. 16.2, p. 569

Cathode ray tube, Ex. 16.8, p. 582
Oscilloscope, Sec. 16.5, p. 582
Electrostatic shielding, Sec. 16.6, p. 585
Electrostatic precipitator, Sec. 16.6, p. 586
Lightning rods, Sec. 16.6, p. 586
Battery-powered lantern, Ex. 17.3, p. 607
van de Graaff generator, Sec. 17.2, p. 610
Transmission of nerve impulses, Sec. 17.2, p. 611
Computer keyboard, Ex. 17.9, p. 619
Camera flash attachments, Sec. 17.5 18.10, pp. 620-670
Condenser microphone, Sec. 17.5, p. 620
Oscilloscopes, Sec. 17.5, p. 620
Random-access memory (RAM) chips, Sec. 17.5, p. 620
Electron drift velocity in household wiring, Ex. 18.2, p. 647
Resistance thermometer, Sec. 18.4, p. 651
Battery connection in a flashlight, Sec. 18.6, p. 656
Resistive heating, Sec. 18.10, p. 665
Camera flash, Sec. 18.10, p. 670
Electric fence, Sec. 18.11, p. 672
Household wiring, Sec. 18.11, 21.2, pp. 673, 787
Magnetic compass, Sec. 19.1, p. 694
Bubble chamber, Sec. 19.3, p. 703
Mass spectrometer, Sec. 19.3, p. 704
Cyclotrons, Ex. 19.5, p. 706
Velocity selector, Sec. 19.5, p. 709
The Hall effect, Sec. 19.5, p. 711
Electric motor, Sec. 19.7, p. 716
Galvanometer, Sec. 19.7, p. 717
Audio speakers, Sec. 19.7, p. 718
Electromagnets, Sec. 19.10, p. 726
Magnetic storage, Sec. 19.10, p. 727
Electric generators, Sec. 20.2, p. 745
DC generator, Sec. 20.2, p. 747
Ground fault interrupter, Sec. 20.3, p. 752
Moving coil microphone, Sec. 20.3, p. 752
Back emf in a motor, Sec. 20.5, p. 756
Transformers, Sec. 20.6, p. 756
Distribution of electricity, Sec. 20.6, p. 758
Eddy-current braking, Sec. 20.7, p. 759
Induction stove, Sec. 20.7, p. 759
Radio tuning circuit, Ex. 21.3, p. 790
Laptop power supply, Ex. 21.5, p. 793
Tuning circuits, Sec. 21.6, p. 795
Radio tuner, Ex. 21.6, p. 796
Rectifiers, Sec. 21.7, p. 796
Crossover networks, Sec. 21.7, p. 798
Electric dipole antenna, Ex. 21.1, p. 815
Microwave ovens, Sec. 22.3, p. 819
Liquid crystal displays, Sec. 22.7, p. 834
Radar guns, Ex. 22.9, p. 838
Periscope, Sec. 23.4, p. 861
Fiber optics, Sec. 23.4, p. 862
Zoom lens, Ex. 23.9, p. 879
Cameras, Sec. 24.2, p. 895
Microscopes, Sec. 24.5, p. 905
Reading a compact disk (CD), Sec. 25.1, p. 927
Michelson interferometer, Sec. 25.2, p. 927
Interference microscope, Sec. 25.2, p. 929
Antireflective coating, Sec. 25.3, p. 933
CD tracking, Sec. 25.5, p. 940
Spectroscopy, Sec. 25.5, p. 941
Diffraction and photolithography, Ex. 25.7, p. 943
Resolution of a laser printer, Ex. 25.9, p. 949
X-ray diffraction, Sec. 25.9, pp. 950-952
Holography, Sec. 25.10, p. 952
Photocells for sound tracks, burglar alarms, garage door openers, Sec. 27.3, p. 1005
Diagnostic x-rays in medicine, Ex. 27.4, p. 1006
Lasers, Sec. 28.9, p. 1034
Quantum corral, Sec. 28.5, p. 1041
Scanning tunneling microscope, Sec. 28.10, p. 1054
Atomic clock, Sec. 28.10, p. 1056
Nuclear fission reactors, Sec. 29.7, p. 1094
Fusion reactors, Sec. 29.8, p. 1098

Preface

College Physics is intended for a two-semester college course in introductory physics using algebra and trigonometry. Our main goals in writing this book are

- to present the basic concepts of physics that students need to know for later courses and future careers,
- to emphasize that physics is a tool for understanding the real world, and
- to teach transferable problem-solving skills that students can use throughout their lives.

We have kept these goals in mind while developing the main themes of the book.

NEW TO THIS EDITION

Although the fundamental philosophy of the book has not changed, detailed feedback from over 130 reviewers (many of whom used the second edition in the classroom) has enabled us to fine-tune our approach to make the text even more user-friendly, conceptually based, and relevant for students. The third edition also has some added features to further facilitate student learning.

A greater emphasis has been placed on fundamental physics concepts:

- **Connections identify areas in each chapter where important concepts are revisited.** A marginal Connections heading and summary adjacent to the coverage in the main text help students easily recognize that a previously introduced concept is being applied to the current discussion. Knowledge is being revisited and further developed—not newly introduced.
- **Checkpoint** questions have been added to applicable sections of the text to **allow students to pause and test their understanding of the concept** explored within the current section. The answers to the Checkpoints are found at the end of the chapter so that students can confirm their knowledge without jumping too quickly to the provided answer.
- The exercises in the **Review & Synthesis** sections have been revised to concentrate even more heavily on **helping students to realize through practice problems how the concepts in the previously covered group of chapters are interrelated**. The number of problems in the Review & Synthesis sections has also been increased in the new edition. (The MCAT review problems have been retained to also help pre-med students focus on the concepts covered in the upcoming exam.)
- **Nonessential coverage and derivations have been moved to the text's website.** This will help students not only to focus further on the fundamental, core concepts in their reading of the text but also allow them to go online for additional information or explanation on topics of interest. identifiers in the text direct students to additional information online.

In addition, the following general revisions occur in chapters of the text:

- The topical question from the chapter-opening vignette now appears in the margin (along with a reduced version of the chapter-opening image) to help students identify where in the main text the answer to the chapter-opening question is addressed.
- Applications have been clearly identified as such in the text with a complete listing in the front matter.
- Many helpful subheadings have been added to the text to help students quickly identify new subtopics.
- Portions of the text now caption images to establish a visual connection between the text's concepts and terms and the art and photos.

"Trust me, College Physics *by G/R/R is as good as it gets as far as a college textbook in physics goes. One of the coauthors of this book has been teaching a course at this level for 30 years. This book is a direct result of her 30 years' worth of personal experience, and there is no better substitute for that. It is, without any doubt, one of the best of its kind."*

Dr. Abu Fasihuddin, University of Connecticut

• Great care was taken by both the authors and the contributors to the third edition to revise the end-of-chapter and Review & Synthesis problems. Approximately 150 problems are new, and an emphasis has been placed on progressing difficulty level to help students gain confidence and reinforce new skills before tackling more challenging problems.

The following lists major chapter-specific revisions to the text:

Chapter 2:   A discussion of unit vectors has been added. Sections 2.1 through 2.4 have been reorganized for a more intuitive presentation.

Chapter 4:   A more concise section on air resistance is provided with a more detailed discussion available online.

Chapter 7:   Section 7.6 Motion of the Center of Mass has been simplified.

Chapter 8:   Example 8.1 has been replaced with a new problem on the rotational inertia of a barbell.

Chapter 10:   Section 10.8 The Pendulum has been made much more concise with a more detailed discussion of the physical pendulum available online.

Chapter 11:   A new "law box" highlights the physical properties that determine wave speed. The discussion on interference has been expanded for added clarity.

Chapter 12:   In Section 12.9, the discussion of shock waves has been shortened. A more detailed discussion is available online.

Chapter 14:   A detailed discussion of convection and Example 14.12 Roller Blading in Still Air have been moved online. Section 14.7 is now a brief, conceptual description of convection. Section 14.8 Thermal Radiation has been revised with a clearer description of solar radiation and global warming.

Chapter 15:   Section 15.5 Heat Engines has been revised to include a more accurate description of the development of the steam engine. The process of the internal combustion engine is now illustrated in Figure 15.12. Details of the Carnot cycle and a discussion of the statistical interpretation of entropy are available online.

Chapter 16:   A new Example 16.7 Electric Field due to Three Point Charges has been added.

Chapter 22:   Section 22.1 has been simplified and is now titled Maxwell's Equations and Electromagnetic Waves. A more detailed discussion appears online. The material on antennas has been made more concise.

Chapter 27:   The derivation of the radii of the Bohr orbits has been moved online. The section on atomic energy levels has been revised and made more concise.

Chapter 28:   Section 28.8 Electron Energy Levels in a Solid has been made much more concise with a more detailed discussion available online.

Chapter 30:   The discussions of quarks and leptons have been expanded and clarified. The discussion of the standard model is significantly more concise. Twenty-first-century particle physics has been updated, and the most recent information will be provided online.

Please see your McGraw-Hill sales representative for a more detailed list of revisions.

COMPREHENSIVE COVERAGE

Students should be able to get the whole story from the book. The first edition text was tested in our self-paced course, where students must rely on the textbook as their primary learning resource. Nonetheless, completeness and clarity are equally advantageous when the book is used in a more traditional classroom setting. *College Physics* frees the instructor from having to try to "cover" everything. The instructor can then tailor class time to more important student needs—reinforcing difficult concepts, working through example problems, engaging the students in cooperative learning activities, describing applications, or presenting demonstrations.

INTEGRATING CONCEPTUAL PHYSICS INTO A QUANTITATIVE COURSE

Some students approach introductory physics with the idea that physics is just the memorization of a long list of equations and the ability to plug numbers into those equations. We want to help students see that a relatively small number of basic physics concepts are applied to a wide variety of situations. Physics education research has shown that students do not automatically acquire conceptual understanding; the concepts must be explained and the students given a chance to grapple with them. Our presentation, based on years of teaching this course, blends conceptual understanding with analytical skills. The **Conceptual Examples** and **Conceptual Practice Problems** in the text and a variety of Conceptual and Multiple-Choice Questions at the end of each chapter give students a chance to check and to enhance their conceptual understanding.

"Conceptual ideas are important, ideas must be motivated, physics should be integrated, a coherent problem-solving approach should be developed. I'm not sure other books are as explicit in these goals, or achieve them as well as Giambattista, Richardson, and Richardson."

Dr. Michael G. Strauss, University of Oklahoma

INTRODUCING CONCEPTS INTUITIVELY

We introduce key concepts and quantities in an informal way by establishing why the quantity is needed, why it is useful, and why it needs a precise definition. Then we make a transition from the informal, intuitive idea to a formal definition and name. Concepts motivated in this way are easier for students to grasp and remember than are concepts introduced by seemingly arbitrary, formal definitions.

For example, in Chapter 8, the idea of rotational inertia emerges in a natural way from the concept of rotational kinetic energy. Students can understand that a rotating rigid body has kinetic energy due to the motion of its particles. We discuss why it is useful to be able to write this kinetic energy in terms of a single quantity common to all the particles (the angular speed), rather than as a sum involving particles with many different speeds. When students understand why rotational inertia is defined the way it is, they are better prepared to move on to the concepts of torque and angular momentum.

We avoid presenting definitions or formulas without any motivation. When an equation is not derived in the text, we at least describe where the equation comes from or give a plausibility argument. For example, Section 9.9 introduces Poiseuille's law with two identical pipes in series to show why the volume flow rate must be proportional to the pressure drop per unit length. Then we discuss why $\Delta V/\Delta t$ is proportional to the fourth power of the radius (rather than to r^2, as it would be for an ideal fluid).

Similarly, we have found that the definitions of the displacement and velocity vectors seem arbitrary and counterintuitive to students if introduced without any motivation. Therefore, we precede any discussion of kinematic quantities with an introduction to Newton's laws, so students know that forces determine how the state of motion of an object changes. Then, when we define the kinematic quantities to give a precise definition of acceleration, we can apply Newton's second law quantitatively to see how forces affect the motion. We give particular attention to laying the groundwork for a concept when its name is a common English word such as *velocity* or *work*.

"The authors are clearly very able to communicate in written English. The text is well written, not concise to the point of density, but not discursive to the point of long-windedness. A real pleasure to read."

Dr. Galen T. Pickett, California State University, Long Beach

WRITTEN IN CLEAR AND FRIENDLY STYLE

We have kept the writing down-to-earth and conversational in tone—the kind of language an experienced teacher uses when sitting at a table working one-on-one with a student. We hope students will find the book pleasant to read, informative, and accurate without seeming threatening, and filled with analogies that make abstract concepts easier to grasp. We want students to feel confident that they can learn by studying the textbook.

While learning correct physics terminology is essential, we avoid all *unnecessary* jargon—terminology that just gets in the way of the student's understanding. For example, we never use the term *centripetal force,* since its use sometimes leads students to add a spurious "centripetal force" to their free-body diagrams. Likewise, we use *radial component of acceleration* because it is less likely to introduce or reinforce misconceptions than *centripetal acceleration.*

INNOVATIVE ORGANIZATION

There are a few places where, for pedagogical reasons, the organization of this text differs from that of most textbooks. The most significant reorganization is in the treatment of forces and motion. In *College Physics,* the central theme of Chapters 2–4 is *force.* Kinematics is introduced as a tool to understand how forces affect motion. Overall, we spend less time on kinematics and more time on forces than other texts do. This approach has the following advantages:

- The first few chapters in any text set up student expectations that are hard to change later. If the course starts with a series of definitions of the kinematic quantities, with no explanation of *why* we are interested in those quantities, students may see physics as a series of equations to memorize and manipulate.
- We explain to students that the kinematic concepts help us understand the effect that a net force has on the motion of an object. Newton's second law is presented as the key reason why we need a precise definition of acceleration. Defining acceleration requires precise definitions of displacement and velocity. If the definitions of these quantities are imprecise, we cannot hope to understand how forces affect the motion of an object.
- Learning constant-acceleration kinematics before forces may suggest to students that physics is not connected to the real world. If they are told that objects all fall with the same acceleration—which they know from experience to be false—they learn not to trust the principles they're learning. With an understanding of forces and Newton's laws, *College Physics* shows that constant acceleration is an approximation and explains how to judge when that approximation is reasonable.
- We use correct vector notation, terminology, and methods from the very beginning. Even in a one-dimensional problem, displacements, velocities, and accelerations are always treated as vector quantities. For example, we carefully distinguish components from magnitudes by writing "$v_x = -5$ m/s" and never "$v = -5$ m/s," even if the object moves only along the *x*-axis. Several professors, who used our first edition in place of a previous textbook, reported a reduction in the number of students struggling with vector components.

- We begin in Chapter 2 with Newton's laws of motion so the students can build a solid conceptual framework in simpler situations before the mathematics gets more complex. If forces were not introduced until Chapter 4, the students would have much less time to overcome conceptual difficulties associated with Newton's laws and would have much less practice applying them.

ACCURACY ASSURANCE

The authors and the publisher acknowledge the fact that inaccuracies can be a source of frustration for both the instructor and students. Therefore, throughout the writing and production of this edition, we have worked diligently to eliminate errors and inaccuracies. Bill Fellers of Fellers Math & Science conducted an independent accuracy check and worked all end-of-chapter questions and problems in the final draft of the manuscript. He then coordinated the resolution of discrepancies between accuracy checks, ensuring the accuracy of the text, the end-of-book answers, and the solutions manuals. Corrections were then made to the manuscript before it was typeset.

The page proofs of the text were double-proofread against the manuscript to ensure the correction of any errors introduced when the manuscript was typeset. The textual examples, practice problems and solutions, end-of-chapter questions and problems, and problem answers were accuracy checked by Fellers Math & Science again at the page proof stage after the manuscript was typeset. This last round of corrections was then cross-checked against the solutions manuals.

PROVIDING STUDENTS WITH THE TOOLS THEY NEED

Problem-Solving Approach

Problem-solving skills are central to an introductory physics course. We illustrate these skills in the example problems. Lists of problem-solving strategies are sometimes useful; we provide such strategies when appropriate. However, the most elusive skills—perhaps the most important ones—are subtle points that defy being put into a neat list. To develop real problem-solving expertise, students must learn how to think critically and analytically. Problem solving is a multidimensional, complex process; an algorithmic approach is not adequate to instill real problem-solving skills.

Strategy   We begin each example with a discussion—in language that the students can understand—of the *strategy* to be used in solving the problem. The strategy illustrates the kind of analytical thinking students must do when attacking a problem: How do I decide what approach to use? What laws of physics apply to the problem and which of them are *useful* in this solution? What clues are given in the statement of the question? What information is implied rather than stated outright? If there are several valid approaches, how do I determine which is the most efficient? What assumptions can I make? What kind of sketch or graph might help me solve the problem? Is a simplification or approximation called for? If so, how can I tell if the simplification is valid? Can I make a preliminary estimate of the answer? Only after considering these questions can the student effectively solve the problem.

Solution   Next comes the detailed *solution* to the problem. Explanations are intermingled with equations and step-by-step calculations to help the student understand the approach used to solve the problem. We want the student to be able to follow the mathematics without wondering, "Where did that come from?"

Discussion   The numerical or algebraic answer is not the end of the problem; our examples end with a *discussion*. Students must learn how to determine whether their answer is consistent and reasonable by checking the order of magnitude of the answer, comparing the answer to a preliminary estimate, verifying the units, and doing an independent calculation when more than one approach is feasible. When there are several different approaches, the discussion looks at the advantages and disadvantages of each approach. We also discuss the implications of the answer—what can we learn from it? We look at special cases and look at "what if" scenarios. The discussion sometimes generalizes the problem-solving techniques used in the solution.

Practice Problem   After each Example, a Practice Problem gives students a chance to gain experience using the same physics principles and problem-solving tools. By comparing their answers to those provided at the end of each chapter, they can gauge their understanding and decide whether to move on to the next section.

Our many years of experience in teaching the college physics course in a one-on-one setting has enabled us to anticipate where we can expect students to have difficulty. In addition to the consistent problem-solving approach, we offer several other means of assistance to the student throughout the text. A boxed problem-solving strategy gives detailed information on solving a particular type of problem, while an icon 🌐 for problem-solving tips draws attention to techniques that can be used in a variety of contexts. A hint in a worked example or end-of-chapter problem provides a clue on what

"The major strength of this text is its approach, which makes students think out the problems, rather than always relying on a formula to get an answer. The way the authors encourage students to investigate whether the answer makes sense, and compare the magnitude of the answer with common sense is good also."

Dr. Jose D'Arruda,
University of North Carolina,
Pembroke

"I understood the math, mostly because it was worked out step-by-step, which I like."

Student, Bradley University

approach to use or what simplification to make. A warning icon ⚠ emphasizes an explanation that clarifies a possible point of confusion or a common student misconception.

An important problem-solving skill that many students lack is the ability to extract information from a graph or to sketch a graph without plotting individual data points. Graphs often help students visualize physical relationships more clearly than they can do with algebra alone. We emphasize the use of graphs and sketches in the text, in worked examples, and in the problems.

Using Approximation, Estimation, and Proportional Reasoning

College Physics is forthright about the constant use of simplified models and approximations in solving physics problems. One of the most difficult aspects of problem solving that students need to learn is that some kind of simplified model or approximation is usually required. We discuss how to know when it is reasonable to ignore friction, treat *g* as constant, ignore viscosity, treat a charged object as a point charge, or ignore diffraction.

Some Examples and Problems require the student to make an estimate—a useful skill both in physics problem solving and in many other fields. Similarly, we teach proportional reasoning as not only an elegant shortcut but also as a means to understanding patterns. We frequently use percentages and ratios to give students practice in using and understanding them.

Showcasing an Innovative Art Program

To help show that physics is more than a collection of principles that explain a set of contrived problems, in every chapter we have developed a system of illustration's, ranging from simpler diagrams to elaborate and beautiful illustrations, that brings to life the connections between physics concepts and the complex ways in which they are applied. We believe these illustrations, with subjects ranging from three-dimensional views of electric field lines to the biomechanics of the human body and from representations of waves to the distribution of electricity in the home, will help students see the power and beauty of physics.

Helping Students See the Relevance of Physics in Their Lives

Students in an introductory college physics course have a wide range of backgrounds and interests. We stimulate interest in physics by relating the principles to applications relevant to students' lives and in line with their interests. The text, examples, and end-of-chapter problems draw from the everyday world; from familiar technological applications; and from other fields such as biology, medicine, archaeology, astronomy, sports, environmental science, and geophysics. (Applications in the text are identified with a text heading or marginal note. An icon (⚕) identifies applications in the biological or medical sciences.)

The **Physics at Home** experiments give students an opportunity to explore and see physics principles operate in their everyday lives. These activities are chosen for their simplicity and for the effective demonstration of physics principles.

Each **Chapter Opener** includes a photo and vignette, designed to capture student interest and maintain it throughout the chapter. The vignette describes the situation shown in the photo and asks the student to consider the relevant physics. A reduced version of the chapter opener photo and question marks where the topic from the vignette is addressed within the chapter.

Focusing on the Concepts

To focus on the basic, core concepts of physics and reinforce for students that all of physics is based on a few, fundamental ideas, within chapters we have developed **Connections** to identify areas where important concepts are revisited. A marginal Connections heading and summary adjacent to the coverage in the main text help

"The warning signs about many of the misconceptions, traps, and common mistakes is a very helpful and novel idea. Those of us who have taught undergraduate students in service courses have spent considerable time on these. It is good to see them in a book."

Dr. H.R. Chandrasekhar,
University of Missouri, Columbia

"I have tried a number of texts in this course over the past 30 years that I have taught Physics 116–117, and I can assure you that G/R/R is the one I (and the students . . .) like the best. The explanations are clear, and the graphics are excellent—the best I have seen anywhere. And the structure of the question and problem sets is very good. G/R/R is the best standard algebra-based text I have ever seen."

Dr. Carey E. Stronach,
Virginia State University

students easily recognize that a previously introduced concept is being applied to the current discussion. Knowledge is being built-up—not newly introduced.

The exercises in the **Review & Synthesis sections** have been revised to increase the number of available exercises and to also concentrate even more heavily on helping students to realize through practice problems how the concepts in the previously covered group of chapters are interrelated.

Checkpoint questions have been added to applicable sections of the text to allow students to pause and test their understanding of the concept explored within the current section. The answers to the Checkpoints are found at the end of the chapter so that students can confirm their knowledge without jumping too quickly to the provided answer.

Applications are clearly identified as such in the text with a complete listing in the front matter. With Applications, students have the opportunity to see how physics concepts are experienced through their everyday lives.

icons identify opportunities for students to access additional information or explanation of topics of interest online. This will help students to focus even further on just the very fundamental, core concepts in their reading of the text.

ADDITIONAL RESOURCES FOR INSTRUCTORS AND STUDENTS

Online Homework and Resources

McGraw-Hill's *College Physics* website offers online electronic homework along with a myriad of resources for both instructors and students. Instructors can create homework with easy-to-assign algorithmically generated problems from the text and the simplicity of automatic grading and reporting:

- The end-of-chapter problems and Review & Synthesis exercises appear in the online homework system in diverse formats and with various tools.
- The online homework system incorporates new and exciting interactive tools and problem types: ranking problems, a graphing tool, a free-body diagram drawing tool, symbolic entry, a math palette, and multi-part problems.

Instructors also have access to PowerPoint lecture outlines, an Instructor's Resource Guide with solutions, suggested demonstrations, electronic images from the text, clicker questions, quizzes, tutorials, interactive simulations, and many other resources directly tied to text-specific materials in *College Physics*. Students have access to self-quizzing, interactive simulations, tutorials, selected solutions for the text's problems, and more.

See www.mhhe.com/grr to learn more and to register.

Electronic Media Integrated with the Text

McGraw-Hill is proud to bring you an assortment of outstanding interactives and tutorials like no other. These activities offer a fresh and dynamic method to teach the physics basics by providing students with activities that work with real data. icons identify areas in the text where additional understanding can be gained through work with an interactive or tutorial on the text website.

The interactives allow students to manipulate parameters and gain a better understanding of the more difficult physics concepts by watching the effect of these manipulations. Each interactive includes:

- Analysis tool (interactive model)
- Tutorial describing its function
- Content describing its principle themes

The text website contains accompanying interactive quizzes. An instructor's guide for each interactive with a complete overview of the content and navigational tools, a quick demonstration description, further study with the textbook, and suggested end-of-chapter follow-up questions is also provided as an online instructor's resource.

The tutorials, developed and integrated by Raphael Littauer of Cornell University, provide the opportunity for students to approach a concept in steps. Detailed feedback is provided when students enter an incorrect response, which encourages students to further evaluate their responses and helps them progress through the problem.

Electronic Book Images and Assets for Instructors

Build instructional materials wherever, whenever, and however you want!

Accessed from the *College Physics* website, an online digital library containing photos, artwork, interactives, and other media types can be used to create customized lectures, visually enhanced tests and quizzes, compelling course websites, or attractive printed support materials. Assets are copyrighted by McGraw-Hill Higher Education, but can be used by instructors for classroom purposes. The visual resources in this collection include

- **Art** Full-color digital files of all illustrations in the book can be readily incorporated into lecture presentations, exams, or custom-made classroom materials. In addition, all files are preinserted into PowerPoint slides for ease of lecture preparation.
- **Active Art Library** These key art pieces—formatted as PowerPoint slides—allow you to illustrate difficult concepts in a step-by-step manner. The artwork is broken into small, incremental pieces, so you can incorporate the illustrations into your lecture in whatever sequence or format you desire.
- **Photos** The photos collection contains digital files of photographs from the text, which can be reproduced for multiple classroom uses.
- **Worked Example Library, Table Library, and Numbered Equations Library** Access the worked examples, tables, and equations from the text in electronic format for inclusion in your classroom resources.
- **Interactives** Flash files of the physics interactives described earlier are included so that you can easily make use of the interactives in a lecture or classroom setting.

Also residing on your textbook's website are

- **PowerPoint Lecture Outlines** Ready-made presentations that combine art and lecture notes are provided for each chapter of the text.
- **PowerPoint Slides** For instructors who prefer to create their lectures from scratch, all illustrations and photos are preinserted by chapter into blank PowerPoint slides.

Computerized Test Bank Online

A comprehensive bank of over 2000 test questions in multiple-choice format at a variety of difficulty levels is provided within a computerized test bank powered by McGraw-Hill's flexible electronic testing program—EZ Test Online (www.eztestonline.com). EZ Test Online allows you to create paper and online tests or quizzes in this easy-to-use program!

Imagine being able to create and access your test or quiz anywhere, at any time without installing the testing software. Now, with EZ Test Online, instructors can select questions from multiple McGraw-Hill test banks or create their own, and then either print the test for paper distribution or give it online. See www.mhhe.com/grr for more information.

Electronic Books

If you or your students are ready for an alternative version of the traditional textbook, McGraw-Hill brings you innovative and inexpensive electronic textbooks. By purchasing

E-books from McGraw-Hill, students can save as much as 50% on selected titles delivered on the most advanced E-book platforms available.

E-books from McGraw-Hill are smart, interactive, searchable, and portable, with such powerful built-in tools as detailed searching, highlighting, note taking, and student-to-student or instructor-to-student note sharing. E-books from McGraw-Hill will help students to study smarter and quickly find the information they need. E-books also saves students money. Contact your McGraw-Hill sales representative to discuss E-book packaging options.

Personal Response Systems

Personal response systems, or "clickers," bring interactivity into the classroom or lecture hall. Wireless response systems give the instructor and students immediate feedback from the entire class. The wireless response pads are essentially remotes that are easy to use and engage students, allowing instructors to motivate student preparation, interactivity, and active learning. Instructors receive immediate feedback to gauge which concepts students understand. Questions covering the content of the *College Physics* text (formatted in PowerPoint) are available on the website for *College Physics*.

Instructor's Resource Guide

The *Instructor's Resource Guide* includes many unique assets for instructors, such as demonstrations, suggested reform ideas from physics education research, and ideas for incorporating just-in-time teaching techniques. It also includes answers to the end-of-chapter conceptual questions and complete, worked-out solutions for all the end-of-chapter problems from the text. The Instructors Resource Guide is available in the Instructor Resources on the text's website.

ALEKS®

Help students master the math skills needed to understand difficult physics problems. ALEKS® [Assessment and LEarning in Knowledge Spaces] is an artificial intelligence–based system for individualized math learning available via the World Wide Web.

ALEKS® is

- A robust course management system. It tells you exactly what your students know and don't know.
- Focused and efficient. It enables students to quickly master the math needed for college physics.
- Artificial intelligence. It totally individualizes assessment and learning.
- Customizable. Click on or off each course topic.
- Web based. Use a standard browser for easy Internet access.
- Inexpensive. There are no setup fees or site license fees.

ALEKS® is a registered trademark of ALEKS Corporation.

Student Solutions Manual

The *Student Solutions Manual* contains complete worked-out solutions to selected end-of-chapter problems and questions, selected Review & Synthesis problems, and the MCAT Review Exercises from the text. The solutions in this manual follow the problem-solving strategy outlined in the text's examples and also guide students in creating diagrams for their own solutions.

For more information, contact a McGraw-Hill customer service representative at (800) 338–3987, or by email at www.mhhe.com. To locate your sales representative, go to www.mhhe.com for Find My Sales Rep.

To the Student

HOW TO SUCCEED IN YOUR PHYSICS CLASS

It's true—how much you get out of your studies depends on how much you put in. Success in a physics class requires:

- Commitment of time and perseverance
- Knowing and motivating yourself
- Getting organized
- Managing your time

This section will help you learn how to be effective in these areas, as well as offer guidance in:

- Getting the most out of your lecture
- Finding extra help when you need it
- Getting the most out of your textbook
- How to study for an exam

Commitment of Time and Perseverance

A good rule of thumb is to allow 2 hours of study time for every hour you spend in lecture. For instance, a 3-hour lecture deserves 6 hours of study time per week. If you commit to studying for this course daily, you're investing a little less than one hour per day, including the weekend.

Learning and mastering takes time and patience. Nothing worthwhile comes easily. Be committed to your studies and you will reap the benefits in the long run. A regular, sustained effort is much more effective than sporadic bouts of cramming.

Knowing and Motivating Yourself

What kind of learner are you? When are you most productive? Know yourself and your limits, and work within them. Know how to motivate yourself to give your all to your studies and achieve your goals.

There are many types of learners, and no right or wrong way of learning. Which category do you fall into?

Begin each of the tasks assigned in your course with the goal of understanding the material. Simply completing the assignment does not mean that learning has taken place. Your fellow students, your instructor, and this textbook can all be important resources in broadening your knowledge.

- **Visual learner** You respond best to "seeing" processes and information. Focus on text illustrations and graphs. Use course handouts and the animations on the course and text websites to help you. Draw diagrams in your notes to illustrate concepts.
- **Auditory learner** You work best by listening to—and possibly recording—the lecture and by talking information through with a study partner.
- **Tactile/Kinesthetic Learner** You learn best by being "hands on." You'll benefit by applying what you've learned during lab time. Writing and drawing are physical activities, so don't neglect taking notes on your reading and the lecture to explain the content in your own words. Try pacing while you read the text. Stand up and write on a chalkboard during discussions in your study group.

Identify your own personal preferences for learning and seek out the resources that will best help you with your studies. Also remember, even though you have a preferred style of learning, most learners benefit when they engage in all styles of learning.

Getting Organized

It's simple, yet it's fundamental. It seems the more organized you are, the easier things come. Take the time before your course begins to analyze your life and your study habits. Get organized now and you'll find you have a little more time—and a lot less stress.

- **Find a calendar system that works for you.** The best kind is one that you can take with you everywhere. To be truly organized, you should integrate all aspects of your life into this one calendar—school, work, and leisure. Some people also find it helpful to have an additional monthly calendar posted by their desk for "at a glance" dates and to have a visual planner. If you do this, be sure you are consistently synchronizing both calendars so as not to miss anything. *More tips for organizing your calendar can be found in the time management discussion below.*

- By the same token, **keep everything for your course or courses in one place**—and at your fingertips. A three-ring binder works well because it allows you to add or organize handouts and notes from class in any order you prefer. Incorporating your own custom tabs helps you flip to exactly what you need at a moment's notice.
- **Find your space.** Find a place that helps you be organized and focused. If it's your desk in your dorm room or in your home, keep it clean. Clutter adds confusion and stress and wastes time. Perhaps your "space" is at the library. If that's the case, keep a backpack or bag that's fully stocked with what you might need—your text, binder or notes, pens, highlighters, Post-its, phone numbers of study partners. [*Hint:* A good place to keep phone numbers is in your "one place for everything calendar."]

Managing Your Time

Managing your time is the single most important thing you can do to help yourself, but it's probably one of the most difficult tasks to successfully master.

In college, you are expected to work much harder and to learn much more than you ever have before. To be successful you need to invest in your education with a commitment of time. We all lead busy lives, but we all make choices as to how we spend our time. Choose wisely.

- **Know yourself and when you'll be able to study most efficiently.** When are you most productive? Are you a night owl? Or an early bird? Plan to study when you are most alert and can have uninterrupted segments. This could include a quick 5-minute review before class or a one-hour problem-solving study session with a friend.
- **Create a set daily study time for yourself.** Having a set schedule helps you commit to studying and helps you plan instead of cram. Find—and use—a planner that is small enough that you can take it with you everywhere. This may be a simple paper calendar or an electronic version. They all work on the same premise: **organize *all* of your activities in one place**.
- **Schedule study time using shorter, focused blocks with small breaks.** Doing this offers two benefits: (1) You will be less fatigued and gain more from your effort and (2) Studying will seem less overwhelming, and you will be less likely to procrastinate.
- **Plan time for leisure, friends, exercise, and sleep.** Studying should be your main focus, but you need to balance your time—and your life.
- **Log your homework deadlines and exam dates** in your personal calendar.
- Try to **complete tasks ahead of schedule**. This will give you a chance to carefully review your work before it is due. You'll feel less stressed in the end.
- **Know where help can be found.** At the beginning of the semester, find your instructor's office hours, your lab partner's contact information, and the "Help Desk" or Learning Resource Center if your course offers one. Make use of all of the support systems that your college or university has to offer. Ask questions both in class and during your instructor's office hours. Don't be shy—your instructor is there to help you learn.
- **Prioritize!** In your calendar or planner, highlight or number key projects; do them first, and then cross them off when you've completed them. Give yourself a pat on the back for getting them done!
- **Review your calendar and reprioritize *daily*.**
- **Resist distractions by setting and sticking to a designated study time.**
- **Multitask when possible.** You may find a lot of extra time you didn't think you had. Review material in your head or think about how to tackle a tough problem while walking to class or doing laundry.

Add extra "padding" into your personal deadlines. If you have a report due on Friday, set a goal for yourself to have it done on Wednesday. Then, take time on Thursday to look over your project with a fresh eye. Make any corrections or enhancements and have it ready to turn in on Friday.

Plan to study and plan for leisure. Being well balanced will help you focus when it is time to study.

Try combining social time with studying in a group, or social time with mealtime or exercise. Being a good student doesn't mean you have to be a hermit. It does mean you need to know how to smartly budget your time.

Getting the Most Out of Lectures

Your instructors want you to succeed. They put a lot of effort into preparing their lectures and other materials designed to help you learn. Attending class is one of the simplest, most valuable things you can do to help yourself. But it doesn't end there—getting the most out of your lectures means being organized. Here's how:

Prepare Before You Go to Class   Study the text on the lecture topic *before* attending class. Familiarizing yourself with the material gives you the ability to take notes selectively rather than scrambling to write everything down. You'll be able to absorb more of the subtleties and difficult points from the lecture. You may also develop some good questions to ask your instructor.

Don't feel overwhelmed by this task. Spend time the night before class gaining a general overview of the topics for the next lecture using your syllabus. If your schedule does not allow this, plan to arrive at class 5–15 minutes before lecture. Bring your text with you and skim the chapter before lecture begins.

Don't try to read an entire chapter in one sitting; study one or two sections at a time. It's difficult to maintain your concentration in a long session with so many new concepts and skills to learn.

Be a Good Listener   Most people think they are good listeners, but few really are. Are you?

Important points to remember:

- You can't listen if you are talking.
- You aren't listening if you are daydreaming or constantly distracted by other concerns.
- Listening and comprehending are two different things. Listen carefully in class. The language of science is precise; be sure you understand your instructor. If you don't understand something your instructor is saying, ask a question or jot a note and visit the instructor during office hours. You are likely doing others a favor when you ask questions because there are probably others in the class who have the same questions.

Take Good Notes

- Use a standard size notebook, or better yet, a three-ring binder with loose leaf notepaper. The binder will allow you to organize and integrate your notes and handouts, integrate easy-to-reference tabs, and the like.
- Color-code your notes. Use one color of ink pen to take your initial notes. You can annotate later using a pencil, which can be erased if need be.
- Start a new page with each lecture or note-taking session.
- Label each page with the date and a heading for each day.

- Focus on main points and try to use an outline format to take notes to capture key ideas and organize sub-points.
- Take your text to lecture, and keep it open to the topics being discussed. You can also take brief notes in your textbook margin or reference textbook pages in your notebook to help you study later.
- Review and edit your notes shortly after class—within 24 hours—to make sure they make sense and that you've recorded core thoughts. You may also want to compare your notes with a study partner later to make sure neither of you have missed anything.
- This is a very IMPORTANT point: *You can and should also add notes from your reading of the textbook.*

Get a Study Partner   Find a few study partners and get together regularly. Four or five study partners to a group is a good number. Too many students make the group unwieldy, but you want enough students to ensure the group can meet even if one or two people can't make it. Having study partners has many benefits. First, they can help you keep your commitment to this class. By having set study dates, you can combine study and social time, and maybe even make it fun! In addition, you now have several minds to help digest the information from the lecture and the text:

- Talk through concepts and go over the difficulties you may be having. Take turns explaining things to each other. You learn a tremendous amount when you teach someone else.
- Compare your notes and solutions with the Practice Problems.
- Try a new approach to a problem or look at the problem from the perspective of your partner. There are often many ways to do the same problem. You can benefit from the insights of others—and they from you—but resist the temptation to simply copy solutions. You need to learn how to solve the problem yourself.
- Quiz each other and discuss some of the Conceptual Questions from the end of the chapter.
- Don't take advantage of your study partner by skipping class or skipping study dates. You obviously won't have a study partner—or a friend—much longer if it's not a mutually beneficial arrangement!

Getting the Most Out of Your Textbook

We hope that you enjoy your physics course using this text. While studying physics does require hard work, we have tried to remove the obstacles that sometimes make introductory physics unnecessarily difficult. We have also tried to reveal the beauty inherent in the principles of physics and how these principles are manifest all around you.

In our years of teaching experience, we have found that studying physics is a skill that must be learned. It's much more effective to *study* a physics textbook, which involves active participation on your part, than to read through passively. Even though active study takes more time initially, in the long run it will save you time; you learn more in one active study session than in three or four superficial readings.

As you study, take particular note of the following elements:

Consider the **chapter opener**. It will help you make the connection between the physics you are about to study and how it affects the world around you. Each chapter opener includes a photo and vignette designed to pique your interest in the chapter. The vignette describes the situation shown in the photo and asks you to consider the relevant physics. The question is then answered within the chapter. Look for the reduced opener photo and question on the referenced page.

CHAPTER

Optical Instruments

24

The Hubble Space Telescope, orbiting Earth at an altitude of about 600 km, was launched in 1990 by the crew of the Space Shuttle *Discovery*. What is the advantage of having a telescope in space when there are telescopes on Earth with larger light-gathering capabilities? What justifies the cost of $2 billion to place this 12.5-ton instrument into orbit? (See p. 910 for the answer.)

Evaluate the **Concepts & Skills to Review** on the first page of each chapter. It lists important material from previous chapters that you should understand before you start reading. If you have problems recalling any of the concepts, you can revisit the sections referenced in the list.

Concepts & Skills to Review

- distinction between real and virtual images (Section 23.6)
- magnification (Section 23.8)
- refraction (Section 23.3)
- thin lenses (Section 23.9)
- finding images with ray diagrams (Section 23.6)
- small-angle approximations (Appendix A.7)

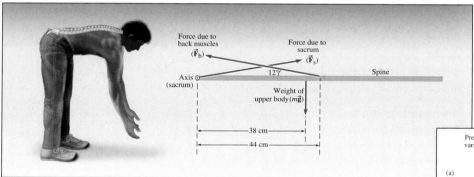

Force due to back muscles ($\vec{F}_b$)

Force due to sacrum ($\vec{F}_s$)

Axis (sacrum)

Spine

$12°$

Weight of upper body ($m\vec{g}$)

38 cm

44 cm

Study the figures and graphs carefully. **Some elaborate illustrations** and more straightforward **diagrammatic illustrations** are used in combination throughout the text to help you grasp concepts. Complex illustrations help you visualize the most difficult concepts. When looking at graphs, try to see the wealth of information displayed. Ask yourself about the physical meaning of the slope, the area under the curve, the overall shape of the graph, the vertical and horizontal intercepts, and any maxima and minima.

(a) Pressure variation p $t = 0$
p_0
$-p_0$
x
Rarefaction Compression Rarefaction Compression

(b) $\vec{F}$ $\vec{F}$ $\vec{F}$ $\vec{F}$ $\vec{F}$

(c) Displacement of air elements s $t = 0$
s_0
Right (+)
Left (−)
$-s_0$
$\vec{s}$ $\vec{s}$ $\vec{s}$ $\vec{s}$
x

Compression
Rarefaction

Wavelength

Marginal **Connections** headings and summaries adjacent to the coverage in the main text identify areas where important concepts are revisited. Consider the notes carefully to help you recognize how a previously introduced concept is being applied to the current discussion.

Checkpoint questions appear in applicable sections of the text to allow you to test your understanding of the concept explored within the current section. The answers to the Checkpoints are found at the end of the chapter so that you can confirm your knowledge without jumping too quickly to the provided answer.

✓ CHECKPOINT 8.2

You are trying to loosen a nut, without success. Why might it help to switch to a wrench with a longer handle?

---

 icons identify opportunities for you to access additional information or explanation of topics of interest online.

Various **Reinforcement Notes** appear in the margin to emphasize the important points in the text.

Definition of displacement:

$$\Delta \vec{r} = \vec{r}_f - \vec{r}_i \qquad \text{(3-1)}$$

Reminder: the symbol Δ stands for *the change in*. If the initial value of a quantity Q is Q_i and the final value is Q_f, then $\Delta Q = Q_f - Q_i$. ΔQ is read "delta Q."

Important **Equations** are numbered for easier reference. Equations that correspond to important laws are boxed for quick identification.

Statements of important physics **Rules and Laws** are boxed to highlight the most important and central concepts.

The Law of Conservation of Energy

The total energy in the universe is unchanged by any physical process:

total energy before = total energy after.

Boxed **Problem-Solving Strategies** give detailed information on solving a particular type of problem. These are supplied for the most fundamental physical rules and laws.

Problem-Solving Strategy for Newton's Second Law

- Decide what objects will have Newton's second law applied to them.
- Identify all the *external* forces acting on that object.
- Draw an FBD to show all the forces acting on the object.
- Choose a coordinate system. If the direction of the net force is known, choose axes so that the net force (and the acceleration) are along one of the axes.
- Find the net force by adding the forces as vectors.
- Use Newton's second law to relate the net force to the acceleration.
- Relate the acceleration to the change in the velocity vector during a time interval of interest.

x-axis: $a_x = 0$	y-axis: constant a_y	
$\Delta v_x = 0$ (v_x is constant)	$\Delta v_y = a_y \Delta t$	(4-7)
$\Delta x = v_x \Delta t$	$\Delta y = \frac{1}{2}(v_{fy} + v_{iy}) \Delta t$	(4-8)
	$\Delta y = v_{iy} \Delta t + \frac{1}{2}a_y(\Delta t)^2$	(4-9)
	$v_{fy}^2 - v_{iy}^2 = 2a_y \Delta y$	(4-10)

Why are only two equations shown in the column for the x-axis? The other two are redundant when $a_x = 0$.

Note that there is no mixing of components in Eqs. (4-7) through (4-10). Each equation pertains either to the x-components or to the y-components; none contains the x-component of one vector quantity and the y-component of another. The only quantity that appears in both x- and y-component equations is the time interval—a scalar.

An object in free fall near the Earth's surface has a constant acceleration. As long as air resistance is negligible, the constant downward pull of gravity gives the object a constant downward acceleration equal to $\vec{g}$. In Section 4.3 we considered objects in free fall, but only when they had no horizontal velocity component, so they moved straight up or straight down. Now we consider objects (called **projectiles**) in free fall that have a *nonzero* horizontal velocity component. The motion of a projectile takes place in a vertical plane.

Suppose some medieval marauders are attacking a castle. They have a catapult that propels large stones into the air to bombard the walls of the castle (Fig. 4.23). Picture a stone leaving the catapult with initial velocity $\vec{v}_i$. ($\vec{v}_i$ is the *initial* velocity for the time interval during which it moves as a projectile. It is also the *final* velocity for the time interval during which it is in contact with the catapult.) The **angle of elevation** is the angle of

 A **problem-solving tip** will guide you in applying problem-solving techniques.

⚠ A **warning note** describes possible points of confusion or any common misconceptions that may apply to a particular concept.

Bungee Jumping

A bungee jumper makes a jump in the Gorge du Verdon in southern France. The jumping platform is 182 m above the bottom of the gorge. The jumper weighs 780 N. If the jumper falls to within 68 m of the bottom of the gorge, how much work is done by the bungee cord on the jumper during his descent? Ignore air resistance.

Strategy Ignoring air resistance, only two forces act on the jumper during the descent: gravity and the tension in the cord. Since the jumper has zero kinetic energy at both the highest and lowest points of the jump, the change in kinetic energy for the descent is zero. Therefore, the total work done by the two forces on the jumper must equal zero.

Solution Let W_g and W_c represent the work done on the jumper by gravity and by the cord. Then

$$W_{total} = W_g + W_c = \Delta K = 0$$

The work done by gravity is

$$W_g = F_y \, \Delta y = -mg \, \Delta y$$

where the weight of the jumper is $mg = 780$ N. With $y = 0$ at the bottom of the gorge, the vertical component of the displacement is

$$\Delta y = y_f - y_i = 68 \text{ m} - 182 \text{ m} = -114 \text{ m}$$

Then the work done by gravity is

$$W_g = -(780 \text{ N}) \times (-114 \text{ m}) = +89 \text{ kJ}$$

The work done by the cord is $W_c = W_{total} - W_g = -89$ kJ.

Discussion The work done by gravity is positive, since the force and the displacement are in the same direction (downward). If not for the negative work done by the cord, the jumper would have a kinetic energy of 89 kJ after falling 114 m.

The length of the bungee cord is not given, but it does not affect the answer. At first the jumper is in free fall as the cord plays out to its full length; only then does the cord begin to stretch and exert a force on the jumper, ultimately bringing him to rest again. Regardless of the length of the cord, the total work done by gravity and by the cord must be zero since the change in the jumper's kinetic energy is zero.

Practice Problem 6.4 The Bungee Jumper's Speed

Suppose that during the jumper's descent, at a height of 111 m above the bottom of the gorge, the cord has done −21.7 kJ of work on the jumper. What is the jumper's speed at that point?

✓ **CHECKPOINT 6.3**

Kinetic energy and work are related. Can kinetic energy ever be negative? Can work ever be negative?

6.4 GRAVITATIONAL POTENTIAL ENERGY (1)

Gravitational Potential Energy When Gravitational Force Is Constant

Toss a stone up with initial speed v_i. Ignoring air resistance, how high does the stone go? We can solve this problem with Newton's second law, but let's use work and energy instead. The stone's initial kinetic energy is $K_i = \frac{1}{2}mv_i^2$. For an upward displacement Δy, gravity does negative work $W_{grav} = -mg \, \Delta y$. No other forces act, so this is the total work done on the stone. The stone is momentarily at rest at the top, so $K_f = 0$. Then

---

When you come to an **Example**, pause after you've read the problem. Think about the strategy you would use to solve the problem. See if you can work through the problem on your own. Now study the **Strategy**, **Solution**, and **Discussion** in the textbook. Sometimes you will find that your own solution is right on the mark; if not, you can focus your attention on the areas of misunderstanding or any mistakes you may have made.

Work the **Practice Problem** after each Example to practice applying the physics concepts and problem-solving skills you've just learned. Check your answer with the one given at the end of the chapter. If your answer isn't correct, review the previous section in the textbook to try to find your mistake.

Application headings identify places in the text where physics can be applied to other areas of your life. Familiar topics and interests are discussed in the accompanying text, including examples from biology, archaeology, astronomy, sports, and the everyday world. The biology/life science examples have a special icon. ——————→

Banked Curves To help prevent cars from going into a skid or losing control, the roadway is often banked (tilted at a slight angle) around curves so that the outer portion of the road—the part farthest from the center of curvature—is higher than the inner portion. Banking changes the angle and magnitude of the normal force, $\vec{N}$, so that it has a horizontal component N_x directed toward the center of curvature (in the

Application of radial acceleration and contact forces: banked roadways

Application of the manometer: measuring blood pressure

Try the *Physics at Home* experiments in your dorm room or at home. They reinforce key physics concepts and help you see how these concepts operate in the world around you.

Drop a very tiny speck of dust or lint into a container of water and push the speck below the surface. The motion of the speck—called *Brownian motion*—is easily observed as it is pushed and bumped about randomly by collisions with water molecules. The water molecules themselves move about randomly, but at much higher speeds than the speck of dust due to their much smaller mass.

Master the Concepts

- Fluids are materials that flow and include both liquids and gases. A liquid is nearly incompressible, whereas a gas expands to fill its container.
- Pressure is the perpendicular force per unit area that a fluid exerts on any surface with which it comes in contact ($P = F/A$). The SI unit of pressure is the pascal ($1\ \text{Pa} = 1\ \text{N/m}^2$).
- The average air pressure at sea level is 1 atm = 101.3 kPa.
- Pascal's principle: A change in pressure at any point in a confined fluid is transmitted everywhere throughout the fluid.
- The average density of a substance is the ratio of its mass to its volume

$$\rho = \frac{m}{V} \qquad (9\text{-}2)$$

- The specific gravity of a material is the ratio of its density to that of water at 4°C.
- Pressure variation with depth in a static fluid:

$$P_2 = P_1 + \rho g d \qquad (9\text{-}3)$$

where point 2 is a depth d
- Instruments to measure p and the barometer. The sure of the atmosphere. pressure difference.

equal in magnitude to the weight of the volume of fluid displaced by the object:

$$F_B = \rho g V \qquad (9\text{-}7)$$

where V is the volume of the part of the object that is submerged and ρ is the density of the fluid.

- In steady flow, the velocity of the fluid *at any point* is constant in time. In laminar flow, the fluid flows in neat layers so that each small portion of fluid that passes a particular point follows the same path as every other portion of fluid that passes the same point. The path that the fluid follows, starting from any point, is called a streamline. Laminar flow is steady. Turbulent flow is chaotic and unsteady. The viscous force opposes the flow of the fluid; it is the counterpart to the frictional force for solids.
- An ideal fluid exhibits laminar flow, has no viscosity, and is incompressible. The flow of an ideal fluid is governed by two principles: the continuity equation and Bernoulli's equation

5.1 Description of Uniform Circular Motion

1. A carnival swing is fixed on the end of an 8.0-m-long beam. If the swing and beam sweep through an angle of 120°, what is the distance through which the riders move?

2. A soccer ball of diameter 31 cm rolls without slipping at a linear speed of 2.8 m/s. Through how many revolutions has the soccer ball turned as it moves a linear distance of 18 m?

3. Find the average angular speed of the second hand of a

Problems

 Combination conceptual/quantitative problem
 Biological or medical application
 Challenging problem
Blue #   Detailed solution in the Student Solutions Manual
(1) (2)   Problems paired by concept
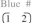 Text website interactive or tutorial

5.1 Description of Uniform Circular Motion

1. A carnival swing is fixed on the end of an 8.0-m-l beam. If the swing and beam sweep through an angl 120 mov

114. A student's head is bent over her physics book. The head weighs 50.0 N and is supported by the muscle force $\vec{F}_m$ exerted by the neck extensor muscles and by the contact force $\vec{F}_c$ exerted at the atlantooccipital joint. Given that the magnitude of $\vec{F}_m$ is 60.0 N and is directed 35° below the horizontal, find (a) the magnitude and (b) the direction of $\vec{F}_c$.

Write your *own* chapter summary or outline, adding notes from class where appropriate, and then compare it with the **Master the Concepts** provided at the end of the chapter. This will help you identify the most important and fundamental concepts in each chapter.

Along with working the problems assigned by your instructor, try quizzing yourself on the **Multiple-Choice Questions.** Check your answers against the answers at the end of the book. Consider the **Conceptual Questions** to check your qualitative understanding of the key ideas from the chapter. Try writing some responses to practice your writing skills and to help prepare for any essay problems on the exam.

When working the **Problems** and **Comprehensive Problems** assigned by your instructor, pay special attention to the explanatory paragraph below the Problem heading and the keys accompanying each problem.

- *Paired Problems* are connected with a bracket. Your instructor may assign the even-numbered problem, which has no answer at the end of the book. However, working the connected odd-numbered problem will allow you to check your answer at the back of the book and apply what you have learned to working the even-numbered problem.
- Problem numbers highlighted in blue have a solution available in the **Student Solutions Manual** if you need additional help or would like to double-check your work.
- The *difficulty level* for each problem is indicated. The least difficult problems and problems of intermediate difficulty have no diamond. The more challenging problems have one diamond ◆.

Read through all of the assigned problems and budget your time accordingly.
- indicates a combination **Conceptual and Quantitative** problem.
- indicates a problem with a biological or medical application.
- 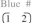 indicates a problem that has an accompanying interactive or tutorial online.

While working your solutions to problems, try to **keep your work in symbolic form** until the very end. Symbolic solutions will allow you to view which factors affect the results and how the answer would change should any one of the variables in the problem change their value. In this fashion, your solution to any one problem becomes a solution to a whole series of similar problems.

Substituting values into your final symbolic solution will then enable you to judge if your answer is reasonable and provide greater ease in troubleshooting your error if it is not. Always perform a "reality check" at the end of each problem. Did you obtain a reasonable answer given the question being asked?

After a group of related chapters, you will find a **Review & Synthesis** section. This section will provide *Review Exercises* that require you to combine two or more concepts learned in the previous chapters. Working these problems will help you to prepare for cumulative exams. This section also contains *MCAT Review* exercises. These problems were written for the actual MCAT exam and will provide additional practice if this exam is part of your future plans.

How to Study for an Exam

- Be an active learner:
  - read
  - be an active participant in class; ask questions
  - apply what you've learned; think through scenarios rather than memorizing your notes
- Finish reading all material—text, notes, handouts—at least three days prior to the exam.
- Three days prior to the exam, set aside time each day to do self-testing, work practice problems, and review your notes. Useful tools to help:
  - end-of-chapter summaries
  - questions and practice problems
  - text website
  - your professor's course website
  - the Student Solutions Manual
  - your study partner
- Analyze your weaknesses, and create an "I don't know this yet" list. Focus on strengthening these areas and narrow your list as you study.
- If you find that you were unable to allow the full three days to study for the exam, the most important thing you can do is try some practice problems that are similar to those your instructor assigned for homework. Choose odd-numbered problems so that you can check your answer. The Review & Synthesis problems are designed to help you prepare for exams. Try to solve each problem under exam conditions—use a formula sheet, if your instructor provides one with the exam, but don't look at the book or your notes. If you can't solve the problem, then you have found an area of weakness. Study the material needed to solve that problem and closely related material. Then try another similar problem.
- VERY IMPORTANT—Be sure to sleep and eat well before the exam. Staying up late and memorizing the night before an exam doesn't help much in physics. On a physics exam, you will be asked to demonstrate reasoning and analytical skills acquired by much practice. If you are fatigued or hungry, you won't perform at your highest level.

We hope that these suggestions will help you get the most out of your physics course. After many years working with students, both in the classroom and one-on-one in a self-paced course, we wrote this book so you could benefit from our experience. In *College Physics*, we have tried to address the points that have caused difficulties for our students in the past. We also wish to share with you some of the pleasure and excitement we have found in learning about the physical laws that govern our world.

Alan Giambattista

Betty Richardson

Bob Richardson

Acknowledgments

We are grateful to the faculty, staff, and students at Cornell University, who helped us in a myriad of ways. We especially thank our friend and colleague Bob Lieberman who shepherded us through the process as our literary agent and who inspired us as an exemplary physics teacher. Donald F. Holcomb, Persis Drell, Peter Lepage, and Phil Krasicky read portions of the manuscript and provided us with many helpful suggestions. Raphael Littauer contributed many innovative ideas and served as a model of a highly creative, energetic teacher.

We are indebted to Jeevak Parpia, David G. Cassel, Edith Cassel, Richard Galik, Lou Hand, Chris Henley, and Tomás Arias for many helpful discussions while they taught Physics 101–102 using the second edition. We also appreciate the assistance of Leonard J. Freelove and Rosemary French. We thank our enthusiastic and capable graduate teaching assistants and, above all, the students in Physics 101–102, who patiently taught us how to teach physics.

We are grateful for the guidance and enthusiasm of Debra Hash and Mary Hurley at McGraw-Hill, whose tireless efforts were invaluable in bringing this project to fruition. We would like to thank the entire team of talented professionals assembled by McGraw-Hill to publish this book, including Traci Andre, Tammy Ben, Carrie Burger, Linda Davoli, Laura Fuller, David Hash, Tammy Juran, Mary Jane Lampe, Lisa Nicks, Mary Reeg, Gloria Schiesl, Thomas Timp, Dan Wallace, and many others whose hard work has contributed to making the book a reality.

We are grateful to Bill Fellers for accuracy-checking the manuscript and for many helpful suggestions.

Our thanks to Janet Scheel, Warren Zipfel, Rebecca Williams, and Mike Nichols for contributing some of the medical and biological applications; to Nick Taylor and Mike Strauss for contributing to the end-of-chapter and Review & Synthesis problems; and to Nick Taylor for writing answers to the Conceptual Questions.

From Alan: Above all, I am deeply grateful to my family. Marion, Katie, Charlotte, Julia, and Denisha, without your love, support, encouragement, and patience, this book could never have been written.

From Bob and Betty: We thank our daughter Pamela's classmates and friends at Cornell and in the Vanderbilt Master's in Nursing program who were an early inspiration for the book, and we thank Dr. Philip Massey who was very special to Pamela and is dear to us. We thank our friends at *blur,* Alex, Damon, Dave, and Graham, who love physics and are inspiring young people of Europe to explore the wonders of physics through their work with the European Space Agency's Mars mission. Finally we thank our daughter Jennifer, our grandsons Jasper, Dashiell, Oliver, and Quintin, and son-in-law Jim who endured our protracted hours of distraction while this book was being written.

REVIEWERS, CLASS TESTERS, AND ADVISORS

This text reflects an extensive effort to evaluate the needs of college physics instructors and students, to learn how well we met those needs, and to make improvements where we fell short. We gathered information from numerous reviews, class tests, and focus groups.

The primary stage of our research began with commissioning reviews from instructors across the United States and Canada. We asked them to submit suggestions for improvement on areas such as content, organization, illustrations, and ancillaries. The detailed comments of these reviewers constituted the basis for the revision plan.

We organized focus groups across the United States from 2006 through 2008. Participants reviewed our text in comparison to other books and suggested improvements to *College Physics* and ways in which we as publishers could help to improve the content of the college physics course.

Finally, we received extremely useful advice on the instructional design, quality, and content of the print and media ancillary packages from Pete Anderson, Gerry Feldman, Ajawad Haija, Hong Luo, David Mast, John Prineas, Michael Pravica, and Craig Wiegert.

Considering the sum of these opinions, this text now embodies the collective knowledge, insight, and experience of hundreds of college physics instructors. Their influence can be seen in everything from the content, accuracy, and organization of the text to the quality of the illustrations.

We are grateful to the following instructors for their thoughtful comments and advice:

REVIEWERS AND FOCUS GROUP ATTENDEES

David Aaron   *South Dakota State University*

Bruce Ackerson   *Oklahoma State University*

Iftikhar Ahmad   *Louisiana State University—Baton Rouge*

Peter Anderson   *Oakland Community College*

Karamjeet Arya   *San Jose State University*

Charles Bacon   *Ferris State University*

Becky Baker   *Missouri State University*

David Bannon   *Oregon State University*

Natalie Batalha   *San Jose State University*

David Baxter   *Indiana University*

Philip Best   *University of Connecticut—Storrs*

George Bissinger   *East Carolina University*

Julio Blanco   *California State University, Northridge*

Werner Boeglin   *Florida International University—Miami*

Thomas K. Bolland   *The Ohio State University*

Richard Bone   *Florida International University*

Arthur Braundmeier, Jr.   *Southern Illinois University—Edwardsville*

Hauke Busch   *Augusta State University*

David Carleton   *Missouri State University*

Soumitra Chattopadhyay   *Georgia Highlands College*

Lee Chow   *University of Central Florida*

Rambis Chu   *Texas Southern University*

Francis Cobbina   *Columbus State Community College*

John Cockman   *Appalachian State University*

Teman Cooke   *Georgia Perimeter College*

Andrew Cornelius   *University of Nevada, Las Vegas*

Carl Covatto   *Arizona State University*

Orville Day   *East Carolina University*

Keith Dienes   *University of Arizona*

Russell Doescher   *Texas State University, San Marcos*

Gregory Dolise   *Harrisburg Area Community College—Harrisburg*

Aaron Dominguez   *University of Nebraska—Lincoln*

James Eickemeyer   *Cuesta College*

Steven Ellis   *University of Kentucky—Lexington*

Abu Fasihuddin   *University of Connecticut—Storrs*

Gerald Feldman   *George Washington University*

Frank Ferrone   *Drexel University*

John Fons   *University of Wisconsin—Rock County*

Lyle Ford   *University of Wisconsin—Eau Claire*

Gregory Francis   *Montana State University*

Carl Frederickson   *University of Central Arkansas*

David Gerdes   *University of Michigan*

Jim Goff   *Pima Community College—West*

Omar Guerrero   *University of Delaware*

Gemunu Gunaratne   *University of Houston*

Robert Hagood   *Washtenaw Community College*

Ajawad Haija   *Indiana University of Pennsylvania*

Hussein Hamdeh   *Wichita State University*

James Heath   *Austin Community College*

Paul Heckert   *Western Carolina University*

Thomas Hemmick   *Stony Brook University*

Gerald Hite   *Texas A&M University—Galveston*

James Ho   *Wichita State University*

Laurent Hodges   *Iowa State University*

William Hollerman   *University of Louisiana at Lafayette*

Klaus Honscheid   *The Ohio State University*

Chuck Hughes   *University of Central Oklahoma*

Yong Suk Joe   *Ball State University*

Linda Jones   *College of Charleston*

Nikolaos Kalogeropoulos   *Borough of Manhattan, Community College/CUNY*

Daniel Kennefick   *University of Arkansas*

Raman Kolluri   *Camden County College*

Dorina Kosztin   *University of Missouri, Columbia*

Liubov Kreminska   *Truman State University*

Allen Landers   *Auburn University*

Eric Lane   *University of Tennessee at Chattanooga*

Mary Lu Larsen   *Towson University*

Kwong Lau   *University of Houston*

Paul Lee   *California State University—Northridge*

Geoff Lenters   *Grand Valley State University*

Alfred Leung   *California State University—Long Beach*

Pui-Tak Leung   *Portland State University*

Jon Levin   *University of Tennessee, Knoxville*

Mark Lucas   *Ohio State University*

Hong Luo   *University at Buffalo*

Lisa Madewell   *University of Wisconsin—Superior*

Rizwan Mahmood   *Slippery Rock University of Pennsylvania*

George Marion   *Texas State University, San Marcos*

Pete Markowitz   *Florida International University*

Perry Mason   *Lubbock Christian University*

David Mast   *University of Cincinnati*

Mark Mattson   *James Madison University*

Richard Matzner   *University of Texas*

Dan Mazilu   *Virginia Polytechnic Institute & State University*

Joseph McCullough   *Cabrillo College*

Rahul Mehta   *University of Central Arkansas*

Nathan Miller   *University of Wisconsin—Eau Claire*

John Milsom   *University of Arizona*

Kin-Keung Mon   *University of Georgia*

Ted Morishige   *University of Central Oklahoma*

Krishna Mukherjee   *Slippery Rock University*

Hermann Nann   *Indiana University*

Meredith Newby   *Clemson University*

Galen Pickett   *California State University—Long Beach*

Christopher Pilot   *Maine Maritime Academy*

Amy Pope   *Clemson University*

Scott Pratt   *Michigan State University*

Michael Pravica   *University of Nevada, Las Vegas*

Roger Pynn   *Indiana University*

Oren Quist   *South Dakota State University*

W. Steve Quon   *Ventura College*

Natarajan Ravi   *Spelman College*

Michael Roth   *University of Northern Iowa*

Alberto Sadun   *University of Colorado—Denver*

G. Mackay Salley   *Wofford College*

Phyllis Salmons   *Embry Riddle Aeronautical University*

Jyotsna Sau   *Delaware Technical & Community College*

Douglas Sherman   *San Jose State University*

Natalia Sidorovskaia   *University of Louisiana at Lafayette*

Bjoern Siepel   *Portland State University*

Joseph Slawny   *Virginia Polytechnic Institute & State University*

Clark Snelgrove   *Virginia Polytechnic Institute & State University*

John Stanford   *Georgia Perimeter College*

Michael Strauss   *University of Oklahoma*

Elizabeth Stoddard   *University of Missouri—Kansas City*

Donna Stokes   *University of Houston*

Colin Terry   *Ventura College*

Cheng Ting   *Houston Community College—Southeast*

Bruno Ullrich   *Bowling Green State University*

Gautam Vemuri   *IUPUI*

Melissa Vigil   *Marquette University*

Judy Vondruska   *South Dakota State University*

Carlos Wexler   *University of Missouri, Columbia*

Joe Whitehead   *University of Southern Mississippi*

Daniel Whitmire   *University of Louisiana at Lafayette*

Craig Wiegert   *University of Georgia*

Arthur Wiggins   *Oakland Community College*

Weldon Wilson   *University of Central Oklahoma*

Scott Wissink   *Indiana University*

Sanichiro Yoshida   *Southeastern Louisiana University*

David Young   *Louisiana State University*

Richard Zajac   *Kansas State University at Salina*

Steven Zides   *Wofford College*

We are also grateful to our international reviewers for their comments and suggestions:

Goh Hock Leong   *National Junior College—Singapore*

Mohammed Saber Musazay   *King Fahd University of Petroleum and Minerals*

Contributors

We are deeply indebted to:

Professor Suzanne Willis of Northern Illinois University and Professor Susanne M. Lee, Visiting Scientist Rensselaer Polytechnic Institute, for creating the instructor resources and demonstrations in the *College Physics Instructors' Resource Guide.*

Professor Jack Cuthbert of Holmes Community College, Ridgeland for the Test Bank to accompany *College Physics.*

Professor Lorin Swint Matthews of Baylor University for the clicker questions to accompany *College Physics.*

Professor Carl Covatto of Arizona State University for the PowerPoint Lectures to accompany *College Physics.*

Professor Allen Landers of Auburn University for his work on the *College Physics* collection of Active Art on the text's website.

Introduction

In 2004, the exploration rovers *Spirit* and *Opportunity* landed on sites on opposite sides of Mars. The primary goal of the mission was to examine a wide variety of rocks and soils that might provide evidence of the past presence of water on Mars and clues to where the water went. The mission sent back tens of thousands of photographs and a wealth of geologic data. By contrast, in a previous mission to Mars, a simple mistake caused the loss of the Mars Climate Orbiter as it entered orbit around Mars. In this chapter, you will learn how to avoid making this same mistake. (See p. 9.)

The Mars Exploration Rover *Opportunity* looks back toward its lander in "Eagle Crater" on the surface of Mars.

Concepts & Skills to Review

- algebra, geometry, and trigonometry (Appendix A)
- To the Student: How to Succeed in Your Physics Class (p. xxii)

1.1   WHY STUDY PHYSICS?

Physics is the branch of science that describes matter, energy, space, and time at the most fundamental level. Whether you are planning to study biology, architecture, medicine, music, chemistry, or art, some principles of physics are relevant to your field.

Physicists look for patterns in the physical phenomena that occur in the universe. They try to explain what is happening, and they perform experiments to see if the proposed explanation is valid. The goal is to find the most basic laws that govern the universe and to formulate those laws in the most precise way possible.

The study of physics is valuable for several reasons:

- Since physics describes matter and its basic interactions, all natural sciences are built on a foundation of the laws of physics. A full understanding of chemistry requires a knowledge of the physics of atoms. A full understanding of biological processes in turn is based on the underlying principles of physics and chemistry. Centuries ago, the study of *natural philosophy* encompassed what later became the separate fields of biology, chemistry, geology, astronomy, and physics. Today there are scientists who call themselves biophysicists, chemical physicists, astrophysicists, and geophysicists, demonstrating how thoroughly the sciences are intertwined.
- In today's technological world, many important devices can be understood correctly only with a knowledge of the underlying physics. Just in the medical world, think of laser surgery, magnetic resonance imaging, instant-read thermometers, x-ray imaging, radioactive tracers, heart catheterizations, sonograms, pacemakers, microsurgery guided by optical fibers, ultrasonic dental drills, and radiation therapy.
- By studying physics, you acquire skills that are useful in other disciplines. These include thinking logically and analytically; solving problems; making simplifying assumptions; constructing mathematical models; using valid approximations; and making precise definitions.
- Society's resources are limited, so it is important to use them in beneficial ways and not squander them on scientifically impossible projects. Political leaders and the voting public are too often led astray by a lack of understanding of scientific principles. Can a nuclear power plant supply energy safely to a community? What is the truth about the greenhouse effect, the ozone hole, and the danger of radon in the home? By studying physics, you learn some of the basic scientific principles and acquire some of the intellectual skills necessary to ask probing questions and to formulate informed opinions on these important matters.
- Finally, by studying physics, we hope that you develop a sense of the beauty of the fundamental laws governing the universe.

A patient being prepared for magnetic resonance imaging (MRI). MRI provides a detailed image of the internal structures of the patient's body.

1.2   TALKING PHYSICS

Some of the words used in physics are familiar from everyday speech. This familiarity can be misleading, since the scientific definition of a word may differ considerably from its common meaning. In physics, words must be precisely defined so that anyone reading a scientific paper or listening to a science lecture understands exactly what is meant. Some of the basic defined quantities, whose names are also words used in everyday speech, include time, length, force, velocity, acceleration, mass, energy, momentum, and temperature.

In everyday language, *speed* and *velocity* are synonyms. In physics, there is an important distinction between the two. In physics, *velocity* includes the *direction* of motion as well as the distance traveled per unit time. When a moving object changes direction, its velocity changes even though its speed may not have changed. Confusion of the scientific definition of *velocity* with its everyday meaning will prevent a correct understanding of some of the basic laws of physics and will lead to incorrect answers.

Mass, as used in everyday language, has several different meanings. Sometimes *mass* and *weight* are used interchangeably. In physics, mass and weight are *not* interchangeable. Mass is a measure of inertia—the tendency of an object at rest to remain at rest or, if moving, to continue moving with the same velocity. Weight, on the other hand, is a measure of the gravitational pull on an object. (Mass and weight are discussed in more detail in Chapter 2.)

There are two important reasons for the way in which we define physical quantities. First, physics is an experimental science. The results of an experiment must be stated unambiguously so that other scientists can perform similar experiments and compare their results. Quantities must be defined precisely to enable experimental measurements to be uniform no matter where they are made. Second, physics is a mathematical science. We use mathematics to quantify the relationships among physical quantities. These relationships can be expressed mathematically only if the quantities being investigated have precise definitions.

1.3 THE USE OF MATHEMATICS

A working knowledge of algebra, trigonometry, and geometry is essential to the study of introductory physics. Some of the more important mathematical tools are reviewed in Appendix A. If you know that your mathematics background is shaky, you might want to test your mastery by doing some problems from a math textbook. You may find it useful to visit www.mhhe.com to explore the Schaum's Outline series, especially the Schaum's Outlines of *Precalculus, College Physics,* or *Physics for Pre-Med, Biology, and Allied Health Students.*

Mathematical equations are shortcuts for expressing concisely in symbols relationships that are cumbersome to describe in words. Algebraic symbols in the equations stand for quantities that consist of numbers *and units*. The number represents a measurement and the measurement is made in terms of some standard; the unit indicates what standard is used. In physics, a number to specify a quantity is useless unless we know the unit attached to the number. When buying silk to make a sari, do we need a length of 5 millimeters, 5 meters, or 5 kilometers? Is the term paper due in 3 minutes, 3 days, or 3 weeks? Systems of units are discussed in Section 1.5.

There are not enough letters in the alphabet to assign a unique letter to each quantity. The same letter V can represent volume in one context and voltage in another. Avoid attempting to solve problems by picking equations that seem to have the correct letters. A skilled problem-solver understands *specifically* what quantity each symbol in a particular equation represents, can specify correct units for each quantity, and understands the situations to which the equation applies.

Ratios and Proportions In the language of physics, the word **factor** is used frequently, often in a rather idiosyncratic way. If the power emitted by a radio transmitter has doubled, we might say that the power has "increased by a factor of two." If the concentration of sodium ions in the bloodstream is half of what it was previously, we might say that the concentration has "decreased by a factor of two," or, in a blatantly inconsistent way, someone else might say that it has "decreased by a factor of one-half." The *factor* is the number by which a quantity is multiplied or divided when it is changed from one value to another. In other words, the factor is really a ratio. In the case of the radio transmitter, if P_0 represents the initial power and P represents the power after new equipment is installed, we write

$$\frac{P}{P_0} = 2$$

It is also common to talk about "increasing 5%" or "decreasing 20%." If a quantity increases $n\%$, that is the same as saying that it is multiplied by a factor of $1 + (n/100)$. If a quantity decreases $n\%$, then it is multiplied by a factor of $1 - (n/100)$. For example, an increase of 5% means something is 1.05 times its original value and a decrease of 4% means it is 0.96 times the original value.

Physicists talk about increasing "by some factor" because it often simplifies a problem to think in terms of **proportions**. When we say that A is proportional to B (written $A \propto B$), we mean that if B increases by some factor, then A must increase by the same factor. For instance, the circumference of a circle equals 2π times the radius: $C = 2\pi r$. Therefore $C \propto r$. If the radius doubles, the circumference also doubles. The area of a circle is proportional to the *square* of the radius ($A = \pi r^2$, so $A \propto r^2$). The area must increase by the same factor as the radius *squared*, so if the radius doubles, the area increases by a factor of $2^2 = 4$.

$A \propto B$ means $A_1/A_2 = B_1/B_2$

Example 1.1

Effect of Increasing Radius on the Volume of a Sphere

The volume of a sphere is given by the equation

$$V = \tfrac{4}{3}\pi r^3$$

where V is the volume and r is the radius of the sphere. If a basketball has a radius of 12.4 cm and a tennis ball has a radius of 3.20 cm, by what factor is the volume of the basketball larger than the volume of the tennis ball?

Strategy   The problem gives the values of the radii for the two balls. To keep track of which ball's radius and volume we mean, we use subscripts "b" for basketball and "t" for tennis ball. The radius of the basketball is r_b and the radius of the tennis ball is r_t. Since $\tfrac{4}{3}$ and π are constants, we can work in terms of proportions.

Solution   The ratio of the basketball radius to that of the tennis ball is

$$\frac{r_b}{r_t} = \frac{12.4 \text{ [cm]}}{3.20 \text{ [cm]}} = 3.875$$

The volume of a sphere is proportional to the cube of its radius:

$$V \propto r^3$$

Since the basketball radius is larger by a factor of 3.875, and volume is proportional to the cube of the radius, the new volume should be bigger by a factor of $3.875^3 \approx 58.2$.

Discussion   A slight variation on the solution is to write out the proportionality in terms of ratios of the corresponding sides of the two equations:

$$\frac{V_b}{V_t} = \frac{\tfrac{4}{3}\pi r_b^3}{\tfrac{4}{3}\pi r_t^3} = \left(\frac{r_b}{r_t}\right)^3$$

Substituting the ratio of r_b to r_t yields

$$\frac{V_b}{V_b} = 3.875^3 \approx 58.2$$

which says that V_b is approximately 58.2 times V_t.

Practice Problem 1.1   Power Dissipated by a Lightbulb

The electric power P dissipated by a lightbulb of resistance R is $P = V^2/R$, where V represents the line voltage. During a brownout, the line voltage is 10.0% less than its normal value. How much power is drawn by a lightbulb during the brownout if it normally draws 100.0 W (watts)? Assume that the resistance does not change.

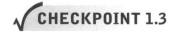

CHECKPOINT 1.3

If the radius of the sphere is increased by a factor of 3, by what factor does the volume of the sphere change?

1.4   SCIENTIFIC NOTATION AND SIGNIFICANT FIGURES

In physics, we deal with some numbers that are very small and others that are very large. It can get cumbersome to write numbers in conventional decimal notation. In **scientific notation**, any number is written as a number between 1 and 10 times an integer power of ten. Thus the radius of Earth, approximately 6 380 000 m at the equator, can be written 6.38×10^6 m; the radius of a hydrogen atom, 0.000 000 000 053 m, can be written 5.3×10^{-11} m. Scientific notation eliminates the need to write zeros to locate the decimal point correctly.

In science, a measurement or the result of a calculation must indicate the **precision** to which the number is known. The precision of a device used to make a measurement is limited by the finest division on the scale. Using a meterstick with millimeter divisions as the smallest separations, we can measure a length to a precise number of millimeters and we can estimate a fraction of a millimeter between two divisions. If the meterstick has centimeter divisions as the smallest separations, we measure a precise number of centimeters and estimate the fraction of a centimeter that remains.

Significant Figures   The most basic way to indicate the precision of a quantity is to write it with the correct number of **significant figures**. The significant figures are all the digits that are known accurately plus the one estimated digit. If we say that the distance from here to the state line is 12 km, that does not mean we know the distance to be *exactly* 12 kilometers. Rather, the distance is 12 km *to the nearest kilometer.* If instead we said that the distance is 12.0 km, that would indicate that we know the distance to the nearest *tenth* of a kilometer. More significant figures indicate a greater degree of precision.

> Learn how to use the button on your calculator (usually labeled EE) to enter a number in scientific notation. To enter 1.2×10^8, press 1.2, EE, 8.

Rules for Identifying Significant Figures

1. Nonzero digits are always significant.
2. Final or ending zeros written to the right of the decimal point are significant.
3. Zeros written to the right of the decimal point for the purpose of spacing the decimal point are not significant.
4. Zeros written to the left of the decimal point may be significant, or they may only be there to space the decimal point. For example, 200 cm could have one, two, or three significant figures; it's not clear whether the distance was measured to the nearest 1 cm, to the nearest 10 cm, or to the nearest 100 cm. On the other hand, 200.0 cm has four significant figures (see rule 5). Rewriting the number in scientific notation is one way to remove the ambiguity. In this book, when a number has zeros to the left of the decimal point, you may *assume a minimum of two significant figures.*
5. Zeros written between significant figures are significant.

Example 1.2

Identifying the Number of Significant Figures

For each of these values, identify the number of significant figures and rewrite it in standard scientific notation.

(a) 409.8 s
(b) 0.058700 cm
(c) 9500 g
(d) 950.0×10^1 mL

Strategy   We follow the rules for identifying significant figures as given. To rewrite a number in scientific notation, we move the decimal point so that the number to the left of the decimal point is between 1 and 10 and compensate by multiplying by the appropriate power of ten.

continued on next page

Example 1.2 continued

Solution   (a) All four digits in 409.8 s are significant. The zero is between two significant figures, so it is significant. To write the number in scientific notation, we move the decimal point two places to the left and compensate by multiplying by 10^2: 4.098×10^2 s.

(b) The first two zeros in 0.058700 cm are not significant; they are used to place the decimal point. The digits 5, 8, and 7 are significant, as are the two final zeros. The answer has five significant figures: 5.8700×10^{-2} cm.

(c) The 9 and 5 in 9500 g are significant, but the zeros are ambiguous. This number could have two, three, or four significant figures. If we take the most cautious approach and assume the zeros are not significant, then the number in scientific notation is 9.5×10^3 g.

(d) The final zero in 950.0×10^1 mL is significant since it comes after the decimal point. The zero to its left is also significant since it comes between two other significant digits.

The result has four significant figures. The number is not in *standard* scientific notation since 950.0 is not between 1 and 10; in scientific notation we write 9.500×10^3 mL.

Discussion   Scientific notation clearly indicates the number of significant figures since all zeros are significant; none are used only to place the decimal point. In (c), if we want to show that the zeros were significant, we would write 9.500×10^3 g.

Practice Problem 1.2   Identifying Significant Figures

State the number of significant figures in each of these measurements and rewrite them in standard scientific notation.

(a) 0.000 105 44 kg   (b) 0.005 800 cm   (c) 602 000 s

Significant Figures in Calculations

1. When two or more quantities are added or subtracted, the result is as precise as the *least precise* of the quantities (Example 1.3). If the quantities are written in scientific notation with different powers of ten, first rewrite them with the same power of ten. After adding or subtracting, round the result, keeping only as many decimal places as are significant in *all* of the quantities that were added or subtracted.

2. When quantities are multiplied or divided, the result has the same number of significant figures as the quantity with the *smallest number of significant figures* (Example 1.4).

3. In a series of calculations, rounding to the correct number of significant figures should be done only at the end, *not at each step*. Rounding at each step would increase the chance that roundoff error could snowball and have an adverse effect on the accuracy of the final answer. It's a good idea to keep *at least two* extra significant figures in calculations, then round at the end.

Example 1.3

Significant Figures in Addition

Calculate the sum 44.56005 s + 0.0698 s + 1103.2 s.

Strategy   The sum cannot be more precise than the least precise of the three quantities. The quantity 44.56005 s is known to the nearest 0.00001 s, 0.0698 s is known to the nearest 0.0001 s, and 1103.2 s is known to the nearest 0.1 s.

Therefore the least precise is 1103.2 s. The sum has the same precision; it is known to the nearest tenth of a second.

Solution   According to the calculator,

$$44.56005 + 0.0698 + 1103.2 = 1147.82985$$

continued on next page

Example 1.3 continued

We do *not* want to write all of those digits in the answer. That would imply greater precision than we actually have. Rounding to the nearest tenth of a second, the sum is written

$$= 1147.8 \text{ s}$$

and there are five significant figures in the result.

⚠ **Discussion** Note that the least precise measurement is not necessarily the one with the fewest number of significant figures. The least precise is the one whose rightmost significant figure represents the largest unit: the "2" in 1103.2 s represents 2 tenths of a second. In addition or subtraction, we are concerned with the precision rather than the number of significant figures. The three quantities to be added have seven, three, and five significant figures, respectively, while the sum has five significant figures.

Practice Problem 1.3   Significant Figures in Subtraction

Calculate the difference 568.42 m − 3.924 m and write the result in scientific notation. How many significant figures are in the result?

Example 1.4

Significant Figures in Multiplication

Find the product of 45.26 m/s and 2.41 s. How many significant figures does the product have?

Strategy The product should have the same number of significant figures as the factor with the least number of significant figures.

Solution A calculator gives

$$45.26 \times 2.41 = 109.0766$$

Since the answer should have only three significant figures, we round the answer to

$$45.26 \text{ m/s} \times 2.41 \text{ s} = 109 \text{ m}$$

Discussion Writing the answer as 109.0766 m would give the false impression that we know the answer to a precision of about 0.0001 m, whereas we actually have a precision of only about 1 m.

Note that although both factors were known to two decimal places, our solution is properly given with no decimal places. It is the number of significant figures that matters in multiplication or division. In scientific notation, we write 1.09×10^2 m.

Practice Problem 1.4   Significant Figures in Division

Write the solution to 28.84 m divided by 6.2 s with the correct number of significant figures.

When an integer, or a fraction of integers, is used in an equation, the precision of the result is not affected by the integer or the fraction; the number of significant figures is limited only by the measured values in the problem. The fraction $\frac{1}{2}$ in an equation is *exact*; it does not reduce the number of significant figures to one. In an equation such as $C = 2\pi r$ for the circumference of a circle of radius r, the factors 2 and π are exact. We use as many digits for π as we need to maintain the precision of the other quantities.

Order-of-Magnitude Estimates Sometimes a problem may be too complicated to solve precisely, or information may be missing that would be necessary for a precise calculation. In such a case, an **order-of-magnitude** solution is the best we can do. By *order of magnitude*, we mean "roughly what power of ten?" An order of magnitude calculation is done to at most one significant figure. Even when a more precise solution is feasible, it is often a good idea to start with a quick, "back-of-the-envelope estimate." Why? Because we can often make a good guess about the correct order of magnitude of the answer to a problem, even before we start solving the problem. If the answer comes out with a different order of magnitude, we go back and search out an error. Suppose a problem concerns a vase that is knocked off a fourth-story window ledge. We can guess by experience the order of magnitude of the time it takes the vase to hit the ground. It might be 1 s, or 2 s, but we are certain that it is *not* 1000 s or 0.00001 s.

Back-of-the-envelope estimate: a calculation so short that it could easily fit on the back of an envelope

✓ CHECK POINT 1.4

What are some of the reasons for making order-of-magnitude estimates?

1.5   UNITS

A **metric system** of units has been used for many years in scientific work and in European countries. The metric system is based on powers of ten (Fig. 1.1). In 1960, the General Conference of Weights and Measures, an international authority on units, proposed a revised metric system called the *Système International d'Unités* in French (abbreviated **SI**), which uses the meter (m) for length, the kilogram (kg) for mass, the second (s) for time, and four more base units (Table 1.1). **Derived units** are constructed from combinations of the base units. For example, the SI unit of force is kg·m/s²; the combination of kg·m/s² is given a special name, the newton (N), in honor of Isaac Newton. The newton is a derived unit because it is composed of a combination of base units. When units are named after famous scientists, the name of the unit is written with a lowercase letter, even though it is based on a proper name; the *abbreviation* for the unit is written with an upper-case letter. The inside front cover of the book has a complete listing of the derived SI units used in this book.

kg·m/s² can also be written kg·m·s⁻²

As an alternative to explicitly writing powers of ten, SI uses prefixes for units to indicate power of ten factors. Table 1.2 shows some of the powers of ten and the SI prefixes used for them. These are also listed on the inside front cover of the book. Note that when an SI unit with a prefix is raised to a power, the prefix is *also* raised to that power. For example, $8 \text{ cm}^3 = 2 \text{ cm} \times 2 \text{ cm} \times 2 \text{ cm}$.

SI units are preferred in physics and are emphasized in this book. Since other units are sometimes used, we must know how to convert units. Various scientific fields, even in physics, do use units other than SI units, whether for historical or practical reasons.

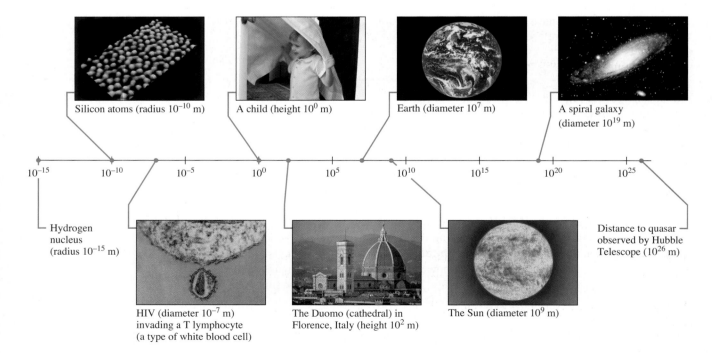

Silicon atoms (radius 10^{-10} m)

A child (height 10^0 m)

Earth (diameter 10^7 m)

A spiral galaxy (diameter 10^{19} m)

10^{-15} 10^{-10} 10^{-5} 10^0 10^5 10^{10} 10^{15} 10^{20} 10^{25}

Hydrogen nucleus (radius 10^{-15} m)

HIV (diameter 10^{-7} m) invading a T lymphocyte (a type of white blood cell)

The Duomo (cathedral) in Florence, Italy (height 10^2 m)

The Sun (diameter 10^9 m)

Distance to quasar observed by Hubble Telescope (10^{26} m)

Figure 1.1 Scientific notation uses powers of ten to express quantities that have a wide range of values.

Table 1.1	SI Base Units		
Quantity	**Unit Name**	**Symbol**	**Definition**
Length	meter	m	The distance traveled by light in vacuum during a time interval of 1/299 792 458 s.
Mass	kilogram	kg	The mass of the international prototype of the kilogram.
Time	second	s	The duration of 9 192 631 770 periods of the radiation corresponding to the transition between the two hyperfine levels of the ground state of the cesium-133 atom.
Electric current	ampere	A	The constant current in two long, thin, straight, parallel conductors placed 1 m apart in vacuum that would produce a force on the conductors of 2×10^{-7} N per meter of length.
Temperature	kelvin	K	The fraction 1/273.16 of the thermodynamic temperature of the triple point of water.
Amount of substance	mole	mol	The amount of substance that contains as many elementary entities as there are atoms in 0.012 kg of carbon-12.
Luminous intensity	candela*	cd	The luminous intensity, in a given direction, of a source that emits radiation of frequency 540×10^{12} Hz and that has a radiant intensity in that direction of 1/683 watts per steradian.

*Not used in this book

For example, in atomic and nuclear physics, the SI unit of energy (the joule, J) is rarely used; instead the energy unit used is usually the electron-volt (eV). Biologists and chemists use units that are not familiar to physicists. One reason that SI is preferred is that it provides a common denominator—all scientists are familiar with the SI units.

In most of the world, SI units are used in everyday life and in industry. In the United States, the U.S. customary units—sometimes called English units—are still used. The base units for this system are the foot, the second, and the pound. The pound is legally defined in the United States as a unit of mass, but it is also commonly used as a unit of force (in which case it is sometimes called *pound-force*). Since mass and force are entirely different concepts in physics, this inconsistency is one good reason to use SI units.

In the autumn of 1999, to the chagrin of NASA, a $125 million spacecraft was destroyed as it was being maneuvered into orbit around Mars. The company building the booster rocket provided information about the rocket's thrust in U.S. customary units, but the NASA scientists who were controlling the rocket thought the figures provided were in metric units. Arthur Stephenson, chairman of the Mars Climate Orbiter Mission Failure Investigation Board, stated that, "The 'root cause' of the loss of the spacecraft was the failed translation of English units into metric units in a segment of ground-based, navigation-related mission software." After a journey of 122 million miles, the Climate Orbiter dipped about 15 miles too deep into the Martian atmosphere, causing the propulsion system to overheat. The discrepancy in units unfortunately caused a dramatic failure of the mission.

Converting Units If the statement of a problem includes a mixture of different units, the units must be converted to a single, consistent set before the problem is solved. Quantities to be added or subtracted *must be expressed in the same units*. Usually the best way is to convert everything to SI units. Common conversion factors are listed on the inside front cover of this book.

Examples 1.5 and 1.6 illustrate the technique for converting units. The quantity to be converted is multiplied by one or more conversion factors written as a fraction equal to 1. The units are multiplied or divided as algebraic quantities.

What happened to the Mars Climate Orbiter?

Table 1.2	SI Prefixes
Prefix (abbreviation)	**Power of Ten**
peta- (P)	10^{15}
tera- (T)	10^{12}
giga- (G)	10^{9}
mega- (M)	10^{6}
kilo- (k)	10^{3}
deci- (d)	10^{-1}
centi- (c)	10^{-2}
milli- (m)	10^{-3}
micro- (μ)	10^{-6}
nano- (n)	10^{-9}
pico- (p)	10^{-12}
femto- (f)	10^{-15}

Some conversions are exact by definition. One meter is defined to be *exactly* equal to 100 cm; all SI prefixes are exactly a power of ten. The use of an exact conversion factor such as 1 m = 100 cm, or 1 foot = 12 inches, does not affect the precision of the result; the number of significant figures is limited only by the other quantities in the problem.

Example 1.5

Buying Clothes in a Foreign Country

Michel, an exchange student from France, is studying in the United States. He wishes to buy a new pair of jeans, but the sizes are all in *inches*. He does remember that 1 m = 3.28 ft and that 1 ft = 12 in. If his waist size is 82 cm, what is his waist size in inches?

Strategy   Each conversion factor can be written as a fraction. If 1 m = 3.28 ft, then

$$\frac{3.28 \text{ ft}}{1 \text{ m}} = 1$$

We can multiply any quantity by 1 without changing its value. We arrange each conversion factor in a fraction and multiply one at a time to get from centimeters to inches.

Solution   We first convert cm to meters.

$$82 \text{ cm} \times \frac{1 \text{ m}}{100 \text{ cm}}$$

Now, we convert meters to feet.

$$82 \text{ cm} \times \frac{1 \text{ m}}{100 \text{ cm}} \times \frac{3.28 \text{ ft}}{1 \text{ m}}$$

Finally, we convert feet to inches.

$$82 \text{ cm} \times \frac{1 \text{ m}}{100 \text{ cm}} \times \frac{3.28 \text{ ft}}{1 \text{ m}} \times \frac{12 \text{ in}}{1 \text{ ft}} = 32 \text{ in}$$

In each case, the fraction is written so that the unit we are converting *from* cancels out.

As a check:

$$\text{cm} \times \frac{\text{m}}{\text{cm}} \times \frac{\text{ft}}{\text{m}} \times \frac{\text{in}}{\text{ft}} = \text{in}$$

Discussion   This problem could have been done in one step using a direct conversion factor from inches to cm (1 in = 2.54 cm). One of the great advantages of SI units is that all the conversion factors are powers of ten (see Table 1.2); there is no need to remember that there are 12 inches in a foot, 4 quarts in a gallon, 16 ounces in a pound, 5280 feet in a mile, and so on.

Practice Problem 1.5   **Driving on the Autobahn**

A BMW convertible travels on the German autobahn at a speed of 128 km/h. What is the speed of the car (a) in meters per second? (b) in miles per hour?

Example 1.6

Conversion of Volume

A beaker of water contains 255 mL of water. (1 mL = 1 milliliter; 1 L = 1000 cm^3.) What is the volume of the water in (a) cubic centimeters? (b) cubic meters?

Strategy   First convert milliliters to liters; then convert liters to cubic centimeters. To convert cubic centimeters to cubic meters, use 100 cm = 1 m. Since there are *three* factors of centimeters to convert, we have to multiply by $\left(\frac{1 \text{ m}}{100 \text{ cm}}\right)$ *three times*.

Solution   (a) The prefix milli- means 10^{-3}, so 1 mL = 10^{-3} L. Then

$$255 \text{ mL} \times \frac{10^{-3} \text{ L}}{1 \text{ mL}} \times \frac{1000 \text{ cm}^3}{1 \text{ L}} = 255 \text{ cm}^3$$

(b) 1 m = 100 cm. Since we need to convert *cubic* centimeters to *cubic* meters, we must raise the conversion factor to the third power:

$$255 \text{ cm}^3 \times \left(\frac{1 \text{ m}}{100 \text{ cm}}\right)^3 = 255 \text{ cm}^3 \times \frac{(1 \text{ m})^3}{(100 \text{ cm})^3}$$

$$255 \text{ cm}^3 \times \frac{1 \text{ m}^3}{100^3 \text{ cm}^3} = 2.55 \times 10^{-4} \text{ m}^3$$

Discussion   Be careful when a unit is raised to a power other than one; the conversion factor must be raised to the same power. Writing out the units to make sure they cancel prevents mistakes. When a quantity is raised to a power, both the number and the unit must be raised to the same power. $(100 \text{ cm})^3$ is equal to $100^3 \text{ cm}^3 = 10^6 \text{ cm}^3$; it is *not* equal to 100 cm^3, nor is it equal to 10^6 cm.

Practice Problem 1.6   **Surface Area of Earth**

The radius of Earth is 6.4×10^3 km. Find the surface area of Earth in square meters and in square miles. (Surface area of a sphere = $4\pi r^2$.)

Whenever a calculation is performed, always write out the units with each quantity. Combine the units algebraically to find the units of the result. This small effort has three important benefits:

1. It shows what the units of the result are. A common mistake is to get the correct numerical result of a calculation but to write it with the wrong units, making the answer wrong.
2. It shows where unit conversions must be done. If units that should have canceled do not, we go back and perform the necessary conversion. When a distance is calculated and the result comes out with units of meter-seconds per hour (m·s/h), we should convert hours to seconds.
3. It helps locate mistakes. If a distance is calculated and the units come out as m/s, we know to look for an error.

✓ CHECKPOINT 1.5

If 1 fluid ounce (fl oz) is approximately 30 mL, how many liters are in a half gallon (64 fl oz) of milk?

1.6   DIMENSIONAL ANALYSIS

Dimensions are basic *types* of units, such as time, length, and mass. (Warning: The word *dimension* has several other meanings, such as in "three-dimensional space" or "the dimensions of a soccer field.") Many different units of length exist: meters, inches, miles, nautical miles, fathoms, leagues, astronomical units, angstroms, and cubits, just to name a few. All have dimensions of length; each can be converted into any other.

We can add, subtract, or equate quantities only if they have the same dimensions (although they may not necessarily be given in the same units). It is possible to add 3 meters to 2 inches (after converting units), but it is not possible to add 3 meters to 2 kilograms. To analyze dimensions, treat them as algebraic quantities, just as we did

---

Example 1.7

Dimensional Analysis for a Distance Equation

Analyze the dimensions of the equation $d = vt$, where d is distance traveled, v is speed, and t is elapsed time.

Strategy   Replace each quantity with its dimensions. Distance has dimensions [L]. Speed has dimensions of length per unit time [L/T]. The equation is dimensionally consistent if the dimensions are the same on both sides.

Solution   The right side has dimensions

$$\frac{[L]}{[T]} \times [T] = [L]$$

Since both sides of the equation have dimensions of length, the equation is dimensionally consistent.

Discussion   If, by mistake, we wrote $d = v/t$ for the relation between distance traveled and elapsed time, we could

quickly catch the mistake by looking at the dimensions. On the right side, v/t would have dimensions $[L/T^2]$, which is not the same as the dimensions of d on the left side.

A quick dimensional analysis of this sort is a good way to catch algebraic errors. Whenever we are unsure whether an equation is correct, we can check the dimensions.

Practice Problem 1.7   Testing Dimensions of Another Equation

Test the dimensions of the following equation:

$$d = \frac{1}{2} at$$

where d is distance traveled, a is acceleration (which has SI units m/s^2), and t is the elapsed time. If incorrect, can you suggest what might have been omitted?

with units in Section 1.5. Usually [M], [L], and [T] are used to stand for mass, length, and time dimensions, respectively. Equivalently, we can use the SI base units: kg for mass, m for length, and s for time.

Applying Dimensional Analysis   Dimensional analysis is good for more than just checking equations. In some cases, we can completely solve a problem—up to a dimensionless factor like $1/(2\pi)$ or $\sqrt{3}$—using dimensional analysis. To do this, first list all the relevant quantities on which the answer might depend. Then determine what combinations of them have the same dimensions as the answer for which we are looking. If only one such combination exists, then we have the answer, except for a possible dimensionless multiplicative constant.

Example 1.8

Violin String Frequency

While it is being played, a violin string produces a tone with frequency f in s^{-1}; the frequency is the number of vibrations *per second* of the string. The string has mass m, length L, and tension T. If the tension is increased 5.0%, how does the frequency change? Tension has SI unit kg·m/s².

Strategy   We could make a study of violin strings, but let us see what we can find out by dimensional analysis. We want to find out how the frequency f can depend on m, L, and T. We won't know if there is a dimensionless constant involved, but we can work by proportions so any such constant will divide out.

Solution   The unit of tension T is kg·m/s². The units of f do not contain kg or m; we can get rid of them from T by dividing the tension by the length and the mass:

$$\frac{T}{mL} \text{ has SI unit } s^{-2}$$

That is almost what we want; all we have to do is take the square root:

$$\sqrt{\frac{T}{mL}} \text{ has SI unit } s^{-1}$$

Therefore,

$$f = C\sqrt{\frac{T}{mL}}$$

where C is some dimensionless constant. To answer the question, let the original frequency and tension be f and T and the new frequency and tension be f' and T', where $T' = 1.050T$. Frequency is proportional to the square root of tension, so

$$\frac{f'}{f} = \sqrt{\frac{T'}{T}} = \sqrt{1.050} = 1.025$$

The frequency increases 2.5%.

Discussion   We'll learn in Chapter 11 how to calculate the value of C, which is 1/2. That is the *only* thing we cannot get by dimensional analysis. There is *no* other way to combine T, m, and L to come up with a quantity that has the units of frequency.

Practice Problem 1.8   Increase in Kinetic Energy

When a body of mass m is moving with a speed v, it has kinetic energy associated with its motion. Energy is measured in kg·m²·s⁻². If the speed of a moving body is increased by 25% while its mass remains constant, by what percentage does the kinetic energy increase?

CHECKPOINT 1.6

If two quantities have different dimensions, is it possible to (a) multiply; (b) divide; (c) add; (d) subtract them?

1.7   PROBLEM-SOLVING TECHNIQUES

No single method can be used to solve every physics problem. We demonstrate useful problem-solving techniques in the examples in every chapter of this text. Even for a particular problem, there may be more than one correct way to approach the solution. Problem-solving techniques are *skills* that must be *practiced* to be learned.

Think of the problem as a puzzle to be solved. Only in the easiest problems is the solution method immediately apparent. When you do not know the entire path to a solution, see where you can get by using the given information—find whatever you can. Exploration of this sort may lead to a solution by suggesting a path that had not been considered. Be willing to take chances. You may even find the challenge enjoyable!

When having some difficulty, it helps to work with a classmate or two. One way to clarify your thoughts is to put them into words. After you have solved a problem, try to explain it to a friend. If you can explain the problem's solution, you really do understand it. Both of you will benefit. But do not rely too much on help from others; the goal is for each of you to develop your own problem-solving skills.

General Guidelines for Problem Solving

1. Read the problem *carefully* and *all the way through.*
2. Reread the problem one sentence at a time and draw a sketch or diagram to help you visualize what is happening.
3. Write down and organize the given information. Some of the information can be written in labels on the diagram. Be sure that the labels are unambiguous. Identify in the diagram the object, the position, the instant of time, or the time interval to which the quantity applies. Sometimes information might be usefully written in a table beside the diagram. Look at the wording of the problem again for information that is implied or stated indirectly.
4. Identify the goal of the problem. What quantities need to be found?
5. If possible, make an estimate to determine the order of magnitude of the answer. This estimate is useful as a check on the final result to see if it is reasonable.
6. Think about how to get from the given information to the final desired information. Do not rush this step. Which principles of physics can be applied to the problem? Which will help get to the solution? How are the known and unknown quantities related? Are all of the known quantities relevant, or might some of them not affect the answer? Which equations are relevant and may lead to the solution to the problem? This step requires skills developed only with much practice in problem solving.
7. Frequently, the solution involves more than one step. Intermediate quantities might have to be found first and then used to find the final answer. Try to map out a path from the given information to the solution. Whenever possible, a good strategy is to divide a complex problem into several simpler subproblems.
8. Perform algebraic manipulations with algebraic symbols (letters) as far as possible. Substituting the numbers in too early has a way of hiding mistakes.
9. Finally, if the problem requires a numerical answer, substitute the known numerical quantities, *with their units*, into the appropriate equation. Leaving out the units is a common source of error. Writing the units shows when a unit conversion needs to be done—and also may help identify an algebra mistake.
10. Once the solution is found, don't be in a hurry to move on. Check the answer—is it reasonable? Try to think of other ways to solve the same problem. Many problems can be solved in several different ways. Besides providing a check on the answer, finding more than one method of solution deepens our understanding of the principles of physics and develops problem-solving skills that will help solve other problems.

1.8   APPROXIMATION

Physics is about building conceptual and mathematical models and comparing observations of the real world with the model. Simplified models help us to analyze complex situations. In various contexts we assume there is no friction, or no air resistance, no heat loss, or no wind blowing, and so forth. If we tried to take all these things into consideration with every problem, the problems would become vastly more complicated to solve. We never can take account of *every* possible influence. We freely make approximations whenever possible to turn a complex problem into an easier one, as long as the answer will be accurate enough for our purposes.

A valuable skill to develop is the ability to know when an assumption or approximation is reasonable. It might be permissible to ignore air resistance when dropping a stone, but not when dropping a beach ball. Why? We must always be prepared to justify any approximation we make by showing the answer is not changed very much by its use.

As well as making simplifying approximations in models, we also recognize that measurements are approximate. Every measured quantity has some uncertainty; it is impossible for a measurement to be exact to an arbitrarily large number of significant figures. Every measuring device has limits on the precision and accuracy of its measurements.

Approximating the Surface Area of the Human Body   Sometimes it is difficult or impossible to measure precisely a quantity that is needed for a problem. Then we have to make a reasonable estimate. Suppose we need to know the surface area of a human being to determine the heat loss by radiation in a cold room. We can estimate the height of an average person. We can also estimate the average distance around the waist or hips. Approximating the shape of a human body as a cylinder, we can estimate the surface area by calculating the surface area of a cylinder with the same height and circumference (Fig. 1.2a).

If we need a better estimate, we use a slightly more refined model. For instance, we might approximate the arms, legs, trunk, and head and neck as cylinders of various sizes (Fig. 1.2b). How different is the sum of these areas from the original estimate? That gives an idea of how close the first estimate is.

(a)   (b)

Figure 1.2 Approximation of human body by one or more cylinders.

Example 1.9

Number of Cells in the Human Body

Average-sized cells in the human body are about 10 μm in length (Fig. 1.3). How many cells are in the human body? Make an order-of-magnitude estimate.

Strategy   We divide this problem into three subproblems: estimating the volume of a human, estimating the volume of the average cell, and finally estimating the number of cells.

To find the volume of a human body, we approximate the body as a cylinder, as previously discussed. Next we assume the cells are cubical to find the volume of a cell. Third, the ratio of the two volumes (volume of the body to volume of the cell) shows how many cells are in the body.

Solution   Model the body as a cylinder. A typical height is about 2 m. A typical *maximum* circumference (think hip size) is about 1 m. The corresponding radius is $1/(2\pi)$ m, or about 1/6 m. The *average* radius is somewhat smaller; say

Figure 1.3

Scanning electron micrograph of a precursor T lymphocyte (a type of white blood cell in the human body). The cell is approximately 12 μm in diameter.

0.1 m. The volume of a cylinder is the height times the cross-sectional area:

$$V = Ah = \pi r^2 h \approx 3 \times (0.1 \text{ m})^2 \times (2 \text{ m}) = 0.06 \text{ m}^3$$

continued on next page

Example 1.9 continued

The volume of a cube is $V = s^3$. Then the volume of an average cell is about

$$V_{\text{cell}} \approx (1 \times 10^{-5} \text{ m})^3 = 1 \times 10^{-15} \text{ m}^3$$

The number of cells is the ratio of the two volumes:

$$N = \frac{\text{volume of body}}{\text{average volume of cell}} \approx \frac{6 \times 10^{-2} \text{ m}^3}{1 \times 10^{-15} \text{ m}^3} \approx 6 \times 10^{13}$$

Discussion   Based on this rough estimate, we cannot rule out the possibility that a better estimate might be 3×10^{13}. On the other hand, we *can* rule out the possibility that the number of cells is, say, 100 million ($= 10^8$).

Practice Problem 1.9   Drinking Water Consumed in the United States

How many liters of water are swallowed by the people living in the United States in one year? This is a type of problem made famous by the physicist Enrico Fermi (1901–1954), who was a master at this sort of back-of-the-envelope calculation. Such problems are often called *Fermi problems* in his honor. (1 liter = 10^{-3} m^3 ≈ 1 quart.)

1.9   GRAPHS

Graphs are used to help us see a pattern in the relationship between two quantities. It is much easier to see a pattern on a graph than to see it in a table of numerical values. When we do experiments in physics, we change one quantity (the **independent variable**) and see what happens to another (the **dependent variable**). We want to see how one variable *depends on* another. The value of the independent variable is usually plotted along the horizontal axis of the graph. In a plot of p versus q, which means p is plotted on the vertical axis and q on the horizontal axis, normally p is the dependent variable and q is the independent variable.

Some general guidelines for recording data and making graphs are given next.

Recording Data and Making Data Tables

1. Label columns with the names of the data being measured and be sure to include the units for the measurements. Do not erase any data, but just draw a line through data that you think are erroneous. Sometimes you may decide later that the data were correct after all.

2. Try to make a realistic estimate of the precision of the data being taken when recording numbers. For example, if the timer says 2.3673 s, but you know your reaction time can vary by as much as 0.1 s, the time should be recorded as 2.4 s. When doing calculations using measured values, remember to round the final answer to the correct number of significant figures.

3. Do not wait until you have collected all of your data to start a graph. It is much better to graph each data point as it is measured. By doing so, you can often identify equipment malfunction or measurement errors that make your data unreliable. You can also spot where something interesting happens and take data points closer together there. Graphing as you go means that you need to find out the range of values for both the independent and dependent variables.

Graphing Data

1. Make *large*, *neat* graphs. A tiny graph is not very illuminating. Use at least half a page. A graph made carelessly obscures the pattern between the two variables.

2. Label axes with the name of the quantities graphed and their units. Write a meaningful title.

The equation of a straight line on a graph of y versus x can be written $y = mx + b$, where m is the slope and b is the y-intercept (the value of y corresponding to $x = 0$).

The symbol Δ, the Greek uppercase letter delta, stands for the difference between two measurements. The notation Δy is read aloud as "delta y" and represents a change in the value of y.

3. When a linear relation is expected, use a ruler or straightedge to draw the best-fit straight line. Do not *assume* that the line must go through the origin—make a measurement to find out, if possible. Some of the data points will probably fall above the line and some will fall below the line.

4. Determine the slope of a best-fit line by measuring the ratio $\Delta y / \Delta x$ using as large a range of the graph as possible. Do not choose two data points to calculate the slope; instead, read values from two points on the best-fit line. Show the calculations. Do not forget to write the units; slopes of graphs in physics have units, since the quantities graphed have units.

5. When a nonlinear relationship is expected between the two variables, the best way to test that relationship is to manipulate the data algebraically so that a linear graph is expected. The human eye is a good judge of whether a straight line fits a set of data points. It is not so good at deciding whether a curve is parabolic, cubic, or exponential. To test the relationship $x = \frac{1}{2}at^2$, where x and t are the quantities measured, graph x versus t^2 instead of x versus t.

6. If one data point does not lie near the line or smooth curve connecting the other data points, that data point should be investigated to see whether an error was made in the measurement or whether some interesting event is occurring at that point. If something unusual is happening there, obtain additional data points in the vicinity.

7. When the slope of a graph is used to calculate some quantity, pay attention to the equation of the line and the units along the axes. The quantity to be found may be the inverse of the slope or twice the slope or one half the slope. For example, if you wish to find the value of a in the relationship $x = \frac{1}{2}at^2$, and you make a graph of x versus t^2, then the slope of the line is $\frac{1}{2}a$. The value of a you seek is twice the slope.

Example 1.10

Length of a Spring

In an introductory physics laboratory experiment, students are investigating how the length of a spring varies with the weight hanging from it. Various weights (accurately calibrated to 0.01 N) ranging up to 6.00 N can be hung from the spring; then the length of the spring is measured with a meterstick (Fig. 1.4). The goal is to see if the weight F and length L are related by

$$F = kx$$

where $x = (L - L_0)$, L_0 is the length of the spring when no weight is hanging from it, and k is called the *spring constant* of the spring. Graph the data in the table and calculate k for this spring.

F (N):	0	0.50	1.00	2.50	3.00	3.50	4.00	5.00	6.00
L (cm):	9.4	10.2	12.5	17.9	19.7	22.5	23.0	28.8	29.5

Strategy   Weight is the independent variable, so it is plotted on the horizontal axis. After plotting the data points, we draw the best-fit straight line. Then we calculate the slope of the line, using two points on the line that are widely separated

Figure 1.4

A weight causes an extension in the length of a spring.

and that cross gridlines of the graph (so the values are easy to read). The slope of the graph is not k; we must solve the equation for L, since length is plotted on the vertical axis.

continued on next page

Example 1.10 continued

Solution   Figure 1.5 shows a graph with data points and a best-fit straight line. There is some scatter in the data, but a linear relationship is plausible.

Two points where the line crosses gridlines of the graph are (0.80 N, 12.0 cm) and (4.40 N, 25.0 cm). From these, we calculate the slope:

$$\text{slope} = \frac{\Delta L}{\Delta F} = \frac{25.0 \text{ cm} - 12.0 \text{ cm}}{4.40 \text{ N} - 0.80 \text{ N}} = 3.61 \frac{\text{cm}}{\text{N}}$$

By analyzing the units of the equation $F = k(L - L_0)$, it is clear that the slope cannot be the spring constant; k has the same units as weight divided by length (N/cm). Is the slope equal to $1/k$? The units would be correct for that case. To be sure, we solve the equation of the line for L:

$$L = \frac{F}{k} + L_0$$

We recognize the equation of a line with a slope of $1/k$. Therefore,

$$k = \frac{1}{3.61 \text{ cm/N}} = 0.277 \text{ N/cm}$$

Discussion   As discussed in the graphing guidelines, the slope of the straight-line graph is calculated from two widely spaced values *along the best-fit line*. We do not subtract values of actual data points. We are looking for an average value from the data; using two data points to find the slope would defeat the purpose of plotting a graph or of taking more than two data measurements. The values read from the graph, including the units, are indicated in Fig. 1.5. The units for the slope are cm/N, since we plotted centimeters versus newtons. For this particular problem the *inverse* of the slope is the quantity we seek, the spring constant in N/cm.

Practice Problem 1.10   Another Weight on Spring

What is the length of the spring of Example 1.10 when a weight of 8.00 N is suspended? Assume that the relationship found in Example 1.10 still holds for this weight.

Figure 1.5
Spring length versus weight hanging.

Master the Concepts

- Terms used in physics must be precisely defined. A term may have a different meaning in physics from the meaning of the same word in other contexts.

- A working knowledge of algebra, geometry, and trigonometry is essential in the study of physics.

- The *factor* by which a quantity is increased or decreased is the ratio of the new value to the original value.

- When we say that *A* is *proportional* to *B* (written $A \propto B$), we mean that if *B* increases by some factor, then *A* must increase by the same factor.

- In *scientific notation*, a number is written as the product of a number between 1 and 10 and a whole-number power of ten.

- *Significant figures* are the basic *grammar* of precision. They enable us to communicate quantitative information and indicate the precision to which that information is known.

- When two or more quantities are added or subtracted, the result is as precise as the *least precise* of the quantities. When quantities are multiplied or divided, the result has

continued on next page

the same number of significant figures as the quantity with the *smallest number of significant figures.*

- Order-of-magnitude estimates and calculations are made to be sure that the more precise calculations are realistic.
- The units used for scientific work are those from the *Système International* (*SI*). SI uses seven *base units,* which include the meter (m), the kilogram (kg), and the second (s) for length, mass, and time, respectively. Using combinations of the base units, we can construct other *derived units.*
- If the statement of a problem includes a mixture of different units, the units should be converted to a single, consistent set before the problem is solved. Usually the best way is to convert everything to SI units.

- Dimensional analysis is used as a quick check on the validity of equations. Whenever quantities are added, subtracted, or equated, they must have the same dimensions (although they may not necessarily be given in the same units).
- Mathematical approximations aid in simplifying complicated problems.
- Problem-solving techniques are *skills* that must be *practiced* to be learned.
- A graph is plotted to give a picture of the data and to show how one variable changes with respect to another. Graphs are used to help us see a pattern in the relationship between two variables.
- Whenever possible, make a careful choice of the variables plotted so that the graph displays a linear relationship.

Conceptual Questions

1. Give a few reasons for studying physics.
2. Why must words be carefully defined for scientific use?
3. Why are simplified models used in scientific study if they do not exactly match real conditions?
4. By what factor does tripling the radius of a circle increase (a) the circumference of the circle? (b) the area of the circle?
5. What are some of the advantages of scientific notation?
6. After which numeral is the decimal point usually placed in scientific notation? What determines the number of numerical digits written in scientific notation?
7. Are all the digits listed as "significant figures" precisely known? Might any of the significant digits be less precisely known than others? Explain.
8. Why is it important to write quantities with the correct number of significant figures?
9. List three of the base units used in SI.
10. What are some of the differences between the SI and the customary U.S. system of units? Why is SI preferred for scientific work?
11. Sort the following units into three groups of dimensions and identify the dimensions: fathoms, grams, years, kilometers, miles, months, kilograms, inches, seconds.
12. What are the first two steps to be followed in solving almost any physics problem?
13. Why do scientists plot graphs of their data instead of just listing values?
14. A student's lab report concludes, "The speed of sound in air is 327." What is wrong with that statement?
15. Once the solution of a problem has been found, what should be done before moving on to solve another problem?

Multiple-Choice Questions

1. One kilometer is approximately
   (a) 2 miles   (b) 1/2 mile   (c) 1/10 mile (d) 1/4 mile
2. 55 mi/h is approximately
   (a) 90 km/h   (b) 30 km/h   (c) 10 km/h   (d) 2 km/h
3. By what factor does the volume of a cube increase if the length of the edges are doubled?
   (a) 16   (b) 8   (c) 4   (d) 2   (e) $\sqrt{2}$
4. If the length of a box is reduced to one third of its original value and the width and height are doubled, by what factor has the volume changed?
   (a) 2/3   (b) 1   (c) 4/3   (d) 3/2
   (e) depends on relative proportion of length to height and width
5. If the area of a circle is found to be half of its original value after the radius is multiplied by a certain factor, what was the factor used?
   (a) $1/(2\pi)$ (b) 1/2   (c) $\sqrt{2}$ (d) $1/\sqrt{2}$ (e) 1/4
6. In terms of the original diameter d, what new diameter will result in a new spherical volume that is a factor of eight times the original volume?
   (a) $8d$ (b) $2d$ (c) $d/2$ (d) $d \times \sqrt[3]{2}$ (e) $d/8$
7. An equation for potential energy states $U = mgh$. If U is in $kg \cdot m^2 \cdot s^{-2}$, m is in kg, and g is in $m \cdot s^{-2}$, what are the units of h?
   (a) s   (b) s^2 (c) m^{-1} (d) m   (e) g^{-1}

8. The equation for the speed of sound in a gas states that $v = \sqrt{\gamma k_B T/m}$. Speed v is measured in m/s, γ is a dimensionless constant, T is temperature in kelvins (K), and m is mass in kg. What are the units for the Boltzmann constant, k_B?
   (a) $kg \cdot m^2 \cdot s^2 \cdot K$ (b) $kg \cdot m^2 \cdot s^{-2} \cdot K^{-1}$ (c) $kg^{-1} \cdot m^{-2} \cdot s^2 \cdot K$
   (d) $kg \cdot m/s$ (e) $kg \cdot m^2 \cdot s^{-2}$

9. How many significant figures should be written in the sum 4.56 g + 9.032 g + 580.0078 g + 540.439 g?
   (a) 3   (b) 4   (c) 5   (d) 6   (e) 7

10. How many significant figures should be written in the product 0.007 840 6 m × 9.450 20 m?
    (a) 3   (b) 4   (c) 5   (d) 6   (e) 7

Problems

 🕲   Combination conceptual/quantitative problem

⚕   Biological or medical application

✦   Challenging problem

Blue #   Detailed solution in the Student Solutions Manual

① ②   Problems paired by concept

🌐   Text website interactive or tutorial

1.3 The Use of Mathematics

1. The gardener is told that he must increase the height of his fences 37% if he wants to keep the deer from jumping in to eat the foliage and blossoms. If the current fence is 1.8 m high, how high will the new fence be?

2. What is the ratio of the number of seconds in a day to the number of hours in a day?

3. A spherical balloon expands when it is taken from the cold outdoors to the inside of a warm house. If its surface area increases 16.0%, by what percentage does the radius of the balloon change?

4. A spherical balloon is partially blown up and its surface area is measured. More air is then added, increasing the volume of the balloon. If the surface area of the balloon expands by a factor of 2.0 during this procedure, by what factor does the radius of the balloon change? (🌐 tutorial: car on curve)

5. For any cube with edges of length s, what is the ratio of the surface area to the volume?

6. Samantha is 1.50 m tall on her eleventh birthday and 1.65 m tall on her twelfth birthday. By what factor has her height increased? By what percentage?

7. The "scale" of a certain map is 1/10 000. This means the length of, say, a road as represented on the map is 1/10 000 the actual length of the road. What is the ratio of the *area* of a park as represented on the map to the actual area of the park? (🌐 tutorial: scaling)

8. On Monday, a stock market index goes up 5.00%. On Tuesday, the index goes down 5.00%. What is the net percentage change in the index for the two days?

9. According to Kepler's third law, the orbital period T of a planet is related to the radius R of its orbit by $T^2 \propto R^3$. Jupiter's orbit is larger than Earth's by a factor of 5.19. What is Jupiter's orbital period? (Earth's orbital period is 1 yr.)

10. If the radius of a circular garden plot is increased by 25%, by what percentage does the area of the garden increase?

11. A poster advertising a student election candidate is too large according to the election rules. The candidate is told she must reduce the length and width of the poster by 20.0%. By what percentage will the area of the poster be reduced?

12. An architect is redesigning a rectangular room on the blueprints of the house. He decides to double the width of the room, increase the length by 50%, and increase the height by 20%. By what factor has the volume of the room increased?

1.4 Scientific Notation and Significant Figures

13. Perform these operations with the appropriate number of significant figures.
    (a) 3.783×10^6 kg + 1.25×10^8 kg
    (b) $(3.783 \times 10^6$ m$) \div (3.0 \times 10^{-2}$ s$)$

14. Write these numbers in scientific notation: (a) the U.S. population, 290 000 000; (b) the diameter of a helium nucleus, 0.000 000 000 000 003 8 m.

15. In the following calculations, be sure to use an appropriate number of significant figures.
    (a) 3.68×10^7 g − 4.759×10^5 g
    (b) $\dfrac{6.497 \times 10^4 \text{ m}^2}{5.1037 \times 10^2 \text{ m}}$

16. Write your answer to the following problems with the appropriate number of significant figures.
    (a) 6.85×10^{-5} m + 2.7×10^{-7} m
    (b) 702.35 km + 1897.648 km
    (c) 5.0 m × 4.3 m
    (d) $(0.04/\pi)$ cm
    (e) $(0.040/\pi)$ m

17. Solve the following problem and express the answer in scientific notation with the appropriate number of significant figures: (3.2 m) × (4.0×10^{-3} m) × (1.3×10^{-8} m).

18. How many significant figures are in each of these measurements?
    (a) 7.68 g   (b) 0.420 kg
    (c) 0.073 m   (d) 7.68×10^5 g
    (e) 4.20×10^3 kg   (f) 7.3×10^{-2} m
    (g) 2.300×10^4 s

19. Solve the following problem and express the answer in meters per second (m/s) with the appropriate number of significant figures. (3.21 m)/(7.00 ms) = ? [*Hint:* Note that ms stands for milliseconds.]

20. Solve the following problem and express the answer in meters with the appropriate number of significant figures and in scientific notation:

$$3.08 \times 10^{-1} \text{ km} + 2.00 \times 10^{3} \text{ cm}$$

1.5 Units

21. A cell membrane is 7.0 nm thick. How thick is it in inches?

22. The label on a small soda bottle lists the volume of the drink as 355 mL. (a) How many fluid ounces are in the bottle? A competitor's drink is labeled 16.0 fl oz. (b) How many milliliters are in that drink?

23. The length of the river span of the Brooklyn Bridge is 1595.5 ft. The total length of the bridge is 6016 ft. Find the length and the order of magnitude in meters of (a) the river span and (b) the total bridge length?

24. Convert 1.00 km/h to meters per second (m/s).

25. A sprinter can run at a top speed of 0.32 miles per minute. Express her speed in (a) m/s and (b) mi/h.

26. The first modern Olympics in 1896 had a marathon distance of 40 km. In 1908, for the Olympic marathon in London, the length was changed to 42.195 km to provide the British royal family with a better view of the race. This distance was adopted as the official marathon length in 1921 by the International Amateur Athletic Federation. What is the official length of the marathon in miles?

27. At the end of 2006 an expert economist from the Global Economic Institute in Kiel, Germany, predicted a drop in the value of the dollar against the euro of 10% over the next 5 years. If the exchange rate was $1.27 to 1 euro on November 5, 2006, and was $1.45 to 1 euro on November 5, 2007, what was the actual drop in the value of the dollar over the first year?

28. The intensity of the Sun's radiation that reaches Earth's atmosphere is 1.4 kW/m^2 (kW = kilowatt; W = watt). Convert this to W/cm^2.

29. Density is the ratio of mass to volume. Mercury has a density of 1.36×10^{4} kg/m^3. What is the density of mercury in units of g/cm^3?

30. A molecule in air is moving at a speed of 459 m/s. How many meters would the molecule move during 7.00 ms (milliseconds) if it didn't collide with any other molecules?

31. Express this product in units of km^3 with the appropriate number of significant figures: (3.2 km) × (4.0 m) × (13 × 10^{-3} mm).

32. (a) How many square centimeters are in 1 square foot? (1 in. = 2.54 cm.) (b) How many square centimeters are in 1 square meter? (c) Using your answers to parts (a) and (b), but without using your calculator, roughly how many square feet are in one square meter?

33. A snail crawls at a pace of 5.0 cm/min. Express the snail's speed in (a) ft/s and (b) mi/h.

34. An average-sized capillary in the human body has a cross-sectional area of about 150 μm^2. What is this area in square millimeters (mm^2)?

1.6 Dimensional Analysis

35. An equation for potential energy states $U = mgh$. If U is in joules, with m in kg, h in m, and g in m/s^2, find the combination of SI base units that are equivalent to joules.

36. One equation involving force states that $F_{\text{net}} = ma$, where F_{net} is in newtons, m is in kg, and a is in m·s^{-2}. Another equation states that $F = -kx$, where F is in newtons, k is in kg·s^{-2}, and x is in m. (a) Analyze the dimensions of ma and kx to show they are equivalent. (b) What are the dimensions of the force unit newton?

37. An equation for the period T of a planet (the time to make one orbit about the Sun) is $4\pi^2 r^3/(GM)$, where T is in s, r is in m, G is in m^3/(kg·s^2), and M is in kg. Show that the equation is dimensionally correct.

38. The relationship between kinetic energy K (SI unit kg·m^2·s^{-2}) and momentum p is $K = p^2/(2m)$, where m stands for mass. What is the SI unit of momentum?

39. An expression for buoyant force is $F_B = \rho g V$, where F_B has dimensions [MLT^{-2}], ρ (density) has dimensions [ML^{-3}], and g (gravitational field strength) has dimensions [LT^{-2}]. (a) What must be the dimensions of V? (b) Which could be the correct interpretation of V: velocity or volume?

40. Use dimensional analysis to determine how the linear speed (v in m/s) of a particle traveling in a circle depends on some, or all, of the following properties: r is the radius of the circle; ω is an angular frequency in s^{-1} with which the particle orbits about the circle, and m is the mass of the particle. There is no dimensionless constant involved in the relation.

1.8 Approximation

41. What is the approximate distance from your eyes to a book you are reading?

42. What is the approximate volume of your physics textbook in cubic centimeters (cm^3)?

43. (a) Estimate the average mass of a person's leg.
    (b) Estimate the length of a full-size school bus.

44. Estimate the number of times a human heart beats during its lifetime.

45. Estimate the number of automobile repair shops in the city you live in by considering its population, how often an automobile needs repairs, and how many cars each shop can service per day. Then look in the yellow pages of your phone directory to see how accurate your estimate is. By what percentage was your estimate off?

46. What is the order of magnitude of the number of seconds in one year?

47. What is the order of magnitude of the height (in meters) of a 40-story building?

1.9 Graphs

48. You have just performed an experiment in which you measured many values of two quantities, A and B. According to theory, $A = cB^3 + A_0$. You want to verify that the values of c and A_0 are correct by making a graph of your data that enables you to determine their values from a slope and a vertical axis intercept. What quantities do you put on the vertical and horizontal axes of the plot?

49. A nurse recorded the values shown in the temperature chart for a patient's temperature. Plot a graph of temperature versus elapsed time and from the graph find (a) an estimate of the temperature at noon and (b) the slope of the graph. (c) Would you expect the graph to follow the same trend over the next 12 hours? Explain.

Time	Temp (°F)
10:00 A.M.	100.00
10:30 A.M.	100.45
11:00 A.M.	100.90
11:30 A.M.	101.35
12:45 P.M.	102.48

50. A graph of x versus t^4, with x on the vertical axis and t^4 on the horizontal axis, is linear. Its slope is 25 m/s^4 and its vertical axis intercept is 3 m. Write an equation for x as a function of t.

51. A patient's temperature was 97.0°F at 8:05 A.M. and 101.0°F at 12:05 P.M. If the temperature change with respect to elapsed time was linear throughout the day, what would the patient's temperature be at 3:35 P.M.?

52. The weight of a baby measured over an 11-mon period is given in the weight chart for this problem. (a) Plot the baby's weight versus age over the 11 mon. (b) What was the average monthly weight gain for this baby over the period from birth to 5 mon? How do you find this value from the graph? (c) What was the average monthly weight gain for the baby over the period from 5 mon to 10 mon? (d) If a baby continued to grow at the same rate as in the first five months of life, what would the child weigh at age 12 yr?

Weight (lb)	Age (mon)
6.6	0 (birth)
7.4	1.0
9.6	2.0
11.2	3.0
12.0	4.0
13.6	5.0
13.8	6.0
14.8	7.0
15.0	8.0
16.6	9.0
17.5	10.0
18.4	11.0

53. A physics student plots results of an experiment as v versus t. The equation that describes the line is given by $at = v - v_0$. (a) What is the slope of this line? (b) What is the vertical axis intercept of this line?

54. A linear plot of speed versus elapsed time has a slope of 6.0 m/s^2 and a vertical intercept of 3.0 m/s. (a) What is the change in speed in the time interval between 4.0 s and 6.0 s? (b) What is the speed when the elapsed time is equal to 5.0 s?

55. In a laboratory you measure the decay rate of a sample of radioactive carbon. You write down the following measurements:

Time (min)	0	15	30	45	60	75	90
Decays/s	405	237	140	90	55	32	19

(a) Plot the decays per second versus time. (b) Plot the natural logarithm of the decays per second versus the time. Why might the presentation of the data in this form be useful?

56. An object is moving in the x-direction. A graph of the distance it has moved as a function of time is shown. (a) What are the slope and vertical axis intercept? (Be sure to include units.) (b) What physical significance do the slope and intercept on the vertical axis have for this graph?

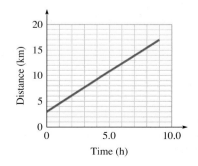

Comprehensive Problems

57. It is useful to know when a small number is negligible. Perform the following computations. (a) 186.300 + 0.0030 (b) 186.300 − 0.0030 (c) 186.300 × 0.0030 (d) 186.300/0.0030 (e) For cases (a) and (b), what percent error will result if you ignore the 0.0030? Explain why you can never ignore the smaller number, 0.0030, for case (c) and case (d)? (f) What rule can you make about ignoring small values?

58. The weight of an object at the surface of a planet is proportional to the planet's mass and inversely proportional to the square of the radius of the planet. Jupiter's radius is 11 times Earth's and its mass is 320 times Earth's. An apple weighs 1.0 N on Earth. How much would it weigh on Jupiter?

59. In cleaning out the artery of a patient, a doctor increases the radius of the opening by a factor of 2.0. By what factor does the cross-sectional area of the artery change?

60. A scanning electron micrograph of xylem vessels in a corn root shows the vessels magnified by a factor of 600. In the micrograph the xylem vessel is 3.0 cm in diameter. (a) What is the diameter of the vessel itself? (b) By what factor has the cross-sectional area of the vessel been increased in the micrograph?

61. The average speed of a nitrogen molecule in air is proportional to the square root of the temperature in kelvins (K). If the average speed is 475 m/s on a warm summer day (temperature = 300.0 K), what is the average speed on a cold winter day (250.0 K)?

62. A furlong is 220 yd; a fortnight is 14 d. How fast is 1 furlong per fortnight (a) in μm/s? (b) in km/day?

63. Given these measurements, identify the number of significant figures and rewrite in scientific notation.
    (a) 0.00574 kg (b) 2 m   (c) 0.450×10^{-2} m
    (d) 45.0 kg   (e) 10.09×10^4 s (f) 0.09500×10^5 mL

64. A car has a gas tank that holds 12.5 U.S. gal. Using the conversion factors from the inside front cover, (a) determine the size of the gas tank in cubic inches. (b) A cubit is an ancient measurement of length that was defined as the distance from the elbow to the tip of the finger, about 18 in. long. What is the size of the gas tank in cubic cubits?

65. You are given these approximate measurements: (a) the radius of Earth is 6×10^6 m, (b) the length of a human body is 6 ft, (c) a cell's diameter is 10^{-6} m, (d) the width of the hemoglobin molecule is 3×10^{-9} m, and (e) the distance between two atoms (carbon and nitrogen) is 3×10^{-10} m. Write these measurements in the simplest possible metric prefix forms (in either nm, Mm, μm, or whatever works best).

66. A typical virus is a packet of protein and DNA (or RNA) and can be spherical in shape. The influenza A virus is a spherical virus that has a diameter of 85 nm. If the volume of saliva coughed onto you by your friend with the flu is 0.010 cm³ and 10^{-9} of that volume consists of viral particles, how many influenza viruses have just landed on you?

67. The smallest "living" thing is probably a type of infectious agent known as a viroid. Viroids are plant pathogens that consist of a circular loop of single-stranded RNA, containing about 300 bases. (Think of the bases as beads strung on a circular RNA string.) The distance from one base to the next (measured along the circumference of the circular loop) is about 0.35 nm. What is the diameter of a viroid in (a) m, (b) μm, and (c) in.?

68. The largest living creature on Earth is the blue whale, which has an average length of 70 ft. The largest blue whale on record (and therefore the largest animal ever found) was 1.10×10^2 ft long. (a) Convert this length to meters. (b) If a double-decker London bus is 8.0 m long, how many double-decker-bus lengths is the record whale?

69. The record blue whale in Problem 68 had a mass of 1.9×10^5 kg. Assuming that its average density was 0.85 g/cm³, as has been measured for other blue whales, what was the volume of the whale in cubic meters (m³)? (Average density is the ratio of mass to volume.)

70. A sheet of paper has length 27.95 cm, width 8.5 in., and thickness 0.10 mm. What is the volume of a sheet of paper in m³? (Volume = length × width × thickness.)

71. An object moving at constant speed v around a circle of radius r has an acceleration a directed toward the center of the circle. The SI unit of acceleration is m/s². (a) Use dimensional analysis to find a as a function of v and r. (b) If the speed is increased 10.0%, by what percentage does the radial acceleration increase?

72. The speed of ocean waves depends on their wavelength λ (measured in meters) and the gravitational field strength g (measured in m/s²) in this way:

$$v = K\lambda^p g^q$$

where K is a dimensionless constant. Find the values of the exponents p and q.

73. In the United States, we often use miles per hour (mi/h) when discussing speed, but the SI unit of speed is m/s. What is the conversion factor for changing m/s to mi/h? If you want to make a quick approximation of the speed in mi/h given the speed in m/s, what might be the easiest conversion factor to use?

74. How many cups of water are required to fill a bathtub?

75. Without looking up any data, make an order-of-magnitude estimate of the annual consumption of gasoline (in gallons) by passenger cars in the United States. Make reasonable order-of-magnitude estimates for any quantities you need. Think in terms of average quantities. (1 gal ≈ 4 L.)

76. Some thieves, escaping after a bank robbery, drop a sack of money on the sidewalk. (a) Estimate the mass of the sack if it contains $5000 in half-dollar coins. (b) Estimate the mass if the sack contains $1 000 000 in $20 bills.

77. The weight W of an object is given by $W = mg$, where m is the object's mass and g is the gravitational field strength. The SI unit of field strength g, expressed in SI base units, is m/s^2. What is the SI unit for weight, expressed in base units?

78. Kepler's law of planetary motion says that the square of the period of a planet (T^2) is proportional to the cube of the distance of the planet from the Sun (r^3). Mars is about twice as far from the Sun as Venus. How does the period of Mars compare with the period of Venus?

79. One morning you read in the *New York Times* that the net worth of the richest man in the world, Carlos Slim Helu of Mexico, is $59 000 000 000. Later that day you see him on the street, and he gives you a $100 bill. What is his net worth now? (Think of significant figures.)

80. Estimate the number of hairs on the average human head. [*Hint:* Consider the number of hairs in an area of 1 in.^{2} and then consider the area covered by hair on the head.]

81. Suppose you have a pair of Seven League Boots. These are magic boots that enable you to stride along a distance of 7.0 leagues with each step. (a) If you march along at a military march pace of 120 paces/min, what will be your speed in km/h? (b) Assuming you could march on top of the oceans when you step off the continents, how long (in minutes) will it take you to march around the Earth at the equator? (1 league = 3 mi = 4.8 km.)

82. The electrical power P drawn from a generator by a lightbulb of resistance R is $P = V^2/R$, where V is the line voltage. The resistance of bulb B is 42% greater than the resistance of bulb A. What is the ratio P_B/P_A of the power drawn by bulb B to the power drawn by bulb A if the line voltages are the same?

83. Three of the fundamental constants of physics are the speed of light, $c = 3.0 \times 10^8$ m/s, the universal gravitational constant, $G = 6.7 \times 10^{-11}$ m^3·kg^{-1}·s^{-2}, and Planck's constant, $h = 6.6 \times 10^{-34}$ kg·m^2·s^{-1}.

(a) Find a combination of these three constants that has the dimensions of time. This time is called the *Planck time* and represents the age of the universe before which the laws of physics as presently understood cannot be applied. (b) Using the formula for the Planck time derived in part (a), what is the time in seconds?

84. Use dimensional analysis to determine how the period T of a swinging pendulum (the elapsed time for a complete cycle of motion) depends on some, or all, of these properties: the length L of the pendulum, the mass m of the pendulum bob, and the gravitational field strength g (in m/s^2). Assume that the amplitude of the swing (the maximum angle that the string makes with the vertical) has no effect on the period.

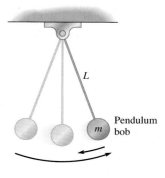

85. The Space Shuttle astronauts use a *massing chair* to measure their mass. The chair is attached to a spring and is free to oscillate back and forth. The frequency of the oscillation is measured and that is used to calculate the total mass m attached to the spring. If the spring constant of the spring k is measured in kg/s^2 and the chair's frequency f is 0.50 s^{-1} for a 62-kg astronaut, what is the chair's frequency for a 75-kg astronaut? The chair itself has a mass of 10.0 kg. [*Hint:* Use dimensional analysis to find out how f depends on m and k.]

86. The average depth of the oceans is about 4 km, and oceans cover about 70% of Earth's surface. Make an order-of-magnitude estimate of the volume of water in the oceans. Do not look up any data in books. (Use your ingenuity to estimate the radius or circumference of Earth.)

87. The population of a culture of yeast cells is studied in the laboratory to see the effects of limited resources (food, space) on population growth. At 2-h intervals, the size of the population (measured as total mass of yeast cells) is recorded (see table on p. 24). (a) Make a graph of the yeast population as a function of elapsed time. Draw a best-fit smooth curve. (b) Notice from the graph of part (a) that after a long time, the population asymptotically approaches a maximum known as the *carrying capacity*. From the graph, estimate the carrying capacity for this population. (c) When the population is much smaller than the carrying capacity, the growth is expected to be exponential: $m(t) = m_0 e^{rt}$, where m is the population at any time t, m_0 is the initial population, r is the *intrinsic growth rate* (i.e., the growth rate in the absence of limits), and e is the base of natural logarithms (see Appendix A.3). To obtain a straight line graph from this exponential relationship, we can plot the natural logarithm of m/m_0:

$$\ln \frac{m}{m_0} = \ln e^{rt} = rt$$

Make a graph of $\ln (m/m_0)$ versus t from $t = 0$ to $t = 6.0$ h, and use it to estimate the intrinsic growth rate *r* for the yeast population. (The term ln stands for the natural logarithm; see Appendix A.3 if you need help with natural logs.)

Time (h)	Mass (g)
0.0	3.2
2.0	5.9
4.0	10.8
6.0	19.1
8.0	31.2
10.0	46.5
12.0	62.0
14.0	74.9
16.0	83.7
18.0	89.3
20.0	92.5
22.0	94.0
24.0	95.1

Answers to Practice Problems

1.1 81.0 W

1.2 (a) five; 1.0544×10^{-4} kg; (b) four; 5.800×10^{-3} cm; (c) ambiguous, three to six; if three, 6.02×10^5 s

1.3 The least precise value is to the nearest hundredth of a meter, so we round the result to the nearest hundredth of a meter: 564.50 m or, in scientific notation, 5.6450×10^2 m; five significant figures.

1.4 4.7 m/s

1.5 (a) 35.6 m/s; (b) 79.5 mi/h

1.6 5.1×10^{14} m^2; 2.0×10^8 mi^2

1.7 The equation is dimensionally inconsistent; the right side has dimensions [L/T]. To have matching dimensions we must multiply the right side by [T]; the equation must involve time squared: $d = \frac{1}{2}at^2$.

1.8 kinetic energy = (constant) $\times mv^2$; kinetic energy increases by 56%.

1.9 10^{11} L (Make a rough estimate of the population to be about 3×10^8 people, each drinking about 1.5 L/day.)

1.10 38.3 cm

Answers to Checkpoints

1.3 The volume increases by a factor of 27.

1.4 Order-of-magnitude estimates provide a quick method for obtaining limited precision solutions to problems. Even if greater accuracy is required, order-of-magnitude calculations are still useful as they provide a check as to the accuracy of the higher precision calculation.

1.5 1.9 L

1.6 (a) and (b) It is possible to multiply or divide quantities with different dimensions. (c) and (d) To be added or subtracted, quantities *must* have the same dimensions.

CHAPTER

2

Force

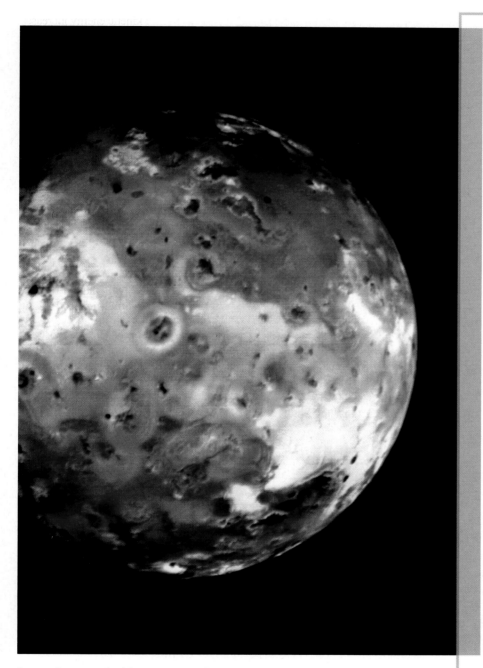

Io, as photographed by Voyager 1 from a distance of 862 000 km.

The Voyager 1 and Voyager 2 space probes were launched in 1977. Between them, they explored all the large planets of the outer solar system (Jupiter, Saturn, Uranus, and Neptune) and 48 of their moons. Voyager 1 discovered volcanoes on Io, one of the moons of Jupiter, and showed that rings of Saturn are made up of thousands of "ringlets" made up of particles of ice and rock. Voyager 2 photographed the extreme geography of Miranda, a moon of Uranus, showing a 6-km cliff on a moon that is only a few hundred kilometers in size. Passing only 5000 km from Neptune, Voyager 2 discovered that the planet is buffeted by 2000 km/h winds.

Almost 30 years after being launched, Voyager 1 is now exploring the outer reaches of the solar system more than 15 billion kilometers from the Sun—about 100 times as far as Earth—and Voyager 2 is not far behind. They are heading out of the solar system at speeds of 17 km/s and 16 km/s, respectively, without being propelled by rockets or any other kind of engine. How can they continue to move at such high speeds for many years without an engine to drive them? (See p. 36 for the answer.)

- scientific notation and significant figures (Section 1.4)
- converting units (Section 1.5)
- Pythagorean theorem (Appendix A.6)
- trigonometric functions: sine, cosine, and tangent (Appendix A.7)
- problem-solving techniques (Section 1.7)
- meanings of *velocity* and *mass* in physics (Section 1.2)

2.1   FORCE

This chapter begins our study of **mechanics**, the branch of physics that considers how interactions between objects affect the motion of those objects. Just as human life would be dull without social interactions, the physical universe would be dull without physical interactions. Social interactions with friends and family change our behavior; physical interactions change the "behavior" (motion, temperature, etc.) of matter.

Force: a push or pull that one object exerts on another

An interaction between two objects can be described and measured in terms of two *forces*, one exerted on each of the two interacting objects. A **force** is a push or a pull. When you play soccer, your foot exerts a force on the ball while the two are in contact, thereby changing the speed and direction of the ball's motion. At the same time, the ball exerts a force on your foot, the effect of which you can feel. To understand the motion of an object, whether it be a soccer ball or the International Space Station, we need to analyze the forces acting on the object.

Long-range Forces   Forces exerted on macroscopic objects—objects that are large enough for us to observe without instrumentation—can be either long-range forces or contact forces. **Long-range forces** do not require the two objects to be touching. These forces can exist even if the two objects are far apart and even if there are other objects between the two. For example, gravity is a long-range force. The gravitational force exerted on the Earth by the Sun keeps the Earth in orbit around the Sun, despite the great distance between them and despite other planets that occasionally come between them. The Earth also exerts a long-range gravitational force on objects on or near its surface. We call the size of the gravitational force (also called the strength, or **magnitude**, of the force) that a planet or moon exerts on a nearby object the object's **weight**.

The weight of an object near a planet or moon is the magnitude of the gravitational force exerted on it by that planet or moon.

PHYSICS AT HOME

Besides gravity, other long-range forces are electric or magnetic in nature. On a dry day, run a comb vigorously through your hair until you hear some crackling. Now hold the comb a few centimeters from small pieces of a torn paper napkin. Observe the long-range electrical interaction between the paper and the comb.

Now take a refrigerator magnet. Hold it near but not touching the refrigerator door. You can feel the effect of a long-range magnetic interaction.

Part 3 of this book treats electromagnetic forces in detail. Until then, you can safely assume that gravity is the only significant long-range interaction unless the statement of a problem indicates otherwise.

Contact forces exist only as long as the objects are touching one another.

Contact Forces   All forces exerted on macroscopic objects, other than long-range gravitational and electromagnetic forces, involve contact. **Contact forces** exist only as long as the objects are touching one another. Your foot has no noticeable effect on a soccer ball's motion until the two come into contact and the force lasts only as long as they are in contact. Once the ball moves away from your foot, your foot has no further influence over the ball's motion.

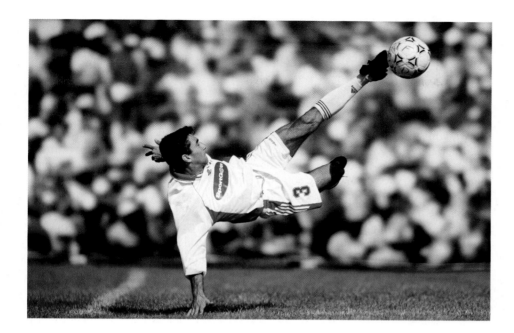

A soccer player's foot exerts a force on the ball only when they are touching.

The idea of contact is a useful simplification for macroscopic objects. What we call a single contact force is really the net effect of enormous numbers of electromagnetic forces between atoms on the surfaces of the two objects. On an atomic scale, the idea of "contact" breaks down. There is no way to define "contact" between two atoms—in other words, there is no unique distance between the atoms at which the forces they exert on each other suddenly become zero.

Measuring Forces

If the concept of force is to be useful in physics, there must be a way to measure forces. Consider a simple spring scale (Fig. 2.1). As the scale's pan is pulled down, a spring is stretched. The harder you pull, the more the spring stretches. As the spring stretches, an attached pointer moves. Then all we have to do to measure the applied force is to calibrate the scale so the amount of stretch measures the magnitude of the force.

In the United States, supermarket scales are generally calibrated to measure forces in pounds (lb). In the SI system, the unit of force is the **newton** (N). To convert pounds to newtons, use the approximate conversion factors

$$1 \text{ lb} = 4.448 \text{ N} \quad \text{or} \quad 1 \text{ N} = 0.2248 \text{ lb} \tag{2-1}$$

There are more sophisticated means for measuring forces than a supermarket scale. Even so, many operate on the same principle as the supermarket scale: a force is measured by the deformation—change of size or shape—it produces in some object.

Force Is a Vector Quantity

The magnitude of a force is *not* a complete description of the force. The *direction* of the force is equally important. The direction of the brief contact force exerted by a soccer player's foot on the ball can make the difference between scoring a goal or not.

Force is one of many quantities in physics that are called **vectors**. All vectors have a direction as well as a magnitude. Section 1.2 mentioned that velocity, as defined in physics, has magnitude and direction. Velocity is another vector quantity: the magnitude of the velocity vector is the speed at which the object moves, and the direction of the velocity vector is the direction of motion. Other vector quantities you will study in this book include position, displacement, acceleration, momentum, angular momentum, torque, and the electric and magnetic fields.

Ceiling pulls up on scale

Newtons

Extension of spring

Hand pulls down on scale

Figure 2.1 As the bottom of a spring scale is pulled downward, the spring stretches. We can measure the force by measuring the extension of the spring. For many springs, the extension is approximately proportional to the force, which makes calibration easy. Note that there is a pull on *both* ends of the scale. The ceiling pulls up on the scale and supports the scale from above.

Vector quantities, such as force and velocity, have both magnitude and direction.

Vector quantities must be added according to special rules that take their directions into account.

The direction of any vector is always a *physical direction in space* such as up, down, north, or 35° south of west. If a homework or exam question has you calculate a vector quantity such as force or velocity, don't forget to specify the direction as well as the magnitude in your answer. One without the other is incomplete.

Scalars and Vectors   Mass is an example of a quantity that is a **scalar** rather than a vector. A scalar quantity can have magnitude, algebraic sign, and units, but not a direction in space. When scalars are added or subtracted, they do so in the usual way: 3 kg of water plus 2 kg of water is always equal to 5 kg of water. Adding vectors is different. All vectors follow the same rules of addition—rules that take into account the directions of the vectors being added. A 300-N force added to a 200-N force gives different results, depending on the directions of the two forces. If two friends are trying to push a car out of a snowbank, they help each other by applying forces *in the same direction* so the sum of the two forces is as large as possible. If they push in *opposite* directions, the net effect of the two forces would be *much* smaller. We introduce the rules for adding vectors in Sections 2.2 and 2.3. Whenever you need to add or subtract quantities, check whether they are vectors. If so, be sure to add them correctly according to the method you will learn later in this chapter. *Do not just add their magnitudes.*

In this book, an arrow over a boldface symbol indicates a vector quantity ($\vec{\mathbf{F}}$). (Some books use boldface without the arrow or the arrow without boldface.) When writing by hand, always draw an arrow over a vector symbol to distinguish it from a scalar. When the symbol for a vector is written without the arrow and in italics rather than boldface (F), it stands for the *magnitude* of the vector (which is a scalar). Absolute value bars are also used to stand for the magnitude of a vector, so $F = |\vec{\mathbf{F}}|$. The magnitude of a vector may have units and is never negative; it can be positive or zero.

Conceptual Example 2.1

Vector or Scalar?

Is temperature a vector quantity?

Strategy   If a quantity is a vector, it must have both a magnitude and a physical direction in space.

Solution and Discussion   Does temperature have a direction? A temperature in Fahrenheit (°F) or Celsius (°C) can be above or below zero—is that a direction? No. A vector must have a *physical direction* in space. It does not make sense to say that the temperature of your coffee is "85° in the southwest direction." "The temperature is up 5° today," means that it has increased, not that it is pointing vertically upward.

Temperature is a scalar. If we need to subtract temperatures to find the change in temperature, we subtract them like ordinary numbers. If the temperature of a cup of coffee changes from 82°C to 67°C, the temperature change is

$$\Delta T = T_{\text{final}} - T_{\text{initial}} = 67°\text{C} - 82°\text{C} = -15°\text{C}$$

Conceptual Practice Problem 2.1   Bank Balance

When you deposit a paycheck, the balance of your checking account "goes up." When you pay a bill, it "goes down." Is the balance of your account a vector quantity?

 A plus sign (+) between vector quantities indicates *vector addition*, not ordinary addition. An equals sign (=) between vector quantities means that the vectors are identical in magnitude *and* direction, *not* simply that their magnitudes are equal.

2.2   GRAPHICAL VECTOR ADDITION

To add two forces graphically, first draw an arrow to represent one of them (Fig. 2.2a). (It does not matter in what order vectors are added; $\vec{\mathbf{F}}_1 + \vec{\mathbf{F}}_2 = \vec{\mathbf{F}}_2 + \vec{\mathbf{F}}_1$.) The arrow points in the direction of the force and its length is proportional to the magnitude of the vector. It doesn't matter where you start drawing the arrow. The value of a vector is not changed by moving it as long as its direction and magnitude are not changed.

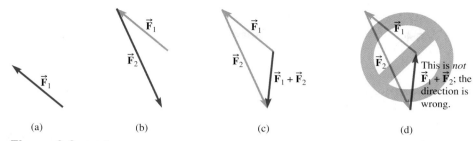

Figure 2.2 Adding two force vectors graphically. (a) Draw one vector arrow. (b) Draw the second, starting where the first arrow ended. (c) The sum of the two. (d) A common mistake.

Figure 2.3 Addition of vectors that are (a) in the same direction and (b) in opposite directions. (c) The sum of two vectors with equal magnitudes and opposite directions is zero. (When adding vectors whose directions are opposite, it sometimes helps to draw them next to each other rather than on top of each other so the vectors and their sum can be clearly seen.)

Now draw the second force arrow starting where the first ends. In other words, place the "tail" of the second arrow at the "tip" of the first (Fig 2.2b). Finally, draw an arrow starting from the *tail* of the first and ending at the *tip* of the second. This arrow represents the vector sum of the two forces (Fig 2.2c). A common error is to draw the sum from the tip of the second to the tail of the first (Fig. 2.2d). If the lengths and directions of the vectors are drawn accurately to scale, using a ruler and a protractor, then the length and direction of the sum can be determined with the ruler and protractor. To add more than two forces, continue drawing them tip to tail.

Adding vectors along the same line, we can draw these conclusions:

- If two forces are in the same direction, their sum is in the same direction (Fig. 2.3a) and its magnitude is the sum of the magnitudes of the two. If you and your friend push a heavy trunk with forces of 200 N and 300 N in the same direction, the net effect is that of a 500-N force in that direction.
- If two forces are in opposite directions, the magnitude of their sum is the *difference* between the magnitudes of the two vectors (Fig. 2.3b)—the larger minus the smaller, since vector magnitudes are never negative. The direction of the vector sum is the direction of the larger of the two. Pushing that trunk with a 400-N force to the right and a 300-N force to the left has the net effect of a 100-N force to the right.
- The only way that two vectors can add to zero is if they are opposites: they must have the same magnitude but opposite directions (Fig. 2.3c).

√ CHECKPOINT 2.2

What is the vector sum of a force of 20 N directed north and a force of 50 N directed south?

Example 2.2

Bringing Home the Maple Syrup

Two draft horses, Sam and Bob, are dragging a sled loaded with jugs of maple syrup. They pull with horizontal forces of equal magnitude 1.50 kN (kilonewtons) on the front of the sled. The force due to Sam is in the direction 15° north of east, and the force due to Bob is 15° south of east (Fig. 2.4). Use the graphical method of vector addition to find the magnitude and direction of the sum of the forces exerted on the sled by the two horses.

Strategy   Forces are vector quantities. To add vectors graphically and get an accurate result, we will use a ruler and a protractor. The protractor is used to draw the vector arrows in the correct directions and the ruler is used to draw them with the correct lengths. We must choose a convenient scale for the lengths of the vector arrows. Here we choose to represent 200 N as a length of 1 cm, so the 1.50-kN forces are drawn as vector arrows of length

$$1.50 \text{ kN} \times \frac{1 \text{ cm}}{200 \text{ N}} = 7.50 \text{ cm}$$

Once the sum is drawn, its direction and magnitude are determined with the ruler and protractor.

Solution   We can redraw any vector starting at any point, as long as we do not change its direction or magnitude. We can either add vector $\vec{\mathbf{F}}_B$ (the force exerted by Bob) to vector $\vec{\mathbf{F}}_S$ (the force exerted by Sam) or add vector $\vec{\mathbf{F}}_S$ to vector $\vec{\mathbf{F}}_B$. Both possibilities are shown in Fig. 2.5.

The drawing shows that the direction of the sum is due east. Measurement of the length of the arrow that represents the vector sum arrow yields 14.5 cm. The magnitude of the sum is, therefore,

$$14.5 \text{ cm} \times \frac{200 \text{ N}}{1 \text{ cm}} = 2.90 \text{ kN}$$

The sum of the two forces is 2.90 kN due east.

Discussion   It makes sense that the sum of the two forces points east since they are equal in magnitude and pull at equal angles on either side of east.

A quick check on the magnitude of the sum: if the two vectors being added were parallel, their sum would have magnitude 3.00 kN. Since they are not parallel, their sum must have a magnitude *smaller* than 3.00 kN. The magnitude of $\vec{\mathbf{F}}_S + \vec{\mathbf{F}}_B$ is only *slightly* smaller than if they were in the same direction because the angle between the two vectors is relatively small.

Practice Problem 2.2   Pulling at Other Angles

(a) If Sam and Bob were to pull with forces of the same magnitude as before (1.50 kN) but angled at 30° north and south of east, respectively, instead of 15°, would the sum of the two be larger, smaller, or the same magnitude as before? Illustrate with a sketch. (b) If Sam pulls at 10° north of east while Bob pulls at 15° south of east, is it still possible for the sum of the two forces to be due east if their magnitudes are not the same? Which force must have the larger magnitude? Illustrate with a sketch.

(a)

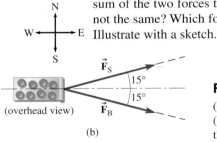

(overhead view)   (b)

Figure 2.4

(a) Hauling the maple syrup (side view). (b) Forces exerted by Sam and Bob on the sled (overhead view).

Scale: 1 cm = 200 N   Each sq = 1 cm × 1 cm

Figure 2.5

Graphical addition of the two force vectors. The tail of the second vector is placed at the tip of the first. The sum is the vector from the tail of the first to the tip of the second. Adding the vectors in a different order gives the same result.

2.3   VECTOR ADDITION USING COMPONENTS

Components of a Vector

Any vector can be expressed as the sum of vectors parallel to the *x*-, *y*-, and (if needed) *z*-axes. The *x*-, *y*-, and *z*-**components** of a vector indicate the magnitude and direction of the three vectors along the axes. A component has magnitude, units, and an algebraic sign (+ or −). The sign of a component indicates the direction along that axis. A positive *x*-component indicates the direction of the positive *x*-axis, but a negative *x*-component indicates the opposite direction (the negative *x*-axis). A vector quantity can be specified either by giving its magnitude and direction or by giving its components; the two representations are equally acceptable. The *x*-, *y*-, and *z*-components of vector $\vec{\mathbf{A}}$ are written with subscripts as follows: A_x, A_y, and A_z. The process of finding the components of a vector is called **resolving** the vector into its components.

Finding Components   Consider force vector $\vec{\mathbf{F}}$ in Fig. 2.6. We can think of $\vec{\mathbf{F}}$ as the sum of two vectors, one parallel to the *x*-axis and the other parallel to the *y*-axis. The magnitudes of these two vectors are the *magnitudes* (absolute values) of the *x*- and *y*-components of $\vec{\mathbf{F}}$. We can find the magnitudes of the components using the right triangle in Fig. 2.6 and the trigonometric functions in Fig. 2.7. The length of the arrow represents the magnitude of the force ($F = 9.4$ N), so

$$\cos 58° = \frac{\text{adjacent}}{\text{hypotenuse}} = \frac{|F_x|}{F} \quad \text{and} \quad \sin 58° = \frac{\text{opposite}}{\text{hypotenuse}} = \frac{|F_y|}{F}$$

Now we must determine the correct algebraic sign for each of the components. From Fig. 2.6, the vector along the *x*-axis points in the *positive x*-direction and the vector along the *y*-axis points in the *negative y*-direction, so in this case,

$$F_x = +F \cos 58° = 5.0 \text{ N} \quad \text{and} \quad F_y = -F \sin 58° = -8.0 \text{ N}$$

Using the right triangle in Fig. 2.8 gives the same values for the *x*- and *y*-components of $\vec{\mathbf{F}}$ since $\cos 32° = \sin 58°$ and $\sin 32° = \cos 58°$.

Figure 2.6 Resolving a force vector $\vec{\mathbf{F}}$ into *x*- and *y*-components.

$$\phi = 90° - \theta$$

$$\sin \theta = \frac{\text{side opposite } \angle\theta}{\text{hypotenuse}} = \frac{b}{c}$$

$$\cos \theta = \frac{\text{side adjacent } \angle\theta}{\text{hypotenuse}} = \frac{a}{c}$$

$$\tan \theta = \frac{\text{side opposite } \angle\theta}{\text{side adjacent } \angle\theta} = \frac{b}{a}$$

Figure 2.7 Trigonometric functions (see Appendix A.7 for more information).

Problem-Solving Strategy: Finding the *x*- and *y*-Components of a Vector from Its Magnitude and Direction

1. Draw a right triangle with the vector as the hypotenuse and the other two sides parallel to the *x*- and *y*-axes.
2. Determine one of the angles in the triangle.
3. Use trigonometric functions to find the magnitudes of the components. Make sure your calculator is in "degree mode" to evaluate trigonometric functions of angles in degrees and "radian mode" for angles in radians.
4. Determine the correct algebraic sign for each component.

Finding Magnitude and Direction   We must also know how to reverse the process to find a vector's magnitude and direction from its components.

Suppose we knew the components of the force vector in Fig. 2.6, but not the magnitude and direction. Let us find the angle θ between $\vec{\mathbf{F}}$ and the +*x*-axis:

$$\theta = \tan^{-1} \frac{\text{opposite}}{\text{adjacent}} = \tan^{-1} \frac{|F_y|}{|F_x|} = \tan^{-1} \frac{8.0 \text{ N}}{5.0 \text{ N}} = 58°$$

The magnitude of $\vec{\mathbf{F}}$ is

$$F = \sqrt{F_x^2 + F_y^2} = \sqrt{(+5.0 \text{ N})^2 + (-8.0 \text{ N})^2} = 9.4 \text{ N}$$

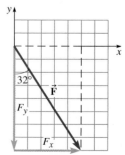

Figure 2.8 Resolving the force vector into components using a different right triangle.

Problem-Solving Strategy: Finding the Magnitude and Direction of a Vector from Its *x*- and *y*-Components

1. Sketch the vector on a set of *x*- and *y*-axes in the correct quadrant, according to the signs of the components.
2. Draw a right triangle with the vector as the hypotenuse and the other two sides parallel to the *x*- and *y*-axes.
3. In the right triangle, choose which of the unknown angles you want to determine.
4. Use the inverse tangent function to find the angle. The lengths of the sides of the triangle represent $|F_x|$ and $|F_y|$. If θ is opposite the side parallel to the *x*-axis, then $\tan \theta = $ opposite/adjacent $= |F_x/F_y|$. If θ is opposite the side parallel to the *y*-axis, then $\tan \theta = $ opposite/adjacent $= |F_y/F_x|$. If your calculator is in "degree mode," then the result of the inverse tangent operation will be in degrees. [In general, the inverse tangent has *two* possible values between 0 and $360°$ because $\tan \alpha = \tan (\alpha + 180°)$. However, when the inverse tangent is used to find one of the angles in a right triangle, the result can never be greater than $90°$, so the value the calculator returns is the one you want.]
5. Interpret the angle: specify whether it is the angle below the horizontal, or the angle west of south, or the angle clockwise from the negative *y*-axis, etc.
6. Use the Pythagorean theorem to find the magnitude of the vector.

$$F = \sqrt{F_x^2 + F_y^2} \tag{2-2}$$

Example 2.3

Exercise Is Good for You

Suppose you are standing on the floor doing your daily exercises. For one exercise, you lift your arms up and out until they are horizontal. In this position, assume that the deltoid muscle exerts a force of 270 N at an angle of 15° above the horizontal on the humerus (Fig. 2.9). What are the *x*- and *y*-components of this force?

Figure 2.9

Force exerted by the deltoid muscle on the humerus.

Strategy This problem gives the magnitude and direction of a force and asks for the components of the force. The directions of the axes are shown in Fig. 2.9. To find the components, we draw a right triangle with the force vector as the hypotenuse and the sides parallel to the *x*- and *y*-axes.

Solution Figure 2.10 shows a right triangle that can be used to find the components. The side of the triangle along

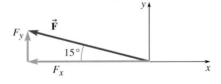

Figure 2.10

Drawing a right triangle to find the force components.

the *x*-axis is adjacent to the 15° angle, so the cosine function is used for the *x*-component.

$$\cos 15° = \frac{\text{adjacent}}{\text{hypotenuse}} = \frac{|F_x|}{F}$$

The *x*-component is negative; the +*x*-axis points to the right, while the *x*-component of the force is to the left. Therefore,

$$F_x = -F \cos 15° = -270 \text{ N} \times 0.9659 = -260 \text{ N}$$

The sine function is used for the *y*-component since the side representing F_y is opposite the 15° angle.

$$\sin 15° = \frac{\text{opposite}}{\text{hypotenuse}} = \frac{|F_y|}{F}$$

The *y*-component is up, along the +*y*-axis, so

$$F_y = +F \sin 15° = 270 \text{ N} \times 0.2588 = 70 \text{ N}$$

continued on next page

Example 2.3 continued

Discussion   To check the answer, we can convert the components back into magnitude and direction.

$$F = \sqrt{(260 \text{ N})^2 + (70 \text{ N})^2} = 270 \text{ N}$$

$$\theta = \tan^{-1}\left|\frac{F_y}{F_x}\right| = \tan^{-1}\frac{70 \text{ N}}{260 \text{ N}} = 15°$$

Practice Problem 2.3   Tilling the Garden

While tilling your garden, you exert a force on the handles of the tiller that has components $F_x = +85$ N and $F_y = -132$ N. The x-axis is horizontal and the y-axis points up. What are the magnitude and direction of this force?

Adding Vectors Using Components

Now that we know how to find components of vectors, we can use components to add vectors. Remember that each vector is thought of as the sum of vectors parallel to the axes (Fig. 2.11a). When adding vectors, we can add them in any order and group them as we please. So we can sum the x-components to find the x-component of the sum (Fig. 2.11b) and then do the same with the y-components (Fig. 2.11c):

$$\vec{C} = \vec{A} + \vec{B} \quad \text{if and only if} \quad C_x = A_x + B_x \quad \text{and} \quad C_y = A_y + B_y \qquad (2\text{-}3)$$

In Eq. (2-3), remember that $A_x + B_x$ represents ordinary addition since the signs of the components carry the direction information.

Problem-Solving Strategy: Adding Vectors Using Components

1. Find the x- and y-components of each vector to be added.
2. Add the x-components (*with their algebraic signs*) of the vectors to find the x-component of the sum. (If the signs are not correct, the sum will not be correct.)
3. Add the y-components (with their algebraic signs) of the vectors to find the y-component of the sum.
4. If necessary, use the x- and y-components of the sum to find the magnitude and direction of the sum.

Unit Vectors   The connection between a vector and its components may be expressed using the **unit vectors** $\hat{\mathbf{x}}$ (read aloud as "x hat"), $\hat{\mathbf{y}}$, and $\hat{\mathbf{z}}$, which are defined as vectors of magnitude 1 that point in the +x-, +y-, and +z-directions, respectively. (In some books, you may see them written as $\hat{\mathbf{i}}$, $\hat{\mathbf{j}}$, and $\hat{\mathbf{k}}$.) They are called *unit* vectors because the magnitude of each is the pure number 1—they do *not* have physical units such as kilograms or meters. Any vector $\vec{F}$ can be written as the sum of three vectors along the coordinate axes:

$$\vec{F} = F_x\hat{\mathbf{x}} + F_y\hat{\mathbf{y}} + F_z\hat{\mathbf{z}}$$

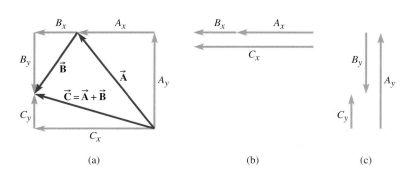

(a)   (b)   (c)

Figure 2.11 (a) $\vec{C} = \vec{A} + \vec{B}$, shown graphically with the x- and y-components of each vector illustrated. (b) $C_x = A_x + B_x$; (c) $C_y = A_y + B_y$.

Here F_x is the x-component of $\vec{F}$, which has physical units and can be positive or negative. $F_x\hat{x}$ is a vector of magnitude $|F_x|$ directed in the $+x$-direction if $F_x > 0$ and in the $-x$-direction if $F_x < 0$. For example, consider the force vector $\vec{F}$ of Fig. 2.8. $\vec{F}$ has x-component $F_x = +5.0$ N and y-component $F_y = -8.0$ N, so $\vec{F} = (+5.0$ N$)\hat{x} + (-8.0$ N$)\hat{y}$.

Using unit vector notation is one way to keep track of vector components in vector addition and subtraction without writing separate equations for each component. Adding two vectors in the xy-plane looks like this:

$$\vec{F}_1 + \vec{F}_2 = \left(F_{1x}\hat{x} + F_{1y}\hat{y}\right) + \left(F_{2x}\hat{x} + F_{2y}\hat{y}\right)$$

Regrouping the terms shows that the x-component of the sum is the sum of the x-components and likewise for the y-components:

$$\vec{F}_1 + \vec{F}_2 = \left(F_{1x} + F_{2x}\right)\hat{x} + \left(F_{1y} + F_{2y}\right)\hat{y}$$

 Estimation Using Graphical Addition   Even when using the component method to add vectors, the graphical method is an important first step. A rough sketch of vector addition, even one made without carefully measuring the lengths or the angles, has important benefits. Sketching the vectors makes it much easier to get the signs of the components correct. The graphical addition also serves as a check on the answer—it provides an estimate of the magnitude and direction of the sum, which can be used to check the algebraic answer. Graphical addition gives you a mental picture of what is going on and an intuitive feel for the algebraic calculations.

Example 2.4

Traction on a Foot

In a traction apparatus, three cords pull on the central pulley, each with magnitude 22.0 N, in the directions shown in Fig. 2.12. What is the sum of the forces exerted on the central pulley by the three cords? Give the magnitude and direction of the sum.

Strategy   First, we sketch the graphical addition of the three forces to get an estimate of the magnitude and direction of the sum. Then, to get an accurate answer, we resolve the three forces into their x- and y-components, sum the components, and then calculate the magnitude and direction of the sum.

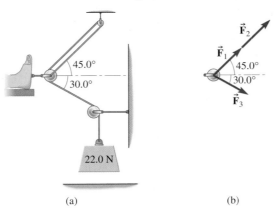

Figure 2.12
(a) A foot in traction; (b) the three forces exerted on the central pulley by the cords.

Solution   Figure 2.13 shows the graphical addition of the three forces exerted on the central pulley by the cords. From this sketch, we can tell that the sum of the three forces is at a relatively small angle above the horizontal (roughly half of 45°) and has a magnitude a bit larger than 44 N.

To find an algebraic solution, we find the components along the x- and y-axes and add them (Fig. 2.14). The x-components of the forces are

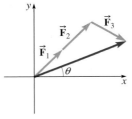

Figure 2.13

Graphical sum of the forces on the pulley due to the cords.

$$F_{1x} = F_{2x} = (22.0 \text{ N}) \cos 45.0°$$
$$F_{3x} = (22.0 \text{ N}) \cos 30.0°$$

The y-components of the forces are

$$F_{1y} = F_{2y} = (22.0 \text{ N}) \sin 45.0°$$
$$F_{3y} = (-22.0 \text{ N}) \sin 30.0°$$

The sum of the x-components is

$$F_x = F_{1x} + F_{2x} + F_{3x}$$
$$= 2 \times (22.0 \text{ N}) \cos 45.0° + (22.0 \text{ N}) \cos 30.0°$$
$$= 31.11 \text{ N} + 19.05 \text{ N} = 50.16 \text{ N}$$

continued on next page

Example 2.4 continued

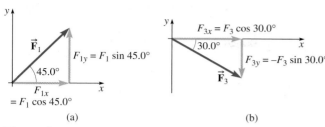

Figure 2.14

Finding the components of (a) $\vec{F}_1$ and (b) $\vec{F}_3$. For clarity, the vector arrows are drawn twice as long as they were in Fig. 2.13.

We keep an extra decimal place for now to minimize round-off error. The sum of the y-components is

$$F_y = F_{1y} + F_{2y} + F_{3y}$$

$$= 2 \times (22.0 \text{ N}) \sin 45.0° + (-22.0 \text{ N}) \sin 30.0°$$

$$= 31.11 \text{ N} - 11.00 \text{ N} = 20.11 \text{ N}$$

The magnitude of the sum is (Fig. 2.15):

$$F = \sqrt{F_x^2 + F_y^2} = \sqrt{(50.16 \text{ N})^2 + (20.11 \text{ N})^2} = 54.0 \text{ N}$$

and the direction of the sum is

$$\theta = \tan^{-1} \frac{\text{opposite}}{\text{adjacent}} = \tan^{-1} \frac{20.11 \text{ N}}{50.16 \text{ N}} = 21.8°$$

Figure 2.15

Finding the sum from its components.

The sum of the forces exerted on the pulley by the three cords is 54.0 N at an angle 21.8° above the +x-axis.

Discussion   To check the answer, look back at the graphical estimate. The magnitude of the sum (54.0 N) is somewhat larger than 44 N and the direction is at an angle very nearly half of 45° above the horizontal.

Practice Problem 2.4   Changing the Pulley Angles

The pulleys are moved, after which $\vec{F}_1$ and $\vec{F}_2$ are at an angle of 30.0° above the x-axis and $\vec{F}_3$ is 60.0° below the x-axis. (a) What is the sum of these three forces in component form? (b) What is the magnitude of the sum? (c) At what angle with the horizontal is the sum?

2.4   INERTIA AND EQUILIBRIUM: NEWTON'S FIRST LAW OF MOTION

Introduction to Newton's Laws of Motion

In 1687, Isaac Newton (1643–1727) published one of the greatest scientific works of all time, his *Philosophiae Naturalis Principia Mathematica* (or *Principia* for short). The Latin title translates as *The Mathematical Principles of Natural Philosophy*. In the *Principia*, Newton stated three laws of motion that form the basis of classical mechanics.

Together with his law of universal gravitation, Newton's laws showed for the first time that the motion of the heavenly bodies (the Sun, the planets, and their satellites) and the motion of earthly bodies can be understood using the same physical principles. To pre-Newtonian thinkers, it seemed that there must be two different sets of physical laws: one set to describe the motion of the heavenly bodies, thought to be perfect and enduring, and another to describe the motion of earthly bodies that always come to rest.

We will study Newton's laws one at a time and will phrase them in modern terms to help you understand them, rather than in a translation of the original Latin.

Net Force

When more than one force acts on an object, the subsequent motion of the object is determined by the *net force* acting on the object. The **net force** is the vector sum of all the forces acting on an object.

> **Definition of net force:**
> If $\vec{F}_1, \vec{F}_2, \ldots, \vec{F}_n$ are *all* the forces acting on an object, then the net force $\vec{F}_{net}$ acting on that object is the vector sum of those forces:
>
> $$\vec{F}_{net} = \sum \vec{F} = \vec{F}_1 + \vec{F}_2 + \cdots + \vec{F}_n \qquad (2\text{-}4)$$

The symbol $\sum$ is a capital Greek letter sigma that stands for "sum."

Newton's First Law of Motion

Newton's first law says that an object acted on by zero net force moves in a straight line with constant speed, or, if it is at rest, remains at rest. Using the concept of the velocity vector (see Sections 1.2 and 2.1), which is a measure of both the speed *and the direction of motion* of an object, we can restate the first law:

> ### Newton's First Law of Motion
>
> An object's velocity vector remains constant if and only if the net force acting on the object is zero.

This concise statement of Newton's first law includes both the case of an object at rest (zero velocity) and a moving object (nonzero velocity). Certainly it makes sense that an object at rest remains at rest unless some force acts on it to make it start to move. On the other hand, it may not be obvious that an object can continue to move with constant speed in a straight line without forces acting to keep it moving. In our experience, most moving objects come to rest because of forces that oppose motion, like friction and air resistance. A hockey puck can slide the entire length of a rink with very little change in speed or direction because the ice is slippery (frictional forces are small). If we could remove *all* the resistive forces, including friction and air resistance, the puck would slide without changing its speed or direction at all.

No force is required to keep an object in motion if there are no forces opposing its motion. When a hockey player strikes the puck with his stick, the brief contact force exerted on the puck by the stick changes the puck's velocity, but once the puck loses contact with the stick, it slides along the ice even though the stick no longer exerts a force on it.

Why Voyager space probes keep moving

The Voyager space probes are so far from the Sun that the gravitational forces exerted on them due to the Sun are negligibly small. To a very good approximation, we can say that the net force acting on them is zero. Therefore, the probes continue moving at constant speed along a straight line. No applied force has to be maintained by an engine to keep them moving because there are no forces that oppose their motion.

Inertia   Newton's first law is also called the **law of inertia**. In physics, **inertia** means resistance to *changes* in velocity. It does *not* mean resistance to the continuation of motion (or the tendency to come to rest). Newton based the law of inertia on the ideas of some of his predecessors, including Galileo Galilei (1564–1642) and René Descartes (1596–1650). In a series of clever experiments in which he rolled a ball up inclines of different angles, Galileo postulated that, if he could eliminate all resistive forces, a ball rolling on a horizontal surface would never stop (Fig. 2.16). Galileo made a brilliant conceptual leap from the real world with friction to an imagined, ideal world, free of friction. The law of inertia contradicted the view of the Greek philosopher Aristotle (384–322 B.C.E.). Almost 2000 years before Galileo, Aristotle had formulated his view that the natural state of an object is to be at rest; and, for an object to remain in motion, a force would have to act on it continuously. Galileo conjectured that, in the absence of friction and other resistive forces, no continued force is needed to keep an object moving.

Figure 2.16 (a) Galileo found that a ball rolled down an incline stops when it reaches *almost* the same height on the second incline. He decided that it would reach the *same* height if resistive forces could be eliminated. (b) As the second incline is made less and less steep, the ball rolls farther and farther before stopping. (c) If the second incline is horizontal, and there are no resistive forces, the ball would never stop.

However, Galileo thought that the sustained motion of an object would be in a great circle around the Earth. Shortly after Galileo's death, Descartes argued that the motion of an object free of any forces should be along a straight line rather than a circle. Newton acknowledged his debt to Galileo, Descartes, and others when he wrote: "If I have seen farther, it is because I was standing on the shoulders of giants."

Conceptual Example 2.5

Snow Shoveling

The task of shoveling newly fallen snow from the driveway can be thought of as a struggle against the inertia of the snow. Without the application of a net force, the snow remains at rest on the ground. However, in an important way the inertia of the snow makes it *easier* to shovel. Explain.

Strategy Think about the physical motions used when shoveling snow. (If you live where there is no snow, think about shoveling gravel from a wheelbarrow to line a garden path.) For the shoveling to be facilitated by the snow's inertia, there must be a time when the snow is moving on its own, without the shovel pushing it.

Solution and Discussion Imagine scooping up a shovelful of snow and swinging the shovel forward toward the side of the driveway. The snow and the shovel are both in motion. Then suddenly the forward motion of the shovel stops, but the snow continues to move forward because of its inertia; it slides forward off the shovel, to be pulled down to the ground by gravity. The snow does not stop moving forward when the forward force due to the shovel is removed.

This procedure works best with fairly dry snow. Wet sticky snow tends to cling to the shovel. The frictional force on the snow due to the shovel keeps it from moving forward and makes the job far more difficult. In this case, it might

help to give the shovel a thin coating of cooking oil to reduce the frictional force the shovel exerts on the snow.

Conceptual Practice Problem 2.5 Inertia on the Subway

Negar, a college student, stands on a subway car, holding on to an overhead strap. As the train starts to pull out of the station, she feels thrust toward the rear of the car; as the train comes to a stop at the next station, she feels thrust forward. Explain the role played by inertia in this situation.

Figure 2.17 A demonstration of inertia.

(a)   (b)   (c)

PHYSICS AT HOME

For an easy demonstration of inertia, place a quarter on top of an index card, or a credit card, balanced on top of a drinking glass (Fig. 2.17a). With your thumb and forefinger, flick the card so it flies out horizontally from under the quarter. What happens to the quarter? The horizontal force on the coin due to friction is small. With a negligibly small horizontal force, the coin tends to remain motionless while the card slides out from under it (Fig. 2.17b). Once the card is gone, gravity pulls the coin down into the glass (Fig. 2.17c).

Free-Body Diagrams

An essential tool used to find the net force acting on an object is a **free-body diagram** (FBD): a simplified sketch of a single object with force vectors drawn to represent *every* force *acting on that object*. It must *not* include any forces that act on other objects. To draw a free-body diagram:

- Draw the object in a simplified way—you don't have to be Michelangelo to solve physics problems! Almost any object can be represented as a box or a circle, or even a dot.
- Identify all the forces that are exerted on the object. Take care not to omit any forces that are exerted on the object. Consider that everything touching the object may exert one or more contact forces. Then identify long-range forces (for now, just gravity unless electric or magnetic forces are specified in the problem).
- Check your list of forces to make sure that each force is exerted *on* the object of interest *by* some other object. Make sure you have not included any forces that are exerted *on other objects.*
- Draw vector arrows representing all the forces acting on the object. We usually draw the vectors as arrows that start on the object and point away from it. Draw the arrows so they correctly illustrate the directions of the forces. If you have enough information to do so, draw the lengths of the arrows so they are proportional to the magnitudes of the forces.

Equilibrium

An object in translational equilibrium has a net force of zero acting on it.

When the net force acting on an object is zero, the object is said to be in **translational equilibrium**. *Equilibrium* conveys the idea that the forces are in balance; there is as much force upward as there is downward, as much to the right as to the left, and so forth. Any object with a constant velocity, whether at rest or moving in a straight line at constant speed, is in translational equilibrium. A vector can only have zero magnitude if all of its components are zero, so

> For an object in equilibrium,
> $$\sum F_x = 0 \quad \text{and} \quad \sum F_y = 0 \quad (\text{and} \quad \sum F_z = 0) \tag{2-5}$$

Using Newton's first law, we can now understand how a spring scale can be used to measure weight (the magnitude of the gravitational force exerted on an object). If a melon remains at rest in the pan of the scale, the net force on the melon must be zero. Only two forces are acting on the melon: gravity pulls down and the scale pulls up. Then these two forces must be equal in magnitude and opposite in direction. The scale measures the magnitude of the force it exerts on the melon, which is equal to the weight of the melon.

Example 2.6

Hawk in Equilibrium

A red-tailed hawk that weighs 8 N is gliding due north at constant speed. What is the force acting on the hawk due to the air? Draw a free-body diagram for the hawk.

Strategy Since the hawk is gliding at constant velocity (constant speed *and* direction), it is in equilibrium—the net force acting on it is zero. We identify the forces acting on the hawk and determine what the force due to the air must be for the net force to be zero.

Solution Only two forces are acting on the hawk. One of them is long-range: the gravitational pull of the Earth ($\vec{F}_{grav}$) whose magnitude is the bird's weight. The other is a contact force due to the air ($\vec{F}_{air}$). Nothing else is in contact with the bird, so there are no other contact forces. Since the bird is in equilibrium, the net force acting on the bird must be zero:

$$\vec{F}_{grav} + \vec{F} = 0$$

If two vectors add to zero, they must have the same magnitude and opposite directions. So the force on the bird due to the air is 8 N, directed upward. Figure 2.18 is the FBD for the hawk.

Figure 2.18
Free-body diagram for a hawk gliding with constant velocity.

Discussion The interaction between the hawk and the air is extremely complex at the microscopic level, but the net effect of all the interactions between air molecules and the hawk produces an upward force of 8 N.

Practice Problem 2.6 A Crate of Apples

An 80-N crate of apples sits at rest on the horizontal bed of a parked pickup truck. What is the force $\vec{C}$ exerted on the crate by the bed of the pickup? Draw a free-body diagram for the crate.

Choosing x- and y-Axes

A problem can be made easier to solve with a good choice of axes. We can choose any direction we want for the *x*- and *y*-axes, as long as they are perpendicular to each other. Three common choices are

- *x*-axis horizontal and *y*-axis vertical, when the vectors all lie in a vertical plane;
- *x*-axis east and *y*-axis north, when the vectors all lie in a horizontal plane; and
- *x*-axis parallel to an inclined surface and *y*-axis perpendicular to it.

In an equilibrium problem, choose *x*- and *y*-axes so the fewest number of force vectors have both *x*- and *y*-components. It is always good practice to make a conscious *choice* of axes and then to draw them in the FBDs and any other sketches that you make in solving the problem.

Example 2.7

Net Force on an Airplane

The forces on an airplane in flight heading eastward are as follows: gravity = 16.0 kN, downward; lift = 16.0 kN, upward; thrust = 1.8 kN, east; and drag = 0.8 kN, west. (Lift, thrust, and drag are three forces that the air exerts on the plane.) What is the net force on the plane?

Strategy　All the forces acting on the plane are given in the statement of the problem. After drawing these forces in the FBD for the plane, we add the forces to find the net force. To resolve the force vectors into components, we choose x- and y-axes pointing east and north, respectively. All four forces are then lined up with the axes, so each will have only one nonzero component, with a sign that indicates the direction along that axis. For example, the drag force points in the $-x$-direction, so its x-component is negative and its y-component is zero.

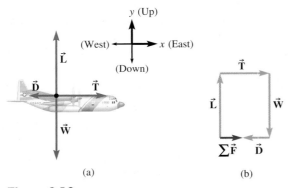

(a)

Figure 2.19
(a) Free-body diagram for the airplane. (b) Graphical addition of the four force vectors.

Solution　Figure 2.19a is the FBD for the plane, using $\vec{\mathbf{L}}, \vec{\mathbf{T}}$, and $\vec{\mathbf{D}}$ for the lift, thrust, and drag, respectively. $\vec{\mathbf{W}}$ stands for the gravitational force on the plane; its magnitude is the plane's weight W.

The sum of the x-components of the forces is

$$\sum F_x = L_x + T_x + W_x + D_x$$
$$= 0 + (1.8\text{ kN}) + 0 + (-0.8\text{ kN}) = 1.0\text{ kN}$$

The sum of the y-components of the forces is

$$\sum F_y = L_y + T_y + W_y + D_y$$
$$= (16\text{ kN}) + 0 + (-16\text{ kN}) + 0 = 0$$

The net force is 1.0 kN east.

Discussion　A graphical check of the vector addition is a good idea. Figure 2.19b shows that the sum of the four forces is indeed in the $+x$-direction (east).

The net force on the airplane is *not* zero, so the airplane's velocity is not constant. To find out how the airplane's velocity changes, we would use Newton's second law of motion, which is the main topic of Chapter 3. Newton's second law relates the net force on an object to the rate of change of its velocity vector.

Practice Problem 2.7　New Forces on the Airplane

Find the net force on the airplane if the forces are gravity = 16.0 kN, downward; lift = 15.5 kN, upward; thrust = 1.2 kN, north; drag = 1.2 kN, south.

Example 2.8

Sliding a Chest

Figure 2.20
Sliding a chest across the floor.

To slide a chest that weighs 750 N across the floor at constant velocity, you must push it horizontally with a force of 450 N (Fig. 2.20). Find the contact force that the floor exerts on the chest.

Strategy　The chest moves with constant velocity, so it is in equilibrium. The net force acting on it is zero. We will identify all the forces acting on the chest, draw an FBD, do a graphical addition of the forces, choose x- and y-axes, resolve the forces into their x- and y-components, and then set $\sum F_x = 0$ and $\sum F_y = 0$.

continued on next page

Example 2.8 continued

Solution Three forces are acting on the chest. The gravitational force $\vec{\mathbf{W}}$ has magnitude 750 N and is directed downward. Your push $\vec{\mathbf{F}}$ has magnitude 450 N and its direction is horizontal. The contact force due to the floor $\vec{\mathbf{C}}$ has unknown magnitude and direction. However, remembering that the chest is in equilibrium, upward and downward force components must balance, as must the horizontal force components. Therefore, $\vec{\mathbf{C}}$ must be roughly in the direction shown in the FBD (Fig. 2.21a), as is confirmed by adding the three forces graphically (Fig. 2.21b). The sum is zero because the tip of the last vector ends up at the tail of the first one.

Choosing the x-axis to the right and the y-axis up means that two of the three force vectors, $\vec{\mathbf{W}}$ and $\vec{\mathbf{F}}$, have one component that is zero:

$$W_x = 0 \quad \text{and} \quad W_y = -750 \text{ N}$$

$$F_x = 450 \text{ N} \quad \text{and} \quad F_y = 0$$

Now we set the x- and y-components of the net force each equal to zero because the chest is in equilibrium.

$$\sum F_x = W_x + F_x + C_x = 0 + 450 \text{ N} + C_x = 0$$

$$\sum F_y = W_y + F_y + C_y = -750 \text{ N} + 0 + C_y = 0$$

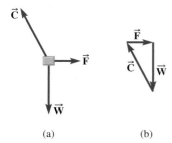

Figure 2.21
(a) A free-body diagram for the chest; (b) graphical addition of the three forces showing that the sum is zero.

(a)   (b)

Figure 2.22
Finding the magnitude and direction of the contact force.

These equations tell us the components of $\vec{\mathbf{C}}$: $C_x = -450$ N and $C_y = +750$ N. Then the magnitude of the contact force is (Fig. 2.22)

$$C = \sqrt{C_x^2 + C_y^2} = \sqrt{(-450 \text{ N})^2 + (750 \text{ N})^2} = 870 \text{ N}$$

$$\theta = \tan^{-1} \frac{\text{opposite}}{\text{adjacent}} = \tan^{-1} \frac{750 \text{ N}}{450 \text{ N}} = 59°$$

The contact force due to the floor is 870 N, directed 59° above the leftward horizontal (−x-axis).

Discussion The x- and y-components of the contact force and its magnitude and direction are all reasonable based on the graphical addition, so we can be confident that we did not make an error such as a sign error with one of the components.

Practice Problem 2.8   The Chest at Rest

Suppose the same chest is at rest. You push it horizontally with a force of 110 N but it does not budge. What is the contact force on the chest due to the floor during the time you are pushing?

2.5   INTERACTION PAIRS: NEWTON'S THIRD LAW OF MOTION

Forces always exist in pairs. Every force is part of an interaction between two objects and each of those objects exerts a force on the other. We call the two forces an **interaction pair**; each force is the **interaction partner** of the other. When you push open a door, the door pushes you. When two cars collide, each exerts a force on the other. Note that interaction partners *act on different objects*—the two objects that are interacting.

Newton's third law of motion says that interaction partners always have the *same magnitude* and are in *opposite directions*.

Newton's Third Law of Motion

In an interaction between two objects, each object exerts a force on the other. These two forces are equal in magnitude and opposite in direction.

Conceptual Example 2.9

An Orbiting Satellite

Earth exerts a gravitational force on an orbiting communications satellite. What is the interaction partner of this force?

Strategy The question concerns a gravitational interaction between two objects: Earth and the satellite. In this interaction, each object exerts a gravitational force on the other.

Solution The interaction partner is the gravitational force exerted on the Earth by the satellite.

Discussion Does the satellite really exert a force on the Earth with the same magnitude as the force Earth exerts on the satellite? If so, why does the satellite orbit Earth rather than Earth orbiting the satellite? Newton's third law says that the interaction partners are equal in magnitude, but does not say that these two forces have equal *effects*. We will see in Chapter 3 that the effect of a net force on an object's motion depends on the object's mass. These two forces of

equal magnitude have different effects due to the great discrepancy between the masses of the Earth and the satellite.

On the other hand, if a massive planet orbits a star in a relatively small orbit, the gravitational force that the planet exerts on the star can make the star wobble enough to be observed. The wobble enables astronomers to discover planets orbiting stars other than the Sun. The planets do not reflect enough light toward Earth to be seen, but their presence can be inferred from the effect they have on the star's motion.

Practice Problem 2.9   Interaction Partner of a Surface Contact Force

In Example 2.8, the contact force exerted on the chest by the floor was 870 N, directed 59° above the leftward horizontal (−x-axis). Describe the interaction partner of this force—in other words, what object exerts it on what other object? What are the magnitude and direction of the interaction partner?

 Do not assume that Newton's third law is involved *every* time two forces *happen* to be equal and opposite—*it ain't necessarily so!* You will encounter many situations in which two equal and opposite forces act *on a single object*. These forces cannot be *interaction partners* because they act on the same object. Interaction partners act on *different objects*, one on each of the two objects that are interacting.

✓ CHECKPOINT 2.5

In the photo, two children are pulling on a toy. If they are exerting equal and opposite forces on the toy, are these two forces interaction partners?

PHYSICS AT HOME

The next time you go swimming, notice that you use Newton's third law to get the water to push you forward. When you push down and backward on the water with your arms and legs, the water pushes up and forward on you. The various swimming strokes are devised so that you exert as large a force as possible backward on the water during the power part of the stroke, and then as small a force as possible forward on the water during the return part of the stroke.

Internal and External Forces

When we say that a baseball has interactions with the Earth (gravity), with a baseball bat, and with the air, we are treating the baseball as a single entity. But the ball really consists of an enormous number of protons, neutrons, and electrons, all interacting with each other. The protons and neutrons interact with each other to form atomic nuclei; the nuclei interact with electrons to form atoms; interactions between atoms form molecules; and the molecules interact to form the structure of the thing we call a base-ball. It would be difficult to have to deal with all of these interactions to predict the motion of a baseball.

Defining a System   Let us call the set of particles that make up the baseball a **system**. Once we have defined a system, we can classify all the interactions that affect the system as either **internal** or **external** to the system. For an internal interaction, *both* interacting objects are part of the system. When we add up all the forces acting on the system to find the net force, every internal interaction contributes two forces—an interaction pair—that always add to zero. For an external interaction, *only one of the two interaction partners is exerted on the system.* The other partner is exerted on an object outside the system and does not contribute to the net force on the system. So to find the net force on the system, we can ignore all the internal forces and just add the external forces.

The insight that internal forces always add to zero is particularly powerful because the choice of what constitutes a system is completely arbitrary. We can choose *any* set of objects and define it to be a system. In one problem, it may be convenient to think of the baseball as a system; in another, we may choose a system consisting of both the baseball and the bat. The second choice might be useful if we do not have detailed information about the interaction between the bat and the ball.

2.6   GRAVITATIONAL FORCES

Now that we know how to add forces, we turn our attention to learning about some forces in more detail, beginning with gravity. According to **Newton's law of universal gravitation**, any two objects exert gravitational forces on each other that are proportional to the masses (m_1 and m_2) of the two objects and inversely proportional to the square of the distance (r) between their centers. Strictly speaking, the law of gravitation as presented here only applies to point particles and symmetrical spheres. (The *point particle* is a common model in physics used when the size of an object is negligibly small and the internal structure is irrelevant.) Nevertheless, the law of gravitation is *approximately* true for any two objects if the distance between their centers is large relative to their sizes.

In mathematical language, the magnitude of the gravitational force is written:

$$F = \frac{Gm_1m_2}{r^2} \qquad (2\text{-}6)$$

where the constant of proportionality ($G = 6.674 \times 10^{-11} \ \text{N·m}^2/\text{kg}^2$) is called the **universal gravitational constant**. Equation (2-6) is only part of the law of universal gravitation because it gives only the magnitudes of the gravitational forces that each object exerts on the other. The directions are equally important: each object is pulled toward the other's center (Fig. 2.23). In other words, gravity is an attractive force. The forces on the two objects are equal in magnitude and the directions are opposite, as they must be since they form an interaction pair.

Gravitational forces exerted *by* ordinary objects on each other are so small as to be negligible in most cases (see Practice Problem 2.10). Gravitational forces exerted by Earth, on the other hand, are much larger due to Earth's large mass.

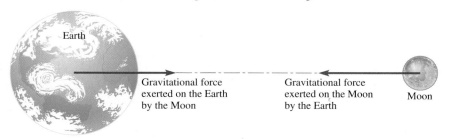

Figure 2.23 Gravity is always an attractive force. The force that each body exerts on the other is equal in magnitude, even though the masses may be very different. The force exerted *on the Moon by the Earth* is of the same magnitude as the force exerted on the Earth by the Moon. The directions are opposite.

Example 2.10

Weight at High Altitude

When you are in a commercial airliner cruising at an altitude of 6.4 km (21 000 ft), by what percentage has your weight (as well as the weight of the airplane) changed compared with your weight on the ground?

Strategy   Your weight is the magnitude of Earth's gravitational force exerted on you. Newton's law of universal gravitation gives the magnitude of the gravitational force at a distance r from the center of the Earth. For your weight on the ground W_1, we can use the mean radius of the Earth R_E as the distance between the Earth's center and you: $r_1 = R_E = 6.37 \times 10^6$ m   (Fig. 2.24). At an altitude of $h = 6.4 \times 10^3$ m above the surface, your weight is W_2 and your distance from Earth's center is $r_2 = R_E + h$. Your mass m, the mass of the Earth M_E ($= 5.97 \times 10^{24}$ kg), and G are the same in the two cases, so it is efficient to write a ratio of the weights and let those factors cancel out.

Figure 2.24

The gravitational force depends on the distance r to the *center* of the Earth.

Solution   The ratio of your weight in the airplane to your weight on the ground is

$$\frac{W_2}{W_1} = \frac{\dfrac{GM_E m}{r_2^2}}{\dfrac{GM_E m}{r_1^2}} = \frac{r_1^2}{r_2^2} = \frac{R_E^2}{(R_E + h)^2}$$

$$= \left(\frac{6.37 \times 10^6 \text{ m}}{6.37 \times 10^6 \text{ m} + 6.4 \times 10^3 \text{ m}} \right)^2 = 0.998$$

Since $0.998 = 1 - 0.002$ and $0.002 = 0.2/100$, your weight decreases by 0.2%.

Discussion   Although 6400 m may seem like a significant altitude to us, it's a small fraction of the Earth's radius (0.10%), so the weight change is a small percentage. When judging whether a quantity is small or large, always ask: "Small (or large) compared with what?"

Practice Problem 2.10   A Creative Defense

After an automobile collision, one driver claims that the gravitational force between the two cars caused the collision. Estimate the magnitude of the gravitational force exerted by one car on another when they are driving side-by-side in parallel lanes and comment on the driver's claim.

Gravitational Field Strength

For an object near Earth's surface, the distance between the object and the Earth's center is very nearly equal to the Earth's mean radius, $R_E = 6.37 \times 10^6$ m. The mass of the Earth is $M_E = 5.97 \times 10^{24}$ kg, so the weight of an object of mass m near Earth's surface is

$$W = \frac{GM_E m}{R_E^2} = m \left(\frac{GM_E}{R_E^2} \right) \tag{2-7}$$

Notice that for objects near Earth's surface, the constants in the parentheses are always the same and the weight of the object is proportional to its mass. Rather than recalculate that combination of constants over and over, we call the combination the **gravitational field strength** g near Earth's surface:

For those who have studied physics before: Chapter 3 shows that 1 N/kg = 1 m/s². For now, we write the units of g as N/kg to emphasize that g relates weight (in newtons) to mass (in kilograms).

$$g = \frac{GM_E}{R_E^2} = \frac{6.674 \times 10^{-11} \text{ N·m}^2\text{·kg}^{-2} \times (5.97 \times 10^{24} \text{ kg})}{(6.37 \times 10^6 \text{ m})^2} \approx 9.8 \text{ N/kg} \tag{2-8}$$

The units *newtons per kilogram* reinforce the conclusion that weight is proportional to mass: g tells us how many newtons of gravitational force are exerted on an object for every kilogram of the object's mass. The weight of a 1.0-kg object near Earth's surface is 9.8 N (2.2 lb). Using g, the weight of an object of mass m near Earth's surface is usually written as follows:

Relationship between mass and weight:

$$W = mg \qquad\qquad (2\text{-}9)$$

Variations in Earth's Gravitational Field   The Earth is not a perfect sphere; it is slightly flattened at the poles. Since the distance from the surface to the center of the Earth is smaller there, the field strength at sea level is greatest at the poles (9.832 N/kg) and smallest at the equator (9.814 N/kg). Altitude also matters; as you climb above sea level, your distance from Earth's center increases and the field strength decreases. Tiny local variations in the field strength are also caused by geologic formations. On top of dense bedrock, g is a little greater than above less dense rock. Geologists and geophysicists measure these variations to study Earth's structure and also to locate deposits of various minerals, water, and oil. The device they use, a *gravimeter*, is essentially a mass hanging on a spring. As the gravimeter is carried from place to place, the extension of the spring increases where g is larger and decreases where g is smaller. The mass hanging from the spring does not change, but its weight does ($W = mg$).

   Furthermore, due to Earth's rotation, the *effective* value of g that we measure in a coordinate system attached to Earth's surface is slightly less than the true value of the field strength. This effect is greatest at the equator, where the effective value of g is 9.784 N/kg, about 0.3% smaller than the true value of g. The effect gradually decreases with latitude to zero at the poles. We learn more about this effect in Chapter 5.

   The most important thing to remember from this is that, unlike G, g is *not* a universal constant. The value of g is a function of position. Near Earth's surface, the variations are small, so we can adopt an average value as a default:

Average value of g near Earth's surface:

$$g = 9.80 \text{ N/kg}$$

Please use this value for g near Earth's surface unless the statement of a problem gives a different value.

Example 2.11

"Weighing" Figs in Kilograms

In most countries other than the United States, produce is sold in mass units (grams or kilograms) rather than in force units (pounds or newtons). The scale still measures a force, but the scale is calibrated to show the mass of the produce instead of its weight. What is the weight of 350 g of fresh figs, in newtons and in pounds?

Strategy   Weight is mass times the gravitational field strength. We will assume $g = 9.80$ N/kg. The weight in newtons can be converted to pounds using the conversion factor 1 N = 0.2248 lb.

Solution   The weight of the figs in newtons is

$$W = mg = 0.35 \text{ kg} \times 9.80 \text{ N/kg} = 3.43 \text{ N}$$

Converting to pounds,

$$W = 3.43 \text{ N} \times 0.2248 \text{ lb/N} = 0.771 \text{ lb}$$

The figs weigh 3.4 N, or 0.77 lb.

Discussion   This is the weight of the figs at a location where g has its average value of 9.80 N/kg. The figs would weigh a little more in the northern city of St. Petersburg, Russia, and a little less in Quito, Ecuador, which is near the equator.

Practice Problem 2.11   Figs on the Moon

What would those figs weigh on the surface of the Moon, where $g = 1.62$ N/kg?

Equation (2-9) can be used to find the weight of an object at or above the surface of *any* planet or moon, but the value of *g* will be different due to the different mass *M* of the planet or moon and the different distance *r* from the planet's center:

$$g = \frac{GM}{r^2} \tag{2-10}$$

✓ CHECKPOINT 2.6

If you climb Mt. McKinley, what happens to the weight of your gear? What happens to its mass?

2.7   CONTACT FORCES

We have already done some problems involving forces exerted between two solid objects in contact. Now we look at those forces in more detail. In Example 2.8, we resolved the contact force on a sliding chest into components perpendicular to and parallel to the contact surface. It is often convenient to think of these components as two separate but related contact forces: the *normal force* and the *frictional force*.

Normal Force

A contact force perpendicular to the contact surface that prevents two objects from passing through one another is called the **normal force**. (In geometry, the word *normal* means *perpendicular*.) Consider a book resting on a horizontal table surface. The normal force due to the table must have just the right magnitude to keep the book from falling through the table. If no other vertical forces act, the normal force on the book is equal in magnitude to the book's weight because the book is in equilibrium (Fig. 2.25a).

According to Newton's third law, a normal force is also exerted on the table by the book; this normal force acts downward and is of equal magnitude. In *everyday* language, we might say that the table "feels the book's weight." That is not an accurate statement in the language of physics. The table cannot "feel" the gravitational force on the book; the table can only feel forces exerted *on the table*. What the table does "feel" is the normal force—a *contact* force—exerted on the table by the book.

If the table's surface is horizontal, the normal force on the book will be vertical and equal in magnitude to the book's weight. If the surface of the table is *not* horizontal, the normal force is not vertical and is not equal in magnitude to the weight of the book. Remember that the normal force is *perpendicular to the contact surface* (Fig. 2.25b). Even on a horizontal surface, if there are other vertical forces acting on the book, then the normal force is *not* equal in magnitude to the book's weight (Fig. 2.25c). Never

CONNECTION:

Normal force and *frictional force* are just names given to two perpendicular components of a surface contact force.

Normal force: a contact force between two solid objects that is perpendicular to the contact surfaces. Each object pushes the other one away.

Figure 2.25 (a) The normal force is equal in magnitude to the weight of the book; the two forces sum to zero. (b) On an incline, the normal force is smaller than the weight of the book and is not vertical. (c) If you push down on the book ($\vec{F}$), the normal force on the book due to the table is larger than the book's weight.

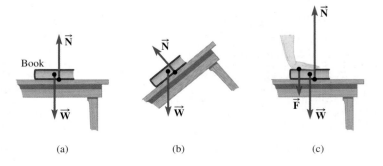

(a)   (b)   (c)

assume anything about the magnitude of the normal force. In general, we can figure out what the magnitude of the normal force must be in various situations if we have enough information about other forces.

How does the table "know" how hard to push on the book? First imagine putting the book on a bathroom scale instead of the table. A spring inside the scale provides the upward force. The spring "knows" how hard to push because, as it is compressed, the force it exerts increases. When the book reaches equilibrium, the spring is exerting just the right amount of force, so there is no tendency to compress it further. The spring is compressed until it pushes up with a force equal to the book's weight. If the spring were stiffer, it would exert the same upward force but with less compression.

The forces that bind atoms together in a rigid solid, like the table, act like extremely stiff springs that can provide large forces with little compression—so little that it's usually not noticed. The book makes a tiny indentation in the surface of the table (Fig. 2.26); a heavier book would make a slightly larger indentation. If the book were to be placed on a soft foam surface, the indentation would be much more noticeable.

✓ CHECKPOINT 2.7

Your laptop is resting on the surface of your desk, which stands on four legs on the floor. Identify the normal forces acting on the desk and give their directions.

Figure 2.26 The book compresses the "atomic springs" in the table until they push up on the book to hold it up. The slight decrease in the distance between atoms is greatly exaggerated here.

Friction

A contact force *parallel* to the contact surface is called **friction**. We distinguish two types: **static friction** and **kinetic** (or **sliding**) **friction**. When the two objects are slipping or sliding across one another, as when a loose shingle slides down a roof, the friction is kinetic. When no slipping or sliding occurs, such as between the tires of a car parked on a hill and the road surface, the friction is called static. Static friction acts to prevent objects from *starting* to slide; kinetic friction acts to try to make sliding objects stop sliding. Note that two objects in contact with one another that move with the same velocity exert *static* frictional forces on one another, because there is no *relative* motion between the two. For example, if a conveyor belt carries an air freight package up an incline and the package is not sliding, the two move with the same velocity and the friction is *static*.

Static Friction Frictional forces are complicated on the microscopic level and are an active field of current research. Despite the complexities, we can make some approximate statements about the frictional forces between dry, solid surfaces. In a simplified model, the maximum magnitude of the force of static friction $f_{s,max}$ that can occur in a particular situation is proportional to the magnitude of the normal force N acting between the two surfaces.

$$f_{s,max} \propto N$$

If you want better traction between the tires of a rear-wheel-drive car and the road, it helps to put something heavy in the trunk to increase the normal force between the tires and the road.

The constant of proportionality is called the **coefficient of static friction** (symbol μ_s):

Maximum force of static friction:

$$f_{s,max} = \mu_s N \tag{2-11}$$

Since $f_{s,max}$ and N are both magnitudes of forces, μ_s is a dimensionless number. Its value depends on the condition and nature of the surfaces. Equation (2-11) provides only an *upper limit* on the force of static friction in a particular situation. The actual force of friction in a given situation is not necessarily the maximum possible. It tells us only that, if sliding does not occur, the magnitude of the static frictional force is less than or equal to this upper limit:

$$f_s \leq \mu_s N \qquad (2\text{-}12)$$

Kinetic (Sliding) Friction   For sliding or kinetic friction, the force of friction is only weakly dependent on the speed and is roughly proportional to the normal force. In the simplified model we will use, the force of kinetic friction is assumed to be proportional to the normal force and independent of speed:

Force of kinetic (sliding) friction:

$$f_k = \mu_k N \qquad (2\text{-}13)$$

where f_k is the magnitude of the force of kinetic friction and μ_k is called the **coefficient of kinetic friction**. The coefficient of static friction is always larger than the coefficient of kinetic friction for an object on a given surface. On a horizontal surface, a larger force is required to start the object moving than is required to keep it moving at a constant velocity.

Direction of Frictional Force   Equations (2-11) through (2-13) relate only the *magnitudes* of the frictional and normal forces on an object. Remember that the frictional force is perpendicular to the normal force between the same two surfaces. Friction is always parallel to the contact surface, but there are many directions parallel to a given contact surface. Here are some rules of thumb for determining the direction of a frictional force.

- The static frictional force acts in whatever direction necessary to prevent the objects from beginning to slide or slip.
- Kinetic friction acts in a direction that tends to make the sliding stop. If a book slides to the left along a table, the table exerts a kinetic frictional force on the book to the right, in the direction opposite to the motion of the book.
- From Newton's third law, frictional forces come in interaction pairs. If the table exerts a frictional force on the sliding book to the right, the book exerts a frictional force on the table to the *left* with the same magnitude.

Example 2.12

Coefficient of Kinetic Friction for the Sliding Chest

Example 2.8 involved sliding a 750-N chest to the right at constant velocity by pushing it with a horizontal force of 450 N. We found that the contact force on the chest due to the floor had components $C_x = -450$ N and $C_y = +750$ N, where the x-axis points to the right and the y-axis points up (see Fig. 2.22). What is the coefficient of kinetic friction for the chest-floor surface?

Strategy   To find the coefficient of friction, we need to know what the normal and frictional forces are. They are the components of the contact force that are perpendicular and parallel to the contact surface. Since the surface is horizontal (in the x-direction), the x-component of the contact force is friction and the y-component is the normal force.

continued on next page

Example 2.12 continued

Solution The magnitude of the force due to sliding friction is $f_k = |C_x| = 450$ N. The magnitude of the normal force is $N = |C_y| = 750$ N. Now we can calculate the coefficient of kinetic friction from $f_k = \mu_k N$:

$$\mu_k = \frac{f_k}{N} = \frac{450 \text{ N}}{750 \text{ N}} = 0.60$$

Discussion If we had written $f_k = C_x = -450$ N, we would have ended up with a negative coefficient of friction. The

coefficient of friction is a relationship between the *magnitudes* of two forces, so it cannot be negative.

Practice Problem 2.12 Chest at Rest

Suppose the same chest is at rest. You push to the right with a force of 110 N but the chest does not budge. What are the normal and frictional forces on the chest due to the floor while you are pushing? Explain why you do not need to know the coefficient of static friction to answer this question.

Conceptual Example 2.13

Horse and Sleigh

A horse pulls a sleigh to the right at constant velocity on level ground (Fig. 2.27). The horse exerts a horizontal force $\vec{F}_{sh}$ on the sleigh. (The subscripts indicate the force on the sleigh due to the horse.) (a) Draw three FBDs, one for the horse, one for the sleigh, and one for the system horse + sleigh. (b) To make the sleigh increase its velocity, there must be a nonzero net force to the right acting on the sleigh. Suppose the horse pulls harder (F_{sh} increases in magnitude). According to Newton's third law, the sleigh always pulls back on the horse with a force of *the same* magnitude as the force with which the horse pulls the sleigh. Does this mean that no matter how hard it pulls, the horse can never make the net force on the sleigh nonzero? Explain. (c) Identify the interaction partner of each force acting on the sleigh.

Strategy (a) In each FBD, we include only the *external* forces acting on that system. All three systems move with constant velocity, so the net force on each is zero. (b) Looking at the FBD for the sleigh, we can determine the conditions under which the net force on the sleigh can be nonzero. (c) For a force exerted on the sleigh by X, its interaction partner must be the force exerted on X by the sleigh.

Solution and Discussion (a) If we think of the normal and frictional forces as separate forces, then there are four forces acting on the sleigh: the force exerted by the horse $\vec{F}_{sh}$, the gravitational force due to Earth $\vec{F}_{sE}$, the normal force on the sleigh due to the ground $\vec{N}_{sg}$, and kinetic (sliding) friction due to the ground $\vec{f}_{sg}$. Figure 2.28 shows the FBD for the sleigh. The net force is zero, so its horizontal and vertical components must each be zero: $\vec{F}_{sh} + \vec{f}_{sg} = 0$ and $\vec{N}_{sg} + \vec{F}_{sE} = 0$.

Similarly, four forces are acting on the horse: the force exerted by the sleigh $\vec{F}_{hs}$, the gravitational force $\vec{F}_{hE}$, the normal force due to the ground $\vec{N}_{hg}$, and friction due to the ground $\vec{f}_{hg}$. Newton's third law says that $\vec{F}_{hs} = -\vec{F}_{sh}$; the sleigh pulls back on the horse with a force equal in magnitude to the forward pull of the horse on the sleigh. Therefore, $\vec{F}_{hs}$ is to the left and has the same magnitude as $\vec{F}_{sh}$. The horse is in equilibrium, so $\vec{F}_{hs} + \vec{f}_{hg} = 0$ and $\vec{N}_{hg} + \vec{F}_{hE} = 0$. The first of these equations means that the frictional force has to be to the *right*. How does the horse get friction to push it *forward*? By pushing *backward* on the ground with its feet. We all do the same thing when taking a step; by pushing backward on the ground, we get the ground to push forward on us. This is *static* friction because the horse's hoof is not sliding along the ground. If there were no friction (imagine the ground to

Figure 2.27
Horse pulling sleigh.

s = sleigh
g = ground
h = horse
E = Earth

Figure 2.28
Free-body diagram for the sleigh.

continued on next page

Conceptual Example 2.13 continued

be icy), the hoof might slide backward. Static friction acts to prevent sliding, so the frictional force on the hoof is forward. Figure 2.29 shows the FBD for the horse.

Of the eight forces acting either on the horse or on the sleigh, two are internal forces for the horse + sleigh system: $\vec{\mathbf{F}}_{sh}$ and $\vec{\mathbf{F}}_{hs}$. They add to zero since they are interaction partners, so we can omit them from the FBD for the system (Fig. 2.30). The two frictional forces on the system horse + sleigh are *not* interaction partners, but they are equal in magnitude and opposite in direction. From the FBDs, $\vec{\mathbf{f}}_{hg} = -\vec{\mathbf{F}}_{hs}$ and $\vec{\mathbf{f}}_{sg} = -\vec{\mathbf{F}}_{sh}$. Because $\vec{\mathbf{F}}_{hs}$ and $\vec{\mathbf{F}}_{sh}$ are interaction partners, they are equal and opposite. Therefore, $\vec{\mathbf{f}}_{hg}$ and $\vec{\mathbf{f}}_{sg}$ are equal and opposite. The system is in equilibrium.

(b) The FBD for the sleigh (see Fig. 2.28) shows that if the horse pulls the sleigh with a force greater in magnitude than the force of friction on the sleigh ($F_{sh} > f_{sg}$), then the net force on the sleigh is nonzero and to the right. From Fig. 2.29, we need $f_{hg} > F_{hs}$ to have a nonzero net force to the right on the horse. So the frictional force on the horse would have to increase to enable it to pull the sleigh with a greater force. Then in Fig. 2.30, the two frictional forces are no longer equal in magnitude. The forward frictional force on the horse is greater than the backward frictional

Figure 2.29

Free-body diagram for the horse.

Figure 2.30

Free-body diagram for the system, horse and sleigh. The internal forces $\vec{\mathbf{F}}_{sh}$ and $\vec{\mathbf{F}}_{hs}$ are omitted—they form an interaction pair, so they add to zero.

force on the sleigh, so the net force on the system horse + sleigh is to the right.

(c)

Force Exerted on Sleigh	Interaction Partner
Force on the sleigh due to the horse $\vec{\mathbf{F}}_{sh}$	Force on the horse due to the sleigh $\vec{\mathbf{F}}_{hs}$
Gravitational force on the sleigh due to Earth $\vec{\mathbf{F}}_{sE}$	Gravitational force on Earth due to the sleigh $\vec{\mathbf{F}}_{Es}$
Normal force on the sleigh due to the ground $\vec{\mathbf{N}}_{sg}$	Normal force on the ground due to the sleigh $\vec{\mathbf{N}}_{gs}$
Friction on the sleigh due to the ground $\vec{\mathbf{f}}_{sg}$	Friction on the ground due to the sleigh $\vec{\mathbf{f}}_{gs}$

Practice Problem 2.13   Passing a Truck

A car is moving north and speeding up to pass a truck on a level road. The combined contact force exerted *on the road by all four tires* has vertical component 11.0 kN downward and horizontal component 3.3 kN southward. The drag force exerted on the car by the air is 1.2 kN southward. (a) Draw the FBD for the car. (b) What is the weight of the car? (c) What is the net force acting on the car?

Microscopic Origin of Friction   What looks like the smooth surface of a solid to the unaided eye is generally quite rough on a microscopic scale (Fig. 2.31). Friction is caused by atomic or molecular bonds between the "high points" on the surfaces of the two objects. These bonds are formed by microscopic electromagnetic forces that hold the atoms or molecules together. If the two objects are pushed together harder, the surfaces deform a little more, enabling more "high points" to bond. That is why the force of kinetic friction and the maximum force of static friction are proportional to the normal force. A bit of lubricant drastically decreases the frictional forces, because the two surfaces can float past each other without many of the "high points" coming into contact.

In static friction, when these molecular bonds are stretched, they pull back harder. The bonds have to be broken before sliding can begin. Once sliding begins, molecular bonds are continually made and broken as "high points" come together in a hit-or-miss fashion. These bonds are generally not as strong as those formed in the absence of sliding, which is why $\mu_s > \mu_k$.

For dry, solid surfaces, the amount of friction depends on how smooth the surfaces are and how many contaminants are present on the surface. Does polishing two steel surfaces decrease the frictional forces when they slide across each other? Not necessarily. In an extreme case, if the surfaces are extremely smooth and all surface contaminants are removed, the steel surfaces form a "cold weld"—essentially, they become one piece of steel. The atoms bond as strongly with their new neighbors as they do with the old.

Equilibrium on an Inclined Plane   Suppose we wish to pull a large box up a *frictionless* incline to a loading dock platform. Figure 2.32 shows the three forces acting on the box. $\vec{F}_a$ represents the applied force with which we pull. The force is parallel to the incline. If we choose the *x*- and *y*-axes to be horizontal and vertical, respectively, then two of the three forces have both *x*- and *y*-components. On the other hand, if we choose the *x*-axis parallel to the incline and the *y*-axis perpendicular to it, then only one of the three forces has both *x*- and *y*-components (the gravitational force).

With axes chosen, the weight of the box is then resolved into two perpendicular components (Fig. 2.33a). To find the *x*- and *y*-components of the gravitational force $\vec{W}$, we must determine the angle that $\vec{W}$ makes with one of the axes. The right triangle of Fig. 2.33b shows that $\alpha + \phi = 90°$, since the interior angles of a triangle add up to 180°. The *x*- and *y*-axes are perpendicular, so $\alpha + \beta = 90°$. Therefore, $\beta = \phi$.

The *y*-component of $\vec{W}$ is perpendicular to the surface of the incline. From Fig. 2.33a, the side parallel to the *y*-axis is adjacent to angle β, so

$$\cos \beta = \frac{\text{adjacent}}{\text{hypotenuse}} = \frac{|W_y|}{|W|}$$

Since W_y is negative and $W = mg$,

$$W_y = -mg \cos \beta = -mg \cos \phi$$

The *x*-component of the weight tends to make the box slide down the incline (in the +*x*-direction). Using the same triangle,

$$W_x = +mg \sin \phi$$

When the box is pulled with a force equal in magnitude to W_x up the incline (in the negative *x*-direction), it will slide up with constant velocity. The component of the box's weight perpendicular to the incline is supported by the normal force $\vec{N}$ that pushes the box away from the incline. Figure 2.33c is an FBD in which the gravitational force is separated into its *x*- and *y*-components.

Figure 2.31 Friction is caused by bonds between atoms that form between the "high points" of the two surfaces that come into contact.

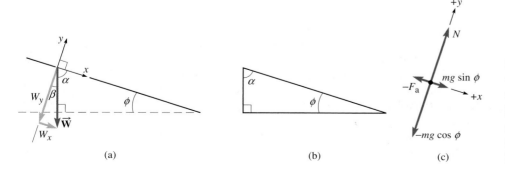

Figure 2.32 A box of mass *m* pulled up an incline.

(a)   (b)   (c)

Figure 2.33 (a) Resolving the weight into components parallel to and perpendicular to the incline. (b) A right triangle shows that $\alpha + \phi = 90°$. (c) Free-body diagram for the box on the incline.

If the box is in equilibrium, whether at rest or moving along the incline at constant velocity, the force components along each axis sum to zero:

$$\sum F_x = (-F_a) + mg \sin \phi = 0$$

and

$$\sum F_y = N + (-mg \cos \phi) = 0$$

The normal force is *not* equal in magnitude to the weight and it does not point straight up. If the applied force has magnitude $mg \sin \phi$, we can pull the box up the incline at constant velocity. If friction acts on the box, we must pull with a force greater than $mg \sin \phi$ to slide the box up the incline at constant velocity.

Example 2.14

Pushing a Safe up an Incline

A new safe is being delivered to the Corner Book Store. It is to be placed in the wall at a height of 1.5 m above the floor. The delivery people have a portable ramp, which they plan to use to help them push the safe up and into position. The mass of the safe is 510 kg, the coefficient of static friction along the incline is $\mu_s = 0.42$, and the coefficient of kinetic friction along the incline is $\mu_k = 0.33$. The ramp forms an angle $\theta = 15°$ above the horizontal. (a) How hard do the movers have to push to start the safe moving up the incline? Assume that they push in a direction parallel to the incline. (b) To slide the safe up at a constant speed, with what magnitude force must the movers push?

Strategy (a) When the safe *starts* to move, its velocity is changing, so the safe is *not* in equilibrium. Nevertheless, to find the minimum applied force to start the safe moving, we can find the *maximum* applied force for which the safe *remains at rest*—an equilibrium situation. (b) The safe is in equilibrium as it slides with a constant velocity. Both parts of the problem can be solved by drawing the FBD, choosing axes, and setting the x- and y-components of the net force equal to zero.

Solution First we draw a diagram to show forces acting (Fig. 2.34). Before resolving the forces into components, we must choose x- and y-axes. To use the coefficient of friction,

we have to resolve the contact force on the safe due to the incline into components *parallel and perpendicular to the incline*—friction and the normal force, respectively—rather than into horizontal and vertical components. Therefore, we choose x- and y-axes parallel and perpendicular to the incline so friction is along the x-axis and the normal force is along the y-axis.

The gravitational force $\vec{W}$ can be resolved into its components: $W_x = -mg \sin \theta$ and $W_y = -mg \cos \theta$ (Fig. 2.35a). Now we draw the FBD with $\vec{W}$ replaced by its components (Fig. 2.35b).

(a) Suppose that the safe is initially at rest. As the movers start to push, F_a gets larger and the force of static friction gets larger to "try" to keep the safe from sliding. Eventually, at some value of F_a, static friction reaches its maximum possible value $\mu_s N$. If the movers continue to push harder, increasing F_a further, the force of static friction cannot increase past its maximum value $\mu_s N$, so the safe starts to slide. The direction of the frictional force is along the incline and downward since friction is "trying" to keep the safe from sliding *up* the incline.

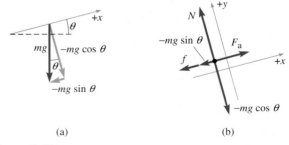

(a)   (b)

Figure 2.35

(a) Resolving the weight into x- and y-components, and (b) a free-body diagram in which the weight is replaced with its x- and y-components.

$\theta = 15°$

Figure 2.34

Forces acting on the safe as it is moved up the incline.

continued on next page

Example 2.14 continued

The normal force is *not* equal in magnitude to the weight of the safe. To find the normal force, sum the *y*-components of the forces:

$$\sum F_y = N + (-mg \cos \theta) = 0$$

Then $N = mg \cos \theta$. The normal force is *less than the weight* since $\cos \theta < 1$.

When the movers push with the largest force for which the safe does *not* slide,

$$\sum F_x = F_{ax} + f_x + W_x + N_x = 0$$

The applied force is in the +*x*-direction, so $F_{ax} = +F_a$. The frictional force has its maximum magnitude and is in the −*x*-direction, so $f_x = -f_{s,\max} = -\mu_s N = -\mu_s mg \cos \theta$. From the FBD, $W_x = -mg \sin \theta$ and $N_x = 0$. Then,

$$\sum F_x = F_a - \mu_s mg \cos \theta - mg \sin \theta + 0 = 0$$

Solving for F_a,

$$F_a = mg \,(\mu_s \cos \theta + \sin \theta)$$
$$= 510 \text{ kg} \times 9.80 \text{ m/s}^2 \times (0.42 \times \cos 15° + \sin 15°)$$
$$= 3300 \text{ N}$$

An applied force that *exceeds* 3300 N starts the box moving up the incline.

(b) Once the safe is sliding, the movers need only push hard enough to make the net force on the safe equal to zero if they want the safe to slide at constant velocity. We are now dealing with sliding friction, so the frictional force is now $f_x = -\mu_k N = -\mu_k mg \cos \theta$.

$$\sum F_x = F_{ax} + f_x + W_x + N_x$$
$$= F_a - \mu_k mg \cos \theta - mg \sin \theta + 0$$
$$= 0$$
$$F_a = mg \,(\mu_k \cos \theta + \sin \theta)$$
$$= 510 \text{ kg} \times 9.80 \text{ m/s}^2 \times (0.33 \times \cos 15° + \sin 15°)$$
$$= 2900 \text{ N}$$

The movers push with a force $\vec{F}_a$ of magnitude 2900 N directed up the incline.

Discussion In (b), the expression $F_a = mg \,(\mu_k \cos \theta + \sin \theta)$ shows that the applied force up the incline has to balance the sum of two forces down the incline: the frictional force ($\mu_k mg \cos \theta$) and the component of the gravitational force down the incline ($mg \sin \theta$). This balance of forces is shown graphically in the FBD (Fig. 2.35b).

Practice Problem 2.14   Smoothing the Infield Dirt

During the seventh-inning stretch of a baseball game, groundskeepers drag mats across the infield dirt to smooth it. A groundskeeper is pulling a mat at a constant velocity by applying a force of 120 N at an angle of 22° above the horizontal. The coefficient of kinetic friction between the mat and the ground is 0.60. Find (a) the magnitude of the frictional force between the dirt and the mat and (b) the weight of the mat.

PHYSICS AT HOME

To estimate the coefficient of static friction between a penny and the cover of your physics book, place the penny on the book and slowly lift the cover. Note the angle of the cover when the penny starts to slide. Explain how you can use this angle to find the coefficient of static friction. Can you devise an experiment to find the coefficient of kinetic friction?

2.8   TENSION

Consider a heavy chandelier hanging by a chain from the ceiling (Fig. 2.36a). The chandelier is in equilibrium, so the upward force on it due to the chain is equal in magnitude to the chandelier's weight. With what force does the chain pull downward on the ceiling? The ceiling has to pull up with a force equal to the total weight of the chain and the chandelier. The interaction partner of this force—the force the chain exerts on the ceiling—is equal in magnitude and opposite in direction. Therefore, if the weight of the chain is negligibly small compared with the weight of the chandelier, then the chain exerts forces of

Figure 2.36 (a) The chain pulls up on the chandelier and pulls down on the ceiling. (b) The chain is under tension. Each link is pulled in opposite directions by its neighbors.

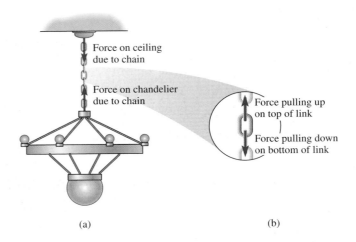

Force on ceiling due to chain

Force on chandelier due to chain

Force pulling up on top of link

Force pulling down on bottom of link

(a)   (b)

equal magnitude at its two ends. The forces at the ends would *not* be equal, however, if you grabbed the chain in the middle and pulled it up or down or if we could not ignore the weight of the chain. We can generalize this observation:

> An *ideal* cord (or rope, string, tendon, cable, or chain) pulls in the direction of the cord with forces of equal magnitude on the objects attached to its ends as long as no external force is exerted on it anywhere between the ends. An ideal cord has zero mass and zero weight.

A single link of the chain (Fig. 2.36b) is pulled at both ends by the neighboring links. The magnitude of these forces is called the **tension** in the chain. Similarly, a little segment of a cord is pulled at both its ends by the tension in the neighboring pieces of the cord. If the segment is in equilibrium, then the net force acting on it is zero. As long as there are no other forces exerted on the segment, the forces exerted by its neighbors must be equal in magnitude and opposite in direction. Therefore, the tension has the same value everywhere and is equal to the force that the cord exerts on the objects attached to its ends.

Example 2.15

Archery Practice

Figure 2.37 shows the bowstring of a bow and arrow just before it is released. The archer is pulling back on the midpoint of the bowstring with a horizontal force of 162 N. What is the tension in the bowstring?

72 cm

162 N

35 cm

Figure 2.37

The force applied to the bowstring by an archer.

Strategy   Consider a small segment of the bowstring that touches the archer's finger. That piece of the string is in equilibrium, so the net force acting on it is zero. We draw the FBD, choose coordinate axes, and apply the equilibrium condition: $\Sigma F_x = 0$ and $\Sigma F_y = 0$. We know the force exerted on the segment of string by the archer's fingers. That segment is also pulled on each end by the tension in the string. Can we assume the tension in the string is the same everywhere? The weight of the string is small compared to the other forces acting on it. The archer pulls sideways on the bowstring, exerting little or no *tangential* force, so we can assume the tension is the same everywhere.

continued on next page

Example 2.15 continued

Solution   Figure 2.38a is an FBD for the segment of bow-string being considered. The forces are labeled with their magnitudes: F_a for the force applied by the archer's finger and T for each of the tension forces. Figure 2.38b shows these three forces adding to zero. From this sketch, we expect the tension T to be roughly the same as F_a. We choose the x-axis to the right and the y-axis upward. To find the components of the forces due to tension in the string, we draw a triangle (Fig. 2.38c). From the measurements given, we can find the angle θ.

$$\sin \theta = \frac{\text{opposite}}{\text{hypotenuse}} = \frac{35 \text{ cm}}{72 \text{ cm}} = 0.486$$

$$\theta = \sin^{-1} 0.486 = 29.1°$$

The x-component of the tension force exerted on the upper end of the segment is

$$T_x = -T \sin \theta$$

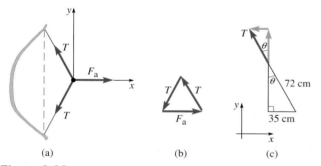

(a)   (b)   (c)

Figure 2.38

(a) Free-body diagram for a point on the bowstring with the magnitudes of the forces labeled. (b) Graphical addition of the three forces showing that the sum is zero. (c) The angle θ is used to find the x- and y-components of the forces exerted at each end of the bowstring.

The x-component of the force exerted on the lower end of the string is the same. Therefore,

$$\sum F_x = -2T \sin \theta + F_a = 0$$

Solving for T,

$$T = \frac{F_a}{2 \sin \theta} = \frac{162 \text{ N}}{2 \times 0.486} = 170 \text{ N}$$

Discussion   The tension is only slightly larger than F_a, a reasonable result given the picture of graphical vector addition in Fig. 2.38b.

In this problem, only the x-components of the forces had to be used. The y-components must also add to zero. At the upper end of the string, the y-component of the force exerted by the bow is $+T \cos \theta$, while at the lower end it is $-T \cos \theta$. Therefore, $\sum F_y = 0$.

The expression $T = F_a/(2 \sin \theta)$ can be evaluated for limiting values of θ to make sure that the expression is correct. As θ approaches 90°, the tension approaches $F_a/(2 \sin 90°) = \frac{1}{2}F_a$. That is correct because the archer would be pulling to the right with a force F_a, while each side of the bowstring would pull to the left with a force of magnitude T. For equilibrium, $F_a = 2T$ or $T = \frac{1}{2}F_a$.

As θ gets smaller, $\sin \theta$ decreases and the tension increases (for a fixed value of F_a). That agrees with our intuition. The larger the tension, the smaller the angle the string needs to make in order to supply the necessary horizontal force.

Practice Problem 2.15   Tightrope Practice

Jorge decides to rig up a tightrope in the backyard so his children can develop a good sense of balance (Fig. 2.39). For safety reasons, he positions a horizontal cable only 0.60 m above the ground. If the 6.00-m-long cable sags by 0.12 m from its taut horizontal position when Denisha (weight 250 N) is standing on the middle of it, what is the tension in the cable? Ignore the weight of the cable.

Figure 2.39

Tightrope for balancing practice.

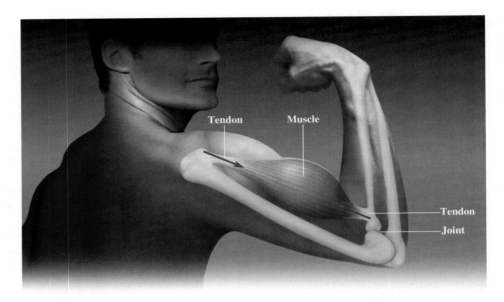

Figure 2.40 A muscle contracts, increasing the tension in the attached tendons. The tendons exert forces on two different bones.

Application: Tensile Forces in the Body   Tensile forces are central in the study of animal motion. Muscles are usually connected by tendons, one at each end of the muscle, to two different bones, which in turn are linked at a joint (Fig. 2.40). Usually one of the bones is more easily moved than the other. When the muscle contracts, the tension in the tendons increases, pulling on both of the bones.

PHYSICS AT HOME

Sit with your arm bent at the elbow with a heavy object on the palm of your hand. You can feel the contraction of the biceps muscle. With your other hand, feel the tendon that connects the biceps muscle to your forearm.

Now place your hand palm down on the desktop and push down. Now it is the triceps muscle that contracts, pulling up on the bone on the other side of the elbow joint. Muscles and tendons cannot push; they can only pull. The biceps muscle cannot push the forearm downward, but the triceps muscle can pull on the other side of the joint. In both cases, the arm acts as a lever.

Figure 2.41 Using a pulley to lift an object by pulling *down-ward* on a rope with force $\vec{F}$.

Application: Ideal Pulleys   A pulley can change the direction of the force exerted by a cord under tension. To lift something heavy, it is easier to stand on the ground and pull *down* on the rope than to get above the weight on a platform and pull up on the rope (Fig. 2.41).

An *ideal* pulley has no mass and no friction. An ideal pulley exerts no forces on the cord that are *tangent* to the cord—it is not pulling in either direction along the cord. As a result, the tension of an ideal cord that runs through an ideal pulley is the same on both sides of the pulley. (The proof of this statement comes in Chapter 3.) An ideal pulley changes the direction of the force exerted by a cord without changing its magnitude. As long as a real pulley has a small mass and negligible amount of friction, we can approximate it as an ideal pulley.

Example 2.16

A Two-Pulley System

A 1804-N engine is hauled upward at constant speed (Fig. 2.42). What are the tensions in the three ropes labeled A, B, and C? Assume the ropes and the pulleys labeled L and R are ideal.

Strategy The engine and pulley L move up at constant speed, so the net force on each of them is zero. Pulley R is at rest, so the net force on it is also zero. We can draw the FBD for any or all of these objects and then apply the equilibrium condition. If the pulleys are ideal, the tension in the rope is the same on both sides of the pulley. Therefore, rope C—which is attached to the ceiling—passes around both pulleys, and is pulled downward at the other end, has the same tension throughout. Call the tensions in the three ropes T_A, T_B, and T_C. To analyze the forces exerted on a pulley, we define our system so the part of the rope wrapped around the pulley is considered part of the pulley. Then there are two cords pulling on the pulley, each with the same tension.

Solution There are two forces acting on the engine: the gravitational force (1804 N, downward) and the upward pull of rope A. These must be equal and opposite (Fig. 2.43a), since the net force is zero. Therefore $T_A = 1804$ N.

The FBD for pulley L (Fig. 2.43b) shows rope A pulling down with a force of magnitude T_A and rope C pulling upward on *each side*. The rope has the same tension throughout, so all forces labeled T_C in Fig. 2.43b,c have the same magnitude. For the net force to equal zero,

$$2T_C = T_A$$

$$T_C = \tfrac{1}{2}T_A = 902.0 \text{ N}$$

Figure 2.43c is the FBD for pulley R. Rope B pulls upward on it with a force of magnitude T_B. On *each side* of the pulley, rope C pulls downward. For the net force to equal zero,

$$T_B = 2T_C = 1804 \text{ N}$$

Discussion The engine is raised by pulling *down* on a rope—the pulleys change the direction of the applied force needed to lift the engine. In this case they also change the *magnitude* of the required force. They do that by making the rope pull up on the engine twice, so the person pulling the rope only needs to exert a force equal to half the engine's weight.

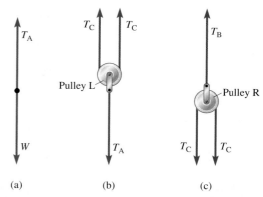

Figure 2.43
(a) Free-body diagram for the engine. (b) Free-body diagram for pulley L and (c) free-body diagram for pulley R.

Practice Problem 2.16   System of Ropes, Pulleys, and Engine

Consider the entire collection of ropes, pulleys, and the engine to be a single system. Draw the FBD for this system and show that the net force is zero. [*Hint:* Remember that only forces exerted by objects *external* to the system are included in the FBD.]

Figure 2.42
A system of pulleys used to raise a heavy weight.

2.9   FUNDAMENTAL FORCES

One of the main goals of physics has been to understand the immense variety of forces in the universe in terms of the fewest number of fundamental laws. Physics has made great progress in this quest for *unification*; today all forces are understood in terms of just four fundamental interactions (Fig. 2.44). At the high temperatures present in the early universe, two of these interactions—the electromagnetic and weak forces—are now understood as the effects of a single electroweak interaction. The ultimate goal is to describe all forces in terms of a single interaction.

Gravity   You may be surprised to learn that gravity is by far the *weakest* of the fundamental forces. Any two objects exert gravitational forces on one another, but the force is tiny unless at least one of the masses is large. We tend to notice the relatively large gravitational forces exerted by planets and stars, but not the feeble gravitational forces exerted by smaller objects, such as the gravitational force this book exerts on your body.

Gravity has an unlimited range. The force gets weaker as the distance between two objects increases, but it never drops exactly to zero, no matter how far apart the objects get.

Newton's law of gravity is an early example of unification. Before Newton, people did not understand that the same kind of force that makes an apple fall from a tree also keeps the planets in their orbits around the Sun. A single law—Newton's law of universal gravitation—describes both.

Electromagnetism   The electromagnetic force is unlimited in range, like gravity. It acts on particles with electric charge. The electric and magnetic forces were unified into a single theoretical framework in the nineteenth century. We study electromagnetic forces in detail in Part 3 of this book.

Electromagnetism is the fundamental interaction that binds electrons to nuclei to form atoms and binds atoms together in molecules and solids. It is responsible for the properties of solids, liquids, and gases and forms the basis of the sciences of chemistry and biology. It is the fundamental interaction behind all macroscopic contact forces such as the frictional and normal forces between surfaces and forces exerted by springs, muscles, and the wind.

Figure 2.44 All forces result from just four fundamental forces: gravity, electromagnetism, and the weak and strong forces.

The electromagnetic force is *much* stronger than gravity. For example, the electrical repulsion of two electrons at rest is about 10^{43} times as strong as the gravitational attraction between them. Macroscopic objects have a nearly perfect balance of positive and negative electric charge, resulting in a nearly perfect balance of attractive and repulsive electromagnetic forces between the objects. Therefore, despite the fundamental strength of the electromagnetic forces, the net electromagnetic force between two macroscopic objects is often negligibly small except when atoms on the two surfaces come very close to each other—what we think of as *in contact*. On a microscopic level, there is no fundamental difference between contact forces and other electromagnetic forces.

The Strong Force   The strong force holds protons and neutrons together in the atomic nucleus. The same force binds quarks (a family of elementary particles) in combinations so they can form protons and neutrons and many more exotic subatomic particles. The strong force is the strongest of the four fundamental forces—hence its name—but its range is short: its effect is negligible at distances much larger than the size of an atomic nucleus (about 10^{-15} m).

The Weak Force   The range of the weak force is even shorter than that of the strong force (about 10^{-17} m). It is manifest in many radioactive decay processes.

Master the Concepts

- A *force* is a push or a pull. Gravity and electromagnetic forces have unlimited range. All other forces exerted on macroscopic objects involve contact. Force is a vector quantity.

- Vectors have magnitude and direction and are added according to special rules. Vectors are added graphically by drawing each vector so that its tail is placed at the tip of the previous vector. The sum is drawn as a vector arrow from the tail of the first vector to the tip of the last.

- To find the components of a vector: draw a right triangle with the vector as the hypotenuse and the other two sides parallel to the x- and y-axes. Then use the trigonometric functions to find the magnitudes of the components. The correct algebraic sign must be determined for each component. The same triangle can be used to find the magnitude and direction of a vector if its components are known.

- To add vectors algebraically, add their components to find the components of the sum:

  if $\vec{A} + \vec{B} = \vec{C}$, then $A_x + B_x = C_x$ and $A_y + B_y = C_y$

- The SI unit of force is the newton. $1.00\ \text{N} = 0.2248\ \text{lb}$.

- The *net force* on a system is the vector sum of all the forces acting on it:

$$\vec{F}_{net} = \sum \vec{F} = \vec{F}_1 + \vec{F}_2 + \cdots + \vec{F}_n \qquad (2\text{-}4)$$

Since all the internal forces form interaction pairs, we need only sum the external forces.

- *Newton's first law of motion*: If zero net force acts on an object, then the object's velocity does not change. Velocity is a vector whose magnitude is the speed at which the object moves and whose direction is the direction of motion.

- A *free-body diagram* (FBD) includes vector arrows representing every force acting on the chosen object due to some other object, but no forces acting on other objects.

- *Newton's third law of motion*: In an interaction between two objects, each object exerts a force on the other. These two forces are equal in magnitude and opposite in direction.

- At the fundamental level, there are four interactions: gravity, the strong and weak interactions, and the electromagnetic interaction. Contact forces are large-scale manifestations of many microscopic electromagnetic interactions.

continued on next page

Master the Concepts continued

- The magnitude of the *gravitational force* between two objects is

$$F = \frac{Gm_1 m_2}{r^2} \qquad (2\text{-}6)$$

where r is the distance between their centers. Each object is pulled toward the other's center.

- The *weight* of an object is the magnitude of the gravitational force acting on it. An object's weight is proportional to its mass: $W = mg$ [Eq. (2-9)], where g is the gravitational field strength. Near Earth's surface, g has an average value of 9.80 N/kg.

- The *normal force* is a contact force perpendicular to the contact surfaces that pushes each object away from the other.

- *Friction* is a contact force parallel to the contact surfaces. In a simplified model, the kinetic frictional force and the maximum static frictional force are proportional to the normal force acting between the same contact surfaces.

$$f_s \leq \mu_s N \qquad (2\text{-}12)$$

$$f_k = \mu_k N \qquad (2\text{-}13)$$

The static frictional force acts in the direction that tends to keep the surfaces from beginning to slide. The direction of the kinetic frictional force is in the direction that would tend to make the sliding stop.

- An ideal cord pulls in the direction of the cord with forces of equal magnitude on the objects attached to its ends as long as no external force tangent to the cord is exerted on it anywhere between the ends. The tension of an ideal cord that runs through an ideal pulley is the same on both sides of the pulley.

Conceptual Questions

1. Explain the need for automobile seat belts in terms of Newton's first law.

2. An American visitor to Finland is surprised to see heavy metal frames outside of all the apartment buildings. On Saturday morning the purpose of the frames becomes evident when several apartment dwellers appear, carrying rugs and carpet beaters to each frame. What role does the principle of inertia play in the rug beating process? Do you see a similarity to the role the principle of inertia plays when you throw a baseball?

3. You are lying on the beach after a dip in the ocean where the waves were buffeting you around. Is it true that there are now no forces acting on you? Explain.

4. A dog goes swimming at the beach and then shakes himself all over to get dry. What principle of physics aids in the drying process? Explain.

5. In an attempt to tighten the loosened steel head of a hammer, a carpenter holds the hammer vertically, raises it up, and then brings it down rapidly, hitting the bottom end of the wood handle on a

two-by-four board. Explain how this tightens the head back onto the handle.

6. When a car begins to move forward, what force makes it do so? Remember that it has to be an *external* force; the internal forces all add to zero. How does the engine facilitate the propelling force?

7. Two cars are headed toward each other in opposite directions along a narrow country road. The cars collide head-on, crumpling up the hoods of both. Describe what happens to the car bodies in terms of the principle of inertia. Does the rear end of the car stop at the same time as the front end?

8. (a) Is it possible for the sum of two vectors to be smaller in magnitude than the magnitude of either vector? (b) Is it possible for the magnitude of the sum of two vectors to be larger than the sum of the magnitudes of the vectors?

9. (a) What assumptions do you make when you call the reading of a bathroom scale your "weight"? What does the scale really tell you? (b) Under what circumstances might the reading of the scale *not* be equal to your weight?

10. A freight train consists of an engine and several identical cars on level ground. Determine whether each of these statements is correct or incorrect and explain why. (a) If the train is moving at constant speed, the engine must be pulling with a force greater than the train's weight. (b) If the train is moving at constant speed, the engine's pull on the first car must exceed that car's backward pull on the engine. (c) If the train is coasting, its inertia makes it slow down and eventually stop.

11. (a) Does a man weigh more at the North Pole or at the equator? (b) Does he weigh more at the top of Mt. Everest or at the base of the mountain?

12. What is the distinction between a vector and a scalar quantity? Give two examples of each.

13. If a wagon starts at rest and pulls back on you with a force equal to the force you pull on it, as required by Newton's third law, how is it possible for you to make the wagon start to move? Explain.

14. Can the *x*-component of a vector ever be greater than the magnitude of the vector? Explain.

15. A heavy ball hangs from a string attached to a sturdy wooden frame. A second string is attached to a hook on the bottom of the lead ball. You pull slowly and steadily on the lower string. Which string do you think will break first? Explain.

16. An SUV collides with a Mini Cooper convertible. Is the force exerted on the Mini by the SUV greater than, equal to, or less than the force exerted on the SUV by the Mini? Explain.

17. You are standing on one end of a light wooden raft that has floated 3 m away from the pier. If the raft is 6 m long by 2.5 m wide and you are standing on the raft end nearest to the pier, can you propel the raft back toward the pier where a friend is standing with a pole and hook trying to reach you? You have no oars. Make suggestions of what to do without getting yourself wet.

18. If two vectors have the same magnitude, are they necessarily equal? If not, why not? Can two vectors with different magnitudes ever be equal?

19. Compare the advantages and disadvantages of the two methods of vector addition (graphical and algebraic).

20. Pulleys and inclined planes are examples of *simple machines*. Explain what these machines do in Examples 2.4, 2.14, and 2.16 to make a task easier to perform.

21. For a problem about a crate sliding along an inclined plane, is it possible to choose the *x*-axis so that it is parallel to the incline?

22. A bird sits on a stretched clothesline, causing it to sag slightly. Is the tension in the line greatest where the bird sits, greater at either end of the line where it is attached to poles, or the same everywhere along the line? Treat the line as an ideal cord with negligible weight.

Multiple-Choice Questions

1. Interaction partners
   (a) are equal in magnitude and opposite in direction and act on the same object.
   (b) are equal in magnitude and opposite in direction and act on different objects.
   (c) appear in an FBD for a given object.
   (d) always involve gravitational force as one partner.
   (e) act in the same direction on the same object.

2. Within a given system, the internal forces
   (a) are always balanced by the external forces.
   (b) all add to zero.
   (c) are determined only by subtracting the external forces from the net force on the system.
   (d) determine the motion of the system.
   (e) can never add to zero.

3. A friction force is
   (a) a contact force that acts parallel to the contact surfaces.
   (b) a contact force that acts perpendicular to the contact surfaces.
   (c) a scalar quantity since it can act in any direction along a surface.
   (d) always proportional to the weight of an object.
   (e) always equal to the normal force between the objects.

4. When a force is called a "normal" force, it is
   (a) the usual force expected given the arrangement of a system.
   (b) a force that is perpendicular to the surface of the Earth at any given location.
   (c) a force that is always vertical.
   (d) a contact force perpendicular to the contact surfaces between two solid objects.
   (e) the net force acting on a system.

5. Your car won't start, so you are pushing it. You apply a horizontal force of 300 N to the car, but it doesn't budge. What force is the interaction partner of the 300 N force you exert?
   (a) the frictional force exerted on the car by the road
   (b) the force exerted on you by the car
   (c) the frictional force exerted on you by the road
   (d) the normal force on you by the road
   (e) the normal force on the car by the road

6. Which of these is *not* a long-range force?
   (a) the force that makes raindrops fall to the ground
   (b) the force that makes a compass point north
   (c) the force that a person exerts on a chair while sitting
   (d) the force that keeps the Moon in its orbital path around the Earth

7. When an object is in translational equilibrium, which of these statements is *not* true?

   (a) The vector sum of the forces acting on the object is zero.
   (b) The object must be stationary.
   (c) The object has a constant velocity.
   (d) The speed of the object is constant.

8. To make an object start moving on a surface with friction requires

   (a) less force than to keep it moving on the surface.
   (b) the same force as to keep it moving on the surface.
   (c) more force than to keep it moving on the surface.
   (d) a force equal to the weight of the object.

9. Vector $\vec{A}$ in the drawing is equal to

   (a) $\vec{C}+\vec{D}$ (b) $\vec{C}+\vec{D}+\vec{E}$ (c) $\vec{C}+\vec{F}$
   (d) $\vec{B}+\vec{C}$ (e) $\vec{B}+\vec{F}$

10. Which vector sum is *not* equal to zero?

    (a) $\vec{C}+\vec{D}+\vec{E}$ (b) $\vec{B}+\vec{C}+\vec{F}$
    (c) $\vec{D}+\vec{F}$ (d) $\vec{A}+\vec{B}+\vec{F}$

Multiple-Choice Questions 9 and 10

Problems

   ⓒ   Combination conceptual/quantitative problem

   ⚕   Biological or medical application

   ✦   Challenging problem

Blue #   Detailed solution in the Student Solutions Manual

 ① ②   Problems paired by concept

 〰   Text website interactive or tutorial

2.1 Force

1. A person is standing on a bathroom scale. Which of the following is *not* a force exerted *on the scale:* a contact force due to the floor, a contact force due to the person's feet, the weight of the person, the weight of the scale?

2. Which item/s in the following list is/are a vector quantity? volume, force, speed, length, time

3. Which item in the following list is *not* a scalar? temperature, test score, stock value, humidity, velocity, mass

4. A sack of flour has a weight of 19.8 N. What is its weight in pounds?

5. An astronaut weighs 175 lb. What is his weight in newtons?

6. Does the concept of a contact force apply to both a macroscopic scale and an atomic scale? Explain.

2.2 Graphical Vector Addition

7. Vectors $\vec{A}$, $\vec{B}$, and $\vec{C}$ are shown in the figure. (a) Draw vectors $\vec{D}$ and $\vec{E}$, where $\vec{D}=\vec{A}+\vec{B}$ and $\vec{E}=\vec{A}+\vec{C}$. (b) Show that $\vec{A}+\vec{B}=\vec{B}+\vec{A}$ by graphical means.

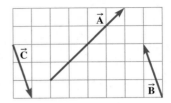

8. In the drawing, what is the vector sum of forces $\vec{A}+\vec{B}+\vec{C}$ if each grid square is 2 N on a side?

9. Two vectors, each of magnitude 4.0 N, are inclined at a small angle α below the horizontal, as shown. Let $\vec{C}=\vec{A}+\vec{B}$. Sketch the direction of $\vec{C}$ and estimate its magnitude. (The grid is 1 N on a side.)

10. In the drawing, what is the vector sum of forces $\vec{D}+\vec{E}+\vec{F}$ if each grid square is 2 N on a side?

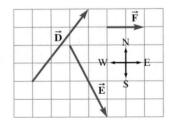

11. Juan is helping his mother rearrange the living room furniture. Juan pushes on the armchair with a force of 30 N directed at an angle of 15° above a horizontal line while his mother pushes with a force of 40 N directed at an angle of 20° below the same horizontal. What is the vector sum of these two forces? Use graph paper, ruler, and protractor to find a graphical solution.

12. Two of Robin Hood's men are pulling a sledge loaded with some gold along a path that runs due north to their hideout. One man pulls his rope with a force of 62 N at an angle of 12° east of north and the other pulls with the same force at an angle of 12° west of north. Use the graphical method to find the sum of these two forces on the sledge. Assume the ropes are parallel to the ground.

2.3 Vector Addition Using Components

13. A force of 20 N is directed at an angle of 60° above the x-axis. A second force of 20 N is directed at an angle of 60° below the x-axis. What is the vector sum of these two forces? Use graph paper to find your answer.

14. In Problem 9, let $\alpha = 10°$ and find the magnitude of vector $\vec{C}$ using the component method.

15. In Problem 8, use the component method to find the vector sum $\vec{A} + \vec{B} + \vec{C}$. Each grid square is 2 N on a side.

16. In Problem 10, use the component method to find the vector sum $\vec{D} + \vec{E} + \vec{F}$.

17. The velocity vector of a sprinting cheetah has x- and y-components $v_x = +16.4$ m/s and $v_y = -26.3$ m/s. (a) What is the magnitude of the velocity vector? (b) What angle does the velocity vector make with the +x- and −y-axes?

18. A vector is 20.0 m long and makes an angle of 60.0° counterclockwise from the y-axis (on the side of the −x-axis). What are the x- and y-components of this vector?

19. Vector $\vec{A}$ has magnitude 4.0 units; vector $\vec{B}$ has magnitude 6.0 units. The angle between $\vec{A}$ and $\vec{B}$ is 60.0°. What is the magnitude of $\vec{A} + \vec{B}$?

20. Vector $\vec{A}$ is directed along the positive y-axis and has magnitude $\sqrt{3.0}$ units. Vector $\vec{B}$ is directed along the negative x-axis and has magnitude 1.0 unit. What are the magnitude and direction of $\vec{A} + \vec{B}$?

21. Vector $\vec{a}$ has components $a_x = -3.0$ m/s² and $a_y = +4.0$ m/s². (a) What is the magnitude of $\vec{a}$? (b) What is the direction of $\vec{a}$? Give an angle with respect to one of the coordinate axes.

22. Find the x- and y-components of the four vectors shown in the drawing.

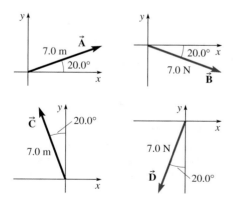

23. In each of these, the x- and y-components of a vector are given. Find the magnitude and direction of the vector. (a) $x = -5.0$ cm, $y = +8.0$ cm. (b) $F_x = +120$ N, $F_y = -60.0$ N. (c) $v_x = -13.7$ m/s, $v_y = -8.8$ m/s. (d) $a_x = 2.3$ m/s², $a_y = 6.5$ cm/s².

24. Vector $\vec{b}$ has magnitude 7.1 and direction 14° below the +x-axis. Vector $\vec{c}$ has x-component $c_x = -1.8$ and y-component $c_y = -6.7$. Compute (a) the x- and y-components of $\vec{b}$; (b) the magnitude and direction of $\vec{c}$; (c) the magnitude and direction of $\vec{c} + \vec{b}$.

2.4 Inertia and Equilibrium: Newton's First Law of Motion

25. A man is lazily floating on an air mattress in a swimming pool. If the weight of the man and air mattress together is 806 N, what is the upward force of the water acting on the system of man and mattress?

26. A hanging potted plant is suspended by a cord from a hook in the ceiling. Draw an FBD for each of these: (a) the system consisting of plant, soil, and pot; (b) the cord; (c) the hook; (d) the system consisting of plant, soil, pot, cord, and hook. Label each force arrow using subscripts (for example, $\vec{F}_{ch}$ would represent the force exerted on the cord by the hook).

27. A car is driving on a straight, level road at constant speed. Draw a free-body diagram for the car, showing the significant forces that act on it.

28. A parked automobile slips out of gear, rolls unattended down a slight incline, and then along a level road until it hits a stone wall. Draw an FBD to show the forces acting on the car while it is in contact with the wall.

29. A sailboat, tied to a mooring with a line, weighs 820 N. The mooring line pulls horizontally toward the west on the sailboat with a force of 110 N. The sails are stowed away and the wind blows from the west. The boat is moored on a still lake—no water currents push on it. Draw a free-body diagram for the sailboat and indicate the magnitude of each force.

30. Two objects, A and B, are acted on by the forces shown in the FBDs. Is the magnitude of the net force acting on object B greater than, less than, or equal to the magnitude of the net force acting on object A? Make a scale drawing on graph paper and explain the result.

31. Find the magnitude and direction of the net force on the object in each of the FBDs for this problem.

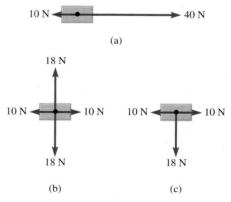

32. A truck driving on a level highway is acted on by the following forces: a downward gravitational force of

52 kN (kilonewtons); an upward contact force due to the road of 52 kN; another contact force due to the road of 7 kN, directed east; and a drag force due to air resistance of 5 kN, directed west. What is the net force acting on the truck?

33. Two forces of magnitudes 3.0 N and 4.0 N act on an object. How are the directions of the two forces related if (a) the net force has magnitude 7.0 N, or (b) if the net force has magnitude 5.0 N? (c) What relationship between the directions gives the smallest magnitude net force and what is this magnitude?

34. A barge is hauled along a straight-line section of canal by two horses harnessed to tow ropes and walking along the tow paths on either side of the canal. Each horse pulls with a force of 560 N at an angle of 15° with the centerline of the canal. Find the sum of these two forces on the barge. Is this sum the net force on the barge? Explain.

35. On her way to visit Grandmother, Red Riding Hood sat down to rest and placed her 1.2-kg basket of goodies beside her. A wolf came along, spotted the basket, and began to pull on the handle with a force of 6.4 N at an angle of 25° with respect to vertical. Red was not going to let go easily, so she pulled on the handle with a force of 12 N. If the net force on the basket is straight up, at what angle was Red Riding Hood pulling?

36. A towline is attached between a car and a glider. As the car speeds due east along the runway, the towline exerts a horizontal force of 850 N on the glider. What is the magnitude and direction of the force exerted by the glider on the towline?

2.5 Interaction Pairs: Newton's Third Law of Motion

37. A bike is hanging from a hook in a garage. Consider the following forces: (a) the force of the Earth pulling down on the bike, (b) the force of the bike pulling up on the Earth, (c) the force of the hook pulling up on the bike, and (d) the force of the hook pulling down on the ceiling. Which two forces are equal and opposite because of Newton's third law? Which two forces are equal and opposite because of Newton's first law?

38. A hummingbird is hovering motionless beside a flower. The blur of its wings shows that they are rapidly beating up and down. If the air pushes upward on the bird with a force of 0.30 N, what is the weight of the hummingbird?

39. A fish is suspended by a line from a fishing rod. Choose two forces acting on the fish and describe the interaction partner of each.

Problems 39 and 40

40. A fisherman is holding a fishing rod with a large fish suspended from the line of the rod. Identify the forces acting on the rod and their interaction partners.

41. Margie, who weighs 543 N, is standing on a bathroom scale that weighs 45 N. (a) With what force does the scale push up on Margie? (b) What is the interaction partner of that force? (c) With what force does the Earth push up on the scale? (d) Identify the interaction partner of that force.

42. A skydiver, who weighs 650 N, is falling at a constant speed with his parachute open. Consider the apparatus that connects the parachute to the skydiver to be part of the parachute. The parachute pulls upward with a force of 620 N. (a) What is the force of the air resistance acting on the skydiver? (b) Identify the forces and the interaction partners of each force exerted on the skydiver. (c) Identify the forces and interaction partners of each force exerted on the parachute.

43. A woman who weighs 600 N sits on a chair with her feet on the floor and her arms resting on the chair's armrests. The chair weighs 100 N. Each armrest exerts an upward force of 25 N on her arms. The seat of the chair exerts an upward force of 500 N. (a) What force does the floor exert on her feet? (b) What force does the floor exert on the chair? (c) Consider the woman and the chair to be a single system. Draw an FBD for this system that includes all of the *external* forces acting on it.

44. Refer to Problem 42. Consider the skydiver and parachute to be a single system. What are the external forces acting on this system?

2.6 Gravitational Forces

45. An astronaut stands at a position on the Moon such that Earth is directly over head and releases a Moon rock that was in her hand. (a) Which way will it fall? (b) What is the gravitational force exerted by the Moon on a 1.0-kg rock resting on the Moon's surface? (c) What is the gravitational force exerted by the Earth on the same 1.0-kg rock resting on the surface of the Moon? (d) What is the net gravitational force on the rock?

46. (a) Calculate your weight in newtons. (b) What is the weight in newtons of 250 g of cheese? (c) Name a common object whose weight is about 1 N.

47. A young South African girl has a mass of 40.0 kg. (a) What is her weight in newtons? (b) If she came to the United States, what would her weight be in pounds as measured on an American scale? Assume $g = 9.80$ N/kg in both locations.

48. A man weighs 0.80 kN on Earth. What is his mass in kilograms?

49. Using the information in the opening paragraphs of this chapter, what is the approximate magnitude of the gravitational force between the Earth and the Voyager 1 spacecraft? Each spacecraft has a mass of approximately 825 kg

during the mission, although the mass at launch was 2100 kg because of expendable Titan-Centaur rockets.

50. How far above the surface of the Earth does an object have to be in order for it to have the same weight as it would have on the surface of the Moon? (Ignore any effects from the Earth's gravity for the object on the Moon's surface or from the Moon's gravity for the object above the Earth.)

51. Find and compare the weight of a 65-kg man on Earth with the weight of the same man on (a) Mars, where $g = 3.7$ N/kg; (b) Venus, where $g = 8.9$ N/kg; and (c) Earth's Moon, where $g = 1.6$ N/kg.

52. Find the altitudes above the Earth's surface where Earth's gravitational field strength would be (a) two-thirds and (b) one-third of its value at the surface. [*Hint:* First find the radius for each situation; then recall that the altitude is the distance from the *surface* to a point above the surface. Use proportional reasoning.]

53. During a balloon ascension, wearing an oxygen mask, you measure the weight of a calibrated 5.00-kg mass and find that the value of the gravitational field strength at your location is 9.792 N/kg. How high above sea level, where the gravitational field strength was measured to be 9.803 N/kg, are you located?

54. At what altitude above the Earth's surface would your weight be half of what it is at the Earth's surface?

55. (a) What is the magnitude of the gravitational force that the Earth exerts on the Moon? (b) What is the magnitude of the gravitational force that the Moon exerts on the Earth? See the inside front and back covers for necessary information.

56. Alex is on stage playing his bass guitar. Estimate the magnitude of the *gravitational* attraction between Alex and Pat, a fan who is standing 8 m from Alex. Alex has a mass of 55 kg and Pat has a mass of 40 kg.

57. The Space Shuttle carries a satellite in its cargo bay and places it into orbit around the Earth. Find the ratio of the Earth's gravitational force on the satellite when it is on a launch pad at the Kennedy Space Center to the gravitational force exerted when the satellite is orbiting 6.00×10^3 km above the launch pad.

2.7 Contact Forces

58. A book rests on the surface of the table. Consider the following four forces that arise in this situation: (a) the force of the Earth pulling on the book, (b) the force of the table pushing on the book, (c) the force of the book pushing on the table, and (d) the force of the book pulling on the Earth. The book is not moving. Which pair of forces must be equal in magnitude and opposite in direction even though they are *not* an interaction pair?

59. You grab a book and give it a quick push across the top of a horizontal table. After a short push, the book slides across the table, and because of friction, comes to a stop.

(a) Draw an FBD of the book while you are pushing it. (b) Draw an FBD of the book after you have stopped pushing it, while it is sliding across the table. (c) Draw an FBD of the book after it has stopped sliding. (d) In which of the preceding cases is the net force on the book not equal to zero? (e) If the book has a mass of 0.50 kg and the coefficient of friction between the book and the table is 0.40, what is the net force acting on the book in part (b)? (f) If there were no friction between the table and the book, what would the FBD for part (b) look like? Would the book slow down in this case? Why or why not?

60. A box sits on a horizontal wooden ramp. The coefficient of static friction between the box and the ramp is 0.30. You grab one end of the ramp and lift it up, keeping the other end of the ramp on the ground. What is the angle between the ramp and the horizontal direction when the box begins to slide down the ramp? (tutorial: crate on ramp)

61. A crate full of artichokes rests on a ramp that is inclined 10.0° above the horizontal. Give the direction of the normal force and the friction force acting on the crate in each of these situations. (a) The crate is at rest. (b) The crate is being pushed and is sliding up the ramp. (c) The crate is being pushed and is sliding down the ramp.

62. A 3.0-kg block is at rest on a horizontal floor. If you push horizontally on the 3.0-kg block with a force of 12.0 N, it just starts to move. (a) What is the coefficient of static friction? (b) A 7.0-kg block is stacked on top of the 3.0-kg block. What is the magnitude F of the force, acting horizontally on the 3.0-kg block as before, that is required to make the two blocks start to move?

63. A horse is trotting along pulling a sleigh through the snow. To move the sleigh, of mass m, straight ahead at a constant speed, the horse must pull with a force of magnitude T. (a) What is the net force acting on the sleigh? (b) What is the coefficient of kinetic friction between the sleigh and the snow?

64. Before hanging new William Morris wallpaper in her bedroom, Brenda sanded the walls lightly to smooth out some irregularities on the surface. The sanding block weighs 2.0 N and Brenda pushes on it with a force of 3.0 N at an angle of 30.0° with respect to the vertical, and angled toward the wall. Draw an FBD for the sanding block as it moves straight up the wall at a constant speed. What is the coefficient of kinetic friction between the wall and the block?

65. Four separate blocks are placed side by side in a left-to-right row on a table. A horizontal force, acting toward the right, is applied to the block on the far left end of the row. Draw FBDs for (a) the second block on the left and for (b) the system of four blocks.

66. (a) In Example 2.14, if the movers stop pushing on the safe, can static friction hold the safe in place without having it slide back down? (b) If not, what minimum force needs to be applied to hold the safe in place?

67. Mechanical advantage is the ratio of the force required without the use of a simple machine to that needed when using the simple machine. Compare the force to lift an object with that needed to slide the same object up a frictionless incline and show that the mechanical advantage of the inclined plane is the length of the incline divided by the height of the incline (d/h in Fig. 2.32).

68. An 80.0-N crate of apples sits at rest on a ramp that runs from the ground to the bed of a truck. The ramp is inclined at 20.0° to the ground. (a) What is the normal force exerted on the crate by the ramp? (b) The inter-action partner of this normal force has what magnitude and direction? It is exerted *by* what object *on* what object? Is it a contact or a long-range force? (c) What is the static frictional force exerted on the crate by the ramp? (d) What is the minimum possible value of the coefficient of static friction? (e) The normal and fric-tional forces are perpendicular components of the con-tact force exerted on the crate by the ramp. Find the magnitude and direction of the contact force.

69. An 85-kg skier is sliding down a ski slope at a constant velocity. The slope makes an angle of 11° above the horizontal direction. (a) Ignoring any air resistance, what is the force of kinetic friction acting on the skier? (b) What is the coefficient of kinetic friction between the skis and the snow?

2.8 Tension

70. You are pulling a suitcase through the airport at a con-stant speed. The handle of the suitcase makes an angle of 60° with respect to the horizontal direction. If you pull with a force of 5.0 N parallel to the handle, what is the force of friction acting on the suitcase?

71. A 200.0-N sign is suspended from a horizontal strut of negligible weight. The force exerted on the strut by the wall is horizontal. Draw an FBD to show the forces acting on the strut. Find the tension T in the diagonal cable sup-porting the strut.

72. Two boxes with different masses are tied together on a frictionless ramp surface. What is the tension in each of the cords?

✦73. A crow perches on a clothesline midway between two poles. Each end of the rope makes an angle of θ below the horizontal where it connects to the pole. If the weight of the crow is W, what is the tension in the rope? Ignore the weight of the rope.

✦74. The drawing shows an elastic cord attached to two back teeth and stretched across a front tooth. The purpose of this arrangement is to apply a force $\vec{F}$ to the front tooth. (The figure has been simplified by running the cord straight from the front tooth to the back teeth.) If the tension in the cord is 1.2 N, what are the magnitude and direction of the force $\vec{F}$ applied to the front tooth?

75. A pulley is attached to the ceiling. Spring scale A is attached to the wall and a rope runs horizontally from it and over the pulley. The same rope is then attached to spring scale B. On the other side of scale B hangs a 120-N weight. What are the readings of the two scales A and B? The weights of the scales are negligible.

76. Spring scale A is attached to the floor and a rope runs vertically upward, loops over the pulley, and runs down on the other side to a 120-N weight. Scale B is attached to the ceiling and the pulley is hung below it. What are the readings of the two spring scales, A and B? Ignore the weights of the pulley and scales.

77. Two springs are connected in series so that spring scale A hangs from a hook on the ceiling and a second spring scale, B, hangs from the hook at the bottom of scale A. Apples weighing 120 N hang from the hook at the bottom of scale B. What are the readings on the upper scale A and the lower scale B? Ignore the weights of the scales.

◆78. A cord, with a spring balance to measure forces attached midway along, is hanging from a hook attached to the ceiling. A mass of 10 kg is hanging from the lower end of the cord. The spring balance indicates a reading of 98 N for the force. Then two people hold the opposite ends of the same cord and pull against each other horizontally until the balance in the middle again reads 98 N. With what force must each person pull to attain this result?

79. A pulley is hung from the ceiling by a rope. A block of mass M is suspended by another rope that passes over the pulley and is attached to the wall. The rope fastened to the wall makes a right angle with the wall. Neglect the masses of the rope and the pulley. Find (a) the tension in the rope from which the pulley hangs and (b) the angle θ that the rope makes with the ceiling.

80. A 2.0-kg ball tied to a string fixed to the ceiling is pulled to one side by a force $\vec{F}$. Just before the ball is released and allowed to swing back and forth, (a) how large is the force $\vec{F}$ that is holding the ball in position and (b) what is the tension in the string?

81. A 45-N lithograph is supported by two wires. One wire makes a 25° angle with the vertical and the other makes a 15° angle with the vertical. Find the tension in each wire. (Ⱳ tutorial: hanging picture)

2.9 Fundamental Forces

82. Which of the fundamental forces governs the motion of planets in the solar system? Is this the strongest or the weakest of the fundamental forces? Explain.

83. Which of the following forces have an unlimited range: strong force, contact force, electromagnetic force, gravitational force?

84. Which of the following forces bind electrons to nuclei to form atoms: strong force, contact force, electromagnetic force, gravitational force?

85. Which of the fundamental forces has the shortest range, yet is responsible for producing the sunlight that reaches Earth?

86. Which of the fundamental forces binds quarks together to form protons, neutrons, and many exotic subatomic particles?

Comprehensive Problems

87. Fernando places a 2.0-kg dictionary on a tabletop, then sits on top of the dictionary. Fernando has a mass of 52 kg. (a) What is the normal force exerted by the table on the dictionary? (b) What is the normal force exerted by the dictionary on Fernando? (c) Is there a normal force exerted by the table on Fernando? If so, what is its magnitude?

◆88. You want to hang a 15-N picture as in the figure (a) using some very fine twine that will break with more than 12 N of tension. Can you do this? What if you have it as illustrated in Figure (b)?

(a)   (b)

89. You want to push a 65-kg box up a 25° ramp. The coefficient of kinetic friction between the ramp and the box is 0.30. With what magnitude force parallel to the ramp should you push on the box so that it moves up the ramp at a constant speed?

◆90. A roller coaster is towed up an incline at a steady speed of 0.50 m/s by a chain parallel to the surface of the incline. The slope is 3.0%, which means that the elevation increases by 3.0 m for every 100.0 m of horizontal distance. The mass of the roller coaster is 400.0 kg. Ignoring friction, what is the magnitude of the force exerted on the roller coaster by the chain?

91. An airplane is cruising along in a horizontal level flight at a constant velocity, heading due west. (a) If the weight of the plane is 2.6×10^4 N, what is the net force on the plane? (b) With what force does the air push upward on the plane?

▼92. A young boy with a broken leg is undergoing traction. (a) Find the magnitude of the total force of the traction apparatus applied to the leg, assuming the weight of the leg is 22 N and the weight hanging from the traction apparatus is also 22 N. (b) What is the horizontal component of the traction force acting on the leg? (c) What is the magnitude of the force exerted on the femur by the lower leg?

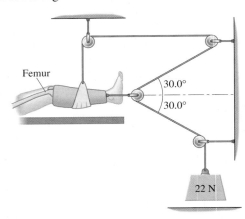

93. The mass of the Moon is 0.0123 times that of the Earth. A spaceship is traveling along a line connecting the centers of the Earth and the Moon. At what distance from the Earth does the spaceship find the gravitational pull of the Earth equal in magnitude to that of the Moon? Express your answer as a percentage of the distance between the centers of the two bodies.

94. A 320-kg satellite is in orbit around the Earth 16 000 km above the Earth's surface. (a) What is the weight of the satellite when in orbit? (b) What was its weight when it was on the Earth's surface, before being launched? (c) While it orbits the Earth, what force does the satellite exert on the Earth?

95. A toy freight train consists of an engine and three identical cars. The train is moving to the right at constant speed along a straight, level track. Three spring scales are used to connect the cars as follows: spring scale A is located between the engine and the first car; scale B is between the first and second cars; scale C is between the second and third cars. (a) If air resistance and friction are negligible, what are the relative readings on the three spring scales A, B, and C? (b) Repeat part (a), taking air resistance and friction into consideration this time. [*Hint*: Draw an FBD for the car in the middle.] (c) If air resistance and friction together cause a force of magnitude 5.5 N on each car, directed toward the left, find the readings of scales A, B, and C.

96. The coefficient of static friction between a block and a horizontal floor is 0.40, while the coefficient of kinetic friction is 0.15. The mass of the block is 5.0 kg. A horizontal force is applied to the block and slowly increased. (a) What is the value of the applied horizontal force at the instant that the block starts to slide? (b) What is the net force on the block after it starts to slide?

97. A box full of books rests on a wooden floor. The normal force the floor exerts on the box is 250 N. (a) You push horizontally on the box with a force of 120 N, but it

refuses to budge. What can you say about the coefficient of static friction between the box and the floor? (b) If you must push horizontally on the box with a force of at least 150 N to start it sliding, what is the coefficient of static friction? (c) Once the box is sliding, you only have to push with a force of 120 N to keep it sliding. What is the coefficient of kinetic friction?

98. The coefficient of static friction between block A and a horizontal floor is 0.45 and the coefficient of static friction between block B and the floor is 0.30. The mass of each block is 2.0 kg and they are connected together by a cord. (a) If a horizontal force $\vec{F}$ pulling on block B is slowly increased, in a direction parallel to the connecting cord, until it is barely enough to make the two blocks start moving, what is the magnitude of $\vec{F}$ at the instant that they start to slide? (b) What is the tension in the cord connecting blocks A and B at that same instant?

99. Four *identical* spring scales, A, B, C, and D are used to hang a 220.0-N sack of potatoes. (a) Assume that the scales have negligible weights and that all four scales show the same reading. What is the reading of each scale? (b) Suppose that each scale has a weight of 5.0 N. If scales B and D show the same reading, what is the reading of each scale?

100. When you hold up a 100-N weight in your hand, with your forearm horizontal and your palm up, the force exerted by your biceps is much larger than 100 N—perhaps as much as 1000 N. How can that be? What other forces are acting on your arm? Draw an FBD for the forearm, showing all of the forces. Assume that all the forces exerted on the forearm are purely vertical—either up or down.

101. In the sport of curling, popular in Canada and the United Kingdom, a player slides a 20.0-kg granite stone down a 38-m-long ice rink. Draw FBDs for the stone (a) while it sits at rest on the ice; (b) while it slides down the rink; (c) during a head-on collision with an opponent's stone that was at rest on the ice.

102. A refrigerator magnet weighing 0.14 N is used to hold up a photograph weighing 0.030 N. The magnet attracts the refrigerator door with a magnetic force of 2.10 N. (a) Identify the interactions between the magnet and other objects. (b) Draw an FBD for the magnet, showing all the forces that act on it. (c) Which of these forces are long-range and which are contact forces? (d) Find the magnitudes of all the forces acting on the magnet.

103. A computer weighing 87 N rests on the horizontal surface of your desk. The coefficient of friction between the computer and the desk is 0.60. (a) Draw an FBD for the computer. (b) What is the magnitude of the frictional force acting on the computer? (c) How hard would you have to push on it to get it to start to slide across the desk?

104. A truck is towing a 1000-kg car at a constant speed up a hill that makes an angle of $\alpha = 5.0°$ with respect to the horizontal. A rope is attached from the truck to the car at an angle of $\beta = 10.0°$ with respect to horizontal. Neglect any friction in this problem. (a) Draw an FBD showing all the forces on the car. Indicate the angle that each force makes with either the vertical or horizontal direction. (b) What is the tension in the rope?

105. The readings of the two spring scales shown in the drawing are the same. (a) Explain why they are the same. [*Hint:* Draw FBDs.] (b) What is the reading?

106. A 50.0-kg crate is suspended between the floor and the ceiling using two spring scales, one attached to the ceiling and one to the floor. If the lower scale reads 120 N, what is the reading of the upper scale? Ignore the weight of the scales.

107. Spring scale A is attached to the ceiling. A 10.0-kg mass is suspended from the scale. A second spring scale, B, is hanging from a hook at the bottom of the 10.0-kg mass and a 4.0-kg mass hangs from the second spring scale. (a) What are the readings of the two scales if the masses of the scales are negligible? (b) What are the readings if each scale has a mass of 1.0 kg?

108. The tallest spot on Earth is Mt. Everest, which is 8850 m above sea level. If the radius of the Earth to sea level is 6370 km, how much does the gravitational field strength change between the sea level value at that location (9.826 N/kg) and the top of Mt. Everest?

109. By what percentage does the weight of an object change when it is moved from the equator at sea level, where the effective value of g is 9.784 N/kg, to the North Pole where $g = 9.832$ N/kg?

110. Two canal workers pull a barge along the narrow waterway at a constant speed. One worker pulls with a force of 105 N at an angle of 28° with respect to the forward motion of the barge and the other worker, on the opposite tow path, pulls at an angle of 38° relative to the barge motion. Both ropes are parallel to the ground. (a) With what magnitude force should the second worker pull to make the sum of the two forces be in the forward direction? (b) What is the magnitude of the force on the barge from the two tow ropes?

111. A large wrecking ball of mass m is resting against a wall. It hangs from the end of a cable that is attached at its upper end to a crane that is just touching the wall. The cable makes an angle of θ with the wall. Ignoring friction between the ball and the wall, find the tension in the cable.

112. The figure shows the quadriceps and the patellar tendons attached to the patella (the kneecap). If the tension T in each tendon is 1.30 kN, what is (a) the magnitude and (b) the direction of the contact force $\vec{F}$ exerted on the patella by the femur?

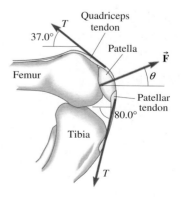

✦113. Tamar wants to cut down a large, dead poplar tree
Ⓒ   with her chain saw, but she does not want it to fall
     onto the nearby gazebo. Yoojin comes to help with a
     long rope. Yoojin, a physicist, suggests they tie the
     rope taut from the poplar to the oak tree and then pull
     sideways on the rope as shown in the figure. If the
     rope is 40.0 m long and Yoojin pulls sideways at the
     midpoint of the rope with a force of 360.0 N, causing
     a 2.00-m sideways displacement of the rope at its
     midpoint, what force will the rope exert on the poplar
     tree? Compare this with pulling the rope directly away
     from the poplar with a force of 360.0 N and explain
     why the values are different. [*Hint:* Until the poplar is
     cut through enough to start falling, the rope is in
     equilibrium.]

Side view

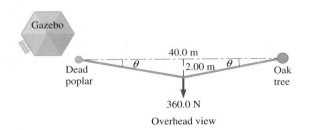

Overhead view

✦114. A student's head is bent over her physics book. The
▼   head weighs 50.0 N and is supported by the muscle
     force $\vec{F}_m$ exerted by the neck extensor muscles and by
     the contact force $\vec{F}_c$ exerted at the atlantooccipital joint.
     Given that the magnitude of $\vec{F}_m$ is 60.0 N and is directed
     35° below the horizontal, find (a) the magnitude and
     (b) the direction of $\vec{F}_c$.

✦115. (a) If a spacecraft moves in a straight line between the
     Earth and the Sun, at what point would the force of
     gravity on the spacecraft due to the Sun be as large as
     that due to the Earth? (b) If the spacecraft is close to,
     but not at, this equilibrium point, does the net force on
     the spacecraft tend to push it toward or away from the
     equilibrium point? [*Hint:* Imagine the spacecraft a
     small distance d closer to the Earth and find out which
     gravitational force is stronger.]

✦116. While trying to decide where to hang a
Ⓒ   framed picture, you press it against the
     wall to keep it from falling. The picture
     weighs 5.0 N and you press against the
     frame with a force of 6.0 N at an angle
     of 40° from the vertical. (a) What is the
     direction of the normal force exerted
     on the picture by your hand? (b) What
     is the direction of the normal force
     exerted on the picture by the wall?
     (c) What is the coefficient of static friction between
     the wall and the picture? The frictional force exerted
     on the picture by the wall can have two possible direc-
     tions. Explain why.

Answers to Practice Problems

2.1 No; the checkbook balance may increase or decrease,
but there is no spatial direction associated with it. When we
say it "goes down," we do not mean that it moves in a direction toward the center of the Earth! Rather, we really mean
that it decreases. The balance is a scalar.

2.2 Answer: (a) smaller (b) yes; $F_S > F_B$.

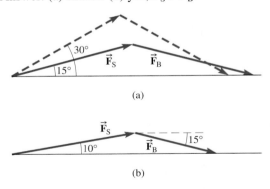

2.3 157 N, 57° below the +x-axis

2.4 (a) $F_x = 49.1$ N, $F_y = 2.9$ N; (b) $F = 49.2$ N; (c) 3.4°
above the horizontal

2.5 In the first case, the principle of inertia says that Negar
tends to stay at rest with respect to the ground as the subway
car begins to move forward, until forces acting on her (exerted
by the strap and the floor) make her move forward. In the second case, Negar keeps moving forward with respect to the
ground with constant speed as the subway car slows down,
until forces acting on her make her slow down as well.

2.6 80 N upward

2.7 0.5 kN downward

2.8 760 N, 81.7° above the $-x$-axis or 8.3° to the left of the $+y$-axis

2.9 The contact force exerted on the floor by the chest. 870 N, 59° below the rightward horizontal ($+x$-axis).

2.10 For $m_1 = m_2 = 1000$ kg and $r = 4$ m, $F \approx 4$ μN, which is about the same magnitude as the weight of a mosquito. The claim that this tiny force caused the collision is ridiculous.

2.11 0.57 N or 0.13 lb

2.12 The chest is in equilibrium, so the net force on it is zero. Setting the net force equal to zero separately for the horizontal and vertical components gives the answer: the normal force is 750 N, up, and the frictional force is 110 N, to the left. The quantity $\mu_s N$ is the *maximum* possible magnitude of the force of static friction for a surface. In this problem, the frictional force does not necessarily have the maximum possible magnitude.

2.13 (a)

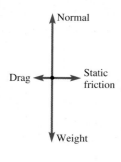

(b) Weight of the car = 11.0 kN; (c) 2.1 kN northward

2.14 (a) 110 N; (b) 230 N

2.15 3100 N

2.16

$T_C = 902.0$ N
$T_B = 1804$ N
$W = 1804$ N

Answers to Checkpoints

2.2 30 N south

2.5 The two forces exerted by the two children on the toy cannot be interaction partners because they act on the *same* object (the toy), not on two different objects. Interaction partners act on different objects, one on each of the two objects that are interacting. The interaction partner of the force exerted by one child on the toy is the force that the toy exerts on that child.

2.6 The weight of the gear decreases as the value of g decreases. The mass of the gear does not change.

2.7 One upward normal force on each leg due to the floor and one downward normal force on the desktop due to the laptop

CHAPTER

3

Acceleration and Newton's Second Law of Motion

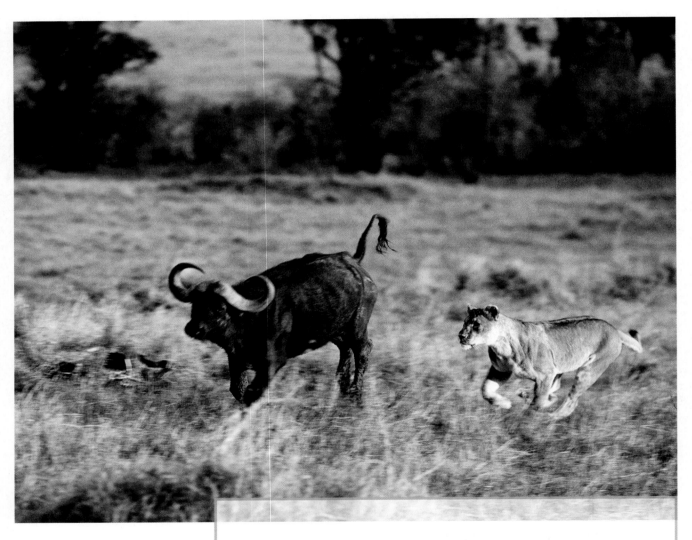

Despite its enormous mass (425 to 900 kg), the Cape buffalo is capable of running at a top speed of about 55 km/h (34 mi/h). Since the top speed of the African lion is about the same, how is it ever possible for a lion to catch the buffalo, especially since the lion typically makes its move from a distance of 20 to 30 m from the buffalo? (See p. 90 for the answer.)

Concepts & Skills to Review

3.1 POSITION AND DISPLACEMENT

Introduction to Newton's Second Law of Motion

In Chapter 2, we concentrated on situations in which the net force acting on an object was zero. Newton's first law of motion states that when the net force is zero, the velocity of the object does not change. If the object is at rest, it remains at rest with zero velocity. If it is moving, it continues moving with the same speed and in the same direction.

When a *nonzero* net force acts on an object, the velocity changes. Newton's second law of motion (presented in Section 3.3) tells us how the net force and the object's mass determine the *change in* velocity. Before discussing Newton's second law in detail, we must introduce a precise definition of velocity as the rate of change of the object's position and then learn how to calculate the rate of change of the *velocity*.

Position

To describe motion unambiguously, we need a way to say *where* an object is located. Suppose that at 3:00 P.M. a train stops on an east-west track as a result of an engine problem. The engineer wants to call the railroad office to report the problem. How can he tell them where to find the train? He might say something like "three kilometers east of the old trestle bridge." Notice that he uses a point of reference: the old trestle bridge. Then he states how far the train is from that point and in what direction. If he omits any of the three pieces (the reference point, the distance, and the direction), then his description of the train's whereabouts is ambiguous.

The same thing is done in physics. First, we choose a reference point, called the **origin**. Then, to describe the location of something, we give its distance from the origin and the direction. These two quantities, direction and distance, together constitute a vector quantity called the **position** of the object (symbol $\vec{r}$, Fig. 3.1). The x-, y-, and z-components of $\vec{r}$ are usually written simply as x, y, and z (instead of r_x, r_y, and r_z) because they are the x-, y-, and z-coordinates of the object. Graphically, the position vector can be drawn as an arrow starting at the origin and ending with the arrowhead on the object. When drawing more than one position vector, choose a scale so the length of the vector arrow is proportional to the actual distance between the object and the origin.

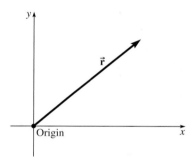

Figure 3.1 A position vector $\vec{r}$.

Displacement and the Subtraction of Vectors

Once the train's engine is repaired and it goes on its way, we might want to describe its motion. At 3:14 P.M., it leaves its initial position, 3 km east of the origin (Fig. 3.2a). At 3:56 P.M., the train is 26 km west of the origin, which is 29 km to the west of its initial position. **Displacement** is defined as the change of the position vector—the final position vector minus the initial position vector. Displacement is written $\Delta\vec{r}$ where the symbol Δ (the uppercase Greek letter delta) means *the change in* the quantity that follows. If the initial and final position vectors are $\vec{r}_i$ and $\vec{r}_f$, then

Displacement: final position vector minus initial position vector

Reminder: the symbol Δ stands for *the change in*. If the initial value of a quantity Q is Q_i and the final value is Q_f, then $\Delta Q = Q_f - Q_i$. ΔQ is read "delta Q."

Definition of displacement:

$$\Delta\vec{r} = \vec{r}_f - \vec{r}_i \tag{3-1}$$

(a)

(b)

Figure 3.2 (a) Initial ($\vec{r}_i$) and final ($\vec{r}_f$) position vectors for a train; (b) the displacement vector $\Delta\vec{r}$ is found by subtracting the vector for the initial position from the vector for the final position. (Train not to scale.)

Vector Subtraction:
$\vec{A} - \vec{B} = \vec{A} + (-\vec{B})$, where $-\vec{B}$ has the same magnitude as $\vec{B}$ but is opposite in direction. Note that the order matters: $\vec{B} - \vec{A} = -(\vec{A} - \vec{B})$.

Since the positions are vector quantities, the operation indicated in Eq. (3-1) is a **vector subtraction**. *To subtract a vector is to add its opposite* (that is, a vector with the same magnitude but opposite direction): $\vec{r}_f - \vec{r}_i = \vec{r}_f + (-\vec{r}_i)$. Multiplying a vector by the scalar −1 reverses the vector's direction while leaving its magnitude unchanged, so $-\vec{r}_i = -1 \times \vec{r}_i$ is a vector equal in magnitude and opposite in direction to $\vec{r}_i$. Figure 3.2b shows the graphical subtraction of position vectors to illustrate the displacement $\Delta\vec{r}$, a vector of magnitude 29 km pointing west.

We can subtract vector components to find the displacement of the train. If we choose the x-axis to the east, then $x_i = +3$ km and $x_f = -26$ km. The x-component of the displacement is

$$\Delta x = x_f - x_i = (-26 \text{ km}) - (+3 \text{ km}) = -29 \text{ km}$$

Δy is zero, so the displacement $\Delta\vec{r}$ is 29 km in the −x-direction (west).

Notice that the magnitude of the displacement vector is not necessarily equal to the *distance traveled.* Suppose the train first travels 7 km to the east, putting it 10 km east of the origin, and then reverses direction and travels 36 km to the west. The total distance traveled in that case is (7 km + 36 km) = 43 km, but the magnitude of the displacement—which is the distance between the initial and final positions—is 29 km. The displacement depends only on the starting and ending positions, not on the path taken.

Example 3.1

A Mule Hauling Corn to Market

A mule hauls the farmer's wagon along a straight road for 4.3 km directly south to the neighboring farm where a few bushels of corn are loaded onto the wagon. Then the farmer drives the mule back along the same straight road, heading north for 7.2 km to the market. Find the displacement of the mule from the starting point to the market.

Strategy The problem gives us two successive displacements. Suppose the mule starts at position $\vec{r}_1$ (Fig. 3.3). It goes south until it reaches the neighbor's farm at position $\vec{r}_2$. The displacement to the neighbor's farm is $\vec{r}_2 - \vec{r}_1 = 4.3$ km south. Then the mule goes 7.2 km north to reach the market at position $\vec{r}_3$. The displacement from the neighbor's farm to the

continued on next page

Example 3.1 continued

market is $\vec{r}_3 - \vec{r}_2 = 7.2$ north. The problem asks for the displacement of the mule from $\vec{r}_1$ to $\vec{r}_3$.

Solution We can eliminate $\vec{r}_2$, the intermediate position, from the two equations for the intermediate displacements by adding them:

$$(\vec{r}_3 - \vec{r}_2) + (\vec{r}_2 - \vec{r}_1) = 7.2 \text{ km north} + 4.3 \text{ km south}$$

$$\vec{r}_3 - \vec{r}_1 = (7.2 \text{ km} - 4.3 \text{ km}) \text{ north} = 2.9 \text{ km north}$$

The displacement is 2.9 km north.

Discussion When we added the two displacements, the intermediate position $\vec{r}_2$ dropped out, as it must since the displacement is independent of the path taken from the initial position to the final position. Generalizing this result, *the total displacement for a trip with several parts is the vector sum of the displacements for each part of the trip.*

We can check the result using components. Since the displacements are directed either north or south, the three displacement vectors have only

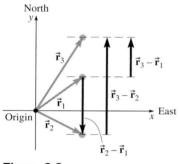

Figure 3.3
The total displacement $\vec{r}_3 - \vec{r}_1$ is the sum of two successive displacements.

y-components; their x-components are zero. As drawn in Fig. 3.3, the *position* vectors do have x-components, but they are all equal, so $x_2 - x_1 = 0$, $x_3 - x_2 = 0$, and $x_3 - x_1 = 0$. If we choose the y-axis to be north, then $y_2 - y_1 = -4.3$ km and $y_3 - y_2 = +7.2$ km. The y-component of the overall displacement is $y_3 - y_1 = (y_3 - y_2) + (y_2 - y_1) = (+7.2 \text{ km}) + (-4.3 \text{ km}) = +2.9$ km. The displacement is 2.9 km in the $+y$-direction (north).

Conceptual Practice Problem 3.1   Around the Bases

Casey hits a long fly ball over the heads of the outfielders. He runs from home plate to first base, to second base, to third base, and slides back to home plate safely (an inside-the-park home run). What is Casey's total displacement?

✓ CHECKPOINT 3.1

In Example 3.1, is the magnitude of the displacement the same as the distance traveled? Explain.

Another Way to Subtract Vectors   Suppose Charlotte and Shona are taking a trip in Ireland from Killarney to Cork to visit Blarney castle. In Fig. 3.4a, we select an origin and then draw position vectors from the origin to the starting and ending points of the trip. The vector drawn from the tip of $\vec{r}_i$ to the tip of $\vec{r}_f$ is the vector $\vec{r}_f - \vec{r}_i$. Why? Because $\Delta\vec{r}$ is the *change in position*, so it takes us *from the initial position $\vec{r}_i$ to the*

(a)   (b)

Blarney castle.

Figure 3.4 (a) Two position vectors, $\vec{r}_i$ and $\vec{r}_f$, drawn from an *arbitrary origin* to the starting point (Killarney) and to the ending point (Cork) of a trip. The final position vector minus the initial position vector is the displacement $\Delta\vec{r}$, drawn from the tip of $\vec{r}_i$ to the tip of $\vec{r}_f$. (b) Adding $-\vec{r}_i + \vec{r}_f$ gives the same result for $\Delta\vec{r}$.

final position $\vec{r}_f$. To double-check, note that the initial position plus the change in position gives the final position:

$$\vec{r}_i + \Delta\vec{r} = \vec{r}_f$$

We draw $\Delta\vec{r}$ so that, when added to $\vec{r}_i$ it gives $\vec{r}_f$. This procedure is equivalent to adding $-\vec{r}_i + \vec{r}_f$ (Fig. 3.4b):

$$\Delta\vec{r} = \vec{r}_f - \vec{r}_i = \vec{r}_f + (-\vec{r}_i) = -\vec{r}_i + \vec{r}_f$$

Although the initial and final position vectors depend on the choice of origin, the displacement (*change* of position) does *not* depend on the choice of origin. This same procedure is used to subtract any kind of vector quantity.

Successive Displacements Can Be Added as Vectors As we saw in Example 3.1, the total displacement for a trip with several parts is the vector sum of the displacements for each part of the trip because

$$\vec{r}_3 - \vec{r}_1 = (\vec{r}_3 - \vec{r}_2) + (\vec{r}_2 - \vec{r}_1)$$

Example 3.2 explores this idea further. We will use compass headings to specify vector directions. Any direction in the horizontal plane can be specified by giving an angle with respect to the directions of the compass. For example, the direction of the vector in Fig. 3.5 is "20° north of east," which means that the vector makes a 20° angle with the east direction and is on the north (rather than the south) side of east. The same direction could be described as "70° east of north," although it is customary to use the smaller angle. Northeast means "45° north of east" or, equivalently, "45° east of north."

Figure 3.5 Measuring angles with respect to compass headings. The direction of this vector is 20° north of east (20° N of E).

Example 3.2

An Irish Adventure

In a trip from Killarney to Cork, Charlotte and Shona drive at a compass heading of 27° west of south for 18 km to Kenmare, then directly south for 17 km to Glengariff, then at a compass heading of 13° north of east for 48 km to Cork. What are the magnitude and direction of the displacement vector for the entire trip?

Strategy Let's call the four positions $\vec{r}_1$ (Killarney), $\vec{r}_2$ (Kenmare), $\vec{r}_3$ (Glengariff), and $\vec{r}_4$ (Cork). The displacement for the whole trip is $\vec{r}_4 - \vec{r}_1$. The problem gives the displacements for the three parts of the trip. Let us define $\vec{A} = \vec{r}_2 - \vec{r}_1$ = 18 km, 27° west of south; $\vec{B} = \vec{r}_3 - \vec{r}_2$ = 17 km, south; and $\vec{C} = \vec{r}_4 - \vec{r}_3$ = 48 km, 13° north of east. The sum of these three

displacements is the total displacement (Fig. 3.6). We add the vectors using x- and y-components. First we choose directions for the x- and y-axes. Then we find the components of the three displacements. Adding the x- or y-components of the three displacements gives the x- or y-component of the total displacement. Finally, from the components we find the magnitude and direction of the total displacement.

Solution A good choice is the conventional one: x-axis to the east and the y-axis to the north. The first displacement ($\vec{A}$) is directed 27° west of south. Both of its components are negative since west is the $-x$-direction and south is the $-y$-direction. Using the triangle in Fig. 3.7, the side of the triangle opposite the 27° angle is parallel to the x-axis. The sine function relates the opposite side to the hypotenuse:

$$A_x = -A \sin 27° = -18 \text{ km} \times 0.454 = -8.17 \text{ km}$$

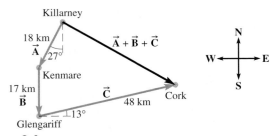

Figure 3.6

Graphical addition of the displacement vectors for the trip from Killarney to Cork via Kenmare and Glengariff.

Figure 3.7

Resolving $\vec{A}$, $\vec{B}$, and $\vec{C}$ into x- and y-components.

continued on next page

Example 3.2 continued

where A is the magnitude of $\vec{A}$. The cosine relates the adjacent side to the hypotenuse:

$$A_y = -A \cos 27° = -18 \text{ km} \times 0.891 = -16.0 \text{ km}$$

Displacement $\vec{B}$ has no x-component since its direction is south. Therefore,

$$B_x = 0 \quad \text{and} \quad B_y = -17 \text{ km}$$

The direction of $\vec{C}$ is 13° north of east. Both its components are positive. From Fig. 3.7, the side of the triangle opposite the 13° angle is parallel to the y-axis, so

$$C_x = +C \cos 13° = +48 \text{ km} \times 0.974 = +46.8 \text{ km}$$
$$C_y = +C \sin 13° = +48 \text{ km} \times 0.225 = +10.8 \text{ km}$$

Now we sum the x- and y-components separately to find the x- and y-components of the total displacement:

$$\Delta x = A_x + B_x + C_x$$
$$= (-8.17 \text{ km}) + 0 + 46.8 \text{ km} = 38.63 \text{ km}$$

and

$$\Delta y = A_y + B_y + C_y$$
$$= (-16.0 \text{ km}) + (-17 \text{ km}) + 10.8 \text{ km} = -22.2 \text{ km}$$

The magnitude and direction of $\Delta \vec{r}$ can be found from the triangle in Fig. 3.8. The magnitude is represented by the hypotenuse:

$$\Delta r = \sqrt{(\Delta x)^2 + (\Delta y)^2} = \sqrt{(38.63 \text{ km})^2 + (-22.2 \text{ km})^2}$$
$$= 45 \text{ km}$$

Figure 3.8
Finding the magnitude and direction of $\Delta \vec{r}$.

The angle θ is

$$\theta = \tan^{-1} \frac{\text{opposite}}{\text{adjacent}} = \tan^{-1} \frac{22.2 \text{ km}}{38.63 \text{ km}} = 30°$$

Since $+x$ is east and $-y$ is south, the direction of the displacement is 30° south of east. The magnitude and direction of the displacement found using components agree with the displacement found graphically in Fig. 3.6.

Discussion Note that the x-component of one displacement was found using the sine function while another was found using the cosine. The x-component (or the y-component) of the vector can be related to *either* the sine or the cosine, depending on which angle in the triangle is used.

Practice Problem 3.2 Changing the Coordinate Axes

Find the x- and y-components of the displacements for the three legs of the trip if the x-axis points south and the y-axis points east.

3.2 VELOCITY

We have already introduced *velocity* as a vector quantity (see Sections 1.2 and 2.1). Its magnitude is the speed with which the object moves and its direction is the direction of motion. Now we develop a more formal, mathematical definition that fits that description. Note that a displacement vector indicates by how much and in what direction the position has changed, but implies nothing about *how long* it took to move from one point to the other. Velocity depends on both the displacement and the time interval.

Average Velocity

When a displacement $\Delta \vec{r}$ occurs during a time interval Δt, the **average velocity** $\vec{v}_{av}$ during that time interval is

Definition of average velocity:

$$\vec{v}_{av} = \frac{\Delta \vec{r}}{\Delta t} = \frac{\vec{r}_f - \vec{r}_i}{t_f - t_i} \tag{3-2}$$

Average velocity is written $\vec{v}_{av}$.

Average velocity is the product of a vector, the displacement ($\Delta\vec{r}$), and a positive scalar, the inverse of the time interval ($1/\Delta t$). Multiplying a vector by a positive scalar other than 1 changes only the magnitude of the vector but does not change the direction, whereas multiplying a vector by a negative scalar changes the magnitude (unless the scalar is −1) and reverses the direction. Since Δt is always positive, the direction of the average velocity vector is the same as the direction of the displacement vector. The *x*- and *y*-components of the average velocity are

$$v_{av,x} = \frac{\Delta x}{\Delta t} \quad \text{and} \quad v_{av,y} = \frac{\Delta y}{\Delta t} \tag{3-3}$$

 The symbol Δ does not stand alone and cannot be canceled in equations because it *modifies* the quantity that follows it; $\frac{\Delta x}{\Delta t}$ means $\frac{x_f - x_i}{t_f - t_i}$, which is *not* the same as $\frac{x}{t}$.

Example 3.3

Average Velocity of a Train

Find the average velocity of the train shown in Fig. 3.2 during the time interval between 3:14 P.M., when the train is 3 km east of the origin, and 3:56 P.M., when it is 26 km west of the origin. (The train first travels 7 km to the east, then travels 36 km to the west.)

Strategy We already know the displacement $\Delta\vec{r}$ from Fig. 3.2. The direction of the average velocity is the direction of the displacement.

Known: Displacement $\Delta\vec{r}$ = 29 km west; start time = 3:14 P.M.; finish time = 3:56 P.M. To find: $\vec{v}_{av}$

Solution From Section 3.1, the displacement is 29 km to the west:

$$\Delta\vec{r} = 29 \text{ km west}$$

The time interval is

$$\Delta t = 56 \text{ min} - 14 \text{ min} = 42 \text{ min}$$

We convert the time interval to hours, so that we may use units of km/h.

$$\Delta t = 42 \text{ min} \times \frac{1 \text{ h}}{60 \text{ min}} = 0.70 \text{ h}$$

The average velocity between 3:14 P.M. and 3:56 P.M. is

$$\vec{v}_{av} = \frac{\text{displacement}}{\text{time interval}} = \frac{\Delta\vec{r}}{\Delta t}$$

$$\vec{v}_{av} = \frac{29 \text{ km west}}{0.70 \text{ h}} = 41 \text{ km/h west}$$

We can also use components to express the answer to this question. Assuming a positive *x*-axis pointing east, the *x*-component of the displacement vector is $\Delta x = -29$ km, where the negative sign indicates that the vector points west. Then,

$$v_{av,x} = \frac{\Delta x}{\Delta t} = \frac{-29 \text{ km}}{0.70 \text{ h}} = -41 \text{ km/h}$$

The negative sign shows that the average velocity is directed along the negative *x*-axis, or to the west.

Discussion If the train had started at the same instant of time, 3:14 P.M., and had traveled directly west at a constant 41 km/h, it would have ended up in exactly the same place— 26 km west of the trestle bridge—at 3:56 P.M.

Had we started measuring time from when we first spotted the motionless train at 3:00 P.M., instead of 3:14 P.M., we would have found the average velocity over a different time interval, changing the average velocity. The average velocity depends on the time interval considered.

The magnitude of the train's average velocity is *not* equal to the total distance traveled divided by the time interval for the complete trip. The latter quantity is called the average *speed*:

$$\text{average speed} = \frac{\text{distance traveled}}{\text{total time}} = \frac{43 \text{ km}}{0.70 \text{ h}} = 61 \text{ km/h}$$

The distinction arises because the average velocity is the constant velocity that would result in the same *displacement vector* (during the given time interval), but the average speed is the constant speed that would result in the same *distance traveled* (during the same time interval).

Practice Problem 3.3   Average Velocity for a Different Time Interval

What is the average velocity of the same train during the time interval from 3:28 P.M., when it is at $x = 10.0$ km, to 3:56 P.M., when it is at $x = -26.0$ km?

Average Speed Versus Average Velocity The *average* velocity does not convey detailed information about the motion during the corresponding time interval Δt. Suppose a butterfly flutters from a point a on one flower to a point e on another flower along the dashed-line path shown in Fig. 3.9 (path *abcde*). The direction of the average velocity is the same as the direction of the displacement vector $\Delta \vec{r}$. The average velocity would be the same for any other path that takes the butterfly from a to e in the same amount of time Δt, because both the displacement and the time interval would be the same. However, the average *speed* would depend on the total *distance* traveled.

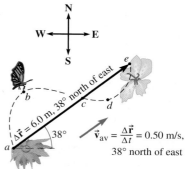

✓ CHECKPOINT 3.2

Can average speed ever be greater than the magnitude of the average velocity? Explain.

Instantaneous Velocity

The speedometer of a car does not indicate the average speed for an entire trip. When a speedometer reads 55 mi/h, it does *not* necessarily mean that the car will travel 55 miles in the next hour; the car could change its speed or direction or stop during that hour. The speedometer reading can be used to calculate how far the car will travel during a *very short time interval*—short enough that the speed does not change appreciably. For instance, at 55 mi/h (= 25 m/s), we can calculate that in 0.010 s the car moves 25 m/s × 0.010 s = 0.25 m—as long as the speed does not change significantly during that 0.010-s interval.

Similarly, the **instantaneous velocity** $\vec{v}$ is a vector quantity whose magnitude is the speed and whose direction is the direction of motion. The instantaneous velocity can be used to calculate the *displacement* of the object *during a very short time interval*. If the car has an instantaneous velocity $\vec{v}$ = 25 m/s in a direction 39° south of west, then the displacement of the car during a 0.010 s time interval is $\Delta \vec{r} = \vec{v} \Delta t$ = 0.25 m, 39° south of west, as long as *neither the speed nor the direction of motion* change significantly during that time interval. Repeating the word *instantaneous* can get cumbersome. When we refer simply to *the velocity*, we always mean the *instantaneous* velocity.

Thus, the velocity $\vec{v}$ at some instant of time t is the average velocity during a *very short* time interval:

> **Definition of instantaneous velocity:**
>
> $$\vec{v} = \lim_{\Delta t \to 0} \frac{\Delta \vec{r}}{\Delta t} \tag{3-4}$$
>
> ($\Delta \vec{r}$ is the displacement during a *very small* time interval Δt)

The notation $\lim_{\Delta t \to 0}$ is read "the limit, as Δt approaches zero, of . . . ." In other words, let the time interval get smaller and smaller, *approaching*—but never reaching—zero. This notation in Eq. (3-4) reminds you that Δt must be a *very small* time interval. How small a time interval is small enough? If you use a smaller time interval and the calculation of $\vec{v}$ always gives the same value (to within the precision of your measurements), then Δt is small enough. In other words, Δt must be small enough that we can treat the velocity as constant during that time interval. When $\vec{v}$ is constant, cutting Δt in half also cuts the displacement $\Delta \vec{r}$ in half, giving the same value for $\Delta \vec{r}/\Delta t$.

A vector equation is always equivalent to a set of equations, one for each component. Equation (3-4) is equivalent to

$$v_x = \lim_{\Delta t \to 0} \frac{\Delta x}{\Delta t} \quad \text{and} \quad v_y = \lim_{\Delta t \to 0} \frac{\Delta y}{\Delta t} \tag{3-5}$$

Suppose you want to know the velocity of the butterfly at point b. We start by dividing the trip into five equal time intervals Δt. Figure 3.10a shows the displacements for

Figure 3.9 Path followed by a butterfly, fluttering from one flower to another. The displacement of the butterfly is the vector arrow $\Delta \vec{r}$ = 6.0 m, 38° north of east. If the time interval that it took the butterfly to go from a to e is Δt = 12.0 s, then the average velocity of the butterfly is the displacement per unit time, $\Delta \vec{r}/\Delta t$ = 0.50 m/s, 38° north of east.

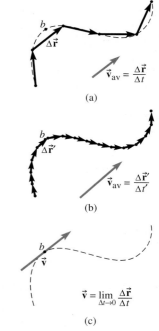

Figure 3.10 (a) The butterfly's displacements during five equal time intervals Δt. The average velocity during the displacement labeled $\Delta \vec{r}$ is $\Delta \vec{r}/\Delta t$. (b) Average velocity during a shorter time interval $\Delta t'$. (c) The instantaneous velocity $\vec{v}$ at point b is tangent to the curved path of the butterfly.

each of the time intervals. The average velocity for the interval during which the butterfly passes through point *b* is also shown. Now we divide the trip into shorter time intervals Δ*t'* (Fig. 3.10b). Again we calculate the average velocity during the time interval that includes point *b*. If we repeat this process, as the time interval gets smaller and smaller, the average velocity calculated for the time interval that includes point *b* approaches the instantaneous velocity at point *b* (Fig. 3.10c). Note that the direction of the velocity vector is along a line tangent to the curved path of the butterfly at that point.

Here we are talking about a tangent to the actual path through space, *not* a tangent line on a graph of position versus time.

Graphical Relationships Between Position and Velocity

For motion along the *x*-axis, the displacement (in component form) is Δ*x*. The average velocity can be represented on the graph of *x*(*t*) as the slope of a line connecting two points (called a *chord*). In Fig. 3.11a, the displacement $\Delta x = x_3 - x_1$ is the *rise* of the graph (the change along the vertical axis) and the time interval $\Delta t = t_3 - t_1$ is the *run* of the graph (the change along the horizontal axis). The slope of the chord is the rise over the run:

$$\text{slope of chord} = \frac{\text{rise}}{\text{run}} = \frac{\Delta x}{\Delta t} = v_{av,x} \qquad (3\text{-}6)$$

The slope of the chord is the average velocity for that time interval.

Finding Instantaneous Velocity on a Graph of Position Versus Time   To find the *instantaneous* velocity at some time $t = t_2$, we draw lines showing the average velocity for smaller and smaller time intervals. As the time interval is reduced (Fig. 3.11b), the average velocity changes. As Δ*t* gets smaller and smaller, the chord approaches a tangent line to the graph at t_2. Thus, v_x is the *slope of the line tangent to the graph of x(t)* at the chosen time.

In Fig. 3.12, the position of the train considered in Section 3.1 is graphed as a function of time, where 3:00 P.M. is chosen as $t = 0$.

> ⚠ If an object moves along a curved path, the velocity vector at any point is tangent to the path at that point.

> The slope of the tangent line on a graph of *x*(*t*) is v_x.

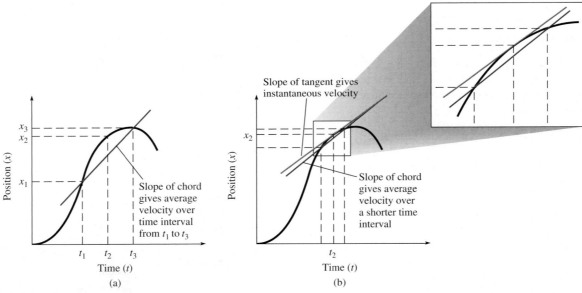

Figure 3.11 A graph of *x*(*t*) for an object moving along the *x*-axis. (a) The average velocity $v_{x,av}$ for the time interval t_1 to t_3 is the slope of the chord connecting those two points on the graph. (b) The average velocity measured over a shorter time interval. As the time interval gets shorter and shorter, the average velocity approaches the *instantaneous* velocity v_x at the instant t_2. The slope of the *tangent line* to the graph is v_x at that instant.

x (km)	t (min)
+3	0
+3	14
+10	23
+10	28
0	40
−26	56

Figure 3.12 Graph of position x versus time t for the train. The positions of the train at various times are marked with a dot. The position of the train would have to be measured at more frequent time intervals to accurately trace out the shape of the graph.

The graph of position versus time shows a curving line, but that does not mean the train travels along a curved path. The motion of the train is along a straight line since the track runs in an east-west direction. The graph shows the x-component of the train's position as a function of time.

A horizontal portion of the graph (as from $t = 0$ to $t = 14$ min and from $t = 23$ min to $t = 28$ min) indicates that the position is not changing during that time interval and, therefore, it is at rest (its velocity is zero). Sloping portions of the graph indicate that the train is moving. The steeper the graph, the larger the speed of the train. The sign of the slope indicates the direction of motion. A positive slope ($t = 14$ min to $t = 23$ min) indicates motion in the +x-direction while a negative slope ($t = 28$ min to $t = 56$ min) indicates motion in the −x-direction.

Example 3.4

Velocity of the Train

Use Fig. 3.12 to estimate the velocity of the train in km/h at $t = 40$ min.

Strategy Figure 3.12 is a graph of $x(t)$. The slope of a line tangent to the graph at $t = 40$ min is v_x at that instant. After sketching a tangent line on the graph, we find its slope from the rise divided by the run.

Solution Figure 3.13 shows a tangent line drawn on the graph. Using the endpoints of the tangent line, the rise is $(-25 \text{ km}) - (15 \text{ km}) = -40$ km. The run is approximately $(57 \text{ min}) - (30 \text{ min}) = 27 \text{ min} = 0.45$ h. Then

$$v_x \approx -40 \text{ km}/(0.45 \text{ h}) \approx -89 \text{ km/h}$$

The velocity is approximately 89 km/h in the −x-direction (west).

Discussion Since the slope of a line is constant, any two points *on the tangent line* would give the same value for the slope. Using widely spaced points tends to give a more accurate estimate for the slope.

Figure 3.13

On the graph of $x(t)$, the slope of a line tangent to the graph at $t = 40$ min is v_x at $t = 40$ min.

Practice Problem 3.4   Maximum Eastward Velocity

Estimate the maximum velocity of the train in kilometers per hour during the time it moves east ($t = 14$ min to $t = 23$ min).

Figure 3.14 Displacement Δx between t_1 and t_2 is represented by the shaded area under the red $v_x(t)$ graph.

Δx is the area under the graph of $v_x(t)$. The area is negative when the graph is beneath the time axis ($v_x < 0$).

Finding Displacement with Constant Velocity   What about the other way around? Given a graph of $v_x(t)$, how can we determine the displacement (change in position)? If v_x is constant during a time interval, then the average velocity is equal to the instantaneous velocity:

$$v_x = v_{\text{av},x} = \frac{\Delta x}{\Delta t} \tag{3-3}$$

and therefore

$$\Delta x = v_x\,\Delta t \quad \text{(for constant } v_x\text{)} \tag{3-7}$$

The graph of Fig. 3.14 shows v_x versus t for an object moving along the x-axis with constant velocity v_1 from time t_1 to t_2. The displacement Δx during the time interval $\Delta t = t_2 - t_1$ is $v_1\Delta t$. The shaded rectangle has "height" v_1 and "width" Δt. Since the area of a rectangle is the product of the height and width, the displacement Δx is represented by the area of the rectangle between the graph of $v_x(t)$ and the time axis for the time interval considered.

When we speak of the area under a graph, we are not talking about the literal number of square centimeters of paper or computer screen. The figurative area under a graph usually does not have dimensions of an ordinary area [L^2]. In a graph of $v_x(t)$, v_x has dimensions [L/T] and time has dimensions [T]; areas on such a graph have dimensions ([L/T]) × [T] = [L], which is correct for a displacement. The *units* of Δx are determined by the units used on the axes of the graph. If v_x is in meters per second and t is in seconds, then the displacement is in meters.

Finding Displacement with Changing Velocity   What if the velocity is not constant? The displacement Δx during a *very small* time interval Δt can be found in the same way as for constant velocity since, during a short enough time interval, the velocity does not change appreciably. Then v_x and Δt are the height and width of a narrow rectangle (Fig. 3.15a) and the displacement during that short time interval is the area of the rectangle. To find the total displacement during any time interval, the areas of all the narrow rectangles are added together (Fig. 3.15b). To improve the approximation, we let the time interval Δt approach zero and find that the displacement Δx during any time interval equals the area under the graph of $v_x(t)$ (Fig. 3.15c). When v_x is negative, x is decreasing and the displacement is in the $-x$-direction, so we must count the area as negative when it is below the time axis.

The magnitude of the train's displacement is represented as the shaded areas in Fig. 3.16. The train's displacement from $t = 14$ min to $t = 23$ min is $+7$ km (area above the t-axis means displacement in the $+x$-direction) and from $t = 28$ min to $t = 56$ min it is -36 km (area below the t-axis means displacement in the $-x$-direction). The total displacement from $t = 0$ to $t = 56$ min is $\Delta x = (+7\text{ km}) + (-36\text{ km}) = -29$ km, which agrees with the displacement vector shown in Fig. 3.2b.

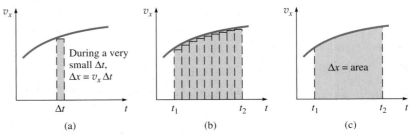

Figure 3.15 (a) Displacement Δx during a short time interval is approximately the area of a rectangle of height v_x and width Δt. (b) During a longer time interval, the displacement is approximately the sum of the areas of the rectangles. (c) The area under the v_x versus t graph for any time interval represents the displacement during that interval.

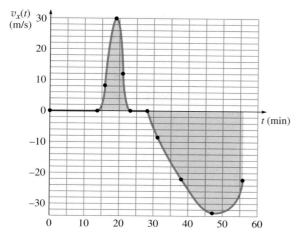

Figure 3.16 A graph of train velocity versus time. The train's displacement from $t = 14$ min to $t = 23$ min is the shaded area under the graph during that time interval. To estimate the area, count the number of grid boxes under the curve, estimating the fraction of the boxes that are only partly below the curve. Each box is 2 m/s in height and 5 min (= 300 s) in width, so each box represents an "area" (displacement) of 2 m/s × 300 s = 600 m = 0.60 km. The total number of shaded boxes for this time interval is about 12, so the displacement is about $\Delta x \approx 12 \times 0.60$ km = +7.2 km, which is close to the actual value of 7 km (during this time interval the train went from +3 km to +10 km). The shaded area for the time interval $t = 28$ min to $t = 56$ min is below the time axis; this negative area represents displacement in the $-x$-direction (west). The number of shaded grid boxes in this interval is about 60, so the displacement during this time interval is $\Delta x \approx -(60) \times 0.60$ km = −36 km.

3.3 NEWTON'S SECOND LAW OF MOTION

The Effect of a Constant Net Force Acting on an Object

When a *constant* net force acts on an object, Newton's second law says that the *rate of change of the velocity* is proportional to the net force and inversely proportional to the mass of the object:

$$\frac{\Delta \vec{\mathbf{v}}}{\Delta t} = \frac{1}{m} \sum \vec{\mathbf{F}} \tag{3-8}$$

where m is the mass of the object, $\Delta \vec{\mathbf{v}} = \vec{\mathbf{v}}_\mathrm{f} - \vec{\mathbf{v}}_\mathrm{i}$ is the change in its velocity during a time interval $\Delta t = t_\mathrm{f} - t_\mathrm{i}$, and $\sum \vec{\mathbf{F}}$ is the net force acting on the object. If the net force is zero, then the change in velocity is zero, in accordance with Newton's first law. If the net force is not zero, then the change in velocity $\Delta \vec{\mathbf{v}}$ has the same direction as the net force. To find the change in velocity, we subtract velocity vectors in the same way that we subtract position vectors (see Section 3.2). The direction of the *change* in velocity $\Delta \vec{\mathbf{v}}$ is not necessarily the same as either the initial or the final velocity direction (see Fig. 3.17).

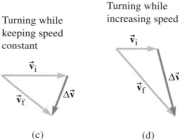

Figure 3.17 Vector diagrams to illustrate initial velocity, final velocity, and change in velocity for four different situations.

Acceleration is the rate of change of the velocity vector.

Definition of Acceleration The rate of change of the velocity—the quantity $\Delta\vec{v}/\Delta t$ in Eq. (3-8)—is called the **acceleration** (symbol $\vec{a}$). The use of the word *acceleration* in everyday language is often imprecise and not in accord with its scientific definition. In everyday language, it usually means "an increase in speed" but sometimes is used almost as a synonym for speed itself. In physics, acceleration does not necessarily indicate an increase in speed. Acceleration can indicate any kind of change in the velocity vector, whether it be a change in direction, an increase in speed, a decrease in speed, or a simultaneous change in speed and direction. A car going around a curve at constant speed has a nonzero acceleration because the *direction* of its velocity vector is changing. Of course, both the magnitude and direction of the velocity can change simultaneously, as when a skateboarder goes up a curved ramp.

Using the symbol $\vec{a}$ for acceleration, Newton's second law is

Newton's Second Law

$$\vec{a} = \frac{1}{m}\sum\vec{F} \quad \text{or} \quad \sum\vec{F} = m\vec{a} \tag{3-9}$$

When the net force is constant, the acceleration is also constant. In component form, Newton's second law is

$$\sum F_x = ma_x \quad \text{and} \quad \sum F_y = ma_y \tag{3-10}$$

where, for constant acceleration, the acceleration components are

$$a_x = \frac{\Delta v_x}{\Delta t} \quad \text{and} \quad a_y = \frac{\Delta v_y}{\Delta t} \tag{3-11}$$

If all the forces acting on an object are known, then Eq. (3-9) can be used to calculate its acceleration. Alternatively, sometimes we know the object's acceleration but we have incomplete information about the forces acting on it; then Eq. (3-9) provides information about the unknown forces.

SI Units of Acceleration and Force

Since acceleration is the change in velocity divided by the corresponding time interval, the SI units of acceleration are $(m/s)/s = m/s^2$, read as "meters per second squared." The SI unit of force, the newton, is *defined* so that a net force of 1 N gives a 1-kg mass an acceleration of 1 m/s^2:

$$1 \text{ N} = 1 \text{ kg·m/s}^2 \tag{3-12}$$

Thinking of m/s^2 as $(m/s)/s$ can help you develop an understanding of what acceleration is. Suppose an object has a constant acceleration with x- and y-components $a_x = +3.0 \text{ m/s}^2$ and $a_y = -2.0 \text{ m/s}^2$. Then v_x increases 3.0 m/s during every second of elapsed time (the change in v_x is +3.0 m/s per second) and v_y decreases 2.0 m/s during every second (the change in v_y is −2.0 m/s per second).

Note that the SI unit of the gravitational field strength, N/kg, is equal to the SI unit of acceleration: $1 \text{ N/kg} = 1 \text{ m/s}^2$. We will discuss the significance of this apparent coincidence in Chapter 4.

Average and Instantaneous Acceleration

Until now we have discussed Newton's second law only in the case of a constant net force. If a constant net force acts on an object, then its acceleration is constant—that is, the velocity vector *changes at a constant rate*. More generally, Newton's second law is a relationship between the net force acting at any instant of time and the *instantaneous* acceleration at that same instant.

What do we mean by instantaneous acceleration? First we define the **average acceleration** during a time interval Δt:

$$\vec{\mathbf{a}}_{av} = \frac{\vec{\mathbf{v}}_f - \vec{\mathbf{v}}_i}{t_f - t_i} = \frac{\Delta \vec{\mathbf{v}}}{\Delta t} \qquad (3\text{-}13)$$

Compare the definitions of average acceleration [Eq. (3-13)] and average velocity [Eq. (3-2)]. Each is the change in a vector quantity divided by the time interval during which the change occurs. Each can have different values for different time intervals. The vector equation [Eq. (3-13)] can be written in component form:

$$a_{av,x} = \frac{\Delta v_x}{\Delta t} \quad \text{and} \quad a_{av,y} = \frac{\Delta v_y}{\Delta t} \qquad (3\text{-}14)$$

To find the **instantaneous acceleration**, we calculate the average acceleration during a very short time interval:

Definition of instantaneous acceleration:

$$\vec{\mathbf{a}} = \lim_{\Delta t \to 0} \frac{\Delta \vec{\mathbf{v}}}{\Delta t} \qquad (3\text{-}15)$$

($\Delta \vec{\mathbf{v}}$ is the change in velocity during a *very small* time interval Δt)

The time interval Δt must be small enough that we can treat the acceleration vector as constant during that time interval. Just as with instantaneous velocity, the word *instantaneous* is not always repeated. *Acceleration* without the adjective means *instantaneous* acceleration. In component form,

$$a_x = \lim_{\Delta t \to 0} \frac{\Delta v_x}{\Delta t} \quad \text{and} \quad a_y = \lim_{\Delta t \to 0} \frac{\Delta v_y}{\Delta t} \qquad (3\text{-}16)$$

Conceptual Example 3.5

Direction of Acceleration While Slowing Down

When Damon approaches a stop sign on his motor scooter, he "decelerates" before coming to a full stop. If he moves in the negative x-direction while he slows down, is the scooter's acceleration component a_x positive or negative? What is the direction of the acceleration vector? What is the direction of the net force acting on the scooter?

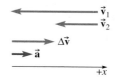

Figure 3.18
The velocity vectors at two different times as the scooter moves to the left with decreasing speed. The change in velocity $\Delta \vec{\mathbf{v}} = \vec{\mathbf{v}}_2 - \vec{\mathbf{v}}_1$ is to the right.

Strategy and Solution The term *decelerate* is not a scientific term. In common usage it means the scooter is slowing: the scooter's velocity is decreasing in magnitude. The acceleration vector $\vec{\mathbf{a}}$ points in the direction of the *change* in the velocity vector $\Delta \vec{\mathbf{v}}$ during a short time interval. Since Damon is slowing down, the direction of $\Delta \vec{\mathbf{v}}$ is opposite to $\vec{\mathbf{v}}$ (Fig. 3.18). The acceleration vector is in the same direction as $\Delta \vec{\mathbf{v}}$—the positive x-direction. Thus, a_x is positive and $\vec{\mathbf{a}}$ is in the $+x$-direction. From Newton's second law, $\Sigma \vec{\mathbf{F}}$ is also in the $+x$-direction.

Discussion Another way to think about it is that Damon is moving in the $-x$-direction, so v_x is negative. He is slowing down so the *absolute value* of v_x is getting smaller. A negative number with a smaller absolute value is *greater than* a negative number with a larger absolute value (for example, $-3 > -4$). Therefore, v_x is increasing ($\Delta v_x > 0$), and a_x is positive.

Practice Problem 3.5   Continuing on His Way

As Damon pulls away from the stop sign, continuing in the $-x$-direction, his speed gradually increases. What is the sign of a_x? What is the direction of $\vec{\mathbf{a}}$? What is the direction of the net force on the scooter?

Interpreting the Directions of Velocity and Acceleration Generalizing Example 3.5, suppose an object moves along the *x*-axis. When the net force is in the same direction as the velocity, the object is speeding up. In terms of components, if v_x and a_x are both positive, the object is moving in the +*x*-direction and is speeding up. If they are both negative, the object is moving in the −*x*-direction and is speeding up.

When the net force and velocity point in opposite directions, so that their *x*-components have opposite signs, the object is slowing down. When v_x is positive and a_x is negative, the object is moving in the positive *x*-direction and is slowing down. When v_x is negative and a_x is positive, the object is moving in the negative *x*-direction and is slowing down.

In straight-line motion, the acceleration is always either in the same direction as the velocity or in the direction opposite to the velocity. For motion that changes direction, the acceleration is not along the same line as the velocity, as illustrated in Example 3.6.

Example 3.6

Skating Uphill

An inline skater is traveling on a level road with a speed of 8.94 m/s; 120.0 s later she is climbing a hill with a 15.0° angle of incline at a speed of 7.15 m/s. (a) What is the change in her velocity? (b) What is her average acceleration during the 120.0-s time interval?

Strategy The change in velocity is *not* 1.79 m/s (= 8.94 m/s − 7.15 m/s). That is the change in *speed*. The change in velocity is found by subtracting the initial velocity *vector* from the final velocity *vector*. After first making a graphical sketch, we use the component method. The average acceleration is the change in velocity divided by the elapsed time.

(a)

(b)

Figure 3.19

(a) Change in velocity as the skater slows going uphill and (b) graphical subtraction of velocity vectors.

Figure 3.20

Initial and final velocity vectors resolved into components.

Figure 3.21

Reconstruction of $\Delta \vec{v}$ from its components (not to scale).

Solution (a) Figure 3.19a shows the initial and final velocity vectors and the slope of the hill. The initial velocity is horizontal as the skater skates on level ground. The final velocity is 15.0° above the horizontal. To subtract the two velocity vectors graphically, we place the tails of the vectors together. The change in velocity $\Delta \vec{v}$ is found by drawing a vector arrow from the tip of $\vec{v}_i$ to the tip of $\vec{v}_f$. Judging by the graphical subtraction in Fig. 3.19b, the change in velocity is roughly at a 45° angle above the −*x*-axis. Its magnitude is smaller than the magnitudes of the initial and final velocity vectors—something like 2 to 3 m/s.

The components v_{fx} and v_{fy} can be found from a right triangle (Fig. 3.20):

$$v_{fx} = v_f \cos \theta = 7.15 \text{ m/s} \times 0.9659 = 6.91 \text{ m/s}$$
$$v_{fy} = v_f \sin \theta = 7.15 \text{ m/s} \times 0.2588 = 1.85 \text{ m/s}$$

continued on next page

Example 3.6 continued

Since v_i has only an x-component,

$$v_{iy} = 0 \quad \text{and} \quad v_{ix} = v_i = 8.94 \text{ m/s}$$

Now we subtract the components to find the components of $\Delta \vec{v}$:

$$\Delta v_x = v_{fx} - v_{ix} = (6.91 - 8.94) \text{ m/s} = -2.03 \text{ m/s}$$

and

$$\Delta v_y = v_{fy} - v_{iy} = (1.85 - 0) \text{ m/s} = +1.85 \text{ m/s}$$

To find the magnitude of $\Delta \vec{v}$, we apply the Pythagorean theorem (Fig. 3.21):

$$(|\Delta \vec{v}|)^2 = (\Delta v_x)^2 + (\Delta v_y)^2 = (-2.03 \text{ m/s})^2 + (1.85 \text{ m/s})^2$$

$$= 7.54 \text{ (m/s)}^2$$

$$|\Delta \vec{v}| = 2.75 \text{ m/s}$$

The angle is found from

$$\tan \phi = \frac{\text{opposite}}{\text{adjacent}} = \left| \frac{\Delta v_y}{\Delta v_x} \right| = \frac{1.85 \text{ m/s}}{2.03 \text{ m/s}} = 0.9113$$

$$\phi = \tan^{-1} 0.9113 = 42.3°$$

The direction of the change in velocity $\Delta \vec{v}$ is 42.3° above the negative x-axis.

(b) The magnitude of the average acceleration is

$$|\vec{a}_{av}| = \frac{|\Delta \vec{v}|}{\Delta t} = \frac{2.75 \text{ m/s}}{120.0 \text{ s}} = 0.0229 \text{ m/s}^2$$

The direction of the average acceleration is the same as the direction of $\Delta \vec{v}$: 42.3° above the negative x-axis.

Discussion Checking back with the graphical subtraction in Fig. 3.19b, the magnitude of $\Delta \vec{v}$ appears to be roughly $\frac{1}{4}$ to $\frac{1}{3}$ the magnitude of $\vec{v}$. Since $\frac{1}{4} \times 8.94$ m/s = 2.24 m/s and $\frac{1}{3} \times 8.94$ m/s = 2.98 m/s, the answer of 2.75 m/s is reasonable.

Figure 3.19b also shows the direction of $\Delta \vec{v}$ to be roughly midway between the +y- and −x-axes. We found the direction of $\Delta \vec{v}$ to be 42.3° above the −x-axis and, therefore, 47.7° from the +y-axis. So the direction we calculated is also reasonable based on the graphical subtraction.

Practice Problem 3.6   Change in Sailboat Velocity

A C&C 30 sailboat is sailing at 12.0 knots (6.17 m/s) heading directly east across the harbor. When a gust of wind comes up, the boat changes its heading to 11.0° north of east and its speed increases to 14.0 knots (7.20 m/s). [A boat's speed is customarily expressed in knots, which means nautical miles per hour. A nautical mile (6076 ft) is a little longer than a statute mile (5280 ft).] (a) What is the magnitude and direction of the change in velocity of the sailboat in m/s? (b) If this velocity change occurs during a 2.0-s time interval and the mass of the sailboat is 3600 kg, what is the average net force on the sailboat during that interval?

CHECKPOINT 3.3A

For an object moving in a straight line how does the direction of the acceleration vector compare with that of the velocity vector?

Graphical Relationships Between Velocity and Acceleration

Both velocity and acceleration measure rates of change: velocity is the rate of change of position and acceleration is the rate of change of velocity. Therefore, the graphical relationship of acceleration to velocity is the same as the graphical relationship of velocity to position (see Sec. 3.2): a_x is the slope on a graph of $v_x(t)$ and Δv_x is the area under a graph of $a_x(t)$.

CONNECTION:

On a graph of *any* quantity Q as a function of time, the slope of the graph represents the instantaneous rate of change of Q. On a graph of the *rate of change of Q* as a function of time, the area under the graph represents ΔQ.

Figure 3.22 In this graph of v_x versus t, as Damon is stopping, v_x is negative, while a_x (the slope) is positive. The value of v_x is increasing, but—since it is less than zero to begin with and is getting closer to zero as time goes on—the speed is *decreasing*. The slopes of the three tangent lines shown represent the instantaneous accelerations (a_x) at three different times.

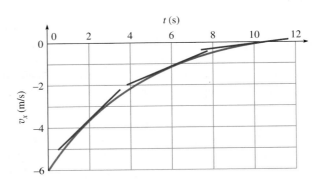

Figure 3.22 shows a graph of v_x versus t for Damon slowing down on his scooter. He is moving in the $-x$-direction, so $v_x < 0$, and his speed is decreasing, so $|v_x|$ is decreasing. The slope of a tangent line to the graph is a_x at that instant. Three tangent lines are drawn, showing that a_x is positive (the slopes are positive) and is not constant (the slopes are not all the same).

Example 3.7

Acceleration of a Sports Car

A sports car starting at rest can achieve 30.0 m/s in 4.7 s according to the advertisements. Figure 3.23 shows data for v_x as a function of time as the sports car starts from rest and travels in a straight line in the $+x$-direction. (a) What is the average acceleration of the sports car from 0 to 30.0 m/s? (b) What is the maximum acceleration of the car? (c) What is the car's displacement from $t = 0$ to $t = 19.1$ s (when it reaches 60.0 m/s)? (d) What is the car's average velocity during the entire 19.1-s interval?

Strategy (a) To find the average acceleration, the change in velocity for the time interval is divided by the time interval. (b) The instantaneous acceleration is the slope of the velocity graph, so it is maximum where the graph is steepest. At that point, the velocity is changing at a high rate. We expect the maximum acceleration to take place early on; the magnitude of acceleration must decrease as the velocity gets higher and higher—there is a maximum velocity for the car, after all. (c) The displacement Δx is the area under the $v_x(t)$ graph. The graph is not a simple shape such as a triangle or rectangle, so an estimate of the area is made. (d) Once we have a value for the displacement, we can apply the definition of average velocity.

Given: Graph of $v_x(t)$ in Fig. 3.23.

To find: (a) $a_{av,x}$ for $v_x = 0$ to 30.0 m/s; (b) maximum value of a_x; (c) Δx from $v_x = 0$ to 60.0 m/s; (d) $v_{av,x}$ from $t = 0$ to 19.1 s

Solution (a) The car starts from rest, so $v_{xi} = 0$. It reaches $v_x = 30.0$ m/s at $t = 4.9$ s, according to the data table. Then for this time interval,

$$a_{av,x} = \frac{\Delta v_x}{\Delta t} = \frac{30.0 \text{ m/s} - 0 \text{ m/s}}{4.9 \text{ s} - 0 \text{ s}} = 6.1 \text{ m/s}^2$$

The average acceleration for this time interval is 6.1 m/s² in the $+x$-direction.

(b) The acceleration component a_x, at any instant of time, is the slope of the tangent line to the $v_x(t)$ graph at that time. To

v_x (m/s)	0	15.0	20.0	25.0	30.0	35.0	40.0	45.0	50.0	55.0	60.0
t (s)	0	2.0	2.9	3.8	4.9	6.2	7.6	9.1	11.2	14.0	19.1

Figure 3.23

Data table and graph of $v_x(t)$ for a sports car.

continued on next page

Example 3.7 continued

find the maximum acceleration, we look for the steepest part of the graph. In this case, the largest slope occurs near $t = 0$, just as the car is starting out. In Fig. 3.23, a tangent line to the $v_x(t)$ graph at $t = 0$ passes through $t = 0$. Values for the rise and run to calculate the slope of the tangent line are read from the graph. The tangent line passes through the two points $(t = 0, v_x = 0)$ and $(t = 6.0 \text{ s}, v_x = 55.0 \text{ m/s})$ on the graph, so the rise is 55.0 m/s for a run of 6.0 s. The slope of this line is

$$a_x = \frac{\text{rise}}{\text{run}} = \frac{55.0 \text{ m/s} - 0 \text{ m/s}}{6.0 \text{ s} - 0 \text{ s}} = +9.2 \text{ m/s}^2$$

The maximum acceleration is 9.2 m/s^2 in the +x-direction.

(c) Δx is the area under the $v_x(t)$ graph shown shaded in Fig. 3.23. The area can be estimated by counting the number of grid boxes under the curve. Each box is 5.0 m/s in height and 2.0 s in width, so each represents an "area" (displacement) of 10 m. When counting the number of boxes under the curve, a best estimate is made for the fraction of the boxes that are only partly below the curve. Approximately 75 boxes lie below the curve, so the displacement is $\Delta x = 75 \times 10 \text{ m} = 750 \text{ m}$. Since the car travels along a straight line and does not change direction, 750 m is also the distance traveled. (d) The average velocity during the 19.1-s interval is

$$v_{\text{av},x} = \frac{\Delta x}{\Delta t} = \frac{750 \text{ m}}{19.1 \text{ s}} = 39 \text{ m/s}$$

Discussion The graph of velocity as a function of time is often the most helpful graph to have when solving a problem. If that graph is not given in the problem, it

is useful to sketch one. The $v_x(t)$ graph shows displacement, velocity, and acceleration at once: the velocity v_x is given by the curve itself, the displacement Δx is the area under the curve, and the acceleration a_x is the slope of the curve.

Why is the average velocity 39 m/s? Why is it not halfway between the initial velocity (0 m/s) and the final velocity (60 m/s)? If the acceleration were constant, the average velocity would indeed be $\frac{1}{2}(0 + 60 \text{ m/s}) = 30 \text{ m/s}$. The actual average velocity is somewhat higher than that—the acceleration is greater at the start, so less of the time interval is spent going (relatively) slow and more is spent going fast. The speed is less than 30 m/s for only 4.9 s, but is greater than 30 m/s for 14.2 s.

___

Practice Problem 3.7   Braking a Car

An automobile is traveling along a straight road heading to the southeast at 24 m/s when the driver sees a deer begin to cross the road ahead of her. She steps on the brake and brings the car to a complete stop in an elapsed time of 8.0 s. A data recording device, triggered by the sudden braking action, records the following velocities and times as the car slows. Let the positive x-axis be directed to the southeast. Plot a graph of v_x versus t and find (a) the average acceleration as the car comes to a stop and (b) the instantaneous acceleration at $t = 2.0$ s.

v_x (m/s)	24	17.3	12.0	8.7	6.0	3.5	2.0	0.75	0
t (s)	0	1.0	2.0	3.0	4.0	5.0	6.0	7.0	8.0

✓ CHECKPOINT 3.3B

What physical quantity does the slope of the tangent to a graph of v_x versus time represent?

What Is Mass?

The acceleration of an object is proportional to the net force on it and is in the same direction (Fig. 3.24). A larger net force causes a more rapid change in the velocity vector. Newton's second law also says that the acceleration is inversely proportional to the object's mass. The same net force acting on two different objects causes a smaller acceleration on the object with greater mass (Fig. 3.25). Mass is a measure of an object's inertia—the amount of resistance to *changes in velocity*. Newton's second law serves as our *definition* of mass.

In everyday language mass and weight are sometimes used as synonyms, but in physics, mass and weight are different physical properties. The mass of an object is a measure of its inertia, but weight is the magnitude of the gravitational force acting on it. Imagine taking a shuffleboard puck to the Moon. Since the Moon's gravitational field is weaker than the Earth's, the puck's weight would be smaller, and a smaller normal force would be required to hold it up. On the other hand, the puck's mass, an intrinsic property, is the same. Ignoring the effects of friction, an astronaut playing shuffleboard on

Figure 3.24 The acceleration of a baseball is proportional to the net force acting on it.

Figure 3.25 The same net force acting on two different objects produces accelerations in inverse proportion to the masses.

the Moon would have to exert the same horizontal force on the puck as on Earth to give it the same acceleration (Fig. 3.26).

The chapter opener asked how an African lion can ever catch a Cape buffalo. Although Cape buffaloes and African lions have about the same top *speed*, lions are capable of much larger *accelerations* than are buffaloes. Starting from rest, it takes a buffalo much longer to get to its top speed. On the other hand, lions have much less stamina. Once the buffalo reaches its top speed, it can maintain that speed much longer than can the lion. Thus, a Cape buffalo is capable of outrunning a lion unless the stalking lion can get fairly close before charging.

Many differences in physiology make the lion capable of much larger accelerations than the buffalo, but one factor is easy to understand. The mass of an African lion is 150 to 250 kg, roughly one-third that of a typical buffalo, and the acceleration produced by a given net force is inversely proportional to mass. The buffalo's leg muscles would have to exert three times the force as the lion's leg muscles to produce the same acceleration.

Can the lion catch the buffalo?

Earth

(a)   (b)   (c)   (d)

Figure 3.26 An astronaut playing shuffleboard (a) on Earth and (c) on the Moon. FBDs for a puck of mass m being given the same acceleration $\vec{a}$ on a *frictionless* court on (b) Earth and (d) on the Moon. The contact force on the puck due to the *pushing stick* ($\vec{F}_C$) must be the same since the mass of the puck is the same: $\Sigma\vec{F} = \vec{F}_{stick} = m\vec{a}$.

3.4   APPLYING NEWTON'S SECOND LAW

The following steps are helpful in most problems that involve Newton's second law.

> ## Problem-Solving Strategy for Newton's Second Law
>
> - Decide what objects will have Newton's second law applied to them.
> - Identify all the *external* forces acting on that object.
> - Draw an FBD to show all the forces acting on the object.
> - Choose a coordinate system. If the direction of the net force is known, choose axes so that the net force (and the acceleration) are along one of the axes.
> - Find the net force by adding the forces as vectors.
> - Use Newton's second law to relate the net force to the acceleration.
> - Relate the acceleration to the change in the velocity vector during a time interval of interest.

Example 3.8

The Broken Suitcase

The wheels fall off Beatrice's suitcase, so she ties a rope to it and drags it along the floor of the airport terminal (Fig. 3.27). The rope makes a 40.0° angle with the horizontal. The suitcase has a mass of 36.0 kg and Beatrice pulls on the rope with a force of 65.0 N. (a) What is the magnitude of the normal force acting on the suitcase due to the floor? (b) If the coefficient of kinetic friction between the suitcase and the marble floor is $\mu_k = 0.13$, find the frictional force acting on the suitcase. (c) What is the acceleration of the suitcase while Beatrice pulls with a 65.0 N force at 40.0°? (d) Starting from rest, for how long a time must she pull with this force until the suitcase reaches a comfortable walking speed of 0.5 m/s?

Strategy   Since the suitcase is dragged horizontally along the floor, the vertical component of its velocity is always zero. The vertical acceleration component of the suitcase is zero because the vertical velocity component does not change. (If it did have a vertical acceleration component, the suitcase would begin to move either down through the floor or up into the air.) If we choose the +y-axis up and the +x-axis to be horizontal, then $a_y = 0$. We resolve the forces acting on the suitcase into their components, draw an FBD for the suitcase, and apply Newton's second law.

Solution   (a) Figure 3.28 shows the forces acting on the suitcase, where $\vec{F}$ is the force exerted by Beatrice. All the other forces are either parallel or perpendicular to the floor, so only $\vec{F}$ needs to be resolved into x- and y-components.

$$F_x = F \cos 40.0° = 65.0 \text{ N} \times 0.766 = 49.8 \text{ N}$$
$$F_y = F \sin 40.0° = 65.0 \text{ N} \times 0.643 = 41.8 \text{ N}$$

Figure 3.29 is an FBD, where $\vec{F}$ is replaced by its components. The vertical force components add to zero since $a_y = 0$.

$$\sum F_y = ma_y = 0$$
$$N + F \sin 40.0° - mg = 0$$

Figure 3.27

Beatrice dragging her suitcase.

Figure 3.28

Forces acting on a suitcase dragged along the floor. The lengths of the vector arrows are not to scale.

continued on next page

Example 3.8 continued

Figure 3.29
FBD for the suitcase, with each force represented by its x- and y-components.

We can solve this equation for the magnitude of the normal force:

$$N = mg - F \sin 40°$$

$$= (36.0 \text{ kg} \times 9.80 \text{ N/kg}) - (65.0 \text{ N} \times \sin 40.0°)$$

$$= 352.8 \text{ N} - 41.8 \text{ N} = 311 \text{ N}$$

(b) The magnitude of the kinetic frictional force is

$$f_k = \mu_k N = 0.13 \times 311 \text{ N} = 40.43 \text{ N}$$

Rounding to two significant figures, the frictional force is 40 N in the −x-direction (opposite the motion of the suitcase).

(c) The y-component of the acceleration is zero. To find the x-component, we apply Newton's second law to the x-components of the forces acting on the suitcase:

$$\sum F_x = +F \cos 40.0° + (-f_k)$$

$$= 49.79 \text{ N} - 40.43 \text{ N} = 9.36 \text{ N}$$

$$a_x = \frac{\sum F_x}{m} = \frac{9.36 \text{ N}}{36.0 \text{ kg}} = 0.260 \text{ m/s}^2$$

Here we have replaced N/kg with the equivalent m/s², the usual way to write the SI units of acceleration. The acceleration is 0.3 m/s² in the +x-direction.

(d) With constant a_x,

$$\Delta v_x = a_x \Delta t$$

The suitcase starts from rest so $v_{ix} = 0$ and $\Delta v_x = v_{fx} - v_{ix} = v_{fx}$. Then,

$$\Delta t = \frac{v_{fx}}{a_x} = \frac{0.5 \text{ m/s}}{0.260 \text{ m/s}^2} = 2 \text{ s}$$

Discussion   What Beatrice probably wants to do is to drag the suitcase along at constant velocity. To do that, she must first accelerate the suitcase from rest. Once the suitcase is moving at the desired velocity, she pulls a little less hard, so the net force is zero and the suitcase slides at constant speed. She would do so without thinking much about it, of course!

Practice Problem 3.8   The Continuing Story . . .

(a) How hard does Beatrice pull at a 40.0° angle while the suitcase slides along the floor at constant velocity? [*Hint:* Do *not* assume that the normal force is the same as in the previous discussion.] (b) The suitcase is moving at 0.50 m/s. Beatrice changes the force to 42 N at 40.0°. How long does it take the suitcase to come to rest?

In the previous example the suitcase was sliding along the flat ground. Now consider a case in which a brick is sliding down an incline. The normal force is no longer vertical; it is perpendicular to the incline.

Example 3.9

A Sliding Brick

A brick of mass 1.0 kg slides down an icy roof inclined at 30.0° with respect to the horizontal. If the brick starts from rest, how fast is it moving when it reaches the edge of the roof 0.90 s later? Ignore friction.

Strategy   First we draw a diagram and indicate the forces acting on the brick. Then we choose coordinate axes. The acceleration of the brick is directed along the roof surface; its velocity component perpendicular to the surface is always zero. We choose the x-axis in the direction of the

acceleration, which is parallel to the roof in the direction the brick slides. The y-axis is then perpendicular to the roof. Next we write Newton's second law and solve it by resolving the forces into components.

Solution   In Fig. 3.30a, $\vec{W}$ is the gravitational force on the brick and $\vec{N}$ is the normal force exerted on the brick by the roof. The gravitational force on the brick must be resolved into its x- and y-components (Fig. 3.30b), after which these components can be shown on the FBD (Fig. 3.30c).

continued on next page

Example 3.9 continued

Ignoring friction, the roof exerts no force in the x-direction on the brick. Then only the gravitational force has an x-component: $W_x = mg \sin 30.0°$. From Newton's second law,

$$\sum F_x = mg \sin 30.0° = ma_x$$

Solving for a_x,

$$a_x = g \sin 30.0°$$

Now that we have the acceleration, we can find the final velocity.

$$\Delta v_x = v_{fx} - v_{ix} = a_x \Delta t$$

Substituting $\Delta t = 0.90$ s and $v_{ix} = 0$ and solving for v_{fx},

$$v_{fx} = v_{ix} + a_x \Delta t$$

$$= 0 + 9.80 \text{ m/s}^2 \times \sin 30.0° \times 0.90 \text{ s} = 4.4 \text{ m/s}$$

The brick is moving at 4.4 m/s down the 30.0° roof.

Discussion   In this problem it was not necessary to apply Newton's second law to the y-components of the forces. Doing so would enable us to find the normal force. If the roof were not frictionless, we would need to find the normal force to calculate the force of kinetic friction.

Practice Problem 3.9   **Effect of Friction on the Sliding Brick**

Repeat Example 3.9 assuming that the coefficient of kinetic friction is 0.20.

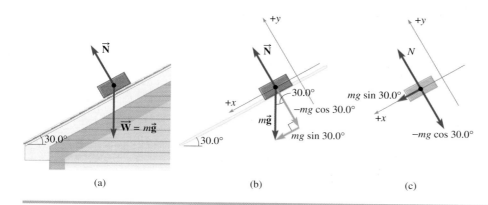

Figure 3.30

(a) Forces acting on a brick sliding down an icy roof, (b) resolving the weight into components, and (c) an FBD in which the weight is replaced by its x- and y-components.

Sometimes two or more objects are constrained to have the same acceleration by the way they are connected. In Example 3.10, we look at a train engine pulling five freight cars. The couplings maintain a fixed distance between the cars, so at any instant the cars move with the same velocity; if they didn't, the distance between them would change. The velocities don't have to be constant, they just have to change in exactly the same way, which implies that the accelerations must also be the same at any instant.

Example 3.10

Coupling Force on First and Last Freight Cars

A train engine pulls out of a station along a straight horizontal track with five identical freight cars behind it, each of which weighs 90.0 kN. The train reaches a speed of 15.0 m/s within 5.00 min of starting out. Assuming the engine pulls with a constant force during this interval, with what magnitude of force does the coupling between cars pull forward on the first and last of the freight cars? Ignore air resistance and friction on the freight cars.

Strategy   A sketch of the situation is shown in Fig. 3.31. To find the force exerted by the first coupling, we consider all five cars to be one system so we do not have to worry about the force exerted on the first car by the second car. The only *external* forces on the group of five cars are the normal force, gravity, and the pull of the first coupling. To find the force exerted by the fifth coupling, we consider car five by

continued on next page

Example 3.10 continued

Figure 3.31

An engine pulling five identical
freight cars. The entire train has a
constant acceleration $\vec{a}$ to the right.

itself to be a system. In each case, once we identify a system, we draw an FBD, choose a coordinate system, and then apply Newton's second law.

As discussed previously, the engine and the cars must all have the same acceleration at any instant. We expect the acceleration to be *constant* because the engine pulls with a constant force. We can calculate the acceleration of the train from the initial and final velocities and the elapsed time.

Solution   For the tension T_1 in the first coupling, we consider the five cars as *one system* of mass M. Figure 3.32 shows the FBD in which cars 1 to 5 are treated as a single object. We choose the x-axis in the direction of motion of the train and the y-axis up. Since the train moves along the x-axis, the acceleration vector is along the x-axis. Therefore, $a_y = 0$. Using the y-component of Newton's second law, the vertical forces add to zero:

$$\sum F_y = Ma_y = N_{1-5} - W_{1-5} = 0$$

The only external horizontal force is the force $\vec{T}_1$ due to the tension in the first coupling. This force is constant according to the problem statement, so we know that the acceleration a_x is constant:

$$\sum F_x = T_1 = Ma_x$$

The mass of the system M is five times the mass of one car m. We are given the *weight* of one car ($W = 90.0$ kN $= 9.00 \times 10^4$ N). From the relation between mass and weight, $W = mg$, the mass of one car is $m = W/g$ and the mass of five cars is $M = 5W/g$.

The constant acceleration of the train is

$$a_x = \frac{\Delta v_x}{\Delta t} = \frac{v_{fx} - v_{ix}}{t_f - t_i} = \frac{15.0 \text{ m/s} - 0}{300 \text{ s} - 0} = 0.0500 \text{ m/s}^2$$

Figure 3.32

FBD for the system consisting
of cars 1 through 5 (but not the
engine).

Therefore,

$$T_1 = Ma_x = \frac{5W}{g} \times \frac{\Delta v_x}{\Delta t} = \frac{5 \times 9.00 \times 10^4 \text{ N}}{9.80 \text{ m/s}^2} \times \frac{15.0 \text{ m/s}}{300 \text{ s}}$$

$$= 2.30 \text{ kN}$$

Now consider the last freight car (car 5). If we ignore friction and air resistance, the only external forces acting are the force $\vec{T}_5$ due to the tension in the fifth coupling, the normal force $\vec{N}_5$, and the gravitational force $\vec{W}_5$; the FBD is shown in Fig. 3.33. Since $\vec{N}_5 + \vec{W}_5 = 0$, the net force is equal to $\vec{T}_5$. From Newton's second law,

$$\sum F_x = T_5 = ma_x = \frac{W}{g} a_x$$

$$T_5 = \frac{W}{g} \times \frac{\Delta v_x}{\Delta t} = \frac{9.00 \times 10^4 \text{ N}}{9.80 \text{ m/s}^2} \times \frac{15.0 \text{ m/s}}{300 \text{ s}} = 459 \text{ N}$$

Figure 3.33

FBD for car 5. (Vector lengths are not to the same
scale as those in Fig. 3.32.)

Discussion   We considered two systems (cars 1 to 5 and car 5) that have the same acceleration and different masses. As expected, the net force is proportional to the mass: the net force on five cars is 5 times the net force on one car.

The solution to this problem is much simpler when Newton's second law is applied to a system comprised of all five cars, rather than to each car individually. Although the problem can be solved by looking at individual cars, to find the tension in the first coupling you would have to draw five FBDs (one for each car) and apply Newton's second law five times. That's because each car, except the fifth, is acted on by the unequal tensions in the couplings on either side. You'd have to first find the tension in the fifth coupling, then the fourth, then the third, and so on.

Practice Problem 3.10   Coupling Force Between First and Second Freight Cars

With what force does the coupling between the first and second cars pull forward on the second car? [*Hint:* Try two methods. One of them is to draw the FBD for the first car and apply Newton's *third* law as well as the second.]

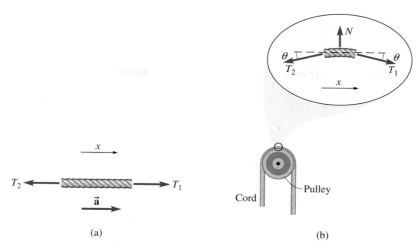

(a)
(b)

Figure 3.34 (a) FBD for an ideal cord with acceleration $\vec{a}$. Applying Newton's second law along the x-axis: $\Sigma F_x = T_1 - T_2 = ma_x$. The ideal cord has mass $m = 0$, so $T_1 = T_2$: the tensions at the ends are equal. (b) An ideal cord passing around an ideal pulley and the FBD for a short segment of the cord at the top of the pulley. Choosing the x-axis to be horizontal, the normal force has no x-component. Applying Newton's second law along the x-axis: $\Sigma F_x = T_1 \cos \theta - T_2 \cos \theta = ma_x$. With $m = 0$, $T_1 = T_2$. The same reasoning can be applied to any segment of cord in contact with the pulley to show that the tensions are the same on either side of the pulley.

Tension in a Cord Attached to Moving Objects   Example 3.11 deals with two objects connected by an ideal cord. Although it may have a nonzero acceleration, the net force on an *ideal* cord is still zero because it has *zero mass*: if $m = 0$, then $\Sigma \vec{F} = m\vec{a} = 0$. As a result, the tension is the same at the two ends as long as no external force acts on the cord between the ends (Fig. 3.34a). An ideal cord that passes over an ideal pulley has the same tension at its ends. The pulley exerts an external force on part of the cord, but this force is everywhere *perpendicular to the cord*. As Fig. 3.34b shows, an external force that has no component tangent to the cord does not affect the tension in the cord.

Example 3.11

Two Blocks Hanging on a Pulley

Figure 3.35

Two hanging blocks connected on either side of a frictionless pulley by a massless, flexible cord that does not stretch.

In Fig. 3.35, two blocks are connected by an ideal cord that does not stretch; the cord passes over an ideal pulley. If the masses are $m_1 = 26.0 \text{ kg}$ and $m_2 = 42.0 \text{ kg}$, what are the accelerations of each block and the tension in the cord?

Strategy   Since m_2 is greater than m_1, the downward force of gravity is stronger on the right side than on the left. We expect block 2's acceleration to be downward and block 1's to be upward.

The cord does not stretch, so blocks 1 and 2 move at the same speed at any instant (in opposite directions). Therefore, the accelerations of the two blocks are equal in magnitude and opposite in

direction. If the accelerations had different magnitudes, then soon the two blocks would be moving with different speeds. That could only happen if the cord either stretches or contracts.

The tension in the cord must be the same everywhere along the cord since the masses of the cord and pulley are negligible and the pulley turns without friction.

We treat each block as a separate system, draw FBDs for each, and then apply Newton's second law to each. It is convenient to choose the positive y-direction differently for the two blocks since we know their accelerations are in opposite directions. For each block, we choose the $+y$-axis in the direction of the acceleration of that block: upward for block m_1 and downward for m_2. Doing so means that a_y has the same magnitude *and sign* (both positive) for the two blocks.

continued on next page

Example 3.11 continued

Solution   Figure 3.36 shows FBDs for the two blocks. Two forces act on each: gravity and the pull of the cord. The acceleration vectors are drawn *next to* the FBDs. Thus, we know the direction of the net force: it is always the same as the direction of the acceleration. Then we know that the tension must be greater than m_1g to give block 1 an upward acceleration and less than m_2g to give block 2 a downward acceleration. The +y-axes are drawn for each block to be in the direction of the acceleration.

From the FBD of block 1, the pull of the cord is in the +y-direction and the gravitational force is in the −y-direction. Then Newton's second law for block 1 is

$$\sum F_{1y} = T - m_1g = m_1a_{1y}$$

For block 2, the pull of the cord is in the −y-direction and the gravitational force is in the +y-direction. Newton's second law for block 2 is

$$\sum F_{2y} = m_2g - T = m_2a_{2y}$$

The tension T in the cord is the same in the two equations. Also a_{1y} and a_{2y} are identical, so we write them simply as a_y. We then have a system of two equations with two unknowns. We can add the equations to obtain

$$m_2g - m_1g = m_2a_y + m_1a_y$$

Solving for a_y, we find

$$a_y = \frac{(m_2 - m_1)g}{m_2 + m_1}$$

Substituting numerical values,

$$a_y = \frac{(42.0 \text{ kg} - 26.0 \text{ kg}) \times 9.80 \text{ N/kg}}{42.0 \text{ kg} + 26.0 \text{ kg}}$$

$$= 2.31 \text{ m/s}^2$$

since

$$1 \frac{\text{N}}{\text{kg}} = 1 \frac{\text{kg·m/s}^2}{\text{kg}} = 1 \text{ m/s}^2$$

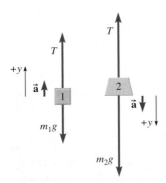

Figure 3.36

FBDs for the hanging blocks with force magnitudes labeled. We draw the acceleration vector *next to* each FBD as a guide—the net force has to be in the direction of the acceleration. However, the acceleration vector is not *part of* the FBD (it is not a force to be added to the others).

The blocks have the same magnitude acceleration. For block 1 the acceleration points upward and for block 2 it points downward.

To find T we can substitute the expression for a_y into either of the two original equations. Using the first equation,

$$T - m_1g = m_1 \frac{(m_2 - m_1)g}{m_2 + m_1}$$

Solving for T yields

$$T = \frac{2m_1m_2}{m_1 + m_2} g$$

Substituting,

$$T = \frac{2 \times 26.0 \text{ kg} \times 42.0 \text{ kg}}{68.0 \text{ kg}} \times 9.80 \text{ N/kg} = 315 \text{ N}$$

Discussion   A few quick checks:

- a_y is positive, which means that the accelerations are in the directions we expect.
- The tension (315 N) is between m_1g (255 N) and m_2g (412 N), as it must be for the accelerations to be in opposite directions.
- The units and dimensions are correct for all equations.
- We can check algebraic expressions in special cases for which we have some intuition. For example, if the masses had been *equal*, we expect the blocks to hang in equilibrium (either at rest or moving at constant velocity) due to the equal pull of gravity on the two blocks. Substituting $m_1 = m_2$ into the expressions for a_y and T gives $a_y = 0$ and $T = m_1g = m_2g$, which is just what we expect.

Note that we did *not* find out which way the blocks move. We found the directions of their *accelerations*. If the blocks start out at rest, then the block of mass m_2 moves downward and the block of mass m_1 moves upward. However, if initially m_2 is moving up and m_1 down, they continue to move in those directions, slowing down since their accelerations are opposite to their velocities. Eventually they come to rest and then reverse directions.

Practice Problem 3.11   Another Check

Using the numerical values of the tension and the acceleration calculated in Example 3.11, verify Newton's second law directly for each of the two blocks.

3.5 VELOCITY IS RELATIVE; REFERENCE FRAMES

The idea of *relativity* arose in physics centuries before Einstein's theory. Nicole Oresme (1323–1382) wrote that motion of one object can only be perceived relative to some other object. Until now, we have tacitly assumed in most situations that displacements, velocities, and accelerations should be measured in a **reference frame** attached to Earth's surface—that is, by choosing an origin fixed in position relative to Earth's surface and a set of axes whose directions are fixed relative to Earth's surface. After learning about relative velocities, we will take another look at this assumption.

Relative Velocity

Suppose Wanda is walking down the aisle of a train moving along the track at a constant velocity (Fig. 3.37). Imagine asking, "How fast is Wanda walking?" This question is not well defined. Do we mean her speed as measured by Tim, a passenger on the train, or her speed as measured by Greg, who is standing on the ground and looking into the train as it passes by? The answer to the question "How fast?" depends on the observer.

Figure 3.38 shows Wanda walking from one end of the car to the other during a time interval Δt. The displacement of Wanda as measured by Tim—her displacement *relative to the train*—is $\Delta \vec{r}_{WT} = \vec{v}_{WT} \Delta t$. During the same time interval, the *train's* displacement *relative to the ground* is $\Delta \vec{r}_{TG} = \vec{v}_{TG} \Delta t$. As measured by Greg, Wanda's displacement is partly due to her motion relative to the train and partly due to the motion of the train relative to the ground. Figure 3.38 shows that $\Delta \vec{r}_{WT} + \Delta \vec{r}_{TG} = \Delta \vec{r}_{WG}$. Dividing by the time interval Δt gives the relationship between the three velocities:

$$\vec{v}_{WT} + \vec{v}_{TG} = \vec{v}_{WG} \tag{3-17}$$

To be sure that you are adding the velocity vectors correctly, think of the subscripts as if they were fractions that get multiplied when the velocity vectors are added. In Eq. (3-17), $\frac{W}{T} \times \frac{T}{G} = \frac{W}{G}$ so the equation is correct.

Relative velocities are of enormous practical interest to pilots of aircraft, sailors, and captains of ocean freighters. The pilot of an airplane is ultimately concerned with the motion of the plane with respect to the ground—the takeoff and landing points are fixed points on the ground. However, the controls of the plane (engines, rudder, ailerons, and spoilers) affect the motion of the plane *with respect to the air*. A sailor has to consider

Applications: relative velocities for pilots and sailors

Figure 3.37 Tim and Greg watch Wanda walk down the aisle of a train. Wanda's velocity with respect to Tim (or with respect to the train) is $\vec{v}_{WT}$; Tim's velocity with respect to Greg (or with respect to the ground) is $\vec{v}_{TG}$.

Figure 3.38 Wanda's displacement relative to the ground is the sum of her displacement relative to the train and the displacement of the train relative to the ground.

three different velocities of the boat: with respect to shore (for launching and landing), with respect to the air (for the behavior of the sails), and with respect to the water (for the behavior of the rudder).

✓ CHECKPOINT 3.5

In Fig. 3.37, if the train is moving at 18.0 m/s with respect to the ground and Wanda walks at 1.5 m/s with respect to the train, how fast is Wanda moving (a) with respect to Greg and (b) with respect to Tim?

Example 3.12

Flight from Denver to Chicago

An airplane flies from Denver to Chicago (1770 km) in 4.4 h when no wind blows. On a day with a tailwind, the plane makes the trip in 4.0 h. (a) What is the wind speed? (b) If a headwind blows with the same speed, how long does the trip take?

Strategy We assume the plane has the same *airspeed*—the same speed relative to the air—in both cases. Once the plane is up in the air, the behavior of the wings, control surfaces, etc., depends on how fast the air is rushing by; the ground speed is irrelevant. But it is not irrelevant for the passengers, who are interested in a displacement relative to the ground.

Solution Let $\vec{v}_{PG}$ and $\vec{v}_{PA}$ represent the velocity of the plane relative to the ground and the velocity of the plane relative to the air, respectively. The wind velocity—the velocity of the air relative to the ground—can be written $\vec{v}_{AG}$. Then $\vec{v}_{PA} + \vec{v}_{AG} = \vec{v}_{PG}$. The equation is correct since $\frac{P}{\cancel{A}} \times \frac{\cancel{A}}{G} = \frac{P}{G}$. With no wind,

$$v_{PA} = v_{PG} = \frac{1770 \text{ km}}{4.4 \text{ h}} = 400 \text{ km/h}$$

(a) On the day with the tailwind,

$$v_{PG} = \frac{1770 \text{ km}}{4.0 \text{ h}} = 440 \text{ km/h}$$

We expect v_{PA} to be the same regardless of whether there is a wind. Since we are dealing with a tailwind, $\vec{v}_{PA}$ and $\vec{v}_{AG}$ are

Figure 3.39

Addition of velocity vectors in the case of a tailwind. Lengths of vectors are not to scale.

Figure 3.40

Addition of velocity vectors in the case of a headwind. Lengths of vectors are not to scale.

in the same direction, which we label as the +x-direction in Fig. 3.39. Then,

$$v_{PAx} + v_{AGx} = v_{PGx}$$

$$v_{AGx} = v_{PGx} - v_{PAx} = 440 \text{ km/h} - 400 \text{ km/h} = 40 \text{ km/h}$$

$v_{AGy} = 0$, so the wind speed is $v_{AG} = 40$ km/h.

(b) With a 40 km/h headwind, $\vec{v}_{PA}$ and $\vec{v}_{AG}$ are in opposite directions (Fig. 3.40). The velocity of the plane with respect to the ground is

$$v_{PGx} = v_{PAx} + v_{AGx} = 400 \text{ km/h} + (-40 \text{ km/h}) = 360 \text{ km/h}$$

The ground speed of the plane is 360 km/h and the trip takes

$$\frac{1770 \text{ km}}{360 \text{ km/h}} = 4.9 \text{ h}$$

Discussion Quick check: the trip takes longer with a headwind (4.9 h) than with no wind (4.4 h), as we expect.

Practice Problem 3.12   Rowing Across the Bay

Jamil, practicing to get on the crew team at school, rows a one-person racing shell to the north shore of the bay for a distance of 3.6 km to his friend's dock. On a day when the water is still (no current flowing), it takes him 20 min (1200 s) to reach his friend. On another day when a current flows southward, it takes him 30 min (1800 s) to row the same course. Ignore air resistance. (a) What is the speed of the current in meters per second? (b) How long does it take Jamil to return home with that same current flowing?

Equation (3-17) applies to situations where the velocities are not all along the same line, as illustrated in Example 3.13.

Example 3.13

Rowing Across a River

Jack wants to row directly across a river from the east shore to a point on the west shore. The width of the river is 250 m and the current flows from north to south at 0.61 m/s. The trip takes Jack 4.2 min. In what direction did he head his rowboat to follow a course due west across the river? At what speed with respect to still water is Jack able to row?

Strategy We start with a sketch of the situation (Fig. 3.41). To keep the various velocities straight, we choose subscripts as follows: R = rowboat; W = water; S = shore. The velocity of the current given is the velocity of the water relative to the shore: $\vec{v}_{WS} = 0.61$ m/s, south. The velocity of the rowboat relative to shore ($\vec{v}_{RS}$) is due west. The magnitude of $\vec{v}_{RS}$ can be found from the displacement relative to shore and the time interval, both of which are given. The question asks for the magnitude and direction of the velocity of the rowboat relative to the water ($\vec{v}_{RW}$). The three velocities are related by

$$\vec{v}_{RW} + \vec{v}_{WS} = \vec{v}_{RS}$$

To compensate for the current carrying the rowboat south with respect to shore, Jack heads (points) the rowboat upstream (against the current) at some angle to the north of west.

Solution In a sketch of the vector addition (Fig. 3.42), the velocity of the rowboat with respect to the water is at an angle θ north of west. With respect to shore, Jack travels 250 m in 4.2 min, so his speed with respect to shore is

$$v_{RS} = \frac{250 \text{ m}}{4.2 \text{ min} \times 60 \text{ s/min}} = 0.992 \text{ m/s}$$

Figure 3.41
Rowing across a river.

$\vec{v}_{WS}$	is velocity of water with respect to shore
$\vec{v}_{RS}$	is velocity of rowboat with respect to shore
$\vec{v}_{RW}$	is velocity of rowboat with respect to water

Figure 3.42
Graphical addition of the velocity vectors.

We can find the angle at which the rowboat should be headed by finding the tangent of the angle between $\vec{v}_{RW}$ and $\vec{v}_{RS}$:

$$\tan \theta = \frac{v_{WS}}{v_{RS}} = \frac{0.61 \text{ m/s}}{0.992 \text{ m/s}}$$

$$\theta = 32° \text{ N of W}$$

The speed at which Jack is able to row with respect to still water is the magnitude of $\vec{v}_{RW}$. Since $\vec{v}_{RS}$ and $\vec{v}_{WS}$ are *perpendicular*, the Pythagorean theorem yields

$$|\vec{v}_{RW}| = \sqrt{v_{WS}^2 + v_{RS}^2} = \sqrt{(0.61 \text{ m/s})^2 + (0.992 \text{ m/s})^2}$$

$$= 1.16 \text{ m/s}$$

Jack rows at a speed of 1.16 m/s with respect to the water.

Discussion If $\vec{v}_{RS}$ and $\vec{v}_{WS}$ had not been perpendicular, we could not have used the Pythagorean theorem in this way. Rather, we would use the component method to add the two vectors.

If Jack had headed the rowboat directly west, the current would have carried him south, so he would have traveled in a direction south of west relative to shore. He has to compensate by heading upstream at just such an angle that his velocity relative to shore is directed west.

Practice Problem 3.13 Heading Straight Across

If Jack were to head straight across the river, in what direction with respect to shore would he travel? How long would it take him to cross? How far downstream would he be carried? Assume that he rows at the same speed with respect to the water as in Example 3.13.

Reference Frames

Think back to the train moving at constant velocity with respect to the ground. Suppose Tim does some experiments using the train's reference frame for his measurements. Greg does similar experiments using the reference frame of the ground. Tim and Greg disagree about the numerical value of an object's velocity, but since their velocity measurements *differ by a constant* [see Eq. (3-17)], they will always agree about *changes* in velocity and about accelerations. Both observers can use Newton's second law to relate the net force to the acceleration. The basic laws of physics, such as Newton's laws of motion, work equally well in any two reference frames if they move with a constant relative velocity.

Newton's First Law Defines an Inertial Reference Frame   You might wonder why we need Newton's first law—isn't it just a special case of the second law when $\sum \vec{F} = 0$? No, the first law *defines* what kind of reference frame we can use when applying the second law. For the second law to be valid, we must use an *inertial reference frame*—a reference frame in which the law of inertia holds—to observe the motion of objects. The law of inertia is a *postulate* of classical mechanics—an assumption that is used as a starting point. It is not something we can prove experimentally.

Is a reference frame attached to Earth's surface truly inertial? No, but it is close enough in many circumstances. When analyzing the motion of a soccer ball, the fact that Earth rotates about its axis does not have much effect. But if we want to analyze the motion of a meteor falling from a great distance toward Earth, Earth's rotation must be considered. We will take a closer look at the effect of Earth's rotation in Chapter 5.

Master the Concepts

- Position (symbol $\vec{r}$) is the vector from the origin to an object's location. Its magnitude is the distance from the origin and its direction points from the origin to the object.

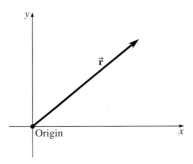

- Displacement is the change in position: $\Delta \vec{r} = \vec{r}_f - \vec{r}_i$. The displacement depends only on the starting and ending positions, not on the path taken. The magnitude of the displacement vector is not necessarily equal to the total distance traveled; it is the straight line distance from the initial position to the final position.

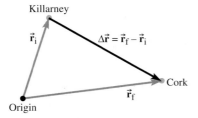

- Average velocity is the constant velocity that would cause the same displacement in the same amount of time.

$$\vec{v}_{av} = \frac{\Delta \vec{r}}{\Delta t} \text{ (for any time interval } \Delta t) \qquad (3\text{-}2)$$

- Velocity is a vector that states how fast and in what direction something moves. Its direction is the direction of the object's motion and its magnitude is the instantaneous speed. It is the instantaneous rate of change of the position vector.

$$\vec{v} = \lim_{\Delta t \to 0} \frac{\Delta \vec{r}}{\Delta t} \text{ (for a } very \text{ } small \text{ time interval } \Delta t) \quad (3\text{-}4)$$

The instantaneous velocity vector is tangent to the path of motion.

$$\vec{v} = \lim_{\Delta t \to 0} \frac{\Delta \vec{r}}{\Delta t}$$

- Average acceleration is the constant acceleration that would cause the same velocity change in the same amount of time.

$$\vec{a}_{av} = \frac{\Delta \vec{v}}{\Delta t} \text{ (for any time interval } \Delta t) \qquad (3\text{-}13)$$

continued on next page

Master the Concepts continued

- Acceleration is the instantaneous rate of change of the velocity vector.

$$\vec{a} = \lim_{\Delta t \to 0} \frac{\Delta \vec{v}}{\Delta t} \text{ (for a } very \ small \text{ time interval } \Delta t) \quad \text{(3-15)}$$

Acceleration does not necessarily mean speeding up. A velocity can also change by decreasing speed or by changing direction. The instantaneous acceleration vector does *not* have to be tangent to the path of motion, since velocities can change both in direction and in magnitude.

- Interpreting graphs: On a graph of $x(t)$, the slope at any point is v_x. On a graph of $v_x(t)$, the slope at any point is a_x, and the area under the graph during any time interval is the displacement Δx during that time interval. If v_x is negative, the displacement is also negative, so we must count the area as negative when it is below the time axis. On a graph of $a_x(t)$, the area under the curve is Δv_x, the change in v_x during that time interval.

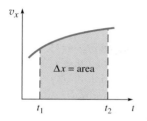

- Newton's second law relates the net force acting on an object to the object's acceleration and its mass:

$$\vec{a} = \frac{\sum \vec{F}}{m} \quad \text{or} \quad \sum \vec{F} = m\vec{a} \quad \text{(3-9)}$$

The acceleration is always in the same direction as the net force. Problems involving Newton's second law—whether equilibrium or nonequilibrium—can be solved by treating the x- and y-components of the forces and the acceleration separately:

$$\sum F_x = ma_x \quad \text{and} \quad \sum F_y = ma_y \quad \text{(3-10)}$$

- The SI unit of force is the newton: $1 \text{ N} = 1 \text{ kg·m/s}^2$. One newton is the magnitude of the net force that gives a 1-kg object an acceleration of magnitude 1 m/s^2.
- To relate the velocities of objects measured in different reference frames, use the equation

$$\vec{v}_{AC} = \vec{v}_{AB} + \vec{v}_{BC} \quad \text{(3-17)}$$

where $\vec{v}_{AC}$ represents the velocity of A relative to C, and so forth.

Conceptual Questions

1. Explain the difference between distance traveled, displacement, and displacement magnitude.

2. Explain the difference between speed and velocity.

3. On a graph of v_x versus time, what quantity does the area under the graph represent?

4. On a graph of v_x versus time, what quantity does the slope of the graph represent?

5. On a graph of a_x versus time, what quantity does the area under the graph represent?

6. On a graph of x versus time, what quantity does the slope of the graph represent?

7. What is the relationship between average velocity and instantaneous velocity? An object can have different instantaneous velocities at different times. Can the same object have different average velocities? Explain.

8. If an object is traveling at a constant velocity, is it necessarily traveling in a straight line? Explain.

9. Can the average speed and the magnitude of the average velocity ever be equal? If so, under what circumstances?

10. Give an example of an object whose acceleration is (a) in the same direction as its velocity, (b) opposite its velocity, and (c) perpendicular to its velocity.

11. Name a situation in which the speed of an object is constant while the velocity is not.

12. Refer to Conceptual Question 15 in Chapter 2. A heavy lead ball hangs from a string attached to a sturdy wooden frame. A second string is attached to a hook on the bottom of the lead ball. In Chapter 2, you imagined pulling slowly and steadily on the lower string and found that the upper string would break first. Now imagine that you reset the apparatus and this time give the lower string a quick, hard pull. Now which string do you think will break first? Explain.

13. Using Newton's laws, explain why a spring *must* exert forces of equal magnitude on the objects attached to each end, assuming that the spring's mass is negligibly small. The same line of reasoning applies to a rope or cord whose mass is negligible.

14. If an object is acted on by a single constant force, is it possible for the object to remain at rest? Is it possible for the object to move with constant velocity? Is it possible for the object's speed to be decreasing? Is it possible for it to change direction?

15. If an object is acted on by two constant forces is it possible for the object to move at constant velocity? If so, what must be true about the two forces?

16. Tell whether each of the following objects has a constant velocity and explain your reasoning. (a) A car driving around a curve at constant speed on a flat road. (b) A car driving straight up a 6° incline at constant speed. (c) The Moon.

17. You are bicycling along a straight north-south road. Let the x-axis point north. Describe your motion in each of the following cases. Example: $a_x > 0$ and $v_x > 0$ means you are moving north and speeding up. (a) $a_x > 0$ and $v_x < 0$. (b) $a_x = 0$ and $v_x < 0$. (c) $a_x < 0$ and $v_x = 0$. (d) $a_x < 0$ and $v_x < 0$. (e) Based on your answers, explain why it is not a good idea to use the expression "negative acceleration" to mean slowing down.

18. An object is subjected to two constant forces that are perpendicular to each other. Can a set of x- and y-axes be chosen so that the acceleration of the object has only one nonzero component? If so, how? Explain.

19. You are given the task of designing a mechanism to trip a switch in an automobile seat belt, causing it to tighten in case of an accident. You decide that if the velocity of the car is high and constant the passenger is in no danger; it is only high acceleration that matters. Explain.

20. While you are supervising playground activity during recess, the children are playing a game of tag. As Marlene and Shelly run past each other in opposite directions, Marlene reaches out and touches the shiny logo on Shelly's jacket. Shelly starts to cry and says that Marlene poked her really hard. Marlene says she didn't poke her, she only touched Shelly's jacket. Each child thinks the other is lying. Can you explain why both children are correct?

Multiple-Choice Questions

1. The term *force* most accurately describes
   (a) the mass of an object.
   (b) the inertia of an object.
   (c) the quantity that causes displacement.
   (d) the quantity that keeps an object moving.
   (e) the quantity that changes the velocity of an object.

2. Which car has a westward acceleration?
   (a) a car traveling westward at constant speed
   (b) a car traveling eastward and speeding up
   (c) a car traveling westward and slowing down
   (d) a car traveling eastward and slowing down
   (e) a car starting from rest and moving toward the east

3. A toy rocket is propelled straight upward from the ground and reaches a height Δy. After an elapsed time Δt, measured from the time the rocket was first fired off, the rocket has fallen back down to the ground, landing at the same spot from which it was launched. The magnitude of the average velocity of the rocket during this time is
   (a) zero (b) $2\dfrac{\Delta y}{\Delta t}$ (c) $\dfrac{\Delta y}{\Delta t}$ (d) $\dfrac{1}{2}\dfrac{\Delta y}{\Delta t}$

4. A toy rocket is propelled straight upward from the ground and reaches a height Δy. After an elapsed time Δt, measured from the time the rocket was first fired off, the rocket has fallen back down to the ground, landing at the same spot from which it was launched. The average speed of the rocket during this time is
   (a) zero (b) $2\dfrac{\Delta y}{\Delta t}$ (c) $\dfrac{\Delta y}{\Delta t}$ (d) $\dfrac{1}{2}\dfrac{\Delta y}{\Delta t}$

5. A space probe leaves the solar system to explore interstellar space. Once it is far from any stars, when must it fire its rocket engines?
   (a) All the time, in order to keep moving.
   (b) Only when it wants to speed up.
   (c) When it wants to speed up or slow down.
   (d) Only when it wants to turn.
   (e) When it wants to speed up, slow down, or turn.

Multiple-Choice Questions 6–15. A jogger is exercising along a long, straight road that runs north-south. She starts out heading north. A graph of $v_x(t)$ is shown on p. 103.

6. What distance does the jogger travel during the first 10.0 min ($t = 0$ to 10.0 min)?
   (a) 8.5 m (b) 510 m (c) 900 m (d) 1020 m

7. What is the displacement of the jogger from $t = 18.0$ min to $t = 24.0$ min?
   (a) 720 m, south   (b) 720 m, north
   (c) 2160 m, south   (d) 3600 m, north

8. What is the displacement of the jogger for the entire 30.0 min?
   (a) 3120 m, south   (b) 2400 m, north
   (c) 2400 m, south   (d) 3840 m, north

9. What is the total distance traveled by the jogger in 30.0 min?
   (a) 3840 m (b) 2340 m (c) 2400 m (d) 3600 m

10. What is the average velocity of the jogger during the 30.0 min?
    (a) 1.3 m/s, north   (b) 1.7 m/s, north
    (c) 2.1 m/s, north   (d) 2.9 m/s, north

11. What is the average speed of the jogger for the 30 min?
    (a) 1.4 m/s (b) 1.7 m/s (c) 2.1 m/s (d) 2.9 m/s

12. In what direction is she running at time $t = 20$ min?
    (a) south (b) north (c) not enough information

13. In which region of the graph is a_x positive?
    (a) A to B (b) C to D (c) E to F (d) G to H

14. In which region is a_x negative?
    (a) A to B (b) C to D (c) E to F (d) G to H

15. In which region is the velocity directed to the south?
   (a) A to B   (b) C to D   (c) E to F   (d) G to H

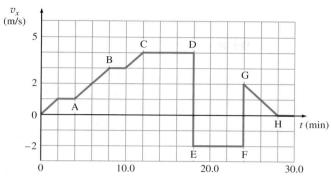

Multiple-Choice Questions 6–15

16. The following figure shows four graphs of x versus time. Which graph shows a constant, positive, nonzero velocity?

17. The four graphs show v_x versus time. (a) Which graph shows a constant velocity? (b) Which graph shows a_x constant and positive? (c) Which graph shows a_x constant and negative? (d) Which graph shows a changing a_x that is always positive?

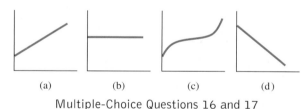

(a)   (b)   (c)   (d)

Multiple-Choice Questions 16 and 17

18. A boy plans to cross a river in a rubber raft. The current flows from north to south at 1 m/s. In what direction should he head to get across the river to the east bank in the least amount of time if he is able to paddle the raft at 1.5 m/s in still water?
   (a) directly to the east
   (b) south of east
   (c) north of east
   (d) The three directions require the same time to cross the river.

19. A boy plans to paddle a rubber raft across a river to the east bank while the current flows downriver from north to south at 1 m/s. He is able to paddle the raft at 1.5 m/s in still water. In what direction should he head the raft to go straight east across the river to the opposite bank?
   (a) directly to the east   (b) south of east
   (c) north of east   (d) north
   (e) south

20. Suppose the signs of v_x, ΣF_x, and a_x are as given in the table for motion along the x-axis. Choose the correct choices for (a), (b), (c), and (d) when either the direction of motion or the changing trend in speed is known for a given set of sign values of v_x, ΣF_x, and a_x.

v_x	ΣF_x	a_x	Direction of motion	Speed increasing or decreasing
+	+	+	$+x$	(a) increasing or decreasing?
+	−	−	(b) $+x$ or $−x$?	decreasing
−	+	+	$−x$	(c) increasing or decreasing?
−	−	−	(d) $+x$ or $−x$?	increasing

Problems

©	Combination conceptual/quantitative problem
✚	Biological or medical application
✦	Challenging problem
Blue #	Detailed solution in the Student Solutions Manual
① ②	Problems paired by concept
🌊	Text website interactive or tutorial

3.1 Position and Displacement

1. Two vectors, each of magnitude 4.0 cm, are inclined at a small angle α below the horizontal as shown. Let $\vec{D} = \vec{A} - \vec{B}$. Sketch the direction of $\vec{D}$ and estimate its magnitude. (🌊 tutorial: vectors)

2. Vector $\vec{A}$ is directed along the positive y-axis and has magnitude $\sqrt{3.0}$ units. Vector $\vec{B}$ is directed along the negative x-axis and has magnitude 1.0 unit. (a) What are the magnitude and direction of $\vec{A} - \vec{B}$? (b) What are the x- and y-components of $\vec{B} - \vec{A}$?

3. Vector $\vec{B}$ has magnitude 7.1 and direction 14° below the $+x$-axis. Vector $\vec{C}$ has x-component $C_x = -1.8$ and y-component $C_y = -6.7$. Compute: (a) the x- and y-components of $\vec{B}$; (b) the magnitude and direction of $\vec{C}$; (c) the magnitude and direction of $\vec{C} - \vec{B}$; (d) the x- and y-components of $\vec{C} - \vec{B}$.

4. Margaret walks to the store using the following path: 0.500 miles west, 0.200 miles north, 0.300 miles east. What is her total displacement? That is, what is the length and direction of the vector that points from her house directly to the store?

5. Jerry bicycles from his dorm to the local fitness center: 3.00 miles east and 2.00 miles north. Cindy's apartment is located 1.50 miles west of Jerry's dorm. If Cindy is able to meet Jerry at the fitness center by bicycling in a straight line, what is the length and direction she must travel?

6. A runner is practicing on a circular track that is 300 m in circumference. From the point farthest to the west on the track, he starts off running due north and follows the track as it curves around toward the east. (a) If he runs halfway around the track and stops at the farthest eastern point of the track, what is the distance he traveled? (b) What is his displacement?

7. Michaela is planning a trip in Ireland from Killarney to Cork to visit Blarney Castle (see Example 3.2). She also wants to visit Mallow, which is located 39 km due east of Killarney and 22 km due north of Cork. Draw the displacement vectors for the trip when she travels from Killarney to Mallow to Cork. (a) What is the magnitude of her displacement once she reaches Cork? (b) How much additional distance does Michaela travel in going to Cork by way of Mallow instead of going directly from Killarney to Cork?

8. A scout troop is practicing its orienteering skills with map and compass. First they walk due east for 1.2 km. Next, they walk 45° west of north for 2.7 km. In what direction must they walk to go directly back to their starting point? How far will they have to walk? Use graph paper, ruler, and protractor to find a geometrical solution.

9. Repeat Problem 8 using the component (algebraic) method.

10. A sailboat sails from Marblehead Harbor directly east for 45 nautical miles, then 60° south of east for 20.0 nautical miles, returns to an easterly heading for 30.0 nautical miles, and sails 30° east of north for 10.0 nautical miles, then west for 62 nautical miles. At that time the boat becomes becalmed and the auxiliary engine fails to start. The crew decides to notify the Coast Guard of their position. Using graph paper, ruler, and protractor, find the sailboat's displacement from the harbor. Then add the displacement vectors using the component method to obtain a more accurate description of their location.

11. You will be hiking to a lake with some of your friends by following the trails indicated on a map at the trailhead. The map says that you will travel 1.6 mi directly north, then 2.2 mi in a direction 35° east of north, then finally 1.1 mi in a direction 15° north of east. At the end of this hike, how far will you be from where you started, and what direction will you be from your starting point?

12. The pilot of a small plane finds that the airport where he intended to land is fogged in. He flies 55 mi west to another airport to find that conditions there are too icy for him to land. He flies 25 mi at 15° east of south and is finally able to land at the third airport. (a) How far and in what direction must he fly the next day to go directly to his original destination? (b) How many extra miles beyond his original flight plan has he flown?

13. We have assumed that the displacement for a trip is equal to the sum of the displacements for each leg of the trip. Prove that this is true. [*Hint:* Imagine a trip that consists of n segments. The trip starts at position $\vec{\mathbf{r}}_1$, proceeds to $\vec{\mathbf{r}}_2$, then to $\vec{\mathbf{r}}_3$, . . . , then to $\vec{\mathbf{r}}_{n-1}$, then finally to $\vec{\mathbf{r}}_n$. Write an expression for each displacement as the difference of two position vectors and then add them.]

3.2 Velocity

14. A cyclist travels 10.0 km east in a time of 11 min 40 s. What is his average velocity in meters per second?

15. If a shot put traveled a linear distance of 23.12 m due north in a time of 1.65 s, what was the average velocity of the shot?

16. In a game against the White Sox, baseball pitcher Nolan Ryan threw a pitch measured at 45.1 m/s. If it was 18.4 m from Nolan's position on the pitcher's mound to home plate, how long did it take the ball to get to the batter waiting at home plate? Treat the ball's velocity as constant and ignore any gravitational effects.

17. A ball thrown by a pitcher on a women's softball team is timed at 65.0 mph. The distance from the pitching rubber to home plate is 43.0 ft. In major league baseball the corresponding distance is 60.5 ft. If the batter in the softball game and the batter in the baseball game are to have equal times to react to the pitch, with what speed must the baseball be thrown? [*Hint:* There is no need to convert units; set up a ratio.]

18. See Problem 7. During Michaela's travel from Killarney to Cork via Mallow, her actual travel time in the car is 48 min. (a) What is her average speed in m/s? (b) What is the magnitude of her average velocity in m/s?

19. For the train in Fig. 3.2 and Example 3.3, find the average velocity between 3:14 P.M. when the train is at 3 km east of the origin and 3:28 P.M. when it is 10 km east of the origin.

20. Jason drives due west with a speed of 35.0 mi/h for 30.0 min, then continues in the same direction with a speed of 60.0 mi/h for 2.00 h, then drives farther west at 25.0 mi/h for 10.0 min. What is Jason's average velocity?

21. Two cars, a Porsche Boxster convertible and a Toyota Scion xB, are traveling in the same direction, although the Boxster is 186 m behind the Scion. The speed of the Boxster is 24.4 m/s and the speed of the Scion is 18.6 m/s. How much time does it take for the Boxster to catch the Scion? [*Hint:* What must be true about the displacement of the two cars when they meet?] (tutorial: catchup)

22. To get to a concert in time, a harpsichordist has to drive 122 mi in 2.00 h. (a) If he drove at an average speed of 55.0 mi/h in a due west direction for the first 1.20 h, what must be his average speed if he is heading 30.0° south of west for the remaining 48.0 min? (b) What is his average velocity for the entire trip?

23. Peggy drives from Cornwall to Atkins Glen in 45 min. Cornwall is 73.6 km from Illium in a direction 25° west of south. Atkins Glen is 27.2 km from Illium in a direction 15° south of west. Using Illium as your origin, (a) draw the initial and final position vectors, (b) find the displacement during the trip, and (c) find Peggy's average velocity for the trip.

24. Speedometer readings are obtained and graphed as a car comes to a stop along a straight-line path. How far does the car move between $t = 0$ and $t = 16$ s? (tutorial: start/stop traffic)

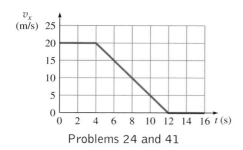

Problems 24 and 41

25. The graph shows speedometer readings, in meters per second (on the vertical axis), obtained as a skateboard travels along a straight-line path. How far does the board move between $t = 3.00$ s and $t = 8.00$ s?

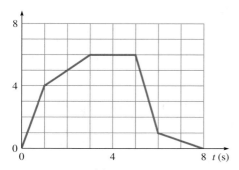

Problems 25–28

26. The graph shows values of $x(t)$ in meters, on the vertical axis, for a skater traveling in a straight line. (a) What is $v_{av,x}$ for the interval from $t = 0$ to $t = 4.0$ s? (b) from $t = 0$ to $t = 5.0$ s?

27. The graph shows values of $x(t)$ in meters for a skater traveling in a straight line. What is v_x at $t = 2.0$ s?

28. The graph shows values of $x(t)$ in meters for an object traveling in a straight line. Plot v_x as a function of time for this object from $t = 0$ to $t = 8$ s.

29. A graph is plotted of the vertical velocity component of an elevator versus time. (a) How high is the elevator above the starting point ($t = 0$) after 20 s have elapsed? (b) When is the elevator at its highest location above the starting point?

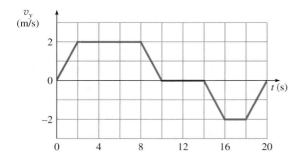

30. To pass a physical fitness test, Massimo must run 1000 m at an average rate of 4.0 m/s. He runs the first 900 m in 250 s. Is it possible for Massimo to pass the test? If so, how fast must he run the last 100 m to pass the test?

31. A speedboat heads west at 108 km/h for 20.0 min. It then travels at 60.0° south of west at 90.0 km/h for 10.0 min. (a) What is the average speed for the trip? (b) What is the average velocity for the trip?

32. A car travels east at 96 km/h for 1.0 h. It then travels 30.0° east of north at 128 km/h for 1.0 h. (a) What is the average speed for the trip? (b) What is the average velocity for the trip?

33. A bicycle travels 3.2 km due east in 0.10 h, then 4.8 km at 15.0° east of north in 0.15 h, and finally another 3.2 km due east in 0.10 h to reach its destination. The time lost in turning is negligible. What is the average velocity for the entire trip?

34. A motor scooter travels east at a speed of 12 m/s. The driver then reverses direction and heads west at 15 m/s. What is the change in velocity of the scooter? Give magnitude and direction.

✦35. A relay race is run along a straight-line track of length 300.0 m running south to north. The first runner starts at the south end of the track and passes the baton to a teammate at the north end of the track. The second runner races back to the start line and passes the baton to a third runner who races 100.0 m northward to the finish line. The magnitudes of the average velocities of the first, second, and third runners during their parts of the race are 7.30 m/s, 7.20 m/s, and 7.80 m/s, respectively. What is the average velocity of the baton for the entire race? [*Hint:* You will need to find the time spent by each runner in completing her portion of the race.]

3.3 Newton's Second Law of Motion

36. If the peak force on a runner's foot during a race is found to be vertical and three times his weight, what is the peak force on the foot of a runner whose mass is 85 kg?

37. (a) In Fig. 3.23, what is the instantaneous acceleration of the sports car of Example 3.7 at the time of 14 s from the start? (b) What is the displacement of the car from $t = 12.0$ s to $t = 16.0$ s? (c) What is the average velocity of the car in the 4.0 s time interval from 12.0 s to 16.0 s?

38. If a pronghorn antelope accelerates from rest in a straight line with a constant acceleration of 1.7 m/s², how long does it take for the antelope to reach a speed of 22 m/s?

39. If a car traveling at 28 m/s is brought to a full stop in 4.0 s after the brakes are applied, find the average acceleration during braking.

40. The graph shows v_x versus t for a body moving along a straight line. (a) What is a_x at $t = 11$ s? (b) What is a_x at

$t = 3$ s? (c) How far does the body travel from $t = 12$ s to $t = 14$ s? ([tutorial icon] tutorial: x, v, a)

41. The graph with Problem 24 shows speedometer readings as a car comes to a stop. What is the magnitude of the acceleration at $t = 7.0$ s?

◆42. The figure shows a plot of $v_x(t)$ for a car traveling in a straight line. (a) What is $a_{av,x}$ between $t = 6$ s and $t = 11$ s? (b) What is $v_{av,x}$ for the same time interval? (c) What is $v_{av,x}$ for the interval $t = 0$ to $t = 20$ s? (d) What is the increase in the car's speed between 10 s and 15 s? (e) How far does the car travel from time $t = 10$ s to time $t = 15$ s?

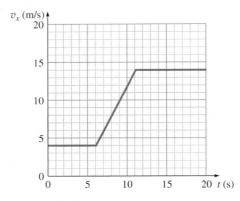

43. An 1100-kg airplane starts from rest and accelerates forward for 8.0 s until it reaches its takeoff speed of 35 m/s. What is the average forward force on the airplane during this time? ([tutorial icon] tutorial: sprinter)

44. At $t = 0$, an automobile traveling north begins to make a turn. It follows one-quarter of the arc of a circle of radius 10.0 m until, at $t = 1.60$ s, it is traveling east. The car does not alter its speed during the turn. Find (a) the car's speed, (b) the change in its velocity during the turn, and (c) its average acceleration during the turn.

◉45. A car travels three-quarters of the way around a circle of radius 20.0 m in a time of 3.0 s at a constant speed. The initial velocity is west and the final velocity is south. (a) Find its average velocity for this trip. (b) What is the car's average acceleration during these 3.0 s? (c) Explain how a car moving at constant speed has a nonzero average acceleration.

46. John drives 16 km directly west from Orion to Chester at a speed of 90 km/h, then directly south for 8.0 km to Seiling at a speed of 80 km/h, then finally 34 km southeast to Oakwood at a speed of 100 km/h. (a) What was the change in velocity during this trip? (b) What was the average acceleration during this trip?

47. At the beginning of a 3.0-h plane trip, you are traveling due north at 192 km/h. At the end, you are traveling 240 km/h in the northwest direction (45° west of north). (a) Draw your initial and final velocity vectors. (b) Find the change in your velocity. (c) What is your average acceleration during the trip?

48. A particle experiences a constant acceleration that is north at 100 m/s². At $t = 0$, its velocity vector is 60 m/s east. At what time will the magnitude of the velocity be 100 m/s?

49. A particle experiences a constant acceleration that is south at 2.50 m/s². At $t = 0$, its velocity is 40.0 m/s east. What is its velocity at $t = 8.00$ s?

50. A 1200-kg airplane starts from rest and, with a constant acceleration of magnitude 5.0 m/s², reaches its takeoff speed in 9.00 s. (a) What is the magnitude of the net force on the airplane during this time? (b) What is its takeoff speed?

51. A rubber ball is attached to a paddle by a rubber band. The ball is initially moving away from the paddle with a speed of 4.0 m/s. After 0.25 s, the ball is moving toward the paddle with a speed of 3.0 m/s. What is the average acceleration of the ball during that 0.25 s? Give magnitude and direction.

3.4 Applying Newton's Second Law

52. In Example 3.10, find T_3, the tension in the coupling between cars 2 and 3. ([tutorial icon] tutorial: towing a train)

◉53. In Fig. 3.26 an astronaut is playing shuffleboard on Earth. The puck has a mass of 2.0 kg. Between the board and puck the coefficient of static friction is 0.35 and of kinetic friction is 0.25. (a) If she pushes the puck with a force of 5.0 N in the forward direction, does the puck move? (b) As she is pushing, she trips and the force in the forward direction suddenly becomes 7.5 N. Does the puck move? (c) If so, what is the acceleration of the puck along the board if she maintains contact between puck and stick as she regains her footing while pushing steadily with a force of 6.0 N on the puck? (d) She carries her game to the Moon and again pushes a moving puck with a force of 6.0 N forward. Will the acceleration of the puck during contact be more, the same, or less than on Earth? Explain. ([tutorial icon] tutorial: rough table)

54. A 2.0-kg toy locomotive is pulling a 1.0-kg caboose. The frictional force of the track on the caboose is 0.50 N backward along the track. If the train's acceleration forward is 3.0 m/s², what is the magnitude of the force exerted by the locomotive on the caboose?

55. A 2010-kg elevator moves with an upward acceleration of 1.50 m/s². What is the tension in the cable that supports the elevator?

56. A 2010-kg elevator moves with a downward acceleration of 1.50 m/s². What is the tension in the cable that supports the elevator?

57. While an elevator of mass 2530 kg moves upward, the tension in the cable is 33.6 kN. (a) What is the acceleration of the elevator? (b) If at some point in the motion the velocity of the elevator is 1.20 m/s upward, what is the elevator's velocity 4.00 s later?

58. An engine pulls a train of 20 freight cars, each having a mass of 5.0×10^4 kg with a constant force. The cars move from rest to a speed of 4.0 m/s in 20.0 s on a straight track. Neglecting friction, what is the force with which the 10th car pulls the 11th one (at the middle of the train)? (tutorial: school bus)

59. In Fig. 3.35, two blocks are connected by a lightweight, flexible cord that passes over a frictionless pulley. (a) If $m_1 = 3.0$ kg and $m_2 = 5.0$ kg, what are the accelerations of each block? (b) What is the tension in the cord?

✦60. A helicopter is lifting two crates simultaneously. One crate with a mass of 200 kg is attached to the helicopter by a cable. The second crate with a mass of 100 kg is hanging below the first crate and attached to the first crate by a cable. As the helicopter accelerates upward at a rate of 1.0 m/s², what is the tension in each of the two cables?

61. An accelerometer—a device to measure acceleration— can be as simple as a small pendulum hanging in the cockpit. Suppose you are flying a small plane in a straight, horizontal line and your accelerometer hangs 12° behind the vertical shown in the figure. What is your acceleration at that time?

Direction of motion of the airplane

12°

62. A model sailboat is slowly sailing west across a pond at 0.33 m/s. A gust of wind blowing at 28° south of west gives the sailboat a constant acceleration of magnitude 0.30 m/s² during a time interval of 2.0 s. (a) If the net force on the sailboat during the 2.0-s interval has magnitude 0.375 N, what is the sailboat's mass? (b) What is the new velocity of the boat after the 2.0-s gust of wind?

63. A rope is attached from a truck to a 1400-kg car. The rope will break if the tension is greater than 2500 N. Ignoring friction, what is the maximum possible acceleration of the truck if the rope does not break? Should the driver of the truck be concerned that the rope might break?

64. The vertical component of the acceleration of a sailplane is zero when the air pushes up against its wings with a force of 3.0 kN. (a) Assuming that the only forces on the sailplane are that due to gravity and that due to the air pushing against its wings, what is the gravitational force on the Earth due to the sailplane? (b) If the wing stalls and the upward force decreases to 2.0 kN, what is the acceleration of the sailplane?

65. A man lifts a 2.0-kg stone vertically with his hand at a constant upward velocity of 1.5 m/s. What is the magnitude of the total force of the stone on the man's hand?

66. A man lifts a 2.0-kg stone vertically with his hand at a constant upward *acceleration* of 1.5 m/s². What is the magnitude of the total force of the stone on the man's hand?

3.5 Velocity Is Relative; Reference Frames

67. A small plane is flying directly west with an airspeed of 30.0 m/s. The plane flies into a region where the wind is blowing at 10.0 m/s at an angle of 30° to the south of west. (a) If the pilot does not change the heading of the plane, what will be the ground speed of the airplane? (b) What will be the new directional heading, relative to the ground, of the airplane? (tutorial: flight of crow)

68. A car is driving directly north on the freeway at a speed of 110 km/h and a truck is leaving the freeway driving 85 km/h in a direction that is 35° west of north. What is the velocity of the truck relative to the car?

69. A Nile cruise ship takes 20.8 h to go upstream from Luxor to Aswan, a distance of 208 km, and 19.2 h to make the return trip downstream. Assuming the ship's speed relative to the water is the same in both cases, calculate the speed of the current in the Nile.

70. Two cars are driving toward each other on a straight, flat Kansas road. The Jeep Wrangler is traveling at 82 km/h north and the Ford Taurus is traveling at 48 km/h south, both measured relative to the road. What is the velocity of the Jeep relative to an observer in the Ford?

71. Two cars are driving toward each other on a straight and level road in Alaska. The BMW is traveling at 100.0 km/h north and the VW is traveling at 42 km/h south, both velocities measured relative to the road. At a certain instant, the distance between the cars is 10.0 km. Approximately how long will it take from that instant for the two cars to meet? [*Hint:* Consider a reference frame in which one of the cars is at rest.]

72. An airplane has a velocity relative to the ground of 210 m/s toward the east. The pilot measures his airspeed (the speed of the plane relative to the air) to be 160 m/s. What is the minimum wind velocity possible?

73. A boat that can travel at 4.0 km/h in still water crosses a river with a current of 1.8 km/h. At what angle must the boat be pointed upstream to travel straight across the river? In other words, in what direction is the velocity of the boat relative to the water?

74. A boy is attempting to swim directly across a river; he is able to swim at a speed of 0.500 m/s relative to the water. The river is 25.0 m wide and the boy ends up at 50.0 m downstream from his starting point. (a) How fast is the current flowing in the river? (b) What is the speed of the boy relative to a friend standing on the riverbank?

75. An aircraft has to fly between two cities, one of which is 600.0 km north of the other. The pilot starts from the southern city and encounters a steady 100.0 km/h wind that blows from the northeast. The plane has a cruising

speed of 300.0 km/h in still air. (a) In what direction (relative to east) must the pilot head her plane? (b) How long does the flight take?

76. At an antique car rally, a Stanley Steamer automobile travels north at 40 km/h and a Pierce Arrow automobile travels east at 50 km/h. Relative to an observer riding in the Stanley Steamer, what are the x- and y-components of the velocity of the Pierce Arrow car? The x-axis is to the east and the y-axis is to the north.

77. Sheena can row a boat at 3.00 mi/h in still water. She needs to cross a river that is 1.20 mi wide with a current flowing at 1.60 mi/h. Not having her calculator ready, she guesses that to go straight across, she should head 60.0° upstream. (a) What is her speed with respect to the starting point on the bank? (b) How long does it take her to cross the river? (c) How far upstream or downstream from her starting point will she reach the opposite bank? (d) In order to go straight across, what angle upstream should she have headed?

78. A small plane is flying directly west with an airspeed of 30.0 m/s. The plane flies into a region where the wind is blowing at 10.0 m/s at an angle of 30° to the south of west. In that region, the pilot changes the directional heading to maintain her due west heading. (a) What is the change she makes in the directional heading to compensate for the wind? (b) After the heading change, what is the ground speed of the airplane?

79. Demonstrate with a vector diagram that a displacement is the same when measured in two different reference frames that are at rest with respect to each other.

80. A dolphin wants to swim directly back to its home bay, which is 0.80 km due west. It can swim at a speed of 4.00 m/s relative to the water, but a uniform water current flows with speed 2.83 m/s in the southeast direction. (a) What direction should the dolphin head? (b) How long does it take the dolphin to swim the 0.80-km distance home?

✦81. In a plate glass factory, sheets of glass move along a conveyor belt at a speed of 15.0 cm/s. An automatic cutting tool descends at preset intervals to cut the glass to size. Since the assembly belt must keep moving at constant speed, the cutter is set to cut at an angle to compensate for the motion of the glass. If the glass is 72.0 cm wide and the cutter moves across the width at a speed of 24.0 cm/s, at what angle should the cutter be set?

Comprehensive Problems

82. (a) If a freestyle swimmer travels 1.50 km in a time of 14 min 53 s, how fast is his average speed? (b) If the pool is rectangular and 50 m in length, how does the speed you found compare with his sustained swimming speed of 1.54 m/s during one length of the pool after he has been swimming for 10 min? What might account for the difference?

83. A jetliner flies east for 600.0 km, then turns 30.0° toward the south and flies another 300.0 km. (a) How far is the plane from its starting point? (b) In what direction could the jetliner have flown directly to the same destination (in a straight-line path)? (c) If the jetliner flew at a constant speed of 400.0 km/h, how long did the trip take? (d) Moving at the same speed, how long would the direct flight have taken?

✦84. A pilot wants to fly from Dallas to Oklahoma City, a distance of 330 km at an angle of 10.0° west of north. The pilot heads directly toward Oklahoma City with an air speed of 200 km/h. After flying for 1.0 h, the pilot finds that he is 15 km off course to the west of where he expected to be after one hour assuming there was no wind. (a) What is the velocity and direction of the wind? (b) In what direction should the pilot have headed his plane to fly directly to Oklahoma City without being blown off course?

✦85. In a playground, two slides have different angles of incline θ_1 and θ_2 ($\theta_2 > \theta_1$). A child slides down the first at constant speed; on the second, his acceleration down the slide is a. Assume the coefficient of kinetic friction is the same for both slides. (a) Find a in terms of θ_1, θ_2, and g. (b) Find the numerical value of a for $\theta_1 = 45°$ and $\theta_2 = 61°$.

86. At 3:00 P.M., a bank robber is spotted driving north on I-15 at milepost 126. His speed is 112.0 mi/h. At 3:37 P.M., he is spotted at milepost 185 doing 105.0 mi/h. During this time interval, what are the bank robber's displacement, average velocity, and average acceleration? (Assume a straight highway.)

87. The coefficient of static friction between a block and a horizontal floor is 0.35, while the coefficient of kinetic friction is 0.22. The mass of the block is 4.6 kg and it is initially at rest. (a) What is the minimum horizontal applied force required to make the block start to slide? (b) Once the block is sliding, if you keep pushing on it with the same minimum starting force as in part (a), does the block move with constant velocity or does it accelerate? (c) If it moves with constant velocity, what is its velocity? If it accelerates, what is its acceleration?

✦88. In a movie, a stuntman places himself on the front of a truck as the truck accelerates. The coefficient of friction between the stuntman and the truck is 0.65. The stuntman is not standing on anything but can "stick" to the front of the truck as long as the truck continues to accelerate. What minimum forward acceleration will keep the stuntman on the front of the truck?

✦89. A crate of oranges weighing 180 N rests on a flatbed truck 2.0 m from the back of the truck. The coefficients of friction between the crate and the bed are $\mu_s = 0.30$ and $\mu_k = 0.20$. The truck drives on a straight, level highway at a constant 8.0 m/s. (a) What is the force of friction acting on the crate? (b) If the truck speeds up with an acceleration of 1.0 m/s², what is the force of the friction on the crate? (c) What is the maximum acceleration the truck can have without the crate starting to slide?

90. A bicycle is moving along a straight line. The graph in the figure shows its position from the starting point as a function of time. (a) In which section(s) of the graph does the object have the highest speed? (b) At which time(s) does the object reverse its direction of motion? (c) How far does the object move from $t = 0$ to $t = 3$ s?

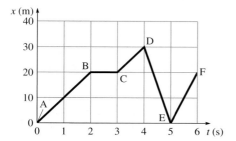

91. A crate of books is to be put on a truck by rolling it up an incline of angle θ using a dolly. The total mass of the crate and the dolly is m. Assume that rolling the dolly up the incline is the same as sliding it up a frictionless surface. (a) What is the magnitude of the *horizontal* force that must be applied just to hold the crate in place on the incline? (b) What horizontal force must be applied to roll the crate up at constant speed? (c) In order to start the dolly moving, it must be accelerated from rest. What horizontal force must be applied to give the crate an acceleration up the incline of magnitude a? (tutorial: cart on ramp)

92. A toy cart of mass m_1 moves on frictionless wheels as it is pulled by a string under tension T. A block of mass m_2 rests on top of the cart. The coefficient of static friction between the cart and the block is μ. Find the maximum tension T that will not cause the block to slide on the cart if the cart rolls on (a) a horizontal surface; (b) up a ramp of angle θ above the horizontal. In both cases, the string is parallel to the surface on which the cart rolls.

93. Imagine a trip where you drive along an east-west highway at 80.0 km/h for 45.0 min and then you turn onto a highway that runs 38.0° north of east and travel at 60.0 km/h for 30.0 min. (a) What is your average velocity for the trip? (b) What is your average velocity on the return trip when you head the opposite way and drive 38.0° south of west at 60.0 km/h for the first 30.0 min and then west at 80.0 km/h for the last 45.0 min?

94. A rocket is launched from rest. After 8.0 min, it is 160 km above the Earth's surface and is moving at a speed of 7.6 km/s. Assuming the rocket moves up in a straight line, what are its (a) average velocity and (b) average acceleration?

95. Based on the information given in Problem 94, is it possible that the rocket moves with constant acceleration? Explain.

96. To pass a physical fitness test, Marcella must run 1000 m at an average speed of 4.00 m/s. She runs the first 500 m at an average of 4.20 m/s. What should be her average speed over the last 500 m in order to finish with an overall average speed of 4.00 m/s?

97. A locomotive pulls a train of 10 identical cars, on a track that runs east-west, with a force of 2.0×10^6 N directed east. What is the force with which the *last* car to the west pulls on the rest of the train?

98. Beatrice needs to drag her suitcase again (see Example 3.8). This time she pulls with a force of 105 N at 38.0° with the horizontal. The coefficients of static and kinetic friction between the suitcase and the floor are 0.273 and 0.117, respectively. (a) Draw an FBD of the suitcase. (b) What is the magnitude of the normal force acting on the suitcase due to the floor? (c) Does the suitcase slide, or does she need to increase her force? (d) If the suitcase slides, what is its acceleration? If it does not slide, to what magnitude should she increase her force?

99. A woman of mass 51 kg is standing in an elevator. (a) If the elevator floor pushes up on her feet with a force of 408 N, what is the acceleration of the elevator? (b) If the elevator is moving at 1.5 m/s as it passes the fourth floor on its way down, what is its speed 4.0 s later?

100. Two blocks lie side by side on a frictionless table. The block on the left is of mass m; the one on the right is of mass $2m$. The block on the right is pushed to the left with a force of magnitude F, pushing the other block in turn. What force does the block on the left exert on the block to its right?

101. A person climbs from a Paris metro station to the street level by walking up a stalled escalator in 94 s. It takes 66 s to ride the same distance when standing on the escalator when it is operating normally. How long would it take for him to climb from the station to the street by walking up the moving escalator?

102. A pilot starting from Athens, New York, wishes to fly to Sparta, New York, which is 320 km from Athens in the direction 20.0° N of E. The pilot heads directly for Sparta and flies at an airspeed of 160 km/h. After flying for 2.0 h, the pilot expects to be at Sparta, but instead he finds himself 20 km due west of Sparta. He has forgotten to correct for the wind. (a) What is the velocity of the plane relative to the air? (b) Find the velocity (magnitude and direction) of the plane relative to the ground. (c) Find the wind speed and direction.

103. Two blocks, masses m_1 and m_2, are connected by a massless cord. If the two blocks are pulled with a constant tension on a frictionless surface by applying a force of magnitude T_2 to a second cord connected to m_2, what is the ratio of the tensions in the two cords T_1/T_2 in terms of the masses?

104. The coefficient of static friction between a brick and a wooden board is 0.40 and the coefficient of kinetic friction between the brick and board is 0.30. You place the brick on the board and slowly lift one end of the board off the ground until the brick starts to slide down the board. (a) What angle does the board make with the ground when the brick starts to slide? (b) What is the acceleration of the brick as it slides down the board?

✦105. In the human nervous system, signals are transmitted along neurons as *action potentials* that travel at speeds of up to 100 m/s. (An action potential is a traveling influx of sodium ions through the membrane of a neuron.) The signal is passed from one neuron to another by the release of neurotransmitters in the synapse. Suppose someone steps on your toe. The pain signal travels along a 1.0-m-long sensory neuron to the spinal column, across a synapse to a second 1.0-m-long neuron, and across a second synapse to the brain. Suppose that the synapses are each 100 nm wide, that it takes 0.10 ms for the signal to cross each synapse, and that the action potentials travel at 100 m/s. (a) At what average speed does the signal cross a synapse? (b) How long does it take the signal to reach the brain? (c) What is the average speed of propagation of the signal?

✦106. An airplane of mass 2800 kg has just lifted off the runway. It is gaining altitude at a constant 2.3 m/s while the horizontal component of its velocity is increasing at a rate of 0.86 m/s². Assume $g = 9.81$ m/s². (a) Find the direction of the force exerted on the airplane by the air. (b) Find the horizontal and vertical components of the plane's acceleration if the force due to the air has the same magnitude but has a direction 2.0° closer to the vertical than its direction in part (a).

✦107. The graph shows the position x of a switch engine in a rail yard as a function of time t. At which of the labeled times t_0 to t_7 is (a) $a_x < 0$, (b) $a_x = 0$, (c) $a_x > 0$, (d) $v_x = 0$, (e) the speed decreasing?

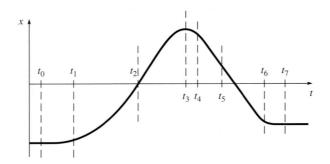

✦108. An elevator starts at rest on the ninth floor. At $t = 0$, a passenger pushes a button to go to another floor. The graph for this problem shows the acceleration a_y of the elevator as a function of time. Let the y-axis point upward. (a) Has the passenger gone to a higher or lower floor? (b) Sketch a graph of the velocity v_y of the elevator versus time. (c) Sketch a graph of the position y of the elevator versus time. (d) If a 63.5-kg person stands on a scale in the elevator, what does the scale read at times t_1, t_2, and t_3?

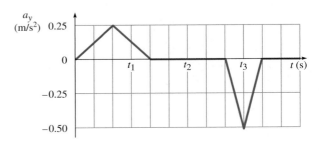

✦109. A helicopter of mass M is lowering a truck of mass m onto the deck of a ship. (a) At first, the helicopter and the truck move downward together (the length of the cable doesn't change). If their downward speed is decreasing at a rate of $0.10g$, what is the tension in the cable? (b) As the truck gets close to the deck, the helicopter stops moving downward. While it hovers, it lets out the cable so that the truck is still moving downward. If the truck's downward speed is decreasing at a rate of $0.10g$, while the helicopter is at rest, what is the tension in the cable?

Answers to Practice Problems

3.1 His displacement is zero, since he ends up at the same place from which he started (home plate).

3.2 $A_x = +16$ km; $A_y = -8.2$ km; $B_x = +17$ km; $B_y = 0$ km; $C_x = -11$ km; $C_y = +47$ km

3.3 77 km/h in the $-x$-direction (west)

3.4 About 100 to 110 km/h in the $+x$-direction (east)

3.5 The velocity is increasing in magnitude, so $\Delta \vec{v}$ and $\vec{a}$ are in the same direction as the velocity (the $-x$-direction). Thus, a_x is negative; $\vec{a}$ and $\Sigma \vec{F}$ are in the $-x$-direction.

3.6 (a) 1.64 m/s directed 33° east of north; (b) 3.0 kN directed 33° east of north

3.7

(a) $a_{\text{av},x} = -3.0$ m/s² where negative sign means the average acceleration is directed to the northwest; (b) $a_x = -4.3$ m/s² (northwest)

3.8 (a) 54 N; (b) 1.8 s

3.9 2.9 m/s

3.10 1.84 kN

3.11 Block 1: $\Sigma F_{1y} = T - m_1 g = 315 \text{ N} - 255 \text{ N} = 60 \text{ N}$; $m_1 a_{1y} = 60 \text{ N}$. Block 2: $\Sigma F_{2y} = m_2 g - T = 412 \text{ N} - 315 \text{ N} = 97 \text{ N}$; $m_2 a_{2y} = 97 \text{ N}$.

3.12 (a) 1.0 m/s; (b) 15 min

3.13 28° S of W; 3.6 min; 130 m

Answers to Checkpoints

3.1 No. The magnitude of the displacement is the shortest possible distance between two points. The distance traveled can be greater than or equal to the displacement, depending on the path taken. In Example 3.1 the displacement is 2.9 km to the north, and the distance traveled is 11.5 km.

3.2 Yes. Average speed is the actual distance traveled divided by the time interval in moving from point A to point B. Average velocity is the displacement from point A to point B divided by the same time interval. The magnitude of the displacement is the *shortest possible* distance from A to B. Thus the average velocity magnitude is equal to or less than the average speed.

3.3a For straight-line motion, the acceleration vector is either in the same or in the opposite direction to the velocity vector.

3.3b The slope of the tangent to a graph of v_x versus time is the instantaneous acceleration a_x at that time.

3.5 (a) 19.5 m/s (b) 1.5 m/s

Motion with Constant Acceleration

A sailplane (or "glider") is a small, unpowered, high-performance aircraft. A sailplane must be initially towed a few thousand feet into the air by a small airplane, after which it relies on regions of upward-moving air such as thermals and ridge currents to ascend further. Suppose a small plane requires about 120 m of runway to take off by itself. When it is towing a sailplane, how much runway does it need? (See p. 118 for the answer.)

- net force and free-body diagrams (Section 2.4)
- position, displacement, velocity, and acceleration (Sections 3.1–3.3)
- Newton's second law (Sections 3.3 and 3.4)
- addition and subtraction of vectors (Sections 2.2, 2.3, and 3.1)
- vector components (Section 2.3)
- internal and external forces (Section 2.5)

4.1   MOTION ALONG A LINE DUE TO A CONSTANT NET FORCE

If the net force acting on an object is constant, then the acceleration of the object is also constant, both in magnitude and direction. A constant acceleration means the velocity vector changes at a constant rate. Now we find how the *position* changes when acceleration is constant.

Two essential relationships between position, velocity, and acceleration enable us to find the position of an object moving along a line with constant acceleration. We write these relationships using these notational conventions:

- Choose axes so that the motion is along one of the axes. Write the position, velocity, and acceleration in terms of their components along that axis.
- At an initial time t_i, the initial position and velocity are x_i and v_{ix}.
- At a later time $t_f = t_i + \Delta t$, the position and velocity are x_f and v_{fx}.

The two essential relationships are

1. Since the acceleration a_x is constant, the change in velocity over a given time interval $\Delta t = t_f - t_i$ is the acceleration—the rate of change of velocity—times the elapsed time:

$$\Delta v_x = v_{fx} - v_{ix} = a_x \Delta t \qquad (4\text{-}1)$$

(if a_x is constant during the entire time interval)

Equation (4-1) is the definition of acceleration [Eq. (3-11)] plus the assumption that a_x is constant.

2. Since the velocity changes linearly with time, the average velocity is given by:

$$v_{av,x} = \tfrac{1}{2}(v_{fx} + v_{ix}) \quad \text{(constant } a_x) \qquad (4\text{-}2)$$

Equation (4-2) is *not* true *in general*, but it is true for constant acceleration. To see why, refer to the $v_x(t)$ graph in Fig. 4.1a. The graph is linear because the acceleration—the slope of the graph—is constant. The displacement during any time interval is represented by the area under the graph. The average velocity is found by forming a rectangle with an area equal to the area under the curve in Fig. 4.1a, because the average velocity should give the same displacement in the same time interval. Figure 4.1b shows that, to make the excluded area above $v_{av,x}$ (triangle 1) equal to the extra area under $v_{av,x}$ (triangle 2), the average velocity must be exactly halfway between the initial and final velocities. Combining Eq. (4-2) with the definition of average velocity,

$$\Delta x = x_f - x_i = v_{av,x} \Delta t \qquad (3\text{-}3)$$

gives our second essential relationship for constant acceleration:

$$\Delta x = \tfrac{1}{2}(v_{fx} + v_{ix})\,\Delta t \qquad (4\text{-}3)$$

(if a_x is constant during the entire time interval)

CONNECTION:

In Chapter 3, we learned that a constant net force produces a constant acceleration and, thus, changes the velocity of an object. Now we learn how the *position* of the object changes as a result of constant acceleration.

(a)

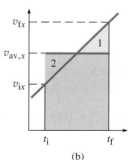
(b)

Figure 4.1 Finding the average velocity when the acceleration is constant.

If the acceleration is *not* constant, there is no reason why the average velocity has to be exactly halfway between the initial and the final velocity. As an illustration, imagine a trip where you drive along a straight highway at 80 km/h for 50 min and then at 60 km/h for 30 min. Your acceleration is zero for the entire trip *except* during the few seconds while you slowed from 80 km/h to 60 km/h. The magnitude of your average velocity is *not* 70 km/h. You spent more time going 80 km/h than you did going 60 km/h, so the magnitude of your average velocity would be greater than 70 km/h.

Other Useful Relationships for Constant Acceleration   Two more useful relationships can be formed among the various quantities (displacement, initial and final velocities, acceleration, and time interval) by eliminating some quantity from Eqs. (4-1) and (4-3). For example, suppose we don't know the final velocity v_{fx}. Then we can solve Eq. (4-1) for v_{fx}, substitute into Eq. (4-3), and simplify:

$$\Delta x = \tfrac{1}{2}(v_{fx} + v_{ix})\,\Delta t = \tfrac{1}{2}[(v_{ix} + a_x \Delta t) + v_{ix}]\,\Delta t$$

$$\Delta x = v_{ix}\,\Delta t + \tfrac{1}{2}a_x(\Delta t)^2 \quad \text{(constant } a_x) \tag{4-4}$$

We can interpret Eq. (4-4) graphically. Figure 4.2 shows a $v_x(t)$ graph for motion with constant acceleration. The displacement that occurs between t_i and a later time t_f is the area under the graph for that time interval. Partition this area into a rectangle plus a triangle. The area of the rectangle is

$$\text{base} \times \text{height} = v_{ix}\,\Delta t$$

The height of the triangle is the change in velocity, which is equal to $a_x \Delta t$. The area of the triangle is

$$\tfrac{1}{2}\text{base} \times \text{height} = \tfrac{1}{2}\Delta t \times a_x\,\Delta t = \tfrac{1}{2}a_x(\Delta t)^2$$

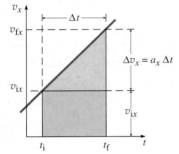

Figure 4.2 Graphical interpretation of Eq. (4-4).

Adding these areas gives Eq. (4-4).

Another useful relationship comes from eliminating the time interval Δt:

$$\Delta x = \frac{1}{2}(v_{fx} + v_{ix})\,\Delta t = \frac{1}{2}(v_{fx} + v_{ix})\left(\frac{v_{fx} - v_{ix}}{a_x}\right) = \frac{v_{fx}^2 - v_{ix}^2}{2a_x}$$

Rearranging terms,

$$v_{fx}^2 - v_{ix}^2 = 2a_x\,\Delta x \quad \text{(constant } a_x) \tag{4-5}$$

✓ CHECKPOINT 4.1

At 3:00 P.M., an airplane is moving due west at 460 km/h. At 3:05 P.M., it is moving due west at 480 km/h. Is its average velocity during the time interval necessarily 470 km/h west? Explain.

Example 4.1

Two Blocks, One Sliding and One Hanging

A block of mass $m_1 = 3.0$ kg rests on a frictionless horizontal surface. A second block of mass $m_2 = 2.0$ kg hangs from an ideal cord of negligible mass, which runs over an ideal pulley and then is connected to the first block (Fig. 4.3). The blocks are released from rest. (a) Find the accelerations of the two blocks after they are released. (b) What is the velocity of the

continued on next page

Example 4.1 continued

Figure 4.3

Two blocks connected by a cord, one supported by a frictionless table and one hanging.

first block 1.2 s after the release of the blocks, assuming the first block does not run out of room on the table and the second block does not land on the floor? (c) How far has block 1 moved during the 1.2-s interval?

Strategy   We consider each block as a separate system and draw an FBD for each. The tension in the cord is the same at both ends of the cord since the cord and pulley are ideal. We choose the $+x$-axis to the right and the $+y$-axis up for both blocks. To find the accelerations of the blocks (which are equal in magnitude because the cord length is fixed), we apply Newton's second law. Then we use equations for constant acceleration to answer (b) and (c). Known: $m_1 = 3.0$ kg; $m_2 = 2.0$ kg; $\vec{v}_i = 0$ for both; $\Delta t = 1.2$ s. To find: $\vec{a}_1$ and $\vec{a}_2$; $\vec{v}_1$ and $\Delta\vec{r}_1$ 1.2 s after release.

Solution   (a) Figure 4.4 shows FBDs for the two blocks. Block 1 slides along the table surface, so the vertical component of acceleration is zero; the normal force must be equal in magnitude to the weight. With the two vertical forces canceling, the only remaining contribution to the net force comes from the pull of the cord, which is horizontal. Then $\Sigma F_{1y} = 0$ and

$$\Sigma F_{1x} = T = m_1 a_{1x}$$

Only vertical forces act on block 2. From the FBD for block 2, we write Newton's second law:

$$\Sigma F_{2y} = T - m_2 g = m_2 a_{2y}$$

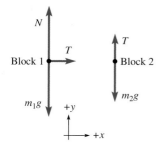

Figure 4.4

FBDs for blocks 1 and 2 with force magnitudes labeled.

The two accelerations have the same magnitude. The acceleration of block 1 is in the $+x$-direction and that of block 2 is in the $-y$-direction. Therefore, we substitute

$$a_{1x} = a \quad \text{and} \quad a_{2y} = -a$$

where a is the magnitude of the acceleration.

Substituting $T = m_1 a$ and $a_{2y} = -a$ into the second equation,

$$m_1 a - m_2 g = -m_2 a$$

Now we solve for a:

$$a = \frac{m_2}{m_1 + m_2} g$$

Substituting the known quantities

$$a = \frac{2.0 \text{ kg}}{3.0 \text{ kg} + 2.0 \text{ kg}} \times 9.80 \text{ m/s}^2 = 3.92 \text{ m/s}^2 \to 3.9 \text{ m/s}^2$$

The arrow indicates rounding to the correct number of significant figures. The acceleration of block 1 is $\vec{a}_1 = 3.9$ m/s^2 to the right and that of block 2 is $\vec{a}_2 = 3.9$ m/s^2 downward.

(b) Next we find the velocity of block 1 after 1.2 s. The problem gives the initial velocity, $v_{ix} = 0$, and the elapsed time, $\Delta t = 1.2$ s.

$$v_{fx} = v_{ix} + a_x \Delta t \tag{4-1}$$
$$= 0 + 3.92 \text{ m/s}^2 \times 1.2 \text{ s} = 4.704 \text{ m/s} \to 4.7 \text{ m/s to the right}$$

(c) The displacement of block 1 during the 1.2-s interval is

$$\Delta x = \tfrac{1}{2}(v_{fx} + v_{ix}) \Delta t \tag{4-3}$$
$$= \tfrac{1}{2}(4.704 \text{ m/s} + 0) \times 1.2 \text{ s} = 2.82 \text{ m} \to 2.8 \text{ m to the right}$$

Discussion   Quick check: the average velocity of block 1 during the 1.2-s interval is $v_{av,x} = \Delta x/\Delta t = (2.82 \text{ m})/(1.2 \text{ s}) = 2.35$ m/s, which is halfway between the initial velocity ($v_{ix} = 0$) and the final velocity ($v_{fx} = 4.7$ m/s), as it must be for constant acceleration. An alternative solution for (c) is to calculate the displacement from Eq. (4-4):

$$\Delta x = v_{ix} \Delta t + \tfrac{1}{2}a_x(\Delta t)^2 = 0 + \tfrac{1}{2}(3.92 \text{ m/s}^2)(1.2 \text{ s})^2 = 2.8 \text{ m}$$

Practice Problem 4.1   Displacement at an Earlier Time

What is the displacement of the blocks from their initial positions 0.40 s after they are released?

Example 4.2

Hauling a Crate Up to a Third-Floor Window

A student is moving into a dorm room on the third floor and he decides to use a block and tackle arrangement (Fig. 4.5) to move a crate of mass 91 kg from the ground up to his window. If the breaking strength of the available rope is 550 N, what is the minimum time required to haul the crate to the level of the window, 30.0 m above the ground, without breaking the rope?

Strategy The tension in the rope is T and is the same at both ends or anywhere along the rope, assuming the rope and pulleys are ideal. Two pieces of rope support the lower pulley, each pulling upward with a force of magnitude T. The gravitational force acts downward. We draw an FBD for the system consisting of the crate and the lower pulley and set the tension equal to the breaking force of the rope to find the maximum possible acceleration of the crate. Then we use the maximum acceleration to find the minimum time to move the required distance to the third-floor window. We choose the y-axis to be upward. Known: $m = 91$ kg; $\Delta y = 30.0$ m; $T_{max} = 550$ N; $v_{iy} = 0$. To find: Δt, the time to raise the crate 30.0 m with the maximum tension in the cable.

Solution From the FBD (Fig. 4.6), if the forces acting up are greater than the force acting down, the net force is upward and the crate's acceleration is upward. In terms of components, with the +y-direction chosen to be upward,

$$\sum F_y = T + T - mg = ma_y$$

Solving for the acceleration,

$$a_y = \frac{T + T - mg}{m}$$

Figure 4.6

FBD for the crate and lower pulley. (This system is outlined by dashed lines in Fig. 4.5.)

Setting $T = 550$ N, the maximum possible value before the cable breaks, and substituting the other known values:

$$a_y = \frac{550 \text{ N} + 550 \text{ N} - 91 \text{ kg} \times 9.80 \text{ m/s}^2}{91 \text{ kg}} = 2.288 \text{ m/s}^2$$

The time to move the crate up a distance Δy starting from rest can be found from

$$\Delta y = v_{iy}\,\Delta t + \tfrac{1}{2}a_y(\Delta t)^2 \qquad (4\text{-}4)$$

Setting $v_{iy} = 0$ and solving for Δt, we find

$$\Delta t = \pm\sqrt{\frac{2\,\Delta y}{a_y}}$$

Our equation applies only for $\Delta t \geq 0$ (the crate reaches the window *after* it leaves the ground). Taking the positive root and substituting numerical values,

$$\Delta t = \sqrt{\frac{2 \times 30.0 \text{ m}}{2.288 \text{ m/s}^2}} = 5.1 \text{ s}$$

This is the minimum possible to haul the crate up without breaking the rope.

Discussion In reality, the student is not likely to achieve this *minimum possible* time. To do so would mean pulling the rope at an unrealistic speed. At the end of the 5.1-s interval, $v_{fy} = 2.288$ m/s$^2 \times 5.1$ s = 12 m/s! More likely, the student would hoist the crate at a roughly constant velocity (except at the beginning, to get it moving, and at the end, to let it come to rest). For motion with a constant velocity, the tension in the rope would be equal to half the weight of the crate (450 N).

Practice Problem 4.2   Hauling the Crate with a Single Pulley

If only a single pulley, attached to the beam above the fourth floor, were available and if the student had a few friends to help him pull on the cable, could they haul the crate up to the third-floor window using the same rope? If so, what is the minimum time required to do so?

Figure 4.5

Block and tackle setup.

Example 4.3

Displacement of a Motorboat

A motorboat starts from rest at a dock and heads due east with a constant acceleration of magnitude 2.8 m/s^2. After traveling for 140 m, the motor is throttled down to slow down the boat at 1.2 m/s^2 (while still moving east) until its speed is 16 m/s. Just as the boat attains a speed of 16 m/s, it passes a buoy due east of the dock. (a) Sketch a qualitative graph of $v_x(t)$ for the motorboat from the dock to the buoy. Let the +x-axis point east. (b) What is the distance between the dock and the buoy?

Strategy   This problem involves two different values of acceleration, so it must be divided into two subproblems. The equations for constant acceleration cannot be applied to a time interval during which the acceleration changes. But for each of two time intervals, the acceleration of the boat is constant: from t_1 to t_2, $a_{1x} = +2.8$ m/s^2; from t_2 to t_3, $a_{2x} = -1.2$ m/s^2. The two subproblems are connected by the position and velocity of the boat at the instant the acceleration changes. This will be reflected in the graph of $v_x(t)$: It will consist of two different straight-line segments with different slopes that connect with the same value of v_x at time t_2.

For the subproblem 1, the boat speeds up with a constant acceleration of 2.8 m/s^2 to the east. We know the acceleration, the displacement (140 m east), and the initial velocity: the boat starts from rest, so the initial velocity v_{1x} is zero. We need to calculate the final velocity v_{2x}, which then becomes the initial velocity for the second subproblem. The boat is always headed to the east, so we let east be the positive x-direction.

Subproblem 1:

Known: $v_{1x} = 0$; $a_{1x} = +2.8$ m/s^2; $\Delta x_{21} = x_2 - x_1 = 140$ m.

To find: v_{2x}.

For subproblem 2, we know acceleration, final velocity v_{3x}, and we have just found the initial velocity v_{2x} from subproblem 1. Because the boat is slowing down, its acceleration is in the direction opposite its velocity; therefore, $\vec{a}_2$ is in the negative x-direction ($a_{2x} < 0$). From these three quantities we can find the displacement of the boat during the second time interval.

Subproblem 2:

Known: v_{2x} from subproblem 1; $a_{2x} = -1.2$ m/s^2; $v_{3x} = +16$ m/s.

To find: $\Delta x_{32} = x_3 - x_2$.

Adding the displacements for the two time intervals gives the total displacement. The magnitude of the total displacement is the distance between the dock and the buoy.

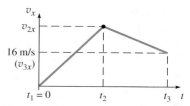

Figure 4.7
Graph of v_x versus t for the motorboat.

Solution   (a) The graph starts with $v_x = 0$ at $t = t_1$. We choose $t_1 = 0$ for simplicity. The graph is a straight line with slope +2.8 m/s^2 until $t = t_2$. Then, starting from where the graph left off, the graph continues as a straight line with slope -1.2 m/s^2 until the graph reaches $v_x = 16$ m/s at $t = t_3$. Figure 4.7 shows the $v_x(t)$ graph. It is not quantitatively accurate because we have not calculated the values of t_2 and t_3.

(b1) To find v_{2x} without knowing the time interval, we eliminate Δt from Eqs. (4-1) and (4-3) for constant acceleration:

$$\Delta x_{21} = \frac{1}{2}(v_{2x} + v_{1x})\,\Delta t = \frac{1}{2}(v_{2x} + v_{1x})\left(\frac{v_{2x} - v_{1x}}{a_{1x}}\right) = \frac{v_{2x}^2 - v_{1x}^2}{2a_{1x}}$$

Solving for v_{2x},

$$v_{2x} = \pm\sqrt{v_{1x}^2 + 2a_{1x}\,\Delta x} = \pm\sqrt{0 + 2 \times 2.8 \text{ m/s}^2 \times 140 \text{ m}}$$
$$= \pm 28 \text{ m/s}$$

The boat is moving east, in the +x-direction, so the correct sign here is positive: $v_{2x} = +28$ m/s.

(b2) The final velocity for the first interval (v_{2x}) is the *initial* velocity for the second interval. The final velocity is v_{3x}. Using the same equation just derived for this time interval,

$$\Delta x = \frac{v_{3x}^2 - v_{2x}^2}{2a_{2x}} = \frac{(16 \text{ m/s})^2 - (28 \text{ m/s})^2}{2 \times (-1.2 \text{ m/s}^2)} = +220 \text{ m}$$

The total displacement is

$$x_3 - x_1 = (x_3 - x_2) + (x_2 - x_1) = 220 \text{ m} + 140 \text{ m} = +360 \text{ m}$$

The buoy is 360 m from the dock.

Discussion   The natural division of the problem into two parts occurs because the boat has two different constant accelerations during two different time periods. In problems that can be subdivided in this way, the final velocity and position found in the first part becomes the initial velocity and position for the second part.

Practice Problem 4.3   Time to Reach the Buoy

What is the time required by the boat in Example 4.3 to reach the buoy?

Example 4.4

Towing a Glider

What length runway does the plane need?

A small plane of mass 760 kg requires 120 m of runway to take off by itself. (120 m is the horizontal displacement of the plane just before it lifts off the runway, not the entire length of the runway.) As a simplified model, ignore friction and drag forces and assume the plane's engine exerts a constant forward force on the plane. (a) When the plane is towing a 330-kg glider, how much runway does it need? (b) If the final speed of the plane just before it lifts off the runway is 28 m/s, what is the tension in the tow cable while the plane and glider are moving along the runway?

Strategy   We draw FBDs for the two cases: plane alone, then plane + glider. The motion in both cases is horizontal (along the runway), because we are told the displacement *before it lifts off the runway*. Until the plane begins to lift off the runway, its vertical acceleration component is zero. We need not be concerned with the vertical forces (gravity, the normal force, and lift—the upward force on the plane's wings due to the air) since they cancel one another to produce zero vertical acceleration. We use Newton's second law to compare the accelerations in the two cases and then use the accelerations to compare the displacements.

Solution   (a) When the plane takes off by itself, four forces act on it (Fig. 4.8). Three are vertical and the third—the thrust due to the engine—is horizontal. Choosing the x-axis to be horizontal, Newton's second law says

$$\sum F_{1x} = F = m_1 a_{1x}$$

where F is the thrust, m_1 is the plane's mass, and a_{1x} is its horizontal acceleration component.

When the glider is towed, we can consider the plane, glider, and cable to be a single system (Fig. 4.9). There is

still only one horizontal external force and it is the same thrust as before. The tension in the cable is an *internal* force. Therefore,

$$\sum F_{2x} = F = (m_1 + m_2)a_x$$

where $m_1 + m_2$ is the total mass of the system (plane mass m_1 plus glider mass m_2) and a_x is the horizontal acceleration component of plane and glider. We ignore the mass of the cable.

The problem statement gives neither the thrust nor either of the accelerations. We can continue by setting the thrusts equal and finding the ratio of the accelerations:

$$m_1 a_{1x} = (m_1 + m_2)a_x \quad \Rightarrow \quad \frac{a_x}{a_{1x}} = \frac{m_1}{m_1 + m_2}$$

The magnitude of the acceleration is inversely proportional to the mass of the system for the same net force.

How is the acceleration related to the runway distance? The plane must get to the same final speed in order to lift off the runway. From our two basic constant acceleration equations

$$\Delta v_x = v_{fx} - v_{ix} = a_x \Delta t \tag{4-1}$$

$$\Delta x = \tfrac{1}{2}(v_{fx} + v_{ix})\,\Delta t \tag{4-3}$$

we can substitute $v_{ix} = 0$ and eliminate Δt to find

$$\Delta x = \tfrac{1}{2}(v_{fx} + 0)\left(\frac{v_{fx}}{a_x}\right) = \frac{v_{fx}^2}{2a_x}$$

In both cases, the displacement is inversely proportional to the acceleration and the acceleration is inversely proportional to the mass of the system. Therefore, the displacement is *directly* proportional to the mass. Letting $\Delta x_1 = 120$ m be the displacement of the plane without the glider, we can set up a proportion:

$$\frac{\Delta x}{\Delta x_1} = \frac{a_{1x}}{a_x} = \frac{m_1 + m_2}{m_1} = \frac{1090 \text{ kg}}{760 \text{ kg}} = 1.434$$

$$\Delta x = 1.434 \times 120 \text{ m} = 172.08 \text{ m} \rightarrow 170 \text{ m}$$

(b) The final speed given enables us to find the acceleration:

$$\Delta x = \frac{v_{fx}^2}{2a_x} \quad \text{or} \quad a_x = \frac{v_{fx}^2}{2\,\Delta x}$$

With $v_{fx} = 28$ m/s, $v_{ix} = 0$, and $\Delta x = 172.08$ m,

$$a_x = \frac{(28 \text{ m/s})^2}{2 \times 172.08 \text{ m}} = 2.278 \text{ m/s}^2$$

The tension in the cable is the only horizontal force acting on the glider. Therefore,

$$\sum F_x = T = m_2 a_x = 330 \text{ kg} \times 2.278 \text{ m/s}^2 = 751.7 \text{ N} \rightarrow 750 \text{ N}$$

Figure 4.8

FBD for the plane.

Figure 4.9

FBD for the system plane + glider.

continued on next page

Example 4.4 continued

Discussion   This solution is based on a simplified model, so we can only regard the answers as approximate. Nevertheless, it illustrates Newton's second law. The same net force produces an acceleration inversely proportional to the mass of the object on which it acts. Here we have the same net force acting on two different objects: first the plane alone, then the plane and glider together.

Alternatively, we can look at forces acting only on the plane. When towing the glider, the cable pulls backward on the plane. The net force *on the plane* is smaller, so its acceleration is smaller. The smaller acceleration means that it takes more time to reach takeoff speed and travels a longer distance before lifting off the runway.

Practice Problem 4.4   Engine Thrust

What is the thrust provided by the airplane's engines in Example 4.4?

4.2   VISUALIZING MOTION ALONG A LINE WITH CONSTANT ACCELERATION

Motion Diagrams   In Fig. 4.10, three carts move in the same direction with three different values of constant acceleration. The position of each cart is depicted in a **motion diagram** as it would appear in a stroboscopic photograph with pictures taken at equal time intervals (here, the time interval is 1.0 s).

The yellow cart has zero acceleration and, therefore, constant velocity. During each 1.0-s time interval its displacement is the same: 1.0 m/s × 1.0 s = 1.0 m to the right.

The red cart has a constant acceleration of 0.2 m/s^2 to the right. Although m/s^2 is normally read "meters per second squared," it can be useful to think of it as "m/s per second": the cart's velocity changes by 0.2 m/s during each 1.0-s time interval. In this case, acceleration is in the same direction as the velocity, so the velocity increases (Fig. 4.11a). The displacement of the cart during successive 1.0-s time intervals gets larger and larger.

The blue cart experiences a constant acceleration of 0.2 m/s^2 in the −x-direction— the direction *opposite* to the velocity. The magnitude of the velocity then decreases (Fig. 4.11b); during each 1.0-s interval, the speed decreases by 0.2 m/s. Now the displacements during 1.0-s intervals get smaller and smaller.

Positions of the carts at 1.0-s intervals

Figure 4.10 Each cart is shown as if photographs were taken at 1.0-s time intervals. The arrows above each cart indicate the instantaneous velocities.

Figure 4.11 (a) If the acceleration is in the same direction as the velocity, then the change in velocity ($\Delta\vec{v} = \vec{a}\,\Delta t$) is also in the same direction as the velocity. The result is an increase in the magnitude of the velocity: the object speeds up. (b) If the acceleration is opposite in direction to the velocity, then the change in velocity ($\Delta\vec{v} = \vec{a}\,\Delta t$) is also opposite in direction to the velocity. The result is a decrease in the magnitude of the velocity: the object slows down.

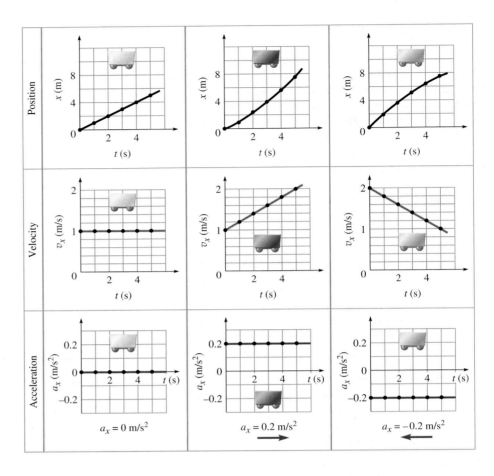

Figure 4.12 Graphs of position, velocity, and acceleration for the carts of Fig. 4.10.

Graphs   Figure 4.12 shows graphs of $x(t)$, $v_x(t)$, and $a_x(t)$ for each of the carts. The acceleration graphs are horizontal since each of the carts has a constant acceleration. All three v_x graphs are straight lines. Since a_x is the rate of change of v_x, the slope of the v_x graph at any value of t is a_x at that value of t. With constant acceleration, the slope is the same everywhere and the graph is linear. Remember that a positive a_x does mean that v_x is increasing, but not necessarily that the *speed* is increasing. If v_x is negative, then a positive a_x indicates a *decreasing* speed. (See Conceptual Example 3.5.) Speed is increasing when the acceleration and velocity are in the same direction (a_x and v_x both positive *or* both negative). Speed is decreasing when acceleration and velocity are in opposite directions—when a_x and v_x have opposite signs.

The position graph is linear for the yellow cart because it has constant velocity. For the red cart, the $x(t)$ graph curves with increasing slope, showing that v_x is increasing. For the blue cart, the $x(t)$ graph curves with decreasing slope, showing that v_x is decreasing.

Example 4.5

Drag Racing Spaceships

Two spaceships are moving from the same starting point in the +x-direction with constant accelerations. In component form, the silver spaceship starts with an initial velocity of +2.00 km/s and has an acceleration of +0.400 km/s². The black spaceship starts with a velocity of +6.00 km/s and has

an acceleration of −0.400 km/s². (a) Find the time at which the silver spaceship just overtakes the black spaceship. (b) Sketch graphs of $v_x(t)$ for the two spaceships. (c) Sketch a motion diagram (similar to Fig. 4.10) showing the positions of the two spaceships at 1.0-s intervals.

continued on next page

Example 4.5 continued

Strategy We can find the positions of the spaceships at later times from the initial velocities and the accelerations. At first, the black spaceship is moving faster, so it pulls out ahead. Later, the silver ship overtakes the black ship at the instant their *positions are equal*.

Solution (a) The position of either spaceship at a later time is given by Eq. (4-4):

$$x_f = x_i + \Delta x = x_i + v_{ix}\,\Delta t + \tfrac{1}{2}a_x(\Delta t)^2$$

We set the final position of the silver spaceship equal to that of the black spaceship ($x_{fs} = x_{fb}$):

$$x_{is} + v_{isx}\,\Delta t + \tfrac{1}{2}a_{sx}(\Delta t)^2 = x_{ib} + v_{ibx}\,\Delta t + \tfrac{1}{2}a_{bx}(\Delta t)^2$$

Although the subscripts might look forbidding, they are there to help you keep from mixing up similar quantities. The x subscripts are there to remind you that we are dealing with x-components. A skilled problem-solver must be able to come up with algebraic symbols that are explicit and unambiguous.

The initial positions are the same: $x_{is} = x_{ib}$. Subtracting the initial positions from each side, moving all terms to one side, and factoring out one power of Δt yields

$$\Delta t(v_{isx} + \tfrac{1}{2}a_{sx}\,\Delta t - v_{ibx} - \tfrac{1}{2}a_{bx}\,\Delta t) = 0$$

This equation has two solutions—there are two times at which the spaceships are at the same position. One solution is $\Delta t = 0$. We already knew that the two spaceships started at the same *initial* position. The other solution, which gives the time at which one spaceship overtakes the other, is found by setting the expression in parentheses equal to zero. Solving for Δt,

$$\Delta t = \frac{2(v_{isx} - v_{ibx})}{a_{bx} - a_{sx}} = \frac{2 \times (2.00\ \text{km/s} - 6.00\ \text{km/s})}{-0.400\ \text{km/s}^2 - 0.400\ \text{km/s}^2} = 10.0\ \text{s}$$

The silver spaceship overtakes the black spaceship 10.0 s after they leave the starting point.

(b) Figure 4.13 shows the $v_x(t)$ graphs with $t_i = 0$. Note that the area under the graphs from t_i to t_f is the same in the two graphs: the spaceships have the same displacement during that interval.

(c) Equation (4-4) can be used to find the position of each spaceship as a function of time. Choosing $x_i = 0$, $t_i = 0$, and $t = t_f$, the position at time t is

$$x(t) = 0 + v_{ix}t + \tfrac{1}{2}a_x t^2$$

Figure 4.14 shows the data table calculated this way and the corresponding motion diagram.

Discussion Quick check: the two ships must have the same displacement at $\Delta t = 10.0$.

$$\Delta x_s = v_{isx}\,\Delta t + \tfrac{1}{2}a_{sx}(\Delta t)^2$$
$$= 2.00\ \text{km/s} \times 10.0\ \text{s} + \tfrac{1}{2} \times 0.400\ \text{km/s}^2 \times (10.0\ \text{s})^2$$
$$= 40.0\ \text{km}$$
$$\Delta x_b = v_{ibx}\,\Delta t + \tfrac{1}{2}a_{bx}(\Delta t)^2$$
$$= 6.00\ \text{km/s} \times 10.0\ \text{s} + \tfrac{1}{2} \times (-0.400\ \text{km/s}^2) \times (10.0\ \text{s})^2$$
$$= 40.0\ \text{km}$$

Practice Problem 4.5   Time to Reach the Same Velocity

When do the two spaceships have the same *velocity*? What is the value of the velocity then?

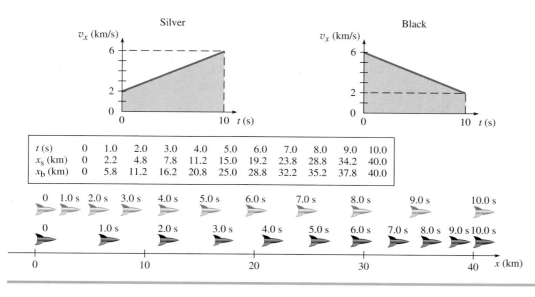

Figure 4.13

Graphs of v_x versus t for the silver and black spaceships. The shaded area under each graph represents the displacement Δx during the time interval.

t (s)	0	1.0	2.0	3.0	4.0	5.0	6.0	7.0	8.0	9.0	10.0
x_s (km)	0	2.2	4.8	7.8	11.2	15.0	19.2	23.8	28.8	34.2	40.0
x_b (km)	0	5.8	11.2	16.2	20.8	25.0	28.8	32.2	35.2	37.8	40.0

Figure 4.14

Calculated positions of the spaceships at 1.0-s time intervals and a motion diagram.

Example 4.6

A Pulley, an Incline, and Two Blocks

A block of mass $m_1 = 2.60$ kg rests on an incline that is angled at 30.0° above the horizontal (Fig. 4.15). An ideal cord is connected from block 1 over an ideal, frictionless pulley to another block of mass $m_2 = 2.20$ kg that is hanging 2.00 m above the ground. The coefficient of kinetic friction between the incline and block 1 is 0.180. The blocks are initially at rest. (a) How long does it take for block 2 to reach the ground? (b) Sketch a motion diagram for block 2 with a time interval of 0.5 s.

Figure 4.15

Block on an incline connected to a hanging block by a cord passing over a pulley.

Strategy The problem says that the blocks start from rest and that block 2 hits the floor, so block 2's acceleration is downward and block 1's is up the incline. For block 1, we choose axes parallel and perpendicular to the incline so that its acceleration has only one nonzero component. The magnitudes of the accelerations of the two blocks are equal since they are connected by an ideal cord that does not stretch. Since the cord and pulley are ideal, the tension is the same at the two ends.

Solution (a) We start by drawing separate FBDs for each block (Figs. 4.16 and 4.17). Since block 1 slides up the incline, the frictional force $\vec{f}_k$ acts down the incline to oppose the sliding. The gravitational force on block 1 is resolved into two components, one along the incline and one perpendicular to the incline.

Using the FBDs, we write Newton's second law in component form for each block. Block 1 has no acceleration component perpendicular to the incline. It does not sink into

Figure 4.16

FBD for block 1 with force magnitudes labeled.

Figure 4.17

FBD for block 2 with the downward direction chosen as +x.

the incline or rise above it; it can only slide along the incline. Thus, the net force on block 1 in the direction perpendicular to the incline—the direction we have chosen as the y-axis for block 1—is zero.

$$\sum F_y = N - m_1 g \cos \theta = 0$$

or

$$N = m_1 g \cos \theta$$

Here $\theta = 30.0°$. Along the incline, in the x-direction for block 1, the acceleration is nonzero:

$$\sum F_x = T - m_1 g \sin \theta - f_k = m_1 a_x$$

The kinetic frictional force is related to the normal force:

$$f_k = \mu_k N = \mu_k m_1 g \cos \theta$$

By substitution,

$$T - m_1 g \sin \theta - \mu_k m_1 g \cos \theta = m_1 a_x \qquad (1)$$

For block 2, we choose an x-axis pointing downward. Doing so simplifies the solution, since then the two blocks have the same a_x. Applying Newton's second law,

$$\sum F_x = m_2 g - T = m_2 a_x \qquad (2)$$

The tension in the cord T and the x-component of acceleration a_x are both unknown in Eqs. (1) and (2). We solve for T in Eq. (2) and substitute into Eq. (1):

$$T = m_2 g - m_2 a_x = m_2(g - a_x)$$
$$m_2(g - a_x) - m_1 g \sin \theta - \mu_k m_1 g \cos \theta = m_1 a_x$$

Rearranging and solving for a_x yields

$$a_x = \frac{m_2 - m_1(\sin \theta + \mu_k \cos \theta)}{m_1 + m_2} g \qquad (3)$$

Substituting the known and given values,

$$a_x = \frac{2.20 \text{ kg} - 2.60 \text{ kg} \times (0.50 + 0.180 \times 0.866)}{2.60 \text{ kg} + 2.20 \text{ kg}} \times 9.80 \text{ m/s}^2$$

$$= 1.01 \text{ m/s}^2$$

Block 2 has a distance of 2.00 m to travel starting from rest with a constant downward acceleration of 1.01 m/s². From Eq. (4-4) with $v_{ix} = 0$,

$$\Delta x = \tfrac{1}{2} a_x (\Delta t)^2$$

The time to travel that distance is

$$\Delta t = \sqrt{\frac{2\Delta x}{a_x}} = \sqrt{\frac{2 \times 2.00 \text{ m}}{1.01 \text{ m/s}^2}} = 2.0 \text{ s}$$

continued on next page

Example 4.6 continued

(b) Figure 4.18 shows the motion diagram for block 2. Choosing $x_i = 0$ and $t_i = 0$, the position as a function of time is $x = \frac{1}{2}a_x t^2$.

Figure 4.18

Motion diagram for block 2.

t (s)	x (m)
0	0
0.5	0.125
1.0	0.50
1.5	1.125
2.0	2.0

Discussion One advantage to solving for a_x algebraically in Eq. (3) before substituting numerical values is that dimensional analysis can easily be used to check for errors. In Eq. (3), the quantity in parentheses is dimensionless—the values of trigonometric functions are pure numbers as are coefficients of friction. Therefore, the numerator is the sum of two quantities with dimensions of force, the denominator is the sum of two masses, and force divided by mass gives an acceleration.

What if the problem did not tell us the directions of the blocks' accelerations? We could figure it out by comparing the force with which gravity pulls down on block 2 ($m_2 g$) with the component of the gravitational force pulling block 1 down the incline ($m_1 g \sin \theta$). Whichever is greater "wins the tug-of-war," assuming that static friction doesn't prevent the blocks from starting to slide. Once we know the direction of block 1's acceleration, we can determine the direction of the kinetic frictional force. If block 1 is not initially at rest, the kinetic frictional force opposes the direction of sliding, even though that may be opposite to the direction of the acceleration.

Practice Problem 4.6   More Fun with a Pulley and an Incline

Suppose that $m_1 = 3.8$ kg and $m_2 = 1.2$ kg and the coefficient of kinetic friction is 0.18. The blocks are released from rest and block 1 starts to slide. (a) Does block 1 slide up or down the incline? (b) In which direction does the kinetic frictional force act? (c) Find the acceleration of block 1.

√ CHECKPOINT 4.2

Is it ever useful to choose the x- and y-axes so the x-axis is not horizontal? If yes, give an example.

4.3   FREE FALL

Suppose you are standing on a bridge over a deep gorge. If you drop a stone into the gorge, how fast does it fall? You know from experience that it does not fall at a constant velocity; the longer it falls, the faster it goes. A better question is: What is the stone's acceleration?

First, let us simplify the problem. If the stone were moving very fast, an appreciable force of air resistance would oppose its motion. When it is not falling so fast, air resistance is negligibly small. If air resistance is negligible, the only appreciable force is that of gravity. In **free fall**, no forces act on an object other than the gravitational force that makes the object fall. On Earth, free fall is an idealization since there is always *some* air resistance.

Free-Fall Acceleration What is the acceleration of an object in free fall? More massive objects are harder to accelerate: The acceleration of an object subjected to a given force is inversely proportional to its mass. However, the stronger gravitational force on a more massive object compensates for its greater inertia, giving it the same acceleration as a less massive object. The gravitational force on an object is $\vec{\mathbf{W}} = m\vec{\mathbf{g}}$, where the gravitational field vector $\vec{\mathbf{g}}$ has magnitude g and is directed downward. From Newton's second law,

$$\sum \vec{\mathbf{F}} = m\vec{\mathbf{g}} = m\vec{\mathbf{a}}$$

CONNECTION:

Free fall is an example of motion with constant acceleration when air resistance is negligible.

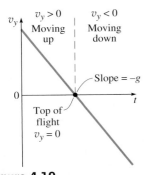

Figure 4.19

Graph of v_y versus t for an object thrown upward.

In free fall, $a_y = -g$ (if the y-axis points up).

Dividing by the mass yields

$$\vec{a} = \vec{g} \qquad (4\text{-}6)$$

The acceleration of an object in free fall is $\vec{g}$, regardless of the object's mass. Since $1\ \text{N} = 1\ \text{kg·m/s}^2$, $1\ \text{N/kg} = 1\ \text{m/s}^2$. An object in free fall has an acceleration equal to the local value of $\vec{g}$. Unless another value of g is given in a particular problem, please assume that the magnitude of the free-fall acceleration near Earth's surface is

$$a_{\text{free-fall}} = g = 9.80\ \frac{\text{N}}{\text{kg}} = 9.80\ \frac{\cancel{\text{N}}}{\cancel{\text{kg}}} \times 1\frac{\cancel{\text{kg}}\text{·m/s}^2}{\cancel{\text{N}}} = 9.80\ \text{m/s}^2$$

The vector $\vec{g}$ is sometimes called *the free-fall acceleration*, because it is the acceleration of an object near the surface of the Earth when the *only* force acting is gravity.

When dealing with vertical motion, the y-axis is usually chosen to be positive pointing upward. (In two-dimensional motion, the x-axis is often used for the horizontal direction and the y-axis for the vertical direction.) The direction of the acceleration is down, so in free fall, $a_y = -g$ (if the y-axis points up). The same techniques and equations used for other constant acceleration situations are used with free fall.

Earth's gravity always pulls downward, so the acceleration of an object in free fall is always downward and constant in magnitude, *regardless of whether the object is moving up, down, or is at rest, and independent of its speed.* If the object is moving downward, the downward acceleration makes it speed up; if it is moving upward, the downward acceleration makes it slow down.

Acceleration at Highest Point   If an object is thrown straight up, its velocity is zero at the highest point of its flight. Why? On the way up, the y-component of its velocity v_y is positive if the positive y-axis is pointing up. On the way down, v_y is negative. Since v_y changes continuously, it must pass through zero to change sign (Fig. 4.19). At the highest point, the velocity is zero but the *acceleration* is *not* zero. If the acceleration were to suddenly become zero at the top of flight, the velocity would no longer change; the object would get *stuck at the top* rather than fall back down. The velocity is zero at the top but it does not *stay* zero; it keeps changing at the same rate.

 CHECKPOINT 4.3

Is it possible for an object in free fall to be moving upward?

Example 4.7

Throwing Stones

Standing on a bridge, you throw a stone straight upward. The stone hits a stream, 44.1 m below the point at which you release it, 4.00 s later. (a) What is the velocity of the stone just after it leaves your hand? (b) What is the velocity of the stone just before it hits the water? (c) Draw a motion diagram for the stone, showing its position at 0.1-s intervals during the first 0.9 s of its motion. (d) Sketch graphs of $y(t)$ and $v_y(t)$. The positive y-axis points up.

Strategy   Ignoring air resistance, the stone is in free fall once your hand releases it and until it hits the water. Therefore,

for the time interval during which the stone is in free fall, the initial velocity is the velocity of the stone *just after* it leaves your hand and the final velocity is the velocity *just before* it hits the water. The FBD (Fig. 4.20) shows the only force acting during free fall: the gravitational force $\vec{W} = m\vec{g}$. From Newton's second law, $\Sigma\vec{F} = \vec{W} = m\vec{g} = m\vec{a}$. During free fall, the stone's acceleration is constant and equal to $\vec{g}$, which we assume to be 9.80 m/s^2

Figure 4.20

FBD for the stone.

continued on next page

Example 4.7 continued

downward. Known: $a_y = -9.80$ m/s^2; $\Delta y = -44.1$ m at $\Delta t = 4.00$ s. To find: v_{iy} and v_{fy}.

Solution (a) Equation (4-4) can be used to solve for v_{iy} since all the other quantities in it (Δy, Δt, and a_y) are known.

$$\Delta y = v_{iy}\,\Delta t + \tfrac{1}{2}a_y\,(\Delta t)^2$$

Solving for v_{iy},

$$v_{iy} = \frac{\Delta y}{\Delta t} - \frac{1}{2}a_y\,\Delta t = \frac{-44.1\text{ m}}{4.00\text{ s}} - \frac{1}{2}(-9.80\text{ m/s}^2 \times 4.00\text{ s}) \quad (1)$$

$$= -11.0\text{ m/s} + 19.6\text{ m/s} = 8.6\text{ m/s}$$

The initial velocity is 8.6 m/s upward.

(b) The change in v_y is $a_y\Delta t$ from Eq. (4-1):

$$v_{fy} = v_{iy} + a_y\,\Delta t$$

Substituting the expression for v_{iy} found previously,

$$v_{fy} = \left(\frac{\Delta y}{\Delta t} - \frac{1}{2}a_y\,\Delta t\right) + a_y\,\Delta t = \frac{\Delta y}{\Delta t} + \frac{1}{2}a_y\,\Delta t \quad (2)$$

$$= \frac{-44.1\text{ m}}{4.00\text{ s}} + \frac{1}{2}(-9.80\text{ m/s}^2 \times 4.00\text{ s})$$

$$= -11.0\text{ m/s} - 19.6\text{ m/s} = -30.6\text{ m/s}$$

The final velocity is 30.6 m/s downward.

(c) Choosing $y_i = 0$ and $t_i = 0$, the position of the stone as a function of time is

$$y(t) = v_{iy}t + \tfrac{1}{2}a_y t^2$$

The motion diagram is shown in Fig. 4.21.

(d) The graphs are shown in Fig. 4.22.

Discussion The final speed is greater than the initial speed, as expected. Equations (1) and (2) have a direct interpretation, which is a good check on their validity. The first term, $\Delta y/\Delta t$, is the average velocity of the stone during the 4.00 s of free fall. The second term, $\tfrac{1}{2}a_y\,\Delta t$, is *half* the change in v_y since $\Delta v_y = a_y\,\Delta t$. Because the acceleration is constant, the average velocity is halfway between the initial and final velocities. Therefore, the initial velocity is the average velocity minus half of the change, and the final velocity is the average velocity plus half of the change.

Figure 4.21

Motion diagram for a stone moving straight up.

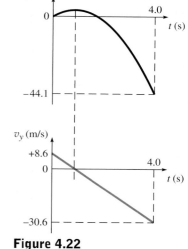

Figure 4.22

Graphs of $y(t)$ and $v_y(t)$ for the stone.

Practice Problem 4.7   Height Attained by Stone

(a) How high above the bridge does the stone go? [*Hint:* What is v_y at the highest point?] (b) If you dropped the stone instead of throwing it, how long would it take to hit the water?

4.4   MOTION OF PROJECTILES

If an object moves in the *xy*-plane with constant acceleration, then both a_x and a_y are constant. By looking separately at the motion along two perpendicular axes, the *y*-direction and the *x*-direction, each component becomes a one-dimensional problem, which we already know how to solve. We can apply any of the constant acceleration relationships from Section 4.1 separately to the *x*-components and to the *y*-components.

CONNECTION:

Projectile motion is free fall for objects with a constant horizontal velocity component. The acceleration is constant and directed downward.

It is generally easiest to choose the axes so that the acceleration has only one non-zero component. Suppose we choose the axes so that the acceleration is in the positive or negative y-direction. Then $a_x = 0$ and v_x is constant. With this choice, the four constant acceleration relationships [Eqs. (4-1), (4-3), (4-4), and (4-5)] become

x-axis: $a_x = 0$	y-axis: constant a_y	
$\Delta v_x = 0$ (v_x is constant)	$\Delta v_y = a_y \Delta t$	(4-7)
$\Delta x = v_x \Delta t$	$\Delta y = \frac{1}{2}(v_{fy} + v_{iy})\,\Delta t$	(4-8)
	$\Delta y = v_{iy}\,\Delta t + \frac{1}{2}a_y(\Delta t)^2$	(4-9)
	$v_{fy}^2 - v_{iy}^2 = 2a_y\,\Delta y$	(4-10)

Why are only two equations shown in the column for the x-axis? The other two are redundant when $a_x = 0$.

Note that there is no mixing of components in Eqs. (4-7) through (4-10). Each equation pertains either to the x-components or to the y-components; none contains the x-component of one vector quantity and the y-component of another. The only quantity that appears in both x- and y-component equations is the time interval—a scalar.

An object in free fall near the Earth's surface has a constant acceleration. As long as air resistance is negligible, the constant downward pull of gravity gives the object a constant downward acceleration equal to $\vec{\mathbf{g}}$. In Section 4.3 we considered objects in free fall, but only when they had no horizontal velocity component, so they moved straight up or straight down. Now we consider objects (called **projectiles**) in free fall that have a *nonzero* horizontal velocity component. The motion of a projectile takes place in a vertical plane.

Suppose some medieval marauders are attacking a castle. They have a catapult that propels large stones into the air to bombard the walls of the castle (Fig. 4.23). Picture a stone leaving the catapult with initial velocity $\vec{\mathbf{v}}_i$. ($\vec{\mathbf{v}}_i$ is the *initial* velocity for the time interval during which it moves as a projectile. It is also the *final* velocity for the time interval during which it is in contact with the catapult.) The **angle of elevation** is the angle of the initial velocity above the horizontal. Once the stone is in the air, the only force acting on it is the downward gravitational force, provided that the air resistance has a negligible effect on the motion. The **trajectory** (path) of the stone is shown in Fig. 4.24. The positive x-axis is chosen in the horizontal direction (to the right) and the positive y-axis is upward.

If the initial velocity $\vec{\mathbf{v}}_i$ is at an angle θ above the horizontal, then resolving it into components gives

$$v_{ix} = v_i \cos\theta \quad \text{and} \quad v_{iy} = v_i \sin\theta \tag{4-11}$$

(+y-axis up, θ measured from the horizontal x-axis)

Figure 4.23 A medieval catapult.

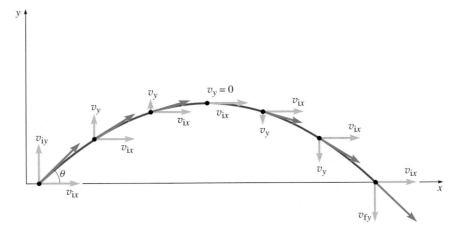

Figure 4.24 Motion diagram showing the trajectory of a projectile. The position is drawn at equal time intervals. Superimposed are the velocity vectors along with their x- and y-components.

Since the gravitational force pulls in the $-y$-direction (downward), the horizontal component of the net force is zero. Therefore, $a_x = 0$ and the stone's horizontal velocity component v_x is *constant*. The vertical velocity component v_y changes at a constant rate, exactly as if the stone were propelled straight up with an initial speed of v_{iy}. The initially positive v_y decreases until, at the top of flight, $v_y = 0$. Then the pull of gravity makes the projectile fall back downward. During the downward trip, v_y is still changing at the same constant rate with which it changed on the way up and at the top of the path. The acceleration has the same constant value—magnitude and direction—for the entire path.

The displacement of the projectile at any instant is the vector sum of the displacements in the two mutually perpendicular directions. The motion of a projectile when air resistance is negligible is the superposition of horizontal motion with constant velocity and vertical motion with constant acceleration. The vertical and horizontal motions each proceed independently, as if the other motion were not present. In the experiment of Fig. 4.25, one ball was dropped and, at the same instant, another was projected horizontally. The strobe photo shows snapshots of the two balls at equally spaced time intervals. The *vertical* motion of the two is identical; at every instant, the two are at the same height. The fact that they have different horizontal motion does not affect their vertical motion. (This statement would *not* be true if air resistance were significant.)

Figure 4.25 Independence of horizontal and vertical motion of a projectile in the absence of air resistance. The vertical motion of the projectile (white) is the same as that of an object (red) that falls straight down.

PHYSICS AT HOME

Take a nickel and a penny to a room with a high table or countertop. Place the penny at the edge of the table and then slide the nickel so it collides with the penny. Listen for the sound of the two coins hitting the floor. The two coins will slide off the table with different horizontal velocities but will land at the same time.

The horizontal and vertical motions of a projectile can be treated separately; they are independent of each other.

Conceptual Example 4.8

Trajectory of a Projectile

The graph of an equation of the form

$$y = kx^2, \quad k = \text{a nonzero constant}$$

is a parabola. Show that the trajectory of a projectile is a parabola. [*Hint:* Choose the origin at the highest point of the trajectory and let $t_i = 0$ at that instant.]

Strategy and Solution We start at the high point of the path and look at displacements from there. The horizontal displacement is proportional to the elapsed time since the horizontal velocity is constant. The vertical displacement is the average vertical velocity component times the elapsed time t. The average vertical velocity component is itself proportional to t since it changes at a constant rate. Therefore, the vertical displacement is proportional to t^2. Thus, the vertical displacement y is proportional to the square of the horizontal displacement x and $y = kx^2$, where k is a constant of proportionality. The path followed by a projectile in free fall is a parabola.

Discussion The same conclusion can be drawn algebraically. With the $+y$-axis upward and the origin and $t = 0$ at the top of flight, x_i, y_i, and v_{iy} are all zero. Then $x = v_{ix}t$ and

$$y = v_{iy}t + \frac{1}{2}a_y t^2 = -\frac{1}{2}gt^2 = -\frac{1}{2}g\left(\frac{x}{v_{ix}}\right)^2 = -\left(\frac{g}{2v_{ix}^2}\right)x^2$$

So y is proportional to x^2 and the constant of proportionality is $-g/(2v_{ix}^2)$.

Practice Problem 4.8   Throwing Stones

You stand at the edge of a cliff and throw stones horizontally into the river below. To double the horizontal displacement of a stone from the cliff to where it lands, by what factor must you increase the stone's initial speed? Ignore air resistance.

Figure 4.26 Projectile motion: separate vertical and horizontal quantities versus time.

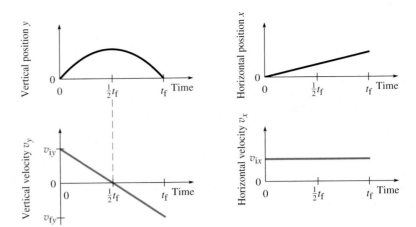

Graphing Projectile Motion   Figure 4.26 shows graphs of the x- and y-components of the velocity and position of a projectile as functions of time. In this case, the projectile is launched above flat ground at $t = 0$ and returns to the same elevation at a later time t_f. Note that the y-component graphs are *symmetrical* about the vertical line through the highest point in the trajectory. The y-component of velocity decreases linearly from its initial value; the slope of the line is $a_y = -g$. When $v_y = 0$, the projectile is at the apex of its trajectory. Then v_y continues to decrease at the same rate and is now negative with its magnitude getting larger and larger. At t_f, when the projectile has returned to its original altitude, the y-component of the velocity has the same magnitude as at $t = 0$ but with the opposite sign ($v_y = -v_{iy}$).

The graph of $y(t)$ indicates that the projectile moves upward, quickly at first and then gradually slowing, until it reaches the maximum height. The slope of the tangent to the $y(t)$ graph at any particular moment of time is v_y at that instant. At the highest point of the $y(t)$ graph, the tangent is horizontal and $v_y = 0$. After that, gravity makes the projectile start to fall downward.

The horizontal velocity is constant because the projectile is not acted on by any horizontal forces ($a_x = \Sigma F_x/m = 0$). Thus, the graph of $v_x(t)$ is a horizontal line. The horizontal position x increases uniformly in time because the object is moving with a constant v_x.

✓ CHECKPOINT 4.4

When a basketball is thrown in an arc toward the net, what can you say about its velocity and acceleration at the highest point of the arc? Assume no air resistance.

Example 4.9

Attacking the Castle Walls

The catapult used by the marauders hurls a stone of mass 32.0 kg with a velocity of 50.0 m/s at a 30.0° angle of elevation (Fig. 4.27). (a) What is the maximum height reached by the stone? (b) What is its *range* (defined as the horizontal distance traveled when the stone returns to its original height)? (c) How long has the stone been in the air when it returns to its original height?

Strategy   The problem gives both the magnitude and direction of the initial velocity of the stone. Ignoring air resistance, the stone has a constant downward acceleration once it has been launched—until it hits the ground or some obstacle. We choose the positive y-axis upward and the positive x-axis in the direction of horizontal motion of the stone (toward the castle). When the stone reaches its maximum height, the velocity component in the y-direction is zero since the stone goes no

continued on next page

Example 4.9 continued

Figure 4.27
A catapult projects a stone into the air in an attack on a castle wall.

higher. When the stone returns to its original height, $\Delta y = 0$ and $v_y = -v_{iy}$. The range can be found once the time of flight t_f is known—time is the quantity that connects the x-component equations to the y-component equations. Therefore, we solve (c) before (b). One way to find t_f is to find the time to reach maximum height and then double it (see Fig. 4.26). (Other methods include setting $\Delta y = 0$ or setting $v_y = -v_{iy}$.)

Solution (a) First we find the x- and y-components of the initial velocity for an angle of elevation $\theta = 30.0°$.

$$v_{iy} = v_i \sin \theta \quad \text{and} \quad v_{ix} = v_i \cos \theta$$

The maximum height is the vertical displacement Δy when $v_{fy} = 0$.

$$\Delta y = \tfrac{1}{2}(v_{fy} + v_{iy}) \, \Delta t = \tfrac{1}{2}(0 + v_i \sin \theta) \, \Delta t$$

Eliminating the time interval using $v_{fy} - v_{iy} = a_y \Delta t$ yields

$$\Delta y = \tfrac{1}{2}(v_i \sin \theta)\left(\frac{0 - v_i \sin \theta}{a_y}\right) = -\frac{(v_i \sin \theta)^2}{2a_y}$$

$$= \frac{-(50.0 \text{ m/s} \times \sin 30.0°)^2}{2 \times (-9.80 \text{ m/s}^2)} = 31.9 \text{ m}$$

The maximum height of the projectile is 31.9 m above its launch height.

(c) The initial and final heights are the same. Due to this symmetry, the time of flight (t_f) is *twice* the time it takes the projectile to reach its maximum height. The time to reach the maximum height can be found from

$$v_{fy} = 0 = v_{iy} + a_y \, \Delta t$$

Solving for Δt,

$$\Delta t = \frac{-v_{iy}}{a_y}$$

The time of flight is

$$t_f = 2 \Delta t = 2 \times \frac{-50.0 \text{ m/s} \times \sin 30.0°}{-9.80 \text{ m/s}^2} = 5.10 \text{ s}$$

(b) The range is

$$\Delta x = v_{ix} t_f = (50.0 \text{ m/s} \times \cos 30.0°) \times 5.10 \text{ s} = 221 \text{ m}$$

Discussion Quick check: using

$$y_f - y_i = v_{iy} \, \Delta t + \tfrac{1}{2} a_y \, (\Delta t)^2$$

we can check that $\Delta y = 31.9$ m when $\Delta t = \tfrac{1}{2} \times 5.10$ s and that $\Delta y = 0$ when $\Delta t = 5.10$ s. Here we check the first of these:

$$\Delta y = (50.0 \text{ m/s}) (\sin 30.0°) (2.55 \text{ s}) + \tfrac{1}{2} (-9.80 \text{ m/s}^2) (2.55 \text{ s})^2$$

$$= 63.8 \text{ m} + (-31.9 \text{ m}) = 31.9 \text{ m}$$

which is correct. This is not an *independent* check, since this equation can be derived from the others, but it can reveal algebra or calculation errors.

Since we analyze the horizontal motion independently from the vertical motion, we start by resolving the given initial velocity into x- and y-components. Time is what connects the horizontal and vertical motions.

Notice that we did not use the mass of the stone in the solution. The mass does not affect the maximum height, the time of flight, or the range, if we are given the initial velocity (that is, its initial velocity *as a projectile*, which is the velocity just when it loses contact with the catapult). Where mass does matter is in the ability of the catapult to accelerate the stone from rest to its launch velocity.

Practice Problem 4.9 **Maximum Height for Arrows**

Archers have joined in the attack on the castle and are shooting arrows over the walls. If the angle of elevation for an arrow is 45°, find an expression for the maximum height of the arrow in terms of v_i and g. [*Hint:* Simplify the expression using $\sin 45° = \cos 45° = 1/\sqrt{2}$.]

Monkey and Hunter

An inexperienced hunter aims and shoots an arrow straight at a coconut that is being held by a monkey sitting in a tree (Fig. 4.28). At the same instant that the arrow leaves the bow, the monkey drops the coconut. Ignoring air resistance, does the arrow hit the coconut, the monkey, or neither?

Strategy and Solution If there were no gravitational field, the arrow would fly straight to the monkey and coconut (along the dashed line from the bow to the monkey on the branch in Fig. 4.28). Since gravity gives the dropped coconut and the released arrow the same constant acceleration downward, they each fall the same vertical distance below the positions they would have had with no gravity. The coconut falls as shown by the dashed red line; the distance fallen at 0.25-s intervals is marked along a vertical axis. At the same time, the arrow drops below the blue dashed line by the amounts marked along its indicated trajectory at 0.25-s intervals.

The arrow ends up hitting the coconut no matter what the initial velocity of the arrow. The higher the velocity of the arrow, the sooner they meet and the shorter the vertical distance that the coconut falls before being hit.

Discussion An experienced hunter would have aimed *above* the initial position of the coconut to compensate for the amount his arrow would drop during the time of flight; he would have missed the dropping coconut but might have hit the monkey unless the monkey jumped down to retrieve the coconut.

Conceptual Practice Problem 4.10 Changes in Position and Velocity for Consecutive Arrows

An arrow is shot into the air. One second later, a second arrow is shot with the same initial velocity. While the two are both in the air, does the difference in their positions ($\vec{r}_2 - \vec{r}_1$) stay constant or does it change with time? Does the difference in their velocities ($\vec{v}_2 - \vec{v}_1$) stay constant or does it change with time?

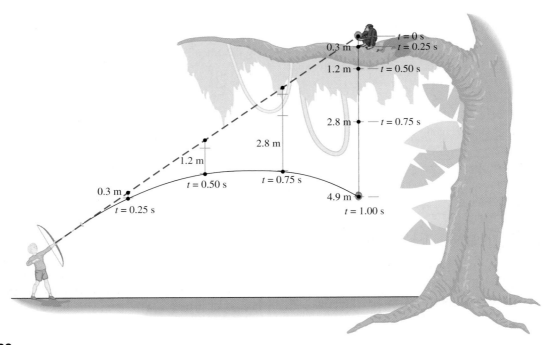

Figure 4.28

A monkey drops a coconut at the very instant an arrow is shot toward the coconut. In each quarter second, the coconut and arrow have fallen the same distance below where their positions would be if there were no gravity.

PHYSICS AT HOME

On a warm day, take a garden hose and aim the nozzle so that the water streams upward at an angle above the horizontal. Set the nozzle for a fast, narrow stream for best effect. Once the water leaves the nozzle, it becomes a projectile subject only to the force of gravity (ignoring the small effect of air resistance). The continuous stream of water lets us see the parabolic path easily. Stand in one place and try aiming the nozzle at different angles of elevation to find an angle that gives the maximum range. Aim for a particular spot on the ground (at a distance less than the maximum range) and see if you can find two different angles of elevated nozzle position that allow the stream to hit the target spot (Fig. 4.29).

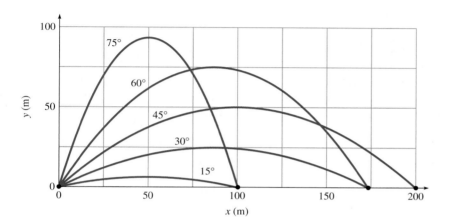

Figure 4.29 Parabolic trajectories of projectiles launched with the same initial speed ($v_i = 44.3$ m/s) at five different angles. The ranges of projectiles launched at angles θ and $90° - \theta$ are the same. The maximum range occurs for $\theta = 45°$.

Example 4.11

A Bullet Fired Horizontally

A bullet is fired horizontally from the top of a cliff that is 20.0 m above a long lake. If the muzzle speed of the bullet is 500.0 m/s, how far from the bottom of the cliff does the bullet strike the surface of the lake? Ignore air resistance.

Strategy We need to find the total time of flight so that we can find the horizontal displacement. The bullet is starting from the high point of the parabolic path because $v_{iy} = 0$. As usual in projectile problems, we choose the y-axis to be the positive vertical direction.

Known: $\Delta y = -20.0$ m; $v_{iy} = 0$; $v_{ix} = 500.0$ m/s. To find: Δx.

Solution The vertical displacement through which the bullet falls is 20.0 m. The relationship between Δy and Δt is

$$\Delta y = \tfrac{1}{2}(v_{fy} + v_{iy}) \Delta t$$

Substituting $v_{iy} = 0$ and $v_{fy} = v_{iy} + a_y \Delta t = a_y \Delta t$ yields

$$\Delta y = \tfrac{1}{2} a_y (\Delta t)^2 \Rightarrow \Delta t = \sqrt{\frac{2\Delta y}{a_y}}$$

The horizontal displacement of the bullet is

$$x = v_{ix} \Delta t = v_{ix} \sqrt{\frac{2\Delta y}{a_y}}$$
$$= 500.0 \text{ m/s} \times \sqrt{\frac{2 \times (-20.0 \text{ m})}{-9.80 \text{ m/s}^2}} = 1.01 \text{ km}$$

Discussion How did we know to start with the y-component equation when the question asks about the *horizontal* displacement? The question gives v_{ix} and asks for Δx. The missing information needed is the time during which the bullet is in the air; the time can be found from analysis of the *vertical* motion.

We ignored air resistance in this problem, which is not very realistic. The actual distance would be less than 1.01 km.

Practice Problem 4.11   Bullet Velocity

Find the horizontal and vertical components of the bullet's velocity just before it hits the surface of the lake. At what angle does it strike the surface?

Air Resistance

So far we have ignored the effect of air resistance on falling objects and projectiles. A skydiver relies on a parachute to provide a large force of air resistance (also called **drag**). Even with the parachute closed, drag is not negligible when the skydiver is falling rapidly. The drag force is similar to friction between two solid surfaces in that the direction of the force *opposes the motion* of the object through the air. However, in contrast to the force of friction, the magnitude of the drag force is strongly dependent on the speed of the object. In many cases, air drag is proportional to the square of the speed. Drag also depends on the size and shape of the object.

Since the drag force increases as the speed increases, a falling object approaches an equilibrium situation in which the drag force is equal in magnitude to the weight but opposite in direction. The speed at which this equilibrium occurs is called the object's *terminal speed*. (See text website for a more detailed treatment of drag.)

PHYSICS AT HOME

Drop a basket-style paper coffee filter (or a cupcake paper) and a penny simultaneously from as close to the ceiling as you can safely do so. Air resistance on the penny is negligible unless it is dropped from a very high balcony. At the other extreme, the effect of air resistance on the coffee filter is very noticeable; it reaches its terminal speed almost immediately. Stack several (two to four) coffee filters together and drop them simultaneously with a single coffee filter. Why is the terminal speed higher for the stack? Crumple a coffee filter into a ball and drop it simultaneously with the penny. Air resistance on the coffee filter is now reduced, but still noticeable.

4.5   APPARENT WEIGHT

Imagine being in an elevator when the cable snaps. Assume that some safety mechanism brings you to rest after you have been in free fall for a while. While you are in free fall, you *seem* to be "weightless," but your weight has not changed; the Earth still pulls downward with the same gravitational force. In free fall, gravity gives the elevator and everything in it a downward acceleration equal to $\vec{\mathbf{g}}$. If you jump up from the elevator floor, you seem to "float" up to the ceiling of the elevator. Your *weight* hasn't changed, but your *apparent* weight is zero while you are in free fall.

Similarly, astronauts in a space station in orbit around the Earth are in free fall (their acceleration is equal to the local value of $\vec{\mathbf{g}}$). Earth exerts a gravitational force on them so they are not weightless; their *apparent* weight is zero.

Imagine an object that appears to be resting on a bathroom scale. The scale measures the object's *apparent* weight W', which is equal to the true weight only if the object and the scale have zero acceleration. Newton's second law requires that

$$\sum \vec{\mathbf{F}} = \vec{\mathbf{N}} + m\vec{\mathbf{g}} = m\vec{\mathbf{a}}$$

where $\vec{\mathbf{N}}$ is the normal force of the scale pushing up. The apparent weight W' is the reading of the scale—that is, the magnitude of $\vec{\mathbf{N}}$:

$$W' = |\vec{\mathbf{N}}| = N$$

In Fig. 4.30a, the acceleration of the elevator is upward. The normal force must be larger than the weight for the net force to be upward (Fig. 4.30b). Writing the forces in component form where the $+y$-direction is upward

$$\sum F_y = N - mg = ma_y$$

Figure 4.30 (a) Apparent weight in an elevator with acceleration upward. (b) FBD for the passenger. (c) The normal force must be greater than the weight to have an upward net force.

Figure 4.31 (a) Apparent weight in an elevator with acceleration downward. (b) FBD for the passenger. (c) The normal force must be less than the weight to have a downward net force.

or

$$N = mg + ma_y$$

Therefore,

$$W' = N = m(g + a_y) \tag{4-12}$$

Since the elevator's acceleration is upward, $a_y > 0$; the apparent weight is greater than the true weight (Fig. 4.30c).

In Fig. 4.31a, the acceleration is downward. Then the net force must also point downward. The normal force is still upward, but it must be smaller than the weight in order to produce a downward net force (Fig. 4.31b). It is still true that $W' = m(g + a_y)$, but now the acceleration is downward ($a_y < 0$). The apparent weight is less than the true weight (Fig. 4.31c). If the elevator is in free fall, then $a_y = -g$ and the apparent weight of the unfortunate passenger is zero.

Example 4.12

Apparent Weight in an Elevator

A passenger weighing 598 N rides in an elevator. What is the apparent weight of the passenger in each of the following situations? In each case, the magnitude of the elevator's acceleration is 0.500 m/s². (a) The passenger is on the first floor and has pushed the button for the fifteenth floor; the elevator is beginning to move upward. (b) The elevator is slowing down as it nears the fifteenth floor.

Strategy   In each case, we sketch the FBD for the passenger. The apparent weight is equal to the magnitude of the normal force exerted by the floor on the passenger. The only other force acting is gravity. Newton's second law lets us find the normal force from the weight and the acceleration. Known: $W = 598$ N; magnitude of the acceleration is $a = 0.500$ m/s². To find: W'.

Solution   (a) Let the +y-axis be upward. When the elevator starts up from the first floor it has acceleration in the upward direction as its speed increases. Since the elevator's acceleration is upward, $a_y > 0$ (as in Fig. 4.30). We expect the apparent weight $W' = N$ to be greater than the true weight—the floor must push up with a force greater than W to cause an upward acceleration. Figure 4.32 is the FBD. Newton's second law says

$$\sum F_y = N - W = ma_y$$

Since $W = mg$, we can substitute $m = W/g$.

$$W' = N = W + ma_y = W + \frac{W}{g}a_y = W\left(1 + \frac{a_y}{g}\right)$$

$$= 598 \text{ N} \times \left(1 + \frac{0.500 \text{ m/s}^2}{9.80 \text{ m/s}^2}\right) = 629 \text{ N}$$

Figure 4.32
FBD for the passenger in an elevator with upward acceleration.

(b) When the elevator approaches the fifteenth floor, it is slowing down while still moving upward; its acceleration is downward ($a_y < 0$) as in Fig. 4.31. The apparent weight is less than the true weight. Figure 4.33 is the FBD. Again, $\sum F_y = N - W = ma_y$, but this time $a_y = -0.500$ m/s².

$$N = W\left(1 + \frac{a_y}{g}\right)$$

$$= 598 \text{ N} \times \left(1 + \frac{-0.500 \text{ m/s}^2}{9.80 \text{ m/s}^2}\right) = 567 \text{ N}$$

Discussion   The apparent weight is greater when the direction of the elevator's acceleration is upward. That can happen in two cases: either the elevator is moving up with increasing speed, or it is moving down with decreasing speed.

Practice Problem 4.12   Elevator Descending

What is the apparent weight of a passenger of mass 42.0 kg traveling in an elevator in each of the following situations? In each case, the magnitude of the elevator's acceleration is 0.460 m/s². (a) The passenger is on the fifteenth floor and has pushed the button for the first floor; the elevator is beginning to move downward. (b) The elevator is slowing down as it nears the first floor.

Figure 4.33
FBD for the passenger in an elevator with downward acceleration.

✓ CHECKPOINT 4.5

You are standing on a bathroom scale in an elevator that is moving downward. Nearing your stop, the elevator's speed is decreasing. Is the scale reading greater or smaller than your weight?

PHYSICS AT HOME

Take a bathroom scale to an elevator. Stand on the scale inside the elevator and push a button for a higher floor. When the elevator's acceleration is upward, you can feel the increase in your apparent weight and can see the increase by the reading on the scale. When the elevator slows down to stop, the elevator's acceleration is downward and your apparent weight is less than your true weight.

What is happening in the body while the elevator accelerates? The inertia principle means that your blood and internal organs cannot have the same acceleration as the elevator until the correct net force acts on them. Blood tends to collect in the lower extremities during acceleration upward and in the upper body during acceleration downward until the forces exerted on the blood by the body readjust to give the blood the same acceleration as the elevator. Likewise, the internal organs shift position within the body cavity, resulting in a funny feeling in the gut as the elevator starts and stops. To avoid this problem, high-speed express elevators in skyscrapers keep the acceleration relatively small, but maintain that acceleration long enough to reach high speeds. That way, the elevator can travel quickly to the upper floors without making the passengers feel too uncomfortable.

Master the Concepts

• Essential relationships for constant acceleration problems: If a_x is constant during the entire time interval Δt from t_i until a later time $t_f = t_i + \Delta t$,

$$\Delta v_x = v_{fx} - v_{ix} = a_x \Delta t \qquad (4\text{-}1)$$

$$\Delta x = \frac{1}{2}(v_{fx} + v_{ix}) \Delta t \qquad (4\text{-}3)$$

$$\Delta x = v_{ix} \Delta t + \frac{1}{2}a_x(\Delta t)^2 \qquad (4\text{-}4)$$

$$v_{fx}^2 - v_{ix}^2 = 2a_x \Delta x \qquad (4\text{-}5)$$

These same relationships hold for the y-components of the position, velocity, and acceleration if a_y is constant.

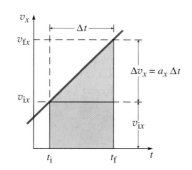

• The only force acting on an object in free fall is gravity. On Earth, free fall is an idealization since there is always *some* air resistance. An object in free fall has an acceleration equal to the local value of the gravitational field $\vec{g}$.

• For a projectile or any object moving with constant acceleration in the $\pm y$-direction, the motion in the x- and y-directions can be treated separately. Since $a_x = 0$, v_x is constant. Thus, the motion is a superposition of constant velocity motion in the x-direction and constant acceleration motion in the y-direction.

• The x- and y-axes are chosen to make the problem easiest to solve. Any choice is valid as long as the two are perpendicular. In an equilibrium problem, choose x- and y-axes so that the fewest number of force vectors have to be resolved into both x- and y-components. In a nonequilibrium problem, if the direction of the acceleration is known, choose x- and y-axes so that the acceleration vector is parallel to one of the axes.

• Problems involving Newton's second law—whether equilibrium or nonequilibrium—can be solved by treating the x- and y-components of the forces and the acceleration separately.

• An object that is accelerating has an apparent weight that differs from its true weight. The apparent weight is equal to the normal force exerted by a supporting surface with the same acceleration. A helpful trick is to think of the apparent weight as the reading of a bathroom scale that supports the object.

Conceptual Questions

1. Why is the muzzle of a rifle not aimed directly at the center of the target?

2. Can the velocity of an object be zero and the acceleration be nonzero at the same time? Explain.

3. Does the monkey, coconut, and hunter demonstration still work if the arrow is pointed *downward* at the monkey and coconut? Explain.

4. Can a body in free fall be in equilibrium? Explain.

5. If a feather and a lead brick are dropped simultaneously from the top of a ladder, the lead brick hits the ground first. What would happen if the experiment is repeated on the surface of the Moon?

6. Why does a 1-kg sandbag fall with the same acceleration as a 5-kg sandbag? Explain in terms of Newton's second law and his law of gravitation.

7. An object is placed on a scale. Under what conditions does the scale read something other than the object's weight, even though the scale is functioning properly and is calibrated correctly? Explain.

8. What does it mean when we refer to a cord as an "ideal cord" and a pulley as an "ideal pulley"?

9. What force(s) act on a parachutist descending to Earth with a constant velocity? What is the acceleration of the parachutist?

10. Is it possible for two identical projectiles with identical initial speeds, but with two different angles of elevation, to land in the same spot? Explain. Ignore air resistance and sketch the trajectories.

11. A baseball is tossed straight up. Taking into consideration the force of air resistance, is the magnitude of the baseball's acceleration zero, less than g, equal to g, or greater than g on the way up? At the top of the flight? On the way down? Explain. [*Hint:* The force of air resistance is directed opposite to the velocity. Assume in this case that its magnitude is less than the weight.]

12. What is the acceleration of an object thrown straight up into the air at the highest point of its motion? Does the answer depend on whether air resistance is negligible or not? Explain.

13. If the trajectory is parabolic in one reference frame, is it always, never, or sometimes parabolic in another reference frame that moves at constant velocity with respect to the first reference frame? If the trajectory can be other than parabolic, what else can it be?

14. If air resistance is ignored, what force(s) act on an object in free fall?

15. Why might an elevator cable break during acceleration when lifting a lighter load than it normally supports at rest or at constant velocity?

16. You are standing on a balcony overlooking the beach. You throw a ball straight up into the air with speed v_i and throw an identical ball straight down with speed v_i. Ignoring air resistance, how do the speeds of the balls compare just before they hit the ground?

17. You throw a ball up with initial speed v_i and when it reaches its high point at height h, you throw another ball into the air with the same initial speed v_i. Will the two balls cross at half the height h, or more than half, or less than half? Explain.

18. When a coin is tossed directly upward, what can you say about its velocity and acceleration at the high point of the toss?

19. The net force acting on an object is constant. Under what circumstances does the object move along a straight line? Under what circumstances does the object move along a curved path?

20. You decide to test your physics knowledge while going over a waterfall in a barrel. You take a baseball into the barrel with you and as you are falling vertically downward, you let go of the ball. What do you expect to see for the motion of the ball relative to the barrel? Will the ball fall faster than you and move toward the bottom of the barrel? Will it move slower than you and approach the top of the barrel. Or will it hover apparently motionless within the falling barrel? Explain. [*Warning:* Do not try this at home.]

Multiple-Choice Questions

1. A ball is thrown straight up into the air. Ignore air resistance. While the ball is in the air its acceleration
   (a) increases.
   (b) is zero.
   (c) remains constant.
   (d) decreases on the way up and increases on the way down.
   (e) changes direction.

2. A leopard starts from rest at $t = 0$ and runs in a straight line with a constant acceleration until $t = 3.0$ s. The distance covered by the leopard between $t = 1.0$ s and $t = 2.0$ s is
   (a) the same as the distance covered during the first second.
   (b) twice the distance covered during the first second.
   (c) three times the distance covered during the first second.
   (d) four times the distance covered during the first second.

3. A kicker kicks a football from the 5-yd line to the 45-yd line (both on the same half of the field). Ignoring air

resistance, where along the trajectory is the speed of the football a minimum?

(a) at the 5-yd line, just after the football leaves the kicker's foot

(b) at the 45-yd line, just before the football hits the ground

(c) at the 15-yd line, while the ball is still going higher

(d) at the 35-yd line, while the ball is coming down

(e) at the 25-yd line, when the ball is at the top of its trajectory

4. Two balls, identical except for color, are projected horizontally from the roof of a tall building at the same instant. The initial speed of the red ball is twice the initial speed of the blue ball. Ignoring air resistance,

(a) the red ball reaches the ground first.

(b) the blue ball reaches the ground first.

(c) both balls land at the same instant with different speeds.

(d) both balls land at the same instant with the same speed.

5. A person stands on the roof garden of a tall building with one ball in each hand. If the red ball is thrown horizontally off the roof and the blue ball is simultaneously dropped over the edge, which statement is true?

(a) Both balls hit the ground at the same time, but the red ball has a higher speed just before it strikes the ground.

(b) The blue ball strikes the ground first, but with a lower speed than the red ball.

(c) The red ball strikes the ground first with a higher speed than the blue ball.

(d) Both balls hit the ground at the same time with the same speed.

6. A ball is thrown into the air and follows a parabolic trajectory. At the highest point in the trajectory,

(a) the velocity is zero, but the acceleration is not zero.

(b) both the velocity and the acceleration are zero.

(c) the acceleration is zero, but the velocity is not zero.

(d) neither the acceleration nor the velocity are zero.

7. A ball is thrown into the air and follows a parabolic trajectory. Point A is the highest point in the trajectory and point B is a point as the ball is falling back to the ground. Choose the correct relationship between the speeds and the magnitudes of the acceleration at the two points.

(a) $v_A > v_B$ and $a_A = a_B$ (b) $v_A < v_B$ and $a_A > a_B$

(c) $v_A = v_B$ and $a_A \neq a_B$ (d) $v_A < v_B$ and $a_A = a_B$

8. You are standing on a bathroom scale in an elevator. In which of these situations must the scale read the same as when the elevator is at rest? Explain.

(a) Moving up at constant speed.

(b) Moving up with increasing speed.

(c) In free fall (after the elevator cable has snapped).

9. A thin string that can support a weight of 35.0 N, but breaks under any larger weight, is attached to the ceiling of an elevator. How large a mass can be attached to the string if the initial acceleration as the elevator starts to ascend is 3.20 m/s^2?

(a) 3.57 kg   (b) 2.69 kg   (c) 4.26 kg

(d) 2.96 kg   (e) 5.30 kg

10. A woman stands on a bathroom scale in an elevator that is not moving. The scale reads 500 N. The elevator then moves downward at a constant velocity of 4.5 m/s. What does the scale read while the elevator descends with constant velocity?

(a) 100 N   (b) 250 N   (c) 450 N

(d) 500 N   (e) 750 N

11. A 70.0-kg man stands on a bathroom scale in an elevator. What does the scale read if the elevator is slowing down at a rate of 3.00 m/s^2 while descending?

(a) 70 kg   (b) 476 N   (c) 686 N

(d) 700 N   (e) 896 N

12. A small plane climbs with a constant velocity of 250 m/s at an angle of 28° with respect to the horizontal. Which statement is true concerning the magnitude of the net force on the plane?

(a) It is equal to zero.

(b) It is equal to the weight of the plane.

(c) It is equal to the magnitude of the force of air resistance.

(d) It is less than the weight of the plane but greater than zero.

(e) It is equal to the component of the weight of the plane in the direction of motion.

13. Two blocks are connected by a light string passing over a pulley (see the figure and tutorial: pulley). The block with mass m_1 slides on the frictionless horizontal surface, while the block with mass m_2 hangs vertically $(m_1 > m_2)$. The tension in the string is

(a) zero.   (b) less than m_2g.   (c) equal to m_2g.

(d) greater than m_2g, but less than m_1g.

(e) equal to m_1g.   (f) greater than m_1g.

Questions 14–16. In Fig. 4.29, two projectiles launched with the same initial speed but at different launch angles 30° and 60° land at the same spot. Ignore air resistance. Answer choices:

(a) Projectile launched at 30°

(b) Projectile launched at 60°

(c) They are equal.

14. Which has the larger horizontal velocity component v_x?

15. Which has a longer time of flight Δt (time interval between launch and hitting the ground)?

16. For which is the product $v_x \Delta t$ larger?

Problems

⊙   Combination conceptual/quantitative problem
☥   Biological or medical application
◆   Challenging problem
Blue #   Detailed solution in the Student Solutions Manual
①   ②   Problems paired by concept
Ⓦ   Text website interactive or tutorial

4.1 Motion Along a Line Due to a Constant Net Force

1. An airplane lands and starts down the runway at a southwest velocity of 55 m/s. What constant acceleration allows it to come to a stop in 1.0 km?

2. A car is speeding up and has an instantaneous velocity of 1.0 m/s in the +x-direction when a stopwatch reads 10.0 s. It has a constant acceleration of 2.0 m/s^2 in the +x-direction. (a) What change in speed occurs between $t = 10.0$ s and $t = 12.0$ s? (b) What is the speed when the stopwatch reads 12.0 s?

3. While passing a slower car on the highway, you accelerate uniformly from 17.4 m/s to 27.3 m/s in a time of 10.0 s. (a) How far do you travel during this time? (b) What is your acceleration magnitude?

4. In a game of shuffleboard, a disk with an initial speed of 3.2 m/s travels 6.0 m before coming to rest. (a) What was the magnitude of the average acceleration of the disk? (b) What was the coefficient of kinetic friction acting on the disk?

5. A skier with a mass of 63 kg starts from rest and skis down an icy (frictionless) slope that has a length of 50 m at an angle of 32° with respect to the horizontal. At the bottom of the slope, the path levels out and becomes horizontal, the snow becomes less icy, and the skier begins to slow down, coming to rest in a distance of 140 m along the horizontal path. (a) What is the speed of the skier at the bottom of the slope? (b) What is the coefficient of kinetic friction between the skier and the horizontal surface?

☥ 6. A cheetah can accelerate from rest to 24 m/s in 2.0 s. Assuming the acceleration is constant over the time interval, (a) what is the magnitude of the acceleration of the cheetah? (b) What is the distance traveled by the cheetah in these 2.0 s? (c) A runner can accelerate from rest to 6.0 m/s in the same time, 2.0 s. What is the magnitude of the acceleration of the runner? By what factor is the cheetah's average acceleration magnitude greater than that of the runner?

7. The forces on a small airplane (mass 1160 kg) in horizontal flight heading eastward are as follows: gravity = 16.000 kN downward, lift = 16.000 kN upward, thrust = 1.800 kN eastward, and drag = 1.400 kN westward. At $t = 0$, the plane's speed is 60.0 m/s. If the forces remain constant, how far does the plane travel in the next 60.0 s?

8. A train of mass 55,200 kg is traveling along a straight, level track at 26.8 m/s (60.0 mi/h). Suddenly the engineer sees a truck stalled on the tracks 184 m ahead. If the maximum possible braking force has magnitude 84.0 kN, can the train be stopped in time?

9. You are driving your car along a country road at a speed of 27.0 m/s. As you come over the crest of a hill, you notice a farm tractor 25.0 m ahead of you on the road, moving in the same direction as you at a speed of 10.0 m/s. You immediately slam on your brakes and slow down with a constant acceleration of magnitude 7.00 m/s^2. Will you hit the tractor before you stop? How far will you travel before you stop or collide with the tractor? If you stop, how far is the tractor in front of you when you finally stop?

10. In a cathode ray tube, electrons are accelerated from rest by a constant electric force of magnitude 6.4×10^{-17} N during the first 2.0 cm of the tube's length; then they move at essentially constant velocity another 45 cm before hitting the screen. (a) Find the speed of the electrons when they hit the screen. (b) How long does it take them to travel the length of the tube?

11. A 10.0-kg watermelon and a 7.00-kg pumpkin are attached to each other via a cord that wraps over a pulley, as shown. Friction is negligible everywhere in this system. (Ⓦ tutorial: pulley) (a) Find the accelerations of the pumpkin and the watermelon. Specify magnitude and direction. (b) If the system is released from rest, how far along the incline will the pumpkin travel in 0.30 s? (c) What is the speed of the watermelon after 0.20 s?

12. Two blocks are connected by a lightweight, flexible cord that passes over a frictionless pulley. If $m_1 = 3.6$ kg and $m_2 = 9.2$ kg, and block 2 is initially at rest 140 cm above the floor, how long does it take block 2 to reach the floor?

◆13. While an elevator of mass 832 kg moves downward, the tension in the supporting cable is a constant 7730 N. Between $t = 0$ and $t = 4.00$ s, the elevator's displacement is 5.00 m downward. What is the elevator's speed at $t = 4.00$ s?

4.2 Visualizing Motion Along a Line with Constant Acceleration

14. The graph is of v_x versus t for an object moving along the x-axis. How far does the object move between $t = 9.0$ s and $t = 13.0$ s? Solve using two methods: a graphical analysis and an algebraic solution.

15. The graph is of v_x versus t for an object moving along the x-axis. What is the average acceleration between $t = 5.0$ s and $t = 9.0$ s? Solve using two methods: a graphical analysis and an algebraic solution.

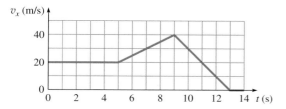

16. A train, traveling at a constant speed of 22 m/s, comes to an incline with a constant slope. While going up the incline, the train slows down with a constant acceleration of magnitude 1.4 m/s². (a) Draw a graph of v_x versus t where the x-axis points up the incline. (b) What is the speed of the train after 8.0 s on the incline? (c) How far has the train traveled up the incline after 8.0 s? (d) Draw a motion diagram, showing the train's position at 2.0-s intervals.

17. The St. Charles streetcar in New Orleans starts from rest and has a constant acceleration of 1.20 m/s² for 12.0 s. (a) Draw a graph of v_x versus t. (b) How far has the train traveled at the end of the 12.0 s? (c) What is the speed of the train at the end of the 12.0 s? (d) Draw a motion diagram, showing the trolley car's position at 2.0-s intervals.

18. A streetcar named Desire travels between two stations 0.60 km apart. Leaving the first station, it accelerates for 10.0 s at 1.0 m/s² and then travels at a constant speed until it is near the second station, when it brakes at 2.0 m/s² in order to stop at the station. How long did this trip take? [*Hint:* What's the average velocity?]

19. In the physics laboratory, a glider is released from rest on a frictionless air track inclined at an angle. If the glider has gained a speed of 25.0 cm/s in traveling 50.0 cm from the starting point, what was the angle of inclination of the track? Draw a graph of $v_x(t)$ when the positive x-axis points down the track.

20. A 10.0-kg block is released from rest on a frictionless track inclined at an angle of 55°. (a) What is the net force on the block after it is released? (b) What is the acceleration of the block? (c) If the block is released from rest, how long will it take for the block to attain a speed of 10.0 m/s? (d) Draw a motion diagram for the block. (e) Draw a graph of $v_x(t)$ for values of velocity between 0 and 10 m/s. Let the positive x-axis point down the track.

21. A 6.0-kg block, starting from rest, slides down a frictionless incline of length 2.0 m. When it arrives at the bottom of the incline, its speed is v_f. At what distance from the top of the incline is the speed of the block 0.50 v_f?

22. A train is traveling south at 24.0 m/s when the brakes are applied. It slows down with a constant acceleration to a speed of 6.00 m/s in a time of 9.00 s. (a) Draw a graph of v_x versus t for a 12-s interval (starting 2 s before the brakes are applied and ending 1 s after the brakes are released). Let the x-axis point to the north. (b) What is the acceleration of the train during the 9.00-s interval? (c) How far does the train travel during the 9.00 s?

4.3 Free Fall

23. Grant Hill jumps 1.3 m straight up into the air to slam-dunk a basketball into the net. With what speed did he leave the floor?

24. A penny is dropped from the observation deck of the Empire State building (369 m above ground). With what velocity does it strike the ground? Ignore air resistance.

25. (a) How long does it take for a golf ball to fall from rest for a distance of 12.0 m? (b) How far would the ball fall in twice that time?

26. A student, looking toward his fourth-floor dormitory window, sees a flowerpot with nasturtiums (originally on a window sill above) pass his 2.0-m high window in 0.093 s. The distance between floors in the dormitory is 4.0 m. From a window on which floor did the flowerpot fall?

27. A balloonist, riding in the basket of a hot air balloon that is rising vertically with a constant velocity of 10.0 m/s, releases a sandbag when the balloon is 40.8 m above the ground. Ignoring air resistance, what is the bag's speed when it hits the ground?

28. A 55-kg lead ball is dropped from the leaning tower of Pisa. The tower is 55 m high. (a) How far does the ball fall in the first 3.0 s of flight? (b) What is the speed of the ball after it has traveled 2.5 m downward? (c) What is the speed of the ball 3.0 s after it is released?

29. Superman is standing 120 m horizontally away from Lois Lane. A villain drops a rock from 4.0 m directly above Lois. (a) If Superman is to intervene and catch the rock just before it hits Lois, what should be his minimum constant acceleration? (b) How fast will Superman be traveling when he reaches Lois?

30. During a walk on the Moon, an astronaut accidentally drops his camera over a 20.0-m cliff. It leaves his hands with zero speed, and after 2.0 s it has attained a velocity of 3.3 m/s downward. How far has the camera fallen after 4.0 s?

31. Glenda drops a coin from ear level down a wishing well. The coin falls a distance of 7.00 m before it strikes the water. If the speed of sound is 343 m/s, how long after Glenda releases the coin will she hear a splash?

32. A stone is launched straight up by a slingshot. Its initial speed is 19.6 m/s and the stone is 1.50 m above the ground when launched. (a) How high above the ground does the stone rise? (b) How much time elapses before the stone hits the ground?

33. A model rocket is fired vertically from rest. It has a net acceleration of 17.5 m/s^2. After 1.5 s, its fuel is exhausted and its only acceleration is that due to gravity. (a) Ignoring air resistance, how high does the rocket travel? (b) How long after liftoff does the rocket return to the ground?

34. The model rocket in Problem 33 has a mass of 87 g and you may assume the mass of the fuel is much less than 87 g. (a) What was the net force on the rocket during the first 1.5 s after liftoff? (b) What force was exerted on the rocket by the burning fuel? (c) What was the net force on the rocket after its fuel was spent? (d) The rocket's vertical velocity was zero instantaneously when it was at the top of its trajectory. What were the net force and acceleration on the rocket at this instant?

◆35. You drop a stone into a deep well and hear it hit the bottom 3.20 s later. This is the time it takes for the stone to fall to the bottom of the well, plus the time it takes for the sound of the stone hitting the bottom to reach you. Sound travels about 343 m/s in air. How deep is the well?

36. A baseball is thrown horizontally from a height of 9.60 m above the ground with a speed of 30.0 m/s. Where is the ball after 1.40 s have elapsed?

37. A clump of soft clay is thrown horizontally from 8.50 m above the ground with a speed of 20.0 m/s. Where is the clay after 1.50 s? Assume it sticks in place when it hits the ground.

38. A tennis ball is thrown horizontally from an elevation of 14.0 m above the ground with a speed of 20.0 m/s. (a) Where is the ball after 1.60 s? (b) If the ball is still in the air, how long before it hits the ground and where will it be with respect to the starting point once it lands?

4.4 Motion of Projectiles

39. A ball is thrown from a point 1.0 m above the ground. The initial velocity is 19.6 m/s at an angle of 30.0° above the horizontal. (a) Find the maximum height of the ball above the ground. (b) Calculate the speed of the ball at the highest point in the trajectory.

40. An arrow is shot into the air at an angle of 60.0° above the horizontal with a speed of 20.0 m/s. (a) What are the x- and y-components of the velocity of the arrow 3.0 s after it leaves the bowstring? (b) What are the x- and y-components of the displacement of the arrow during the 3.0-s interval?

41. You are working as a consultant on a video game designing a bomb site for a World War I airplane. In this game, the plane you are flying is traveling horizontally at 40.0 m/s at an altitude of 125 m when it drops a bomb. (a) Determine how far horizontally from the target you should release the bomb. (b) What direction is the bomb moving just before it hits the target?

◆42. A ballplayer standing at home plate hits a baseball that is caught by another player at the same height above the ground from which it was hit. The ball is hit with an initial velocity of 22.0 m/s at an angle of 60.0° above the horizontal. (ⓦ tutorial: projectile) (a) How high will the ball rise? (b) How much time will elapse from the time the ball leaves the bat until it reaches the fielder? (c) At what distance from home plate will the fielder be when he catches the ball?

43. You are planning a stunt to be used in an ice skating show. For this stunt a skater will skate down a frictionless ice ramp that is inclined at an angle of 15.0° above the horizontal. At the bottom of the ramp, there is a short horizontal section that ends in an abrupt drop off. The skater is supposed to start from rest somewhere on the ramp, then skate off the horizontal section and fly through the air a horizontal distance of 7.00 m while falling vertically for 3.00 m, before landing smoothly on the ice. How far up the ramp should the skater start this stunt?

◆44. A suspension bridge is 60.0 m above the level base of a gorge. A stone is thrown or dropped from the bridge. Ignore air resistance. At the location of the bridge g has been measured to be 9.83 m/s^2. (a) If you drop the stone, how long does it take for it to fall to the base of the gorge? (b) If you *throw* the stone straight down with a speed of 20.0 m/s, how long before it hits the ground? (c) If you throw the stone with a velocity of 20.0 m/s at 30.0° above the horizontal, how far from the point directly below the bridge will it hit the level ground?

45. From the edge of the rooftop of a building, a boy throws a stone at an angle 25.0° above the horizontal. The stone hits the ground 4.20 s later, 105 m away from the base of the building. (Ignore air resistance.) (a) For the stone's path through the air, sketch graphs of x, y, v_x, and v_y as functions of time. These need to be only *qualitatively* correct—you need not put numbers on the axes. (b) Find the initial velocity of the stone. (c) Find the initial height h from which the stone was thrown. (d) Find the maximum height H reached by the stone.

46. Jason is practicing his tennis stroke by hitting balls against a wall. The ball leaves his racquet at a height of 60 cm above the ground at an angle of 80° with respect to the *vertical*. (a) The speed of the ball as it leaves the racquet is 20 m/s and it must travel a distance of 10 m before it reaches the wall. How far above the ground does the ball strike the wall? (b) Is the ball on its way up or down when it hits the wall?

47. You have been employed by the local circus to plan their human cannonball performance. For this act, a spring-loaded cannon will shoot a human projectile, the Great Flyinski, across the big top to a net below. The net is located 5.0 m lower than the muzzle of the cannon from which the Great Flyinski is launched. The cannon will shoot the Great Flyinski at an angle of 35.0° above the horizontal and at a speed of 18.0 m/s. The ringmaster

has asked that you decide how far from the cannon to place the net so that the Great Flyinski will land in the net and not be splattered on the floor, which would greatly disturb the audience. What do you tell the ringmaster? (interactive: projectile motion)

✦48. A circus performer is shot out of a cannon and flies over a net that is placed horizontally 6.0 m from the cannon. When the cannon is aimed at an angle of 40° above the horizontal, the performer is moving in the horizontal direction and just barely clears the net as he passes over it. What is the muzzle speed of the cannon and how high is the net?

49. A cannonball is catapulted toward a castle. The cannonball's velocity when it leaves the catapult is 40 m/s at an angle of 37° with respect to the horizontal and the cannonball is 7.0 m above the ground at this time. (a) What is the maximum height above the ground reached by the cannonball? (b) Assuming the cannonball makes it over the castle walls and lands back down on the ground, at what horizontal distance from its release point will it land? (c) What are the x- and y-components of the cannonball's velocity just before it lands? The y-axis points up.

50. After being assaulted by flying cannonballs, the knights on the castle walls (12 m above the ground) respond by propelling flaming pitch balls at their assailants. One ball lands on the ground at a distance of 50 m from the castle walls. If it was launched at an angle of 53° above the horizontal, what was its initial speed?

51. The citizens of Paris were terrified during World War I when they were suddenly bombarded with shells fired from a long-range gun known as Big Bertha. The barrel of the gun was 36.6 m long and it had a muzzle speed of 1.46 km/s. When the gun's angle of elevation was set to 55°, what would be the range? For the purposes of solving this problem, ignore air resistance. (The actual range at this elevation was 121 km; air resistance cannot be ignored for the high muzzle speed of the shells.)

52. The range R of a projectile is defined as the magnitude of the horizontal displacement of the projectile *when it returns to its original altitude*. In other words, the range is the distance between the launch point and the impact point on flat ground. A projectile is launched at $t = 0$ with initial speed v_i at an angle θ above the horizontal. (a) Find the time t at which the projectile returns to its original altitude. (b) Show that the range is

$$R = \frac{v_i^2 \sin 2\theta}{g}$$

[*Hint:* Use the trigonometric identity $\sin 2\theta = 2 \sin \theta \cos \theta$.]

53. Use the expression in Problem 52 to find (a) the maximum range of a projectile with launch speed v_i and (b) the launch angle θ at which the maximum range occurs.

54. A projectile is launched at $t = 0$ with initial speed v_i at an angle θ above the horizontal. (a) What are v_x and v_y at

the projectile's highest point? (b) Find the time t at which the projectile reaches its maximum height. (c) Show that the maximum height H of the projectile is

$$H = \frac{(v_i \sin \theta)^2}{2g}$$

55. Two angles are complementary when their sum is 90.0°. Find the ranges for two projectiles launched with identical initial speeds of 36.2 m/s at angles of elevation above the horizontal that are complementary pairs. (a) For one trial, the angles of elevation are 36.0° and 54.0°. (b) For the second trial, the angles of elevation are 23.0° and 67.0°. (c) Finally, the angles of elevation are both set to 45.0°. (d) What do you notice about the range values for each complementary pair of angles? At which of these angles was the range greatest?

4.5 Apparent Weight

56. Oliver has a mass of 76.2 kg. He is riding in an elevator that has a downward acceleration of 1.37 m/s². With what magnitude force does the elevator floor push upward on Oliver?

57. Yolanda, whose mass is 64.2 kg, is riding in an elevator that has an upward acceleration of 2.13 m/s². What force does she exert on the floor of the elevator?

58. When on the ground, Ian's weight is measured to be 640 N. When Ian is on an elevator, his apparent weight is 700 N. What is the net force on the system (Ian and the elevator) if their combined mass is 1050 kg?

59. While on an elevator, Jaden's apparent weight is 550 N. When he is on the ground, the scale reading is 600 N. What is Jaden's acceleration?

60. You are standing on a bathroom scale inside an elevator. Your weight is 140 lb, but the reading of the scale is 120 lb. (a) What is the magnitude and direction of the acceleration of the elevator? (b) Can you tell whether the elevator is speeding up or slowing down?

61. Refer to Example 4.12. What is the apparent weight of the same passenger (weighing 598 N) in the following situations? In each case, the magnitude of the elevator's acceleration is 0.50 m/s². (a) After having stopped at the fifteenth floor, the passenger pushes the eighth floor button; the elevator is beginning to move downward. (b) The elevator is moving downward and is slowing down as it nears the eighth floor.

62. Luke stands on a scale in an elevator that has a constant acceleration upward. The scale reads 0.960 kN. When Luke picks up a box of mass 20.0 kg, the scale reads 1.200 kN. (The acceleration remains the same.) (a) Find the acceleration of the elevator. (b) Find Luke's weight.

63. Felipe is going for a physical before joining the swim team. He is concerned about his weight, so he carries his scale into the elevator to check his weight while

heading to the doctor's office on the twenty-first floor of the building. If his scale reads 750 N while the elevator has an upward acceleration of 2.0 m/s², what does the nurse measure his weight to be?

Comprehensive Problems

64. A drag racer crosses the finish line of a 400.0-m track with a final speed of 104 m/s. (a) Assuming constant acceleration during the race, find the racer's time and the minimum coefficient of static friction between the tires and the road. (b) If, because of bad tires or wet pavement, the acceleration were 30.0% smaller, how long would it take to finish the race?

65. An African swallow carrying a very small coconut is flying horizontally with a speed of 18 m/s. (a) If it drops the coconut from a height of 100 m above the Earth, how long will it take before the coconut strikes the ground? (b) At what horizontal distance from the release point will the coconut strike the ground?

66. A ball is thrown horizontally off the edge of a cliff with an initial speed of 20.0 m/s. (a) How long does it take for the ball to fall to the ground 20.0 m below? (b) How long would it take for the ball to reach the ground if it were dropped from rest off the cliff edge? (c) How long would it take the ball to fall to the ground if it were thrown at an initial velocity of 20.0 m/s but 18° below the horizontal?

67. A marble is rolled so that it is projected horizontally off the top landing of a staircase. The initial speed of the marble is 3.0 m/s. Each step is 0.18 m high and 0.30 m wide. Which step does the marble strike first?

68. You are serving as a consultant for the newest James Bond film. In one scene, Bond must fire a projectile from a cannon and hit the enemy headquarters located on the top of a cliff 75.0 m above and 350 m from the cannon. The cannon will shoot the projectile at an angle of 40.0° above the horizontal. The director wants to know what the speed of the projectile must be when it is fired from the cannon so that it will hit the enemy headquarters. What do you tell him? [*Hint:* Don't assume the projectile will hit the headquarters at the highest point of its flight.]

69. An airplane is traveling from New York to Paris, a distance of 5.80×10^3 km. Ignore the curvature of the Earth. (a) If the cruising speed of the airplane is 350.0 km/h, how much time will it take for the airplane to make the round-trip on a calm day? (b) If a steady wind blows from New York to Paris at 60.0 km/h, how much time will the round-trip take? (c) How much time will it take if there is a crosswind of 60.0 km/h?

70. In free fall, we assume the acceleration to be constant. Not only is air resistance ignored, but the gravitational field strength is assumed to be constant. From what height can an object fall to the Earth's surface such that the gravitational field strength changes less than 1.000% during the fall?

71. The graph for this problem shows the vertical velocity component v_y of a bouncing ball as a function of time. The y-axis points up. Answer these questions based on the data in the graph. (a) At what time does the ball reach its maximum height? (b) For how long is the ball in contact with the floor? (c) What is the maximum height of the ball? (d) What is the acceleration of the ball while in the air? (e) What is the average acceleration of the ball while in contact with the floor?

72. A rocket engine can accelerate a rocket launched from rest vertically up with an acceleration of 20.0 m/s². However, after 50.0 s of flight the engine fails. (a) What is the rocket's altitude when the engine fails? (b) When does it reach its maximum height? (c) What is the maximum height reached? [*Hint:* A graphical solution may be easiest.] (d) What is the velocity of the rocket just before it hits the ground?

73. A particle has a constant acceleration of 5.0 m/s² to the east. At time $t = 0$, it is 2.0 m east of the origin and its velocity is 20 m/s north. What are the components of its position vector at $t = 2.0$ s?

74. A baseball batter hits a long fly ball that rises to a height of 44 m. An outfielder on the opposing team can run at 7.6 m/s. What is the farthest the fielder can be from where the ball will land so that it is possible for him to catch the ball?

75. A 15-kg crate starts at rest at the top of a 60.0° incline. The coefficients of friction are $\mu_s = 0.40$ and $\mu_k = 0.30$. The crate is connected to a hanging 8.0-kg box by an ideal rope and pulley. (a) As the crate slides down the incline, what is the tension in the rope? (b) How long does it take the crate to slide 2.00 m down the incline? (c) To push the crate back up the incline at constant speed, with what force P should Pauline push on the crate (parallel to the incline)? (d) What is the smallest mass that you could substitute for the 8.0-kg box to keep the crate from sliding down the incline?

76. A beanbag is thrown horizontally from a dorm room window a height h above the ground. It hits the ground

a horizontal distance h (the *same* distance h) from the dorm directly below the window from which it was thrown. Ignoring air resistance, find the direction of the beanbag's velocity just before impact.

77. An unmarked police car starts from rest just as a speeding car passes at a speed of v. If the police car speeds up with a constant acceleration of a, what is the speed of the police car when it catches up to the speeder, who does not realize she is being pursued and does not vary her speed?

78. A seagull is flying horizontally 8.00 m above the ground at 6.00 m/s. The bird is carrying a clam in its beak and plans to crack the clamshell by dropping it on some rocks below. Ignoring air resistance, (a) what is the horizontal distance to the rocks at the moment that the seagull should let go of the clam? (b) With what speed relative to the rocks does the clam smash into the rocks? (c) With what speed relative to the seagull does the clam smash into the rocks?

79. The minimum stopping distance of a car moving at 30.0 mi/h is 12 m. Under the same conditions (so that the maximum braking force is the same), what is the minimum stopping distance for 60.0 mi/h? Work by proportions to avoid converting units.

80. A car traveling at 29 m/s (65 mi/h) runs into a bridge abutment after the driver falls asleep at the wheel. (a) If the driver is wearing a seat belt and comes to rest within a 1.0-m distance, what is his acceleration (assumed constant)? (b) A passenger who isn't wearing a seat belt is thrown into the windshield and comes to a stop in a distance of 10.0 cm. What is the acceleration of the passenger?

81. Find the point of no return for an airport runway of 1.50 mi in length if a jet plane can accelerate at 10.0 ft/s^2 and decelerate at 7.00 ft/s^2. The point of no return occurs when the pilot can no longer abort the takeoff without running out of runway. What length of time is available from the start of the motion in which to decide on a course of action?

82. A helicopter is flying horizontally at 8.0 m/s and an altitude of 18 m when a package of emergency medical supplies is ejected horizontally backward with a speed of 12 m/s *relative to the helicopter.* Ignoring air resistance, what is the horizontal distance between the package and the helicopter when the package hits the ground?

83. A locust jumps at an angle of 55.0° and lands 0.800 m from where it jumped. (a) What is the maximum height of the locust during its jump? Ignore air resistance. (b) If it jumps with the same initial speed at an angle of 45.0°, would the maximum height be larger or smaller? (c) What about the range? (d) Calculate the maximum height and range for this angle.

84. A toboggan is sliding down a snowy slope. The table shows the speed of the toboggan at various times during its trip. (a) Make a graph of the speed as a function of time. (b) Judging by the graph, is it plausible that the toboggan's acceleration is constant? If so, what is the acceleration? (c) Ignoring friction, what is the angle of incline of the slope? (d) If friction is significant, is the angle of incline larger or smaller than that found in (c)? Explain.

Time Elapsed, t (s)	Speed of Toboggan, v (m/s)
0	0
1.14	2.8
1.62	3.9
2.29	5.6
2.80	6.8

85. Show that for a projectile launched at an angle of 45° the maximum height of the projectile is one quarter of the range (the distance traveled on flat ground).

86. An airtrack glider, 8.0 cm long, blocks light as it goes through a photocell gate. The glider is released from rest on a frictionless inclined track and the gate is positioned so that the glider has traveled 96 cm when it is in the middle of the gate. The timer gives a reading of 333 ms for the glider to pass through this gate. Friction is negligible. What is the acceleration (assumed constant) of the glider along the track?

87. You want to make a plot of the trajectory of a projectile. That is, you want to make a plot of the height y of the projectile as a function of horizontal distance x. The projectile is launched from the origin with an initial speed v_i at an angle θ above the horizontal. Show that the equation of the trajectory followed by the projectile is

$$y = \left(\frac{v_{iy}}{v_{ix}}\right)x + \left(\frac{-g}{2v_{ix}^2}\right)x^2$$

88. Locusts can jump to heights of 0.30 m. (a) Assuming the locust jumps straight up, and ignoring air resistance, what is the takeoff speed of the locust? (b) The locust actually jumps at an angle of about 55° to the horizontal, and air resistance is not negligible. The result is that the takeoff speed is about 40% higher than the value you calculated in part (a). If the mass of the locust is 2.0 g and its body moves 4.0 cm in a straight line while accelerating from rest to the takeoff speed, calculate the acceleration of the locust (assumed constant). (c) Ignore the locust's weight and estimate the force exerted on the hind legs by the ground. Compare this force with the locust's weight. Was it reasonable to ignore the locust's weight?

✦89. In Fig. 4.3, the block of mass m_1 slides to the right with coefficient of kinetic friction μ_k on a horizontal surface. The block is connected to a hanging block of mass m_2 by a light cord that passes over a light, frictionless pulley. (a) Find the acceleration of each of the blocks and the tension in the cord. (b) Check your answers in the special cases $m_1 \ll m_2$, $m_1 \gg m_2$, and $m_1 = m_2$. (c) For what value of m_2 (if any) do the two blocks slide at constant velocity? What is the tension in the cord in that case?

✦90. When salmon head upstream to spawn, they often must make their way up a waterfall. If the water is not moving too fast, the salmon can swim right up through the falling water. If the water is falling with too great a speed, the salmon jump out of the water to get to a place in the waterfall where the water is not falling so fast. When humans build dams that interrupt the usual route followed by the salmon, artificial fish ladders must also be built to allow the salmon to get back uphill to the spawning area. These fish ladders consist of a series of small waterfalls with still pools of water in between them (see the figure). Assume that the water is at rest in the pools at the top and bottom of one "rung" of the fish ladder, that water falls straight down from one pool to the next, and that salmon can swim at 5.0 m/s with respect to the water. (a) What is the maximum height of a waterfall up which the salmon can swim without having to jump? (b) If a waterfall is 1.5 m high, how high must the salmon jump to get to water through which it can swim? Assume that they jump straight up. (c) What initial speed must a salmon have to jump the height found in part (b)? (d) For a 1.0-m-high waterfall, how fast will the salmon be swimming with respect to the ground when it starts swimming up the waterfall?

91. Your current case as an FBI investigator involves a possible assassination attempt. The crime scene is a tall building, about 150 m high. As a foreign official was walking into the building, a flowerpot fell from above him and nearly landed on his head. One witness says that someone accidentally knocked the flowerpot from a twenty-fourth-story window, 94 m above the ground. Another witness was inside the building looking out of an eighteenth-story window when she saw the flowerpot fall. She claims that the flowerpot took exactly 0.044 s to fall from the top of the window to the bottom of the window, a distance of 1.5 m. (She knows this because she was videotaping her pet dachshund doing tricks and the flowerpot falling past the window was filmed in the background.) The top of the eighteenth-story window is 75 m above the ground. Could the flowerpot have fallen with zero initial velocity from the twenty-fourth-story window?

(figure not drawn to scale)

✦92. Jesse James and his gang are planning to rob the train carrying the payroll from the Lost Gulch mine. A Wells Fargo guard on the train spots Jesse astride his horse at a perpendicular distance of 0.300 km from the train tracks. The train is moving at 25.0 m/s on a straight track. The guard wants to frighten Jesse and the desperadoes away by shooting a hole in Jesse's ten-gallon hat, which happens to be at the same height as the guard's gun (see the figure). The muzzle velocity of the guard's gun is 0.350 km/s. Ignore air resistance. (a) Should he aim the gun directly at Jesse's hat, in front of the hat, or behind the hat? Explain. (b) Unsure of the correct angle to aim the gun, the guard decides to aim his gun at a right angle to the track and fire the bullet a little before the time when he will be directly opposite to Jesse. At what distance before the point where the guard is directly opposite Jesse James should the guard fire? (c) Does the guard need to worry about the force of gravity on the bullet? If so, how far above the hat should he aim?

Answers to Practice Problems

4.1 0.31 m to the right (block 1) and 0.31 m down (block 2)

4.2 Impossible to pull the crate up with a single pulley. The entire weight of the crate would be supported by a single strand of cable and that weight exceeds the breaking strength of the cable.

4.3 20 s

4.4 2500 N

4.5 5.00 s after they leave the starting point; 4.00 km/s in the +x-direction

4.6 (a) down the incline; (b) up the incline; (c) 0.2 m/s^2 down the incline

4.7 (a) 3.8 m; (b) 3.00 s

4.8 2

4.9 $v_i^2/(4g)$

4.10 Ignoring air resistance, the two arrows have the same constant horizontal velocity component: $v_{2x} - v_{1x} = 0$ (choosing the x-axis horizontal and the y-axis up). Their vertical velocity components are different, but they *change at the same rate*, so $v_{2y} - v_{1y}$ stays constant. The difference in their velocities ($\vec{v}_2 - \vec{v}_1$) stays constant. This constant difference in their velocities makes the difference in their positions ($\vec{r}_2 - \vec{r}_1$) change with time.

4.11 $v_{fx} = 500.0$ m/s; $v_{fy} = -19.8$ m/s; bullet enters the water at an angle of 2.27° below the horizontal.

4.12 (a) 392 N; (b) 431 N

Answers to Checkpoints

4.1 Only if the plane's acceleration is constant must its average velocity be 470 km/h west. If its acceleration is not constant, the average velocity is not necessarily 470 km/h west. To find the average velocity, we would divide the plane's displacement by the time interval.

4.2 Yes. For motion along an incline, it simplifies the problem to choose one axis parallel to the incline and the other perpendicular to the incline.

4.3 Yes. If you throw a ball upward, it is in free fall as soon as it loses contact with your hand.

4.4 The horizontal velocity component does not change, while the vertical component is zero at the highest point, so the velocity is directed horizontally. The acceleration is constant and directed vertically downward throughout the flight, including at the highest point.

4.5 Your velocity is downward and decreasing in magnitude, so your acceleration is upward. Then the upward normal force exerted on you by the scale must be greater than your weight. The scale reading is greater than your weight.

Circular Motion

German athlete Susanne Keil throws the hammer during the German Athletics championships. Keil qualified for the 2004 Olympics in Athens with a 67.77-m throw.

In the track and field event called the *hammer throw*, the "hammer" is actually a metal ball (mass 4.00 kg for women or 7.26 kg for men) attached by a cable to a grip. The athlete whirls the hammer several times around while not leaving a circle of radius 2.1 m and then releases it. The winner is the athlete whose hammer lands the greatest distance away. How large a force does an athlete have to exert on the grip to whirl the massive hammer around in a circle? What kind of path does the hammer follow once it is released? (See pp. 155–156 for the answer.)

- gravitational forces (Section 2.6)
- Newton's second law: force and acceleration (Sections 3.3 and 3.4)
- velocity and acceleration (Sections 3.2 and 3.3)
- apparent weight (Section 4.5)
- normal and frictional forces (Section 2.7)

Concepts & Skills to Review

5.1   DESCRIPTION OF UNIFORM CIRCULAR MOTION

Ask someone to name the most important machine ever invented by humans and you are likely to get the *wheel* as a response. Rotating objects are so important to modern—and even not-so-modern—technology that we barely notice them. Examples include wheels on cars, bicycles, trains, and lawnmowers; propellers on airplanes and helicopters; CDs and DVDs; computer hard drives; the gears and hands of an analog clock; amusement park rides and centrifuges—the list is endless.

Rotation of a Rigid Body   To describe circular motion, we could use the familiar definitions of displacement, velocity, and acceleration. But much of the circular motion around us occurs in the rotation of a rigid object. A **rigid body** is one for which the distance between any two points of the body remains the same when the body is translated or rotated. When such an object rotates, every point on the object moves in a circular path. The radius of the path for any point is the distance between that point and the axis of rotation. When a compact disk spins inside a CD player, different points on the CD have different velocities and accelerations. The velocity and acceleration of a given point keep changing direction as the CD spins. It would be clumsy to describe the rotation of the CD by talking about the motion of arbitrary points on it. However, some quantities are the *same* for every point on the CD. It is much simpler, for instance, to say "the CD spins at 210 rpm" instead of saying "a point 6.0 cm from the rotation axis of the CD is moving at 1.3 m/s."

In a **rigid body,** the distance between any two points is constant.

The abbreviation rpm means *revolutions per minute.*

Angular Displacement and Angular Velocity   To simplify the description of circular motion, we concentrate on *angles* instead of distances. If a CD spins through $\frac{1}{4}$ of a turn, every point moves through the same angle (90°), but points at different radii move different linear distances. On the CD shown in Fig. 5.1, point 1 near the axis of rotation moves through a smaller distance than point 4 on the circumference. For this reason we define a set of variables that are analogous to displacement, velocity, and acceleration, but use angular measure instead of linear distance. Instead of displacement, we speak of **angular displacement** $\Delta\theta$, the angle through which the CD turns. A point on the CD moves along the circumference of a circle. As the point moves from the angular position θ_i to the angular position θ_f, a radial line drawn between the center of the circle and that point sweeps out an angle $\Delta\theta = \theta_f - \theta_i$, which is the angular displacement of the CD during that time interval (Fig. 5.2).

Definition of angular displacement:

$$\Delta\theta = \theta_f - \theta_i \qquad (5\text{-}1)$$

CONNECTION:

Equations (5-1) through (5-3) have a familiar form because ω is the *rate of change* of θ, just as velocity is the rate of change of position.

The sign of the angular displacement indicates the sense of the rotation. The usual convention is that a positive angular displacement represents counterclockwise rotation and a negative angular displacement represents clockwise rotation. Counterclockwise and clockwise are only well defined for a particular viewing direction; counterclockwise rotation viewed from above is clockwise when viewed from below.

+ Counterclockwise
− Clockwise

Remember that the notation $\lim\limits_{\Delta t \to 0}$ indicates that $\Delta\theta$ is the angular displacement during a *very short* time interval Δt (short enough that the ratio $\Delta\theta/\Delta t$ doesn't change significantly if we make the time interval even shorter).

Figure 5.1 A CD rotates through $\frac{1}{4}$ turn; points 1, 2, 3, and 4 travel through the same angle but different distances to reach their new positions, marked 1′, 2′, 3′, and 4′, respectively.

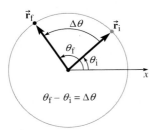

Figure 5.2 Angular positions such as θ_i and θ_f are measured counterclockwise from a reference axis (usually the x-axis).

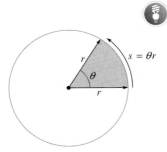

Figure 5.3 Definition of the radian: angle θ in radians is the arc length s divided by the radius r. The angle shown is 1 rad ≈ 57.3°.

The **average angular velocity** ω_{av} is the average rate of change of the angular displacement.

Definition of average angular velocity:

$$\omega_{av} = \frac{\Delta\theta}{\Delta t} \tag{5-2}$$

If we let the time interval Δt become shorter and shorter, we are averaging over smaller and smaller time intervals. In the limit $\Delta t \to 0$, ω_{av} becomes the **instantaneous angular velocity** ω.

Definition of instantaneous angular velocity:

$$\omega = \lim_{\Delta t \to 0} \frac{\Delta\theta}{\Delta t} \tag{5-3}$$

The angular velocity also indicates—through its algebraic sign—in what direction the CD is spinning. Since angular displacements can be measured in degrees or radians, angular velocities have units such as degrees/second, radians/second, degrees/day, and the like.

Radian Measure   You may be most familiar with measuring angles in degrees, but in many situations the most convenient measure is the **radian**. One such situation is when we relate the angular displacement or angular velocity of a rotating object with the distance traveled by, or the speed of, some point on the object.

In Fig. 5.3, an angle θ between two radii of a circle define an arc of length s. We say that θ is the angle *subtended* by the arc. The arc length is proportional to both the radius of the circle and to the angle subtended. The angle θ in radians is *defined* as

$$\theta \text{ (in radians)} = \frac{s}{r} \tag{5-4}$$

where r is the radius of the circle. Since an angle in radians is defined by the ratio of two lengths, it is dimensionless (a pure number). We use the term radians, abbreviated "rad," to keep track of the angular measure used. Since "rad" is not a physical unit like meters or kilograms, it does not have to balance in Eq. (5-4). For the same reason, we can drop "rad" whenever there is no chance of being misunderstood. We can write $\omega = 23 \text{ s}^{-1}$ as long as context makes it clear that we mean 23 radians per second.

In equations that relate linear variables to angular variables [such as Eq. (5-4)], think of r as the number of meters of arc length per radian of angle subtended. In other words, think of r as having units of meters per radian. Doing so, the radians cancel out in these equations. For example, if $\theta = 2.0$ rad and $r = 1.2$ m, then the arc length is

$$s = \theta r = 2.0 \text{ rad} \times 1.2 \frac{\text{m}}{\text{rad}} = 2.4 \text{ m}$$

Since the arc length for an angle of 360° is the circumference of the circle, the radian measure of an angle of 360° is

$$\theta = \frac{s}{r} = \frac{2\pi r}{r} = 2\pi \text{ rad}$$

Therefore, the conversion factor between degrees and radians is

$$360° = 2\pi \text{ rad} \tag{5-5}$$

Example 5.1

Angular Speed of Earth

Earth is rotating about its axis. What is its angular speed in rad/s? (The question asks for angular *speed*, so we do not have to worry about the direction of rotation.)

Strategy The Earth's angular velocity is constant, or nearly so. Therefore, we can calculate the average angular velocity for any convenient time interval and, in turn, the Earth's instantaneous angular speed $|\omega|$.

Solution It takes the Earth 1 day to complete one rotation, during which the angular displacement is 2π rad. More formally, during a time interval $\Delta t = 1$ day, the angular displacement of the Earth is $\Delta\theta = 2\pi$ rad. So the angular speed of the Earth is 2π rad/day, and then convert days to seconds.

$$1 \text{ day} = 24 \text{ h} = 24 \text{ h} \times 3600 \text{ s/h} = 86\,400 \text{ s}$$

$$|\omega| = \frac{2\pi \text{ rad}}{86\,400 \text{ s}} = 7.3 \times 10^{-5} \text{ rad/s}$$

Discussion Notice that this problem is analogous to a problem in linear motion such as: "A car travels in a straight line at constant speed. In 3 h, it has traveled 192 mi. What is its velocity in m/s?" Just about everything in circular motion and rotation has this kind of analog—which means we can draw heavily on what we have already learned.

Earth actually completes one rotation in 23.9345 h (see inside back cover) rather than in 24 h due to Earth's motion around the Sun. This distinction would be important only if we needed a more precise value of $|\omega|$ (more than two significant figures).

Practice Problem 5.1 Angular Speed of Venus

Venus completes one rotation about its axis every 5816 h. What is the angular speed of the rotation of Venus in rad/s?

Relation Between Linear and Angular Speed

For a point moving in a circular path of radius r, the linear distance traveled along the circular path during an angular displacement of $\Delta\theta$ (in radians) is the arc length s where

$$s = r|\Delta\theta| = r|\theta_f - \theta_i| \quad \text{(angles in radians)} \qquad (5\text{-}6)$$

The point in question could be a point particle moving in a circular path, or it could be any point on a rotating rigid object. Since Eq. (5-6) comes directly from the definition of the radian, any equation derived from Eq. (5-6) is valid only when the angles are measured in radians.

What is the linear speed at which the point moves? The average linear speed is the distance traveled divided by the time interval,

$$v_{av} = \frac{s}{\Delta t} = \frac{r|\Delta\theta|}{\Delta t} \quad (\Delta\theta \text{ in radians})$$

We recognize $\Delta\theta/\Delta t$ as the average angular velocity ω_{av}. If we take the limit as Δt approaches zero, both average quantities (v_{av} and ω_{av}) become instantaneous quantities. Therefore, the relationship between linear speed and angular speed is

$$v = r|\omega| \quad (\omega \text{ in radians per unit time}) \qquad (5\text{-}7)$$

Equation (5-7) relates only the *magnitudes* of the linear and angular speeds. The direction of the velocity vector $\vec{v}$ is tangent to the circular path. For a rotating object, points farther from the axis move at higher linear speeds; they have a circle of bigger radius to travel and, therefore, cover more distance in the same time interval. For example, a person standing at the equator has a much higher linear speed due to Earth's rotation than does a person standing at the Arctic Circle (see Fig. 5.4).

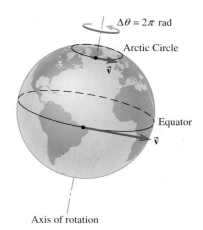

$\Delta\theta = 2\pi$ rad

Arctic Circle

$\vec{v}$

Equator

$\vec{v}$

Axis of rotation

Figure 5.4 A person standing at the Equator is moving much faster than another person standing at the Arctic Circle, but their *angular* speeds are the same.

⚠ In uniform circular motion, speed is constant but velocity is *not* constant because the *direction* of the velocity is changing.

Period and Frequency

When the speed of a point moving in a circle is constant, its motion is called **uniform circular motion**. Even though the speed of the point is constant, the velocity is not: the direction of the velocity is changing. This distinction is important when we find the acceleration of an object in uniform circular motion (Section 5.2). The time for the point to travel completely around the circle is called the **period** of the motion, *T*. The **frequency** of the motion, which is the number of revolutions per unit time, is defined as

$$f = \frac{1}{T} \tag{5-8}$$

since

$$\frac{\text{revolutions}}{\text{second}} = \frac{1}{\text{second/revolution}}$$

✓ CHECKPOINT 5.1

If it takes $\frac{1}{7200}$ of a second for a computer hard drive to spin around once, what is its frequency?

The speed is the total distance traveled divided by the time taken,

$$v = \frac{2\pi r}{T} = 2\pi r f$$

Then, for uniform circular motion

$$|\omega| = \frac{v}{r} = 2\pi f \quad (\omega \text{ in radians per unit time}) \tag{5-9}$$

SI unit of frequency: 1 Hz = 1 rev/s

where, in SI units, angular velocity ω is measured in rad/s and frequency f is measured in hertz (Hz). The hertz is a derived unit equal to 1 rev/s. The dimensions of Eq. (5-9) are correct since both revolutions and radians are pure numbers. The physical dimensions on both sides are a number per second (s^{-1}).

Example 5.2

Speed in a Centrifuge

A centrifuge is spinning at 5400 rpm. (a) Find the period (in s) and frequency (in Hz) of the motion. (b) If the radius of the centrifuge is 14 cm, how fast (in m/s) is an object at the outer edge moving?

Strategy Remember that rpm means *revolutions per minute*. 5400 rpm *is* the frequency, but in a unit other than Hz. After a unit conversion, the other quantities can be found using the relations already discussed.

Solution (a) First convert rpm to Hz:

$$f = 5400 \, \frac{\text{rev}}{\text{min}} \times \frac{1 \, \text{min}}{60 \, \text{s}} = 90 \, \text{rev/s}$$

so the frequency is $f = 90 \, \text{Hz} = 90 \, \text{s}^{-1}$. The period is

$$T = 1/f = 0.011 \, \text{s}$$

(b) To find the linear speed, we first find the angular speed in rad/s:

$$|\omega| = 90 \, \frac{\text{rev}}{\text{s}} \times 2\pi \, \frac{\text{rad}}{\text{rev}} = 180\pi \, \text{rad/s}$$

continued on next page

Example 5.2 continued

So $|\omega| = 2\pi f = 180\pi$ rad/s. The linear speed is

$$v = |\omega|r = 180\pi \, \text{s}^{-1} \times 0.14 \, \text{m} = 79 \, \text{m/s}$$

Discussion   Notice that much of this problem was done with unit conversions. Instead of memorizing a formula such as $|\omega| = 2\pi f$, an understanding of where the formula came

from (in this case, that 2π radians correspond to one revolution) is more useful and less prone to error.

Practice Problem 5.2   Clothing in the Drier

An automatic clothing drier spins at 51.6 rpm. If the radius of the drier drum is 30.5 cm, how fast is the outer edge of the drum moving?

Rolling Without Slipping: Rotation and Translation Combined

When an object is rolling, it is both rotating and translating. The wheel rotates about an axle, but the axle is not at rest; it moves forward or backward. What is the relationship between the angular speed of the wheel and the linear speed of the axle? You might guess that $v = |\omega|r$ is the answer. You would be right, as long as the object rolls without slipping or skidding.

There is no fixed relationship between the linear and angular speeds of a wheel if it is allowed to skid or slip. When an impatient driver guns the engine the instant a traffic light turns green, the automobile wheels are likely to slip. The rubber sliding against the road surface makes the squealing sound and leaves tracks on the road. The driver could actually make the acceleration of the car greater by giving the engine *less* gas. When the wheels are skidding or slipping, *kinetic* friction propels the car forward instead of the potentially larger force of *static* friction.

For a wheel that rolls *without* slipping, as the wheel turns through one complete rotation, the axle moves a distance equal to the circumference of the wheel (Fig. 5.5). Think of a paint roller leaving a line of paint as it rolls along a wall. After one complete

Figure 5.5 (a) As a wheel of radius r that rolls without slipping turns through one complete revolution, the distance its axle moves is equal to the circumference of the wheel ($2\pi r$). (b) As a wheel rolls without slipping through an angle $\Delta\theta$, the distance the axle moves is equal to the arc length s.

rotation, the same point on the roller wheel is touching the wall as was initially touching it. The length of the line of paint is $2\pi r$. The elapsed time is T, so the axle's speed is

$$v_{\text{axle}} = \frac{2\pi r}{T}$$

while the angular speed of the roller is

$$|\omega| = \frac{2\pi}{T}$$

Thus,

$$v_{\text{axle}} = |\omega|r \quad (\omega \text{ in radians per unit time}) \tag{5-10}$$

Example 5.3

Angular Speed of a Rolling Wheel

Kevin is riding his motorcycle at a speed of 13.0 m/s. If the diameter of the rear tire is 65.0 cm, what is the angular speed of the rear wheel? Assume that it rolls without slipping.

Strategy   The given diameter of the tire enables us to find the circumference and, thus, the distance traveled in one revolution of the wheel. From the speed of the motorcycle we can find how many revolutions the tire must make per second.

Solution   During one revolution of the wheel, the motorcycle travels a distance equal to the tire's circumference $2\pi r$ (Fig. 5.5). Then the time to make one revolution is T and the speed v is

$$v = \frac{\text{distance}}{\text{time}} = \frac{2\pi r}{T}$$

Therefore, $T = 2\pi r/v$. For each revolution there is an angular displacement of $\Delta\theta = 2\pi$ radians, so

$$|\omega| = \frac{|\Delta\theta|}{\Delta t} = \frac{2\pi}{T}$$

Substituting $T = 2\pi r/v$ and remembering that the radius is half the diameter,

$$|\omega| = \frac{2\pi}{2\pi r/v} = \frac{v}{r} = \frac{13.0 \text{ m/s}}{(0.650 \text{ m})/2} = 40.0 \frac{\text{rad}}{\text{s}}$$

Discussion   Check: Time for one revolution is

$$\frac{2\pi \text{ rad}}{40.0 \text{ rad/s}} = 0.157 \text{ s}.$$

Time to travel a distance $2\pi r = 2.04$ m is

$$\frac{2.04 \text{ m}}{13.0 \text{ m/s}} = 0.157 \text{ s}.$$

Looks good.

You could have obtained this answer immediately by looking back through the text for the equation $|\omega| = v/r$ and plugging in numbers, but the solution here shows that you can re-create that equation. Here, and in many cases, there is no need to memorize a formula if you understand the concepts behind the formula. You are then less apt to make a mistake by forgetting a factor or constant in the equation, or by using an inappropriate formula. For another example, if an object moves along a straight line at a constant velocity, you know instantly that the displacement is the velocity times the time interval—not because you have memorized an equation ($\Delta\vec{r} = \vec{v}\,\Delta t$), but because you understand the concepts of displacement and velocity. This is the sort of internalization of scientific thinking that you will develop with more and more practice in problem solving.

Practice Problem 5.3   Rolling Drum

A cylindrical steel drum is tipped over and rolled along the floor of a warehouse. If the drum has a radius of 0.40 m and makes one complete turn every 8.0 s, how long does it take to roll the drum 36 m?

5.2   RADIAL ACCELERATION

For a particle undergoing uniform circular motion, the *magnitude* of the velocity vector is constant, but its direction is continuously changing. At any instant of time, the direction of the instantaneous velocity is tangent to the path, as discussed in Section 3.2. Since the *direction* of the velocity continually changes, the particle has a nonzero acceleration.

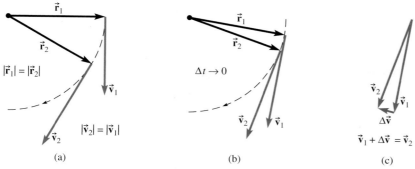

$|\vec{r}_1| = |\vec{r}_2|$

$|\vec{v}_2| = |\vec{v}_1|$

(a)

$\Delta t \to 0$

(b)

$\vec{v}_1 + \Delta\vec{v} = \vec{v}_2$

(c)

Figure 5.6 Uniform circular motion at constant speed. (a) The velocity vector is always tangent to the circular path and perpendicular to the radius at that point. (b) As the time interval between two velocity measurements decreases, the angle between the velocity vectors decreases. (c) The change in velocity ($\Delta\vec{v}$) is found by placing the tails of the two velocity vectors together. Then $\Delta\vec{v}$ is drawn from the tip of the initial velocity ($\vec{v}_1$) to the tip of the final velocity ($\vec{v}_2$) so that $\vec{v}_1 + \Delta\vec{v} = \vec{v}_2$.

In Fig. 5.6a, two velocity vectors of equal magnitude are drawn tangent to a circular path of radius r, representing the velocity at two different times of an object moving around a circular path with constant speed. At any instant, the velocity vector is perpendicular to a radius drawn from the center of the circle to the position of the object. As the time between velocity measurements approaches zero, the radii become closer together (Fig. 5.6b). To find the acceleration, $\vec{a} = \lim_{\Delta t \to 0} \dfrac{\Delta\vec{v}}{\Delta t}$, we must first find the change in velocity $\Delta\vec{v}$ for a very short time interval. Figure 5.6c shows that as the time interval Δt approaches zero, the angle between the two velocities also approaches zero and $\Delta\vec{v}$ becomes perpendicular to the velocity.

Since $\Delta\vec{v}$ is perpendicular to the velocity, it is directed along a radius of the circle. Inspection of Figs. 5.6b and 5.6c shows that $\Delta\vec{v}$ is radially *inward* (toward the center of the circle). Since the acceleration $\vec{a}$ has the same direction as $\Delta\vec{v}$ (in the limit $\Delta t \to 0$), the acceleration is also directed radially inward (Fig. 5.7)—that is, along a radius of the circular path toward the center of the circle. The acceleration of an object undergoing *uniform* circular motion is often called the **radial acceleration $\vec{a}_r$**. The word *radial* here just reminds us of the direction of the acceleration. (A synonym for radial acceleration is *centripetal acceleration. Centripetal* means "toward the center.")

CONNECTION:

Radial acceleration is not a new kind of acceleration. The acceleration vector for an object moving in uniform circular motion is directed radially inward toward the center of the circle.

In uniform circular motion, the direction of the acceleration is radially inward (toward the center of the circular path).

✓ CHECKPOINT 5.2

Does a radial acceleration mean that the speed of the object is changing?

Magnitude of the Radial Acceleration

To find the magnitude of the radial acceleration for uniform circular motion, we must find the change in velocity $\Delta\vec{v}$ for a time interval Δt in the limit $\Delta t \to 0$. The velocity keeps the same magnitude but changes direction at a steady rate, equal to the angular velocity ω. In a time interval Δt, the velocity $\vec{v}$ rotates through an angle equal to the angular displacement $\Delta\theta = \omega \Delta t$. During this time interval, the velocity vector sweeps out an arc of a circle of "radius" v (Fig. 5.8). In the limit $\Delta t \to 0$, the

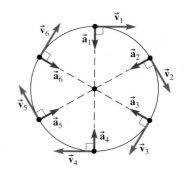

Figure 5.7 In uniform circular motion, the acceleration is always directed toward the center of the circle, perpendicular to the velocity (see ⬛ interactive: circular motion).

Figure 5.8 The velocity vector sweeps out an arc of a circle whose "length" is nearly equal to that of the chord $\Delta\vec{\mathbf{v}}$.

magnitude of $\Delta\vec{\mathbf{v}}$ becomes equal to the arc length, since a very short arc approaches a straight line. Then

$$|\Delta\vec{\mathbf{v}}| = \text{arc length} = \text{radius of circle} \times \text{angle subtended}$$
$$= v\,|\Delta\theta| = v\,|\omega|\,\Delta t$$

Acceleration is the rate of change of velocity, so the magnitude of the radial acceleration is

$$a_r = |\vec{\mathbf{a}}| = \frac{|\Delta\vec{\mathbf{v}}|}{\Delta t} = v|\omega| \quad (\omega \text{ in radians per unit time}) \qquad (5\text{-}11)$$

where absolute value symbols are used with the vector quantities to indicate their magnitudes. Velocity and angular velocity are not independent; $v = |\omega|r$. It is usually most convenient to write the magnitude of the radial acceleration in terms of one or the other of these two quantities. So we write the radial acceleration in two other equivalent ways using $v = |\omega|r$:

$$a_r = \frac{v^2}{r} \quad \text{or} \quad a_r = \omega^2 r \quad (\omega \text{ in radians per unit time}) \qquad (5\text{-}12)$$

Note that Eqs. (5-11) and (5-12) assume that ω is expressed in *radians* per unit time (normally rad/s, but rad/min or rad/h would be correct).

Example 5.4

A Spinning CD

If a CD spins at 210 rpm, what is the radial acceleration of a point on the outer rim of the CD? The CD is 12 cm in diameter.

Strategy   From the number of revolutions per minute, we can find the frequency and the angular velocity. The angular velocity and the radius of the CD enable us to calculate the radial acceleration.

Solution   We convert 210 rpm into a frequency in revolutions per second (Hz).

$$f = 210\,\frac{\text{rev}}{\text{min}} \times \frac{1}{60}\,\frac{\text{min}}{\text{s}} = 3.5\,\frac{\text{rev}}{\text{s}} = 3.5\,\text{Hz}$$

For each revolution, the CD rotates through an angle of 2π radians. The angular velocity is

$$|\omega| = 2\pi f = 2\pi\,\frac{\text{radians}}{\text{rev}} \times 3.5\,\frac{\text{rev}}{\text{s}} = 7.0\pi\,\text{rad/s}$$

Then using Eq. (5-12), the radial acceleration is

$$a_r = \omega^2 r = (7.0\pi\,\text{rad/s})^2 \times 0.060\,\text{m} = 29\,\text{m/s}^2$$

Discussion   When finding the radial acceleration, use whichever form of Eq. (5-12) is more convenient. For rotating objects such as the spinning CD, it's usually easiest to think in terms of the angular velocity. For an object moving around a circle, such as a satellite in orbit whose speed is known, it might be easier to use v^2/r. Since the two equations are equivalent, either can be used in any situation.

Practice Problem 5.4   Radial Acceleration of a Point on an Old Record

What is the radial acceleration of a point 25.4 cm from the center of a record that is rotating at 78 rpm on a turntable?

Applying Newton's Second Law to Uniform Circular Motion

Now that we know the magnitude and direction of the acceleration of any object in uniform circular motion, we can use Newton's second law to relate the net force acting on the object to the speed and radius of its motion. The net force is found in the usual way: each of the individual forces acting on the object is identified and then the forces are added as vectors. Every force acting must be exerted *by some other object*. Resist the temptation to add in a new, separate force just because something moves in a circle. For an object to move in a circle at constant speed, real, physical forces such as gravity, tension, normal forces, and friction must act on it; these forces combine to produce a net force that has the correct magnitude and is always perpendicular to the velocity of the object.

Problem-Solving Strategy for an Object in Uniform Circular Motion

1. Begin as for any Newton's second law problem: identify all the forces acting on the object and draw an FBD.
2. Choose perpendicular axes at the point of interest so that one is radial and the other is tangent to the circular path.
3. Find the radial component of each force.
4. Apply Newton's second law as follows:

$$\sum F_r = ma_r$$

where $\sum F_r$ is the radial component of the net force and the radial component of the acceleration is

$$a_r = \frac{v^2}{r} = \omega^2 r$$

(For uniform circular motion, neither the net force nor the acceleration has a tangential component.)

Example 5.5

The Hammer Throw

 What force does the athlete exert on the grip? What path does the hammer follow after release?

An athlete whirls a 4.00-kg hammer six or seven times around and then releases it. Although the purpose of whirling it around several times is to increase the hammer's speed, assume that *just before* the hammer is released, it moves at constant speed along a circular arc of radius 1.7 m. At the instant she releases the hammer, it is 1.0 m above the ground and its velocity is directed 40° above the horizontal. The hammer lands a horizontal distance of 74.0 m away. What force does the athlete apply to the grip just before she releases it? Ignore air resistance.

Strategy After release, the only force acting on the hammer is gravity. The hammer moves in a parabolic trajectory like any other projectile. By analyzing the projectile motion of the hammer, we can find the speed of the hammer just

after its release. Just *before* release, the forces acting on the hammer are the tension in the cable and gravity. We can relate the net force on the hammer to its radial acceleration, calculated from the speed and radius of its path. The problem becomes two subproblems, one dealing with circular motion and the other with projectile motion. The final velocity for the circular motion is the initial velocity for the projectile motion.

Solution During its projectile motion, the initial velocity has magnitude v_i (to be determined) and direction $\theta = 40°$ above the horizontal. Choosing the $+y$-axis pointing up, the displacement of the hammer (in component form) is $\Delta x = 74.0$ m and $\Delta y = -1.0$ m (Fig. 5.9), the acceleration of the hammer is $a_x = 0$ and $a_y = -g$, and the initial velocity is $v_{ix} = v_i \cos \theta$ and $v_{iy} = v_i \sin \theta$. Then, from Eqs. (4-8) and (4-9),

$$\Delta x = (v_i \cos \theta)\,\Delta t \quad \text{and} \quad \Delta y = (v_i \sin \theta)\,\Delta t - \tfrac{1}{2}g(\Delta t)^2$$

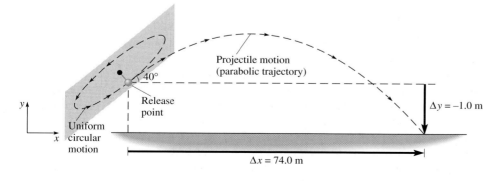

Figure 5.9

Path of the hammer from just before its release until it hits the ground. (Distances are *not* to scale.)

continued on next page

Example 5.5 continued

Solving the left equation for Δt and substituting into the right equation gives

$$\Delta y = \not v_i \sin \theta \, \frac{\Delta x}{\not v_i \cos \theta} - \frac{1}{2} g \left(\frac{\Delta x}{v_i \cos \theta} \right)^2$$

After a bit of algebra, we can solve for v_i. First we multiply through by $2v_i^2 \cos^2 \theta$:

$$2v_i^2 \cos^2 \theta \, \Delta y = 2v_i^2 \cos^2 \theta \, \frac{\Delta x \sin \theta}{\cos \theta}$$

$$- \frac{\cancel{2} \, v_i^2 \cancel{\cos^2 \theta}}{\cancel{2}} \, g \left(\frac{\Delta x}{\cancel{v_i \cos \theta}} \right)^2$$

Subtracting the first term on the right side from both sides and factoring out v_i^2,

$$v_i^2 (2 \, \Delta y \cos^2 \theta - 2 \, \Delta x \cos \theta \, \sin \theta) = -g(\Delta x)^2$$

Now we solve for v_i:

$$v_i = \sqrt{\frac{g(\Delta x)^2}{2\Delta x \cos\theta \, \sin\theta - 2\Delta y \cos^2\theta}}$$

$$= \sqrt{\frac{9.80 \text{ m/s}^2 \times (74.0 \text{ m})^2}{2(74.0 \text{ m}) \cos 40° \sin 40° - 2(-1.0 \text{ m}) \cos^2 40°}}$$

$$= 26.9 \text{ m/s}$$

The net force on the hammer can be found from Newton's second law. The two forces acting on the hammer are due to the tension in the cable and to gravity (Fig. 5.10). We ignore the gravitational force, assuming that the hammer's weight is small compared with the tension in the cable. Then the tension in the cable is the only significant force acting on the hammer. Assuming uniform circular motion, the cable pulls radially inward and causes a radial

Figure 5.10
FBD for the hammer just before its release. (Not to scale.)

acceleration of magnitude v^2/r. Newton's second law in the radial direction is

$$\sum F_r = T = ma_r = \frac{mv^2}{r}$$

Substituting numerical values,

$$T = \frac{4.00 \text{ kg} \times (26.9 \text{ m/s})^2}{1.7 \text{ m}} = 1700 \text{ N}$$

The tension is much larger than the weight of the hammer (≈ 40 N), so the assumption that we could ignore the weight is justified. The athlete must apply a force of magnitude 1700 N—almost 400 lb—to the grip.

Discussion   This example demonstrates the cumulative nature of physics concepts. The basic concepts keep reappearing, to be used over and over and to be extended for use in new contexts. Part of the problem involves new concepts (radial acceleration); the rest of the problem involves old material (Newton's second law, projectile motion, and tension in a cord).

Practice Problem 5.5   Rotating Carousel

A horse located 8.0 m from the central axis of a rotating carousel moves at a speed of 6.0 m/s. The horse is at a fixed height (it does not move up and down). What is the net force acting on a child seated on this horse? The child's weight is 130 N.

Example 5.6

Conical Pendulum

Suppose you whirl a stone in a horizontal circle at a slow speed so that the weight of the stone is *not* negligible compared with the tension in the cord. Then the cord cannot be horizontal—the tension must have a vertical component to cancel the weight and leave a horizontal net force (Fig. 5.11). If the cord has length L, the stone has mass m, and the cord makes an angle ϕ with the vertical direction, what is the constant angular speed of the stone?

Strategy   The net force must point toward the center of the circle, since the stone is in uniform circular motion.

With the stone in the position depicted in Fig. 5.11a, the direction of the net force is along the $+x$-axis. This time the tension in the cord does not pull toward the center, but the *net* force does.

Solution   Start by drawing an FBD (Fig. 5.11b). Now apply Newton's second law in component form. The acceleration has components $a_x = \omega^2 r$ and $a_y = 0$. For the x-components,

$$\sum F_x = T \sin \phi = ma_x = m\omega^2 r$$

continued on next page

Example 5.6 continued

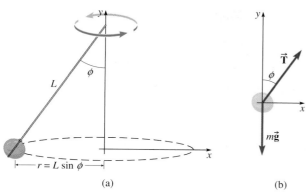

Figure 5.11

(a) A stone is whirled in a horizontal circle of radius $r = L \sin \phi$.
(b) An FBD for the stone.

Since the problem does not specify r, we must express r in terms of L and ϕ. In Fig. 5.11a, the radius forms a right triangle with the cord and the y-axis. Then

$$r = L \sin \phi$$

and

$$\sum F_x = T \sin \phi = m\omega^2 L \sin \phi$$

Therefore, $T = m\omega^2 L$. For the y-components,

$$\sum F_y = T \cos \phi - mg = ma_y = 0 \quad \Rightarrow \quad T \cos \phi = mg$$

Now we eliminate the tension:

$$(m\omega^2 L) \cos \phi = mg$$

Solving for $|\omega|$,

$$|\omega| = \sqrt{\frac{g}{L \cos \phi}}$$

Discussion   We should check the dimensions of the final expression. Since $\cos \phi$ is dimensionless,

$$\sqrt{\frac{[L/T^2]}{[L]}} = \frac{1}{[T]}$$

which is correct for ω (SI unit rad/s).
 Another check is to ask how ω and ϕ are related for a given length cord. As ϕ increases toward 90°, the cord gets closer to horizontal and the radius increases. In our expression, as ϕ increases, $\cos \phi$ decreases and, therefore, ω increases, in accordance with experience: the stone would have to be whirled faster and faster to make the cord more nearly horizontal.

Conceptual Practice Problem 5.6   Conical Pendulum on the Moon

Examine the result of Example 5.6 to see how ω depends on g, all other things being equal. Where the gravitational field is weaker, do you have to whirl the stone faster or more slowly to keep the cord at the same angle ϕ? Is that in accord with your intuition?

5.3 UNBANKED AND BANKED CURVES

Unbanked Curves   When you drive an automobile in a circular path along an unbanked roadway, friction acting on the tires due to the pavement acts to keep the automobile moving in a curved path. This frictional force acts *sideways*, toward the center of the car's circular path (Fig. 5.12). The frictional force might also have a tangential component; for example, if the car is braking, a component of the frictional force makes the car slow down by acting backward (opposite to the car's velocity). For now we assume that the car's speed is constant and that the forward or backward component of the frictional force is negligibly small.

As long as the tires roll without slipping, there is no relative motion between the bottom of the tires and the road, so it is the force of *static* friction that acts (see Section 2.7). If the car is in a skid, then it is the smaller force of kinetic friction that acts as the bottom portion of the tire slides along the pavement. As the speed of the car increases, or for slippery surfaces with low coefficients of friction, the static frictional force may not be enough to hold the car in its curved path.

Banked Curves   To help prevent cars from going into a skid or losing control, the roadway is often banked (tilted at a slight angle) around curves so that the outer portion of the road—the part farthest from the center of curvature—is higher than the inner portion. Banking changes the angle and magnitude of the normal force, $\vec{N}$, so that it has a horizontal component N_x directed toward the center of curvature (in the

Application of radial acceleration and contact forces: banked roadways

(a)   (b)   (c)

Figure 5.12 (a) A car negotiating a curve at constant speed on an *unbanked* roadway. The car's acceleration is toward the center of the circular path. (b) A head-on view of the same car. The center of the circular path is to the left as viewed here. The force vectors $\vec{N}$ and $\vec{f}_s$ are shown acting on one tire, but they represent the *total* normal and frictional forces acting on all four tires. (c) FBD for the car.

radial direction—see Fig. 5.13). Then we need no longer rely solely on friction to keep the car moving in a circular path as it negotiates the curve; this component of the normal force acts to help the car remain on the curved path. Figure 5.13 shows a banked road with the normal force, the gravitational force, and, in parts (b) and (c), the radial component of the normal force N_x. We choose the axes so that the x-axis is in the direction of the acceleration, which is to the left; the axes are *not* parallel and perpendicular to the incline.

Figure 5.13 (a) Head-on view of a car negotiating a curve at constant speed on a *banked* roadway. The car's acceleration is toward the center of the circular path (to the left as viewed here). $\vec{N}$ represents the *total* normal force acting on all four tires. The car moves at just the right speed so that the frictional force is zero. (b) Resolving the normal force into x- and y-components. (c) FBD for the car with the normal force represented by its components.

(a)   (b)   (c)

Example 5.7

A Possible Skid: Unbanked and Banked Curves

A car is going around an unbanked curve at the recommended speed of 11 m/s (see Fig. 5.12). (a) If the radius of curvature of the path is 25 m and the coefficient of static friction between the rubber and the road is $\mu_s = 0.70$, does the car skid as it goes around the curve? (b) What happens if the driver ignores the highway speed limit sign and travels at 18 m/s? (c) What speed is safe for traveling around the curve if the road surface is wet from a recent rainstorm and the

continued on next page

Example 5.7 continued

coefficient of static friction between the wet road and the rubber tires is $\mu_s = 0.50$? (d) For a car to safely negotiate the curve in icy conditions at a speed of 13 m/s, what banking angle would be required (see Fig. 5.13)?

Strategy The force of static friction is the only horizontal force acting on the car when the curve is not banked. The maximum force of static friction, which depends on road conditions, determines the maximum possible radial acceleration of the car. Therefore, we can compare the radial acceleration necessary to go around the curve at the specified speeds with the maximum possible radial acceleration determined by the coefficient of static friction. For part (d), in icy conditions we cannot rely much on friction, but the normal force has a horizontal component when the road is banked.

Solution (a) We find the radial acceleration required for a speed of 11 m/s:

$$a_r = \frac{v^2}{r} = \frac{(11 \text{ m/s})^2}{25 \text{ m}} = 4.8 \text{ m/s}^2$$

In order to have that acceleration, the component of the net force acting toward the center of curvature must be

$$\sum F_r = ma_r = m\frac{v^2}{r}$$

The only force with a horizontal component is the static frictional force acting on the tires due to the road (see the FBD in Fig. 5.12c). Therefore,

$$\sum F_r = f_s = m\frac{v^2}{r}$$

We must check to make sure that the maximum frictional force is not exceeded:

$$f_s \leq \mu_s N$$

Since $N = mg$, the car can go around the curve without skidding as long as

$$\cancel{m}\frac{v^2}{r} \leq \mu_s \cancel{m}g$$

Thus, the radial acceleration cannot exceed $\mu_s g$. That limits the car to speeds satisfying

$$v \leq \sqrt{\mu_s g r}$$

Substituting numerical values,

$$v \leq \sqrt{0.70 \times 9.80 \text{ m/s}^2 \times 25 \text{ m}} = 13 \text{ m/s}$$

Since 11 m/s is less than the maximum safe speed of 13 m/s, the car safely negotiates the curve.

(b) At 18 m/s, the car moves at a speed higher than the maximum safe speed of 13 m/s. The frictional force cannot supply the radial acceleration needed for the car to go around the curve—the car goes into a skid.

(c) In part (a), we found that the car is limited to speeds satisfying

$$v \leq \sqrt{\mu_s g r}$$

With $\mu_s = 0.50$, the maximum safe speed is

$$v_{\max} = \sqrt{\mu_s g r} = \sqrt{0.50 \times 9.80 \text{ m/s}^2 \times 25 \text{ m}} = 11 \text{ m/s}$$

which is the same maximum speed recommended by the road sign. The highway engineer knew what she was doing when she had the sign placed along the road.

(d) Finally, we find the banking angle that would enable cars to travel around the curve at 13 m/s in icy conditions. Assuming that friction is negligible, the horizontal component of the normal force is the only horizontal force. With the x-axis pointing toward the center of curvature and the y-axis vertical (Fig. 5.13),

$$\sum F_x = N \sin \theta = mv^2/r \tag{1}$$

and

$$\sum F_y = N \cos \theta - mg = 0 \tag{2}$$

Dividing Eq. (1) by Eq. (2) gives

$$\frac{N \sin \theta}{N \cos \theta} = \tan \theta = \frac{mv^2/r}{mg} = \frac{v^2}{rg}$$

$$\theta = \tan^{-1}\frac{v^2}{rg} = \tan^{-1}\frac{(13 \text{ m/s})^2}{25 \text{ m} \times 9.80 \text{ m/s}^2} = 35° \tag{3}$$

Discussion Notice that the mass of the car does not appear in Eq. (3); the same banking angle holds for a scooter, motorcycle, car, or tractor-trailer. Notice also that the banking angle depends on the square of the speed. Automobile racetracks and bicycle racetracks have highly banked road surfaces at hairpin curves to minimize skidding of the high-speed vehicles. However, a banking angle of 35° is far greater than those used in practice along public roadways. Careful drivers would not try to drive around this curve in icy conditions at 13 m/s. What do you think might happen in icy conditions to a car that is traveling *very slowly* along a road banked at such a steep angle?

Highway curves are banked at slight angles to help drivers who are driving at reasonable speeds for the road conditions. They are not banked to save speed demons from their folly.

Practice Problem 5.7   A Bobsled Race

A bobsled races down an icy hill and then comes on a horizontal curve, located 60.0 m from the bottom of the hill. The sled is traveling at 22.4 m/s (50 mph) as it approaches the curve that has a radius of curvature of 50.0 m. The curve is banked at an angle of 45° and the frictional force on the sled runners is negligible. Does the sled make it safely around the curve?

If there is *no* friction between the road and the tires, then there is only one speed at which it is safe to drive around a given curve. *With* friction, there is a *range* of safe speeds. The static frictional force can have any magnitude from 0 to $\mu_s N$ and it can be directed either up or down the bank of the road.

When an airplane pilot makes a turn in the air, the pilot makes use of a banking angle. The airplane itself is tilted as if it were traveling over an inclined surface. Because of the shape of the wings, an aerodynamic force called *lift* acts upward when the plane is in level flight. To go around a turn, the wings are tilted; the lift force stays perpendicular to the wings and, therefore, now has a horizontal component (Fig. 5.14), just as the normal force has a horizontal component for a car on a banked curve. This component supplies the necessary radial acceleration, while the vertical component of the lift holds the plane up. Therefore,

$$L_x = ma_r = \frac{mv^2}{r} \quad \text{and} \quad L_y = mg$$

where the x-axis is horizontal and the y-axis is vertical. The lift force is different in its physical origin from the normal force, but its components split up the same way, so a plane in a turn banks its wings at the same angle that a road would be banked for the same speed and radius of curvature. Of course, planes usually move much faster than cars and use large radii of curvature when they turn.

Application of radial acceleration: banking angle of an airplane

Figure 5.14 The lift force $\vec{\mathbf{L}}$ is perpendicular to the wings of the plane. To turn, the pilot tilts the wings so a component of the lift force is directed toward the center of the circular path of the plane.

✓ CHECKPOINT 5.3

A plane can't make a turn without tilting its wings. Why can a car turn on a flat road?

5.4   CIRCULAR ORBITS OF SATELLITES AND PLANETS

A satellite can orbit Earth in a circular path because of the long-range gravitational force on the satellite due to the Earth. The magnitude of the gravitational force on the satellite is

$$F = \frac{Gm_1 m_2}{r^2} \tag{2-6}$$

where the universal gravitational constant is $G = 6.67 \times 10^{-11}$ N·m²/kg². We can use Newton's second law to find the speed of a satellite in circular orbit at constant speed. Let m be the mass of the satellite and M_E be the mass of the Earth. The direction of the gravitational force on the satellite is always toward the center of the Earth, which is the center of the orbit (Fig. 5.15). Since gravity is the only force acting on the satellite,

$$\sum F_r = G\frac{mM_E}{r^2}$$

where r is the distance from the *center* of the Earth to the satellite. Then, from Newton's second law,

$$\sum F_r = ma_r = \frac{mv^2}{r}$$

Setting these equal,

$$G\frac{mM_E}{r^2} = \frac{mv^2}{r}$$

Solving for the speed yields

$$v = \sqrt{\frac{GM_E}{r}} \tag{5-13}$$

Notice that the mass of the satellite does not appear in the equation for speed; it has been algebraically canceled. The greater inertia of a more massive satellite is overcome

Application of radial acceleration: circular orbits

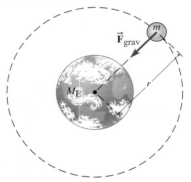

Figure 5.15 Satellite in orbit around Earth.

by a proportionally greater gravitational force acting on it. Thus, the speed of a satellite in a circular orbit does not depend on the mass of the satellite. Equation (5-13) also shows that satellites in lower orbits (smaller radii) have greater speeds.

We have been discussing satellites orbiting Earth, but the same principles apply to the circular orbits of satellites around other planets and to the orbits of the planets around the Sun. For planetary orbits, the mass of the Sun would appear in Eq. (5-13) instead of the Earth's mass, because the *Sun's* gravitational pull keeps the planets in their orbits. The planetary orbits are actually ellipses (Fig. 5.16) instead of circles, although for most of the planets in the solar system the ellipses are nearly circular. Mercury is the exception; its orbit is markedly different from a circle.

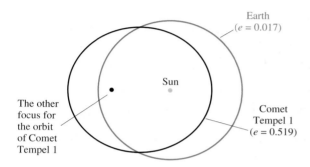

Figure 5.16 The shapes of two elliptical orbits around the Sun. (The *sizes* of the orbits are not to scale.) An ellipse looks like an elongated circle. The degree of elongation is measured by a quantity called the eccentricity *e*. A circle is a special case of an ellipse with *e* = 0. Most of the planetary orbits are nearly circular, with the exception of Mercury. The sum of the distances from any point on an ellipse to each of two fixed points (called the *foci*) is constant. The Sun is at one focus of each orbit. Since Earth's orbit is nearly circular, the second focus is very near the Sun.

Example 5.8

Speed of a Satellite

The Hubble Space Telescope is in a circular orbit 613 km above Earth's surface. The average radius of the Earth is 6.37×10^3 km and the mass of Earth is 5.97×10^{24} kg. What is the speed of the telescope in its orbit?

Strategy We first need to find the orbital radius of the telescope. It is not 613 km; that is the distance from the *surface* of Earth to the telescope. We must add the radius of the Earth to 613 km to find the orbital radius, which is measured from the center of the Earth to the telescope. Then we use Newton's second law, along with what we know about radial acceleration.

Solution The radius of the telescope's orbit is

$$r = 6.13 \times 10^2 \text{ km} + 6.37 \times 10^3 \text{ km} = (0.613 + 6.37) \times 10^3 \text{ km}$$

$$= 6.98 \times 10^3 \text{ km}$$

The net force on the telescope is equal to the gravitational force, given by Newton's law of gravity. Newton's second law relates the net force to the acceleration. Both are directed radially inward.

$$\sum F_r = \frac{GmM_E}{r^2} = \frac{mv^2}{r}$$

where *m* is the mass of the telescope. Solving for the speed, we find

$$v = \sqrt{\frac{GM_E}{r}}$$

$$v = \sqrt{\frac{6.67 \times 10^{-11} \text{ N} \cdot \text{m}^2/\text{kg}^2 \times 5.97 \times 10^{24} \text{ kg}}{6.98 \times 10^6 \text{ m}}}$$

$$v = 7550 \text{ m/s} = 27\,200 \text{ km/h}$$

Discussion *Any* satellite orbiting Earth at an altitude of 613 km has this same speed, regardless of its mass.

Practice Problem 5.8 Speed of Earth in Its Orbit

What is the speed of Earth in its approximately circular orbit about the Sun? The average Earth–Sun distance is 1.50×10^{11} m and the mass of the Sun is 1.987×10^{30} kg. Once you find the speed, use it along with the distance traveled by the Earth during one revolution about the Sun to calculate the time in seconds for one orbit.

Kepler's Laws of Planetary Motion

At the beginning of the seventeenth century, Johannes Kepler (1571–1630) proposed three laws to describe the motion of the planets. These laws predated Newton's laws of motion and his law of gravity. They offered a far simpler description of planetary motion than anything that had been proposed previously. We turn history on its head and look at one of Kepler's laws as a consequence of Newton's laws. The fact that Newton could derive Kepler's laws from his own work on gravity was seen as a confirmation of Newtonian mechanics.

Kepler's laws of planetary motion are

- The planets travel in elliptical orbits (Fig. 5.16) with the Sun at one focus of the ellipse.
- A line drawn from a planet to the Sun sweeps out equal areas in equal time intervals.
- The square of the orbital period is proportional to the cube of the average distance from the planet to the Sun.

Kepler's first law can be derived from the inverse square law of gravitational attraction. The derivation is a bit complicated, but for any two objects that have such an attraction, the orbit of one about the other is an ellipse, with the stationary object located at one focus. (Planetary orbits are also affected by gravitational interactions with other planets; Kepler's laws ignore these small effects.) The circle is a special case of an ellipse where the two foci coincide. We discuss Kepler's second law in Chapter 8.

We can derive Kepler's third law from Newton's law of universal gravitation for the special case of a circular orbit. The gravitational force gives rise to the radial acceleration:

Application of radial acceleration: Kepler's third law for a circular orbit

$$\sum F_r = \frac{GmM_{Sun}}{r^2} = \frac{mv^2}{r}$$

Solving for v yields

$$v = \sqrt{\frac{GM_{Sun}}{r}}$$

The distance traveled during one revolution is the circumference of the circle, which is equal to $2\pi r$. The speed is the distance traveled during one orbit divided by the period:

$$v = \sqrt{\frac{GM_{Sun}}{r}} = \frac{2\pi r}{T}$$

Now we solve for T:

$$T = 2\pi\sqrt{\frac{r^3}{GM_{Sun}}}$$

Squaring both sides yields

$$T^2 = \frac{4\pi^2}{GM_{Sun}} r^3 = \text{constant} \times r^3 \tag{5-14}$$

Equation (5-14) is Kepler's third law: the square of the period of a planet is directly proportional to the cube of the average orbital radius.

Application of radial acceleration: geostationary orbits

Although Kepler's laws were derived for the motion of planets, they apply to satellites orbiting the Earth as well. Many satellites, such as those used for communications, are placed in a *geostationary* (or *geosynchronous*) orbit—a circular orbit in Earth's equatorial plane whose period is equal to Earth's rotational period (Fig. 5.17). A satellite in geostationary orbit remains directly above a particular point on the equator; to observers on the ground, it seems to hover above that point without moving. Due to their fixed positions with respect to Earth's surface, geostationary satellites are used as relay stations for communication signals. In Example 5.9, we find the speed of a geostationary satellite.

 CHECKPOINT 5.4

Do all geostationary satellites, no matter their masses, have to be the same height above Earth? Explain.

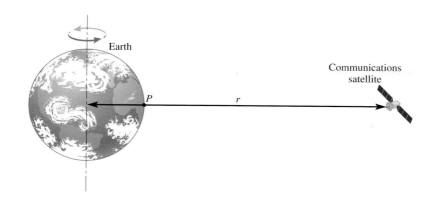

Figure 5.17 Geostationary satellite orbiting the Earth. The satellite has the same angular velocity as Earth, so it is always directly above point *P*.

Example 5.9

Geostationary Satellite

A 300.0-kg communications satellite is placed in a geostationary orbit 35,800 km above a relay station located in Kenya. What is the speed of the satellite in orbit?

Strategy The period of the satellite is 1 d or approximately 24 h. To find the speed of the satellite in orbit we use Newton's law of gravity and his second law of motion along with what we know about radial acceleration.

Solution Let m be the mass of the satellite and let M_E be the mass of the Earth. Gravity is the only force acting on the satellite in its orbit. From Newton's law of universal gravitation, Newton's second law, and the expression for radial acceleration,

$$\sum F_r = \frac{GmM_E}{r^2} = \frac{mv^2}{r}$$

Solving for the speed yields

$$v = \sqrt{\frac{GM_E}{r}}$$

We must add the mean radius of the Earth, $R_E = 6.37 \times 10^6$ m, to the height of the satellite above the Earth's surface to find the orbital radius.

$$r = h + R_E = 3.58 \times 10^7 \text{ m} + 0.637 \times 10^7 \text{ m}$$

$$= 4.217 \times 10^7 \text{ m}$$

Substituting numerical values into the speed equation,

$$v = \sqrt{\frac{6.67 \times 10^{-11} \text{ N·m}^2/\text{kg}^2 \times 5.97 \times 10^{24} \text{ kg}}{4.217 \times 10^7 \text{ m}}}$$

$$= \sqrt{9.443 \times 10^6 \text{ m}^2/\text{s}^2}$$

$$v = 3.07 \times 10^3 \text{ m/s}$$

Discussion This result, an orbital speed of 3.07 km/s and a distance above Earth's surface of 35,800 km, applies to *all*

geostationary satellites. The mass of the satellite does not matter; it cancels out of the equations for orbital radius and for speed.

If we were actually putting a satellite into orbit, we would use a more accurate value for the period. We should use a time of 23 h and 56 min, which is the length of a *sidereal day*—the time for Earth to complete one rotation about its axis relative to the fixed stars. The solar day, 24 h, is the period of time between the daily appearances of the Sun at its highest point in the sky. The fact that Earth moves around the Sun is what causes the difference between these two ways of measuring the length of a day. The error introduced by using the longer time is negligible in this problem.

We can use Kepler's third law to check the result. Examples 5.8 and 5.9 both concern circular orbits around the Earth. Is the square of the period proportional to the cube of the orbital radius? From Example 5.8, $r_1 = 6.98 \times 10^3$ km and

$$T_1 = \frac{2\pi r_1}{v} = \frac{2\pi \times 6.98 \times 10^3 \text{ km}}{7.55 \text{ km/s}} = 5810 \text{ s}$$

From the present example, $r_2 = 4.22 \times 10^7$ m and

$$T_2 = 24 \text{ h} \times \frac{3600 \text{ s}}{1 \text{ h}} = 86\,400 \text{ s}$$

The ratio of the squares of the periods is

$$\left(\frac{T_2}{T_1}\right)^2 = \left(\frac{86\,400 \text{ s}}{5810 \text{ s}}\right)^2 = 221$$

The ratio of the cubes of the radii is

$$\left(\frac{r_2}{r_1}\right)^3 = \left(\frac{4.22 \times 10^7 \text{ m}}{6.98 \times 10^6 \text{ m}}\right)^3 = 221$$

Practice Problem 5.9   Orbital Radius of Venus

The period of the orbit of Venus around the Sun is 0.615 Earth years. Using this information, find the radius of its orbit in terms of R, the radius of Earth's orbit around the Sun.

Example 5.10

Orbiting Satellites

A satellite revolves about Earth with an orbital radius of r_1 and speed v_1. If an identical satellite were set into circular orbit with the same speed about a planet of mass three times that of Earth, what would its orbital radius be?

Strategy   We can apply Newton's law of universal gravitation and set up a ratio to solve for the new orbital radius.

Solution   From Newton's second law, the magnitude of the gravitational force on the satellite is equal to the satellite's mass times the magnitude of its radial acceleration:

$$\frac{Gm M_{\mathrm{E}}}{r_1^2} = \frac{m v_1^2}{r_1}$$

where M_{E} and m are the masses of Earth and of the satellite, respectively. Solving for r_1 yields

$$r_1 = \frac{GM_{\mathrm{E}}}{v_1^2}$$

Now we apply Newton's second law to the orbit of the second satellite about the planet of mass $3M_{\mathrm{E}}$:

$$\frac{Gm \times 3M_{\mathrm{E}}}{r_2^2} = \frac{m v_1^2}{r_2}$$

$$r_2 = \frac{G \times 3M_{\mathrm{E}}}{v_1^2}$$

The ratio of r_2 to r_1 is

$$\frac{r_2}{r_1} = \frac{G \times 3M_{\mathrm{E}}/v_1^2}{GM_{\mathrm{E}}/v_1^2} = 3$$

Thus, $r_2 = 3r_1$.

Discussion   Notice that we did not rush to substitute numerical values for the constants G and M_{E} into the equations. We took the ratio r_2/r_1 so that these constants cancel.

Practice Problem 5.10   Period of Lunar Lander

A lunar lander is orbiting about the Moon. If the radius of its orbit is $\frac{1}{3}$ the radius of Earth, what is the period of its orbit?

5.5   NONUNIFORM CIRCULAR MOTION

So far we have focused on *uniform* circular motion. Now we can extend the discussion to nonuniform circular motion, where the angular velocity changes with time.

Figure 5.18a shows the velocity vectors $\vec{v}_1$ and $\vec{v}_2$ at two different times for an object moving in a circle with changing speed. In this case, the speed is increasing ($v_2 > v_1$). In Fig. 5.18b, we subtract $\vec{v}_1$ from $\vec{v}_2$ to find the change in velocity. In the limit $\Delta t \to 0$, $\Delta\vec{v}$ does *not* become perpendicular to the velocity, as it did for uniform circular motion. Thus, the direction of the acceleration is *not* radial if the speed is changing. However, we can resolve the acceleration into tangential and radial components

Figure 5.18 Motion along a circular path with a changing speed: (a) the magnitude of velocity $\vec{v}_2$ is greater than the magnitude of velocity $\vec{v}_1$, (b) the direction of $\Delta\vec{v}$ is not radial when the speed is changing, and (c) components of $\vec{a}$ can be taken along a tangent to the curved path (a_t) and along a radius (a_r).

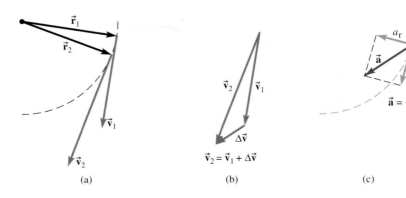

(Fig. 5.18c). The radial component a_r changes the *direction* of the velocity, and the tangential component a_t changes the *magnitude* of the velocity. Since these are perpendicular components of the acceleration, the magnitude of the acceleration is

$$a = \sqrt{a_r^2 + a_t^2}$$

Using the same method as in Section 5.2 to find the radial acceleration, but working here with only the radial *component* of the acceleration, we find that

$$a_r = \frac{v^2}{r} = \omega^2 r \quad (\omega \text{ in radians per unit time}) \tag{5-12}$$

For circular motion, *whether uniform or nonuniform*, the radial component of the acceleration is given by Eq. (5-12). However, in *uniform* circular motion the radial component of the acceleration a_r is constant in magnitude, but for nonuniform circular motion a_r changes as the speed changes.

Also still true for nonuniform circular motion is the relationship between speed and angular speed:

$$v = r\,|\omega| \tag{5-7}$$

Many problems involving nonuniform circular motion are solved in the same way as for uniform circular motion. We find the *radial component of the net force* and then apply Newton's second law along the radial direction:

$$\sum F_r = ma_r$$

Problem-Solving Strategy for an Object in Nonuniform Circular Motion

1. Begin as for any Newton's second law problem: Identify all the forces acting on the object and draw an FBD.
2. Choose perpendicular axes at the point of interest so that one axis is radial and the other is tangent to the circular path.
3. Find the radial component of each force.
4. Apply Newton's second law along the radial direction:

$$\sum F_r = ma_r$$

   where

$$a_r = \frac{v^2}{r} = \omega^2 r$$

5. If necessary, apply Newton's second law to the tangential force components:

$$\sum F_t = ma_t$$

   The tangential acceleration component a_t determines how the speed of the object changes.

✓ CHECKPOINT 5.5

For an object in circular motion, what is it about the radial acceleration that distinguishes between uniform and nonuniform circular motion?

Example 5.11

Vertical Loop-the-Loop

A roller coaster includes a vertical circular loop of radius 20.0 m (Fig. 5.19a). What is the minimum speed at which the car must move at the top of the loop so that it doesn't lose contact with the track?

Strategy   A roller coaster car moving around a vertical loop is in nonuniform circular motion; its speed decreases on the way up and increases on the way back down. Nevertheless, it is moving in a circle and has a radial acceleration component as given in Eq. (5-12) as long as it moves in a circle. The only forces acting on the car are gravity and the normal force of the track pushing the car. Even if frictional or drag forces are present, at the top of the loop they act in the tangential direction and, thus, do not contribute to the radial component of the net force. At the top of the loop, the track exerts a normal force on the car as long as the car

moves with a speed great enough to stay on the track. If the car moves too slowly, it loses contact with the track and the normal force is then zero.

Solution   The normal force exerted by the track on the car at the top pushes the car *away* from the track (downward); the normal force cannot pull up on the car. Then, at the top of the loop, the gravitational force and the normal force both point straight down toward the center of the loop. Figure 5.19b is an FBD for the car. From Newton's second law,

$$\sum F_r = N + mg = ma_r = \frac{mv_{\text{top}}^2}{r}$$

or

$$N = \frac{mv_{\text{top}}^2}{r} - mg$$

continued on next page

Figure 5.19 (a) A roller coaster car on a vertical circular loop. At the bottom of the loop, the car's acceleration $\vec{a}_{\text{bottom}}$ points upward toward the center of the circle. At the top of the loop, the car's acceleration $\vec{a}_{\text{top}}$ points downward. The magnitude of $\vec{a}_{\text{top}}$ is smaller than that of $\vec{a}_{\text{bottom}}$ because the speed is smaller at the top than at the bottom. (b) FBD for the car at the top of the loop. The track is above the car, so the normal force on the car due to the track is *downward*. (c) FBD for the car at the bottom of the loop.

Example 5.11 continued

where v_{top} stands for the speed at the top. In this expression, N stands for the magnitude of the normal force. Since $N \geq 0$,

$$m\left(\frac{v_{top}^2}{r} - g\right) \geq 0$$

or

$$v_{top} \geq \sqrt{gr}$$

Imagine sending a roller coaster car around the loop many times with a slightly smaller speed at the top each time. As v_{top} approaches $\sqrt{gr}$, the normal force at the top gets smaller and smaller. When $v_{top} = \sqrt{gr}$, the normal force just becomes zero at the top of the loop. Any slower and the car loses contact with the track *before* getting to the highest point and would fall off the track unless prevented from falling by a backup safety mechanism. Therefore, the minimum speed at the top is

$$v_{top} = \sqrt{gr} = \sqrt{9.80 \text{ m/s}^2 \times 20.0 \text{ m}} = 14.0 \text{ m/s}$$

Discussion If the car is going faster than 14 m/s at the top, its radial acceleration is larger. The track pushing on the car provides the additional net force component that results in a larger radial acceleration. The minimum speed occurs when gravity alone provides the radial acceleration at the top of the loop. In other words, $a_r = g$ at the top of the loop for minimum speed.

Practice Problem 5.11   Normal Force at the Bottom of the Track

If the speed of the roller coaster at the *bottom* of the loop is 25 m/s, what is the normal force exerted on the car by the track in terms of the car's weight mg? (See Fig. 5.19c.)

PHYSICS AT HOME

Go outside on a warm day and fill a bucket with water. Swing the bucket around in a vertical circle over your head. What, if anything, keeps the water in the bucket when the bucket is upside down over your head? Why doesn't the water spill out? Do any upward forces act on the water at that point? [*Hint:* The FBD for the water when it is directly overhead is similar to the FBD for a roller coaster car at the top of a loop.]

Conceptual Example 5.12

Acceleration of a Pendulum Bob

A pendulum is released from rest at point A (Fig. 5.20). Sketch qualitatively an FBD and the acceleration vector for the pendulum bob at points B and C.

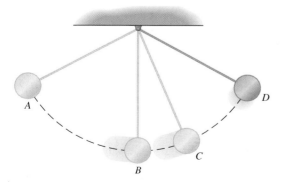

Figure 5.20
A pendulum swings to the right, starting from rest at point A.

Strategy Two forces appear on each FBD: gravity and the force due to the cord. The gravitational force is the same at both points (magnitude mg, direction down), but the force due to the cord varies in magnitude and in direction. Its direction is always along the cord. The net force on the bob is the sum of these two forces and its direction is the same as the direction of the acceleration. We can use what we know about the acceleration to guide us in drawing the forces.

The pendulum bob moves along the arc of a circle, but not at constant speed. At any point, the radial component of the acceleration is $a_r = v^2/r$. Unless $v = 0$, the radial acceleration component is nonzero. As the pendulum bob swings toward the bottom (from A to B), its speed is increasing; as it rises on the other side, its speed is decreasing. When the speed is increasing, the tangential component of the acceleration a_t is in the same direction as the velocity. From B to D, the speed is decreasing and a_t is in the direction *opposite* to

continued on next page

Conceptual Example 5.12 continued

the velocity. At point B, the speed is neither increasing nor decreasing and $a_t = 0$.

Solution and Discussion   At point B, the tangential acceleration is zero, so the acceleration points in the radial direction: straight up (Fig. 5.21). The tension in the cord pulls straight up and gravity pulls down, so the tension must be larger than the weight of the bob to give an upward net force.

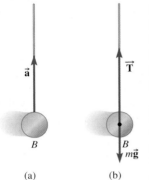

Figure 5.21

(a) Acceleration of the bob at point B. (b) FBD for the bob at B.

The acceleration at point C has both tangential and radial components. The tangential acceleration is opposite to the velocity because the bob is slowing down. Figure 5.22 shows the tangential and radial acceleration components added to form the acceleration vector $\vec{a}$ and the FBD for the bob.

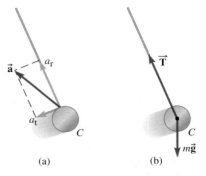

Figure 5.22

(a) At point C, the bob has both tangential and radial acceleration components. (b) FBD for the bob at C.

When the two forces are added, they give a net force in the same direction as the acceleration vector.

Conceptual Practice Problem 5.12   Analysis of the Bob at Point D

Sketch the FBD and the acceleration vector for the pendulum bob at point D, the highest point in its swing to the right.

5.6   TANGENTIAL AND ANGULAR ACCELERATION

An object in nonuniform circular motion has a changing speed and a changing angular velocity. To describe how the angular velocity changes, we define an angular acceleration. If the angular velocity is ω_1 at time t_1 and is ω_2 at time t_2, the change in angular velocity is

$$\Delta \omega = \omega_2 - \omega_1$$

The time interval during which the angular velocity changes is $\Delta t = t_2 - t_1$. The average rate at which the angular velocity changes is called the **average angular acceleration**, α_{av}.

$$\alpha_{av} = \frac{\omega_2 - \omega_1}{t_2 - t_1} = \frac{\Delta \omega}{\Delta t} \tag{5-15}$$

As we let the time interval become shorter and shorter, α_{av} approaches the **instantaneous angular acceleration**, α.

$$\alpha = \lim_{\Delta t \to 0} \frac{\Delta \omega}{\Delta t} \tag{5-16}$$

If ω is in units of rad/s, α is in units of rad/s^2.

The angular acceleration is closely related to the tangential component of the acceleration. The tangential component of velocity is

$$v_t = r \,|\omega| \tag{5-7}$$

Equation (5-7) gives us a way to relate tangential acceleration to the angular acceleration. The tangential acceleration is the rate of change of the tangential velocity, so

$$a_t = \frac{\Delta v_t}{\Delta t} = r \left| \frac{\Delta \omega}{\Delta t} \right| \quad \text{(in the limit } \Delta t \to 0)$$

Therefore,

$$a_t = r \,|\alpha| \tag{5-17}$$

Table 5.1	Relationships Between θ, ω, and α for Constant Angular Acceleration

Constant Acceleration Along x-Axis		Constant Angular Acceleration	
$\Delta v_x = v_{fx} - v_{ix} = a_x \Delta t$	(4-1)	$\Delta \omega = \omega_f - \omega_i = \alpha \Delta t$	(5-18)
$\Delta x = \frac{1}{2}(v_{fx} + v_{ix}) \Delta t$	(4-3)	$\Delta \theta = \frac{1}{2}(\omega_f + \omega_i) \Delta t$	(5-19)
$\Delta x = v_{ix} \Delta t + \frac{1}{2}a_x(\Delta t)^2$	(4-4)	$\Delta \theta = \omega_i \Delta t + \frac{1}{2}\alpha(\Delta t)^2$	(5-20)
$v_{fx}^2 - v_{ix}^2 = 2a_x \Delta x$	(4-5)	$\omega_f^2 - \omega_i^2 = 2\alpha \Delta \theta$	(5-21)

> **CONNECTION:**
> Because α is the rate of change of ω, and ω is the rate of change of θ, the equations for constant α have the same form as those for constant a_x.

Constant Angular Acceleration

The mathematical relationships between θ, ω, and α are the same as the mathematical relationships between x, v_x, and a_x that we developed in Chapter 4. Each quantity is the instantaneous rate of change of the preceding quantity. For example, a_x is the rate of change of v_x and α is the rate of change of ω. Because the mathematical relationships are the same, we can draw upon the skills and equations we developed to solve problems with constant acceleration a_x. All we have to do is take the equations for constant acceleration and replace x with θ, v_x with ω, and a_x with α (see Table 5.1).

Equation (5-18) is the definition of average angular acceleration, with α_{av} replaced by α since the angular acceleration is constant. Constant α means that ω changes linearly with time; therefore, the average angular velocity is halfway between the initial and final angular velocities for any time interval $\omega_{av} = \frac{1}{2}(\omega_i + \omega_f)$. Using this form for ω_{av} along with the definition of ω_{av} ($\omega_{av} = \Delta\theta/\Delta t$) yields Eq. (5-19). Equations (5-20) and (5-21) can be derived from the preceding two relations in a manner analogous to the derivations of Eqs. (4-4) and (4-5) in Section 4.1.

✓ CHECKPOINT 5.6

A centrifuge is "spinning up" with a constant angular acceleration. Can the radial acceleration of a sample in the centrifuge be constant? Explain.

Example 5.13

A Rotating Potter's Wheel

A potter's wheel rotates from rest to 210 rpm in a time of 0.75 s. (a) What is the angular acceleration of the wheel during this time, assuming constant angular acceleration? (b) How many revolutions does the wheel make during this time interval? (c) Find the tangential and radial components of the acceleration of a point 12 cm from the rotation axis when the wheel is spinning at 180 rpm.

Strategy We know the initial and final frequencies, so we can find the initial and final angular velocities. We also know the time it takes for the wheel to get to the final angular velocity. That is all we need to find the average angular

acceleration that, for constant angular acceleration, is equal to the instantaneous angular acceleration. To find the number of revolutions, we can find the angular displacement $\Delta\theta$ in radians and then divide by 2π rad/rev. We can find the angular velocity at $t = 0.75$ s and use it to find the radial acceleration component. The tangential acceleration is calculated from α.

continued on next page

Example 5.13 continued

Solution (a) Initially the wheel is at rest, so the initial angular velocity is zero.

$$\omega_i = 0 \text{ rad/s}$$

Converting 210 rpm to rad/s gives the final angular velocity:

$$\omega_f = 210 \frac{\text{rev}}{\text{min}} \times \frac{1}{60} \frac{\text{min}}{\text{s}} \times 2\pi \frac{\text{rad}}{\text{rev}} = 7.0\pi \text{ rad/s}$$

The angular acceleration is the rate of change of the angular velocity. Since α is constant, we can calculate it by finding the *average* angular acceleration for the time interval:

$$\alpha = \frac{\omega_f - \omega_i}{t_f - t_i} = \frac{7.0\pi \text{ rad/s} - 0}{0.75 \text{ s} - 0} = \frac{7.0\pi \text{ rad/s}}{0.75 \text{ s}} = 29 \text{ rad/s}^2$$

(b) The angular displacement is

$$\Delta\theta = \tfrac{1}{2}(\omega_f + \omega_i)\,\Delta t = \tfrac{1}{2}(7.0\pi \text{ rad/s} + 0)(0.75 \text{ s}) = 8.25 \text{ rad}$$

Since 2π rad = one revolution, the number of revolutions is

$$\frac{8.25 \text{ rad}}{2\pi \text{ rad/rev}} = 1.3 \text{ rev}$$

(c) At 180 rpm, the angular velocity is

$$\omega = 180 \frac{\text{rev}}{\text{min}} \times \frac{1}{60} \frac{\text{min}}{\text{s}} \times 2\pi \frac{\text{rad}}{\text{rev}} = 6.0\pi \text{ rad/s}$$

The radial acceleration component is

$$a_r = \omega^2 r = (6.0\pi \text{ rad/s})^2 \times 0.12 \text{ m} = 43 \text{ m/s}^2$$

and the tangential acceleration component is

$$a_t = \alpha r = 29 \text{ rad/s}^2 \times 0.12 \text{ m} = 3.5 \text{ m/s}^2$$

Discussion A quick check involves another of the equations for constant acceleration:

$$\omega_f^2 - \omega_i^2 = 2\alpha\Delta\theta$$

Since $\omega_i = 0$, we can check

$$\omega_f = \sqrt{2\alpha\Delta\theta}$$

From the answers to (a) and (b),

$$\sqrt{2\alpha\Delta\theta} = \sqrt{2 \times 29 \text{ rad/s}^2 \times 8.25 \text{ rad}} = 22 \text{ rad/s}$$

The original value for ω_f in rad/s was 7.0π rad/s. Since $\pi \approx 22/7$, the check is successful.

Practice Problem 5.13   The London Eye

The London Eye, a Ferris wheel on the banks of the Thames, has radius 67.5 m. At its cruising angular speed, it takes 30.0 min to make one complete revolution. Suppose that it takes 20.0 s to bring the wheel from rest to its cruising speed and that the angular acceleration is constant during startup. (a) What is the angular acceleration during startup? (b) What is the angular displacement of the wheel during startup?

The London Eye

5.7   APPARENT WEIGHT AND ARTIFICIAL GRAVITY

Application of apparent weight and circular motion: apparent weightlessness of orbiting astronauts

You are no doubt familiar with pictures of astronauts "floating" while in orbit around the Earth. It seems as if the astronauts are weightless. To be truly weightless, the force of gravity acting on the astronauts due to Earth would have to be zero, or at least close to zero. Is it? We can calculate the weight of an astronaut in orbit. The orbital altitude for the space shuttle is typically about 600 km above the Earth. Then the orbital radius is 600 km + 6400 km = 7000 km. Comparing the astronaut's weight in orbit to his or her weight on Earth's surface,

$$\frac{W_{\text{orbit}}}{W_{\text{surface}}} = \frac{\dfrac{GM_E m}{(R_E + h)^2}}{\dfrac{GM_E m}{R_E^2}} = \frac{R_E^2}{(R_E + h)^2} = \frac{(6400 \text{ km})^2}{(7000 \text{ km})^2} = 0.84$$

The weight in orbit is 0.84 times the weight on the surface. The astronaut weighs less but certainly isn't *weightless*! Then why does the astronaut *seem* to be weightless?

Recall Section 4.5 on the apparent weightlessness of someone unfortunate enough to be in an elevator when the cable snaps. In that situation, the elevator and the passenger both have the same acceleration ($\vec{\mathbf{a}} = \vec{\mathbf{g}}$). Similarly, the astronaut has the same acceleration as the space shuttle, which is equal to the *local* gravitational field $\vec{\mathbf{g}}$. Apparent weightlessness occurs when $\vec{\mathbf{a}} = \vec{\mathbf{g}}$, where $\vec{\mathbf{g}}$ is the *local* gravitational field.

Application: Artificial Gravity   In order for astronauts to spend long periods of time living in a space station without the deleterious effects of apparent weightlessness, *artificial gravity* would have to be created on the station. Many science fiction novels and movies feature ring-shaped space stations that rotate in order to create artificial gravity for the occupants. In a rotating space station, the acceleration of an astronaut is inward (toward the rotation axis), but the apparent gravitational field is outward. Therefore, the ceiling of rooms on the station are closest to the rotation axis and the floor is farthest away (Fig. 5.23).

The centrifuge is a device that creates artificial gravity on a smaller scale. Centrifuges are common not only in scientific and medical laboratories but also in everyday life. The first successful centrifuge was used to separate cream from milk in the 1880s. Water drips out of sopping wet clothes due to the pull of gravity when the clothes are hung on a clothesline, but the water is removed much faster by the artificial gravity created in the spin cycle of a washing machine.

The human body can be adversely affected not only by too little artificial gravity, but also by too much. Stunt pilots have to be careful about the accelerations to which they subject their bodies. An acceleration of about $3g$ can cause temporary blindness due to an inadequate supply of oxygen to the retina; the heart has difficulty pumping blood up to the head due to the blood's increased apparent weight. Larger accelerations can cause unconsciousness. Pressurized flight suits enable pilots to sustain accelerations up to about $5g$.

Figure 5.23 A rotating space station from the movie *2001: A Space Odyssey*. Note jogger in the upper half running on the floor.

Example 5.14

Stunt Pilot

Dave wants to practice vertical circles for a flying show exhibition. (a) What must the minimum radius of the circle be to ensure that his acceleration at the bottom does not exceed $3.0g$? The speed of the plane is 78 m/s at the bottom of the circle. (b) What is Dave's apparent weight at the bottom of the circular path? Express your answer in terms of his true weight.

Figure 5.24

Velocity and acceleration vectors for the plane at the bottom of the circle.

Strategy   For the *minimum* radius, we use the maximum possible radial acceleration since $a_r = v^2/r$. For the maximum radial acceleration, the *tangential* acceleration must be zero (Fig. 5.24)—the magnitude of the acceleration is $a = \sqrt{a_r^2 + a_t^2}$. Therefore, the radial acceleration component has magnitude $3.0g$ at the bottom. To find Dave's apparent weight, we do not need to use the numerical value of the radius found in part (a); we already know that his acceleration is upward and has magnitude $3.0g$.

Solution   (a) The magnitude of the radial acceleration is

$$a_r = v^2/r$$

Solving for the radius,

$$r = \frac{v^2}{a_r} = \frac{v^2}{3.0g}$$

$$= \frac{(78 \text{ m/s})^2}{3.0 \times 9.8 \text{ m/s}^2} = 210 \text{ m}$$

continued on next page

Example 5.14 continued

(b) Dave's apparent weight is the magnitude of the normal force of the plane pushing up on him. Let the y-axis point upward. The normal force is up and the gravitational force is down (Fig. 5.25). Then

$$\sum F_y = N - mg = ma_y$$

where $a_y = +3.0g$. Therefore,

$$W' = N = m(g + a_y) = 4.0mg$$

His apparent weight is 4.0 times his true weight.

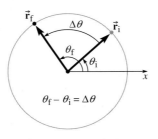

Figure 5.25
FBD for Dave.

Discussion   It might have been tempting to jump to the conclusion that an acceleration of $3.0g$ means that his apparent weight is $3.0mg$. But is his apparent weight zero when his acceleration is zero? No.

___

Practice Problem 5.14   Astronaut's Apparent Weight

What is the apparent weight of a 730-N astronaut when her spaceship has an acceleration of magnitude $2.0g$ in the following two situations: (a) just above the surface of Earth, acceleration straight up; (b) far from any stars or planets?

Application of Apparent Weight to Objects at Rest with Respect to Earth's Surface   Due to Earth's rotation, the *effective* value of g measured in a coordinate system attached to Earth's surface is slightly less than the true value of the gravitational field strength (see Section 2.6). The net force of an object placed on a scale is *not* zero because the object has a radial acceleration $a_r = \omega^2 r$ directed toward Earth's axis of rotation (Fig. 5.26). This relatively small effect is greatest where r is greatest—at the equator, where the effective value of g is about 0.3% smaller than the true value of g.

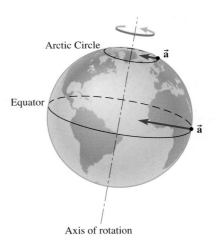

Figure 5.26   An object at rest with respect to Earth's surface has a radial acceleration due to Earth's rotation. The angular frequency ω is the same everywhere, so the radial acceleration $a_r = \omega^2 r$ is proportional to the distance from the axis of rotation.

Master the Concepts

- The angular displacement $\Delta\theta$ is the angle through which an object has turned. Positive and negative angular displacements indicate rotation in different directions. Conventionally, positive represents counterclockwise motion.

- Average angular velocity:

$$\omega_{av} = \frac{\theta_2 - \theta_1}{t_2 - t_1} = \frac{\Delta\theta}{\Delta t} \tag{5-2}$$

- Average angular acceleration:

$$\alpha_{av} = \frac{\omega_2 - \omega_1}{t_2 - t_1} = \frac{\Delta\omega}{\Delta t} \tag{5-15}$$

continued on next page

- The instantaneous angular velocity and acceleration are the limits of the average quantities as $\Delta t \to 0$.
- A useful measure of angle is the radian:

$$2\pi \text{ radians} = 360°$$

Using radian measure for θ, the arc length s of a circle of radius r subtended by an angle θ is

$$s = \theta r \quad (\theta \text{ in radian measure}) \qquad (5\text{-}4)$$

- Using radian measure for ω, the speed of an object in circular motion (including a point on a rotating object) is

$$v = r |\omega| \quad (\omega \text{ in radians per unit time}) \qquad (5\text{-}7)$$

- Using radian measure for α, the tangential acceleration component is related to the angular acceleration by

$$a_t = r |\alpha| \quad (\alpha \text{ in radians per time}^2) \qquad (5\text{-}17)$$

- An object moving in a circle has a radial acceleration component given by

$$a_r = \frac{v^2}{r} = \omega^2 r \quad (\omega \text{ in radians per unit time}) \qquad (5\text{-}12)$$

- The tangential and radial acceleration components are two perpendicular components of the acceleration vector. The radial acceleration component changes the direction of the velocity and the tangential acceleration component changes the speed.

- Uniform circular motion means that v and ω are constant. In uniform circular motion, the time to complete one revolution is constant and is called the period T. The frequency f is the number of revolutions completed per second.

$$f = 1/T \qquad (5\text{-}8)$$

$$|\omega| = v/r = 2\pi f \qquad (5\text{-}9)$$

where the SI unit of angular velocity is rad/s and that of frequency is rev/s = Hz.

- A rolling object is both rotating and translating. If the object rolls without skidding or slipping, then

$$v_{\text{axle}} = r |\omega| \qquad (5\text{-}10)$$

- Kepler's third law says that the square of the period of a planetary orbit is proportional to the cube of the orbital radius:

$$T^2 = \text{constant} \times r^3 \qquad (5\text{-}14)$$

- For constant angular acceleration, we can use equations analogous to those we developed for constant acceleration a_x:

$$\Delta \omega = \omega_f - \omega_i = \alpha \Delta t \qquad (5\text{-}18)$$

$$\Delta \theta = \frac{1}{2}(\omega_f + \omega_i) \Delta t \qquad (5\text{-}19)$$

$$\Delta \theta = \omega_i \Delta t + \frac{1}{2}\alpha (\Delta t)^2 \qquad (5\text{-}20)$$

$$\omega_f^2 - \omega_i^2 = 2\alpha \Delta \theta \qquad (5\text{-}21)$$

Conceptual Questions

1. Is depressing the "accelerator" (gas pedal) of a car the only way that the driver can make the car accelerate (in the physics sense of the word)? If not, what else can the driver do to give the car an acceleration?

2. Two children ride on a merry-go-round. One is 2 m from the axis of rotation and the other is 4 m from it. Which child has the larger (a) linear speed, (b) acceleration, (c) angular speed, and (d) angular displacement?

3. Explain why the orbital radius and the speed of a satellite in circular orbit are not independent.

4. In uniform circular motion, is the velocity constant? Is the acceleration constant? Explain.

5. In uniform circular motion, the net force is perpendicular to the velocity and changes the direction of the velocity but not the speed. If a projectile is launched horizontally, the net force (ignoring air resistance) is perpendicular to the initial velocity, and yet the projectile gains speed as it falls. What is the difference between the two situations?

6. The speed of a satellite in circular orbit around a planet does not depend on the mass of the satellite. Does it depend on the mass of the planet? Explain.

7. A flywheel (a massive disk) rotates with constant angular acceleration. For a point on the rim of the flywheel, is the tangential acceleration component constant? Is the radial acceleration component constant?

8. Explain why the force of gravity due to the Earth does not pull the Moon in closer and closer on an inward spiral until it hits Earth's surface.

9. When a roller coaster takes a sharp turn to the right, it feels as if you are pushed toward the left. Does a force push you to the left? If so, what is it? If not, why does there *seem* to be such a force?

10. Is there anywhere on Earth where a bathroom scale reads your true weight? If so, where? Where does your apparent weight due to Earth's rotation differ most from your true weight?

11. A physics teacher draws a cut-away view of a car rounding a banked curve as a rectangle atop a right triangle. A student draws a coordinate system based on the drawing. Is there another choice of axes that would make the problem easier to solve?

12. A bridal party is at a rehearsal dinner. The best man challenges the bride-groom to pick up an olive using only a brandy snifter. How does the groom accomplish this task?

Brandy snifter

Olive

Multiple-Choice Questions

1. A spider sits on a turntable that is rotating at a constant 33 rpm. The acceleration $\vec{a}$ of the spider is
   (a) greater the closer the spider is to the central axis.
   (b) greater the farther the spider is from the central axis.
   (c) nonzero and independent of the location of the spider on the turntable.
   (d) zero.

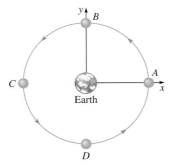

Multiple-Choice Questions 2–5 and Problem 36

Questions 2–5: A satellite in orbit travels around the Earth in uniform circular motion. In the figure, the satellite moves counterclockwise (*ABCDA*). Answer choices:
   (a) +x   (b) +y   (c) −x   (d) −y
   (e) 45° above +x (toward +y)
   (f) 45° below +x (toward −y)
   (g) 45° above −x (toward +y)
   (h) 45° below −x (toward −y)

2. What is the direction of the satellite's instantaneous velocity at point *D*?

3. What is the direction of the satellite's average velocity for one quarter of an orbit, starting at *C* and ending at *D*?

4. What is the direction of the satellite's average acceleration for one half of an orbit, starting at *C* and ending at *A*?

5. What is the direction of the satellite's instantaneous acceleration at point *C*?

6. Two satellites are in orbit around Mars with the same orbital radius. Satellite 2 has twice the mass of satellite 1. The radial acceleration of satellite 2 has
   (a) twice the magnitude of the radial acceleration of satellite 1.
   (b) the same magnitude as the radial acceleration of satellite 1.
   (c) half the magnitude of the radial acceleration of satellite 1.
   (d) four times the magnitude of the radial acceleration of satellite 1.

Questions 7–8: A boy swings in a tire swing. Answer choices:
   (a) At the highest point of the motion
   (b) At the lowest point of the motion
   (c) At a point neither highest nor lowest
   (d) It is constant.

7. When is the tension in the rope the greatest?

8. When is the tangential acceleration the greatest?

Questions 9–10 concern these three statements:
   (1) Its acceleration is constant.
   (2) Its radial acceleration component is constant in magnitude.
   (3) Its tangential acceleration component is constant in magnitude.

9. An object is in uniform circular motion. Identify the correct statement(s).
   (a) 1 only   (b) 2 only   (c) 3 only
   (d) 1, 2, and 3   (e) 2 and 3   (f) 1 and 2
   (g) 1 and 3   (h) None of them

10. An object is in nonuniform circular motion with constant angular acceleration. Identify the correct statement(s). (Use the same answer choices as Question 9.)

11. An astronaut is out in space far from any large bodies. He uses his jets to start spinning, then releases a baseball he has been holding in his hand. Ignoring the gravitational force between the astronaut and the baseball, how would you describe the path of the baseball after it leaves the astronaut's hand?
   (a) It continues to circle the astronaut in a circle with the same radius it had before leaving the astronaut's hand.
   (b) It moves off in a straight line.
   (c) It moves off in an ever-widening arc.

12. An object moving in a circle at a constant speed has an acceleration that is
    (a) in the direction of motion
    (b) toward the center of the circle
    (c) away from the center of the circle
    (d) zero

Problems

☤   Combination conceptual/quantitative problem
☤   Biological or medical application
◆   Challenging problem
Blue #   Detailed solution in the Student Solutions Manual
(1 2)   Problems paired by concept
🌐   Text website interactive or tutorial

5.1 Description of Uniform Circular Motion

1. A carnival swing is fixed on the end of an 8.0-m-long beam. If the swing and beam sweep through an angle of 120°, what is the distance through which the riders move?

2. A soccer ball of diameter 31 cm rolls without slipping at a linear speed of 2.8 m/s. Through how many revolutions has the soccer ball turned as it moves a linear distance of 18 m?

3. Find the average angular speed of the second hand of a clock.

4. Convert these to radian measure: (a) 30.0°, (b) 135°, (c) $\frac{1}{4}$ revolution, (d) 33.3 revolutions.

5. A bicycle is moving at 9.0 m/s. What is the angular speed of its tires if their radius is 35 cm? (🌐 tutorial: car tire)

6. An elevator cable winds on a drum of radius 90.0 cm that is connected to a motor. (a) If the elevator is moving down at 0.50 m/s, what is the angular speed of the drum? (b) If the elevator moves down 6.0 m, how many revolutions has the drum made?

7. Grace is playing with her dolls and decides to give them a ride on a merry-go-round. She places one of them on an old record player turntable and sets the angular speed at 33.3 rpm. (a) What is their angular speed in rad/s? (b) If the doll is 13 cm from the center of the spinning turntable platform, how fast (in m/s) is the doll moving?

8. A wheel is rotating at a rate of 2.0 revolutions every 3.0 s. Through what angle, in radians, does the wheel rotate in 1.0 s?

◆ 9. In the construction of railroads, it is important that curves be gentle, so as not to damage passengers or freight. Curvature is not measured by the radius of curvature, but in the following way. First a 100.0-ft-long chord is measured. Then the curvature is reported as the angle subtended by two radii at the endpoints of the chord. (The angle is measured by determining the angle between two tangents 100 ft apart; since each tangent is perpendicular to a radius, the angles are the same.) In modern railroad construction, track curvature is kept below 1.5°. What is the radius of curvature of a "1.5° curve"? [*Hint:* Since the angle is small, the length of the chord is approximately equal to the arc length along the curve.]

5.2 Radial Acceleration

10. Verify that all three expressions for radial acceleration ($v\omega$, v^2/r, and $\omega^2 r$) have the correct dimensions for an acceleration.

☤ 11. An apparatus is designed to study insects at an acceleration of magnitude 980 m/s^2 (= 100g). The apparatus consists of a 2.0-m rod with insect containers at either end. The rod rotates about an axis perpendicular to the rod and at its center. (a) How fast does an insect move when it experiences a radial acceleration of 980 m/s^2? (b) What is the angular speed of the insect? (🌐 tutorial: centrifuge)

12. The rotor is an amusement park ride where people stand against the inside of a cylinder. Once the cylinder is spinning fast enough, the floor drops out. (a) What force keeps the people from falling out the bottom of the cylinder? (b) If the coefficient of friction is 0.40 and the cylinder has a radius of 2.5 m, what is the minimum angular speed of the cylinder so that the people don't fall out? (Normally the operator runs it considerably faster as a safety measure.)

13. Objects that are at rest relative to Earth's surface are in circular motion due to Earth's rotation. What is the radial acceleration of an African baobab tree located at the equator?

14. Earth's orbit around the Sun is nearly circular. The period is 1 yr = 365.25 d. (a) In an elapsed time of 1 d, what is Earth's angular displacement? (b) What is the change in Earth's velocity, $\Delta \vec{v}$? (c) What is Earth's average acceleration during 1 d? (d) Compare your answer for (c) to the magnitude of Earth's instantaneous radial acceleration. Explain.

15. A 0.700-kg ball is on the end of a rope that is 1.30 m in length. The ball and rope are attached to a pole and the entire apparatus, including the pole, rotates about the pole's symmetry axis. The rope makes an angle of 70.0° with respect to the vertical. What is the tangential speed of the ball?

70.0°

Axis of rotation

16. A child's toy has a 0.100-kg ball attached to two strings, *A* and *B*. The strings are also attached to a stick and the ball swings around the stick along a circular path in a horizontal plane. Both strings are 15.0 cm long and make an angle of 30.0° with respect to the horizontal. (a) Draw an FBD for the ball showing the tension forces and the gravitational force. (b) Find the magnitude of the tension in each string when the ball's angular speed is 6.00π rad/s.

A

B

17. A child swings a rock of mass *m* in a horizontal circle using a rope of length *L*. The rock moves at constant speed *v*. (a) Ignoring gravity, find the tension in the rope. (b) Now include gravity (the weight of the rock is no longer negligible, although the weight of the rope still is negligible). What is the tension in the rope? Express the tension in terms of *m*, *g*, *v*, *L*, and the angle θ that the rope makes with the horizontal. (tutorial: skip rope)

18. A *conical pendulum* consists of a bob (mass *m*) attached to a string (length *L*) swinging in a horizontal circle (Fig. 5.11). As the string moves, it sweeps out the area of a cone. The angle that the string makes with the vertical is ϕ. (a) What is the tension in the string? (b) What is the period of the pendulum?

5.3 Unbanked and Banked Curves

19. A curve in a stretch of highway has radius *R*. The road is unbanked. The coefficient of static friction between the tires and road is μ_s. (a) What is the fastest speed that a car can safely travel around the curve? (b) Explain what happens when a car enters the curve at a speed greater than the maximum safe speed. Illustrate with an FBD. (interactive: banked curve)

20. A highway curve has a radius of 825 m. At what angle should the road be banked so that a car traveling at 26.8 m/s (60 mph) has no tendency to skid sideways on the road? [*Hint:* No tendency to skid means the frictional force is zero.]

21. A curve in a highway has radius of curvature 120 m and is banked at 3.0°. On a day when the road is icy, what is the safest speed to go around the curve?

22. A roller coaster car of mass 320 kg (including passengers) travels around a horizontal curve of radius 35 m. Its speed is 16 m/s. What is the magnitude and direction of the total force exerted on the car by the track?

23. A velodrome is built for use in the Olympics. The radius of curvature of the surface is 20.0 m. At what angle should the surface be banked for cyclists moving at 18 m/s? (Choose an angle so that no frictional force is needed to keep the cyclists in their circular path. Large banking angles *are* used in velodromes.)

24. A car drives around a curve with radius 410 m at a speed of 32 m/s. The road is not banked. The mass of the car is 1400 kg. (a) What is the frictional force on the car? (b) Does the frictional force necessarily have magnitude $\mu_s N$? Explain.

25. A car drives around a curve with radius 410 m at a speed of 32 m/s. The road is banked at 5.0°. The mass of the car is 1400 kg. (a) What is the frictional force on the car? (b) At what speed could you drive around this curve so that the force of friction is zero?

26. A curve in a stretch of highway has radius *R*. The road is banked at angle θ to the horizontal. The coefficient of static friction between the tires and road is μ_s. What is the fastest speed that a car can travel through the curve?

27. An airplane is flying at constant speed *v* in a horizontal circle of radius *r*. The lift force on the wings due to the air is perpendicular to the wings. At what angle to the vertical must the wings be banked to fly in this circle? (tutorial: plane in turn)

28. A road with a radius of 75.0 m is banked so that a car can navigate the curve at a speed of 15.0 m/s without any friction. When a car is going 20.0 m/s on this curve, what minimum coefficient of static friction is needed if the car is to navigate the curve without slipping?

5.4 Circular Orbits of Satellites and Planets

29. What is the average linear speed of the Earth about the Sun?

30. The orbital speed of Earth about the Sun is 3.0×10^4 m/s and its distance from the Sun is 1.5×10^{11} m. The mass of Earth is approximately 6.0×10^{24} kg and that of the Sun is 2.0×10^{30} kg. What is the magnitude of the force exerted by the Sun on Earth? [*Hint:* Two different methods are possible. Try both.]

31. Two satellites are in circular orbits around Jupiter. One, with orbital radius r, makes one revolution every 16 h. The other satellite has orbital radius $4.0r$. How long does the second satellite take to make one revolution around Jupiter?

32. The Hubble Space Telescope orbits Earth 613 km above Earth's surface. What is the period of the telescope's orbit?

33. Io, one of Jupiter's satellites, has an orbital period of 1.77 d. Europa, another of Jupiter's satellites, has an orbital period of about 3.54 d. Both moons have nearly circular orbits. Use Kepler's third law to find the distance of each satellite from Jupiter's center. Jupiter's mass is 1.9×10^{27} kg.

34. A spy satellite is in circular orbit around Earth. It makes one revolution in 6.00 h. (a) How high above Earth's surface is the satellite? (b) What is the satellite's acceleration?

35. Mars has a mass of about 6.42×10^{23} kg. The length of a day on Mars is 24 h and 37 min, a little longer than the length of a day on Earth. Your task is to put a satellite into a circular orbit around Mars so that it stays above one spot on the surface, orbiting Mars once each Mars day. At what distance from the center of the planet should you place the satellite?

36. A satellite travels around Earth in uniform circular motion at an altitude of 35 800 km above Earth's surface. The satellite is in geosynchronous orbit (that is, the time for it to complete one orbit is exactly 1 d). In the figure with Multiple-Choice Questions 2–5, the satellite moves counterclockwise (*ABCDA*). State directions in terms of the *x*- and *y*-axes. (a) What is the satellite's instantaneous velocity at point *C*? (b) What is the satellite's average velocity for one quarter of an orbit, starting at *A* and ending at *B*? (c) What is the satellite's average acceleration for one quarter of an orbit, starting at *A* and ending at *B*? (d) What is the satellite's instantaneous acceleration at point *D*?

37. A spacecraft is in orbit around Jupiter. The radius of the orbit is 3.0 times the radius of Jupiter (which is $R_J = 71\,500$ km). The gravitational field at the surface of Jupiter is 23 N/kg. What is the period of the spacecraft's orbit? [*Hint:* You don't need to look up any more data about Jupiter to solve the problem.]

5.5 Nonuniform Circular Motion

38. A roller coaster has a vertical loop with radius 29.5 m. With what minimum speed should the roller coaster car be moving at the top of the loop so that the passengers do not lose contact with the seats?

39. A pendulum is 0.80 m long and the bob has a mass of 1.0 kg. At the bottom of its swing, the bob's speed is 1.6 m/s. (a) What is the tension in the string at the bottom of the swing? (b) Explain why the tension is greater than the weight of the bob.

40. A 35.0-kg child swings on a rope with a length of 6.50 m that is hanging from a tree. At the bottom of the swing, the child is moving at a speed of 4.20 m/s. What is the tension in the rope?

41. A car approaches the top of a hill that is shaped like a vertical circle with a radius of 55.0 m. What is the fastest speed that the car can go over the hill without losing contact with the ground?

5.6 Tangential and Angular Acceleration

42. A child pushes a merry-go-round from rest to a final angular speed of 0.50 rev/s with constant angular acceleration. In doing so, the child pushes the merry-go-round 2.0 revolutions. What is the angular acceleration of the merry-go-round?

43. A cyclist starts from rest and pedals so that the wheels make 8.0 revolutions in the first 5.0 s. What is the angular acceleration of the wheels (assumed constant)?

44. During normal operation, a computer's hard disk spins at 7200 rpm. If it takes the hard disk 4.0 s to reach this angular velocity starting from rest, what is the average angular acceleration of the hard disk in rad/s²?

45. Derive Eq. 5-20 from Eqs. 5-18 and 5-19. [*Hint:* See the derivation of Eq. (4-4) in Section 4.1.]

46. Derive Eq. 5-21 from Eqs. 5-18 and 5-19.

47. A pendulum is 0.800 m long and the bob has a mass of 1.00 kg. When the string makes an angle of $\theta = 15.0°$ with the vertical, the bob is moving at 1.40 m/s. Find the tangential and radial acceleration components and the tension in the string. [*Hint:* Draw an FBD for the bob. Choose the *x*-axis to be tangential to the motion of the bob and the *y*-axis to be radial. Apply Newton's second law.]

Problems 47 and 48

48. Find the tangential acceleration of a freely swinging pendulum when it makes an angle θ with the vertical.

49. A turntable reaches an angular speed of 33.3 rpm in 2.0 s, starting from rest. (a) Assuming the angular acceleration is constant, what is its magnitude? (b) How many revolutions does the turntable make during this time interval?

50. A wheel's angular acceleration is constant. Initially its angular velocity is zero. During the first 1.0-s time interval, it rotates through an angle of 90.0°. (a) Through what angle does it rotate during the next 1.0-s time interval? (b) Through what angle during the third 1.0-s time interval?

51. A car that is initially at rest moves along a circular path with a constant tangential acceleration component of 2.00 m/s². The circular path has a radius of 50.0 m. The initial position of the car is at the far west location on the circle and the initial velocity is to the north. (a) After the car has traveled $\frac{1}{4}$ of the circumference, what is the speed of the car? (b) At this point, what is the radial acceleration component of the car? (c) At this same point, what is the total acceleration of the car?

52. A disk rotates with constant angular acceleration. The initial angular speed of the disk is 2π rad/s. After the disk rotates through 10π radians, the angular speed is 7π rad/s. (a) What is the magnitude of the angular acceleration? (b) How much time did it take for the disk to rotate through 10π radians? (c) What is the tangential acceleration of a point located at a distance of 5.0 cm from the center of the disk?

53. In a Beams ultracentrifuge, the rotor is suspended magnetically in a vacuum. Since there is no mechanical connection to the rotor, the only friction is the air resistance due to the few air molecules in the vacuum. If the rotor is spinning with an angular speed of 5.0×10^5 rad/s and the driving force is turned off, its spinning slows down at an angular rate of 0.40 rad/s². (a) How long does the rotor spin before coming to rest? (b) During this time, through how many revolutions does the rotor spin?

54. The rotor of the Beams ultracentrifuge (see Problem 53) is 20.0 cm long. For a point at the end of the rotor, find the (a) initial speed, (b) tangential acceleration component, and (c) maximum radial acceleration component.

5.7 Apparent Weight and Artificial Gravity

55. If a washing machine's drum has a radius of 25 cm and spins at 4.0 rev/s, what is the strength of the artificial gravity to which the clothes are subjected? Express your answer as a multiple of g.

56. A space station is shaped like a ring and rotates to simulate gravity. If the radius of the space station is 120 m, at what frequency must it rotate so that it simulates Earth's gravity? [*Hint:* The apparent weight of the astronauts must be the same as their weight on Earth.] (tutorial: space station)

57. A biologist is studying growth in space. He wants to simulate Earth's gravitational field, so he positions the plants on a rotating platform in the spaceship. The distance of each plant from the central axis of rotation is $r = 0.20$ m. What angular speed is required?

58. A biologist is studying plant growth and wants to simulate a gravitational field twice as strong as Earth's. She places the plants on a horizontal rotating table in her laboratory on Earth at a distance of 12.5 cm from the axis of rotation. What angular speed will give the plants an effective gravitational field $\vec{\mathbf{g}}_{eff}$, whose magnitude is $2.0g$? [*Hint:* Remember to account for Earth's gravitational field as well as the artificial gravity when finding the apparent weight.]

59. Objects that are at rest relative to the Earth's surface are in circular motion due to Earth's rotation. (a) What is the radial acceleration of an object at the equator? (b) Is the object's apparent weight greater or less than its weight? Explain. (c) By what percentage does the apparent weight differ from the weight at the equator? (d) Is there any place on Earth where a bathroom scale reading is equal to your true weight? Explain.

60. A person of mass M stands on a bathroom scale inside a Ferris wheel compartment. The Ferris wheel has radius R and angular velocity ω. What is the apparent weight of the person (a) at the top and (b) at the bottom?

61. A person rides a Ferris wheel that turns with constant angular velocity. Her weight is 520.0 N. At the top of the ride her apparent weight is 1.5 N different from her true weight. (a) Is her apparent weight at the top 521.5 N or 518.5 N? Why? (b) What is her apparent weight at the bottom of the ride? (c) If the angular speed of the Ferris wheel is 0.025 rad/s, what is its radius?

62. Objects that are at rest relative to Earth's surface are in circular motion due to Earth's rotation. What is the radial acceleration of a painting hanging in the Prado Museum in Madrid, Spain, at a latitude of 40.2° North? (Note that the object's radial acceleration is not directed toward the center of the Earth.)

Three-dimensional view   Rotation axis
                              Cross-sectional view

63. A rotating flywheel slows down at a constant rate due to friction in its bearings. After 1 min, its angular velocity has diminished to 0.80 of its initial value ω. At the end of the third minute, what is the angular velocity in terms of the initial value?

Comprehensive Problems

64. The Earth rotates on its own axis once per day (24.0 h). What is the tangential speed of the summit of Mt. Kilimanjaro (elevation 5895 m above sea level), which is located approximately on the equator, due to the rotation of the Earth? The equatorial radius of Earth is 6378 km.

65. A trimmer for cutting weeds and grass near trees and borders has a nylon cord of 0.23-m length that whirls about an axle at 660 rad/s. What is the linear speed of the tip of the nylon cord?

66. A high-speed dental drill is rotating at 3.14×10^4 rad/s. Through how many degrees does the drill rotate in 1.00 s?

67. A jogger runs counterclockwise around a path of radius 90.0 m at constant speed. He makes 1.00 revolution in 188.4 s. At $t = 0$, he is heading due east. (a) What is the jogger's instantaneous velocity at $t = 376.8$ s? (b) What is his instantaneous velocity at $t = 94.2$ s?

68. Two gears A and B are in contact. The radius of gear A is twice that of gear B. (a) When A's angular velocity is 6.00 Hz counterclockwise, what is B's angular velocity? (b) If A's radius to the tip of the teeth is 10.0 cm, what is the linear speed of a point on the tip of a gear tooth? What is the linear speed of a point on the tip of B's gear tooth?

Problems 68 and 69

69. If gear A in Problem 68 has an initial frequency of 0.955 Hz and an angular acceleration of 3.0 rad/s², how many rotations does each gear go through in 2.0 s?

70. The time to sunset can be estimated by holding out your arm, holding your fingers horizontally in front of your eyes, and counting the number of fingers that fit between the horizon and the setting Sun. (a) What is the angular speed, in radians per second, of the Sun's apparent circular motion around the Earth? (b) Estimate the angle subtended by one finger held at arm's length. (c) How long in minutes does it take the Sun to "move" through this same angle?

71. In the professional videotape recording system known as quadriplex, four tape heads are mounted on the circumference of a drum of radius 2.5 cm that spins at 1500 rad/s. (a) At what speed are the tape heads moving? (b) Why are moving tape heads used instead of stationary ones, as in audiotape recorders? [*Hint:* How fast would the tape have to move if the heads were stationary?]

72. The Milky Way galaxy rotates about its center with a period of about 200 million yr. The Sun is 2×10^{20} m from the center of the galaxy. How fast is the Sun moving with respect to the center of the galaxy?

73. A small body of mass 0.50 kg is attached by a 0.50-m-long cord to a pin set into the surface of a frictionless table top. The body moves in a circle on the horizontal surface with a speed of 2.0π m/s. (a) What is the magnitude of the radial acceleration of the body? (b) What is the tension in the cord?

74. Two blocks, one with mass $m_1 = 0.050$ kg and one with mass $m_2 = 0.030$ kg, are connected to one another by a string. The inner block is connected to a central pole by another string as shown in the figure with $r_1 = 0.40$ m and $r_2 = 0.75$ m. When the blocks are spun around on a horizontal frictionless surface at an angular speed of 1.5 rev/s, what is the tension in each of the two strings?

75. What's the fastest way to make a U-turn at constant speed? Suppose that you need to make a 180° turn on a circular path. The minimum radius (due to the car's steering system) is 5.0 m, while the maximum (due to the width of the road) is 20.0 m. Your acceleration must never exceed 3.0 m/s² or else you will skid. Should you use the smallest possible radius, so the distance is small, or the largest, so you can go faster without skidding, or something in between? What is the minimum possible time for this U-turn?

76. The Milky Way galaxy rotates about its center with a period of about 200 million yr. The Sun is 2×10^{20} m from the center of the galaxy. (a) What is the Sun's radial acceleration? (b) What is the net gravitational force on the Sun due to the other stars in the Milky Way?

77. Bacteria swim using a corkscrew-like helical flagellum that rotates. For a bacterium with a flagellum that has a pitch of 1.0 μm that rotates at 110 rev/s, how fast could it swim if there were no "slippage" in the medium in which it is swimming? The pitch of a helix is the distance between "threads."

78. You place a penny on a turntable at a distance of 10.0 cm from the center. The coefficient of static friction between the penny and the turntable is 0.350. The turntable's

angular acceleration is 2.00 rad/s². How long after you turn on the turntable will the penny begin to slide off of the turntable?

79. A coin is placed on a turntable that is rotating at 33.3 rpm. If the coefficient of static friction between the coin and the turntable is 0.1, how far from the center of the turntable can the coin be placed without having it slip off?

80. Grace, playing with her dolls, pretends the turntable of an old phonograph is a merry-go-round. The dolls are 12.7 cm from the central axis. She changes the setting from 33.3 rpm to 45.0 rpm. (a) For this new setting, what is the linear speed of a point on the turntable at the location of the dolls? (b) If the coefficient of static friction between the dolls and the turntable is 0.13, do the dolls stay on the turntable?

81. Your car's wheels are 65 cm in diameter and the wheels are spinning at an angular velocity of 101 rad/s. How fast is your car moving in kilometers per hour (assume no slippage)?

82. In an amusement park rocket ride, cars are suspended from 4.25-m cables attached to rotating arms at a distance of 6.00 m from the axis of rotation. The cables swing out at an angle of 45.0° when the ride is operating. What is the angular speed of rotation?

83. Centrifuges are commonly used in biological laboratories for the isolation and maintenance of cell preparations. For cell separation, the centrifugation conditions are typically 1.0×10^3 rpm using an 8.0-cm-radius rotor. (a) What is the radial acceleration of material in the centrifuge under these conditions? Express your answer as a multiple of g. (b) At 1.0×10^3 rpm (and with a 8.0-cm rotor), what is the net force on a red blood cell whose mass is 9.0×10^{-14} kg? (c) What is the net force on a virus particle of mass 5.0×10^{-21} kg under the same conditions? (d) To pellet out virus particles and even to separate large molecules such as proteins, super-high-speed centrifuges called ultracentrifuges are used in which the rotor spins in a vacuum to reduce heating due to friction. What is the radial acceleration inside an ultracentrifuge at 75 000 rpm with an 8.0-cm rotor? Express your answer as a multiple of g.

84. You take a homemade "accelerometer" to an amusement park. This accelerometer consists of a metal nut attached to a string and connected to a protractor, as shown in the figure. While riding a roller coaster that is moving at a uniform speed around a circular path, you hold up the accelerometer and notice that the string is making an angle of 55° with respect to the vertical with the nut pointing away from the center of the circle, as shown. (a) What is the radial acceleration of the roller coaster? (b) What is your radial acceleration expressed as a multiple of g? (c) If the roller coaster track is turning in a radius of 80.0 m, how fast are you moving?

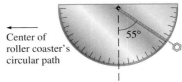

Center of roller coaster's circular path

85. Massimo, a machinist, is cutting threads for a bolt on a lathe. He wants the bolt to have 18 threads per inch. If the cutting tool moves parallel to the axis of the would-be bolt at a linear velocity of 0.080 in./s, what must the rotational speed of the lathe chuck be to ensure the correct thread density? [*Hint:* One thread is formed for each complete revolution of the chuck.]

86. In Chapter 19 we will see that a charged particle can undergo uniform circular motion when acted on by a magnetic force and no other forces. (a) For that to be true, what must be the angle between the magnetic force and the particle's velocity? (b) The magnitude of the magnetic force on a charged particle is proportional to the particle's speed, $F = kv$. Show that two identical charged particles moving in circles at different speeds in the same magnetic field must have the same period. (c) Show that the radius of the particle's circular path is proportional to the speed.

87. Find the orbital radius of a geosynchronous satellite. Do not assume the speed found in Example 5.9. Start by writing an equation that relates the period, radius, and speed of the orbiting satellite. Then apply Newton's second law to the satellite. You will have two equations with two unknowns (the speed and radius). Eliminate the speed algebraically and solve for the radius.

Answers to Practice Problems

5.1 3.001×10^{-7} rad/s

5.2 1.65 m/s

5.3 1.9 min

5.4 17 m/s²

5.5 60 N toward the center of the circular path

5.6 More slowly

5.7 No

5.8 29.7 km/s; 3.17×10^7 s

5.9 0.723R

5.10 2.44 h

5.11 4.2mg

5.12 Acceleration is purely tangential:

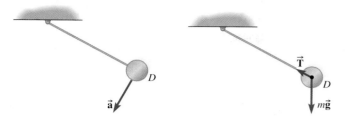

5.13 (a) 1.75×10^{-4} rad/s^2; (b) 0.0349 rad (2.00°)

5.14 (a) 2200 N; (b) 1500 N

Answers to Checkpoints

5.1 7200 Hz

5.2 No, for uniform circular motion the *direction* of the velocity vector is continuously changing but the magnitude of the velocity (the speed) is unchanged.

5.3 The car has friction between the road and the tires to exert a horizontal force that causes the radial acceleration.

5.4 To be geosynchronous the satellites must have an orbital period of 1 d. The only quantities that affect the period are the mass of Earth and the radial distance from Earth's center. These quantities are the same for all satellites no matter the mass.

5.5 For nonuniform circular motion, the direction and the magnitude of the velocity are both changing. There are tangential and radial components to the acceleration. The magnitude of the radial component changes as the speed changes. For uniform circular motion, the magnitude of the velocity is constant but the direction changes. The radial acceleration is constant in magnitude (and the tangential acceleration is zero).

5.6 The radial acceleration cannot be constant because the radius r is constant but the angular velocity ω is changing $a_r = \omega^2 r$.

Review & Synthesis: Chapters 1–5

Review Exercises

1. From your knowledge of Newton's second law and dimensional analysis, find the units (in SI base units) of the spring constant k in the equation $F = kx$, where F is a force and x is a distance.

2. Harrison traveled 2.00 km west, then 5.00 km in a direction 53.0° south of west, then 1.00 km in a direction 60.0° north of west. (a) In what direction, and for how far, should Harrison travel to return to his starting point? (b) If Harrison returns directly to his starting point with a speed of 5.00 m/s, how long will the return trip take?

3. (a) How many center-stripe road reflectors, separated by 17.6 yd, are required along a 2.20-mile section of curving mountain roadway? (b) Solve the same problem for a road length of 3.54 km with the markers placed every 16.0 m. Would you prefer to be the highway engineer in a country with a metric system or U.S. customary units?

4. A baby was spitting up after nursing and the pediatrician prescribed Zantac syrup to reduce the baby's stomach acid. The prescription called for 0.75 mL to be taken twice a day for a month. The pharmacist printed a label for the bottle of syrup that said "3/4 tsp. twice a day." By what factor was the baby overmedicated before the error was discovered at the baby's next office visit two weeks later? [*Hint:* 1 tsp = 4.9 mL.]

5. Mike swims 50.0 m with a speed of 1.84 m/s, then turns around and swims 34.0 m in the opposite direction with a speed of 1.62 m/s. (a) What is his average speed? (b) What is his average velocity?

6. You are watching a television show about Navy pilots. The narrator says that when a Navy jet takes off, it accelerates because the engines are at full throttle and because there is a catapult that propels the jet forward. You begin to wonder how much force is supplied by the catapult. You look on the Web and find that the flight deck of an aircraft carrier is about 90 m long, that an F-14 has a mass of 33 000 kg, that each of the two engines supplies 27 000 lb of force, and that the takeoff speed of such a plane is about 160 mi/h. Estimate the average force on the jet due to the catapult.

7. On April 15, 1999, a Korean cargo plane crashed due to a confusion over units. The plane was to fly from Shanghai, China, to Seoul, Korea. After take-off the plane climbed to 900 m. Then the first officer was instructed by the Shanghai tower to climb to 1500 m and maintain that altitude. The captain, after reaching 1450 m, twice asked the first officer at what altitude they should fly. He was twice told incorrectly they were to be at 1500 ft. The captain pushed the control column quickly forward and started a steep descent. The plane could not recover from the dive and crashed. How much above the correct altitude did the captain think they were when he started his rapid descent and lost control? (It turns out that aircraft altitudes are given in feet throughout the world except in China, Mongolia, and the former Soviet states where meters are used.)

8. Paula swims across a river that is 10.2 m wide. She can swim at 0.833 m/s in still water, but the river flows with a speed of 1.43 m/s. If Paula swims in such a way that she crosses the river in as short a time as possible, how far downstream is she when she gets to the opposite shore?

9. Peter is collecting paving stones from a quarry. He harnesses two dogs, Sandy and Rufus, in tandem to the loaded cart. Sandy pulls with force $\vec{F}$ at a 15° angle to the north of east; Rufus pulls with 1.5 times the force of Sandy and at an angle of 30.0° south of east. Use a ruler and protractor to draw the force vectors to scale (choose a simple scale, such as 2.0 cm ↔ F). Find the sum of the two force vectors graphically. Measure its length and find the magnitude of the sum from the scale used and the direction with the protractor. Will the cart stay on the road that runs directly west to east?

10. A tire swing hangs at a 12° angle to the vertical when a stiff breeze is blowing. In terms of the tire's weight W, (a) what is the magnitude of the horizontal force exerted on the tire by the wind? (b) What is the tension in the rope supporting the tire? Ignore the weight of the rope.

11. An astronaut of mass 60.0 kg and a small asteroid of mass 40.0 kg are initially at rest with respect to the space station. The astronaut pushes the asteroid with a constant force of magnitude 250 N for 0.35 s. Gravitational forces are negligible. (a) How far apart are the astronaut and the asteroid 5.00 s after the astronaut stops pushing? (b) What is their relative speed at this time?

12. In the fairy tale, Rapunzel, the beautiful maiden let her long golden hair hang down from the tower in which she was held prisoner so that her prince could use her hair as a climbing rope to climb the tower and rescue her. (a) Estimate how much force is required to pull a strand of hair out of your head. (b) There are about 10^5 hairs growing out of Rapunzel's head. If the prince has a mass of 60 kg, estimate the average force pulling on each strand of hair. Will Rapunzel be bald by the time the prince reaches the top of the 30-m tower?

13. Marie slides a paper plate with a slice of pizza across a horizontal table to her friend Jaden. The coefficient of friction between the table and plate is 0.32. If the pizza must travel 44 cm to get from Marie to Jaden, what initial speed should Marie give the plate of pizza so that it just stops when it gets to Jaden?

14. Two wooden crates with masses as shown are tied together by a horizontal cord. Another cord is tied to the first crate and it is pulled with a force of 195 N at an angle of 20.0°, as shown. Each crate has a coefficient of

kinetic friction of 0.550. Find the tension in the rope between the crates and the magnitude of the acceleration of the system.

15. A boy has stacked two blocks on the floor so that a 5.00-kg block is on top of a 2.00-kg block. (a) If the coefficient of static friction between the two blocks is 0.400 and the coefficient of static friction between the bottom block and the floor is 0.220, with what minimum force should the boy push horizontally on the upper block to make both blocks start to slide together along the floor? (b) If he pushes too hard, the top block starts to slide off the lower block. What is the maximum force with which he can push without that happening if the coefficient of kinetic friction between the bottom block and the floor is 0.200?

16. A binary star consists of two stars of masses M_1 and $4.0M_1$ a distance d apart. Is there any point where the gravitational field due to the two stars is zero? If so, where is that point?

17. Two boys are trying to break a cord. Gerardo says they should each pull in opposite directions on the two ends; Stefan says they should tie the cord to a pole and both pull together on the opposite end. Which plan is more likely to work?

18. Fish don't move as fast as you might think. A small trout has a top swimming speed of only about 2 m/s, which is about the speed of a brisk walk (for a human, not a fish!). It may seem to move faster because it is capable of large *accelerations*—it can dart about, changing its speed or direction very quickly. (a) If a trout starts from rest and accelerates to 2 m/s in 0.05 s, what is the trout's average acceleration? (b) During this acceleration, what is the average net force on the trout? Express your answer as a multiple of the trout's weight. (c) Explain how the trout gets the water to push it forward.

19. A spotter plane sees a school of tuna swimming at a steady 5.00 km/h northwest. The pilot informs a fishing trawler, which is just then 100.0 km due south of the fish. The trawler sails along a straight-line course and intercepts the tuna after 4.0 h. How fast did the trawler move? [*Hint:* First find the velocity of the trawler relative to the tuna.]

20. Julia is delivering newspapers. Suppose she is driving at 15 m/s along a straight road and wants to drop a paper out the window from a height of 1.00 m so it slides along the shoulder and comes to rest in the customer's driveway. At what horizontal distance before the driveway should she drop the paper? The coefficient of kinetic friction between the newspaper and the ground is 0.40. Ignore air resistance and assume no bouncing or rolling.

21. Three rocks are thrown from a cliff with the same initial speeds but in different directions: one straight down, one straight up, and one horizontally. Ignore air resistance. (a) Compare the speeds of the three rocks just before they hit the flat ground at the bottom of the cliff. (b) Illustrate your answer by calculating the final speeds for three rocks thrown in the specified directions with initial speeds of 10.0 m/s from a cliff that is 15.00 m high. [*Hint:* Remember that the speed is the magnitude of the velocity vector.]

22. You are watching the Super Bowl where your favorite team is leading by a score of 21 to 20. The other team is lining up to try to kick the winning field goal. You watched their kicker warm up and you saw that he could kick the football with a velocity of 21 m/s. He lines up for a 45-yd kick. You watch as he kicks the ball at an angle of 35° above the horizontal. Assuming he kicks the ball straight and with the same speed as during the warmup, will the ball clear the 10-ft-high goal post, or will your favorite team win the Super Bowl?

23. A coin is placed on a turntable 13.0 cm from the center. The coefficient of static friction between the coin and the turntable is 0.110. Once the turntable is turned on, its angular acceleration is 1.20 rad/s². How long will it take until the coin begins to slide?

24. Carlos and Shannon are sledding down a snow-covered slope that is angled at 12° below the horizontal. When sliding on snow, Carlos's sled has a coefficient of friction $\mu_k = 0.10$; Shannon has a "supersled" with $\mu_k = 0.010$. Carlos takes off down the slope starting from rest. When Carlos is 5.0 m from the starting point, Shannon starts down the slope from rest. (a) How far have they traveled when Shannon catches up to Carlos? (b) How fast is Shannon moving with respect to Carlos as she passes by?

25. A proposed "space elevator" consists of a cable going all the way from the ground to a space station in geosynchronous orbit (always above the same point on Earth's surface). Elevator "cars" would climb the cable to transport cargo to outer space. Consider a cable connected between the equator and a space station at height H above the surface. Ignore the mass of the cable*. (a) Find the height H. (b) Suppose there is an elevator car of mass 100 kg sitting halfway up at height $H/2$. What tension T would be required in the cable to hold the car in place? Which part of the cable would be under tension (above the car or below it)?

26. Anthony is going to drive a flat-bed truck up a hill that makes an angle of 10° with respect to the horizontal direction. A 36.0-kg package sits in the back of the truck. The coefficient of static friction between the package

---

*More realistically, the mass of the cable is one of the primary engineering challenges of a space elevator. The cable is so long that it would have a very large mass and would have to withstand an enormous tension to support its own weight. The cable would need to be supported by a counterweight positioned beyond the geosynchronous orbit. Some believe *carbon nanotubes* hold the key to producing a cable with the required properties.

and the truck bed is 0.380. What is the maximum acceleration the truck can have without the package falling off the back?

27. A road with a radius of 75.0 m is banked so that a car can navigate the curve at a speed of 15.0 m/s without any friction. On a cold day when the street is icy, the coefficient of static friction between the tires and the road is 0.120. What is the *slowest* speed the car can go around this curve without sliding *down* the bank?

28. You want to lift a heavy box with a mass of 98.0 kg using the two-pulley system as shown. With what minimum force do you have to pull down on the rope in order to lift the box at a constant velocity? One pulley is attached to the ceiling and one to the box.

98.0 kg

✦29. At time $t = 0$, block A of mass 0.225 kg and block B of mass 0.600 kg rest on a horizontal frictionless surface a distance 3.40 m apart, with block A located to the left of block B. A horizontal force of 2.00 N directed to the right is applied to block A for a time interval $\Delta t = 0.100$ s. During the same time interval, a 5.00-N horizontal force directed to the left is applied to block B. How far from B's initial position do the two blocks meet? How much time has elapsed from $t = 0$ until the blocks meet?

A ← 3.40 m → B

30. A hamster of mass 0.100 kg gets onto his 20.0-cm-diameter exercise wheel and runs along inside the wheel for 0.800 s until its frequency of rotation is 1.00 Hz. (a) What is the tangential acceleration of the wheel, assuming it is constant? (b) What is the normal force on the hamster just before he stops? The hamster is at the bottom of the wheel during the entire 0.800 s.

31. A pellet is fired from a toy cannon with a velocity of 12 m/s directed 60° above the horizontal. After 0.10 s, a second identical pellet is fired with the same initial velocity. After an additional 0.15 s have passed, what is the velocity of the first pellet with respect to the second? Ignore air resistance.

32. A crate is sliding down a frictionless ramp that is inclined at 35.0°. (a) If the crate is released from rest, how far does it travel down the incline in 2.50 s if it does not get to the bottom of the ramp before the time has elapsed? (b) How fast is the crate moving after 2.50 s of travel?

✦33. The invention of the cannon in the fourteenth century made the catapult unnecessary and ended the safety of castle walls. Stone walls were no match for balls shot from cannons. Suppose a cannonball of mass 5.00 kg is launched from a height of 1.10 m, at an angle of elevation of 30.0° with an initial velocity of 50.0 m/s, toward a castle wall of height 30 m and located 215 m away from the cannon. (a) The range of a projectile is defined as the horizontal distance traveled when the projectile returns to its

original height. Derive an equation for the range in terms of v_i, g, and angle of elevation θ. (b) What will be the range reached by the projectile, if it is not intercepted by the wall? (c) If the cannonball travels far enough to hit the wall, find the height at which it strikes.

✦34. Two blocks are connected by a lightweight, flexible cord that passes over a single frictionless pulley. If $m_1 \gg m_2$, find (a) the acceleration of each block and (b) the tension in the cord.

35. A runner runs three-quarters of the way around a circular track of radius 60.0 m, when she collides with another runner and trips. (a) How far had the runner traveled on the track before the collision? (b) What was the magnitude of the displacement of the runner from her starting position when the accident occurred?

36. A solar sailplane is going from Earth to Mars. Its sail is oriented to give a solar radiation force of 8.00×10^2 N. The gravitational force due to the Sun is 173 N and the gravitational force due to the Earth is 1.00×10^2 N. All forces are in the plane formed by Earth, Sun, and sailplane. The mass of the sailplane is 14 500 kg. (a) What is the net force (magnitude and direction) acting on the sailplane? (b) What is the acceleration of the sailplane?

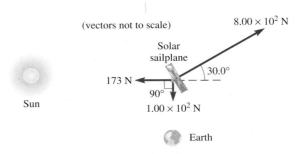

(vectors not to scale) 8.00×10^2 N

Solar sailplane

173 N ←   30.0°

90°

Sun 1.00×10^2 N

Earth

37. A star near the visible edge of a galaxy travels in a uniform circular orbit. It is 40 000 ly (light-years) from the galactic center and has a speed of 275 km/s. (a) Estimate the total mass of the galaxy based on the motion of the star? [*Hint:* For this estimate, assume the total mass to be concentrated at the galactic center and relate it to the gravitational force on the star.] (b) The total *visible* mass (i.e., matter we can detect via electromagnetic radiation) of the galaxy is 10^{11} solar masses. What fraction of the total mass of the galaxy is visible*, according to this estimate?

✦38. One of the tricky things about learning to sail is distinguishing the true wind from the apparent wind. When you are on a sailboat and you feel the wind on your face, you are experiencing the *apparent wind*—the motion of

---

*In many galaxies the stars appear to have roughly the *same orbital speed* over a large range of distances from the center. A popular hypothesis to explain such galaxy rotation velocities is the existence of *dark matter*—matter that we cannot detect via electromagnetic radiation. Dark matter is thought to account for the majority of the mass of some galaxies and nearly a fourth of the total mass of the universe.

the air relative to you. The true wind is the speed and direction of the air relative to the water while the apparent wind is the speed and direction of the air relative to the *sailboat*. The figure shows three different directions for the true wind along with one possible sail orientation as indicated by the position of the boom attached to the mast. (a) In each case, draw a vector diagram to establish the magnitude and direction of the apparent wind. (b) In which of the three cases is the apparent wind speed greater than the true wind speed? (Assume that the speed of the boat relative to the water is less than the true wind speed.) (c) In which of the three cases is the direction of the apparent wind direction forward of the true wind? ["Forward" means coming from a direction more nearly straight ahead. For example, (1) is forward of (2), which is forward of (3).]

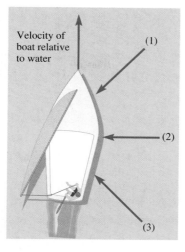

Velocity of boat relative to water

(1)
(2)
(3)

MCAT Review

The section that follows includes MCAT exam material and is reprinted with permission of the Association of American Medical Colleges (AAMC).

Read the paragraph and then answer the following four questions:

The study of the flight of projectiles has many practical applications. The main forces acting on a projectile are air resistance and gravity. The path of a projectile is often approximated by ignoring the effects of air resistance. Gravity is then the only force acting on the projectile. When air resistance is included in the analysis, another force, $\vec{F}_R$, is introduced. F_R is proportional to the square of the velocity, v. The direction of the air resistance is exactly opposite the direction of motion. The equation for air resistance is $F_R = bv^2$, where b is a proportionality constant that depends on such factors as the density of the air and the shape of the projectile.

Air resistance was studied by launching a 0.5-kg projectile from a level surface. The projectile was launched with a speed of 30 m/s at a 40° angle to the surface. (Note: Assume air resistance is present unless otherwise specified.)

1. What is the magnitude of the vertical acceleration of the projectile immediately after it is launched? (Note: v_y = vertical velocity component.)

    A. $-g + (bvv_y)$

    B. $-g - (bvv_y)$

    C. $-g + (bvv_y)/(0.5\ \text{kg})$

    D. $-g - (bvv_y)/(0.5\ \text{kg})$

2. Approximately what horizontal distance does the projectile travel before returning to the elevation from which it was launched? (Note: Assume that the effects of air resistance are negligible.)

    A. 45 m   B. 60 m   C. 90 m   D. 120 m

3. What is the magnitude of the *horizontal component of air resistance* on the projectile at any point during flight? (Note: v_x = horizontal velocity component.)

    A. $(bvv_x) \cos 40°$

    B. $(bvv_x)/2$

    C. $(bvv_x) \sin 40°$

    D. bvv_x

4. How does the amount of time it takes a projectile to reach its maximum height compare to the time it takes to fall from its maximum height back to the ground? (Note: b is greater than zero.)

    A. The times are the same.

    B. The time to reach its maximum height is greater.

    C. The time to fall back to the ground is greater.

    D. Either can be greater depending on the magnitude of b.

Read the paragraph and then answer the following questions:

A raft is constructed from wood and used in a river that varies in depth, width, and current at several points along its length. The river at point A has a current of 2 m/s, a width of 200 m, and an average depth of 3 m.

5. Near point A, the raft is rowed at a constant velocity of 2 m/s relative to the river current and perpendicular to it. How far does the raft travel before it reaches the other side?

    A. 224 m

    B. 250 m

    C. 283 m

    D. 400 m

6. A rower at point A rows the raft at 3 m/s relative to the river current and wants to end up directly across the river from the point of origin. At what angle to the shore should the rower direct the raft?

    A. $\cos^{-1} \frac{5}{3}$

    B. $\cos^{-1} \frac{2}{5}$

    C. $\cos^{-1} \frac{3}{2}$

    D. $\cos^{-1} \frac{2}{3}$

7. A rock is dropped from a cliff that is 100 m above ground level. How long does it take the rock to reach the ground? (Note: Use $g = 10\ \text{m/s}^2$.)

    A. 4.5 s

    B. 10 s

    C. 14 s

    D. 20 s

Conservation of Energy

As a kangaroo hops along, the maximum height of each hop might be around 2.8 m. This height is only slightly higher than that achieved by an Olympic high jumper, but the kangaroo is able to achieve this height hop after hop as it travels with a horizontal velocity of 15 m/s or more. What features of kangaroo anatomy make this feat possible? It cannot simply be a matter of having more powerful leg muscles. If it were, the kangaroo would have to consume large amounts of energy-rich food to supply the muscles with enough chemical energy for each jump, but in reality a kangaroo's diet consists largely of grasses that are poor in energy content. (See p. 210 for the answer.)

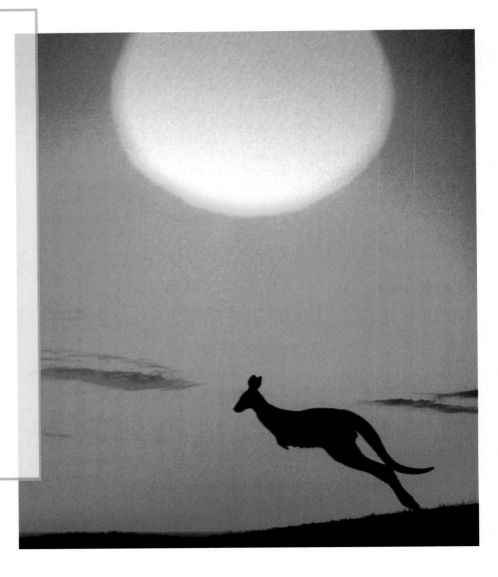

- gravitational forces (Section 2.6)
- Newton's second law: force and acceleration (Sections 3.3–3.4)
- components of vectors (Section 2.3)
- circular orbits (Section 5.4)
- area under a graph (Sections 3.2 and 3.3)

Concepts & Skills to Review

6.1 THE LAW OF CONSERVATION OF ENERGY

Until now, we have relied on Newton's laws of motion to be the fundamental physical laws used to analyze the forces that act on objects and to predict the motion of objects. Now we introduce another physical principle: the conservation of energy. A **conservation law** is a physical principle that identifies some quantity that does not change with time. Conservation of energy means that every physical process leaves the total energy in the universe unchanged. Energy can be converted from one form to another, or transferred from one place to another. If we are careful to account for all the energy transformations, we find that the total energy remains the same.

Conservation law: a physical law that identifies a quantity that does not change with time.

The Law of Conservation of Energy

The total energy in the universe is unchanged by any physical process:

total energy before = total energy after.

"Turn down the thermostat—we're trying to conserve energy!" In ordinary language, *conserving energy* means trying not to waste useful energy resources. In the scientific meaning of *conservation*, energy is *always* conserved no matter what happens. When we "produce" or "generate" electric energy, for instance, we aren't creating any new energy; we're just converting energy from one form into another that's more useful to us.

Conservation of energy is one of the few universal principles of physics. No exceptions to the law of conservation of energy have been found. Conservation of energy is a powerful tool in the search to understand nature. It applies equally well to radioactive decay, the gravitational collapse of a star, a chemical reaction, a biological process such as respiration, and to the generation of electricity by a wind turbine (Fig. 6.1). Think about the energy conversions that make life possible. Green plants use photosynthesis to convert the energy they receive from the Sun into stored chemical energy. When animals eat the plants, that stored energy enables motion, growth, and maintenance of body temperature. Energy conservation governs every one of these processes.

Figure 6.1 At a California "wind farm," these wind turbines convert the energy of motion of the air into electric energy.

Choosing Between Alternative Solution Methods   Some problems can be solved using either energy conservation *or* Newton's second law. Usually the energy method is easier. We often don't know the details of all the forces acting on an object, making a direct application of Newton's second law difficult. Using conservation of energy enables us to solve some of these problems more easily. When deciding which of these two approaches to use to solve a problem, try using energy conservation first. If the energy method does not lead to the solution, then try Newton's second law.

Historical Development of the Principle of Energy Conservation   While many scientists contributed to the development of the law of conservation of energy, the law's first clear statement was made in 1842 by the German surgeon Julius Robert von Mayer (1814–1878). As a ship's physician on a voyage to what is now Indonesia, Mayer had noticed that the sailors' venous blood was a much deeper red in the tropics than it was in Europe. He concluded that less oxygen was being used because they didn't need to "burn" as much fuel to keep the body warm in the warmer climate.

Figure 6.2 The stored chemical energy in food enables a weightlifter to lift the barbell over her head.

Table 6.1	Some Common Forms of Energy
Form of Energy	**Brief Description**
Translational kinetic	Energy of translational motion (Chapter 6)
Elastic	Energy stored in a "springy" object or material when it is deformed (Chapter 6)*
Gravitational	Energy of gravitational interactions (Chapter 6)
Rotational kinetic	Energy of rotational motion (Chapter 8)*
Vibrational, acoustic, seismic	Energy of the oscillatory motions of atoms and molecules in a substance caused by a mechanical wave passing through it (Chapters 11 and 12)*
Internal	Energies of motion and interaction of atoms and molecules in solids, liquids, and gases, related to our sensation of temperature (Chapters 14 and 15)*
Electromagnetic	Energy of interaction of electric charges and currents; energy of electromagnetic fields, including electromagnetic waves such as light (Chapters 14, 17–22)
Rest	The total energy of a particle of mass m when it is at rest, given by Einstein's famous equation $E = mc^2$ (Chapters 26, 29, and 30)
Chemical	Energies of motion and interaction of electrons in atoms and molecules (Chapter 28)*
Nuclear	Energies of motion and interaction of protons and neutrons in atomic nuclei (Chapters 29 and 30)

*Not a *fundamental* form of energy; made up of microscopic kinetic or electromagnetic energy.

In 1843, the English physicist James Prescott Joule (1818–1889), whose "day job" was running the family brewery, performed precise experiments to show that gravitational potential energy could be converted into a previously unrecognized form of energy (internal energy). It had previously been thought that forces like friction "use up" energy. Thanks to Mayer, Joule, and others, we now know that friction converts mechanical forms of energy into internal energy and that total energy is always conserved.

Forms of Energy

Energy comes in many different forms (Fig. 6.2). Table 6.1 summarizes the main forms of energy discussed in this text and indicates the principal chapters that discuss each one. At the most fundamental level, there are only three kinds of energy: energy due to motion (**kinetic energy**), stored energy due to interaction (**potential energy**), and rest energy.

To apply the energy conservation principle, we need to learn how to calculate the amount of each form of energy. There isn't one formula that applies to all. Fortunately, we don't have to learn about all of them at once. This chapter focuses on three forms of macroscopic mechanical energy (kinetic energy, gravitational potential energy, and elastic potential energy). For now, we use energy conservation as a tool to understand the **translational** motion of objects, but we do not consider rotational motion or changes in the *internal* energy of an object. We assume that these moving objects are perfectly rigid, so every point on the object moves through the same displacement.

Kinetic energy: energy of motion.

Potential energy: stored energy due to interaction.

Translation: motion of an object in which any point of the object moves with the same velocity as any other point. (That is, the object does not rotate or change shape.)

6.2   WORK DONE BY A CONSTANT FORCE

To apply the principle of energy conservation, we need to learn how energy can be converted from one form to another. We begin with an example. Suppose the trunk in Fig. 6.3a weighs 220 N and must be lifted a height $h = 4.0$ m. To lift it at constant speed, Rosie must exert a force of 220 N on the rope, assuming an ideal pulley and rope. (We

(a) Single pulley

Initial   Final

(b) Two pulleys

Initial   Final

Figure 6.3 (a) Rosie moves a trunk into her dorm room through the window. (b) The two-pulley system makes it easier for Rosie to lift the trunk: the *force* she must exert is halved. Is she getting something for nothing, or does she still have to do the same amount of *work* to lift the trunk?

ignore for now the brief initial time when she pulls with more than 220 N to accelerate the trunk from rest to its constant speed and the brief time she pulls with less than 220 N to let it come to rest.)

As discussed in Example 2.16, she would only have to exert half the force (110 N) if she were to use the two-pulley system of Fig. 6.3b. She doesn't get something for nothing, though. To lift the trunk 4.0 m, the sections of rope on *both* sides of pulley 2 must be shortened by 4.0 m, so Rosie must pull an 8.0-m length of rope. The two-pulley system enables her to pull with half the force, but now she must pull the rope through *twice the distance.*

Notice that the *product* of the magnitude of the force and the distance is the same in both cases:

$$220 \text{ N} \times 4.0 \text{ m} = 110 \text{ N} \times 8.0 \text{ m} = 880 \text{ N·m} = W$$

This product is called the **work** (*W*) done by Rosie on the rope. Work is a scalar quantity; it does not have a direction. The same symbol *W* is often used for the weight of an object. To avoid confusion, we write *mg* for weight and let *W* stand for work.

Don't be misled by the many different meanings the word *work* has in ordinary conversation. We talk about doing homework, or going to work, or having too much work to do. Not everything we call "work" in conversation is *work* as defined in physics.

The SI unit of work and energy is the newton-meter (N·m), which is given the name joule (symbol: J). Using either method, Rosie must do 880 J of work on the rope to lift the trunk. When we say that Rosie does 880 J of work, we mean that Rosie supplies 880 J of energy—the amount of energy required to lift the trunk 4.0 m. *Work is an energy transfer that occurs when a force acts on an object that moves.*

Rosie does no work on the rope while she holds it in one place because the displacement is zero. She can just as well fasten it and walk away (Fig. 6.4). *If there is no displacement, no work is done and no energy is transferred.* Why then does she get tired if she holds the rope in place for a long time? Although Rosie does no work *on the rope* when holding it in place, work *is* done inside her body by muscle fibers, which have to contract and expand continually to maintain tension in the muscle. This internal work converts chemical energy into internal energy—the muscle warms up—but no energy is transferred *to the trunk.*

Work Done by a Force not Parallel to the Displacement

The force that Rosie exerts on the rope is in the same direction as the displacement of that end of the rope. More generally, how much work is done by a constant force that is at some angle to the displacement? It turns out that only the *component* of the force *in the direction of the displacement*

Figure 6.4 While the trunk is held in place by tying the rope, no work is done and no energy transfers occur.

SI unit of work and energy is the joule: 1 J = 1 N·m.

Work: an energy transfer that occurs when a force acts on an object that moves.

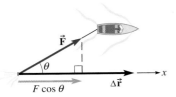

Figure 6.5 The work done by the force of the towrope on the water-skier during a displacement $\Delta\vec{r}$ is $(F\cos\theta)\,\Delta r$, where $(F\cos\theta)$ is the component of $\vec{F}$ in the direction of $\Delta\vec{r}$.

The **scalar product** (or **dot product**) of two vectors is defined by the equation $\vec{A}\cdot\vec{B} = AB\cos\theta$, where θ is the angle between $\vec{A}$ and $\vec{B}$ when they are drawn starting at the same point. The special name and notation are used because this pattern occurs often in physics and mathematics. Work can be expressed using the scalar product: $W = \vec{F}\cdot\Delta\vec{r}$. See Appendix A.8 for more information on the scalar product.

does work. So, in general, the work done by a constant force is defined as the product of the magnitude of the displacement and the *component* of the force *in the direction of the displacement*. If θ represents the angle between the force and displacement vectors when they are drawn starting at the same point, then the force component in the direction of the displacement is $F\cos\theta$ (Fig. 6.5). Therefore, work done by a constant force on an object can be written $W = F\,\Delta r\cos\theta$, where F is the magnitude of the force and Δr is the magnitude of the displacement of the object.

Work done by a constant force $\vec{F}$ acting on an object whose displacement is $\Delta\vec{r}$:

$$W = F\,\Delta r\cos\theta \tag{6-1}$$

(θ is the angle between $\vec{F}$ and $\Delta\vec{r}$)

If we choose the x-axis parallel to the displacement, then the component of the force in the direction of the displacement is $F_x = F\cos\theta$, so $W = F_x\Delta x$. Alternatively, we can identify $\Delta r\cos\theta$ in Eq. (6-1) as the component of the *displacement* in the direction of the *force* (Fig. 6.6). Therefore, if we choose the x-axis parallel to the *force*, then the component of the displacement in the direction of the force is Δx and $W = F_x\Delta x$, as before:

Work done by a constant force $\vec{F}$ acting on an object whose displacement is $\Delta\vec{r}$:

$$W = F_x\,\Delta x \tag{6-2}$$

($\vec{F}$ and/or $\Delta\vec{r}$ parallel to the x-axis)

Work Can Be Positive, Negative, or Zero   When the angle between $\vec{F}$ and $\Delta\vec{r}$ is less than $90°$, $\cos\theta$ in Eq. (6-1) is positive, so the work done by the force is positive ($W > 0$). If the angle between $\vec{F}$ and $\Delta\vec{r}$ is greater than $90°$, $\cos\theta$ is negative and the work done by the force is negative ($W < 0$). Pay careful attention to the algebraic sign when calculating work. For example, the rope pulls Rosie's trunk in the direction of its displacement, so $\theta = 0$ and $\cos\theta = 1$; the rope does positive work on the trunk. At the same time, gravity pulls downward in the direction opposite to the displacement, so $\theta = 180°$ and $\cos\theta = -1$; gravity does *negative* work on the trunk.

If the force is perpendicular to the displacement, $\theta = 90°$ and $\cos 90° = 0$, so the work done is zero. For example, the normal force exerted by a stationary surface on a sliding object does no work because it is perpendicular to the displacement of the object (Fig. 6.7a). Even if the surface is curved, at any instant the normal force is perpendicular to the velocity of the object. During a short time interval, then, the normal force is perpendicular to the displacement $\Delta\vec{r} = \vec{v}\,\Delta t$ (Fig. 6.7b), so the normal force still does zero work.

On the other hand, if the surface exerting the normal force is moving, then the normal force can do work. In Fig. 6.7c, the normal force exerted by the forklift on the pallet does positive work as it lifts the pallet.

Figure 6.6 The work done by the force of gravity on the hang glider during a displacement $\Delta\vec{r}$ is $F(\Delta r\cos\theta)$, which is F times the component of $\Delta\vec{r}$ in the direction of $\vec{F}$.

(a)   (b)   (c)

Figure 6.7 (a) The normal force does no work because it is perpendicular to the displacement. (b) Even while sliding on a curved surface, the direction of the normal force is always perpendicular to the displacement during a short Δt, so it does no work. (c) The normal force that the forklift exerts on the pallet does work; it is not perpendicular to the displacement.

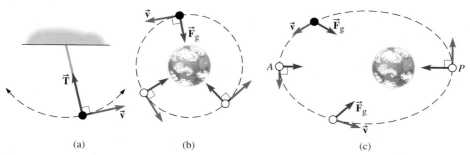

(a)   (b)   (c)

Figure 6.8 (a) The tension in the string of a pendulum is always perpendicular to the velocity of the pendulum bob, so the string does no work on the bob. (b) No matter where the satellite is in its circular orbit, it experiences a gravitational force directed toward the center of the Earth. This force is always perpendicular to the satellite's velocity; thus, gravity does no work on the satellite. (c) In an elliptical orbit, the gravitational force is *not* always perpendicular to the velocity. As the satellite moves counterclockwise in its orbit from point P to point A, gravity does negative work; from A to P, gravity does positive work.

No work is done by the tension in the string on a swinging pendulum bob because the tension is always perpendicular to the velocity of the bob (Fig. 6.8a). Similarly, no work is done by the Earth's gravitational force on a satellite in circular orbit (Fig. 6.8b). In a circular orbit, the gravitational force is always directed along a radius from the satellite to the center of the Earth. At every point in the orbit, the gravitational force is perpendicular to the velocity of the satellite (which is tangent to the circular orbit).

By contrast, gravity does work on a satellite in a noncircular orbit (Fig. 6.8c). Only at points A and P are the gravitational force and the satellite's velocity perpendicular. Wherever the angle between the gravitational force and the velocity is less than 90°, gravity is doing positive work, increasing the satellite's kinetic energy by making it move faster. Wherever the angle between the gravitational force and the velocity is greater than 90°, gravity is doing negative work, decreasing the satellite's kinetic energy by slowing it down.

Application of work: elliptical orbits

✓ CHECKPOINT 6.2

A force is applied to a moving object, but no work is done. How is that possible?

Example 6.1

Antique Chest Delivery

A valuable antique chest, made in 1907 by Gustav Stickley, is to be moved into a truck. The weight of the chest is 1400 N. To get the chest from the ground onto the truck bed, which is 1.0 m higher, the movers must decide what to do. Should they lift it straight up, or should they push it up their 4.0-m-long ramp? Assume they push the chest on a wheeled dolly, which in a simplified model is equivalent to sliding it up a *frictionless* ramp.

(a) Find the work done by the movers on the chest if they lift it straight up 1.0 m at constant speed.
(b) Find the work done by the movers on the chest if they slide the chest up the 4.0-m-long *frictionless* ramp at constant speed by pushing parallel to the ramp.
(c) Find the work done by gravity on the chest in each case.
(d) Find the work done by the normal force of the ramp on the chest. Assume that all forces are constant.

Strategy   To calculate work, we use either Eq. (6-1) or Eq. (6-2), whichever is easier. For (a) and (b), we must calculate the force exerted by the movers. Drawing the FBD helps us calculate the forces. The ramp is a simple machine—just as for Rosie's pulleys, the ramp cannot reduce the amount of work that must be done, so we expect the work done by the movers to be the same in both cases (ignoring friction). We expect the work done by gravity to be negative in both cases, since the chest is moving up while gravity pulls down. The normal force due to the ramp is perpendicular to the displacement, so it does zero work on the chest. Since more than one force does work on the chest, we use subscripts to clarify which work is being calculated.

$\vec{\mathbf{F}}_m$

$m\vec{\mathbf{g}}$

Figure 6.9
FBD for the chest as the movers lift it straight up at constant speed.

Given: Weight of chest $mg = 1400$ N; length of ramp $d = 4.0$ m; height of ramp $h = 1.0$ m
To find: Work done by movers on the chest W_m and work done by gravity on the chest W_g in the two cases; work done by the normal force on the chest W_N.

Solution   (a) The displacement is 1.0 m straight up. The movers must exert an upward force $\vec{\mathbf{F}}_m$ equal in magnitude to the weight of the chest to move it at constant speed (Fig. 6.9). The work done to lift it 1.0 m is

$$W_m = F_m \, \Delta r \cos \theta = 1400 \text{ N} \times 1.0 \text{ m} \times \cos 0 = +1400 \text{ J}$$

where $\theta = 0$ because $\vec{\mathbf{F}}_m$ and $\Delta \vec{\mathbf{r}}$ are in the same direction (upward).

(b) Figure 6.10 shows a sketch of the situation. We take the x-axis along the inclined ramp and the y-axis perpendicular to the ramp and resolve the gravitational force into its x- and y-components (Fig. 6.11a). Figure 6.11b is the FBD for the chest. Sliding along at constant speed, the chest's acceleration is zero, so the x-components of the forces add to zero.

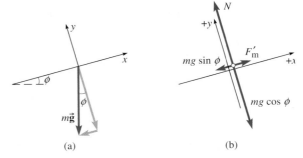

(a)   (b)

Figure 6.11
(a) Resolving $m\vec{\mathbf{g}}$ into x- and y-components; (b) FBD for the chest.

continued on next page

Figure 6.10   An antique chest is pushed up a ramp into a truck.

Example 6.1 continued

The *x*-component of the gravitational force acts in the −*x*-direction and the force exerted by the movers $\vec{F}'_{\mathrm{m}}$ acts in the +*x*-direction. [The *prime* symbol indicates that the force exerted by the movers is different from what it was in part (a).]

$$\sum F_x = F'_{\mathrm{m}} - mg \sin \phi = 0$$

From the right triangle formed by the ramp, the ground, and the truck bed in Fig. 6.12:

$$\sin \phi = \frac{\text{height of truck bed}}{\text{distance along ramp}} = \frac{h}{d}$$

We can now solve for F'_{m}:

$$F'_{\mathrm{m}} = mg \sin \phi = \frac{mgh}{d}$$

The force and displacement are in the same direction, so $\theta = 0$:

$$W_{\mathrm{m}} = F'_{\mathrm{m}} d \cos 0 = \frac{mgh}{d} \times d \times 1 = mgh = +1400 \text{ J}$$

The work done by the movers is the same as in (a).

(c) In both cases, the force of gravity has magnitude *mg* and acts downward. Choosing the *y*-axis so it now points upward, $F_{gy} = -mg$. In both cases, the component of the displacement

4.0 m

1.0 m

ϕ

Figure 6.12

Finding the angle of the incline.

along the *y*-axis is $\Delta y = h = 1.0$ m. The work done by gravity is the same for the two cases. Using Eq. (6-2),

$$W_g = F_{gy} \Delta y = -mg \Delta y$$

$$= -1400 \text{ N} \times 1.0 \text{ m} = -1400 \text{ J}$$

(d) The normal force of the ramp on the chest does no work because it acts in a direction perpendicular to the displacement of the chest.

$$W_N = N \Delta r \cos 90° = 0$$

Discussion   Since *d*, the length of the ramp, cancels when multiplying the force times the distance, the work done by the movers is the same for *any* length ramp (as long as the height is the same). Using the ramp, the movers apply one quarter the force over a displacement that is four times larger. With a *real* ramp, friction acts to oppose the motion of the chest, so the movers would have to do *more* than 1400 J of work to slide the chest up the ramp. There's no getting around it; if the movers want to get that chest into the truck, they're going to have to do *at least* 1400 J of work.

Practice Problem 6.1   Bicycling Uphill

A bicyclist climbs a 2.0-km-long hill that makes an angle of 7.0° with the horizontal. The total weight of the bike and the rider is 750 N. How much work is done on the bike and rider by gravity?

Total Work

When several forces act on an object, the total work is the sum of the work done by each force individually:

$$W_{\text{total}} = W_1 + W_2 + \cdots + W_N \qquad \text{(6-3)}$$

Total work is sometimes called *net* work because the work done by each force can be positive, negative, or zero, so the total work is often smaller than the work done by any one of the forces. Because we assume a rigid object with no rotational or internal motion, another way to calculate the total work is to find the work done by the *net* force as if there were a single force acting:

$$W_{\text{total}} = F_{\text{net}} \Delta r \cos \theta \qquad \text{(6-4)}$$

To show that these two methods give the same result, let's choose the *x*-axis in the direction of the displacement. Then the work done by each individual force is the *x*-component of the force times Δ*x*. From Eq. (6-3),

$$W_{\text{total}} = F_{1x} \Delta x + F_{2x} \Delta x + \cdots + F_{Nx} \Delta x$$

Factoring out the Δ*x* from each term,

$$W_{\text{total}} = (F_{1x} + F_{2x} + \cdots + F_{Nx}) \Delta x = \left(\sum F_x \right) \Delta x$$

$\sum F_x$ is the *x*-component of the net force. In Eq. (6-4), $F_{\text{net}} \cos \theta$ is the component of the net force in the direction of the displacement, which is the *x*-component of the net force. The two methods give the same total work.

Example 6.2

Fun on a Sled

Diane pulls a sled along a snowy path on level ground with her little brother Jasper riding on the sled (Fig. 6.13). The total mass of Jasper and the sled is 26 kg. The cord makes a 20.0° angle with the ground. As a simplified model, assume that the force of friction on the sled is determined by $\mu_k = 0.16$, even though the surfaces are not dry (some snow melts as the runners slide along it). Find (a) the work done by Diane and (b) the work done by the ground on the sled while the sled moves 120 m along the path at a constant 3 km/h. (c) What is the total work done on the sled?

Strategy   (a,b) To find the work done by a force on an object, we need to know the magnitudes and directions of the force and of the displacement of the object. The sled's acceleration is zero, so the vector sum of all the external forces (gravity, friction, rope tension, and the normal force) is zero. We draw the FBD and use Newton's second law to find the tension in the rope and the force of kinetic friction on the sled. Then we apply Eq. (6-1) or Eq. (6-2) to find the work done by each. (c) We have two methods to find the total work. We'll use Eq. (6-3) to calculate the total work and Eq. (6-4) as a check.

Solution   (a) The FBD is shown in Fig. 6.14. The x- and y-axes are parallel and perpendicular to the ground, respectively. After resolving the tension into its components (Fig. 6.15), Newton's second law with zero acceleration yields

$$\sum F_x = +T \cos \theta - f_k = 0 \tag{1}$$

$$\sum F_y = +T \sin \theta - mg + N = 0 \tag{2}$$

where T is the tension and $\theta = 20.0°$. The force of kinetic friction is

$$f_k = \mu_k N$$

Substituting this into Eq. (1)

$$T \cos \theta - \mu_k N = 0 \tag{3}$$

Figure 6.13
Jasper being pulled on a sled.

To find the tension, we need to eliminate the unknown normal force N. Equation (2) also involves the normal force N. We multiply Eq. (2) by μ_k,

$$\mu_k T \sin \theta - \mu_k mg + \mu_k N = 0 \tag{4}$$

Adding Eqs. (3) and (4) eliminates N. Then we solve for T.

$$T \cos \theta + \mu_k T \sin \theta - \mu_k mg = 0$$

$$T = \frac{\mu_k mg}{\mu_k \sin \theta + \cos \theta}$$

$$= \frac{0.16 \times 26 \text{ kg} \times 9.80 \text{ m/s}^2}{0.16 \times \sin 20.0° + \cos 20.0°} = 41 \text{ N}$$

Now that we know the tension, we find the work done by Diane. The component of the tension T acting parallel to the displacement is $T_x = T \cos \theta$ and the displacement is $\Delta x = 120$ m. The work done by Diane is

$$W_T = (T \cos \theta)\Delta x$$

$$= 41 \text{ N} \times \cos 20.0° \times 120 \text{ m} = +4600 \text{ J}$$

(b) The force on the sled due to the ground has two components: N and f_k. The normal force does no work since it is perpendicular to the displacement of the sled. Friction acts in a direction opposite to the displacement, so the angle between the force and displacement is 180°. The work done by friction is

$$W_f = f_k \Delta x \cos 180° = -f_k \Delta x$$

From Eq. (1),

$$f_k = T \cos \theta$$

Therefore, the work done by the ground—the work done by the frictional force—is

$$W_f = -f_k \Delta x = -(T \cos \theta) \Delta x$$

Except for the negative sign, W_f is the same as W_T: $W_f = -4600$ J.

Figure 6.14
FBD.

$\theta = 20.0°$

Figure 6.15
Resolving the tension into x- and y-components.

continued on next page

Example 6.2 continued

(c) The tension and friction are the only forces that do work on the sled. The normal force and gravity are both perpendicular to the displacement, so they do zero work.

$$W_{total} = W_T + W_f = 4600 \text{ J} + (-4600 \text{ J}) = 0$$

Discussion To check (c), note that the sled travels with constant velocity, so the net force acting on it is zero. $W_{total} = F_{net} \Delta r \cos \theta = 0$.

The speed (3 km/h) was not used in the solution. Assuming that the frictional force on the sled is independent of speed, Diane would exert the same force to pull the sled at *any* constant speed. Then the work she does is the same for a 120-m displacement. At a higher speed, though, she would have to do that amount of work in a shorter time interval.

Practice Problem 6.2   A Different Angle

Find the tension if Diane pulls at an angle $\theta = 30.0°$ instead of 20.0°, assuming the same coefficient of friction. What is the work done by Diane on the sled in this case for a 120-m displacement? Explain how the tension can be greater but the work done by Diane smaller.

Work Done by Dissipative Forces

The work done by kinetic friction was calculated in Example 6.2 according to a simplified model of friction. In this model, when friction truly does −4600 J of work on the sled, it transfers 4600 J of energy from the sled to the ground's internal energy—the ground warms up a bit. In reality, 4600 J of energy is converted into internal energy *shared* between the ground and the sled—both the ground and the sled warm up a little. So the 4600 J is not all transferred to the ground; some stays in the sled but is converted to a different form of energy.

Rather than saying friction does −4600 J of work, a more accurate statement is that friction *dissipates* 4600 J of energy. **Dissipation** is the conversion of energy from an organized form to a disorganized form such as the kinetic energy associated with the random motions of the atoms and molecules within an object, which is part of the object's internal energy. As a practical matter, we usually are not concerned with *where* the internal energy appears. When we can calculate the work done by friction using Eq. (6-1), we get the correct amount of energy dissipated; we just don't know how much of it is transferred to the stationary surface and how much remains in the sliding object. This is how we apply the term *work* to kinetic friction or to other dissipative forces such as air resistance. (In Chapters 14 and 15, when we study internal energy in detail, we will look at situations in which we *do* care where the internal energy appears.)

6.3   KINETIC ENERGY

Suppose a constant net force $\vec{F}_{net}$ acts on a rigid object of mass m during a displacement $\Delta \vec{r}$. Choosing the x-axis in the direction of the net force, the total work done on the object is

$$W_{total} = F_{net} \, \Delta x$$

where Δx is the x-component of the displacement. Newton's second law tells us that $\vec{F}_{net} = m\vec{a}$, so

$$W_{total} = m a_x \, \Delta x \qquad (6\text{-}5)$$

Since the acceleration is constant, we can use any of the equations for constant acceleration from Chapter 4. From Eq. (4-5), $v_{fx}^2 - v_{ix}^2 = 2a_x \Delta x$ or

$$a_x \, \Delta x = \tfrac{1}{2}(v_{fx}^2 - v_{ix}^2)$$

Substituting into Eq. (6-5) yields

$$W_{total} = \tfrac{1}{2}m(v_{fx}^2 - v_{ix}^2)$$

Since the net force is in the x-direction, a_y and a_z are both zero. Only the x-component of the velocity changes; v_y and v_z are constant. As a result,

$$v_f^2 - v_i^2 = (v_{fx}^2 + \cancel{v_{fy}^2} + \cancel{v_{fz}^2}) - (v_{ix}^2 + \cancel{v_{iy}^2} + \cancel{v_{iz}^2}) = v_{fx}^2 - v_{ix}^2$$

Therefore, the total work done is

$$W_{total} = \tfrac{1}{2}m(v_f^2 - v_i^2) = \tfrac{1}{2}mv_f^2 - \tfrac{1}{2}mv_i^2$$

The total work done is equal to the change in the quantity $\tfrac{1}{2}mv^2$, which is called the object's **translational kinetic energy** (symbol K). (Often we just say *kinetic energy* if it is understood that we mean translational kinetic energy.) Translational kinetic energy is the energy associated with motion of the object as a whole; it does not include the energy of rotational or internal motion.

Translational kinetic energy:

$$K = \tfrac{1}{2}mv^2 \tag{6-6}$$

Relation between total work and kinetic energy

Work-kinetic energy theorem:

$$W_{total} = \Delta K \tag{6-7}$$

Kinetic energy is a scalar quantity and is always positive if the object is moving or zero if it is at rest. Kinetic energy is never negative, although a *change* in kinetic energy can be negative. The kinetic energy of an object moving with speed v is equal to the work that must be done on the object to accelerate it to that speed starting from rest. When the total work done is positive, the object's speed increases, increasing the kinetic energy. When the total work done is negative, the object's speed decreases, decreasing the kinetic energy.

Conceptual Example 6.3

Collision Damage

Why is the damage caused by an automobile collision so much worse when the vehicles involved are moving at high speeds?

Strategy   When a collision occurs, the kinetic energy of the automobiles gets converted into other forms of energy. We can use the kinetic energy as a rough measure of how much damage can be done in a collision.

Solution and Discussion   Suppose we compare the kinetic energy of a car at two different speeds: 60.0 mi/h and 72.0 mi/h (which is 20.0% greater than 60.0 mi/h). If kinetic energy were proportional to speed, then a 20.0% increase in speed would mean a 20.0% increase in kinetic energy. However, since kinetic energy is proportional to the *square* of the speed, a 20.0% speed increase causes an increase in kinetic energy greater than 20.0%. Working by proportions, we can find the percent increase in kinetic energy:

$$\frac{K_2}{K_1} = \frac{\tfrac{1}{2}\cancel{m}v_2^2}{\tfrac{1}{2}\cancel{m}v_1^2} = \left(\frac{72.0 \text{ mi/h}}{60.0 \text{ mi/h}}\right)^2 = 1.44$$

Therefore, a 20.0% increase in speed causes a 44% increase in kinetic energy. What seems like a relatively modest difference in speed makes a lot of difference when a collision occurs.

Practice Problem 6.3   Two Different Cars Collide with a Stone Wall

Suppose a sports utility vehicle and a small electric car both collide with a stone wall and come to a dead stop. If the SUV mass is 2.5 times that of the small car and the speed of the SUV is 60.0 mph while that of the other car is 40.0 mph, what is the ratio of the kinetic energy changes for the two cars (SUV to small car)?

Example 6.4

Bungee Jumping

A bungee jumper makes a jump in the Gorge du Verdon in southern France. The jumping platform is 182 m above the bottom of the gorge. The jumper weighs 780 N. If the jumper falls to within 68 m of the bottom of the gorge, how much work is done by the bungee cord on the jumper during his descent? Ignore air resistance.

Strategy   Ignoring air resistance, only two forces act on the jumper during the descent: gravity and the tension in the cord. Since the jumper has zero kinetic energy at both the highest and lowest points of the jump, the change in kinetic energy for the descent is zero. Therefore, the total work done by the two forces on the jumper must equal zero.

Solution   Let W_g and W_c represent the work done on the jumper by gravity and by the cord. Then

$$W_{\text{total}} = W_g + W_c = \Delta K = 0$$

The work done by gravity is

$$W_g = F_y \, \Delta y = -mg \, \Delta y$$

where the weight of the jumper is $mg = 780$ N. With $y = 0$ at the bottom of the gorge, the vertical component of the displacement is

$$\Delta y = y_f - y_i = 68 \text{ m} - 182 \text{ m} = -114 \text{ m}$$

Then the work done by gravity is

$$W_g = -(780 \text{ N}) \times (-114 \text{ m}) = +89 \text{ kJ}$$

The work done by the cord is $W_c = W_{\text{total}} - W_g = -89$ kJ.

Discussion   The work done by gravity is positive, since the force and the displacement are in the same direction (downward). If not for the negative work done by the cord, the jumper would have a kinetic energy of 89 kJ after falling 114 m.

  The length of the bungee cord is not given, but it does not affect the answer. At first the jumper is in free fall as the cord plays out to its full length; only then does the cord begin to stretch and exert a force on the jumper, ultimately bringing him to rest again. Regardless of the length of the cord, the total work done by gravity and by the cord must be zero since the change in the jumper's kinetic energy is zero.

Practice Problem 6.4   The Bungee Jumper's Speed

Suppose that during the jumper's descent, at a height of 111 m above the bottom of the gorge, the cord has done −21.7 kJ of work on the jumper. What is the jumper's speed at that point?

✓ CHECKPOINT 6.3

Kinetic energy and work are related. Can kinetic energy ever be negative? Can work ever be negative?

6.4   GRAVITATIONAL POTENTIAL ENERGY (1)

Gravitational Potential Energy When Gravitational Force Is Constant

Toss a stone up with initial speed v_i. Ignoring air resistance, how high does the stone go? We can solve this problem with Newton's second law, but let's use work and energy instead. The stone's initial kinetic energy is $K_i = \frac{1}{2}mv_i^2$. For an upward displacement Δy, gravity does negative work $W_{\text{grav}} = -mg \, \Delta y$. No other forces act, so this is the total work done on the stone. The stone is momentarily at rest at the top, so $K_f = 0$. Then

$$W_{\text{grav}} = K_f - K_i$$

$$-mg \, \Delta y = -\frac{1}{2} \, mv_i^2 \quad \Rightarrow \quad \Delta y = \frac{v_i^2}{2g}$$

  From the standpoint of energy conservation, where did the stone's initial kinetic energy go? If total energy cannot change, it must be "stored" somewhere. Furthermore, the stone gets its kinetic energy back as it falls from its highest point to its initial position, so the energy is stored in a way that is easily recovered as kinetic energy. Stored energy due to the interaction of an object with something else (here, Earth's gravitational field) that can easily be recovered as kinetic energy is called **potential energy** (symbol U).

The change in gravitational potential energy when an object moves up or down is the *negative* of the work done by gravity:

Change in gravitational potential energy:

$$\Delta U_{\text{grav}} = -W_{\text{grav}} \qquad (6\text{-}8)$$

If the gravitational field is uniform, the work done by gravity is

$$W_{\text{grav}} = F_y \, \Delta y = -mg \, \Delta y$$

where the y-axis points up. Therefore,

Change in gravitational potential energy:

$$\Delta U_{\text{grav}} = mg \, \Delta y \qquad (6\text{-}9)$$

(uniform $\vec{\mathbf{g}}$, y-axis up)

Equation (6-9) holds even if the object does not move in a straight-line path.

Significance of the Negative Sign in Eq. (6-8)   When the stone moves up, Δy is positive. The gravitational force and the displacement of the stone are in opposite directions, so the work done by gravity is negative, gravity is taking away kinetic energy and adding it to its stored potential energy, so the potential energy increases (Fig. 6.16a). If the stone moves down, Δy is negative. The work done by gravity is positive; gravity is giving back kinetic energy by depleting its storage of potential energy, so the potential energy decreases (Fig. 6.16b).

✓ CHECKPOINT 6.4

A stone is tossed straight up in the air and is moving upward. (a) Does the gravitational potential energy increase, decrease, or stay the same? (b) What about the kinetic energy? (c) What force, if any, does work on the stone once it leaves the hand of the one who threw it?

The symbol for potential energy is U.

Figure 6.16 (a) When the stone moves up, the gravitational potential energy increases. (b) When the stone moves down, the gravitational potential energy decreases.

Other Forms of Potential Energy   In addition to gravitational potential energy, other kinds of potential energy include elastic potential energy (Section 6.7) and electric potential energy (Chapter 17). Forces that have potential energies associated with them are called **conservative forces**, for reasons we explain shortly. Not every force has an associated potential energy. For instance, there is no such thing as "frictional potential energy." When kinetic friction does work, it converts energy into a disorganized form that is not easily recoverable as kinetic energy.

Mechanical Energy   The total work done on an object can always be written as the sum of the work done by conservative forces (W_{cons}) plus the work done by nonconservative forces (W_{nc}). Since the total work is equal to the change in the object's kinetic energy [Eq. (6-7)],

$$W_{total} = W_{cons} + W_{nc} = \Delta K \quad \Rightarrow \quad W_{nc} = \Delta K - W_{cons} \qquad (6\text{-}10)$$

Following the same reasoning we used for gravity [see Eq. (6-8)], the change in the total potential energy is equal to the negative of the work done by the conservative forces:

$$\Delta U = -W_{cons} \qquad (6\text{-}11)$$

Combining Eqs. (6-10) and (6-11) yields

$$W_{nc} = \Delta K + \Delta U = \Delta E_{mech} \qquad (6\text{-}12)$$

or

$$(K_i + U_i) + W_{nc} = (K_f + U_f)$$

The sum of the kinetic and potential energies ($K + U$) is called the **mechanical energy** (E_{mech}). W_{nc} is equal to the change in mechanical energy. When finding the change in mechanical energy, do not include the work done by conservative forces. Conservative forces such as gravity do not change the mechanical energy; they just change one form of mechanical energy into another. Work done by conservative forces is already accounted for by the change in potential energy.

The term *conservative force* comes from a time before the general law of conservation of energy was understood and when no forms of energy other than mechanical energy were recognized. Back then, it was thought that certain forces conserved energy and others did not. Now we believe that *total* energy is *always* conserved. Nonconservative forces do not conserve *mechanical* energy, but they do conserve *total* energy.

Mechanical energy: the sum of the kinetic and potential energies

---

Conservation of Mechanical Energy

When nonconservative forces do no work, mechanical energy is conserved:

$$E_i = E_f$$

Example 6.5

Rock Climbing in Yosemite

A team of climbers is rappelling down steep terrain in the Yosemite valley (Fig. 6.17). Mei-Ling (mass 60.0 kg) slides down a line starting from rest 12.0 m above a horizontal shelf. If she lands on the shelf below with a speed of 2.0 m/s, calculate the energy dissipated by the kinetic frictional forces acting between her and the line. The local value of g is 9.78 N/kg. Ignore air resistance.

continued on next page

Example 6.5 continued

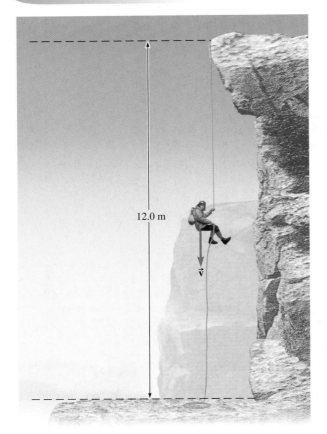

Figure 6.17
Mei-Ling rappelling downward from a position 12.0 m above a shelf.

Strategy   The forces acting on Mei-Ling are gravity and kinetic friction (Fig. 6.18). The only force whose work is not included in the change in potential energy is the work done by kinetic friction. Therefore, the change in the mechanical energy, $\Delta K + \Delta U$, is equal to the work done by friction. Since we know Mei-Ling's initial and final speeds as well as her mass, we can calculate the change in her kinetic energy. From the change in height, we can calculate the change in potential energy.

Figure 6.18
FBD for Mei-Ling.

Given: mass of climber, $m = 60.0$ kg; $\Delta y = -12.0$ m; $v_i = 0$ m/s and $v_f = 2.0$ m/s, just before stopping; local field strength $g = 9.78$ N/kg.

To find: change in mechanical energy ΔE.

Solution $W_{nc} = \Delta E_{mech} = \Delta K + \Delta U$, so we need to calculate the changes in kinetic and potential energy. Mei-Ling's kinetic energy is initially zero since she starts at rest. The change in her kinetic energy is

$$\Delta K = \tfrac{1}{2}mv_f^2 - \tfrac{1}{2}mv_i^2 = \tfrac{1}{2}mv_f^2 - 0 = \tfrac{1}{2}(60.0 \text{ kg}) \times (2.0 \text{ m/s})^2$$
$$= +120 \text{ J}$$

The change in her potential energy is

$$\Delta U = mg\,\Delta y = 60.0 \text{ kg} \times 9.78 \text{ m/s}^2 \times (0 - 12.0 \text{ m}) = -7040 \text{ J}$$

The work done by friction is

$$\Delta E_{mech} = \Delta K + \Delta U = 120 \text{ J} + (-7040 \text{ J}) = -6920 \text{ J}$$

The amount of energy dissipated by friction (converted from mechanical energy into internal energy) is 6920 J. Fortunately, Mei-Ling is wearing gloves, so her hands don't get burned.

Discussion   If the line had broken when Mei-Ling was at the top, her final kinetic energy would have been +7040 J—disastrously large since it corresponds to a final speed of

$$v = \sqrt{\frac{K}{\tfrac{1}{2}m}} = \sqrt{\frac{7040 \text{ J}}{30.0 \text{ kg}}} = 15.3 \text{ m/s}$$

Instead, kinetic friction reduces her final kinetic energy to a manageable +120 J (which corresponds to a final speed of 2.0 m/s). Mei-Ling can absorb this much kinetic energy safely by landing on the shelf while bending her knees.

Practice Problem 6.5   Energy Dissipated by Air Resistance

A ball thrown straight up at an initial speed of 14.0 m/s reaches a maximum height of 7.6 m. What fraction of the ball's initial kinetic energy is dissipated by air resistance as the ball moves upward?

Choosing Where the Potential Energy Is Zero

Notice that when we apply Eq. (6-12), only the *change* in potential energy enters the calculation. Therefore, we can always assign the value of the potential energy for any *one* position. Most often, we choose some convenient position and assign it to have zero potential energy. Once that choice is made, the potential energy of every other configuration is determined by Eq. (6-11).

For gravitational potential energy in a uniform gravitational field, we usually choose the potential energy to be zero at some convenient place: on the floor, on a table, or at the top of a ladder. After assigning $y = 0$ to that place, the potential energy at any other place is $U = mgy$.

> **Gravitational potential energy:**
> $$U_{\text{grav}} = mgy \qquad (6\text{-}13)$$
> (uniform $\vec{g}$, y-axis up, assign $U = 0$ to $y = 0$)

Potential energy is then positive above $y = 0$ and negative below it. There is no special significance to the sign of the potential energy. What matters is the sign of the potential energy *change.*

Example 6.6

A Quick Descent

A ski trail makes a vertical descent of 78 m. A novice skier, unable to control his speed, skis down this trail and is lucky enough not to hit any trees. What is his speed at the bottom of the trail, ignoring friction and air resistance?

Strategy When nonconservative forces do no work, $W_{\text{nc}} = \Delta E_{\text{mech}} = 0$ and mechanical energy does not change. A skilled skier can control his speed by, in effect, controlling how much work the frictional force does on the skis. Here we assume *no* friction or air resistance. Then the only forces acting on the skier are the normal force and gravity (Fig. 6.19). The normal force does no work, since it is always perpendicular to the skier's velocity, so $W_{\text{nc}} = 0$.

continued on next page

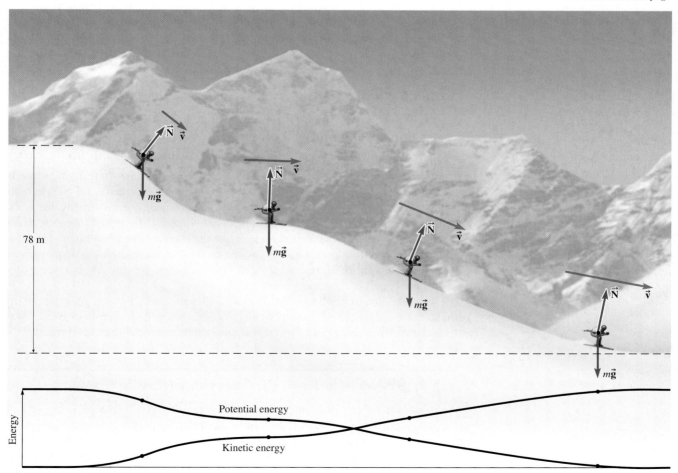

Figure 6.19 The final speed of the skier depends only on the initial and final altitudes if no friction acts.

Example 6.6 continued

Solution   Because $W_{nc} = 0$, the mechanical energy does not change:

$$K_i + U_i = K_f + U_f$$

If we choose the y-axis up and $y = 0$ at the bottom of the hill, $y_i = 78$ m and $y_f = 0$. Then

$$U_i = mgy_i \quad \text{and} \quad U_f = 0$$

If the skier starts with zero kinetic energy, then $K_i = 0$ and $K_f = \frac{1}{2}mv_f^2$. Setting the mechanical energies equal,

$$0 + mgy_i = \frac{1}{2}mv_f^2 + 0$$

Solving for the final speed v_f,

$$v_f = \sqrt{2gy_i} = \sqrt{2 \times 9.80 \text{ m/s}^2 \times 78 \text{ m}} = 39 \text{ m/s}$$

Discussion   Notice that the solution did not depend on the detailed shape of the path. If the slope were constant (Fig. 6.20), we could use Newton's second law to find the skier's acceleration and then the change in velocity:

$$\sum F_x = mg \sin\theta = ma_x \implies a_x = g\sin\theta$$

From Eq. (4-5),

$$\Delta x = \frac{v_{fx}^2 - v_{ix}^2}{2a_x} = \frac{v_{fx}^2}{2g\sin\theta} = \frac{h}{\sin\theta} \implies v_{fx} = \sqrt{2gh}$$

where $h = 78$ m.

This method shows that the final speed does not depend on the angle of the slope, but the energy method shows that the final speed is the same for *any* shape path, not just for constant slopes. On the other hand, the *time* that it takes the skier to reach the bottom *does* depend on the length and contour of the trail.

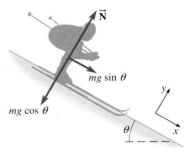

Figure 6.20
FBD for the skier on a constant slope.

A final speed of 39 m/s (87 mi/h) is dangerously fast. In reality, friction and air resistance would do negative work on the skier, so the final speed would be smaller.

Practice Problem 6.6   **Speeding Roller Coaster**

A roller coaster is hauled to the top of the first hill of the ride by a motorized chain drive. After that, the train of cars is released and no more energy is supplied by an external motor. The cars are moving at 4.0 m/s at the top of the first hill, 35.0 m above the ground. How fast are they moving at the top of the second hill, 22.0 m above the ground? Ignore friction and air resistance.

Recognizing a Conservative Force

In Example 6.6, the final speed doesn't depend on the shape of the trail: it could have been a steep descent, or a long gradual one, or have a complicated profile with varying slope. It could even be a vertical descent—the final speed is the same for free fall off a 78-m-high building. Any time the work done by a force is *independent of path*—that is, the work depends only on the initial and final positions—the force is conservative. We depend on the path-independence of the work done to define the potential energy in Eq. (6-11).

Energy stored as potential energy by a conservative force during a displacement from point A to point B can be recovered as kinetic energy. We can simply reverse displacement to get all of the energy back: $\Delta U_{B \to A} = -\Delta U_{A \to B}$.

The work done by friction, air resistance, and other contact forces *does* depend on path, so these forces cannot have potential energies associated with them. We cannot use friction to store energy in a form that is completely recoverable as kinetic energy.

6.5   GRAVITATIONAL POTENTIAL ENERGY (2)

The expressions for gravitational potential energy developed in Section 6.4 apply when the gravitational force is *constant* (or nearly constant). If the gravitational force is not constant, such as when a satellite is placed into orbit around the Earth, Eqs. (6-9) and (6-13) cannot be used. Instead, we need to use an expression for gravitational potential energy that corresponds to Newton's law of universal gravitation. Recall that the magnitude of the gravitational force that one body exerts on another is

$$F = \frac{Gm_1 m_2}{r^2} \qquad (2\text{-}6)$$

where r is the distance between the centers of the bodies. The corresponding expression for gravitational potential energy in terms of the distance between two bodies is

Gravitational potential energy:

$$U = -\frac{Gm_1 m_2}{r} \qquad (6\text{-}14)$$

(assign $U = 0$ when $r = \infty$)

A graph showing the gravitational potential energy as a function of r is shown in Fig. 6.21. Note that we have assigned the potential energy to be zero at infinite separation ($U = 0$ when $r = \infty$). Why this choice? Simply put, any other choice would mean adding a constant term to the expression for U. This constant term would *always subtract out* of our equations, which involve only *changes* in potential energy.

This choice ($U = 0$ when $r = \infty$) means that the gravitational potential energy is *negative* for any finite value of r, because potential energy decreases as the bodies get closer together and increases as they get farther apart.

Does Eq. (6-14) Contradict Eq. (6-9)?

Calculus is used to derive Eq. (6-14), but we can *verify* that it is consistent with Eq. (6-9) without using calculus. For a *very small* displacement from r_i to $r_f = r_i + \Delta y$ (Fig. 6.22), the potential energy change given by Eq. (6-14) must reduce to the constant-force case:

$$\Delta U = U_f - U_i = \left(-\frac{GM_E m}{r_i + \Delta y}\right) - \left(-\frac{GM_E m}{r_i}\right)$$

Rearranging and factoring out the common factors $GM_E m$ and then rewriting with a common denominator,

$$\Delta U = GM_E m \left(\frac{1}{r_i} - \frac{1}{r_i + \Delta y}\right) = GM_E m \, \frac{\cancel{r_i} + \Delta y - \cancel{r_i}}{r_i(r_i + \Delta y)} \qquad (6\text{-}15)$$

For values of Δy that are small compared with r_i, $r_i + \Delta y \approx r_i$. Making that approximation in the denominator of Eq. (6-15),

$$\Delta U = m\left(\frac{GM_E}{r_i^2}\right)\Delta y \quad (\Delta y \ll r_i) \qquad (6\text{-}16)$$

The quantity in the parentheses in Eq. (6-16) is the gravitational field strength g, the gravitational force on the object divided by its mass m. Then, $\Delta U = mg\,\Delta y$, in agreement with Eq. (6-9).

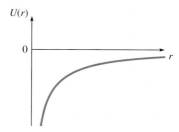

Figure 6.21 Gravitational potential energy as a function of r, the distance between the centers of the two bodies. The potential energy increases as the distance increases.

Figure 6.22 An object at a distance r from Earth's center moves up a small distance Δy (greatly exaggerated in the figure).

✓ CHECKPOINT 6.5

As Mercury travels in its elliptical orbit about the Sun, how does its mechanical energy at its nearest point (*perihelion*) to the Sun compare with that at its farthest point (*aphelion*) from the Sun? How does its potential energy compare at the same two points?

Example 6.7

Orbital Speed of Mercury

The orbit of the planet Mercury around the Sun is an ellipse. At its perihelion (4.60×10^7 km), its orbital speed is 59 km/s. What is its orbital speed at aphelion (6.98×10^7 km)?

Strategy   Ignoring the small gravitational forces exerted by other planets, the only force acting on Mercury is the gravitational force due to the Sun. Gravity is a conservative force, so the mechanical energy is constant. Figure 6.23 is a sketch of the orbit. At aphelion, Mercury is farther from the Sun than at perihelion, so the potential energy is greater. Then the kinetic energy must be smaller, so the answer must be less than 59 km/s.

Given: $v_p = 5.9 \times 10^4$ m/s, $r_p = 4.60 \times 10^{10}$ m,
$r_a = 6.98 \times 10^{10}$ m.
To find: v_a.

Solution   Mechanical energy is constant:

$$K_p + U_p = K_a + U_a$$

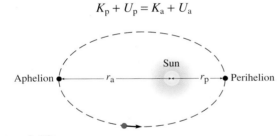

Figure 6.23
Sketch of Mercury's orbit.

The kinetic energy of Mercury at perihelion is $K_p = \frac{1}{2}mv_p^2$, where m is the mass of Mercury; the kinetic energy at aphelion is $K_a = \frac{1}{2}mv_a^2$. The potential energies at perihelion and at aphelion are

$$U_p = -\frac{GM_S m}{r_p} \quad \text{and} \quad U_a = -\frac{GM_S m}{r_a}$$

respectively, where $M_S = 1.99 \times 10^{30}$ kg is the mass of the Sun. From conservation of energy:

$$\frac{1}{2}mv_p^2 + \left(-\frac{GM_S m}{r_p}\right) = \frac{1}{2}mv_a^2 + \left(-\frac{GM_S m}{r_a}\right)$$

The mass of Mercury cancels out. Solving for v_a,

$$\frac{1}{2}v_a^2 = \frac{1}{2}v_p^2 + \left(-\frac{GM_S}{r_p}\right) - \left(-\frac{GM_S}{r_a}\right)$$

$$v_a = \sqrt{v_p^2 + 2GM_S\left(\frac{1}{r_a} - \frac{1}{r_p}\right)}$$

Substituting numerical values yields $v_a = 39$ km/s.

Discussion   The speed at aphelion is less than the speed at perihelion, as expected.

Practice Problem 6.7   Speed at a Different Distance

What is Mercury's orbital speed when its distance from the Sun is 5.80×10^7 km?

Example 6.8

Escape Speed

Ignoring air resistance, what is the minimum initial speed a projectile must have at Earth's surface if the projectile is to escape Earth's gravitational pull?

Strategy   What does "escape Earth's gravitational pull" mean? The gravitational force on the projectile due to Earth *approaches* zero at large distances, but never *reaches* zero. We are looking for the initial speed so that, even though Earth's gravity keeps pulling the projectile back, the projectile can keep moving away from Earth. The gravitational force is not constant, and the trajectory of the projectile may be complicated, so using $\Sigma\vec{F} = m\vec{a}$ is impractical. We try an energy approach.

The only force acting on the projectile is gravity, so the mechanical energy is constant. To escape, the projectile must have enough initial kinetic energy so that it can reach an unlimited distance from Earth.

Solution   The mechanical energy is constant:

$$K_i + U_i = K_f + U_f$$

Initially the projectile is at a distance R_E from Earth's center and is moving at initial speed v_i. At some later time, the projectile has speed v_f at distance r_f from Earth. Then

$$\frac{1}{2}mv_i^2 + \left(-\frac{GM_E m}{R_E}\right) = K_f + U_f$$

continued on next page

Example 6.8 continued

To escape, the projectile must be able to reach any value of r_f, no matter how large. As r_f gets larger and larger, the potential energy approaches its maximum value, which is zero. (Mathematically, as $r_f \rightarrow \infty$, $U_f \rightarrow 0$.) The *minimum* value of v_i gives the projectile *just enough* energy. So we assume that the projectile can reach its maximum potential energy without any kinetic energy left over ($K_f = 0$):

$$\frac{1}{2}mv_i^2 + \left(-\frac{GM_E m}{R_E}\right) = 0 + 0$$

Solving for v_i,

$$\frac{1}{2}\cancel{m}v_i^2 = \frac{GM_E \cancel{m}}{R_E} \quad \Rightarrow \quad v_i = \sqrt{\frac{2GM_E}{R_E}} = 11.2 \text{ km/s}$$

Discussion This speed is called the **escape speed** of Earth. Note that the escape speed is independent of the mass of the projectile because both the kinetic energy and the potential energy are proportional to the projectile's mass.

The concept of escape speed helps explain why there is little hydrogen gas (H_2) or helium gas (He) in Earth's atmosphere. We will see in Chapter 13 that the molecules in a gas have an average kinetic energy determined by the temperature of the gas. In a mixture of gases, the molecules with the smallest mass have the highest average speeds. The average speeds of hydrogen and helium in our atmosphere are large enough that they can escape the atmosphere. A negligible fraction of the nitrogen, oxygen, or water molecules have speeds greater than the escape speed, so they persist in the atmosphere.

Practice Problem 6.8   Protons Streaming Away from the Sun

Particles such as protons and electrons are continually streaming away from the Sun in all directions. They carry off some of the energy released in the thermonuclear reactions occurring in the Sun. How fast must a proton be moving at a distance of 7.00×10^9 m from the center of the Sun for it to escape the Sun's gravitational pull and leave the solar system?

6.6   WORK DONE BY VARIABLE FORCES: HOOKE'S LAW

So far we have considered only constant forces when calculating work. The advantage of using energy methods really shines in problems dealing with variable forces, where it's difficult to use Newton's second law. How can we calculate the work done by a variable force? Consider an archer drawing back a compound bow (Fig. 6.24). The compound bow is designed to make it easier to draw the string back and hold it back because, at a certain point, the force required to draw the string farther stops increasing. A convenient way to describe how the force varies with string position is to plot a graph. Figure 6.25 shows the force that must be applied to hold the string back as a function of distance. How can we calculate the work done by the archer as he draws the string back 40 cm?

We've asked analogous questions in previous chapters. Recall how we find the displacement Δx when the velocity v_x is not constant (Section 3.2). We divide the time interval into a series of *short* time intervals and sum up the displacements that occur during each one.

To approximate the work done by a variable force F_x, we divide the overall displacement into a series of small displacements Δx. During each small displacement, the work done is

$$\Delta W = F_x \, \Delta x \tag{6-17}$$

On a graph of $F_x(x)$, each ΔW is the area of a rectangle of height F_x and width Δx (Fig. 6.26). The total work done is the sum of the areas of these rectangles. This approximation gets better as we make the rectangles thinner and thinner, so *the total work done is the area under the graph of $F_x(x)$ from x_i to x_f.*

In Fig. 6.25, the "area" of each rectangle represents (0.050 m × 20.0 N) = 1.0 J of work. There are approximately 36 rectangles under the graph between $x = 0$ and $x = 40$ cm, so the work done by the archer is +36 J.

Figure 6.24 Application of work done by a variable force: drawing a compound bow.

CONNECTION

See Sections 3.2 and 3.3 to review how we found that the area under a graph of $v_x(t)$ is Δx and that the area under a graph of $a_x(t)$ is Δv_x.

W = the area under a graph of $F_x(x)$

Figure 6.25 The force to draw back the compound bow depends on how far it is drawn. In this graph, the "area" represented by each rectangle is 0.050 m × 20.0 N = 1.0 J.

Figure 6.26 Each rectangle's area approximates the work done during a small displacement. The total area of the rectangles approximates the total work done.

Example 6.9

Archery Practice

To draw back a *simple* bow, the force the archer exerts on the string continues to increase as the displacement of the string increases and the bow bends slightly. The force-versus-position graph of Fig. 6.27 describes such a bow. Calculate the work done by the archer on the string as he draws the string back 40.0 cm.

Strategy The work done by the archer is the area under the force-versus-position graph. This time, instead of counting rectangles, we can calculate the triangular area formed by the force-versus-position graph.

Figure 6.27
A simple bow requires a force proportional to the displacement of the string.

Solution We want to find the work done by the archer to draw the string back 40.0 cm, so the base of the triangle is 40.0 cm. The altitude of the triangle is the force at 40.0 cm: 160 N. The area of a triangle is $\frac{1}{2}$(base × altitude), so

$$W = \tfrac{1}{2}(0.400 \text{ m} \times 160 \text{ N}) = +32 \text{ J}$$

Discussion To check, we can count the number of rectangles (including the half rectangles) that lie under the graph. There are 32 rectangles and each represents 20 N × 0.05 m = 1 J of work, so the answer is correct.

By doing 32 J of work on the bowstring, the archer stores this much energy in the bow. When the arrow is released, the bowstring does 32 J of work on the arrow, giving the arrow a kinetic energy of 32 J.

Practice Problem 6.9   A Gentle Pull

How much work would you do to draw the string of the compound bow (Fig. 6.25) back 10.0 cm instead of 40.0 cm?

Hooke's Law and Ideal Springs

Hooke's law: the deformation is proportional to the deforming force.

In Example 6.9, the displacement of the bowstring is proportional to the force exerted by the archer. Robert Hooke (1635–1703) observed that, for many objects, the deformation—change in size or shape—of the object is proportional to the magnitude of the force that causes the deformation. This observation, called **Hooke's law**, is an approximation and is valid only within limits. For example, the compound bow of Fig. 6.25 is described by Hooke's law only for an applied force less than 80 N.

Many springs are described by Hooke's law as long as they are not stretched or compressed too far. That is, the extension or compression—the increase or decrease in length from the relaxed length—is proportional to the force applied to the ends of the spring. When we refer to an **ideal spring**, we mean a spring that is described by Hooke's law and is also massless.

Hooke's law for an ideal spring:

$$F = k \,\Delta L \tag{6-18}$$

In Eq. (6-18), F is the *magnitude* of the force exerted *on each end* of the spring and ΔL is the distance that the spring is stretched or compressed from its relaxed length.

The constant k is called the **spring constant** for a particular spring. The SI unit of force is the newton and the SI unit of length is the meter, so the SI units of a spring constant are N/m. The spring constant is a measure of how hard it is to stretch or compress a spring. A stiffer spring has a larger spring constant because larger forces must be exerted on the ends of the spring to stretch or compress it. Example 1.10 describes an experiment to measure the spring constant of a real spring and shows a graph of length of the spring as a function of the forces applied to its ends (Fig. 1.5).

In many situations, we are more interested in the forces exerted *by* the spring than in the forces exerted *on* it. From Newton's third law, the forces exerted *by* the spring on whatever is attached to its ends are equal in magnitude and opposite in direction to the forces exerted *by* those objects *on* the ends of the spring. Suppose that an ideal spring is aligned with the *x*-axis. One end is fixed in place and the other end can move along the *x*-axis (Fig. 6.28). Choose the origin so the moveable end is at $x = 0$ when the spring is relaxed. Then the force exerted by the moveable end of the spring on whatever is attached to it is

Figure 6.28 An ideal spring is stretched a distance x beyond its relaxed length.

Force exerted *by* an ideal spring (Hooke's law):

$$F_x = -kx \tag{6-19}$$

(F_x is the force exerted *by* the moveable end when its position is x; the spring is relaxed at $x = 0$.)

The negative sign in Eq. (6-19) indicates the direction of the force. The moveable end of the spring always pushes or pulls toward its relaxed position. If it is displaced in the $+x$-direction, the force it exerts is in the $-x$-direction (back toward $x = 0$). If it is displaced in the $-x$-direction, the force it exerts is in the $+x$-direction (again, back toward $x = 0$).

Example 6.10

Getting Down to Nuts and Bolts

In many hardware stores, bulk nuts and bolts are sold by weight. A spring scale in the store stretches 4.8 cm when 24.0 N of bolts are weighed. On the scale, what is the distance in centimeters between calibration marks that are marked in increments of 1 N? Assume an ideal spring.

Strategy   The bolts are in equilibrium, so the spring scale is pulling upward on them with a force of 24.0 N (see Fig. 6.29). Using Hooke's law and the data given, we can find the spring constant k. Then we can use Hooke's law again to find out how much the spring stretches when the applied force is increased by 1 N.

Solution   Let the *x*-axis point up. When the pan of the scale is at $x = -4.8$ cm, it exerts a force $F_x = +24.0$ N on the bolts. From Hooke's law, $F_x = -kx$ and the spring constant is

$$k = -\frac{F_x}{x} = \frac{-24.0 \text{ N}}{-4.8 \text{ cm}} = 5.0 \text{ N/cm}$$

Now let $F_x = 1.00$ N and solve for x:

$$x = -\frac{F_x}{k} = -\frac{1.00 \text{ N}}{5.0 \text{ N/cm}} = -0.20 \text{ cm}$$

Since the relation between F and x is linear, the spring stretches an additional 0.20 cm for each additional newton of force. Therefore, the 1-N marks should be 0.20 cm apart.

Discussion   A variation on the solution is to look back at the question and notice that we are asked how many centimeters the spring stretches for each newton of force, which is the *reciprocal* of the spring constant. The reciprocal of the spring constant is

$$\frac{1}{k} = -\frac{x}{F} = -\frac{-4.8 \text{ cm}}{24.0 \text{ N}} = 0.20 \text{ cm/N}$$

The answer is reasonable: since it takes 5 N to make the spring stretch 1 cm, 1 N makes the spring stretch $\frac{1}{5}$ cm.

Figure 6.29
FBD for the pan of the scale.

Practice Problem 6.10   Stretching a Spring

16.0 N of nuts are placed in the pan of the scale of Example 6.10. How far does the spring stretch?

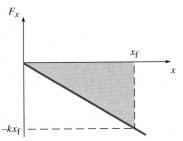

Figure 6.30 The work done by the spring is the (negative) area under the $F_x(x)$ graph.

Work Done by an Ideal Spring

To find the work done by an ideal spring, first we draw the $F_x(x)$ graph (Fig. 6.30). The unstretched position of the moveable end is $x = 0$. The work done by the spring as its moveable end moves from equilibrium ($x_i = 0$) to the final position x_f is the area of the shaded right triangle whose base is x and altitude is $-kx$:

$$W = \tfrac{1}{2}(\text{base} \times \text{altitude}) = -\tfrac{1}{2}kx^2 \qquad (6\text{-}20)$$

The area is negative because the graph is underneath the x-axis. Think of $-\tfrac{1}{2}kx^2$ as the average force ($-\tfrac{1}{2}kx$) times the displacement (x).

More generally, if the moveable end starts at position x_i, not necessarily at the equilibrium point, the work done by the spring is

$$W_{\text{spring}} = (-\tfrac{1}{2}kx_f^2) - (-\tfrac{1}{2}kx_i^2) = -\tfrac{1}{2}kx_f^2 + \tfrac{1}{2}kx_i^2 \qquad (6\text{-}21)$$

Imagine the spring starting at equilibrium and ultimately ending up at a displacement x_f after passing through x_i. The total work done by the spring is $-\tfrac{1}{2}kx_f^2$; then we subtract the work that was done to get the spring to position x_i from equilibrium ($-\tfrac{1}{2}kx_i^2$) to get the work done from x_i to x_f.

6.7   ELASTIC POTENTIAL ENERGY

The work done by an ideal spring [Eq. (6-21)] depends on the initial and final positions of the moveable end, but *not* on the path that was taken. Therefore, the force exerted by an ideal spring is *conservative* and we can associate a potential energy with it. The kind of potential energy stored in a spring is called **elastic potential energy**.

Just as for gravity [see Eqs. (6-8) and (6-11)], the change in elastic potential energy is the *negative* of the work done by the spring:

$$\Delta U_{\text{elastic}} = -W_{\text{spring}} \qquad (6\text{-}22)$$

CONNECTION:

The change in potential energy is always equal to the negative of the work done by the associated force. See Eq. (6-11).

For example, if you increase the elastic energy stored in a spring by compressing it, the spring does *negative* work because the force its end exerts on your hand is in the direction opposite to its displacement. This stored elastic energy can be recovered as kinetic energy by, say, using the spring to shoot a stone. As the spring expands back to its original length, it does positive work on the stone to increase the stone's kinetic energy and the stored elastic energy decreases.

From Eqs. (6-21) and (6-22),

$$\Delta U_{\text{elastic}} = \tfrac{1}{2}kx_f^2 - \tfrac{1}{2}kx_i^2 \qquad (6\text{-}23)$$

Remember that only changes in potential energy enter our calculations, so we can assign $U = 0$ to any convenient position. The most convenient choice is to assign $U = 0$ when the spring is relaxed ($x = 0$):

Elastic potential energy stored in an ideal spring:

$$U_{\text{elastic}} = \tfrac{1}{2}kx^2 \qquad (6\text{-}24)$$

$U = 0$ when $x = 0$ (relaxed spring)

Conservation of Energy with More than One Form of Potential Energy   When applying conservation of energy using $W_{\text{nc}} = \Delta K + \Delta U$ [Eq. (6-12)], ΔU must include the change in all forms of potential energy. For now, with two forms of potential energy,

$$\Delta U = \Delta U_{\text{grav}} + \Delta U_{\text{elastic}} \qquad (6\text{-}25)$$

W_{nc} is the work done by all forces *other than* those included in the potential energy. When $W_{nc} = 0$, the mechanical energy $K + U$ is constant.

CHECKPOINT 6.7

If a spring is compressed horizontally on a table and then released so it expands to its original relaxed position, where does the spring have the greatest elastic potential energy?

Example 6.11

The Dart Gun

In a dart gun (Fig. 6.31), a spring with $k = 400.0$ N/m is compressed 8.0 cm when the dart (mass $m = 20.0$ g) is loaded (Fig. 6.31a). What is the muzzle speed of the dart when the spring is released (Fig. 6.31b)? Ignore friction.

Strategy The elastic energy initially stored in the spring is converted into the kinetic energy of the dart as the spring expands. There is no change in gravitational potential energy since the motion of the dart is horizontal. The vertical normal forces do no work because they are perpendicular to the displacement of the dart. The spring pushes the dart to the right until it reaches its relaxed length. Assuming the spring can't pull the dart to the left (as it would if they stick together), the dart loses contact with the spring when the spring is at its relaxed length. We choose the origin at the relaxed position of the spring; therefore, $x_f = 0$. Using the x-axis in Fig. 6.31, $x_i = -8.0$ cm. The dart starts from rest, so $v_i = 0$. To find: v_f.

Solution Since we ignore friction, no work is done by nonconservative forces. Therefore, the mechanical energy is constant:

$$K_i + U_i = K_f + U_f$$

We can ignore the gravitational potential energy because it does not change. Using Eq. (6-24) for the elastic potential energy in the spring,

$$\tfrac{1}{2}mv_i^2 + \tfrac{1}{2}kx_i^2 = \tfrac{1}{2}mv_f^2 + \tfrac{1}{2}kx_f^2$$

After setting $x_f = 0$ and $v_i = 0$,

$$0 + \tfrac{1}{2}kx_i^2 = \tfrac{1}{2}mv_f^2 + 0$$

Solving for v_f,

$$v_f = \sqrt{\frac{k}{m}}\, x_i = \sqrt{\frac{400.0 \text{ N/m}}{0.0200 \text{ kg}}} \times 0.080 \text{ m} = 11 \text{ m/s}$$

Discussion Checking the units,

$$\sqrt{\frac{\text{N/m}}{\text{kg}}} \times \text{m} = \sqrt{\frac{(\text{kg} \cdot \text{m/s}^2)/\text{m}}{\text{kg}}} \times \text{m} = \frac{\text{m}}{\text{s}}$$

Notice that the muzzle speed is proportional to the distance the spring is compressed when the gun is cocked. If the spring is compressed halfway, it stores only *one quarter* as much elastic energy. The dart then acquires one quarter the kinetic energy, which means its speed is half as much. A more massive dart fired from the same gun would have a smaller muzzle speed, but the *same* kinetic energy.

Practice Problem 6.11   A Misfire

The same dart gun is cocked by compressing the spring the same distance (8.0 cm). This time the spring gets caught inside the gun, stopping at the point where it is still compressed by 4.0 cm. The dart is not caught inside the gun, but is released. Find the muzzle speed of the dart. [*Hint:* What is x_f in this case?]

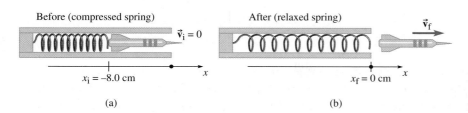

Before (compressed spring)   After (relaxed spring)

$\vec{v}_i = 0$ $\vec{v}_f$

$x_i = -8.0$ cm x $x_f = 0$ cm x

(a)   (b)

Figure 6.31

Dart gun (a) before and (b) after firing. The spring was compressed by 8.0 cm when the gun was cocked.

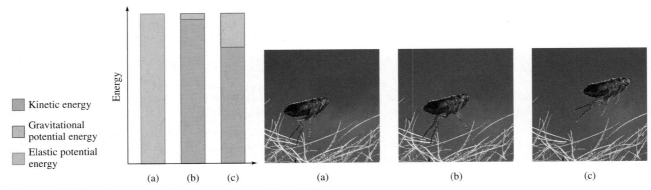

Figure 6.32 Energy transformations in the jump of a flea.

Application of Energy Conversion: Jumping

How does the kangaroo keep jumping?

When a human jumps, the muscles supply the energy to propel the body upward. Try jumping as high as you can from a standing start. You no doubt start by crouching down. Then you accelerate upward, straightening your legs and your body; your muscles convert chemical energy into the mechanical energy of your jump. If you are very athletic, you might be able to jump about 1 m above the floor.

The kangaroo uses a different mechanism. It has long, elastic tendons and small muscles in its hind legs, in contrast to the relatively large muscles and short, stiffer tendons found in humans. The kangaroo folds its legs before a jump, using its muscles to stretch the tendons and converting chemical energy into elastic potential energy. The kangaroo then quickly extends its legs, relaxing the tendons like a released spring. The elastic energy stored in the tendons supplies much of the energy needed for the jump; the rest is supplied by the kangaroo's leg muscles, which convert some more chemical energy into mechanical energy.

When the kangaroo lands on the ground, the tendons are stretched again as its legs bend. Thus, rather than dissipating all of the energy from the previous jump, a large fraction of it is recaptured as elastic energy in the tendons and then released to assist the next jump. This process reduces the amount of energy the muscles must supply for subsequent jumps and makes the kangaroo one of the most energy-efficient travelers among animals. The human body also stores some elastic energy in stretched tendons and in flexed foot bones when we run or jump, but not to the extent that its specialized anatomy enables the kangaroo to do.

Some insects jump using a catapult technique. The knee joint of a flea contains an elastic material called resilin (a rubber-like protein). The flea slowly bends its knee, stretching out the resilin and storing elastic energy, and then locks its knee in place (Fig. 6.32a). When the flea is ready to jump, the knee is unlocked and the resilin quickly contracts with a sudden conversion of the stored elastic energy into kinetic energy (Fig. 6.32b). Some of this kinetic energy is then converted into gravitational potential energy as the flea moves higher and higher (Fig. 6.32c). Ignoring air resistance and other dissipative forces, the total mechanical energy (kinetic energy + gravitational potential energy + elastic potential energy) does not change during the jump.

Example 6.12

The Hopping Kangaroo

Suppose the height h of a kangaroo's hop (Fig. 6.33) after it stretches its tendons a distance x_1 (beyond their unstretched length) is 2.0 m. How high would the hop be after it stretched the tendons 10% more than before (that is, a distance $1.10x_1$

beyond their unstretched length)? In a simplified model, we assume that all the energy for a kangaroo's hop comes from the elastic energy stored in the tendons, which behave as ideal springs. Ignore air resistance and other energy dissipation.

continued on next page

Example 6.12 continued

Strategy Ignoring dissipation, the mechanical energy does not change. We have to include both gravitational and elastic potential energies in the mechanical energy. At first we consider a kangaroo jumping straight up. Then we try to generalize to more typical hopping with forward motion as well as upward motion.

Solution The mechanical energy does not change:

$$K_i + U_{i,grav} + U_{i,elastic} = K_f + U_{f,grav} + U_{f,elastic}$$

Initially, when the kangaroo is crouched before the jump, it has zero kinetic energy. For convenience, we choose the initial gravitational potential energy to be zero. Thinking of the elastic potential energy as being stored in a single ideal spring with spring constant k, the initial mechanical energy is

$$K_i + U_{i,grav} + U_{i,elastic} = 0 + 0 + \tfrac{1}{2}kx_i^2$$

where x_i represents the initial stretch of the tendons. With the kangaroo at the high point of the jump, the kinetic energy is again zero if it jumped straight up. The tendons are no longer stretched, so the elastic potential energy is zero. But now there is gravitational potential energy. At a height h above the initial point, the final mechanical energy is

$$K_f + U_{f,grav} + U_{f,elastic} = 0 + mgh + 0$$

where m is the kangaroo's mass. Setting the mechanical energies equal,

$$\tfrac{1}{2}kx_i^2 = mgh \quad \Rightarrow \quad h = \frac{kx_i^2}{2mg}$$

We don't know all of the constants (mass, spring constant, initial amount of stretch), so we set up a ratio:

$$\frac{h_2}{h_1} = \frac{kx_2^2/(2mg)}{kx_1^2/(2mg)} = \frac{x_2^2}{x_1^2}$$

(a)   (b)

Figure 6.33

(a) Kangaroo crouched and ready to hop. (b) Kangaroo at the highest point in its hop.

For a 10% increase in stretch, $x_2 = 1.10x_1$ and

$$h_2 = \left(\frac{x_2}{x_1}\right)^2 h_1 = (1.10)^2 h_1 = 1.21 \times 2.0 \text{ m} = 2.4 \text{ m}$$

Using a 10% increase in the stretch of the tendon, the kangaroo jumps about 21% higher.

When the kangaroo is hopping along, it does not jump straight up. Will the kangaroo's jump still be 21% higher when jumping at another angle? Imagine the kangaroo hopping along so that it leaves the ground at a 45° angle, which gives the maximum horizontal range per hop in the absence of air resistance. The elastic energy in the tendon is first converted to kinetic energy. This time, not all of the kinetic energy is converted to gravitational potential energy. The kinetic energy at the highest point of the jump is *not* zero because the kangaroo is still moving forward. The initial velocity can be resolved into components:

$$v^2 = v_x^2 + v_y^2 = 2v_x^2 \quad \text{(since } v_x = v_y \text{ for a 45° angle)}$$

At the highest point of the jump, the kinetic energy is $\tfrac{1}{2}mv_x^2$, which is half of the initial kinetic energy. Overall, *half* of the elastic energy of the tendon is converted to gravitational potential energy:

$$\tfrac{1}{2} \times \left(\tfrac{1}{2}kx_i^2\right) = mgh$$

Since h is still proportional to x_i^2, the height of the jump still increases by 21% if the stretch of the tendon is increased by 10%.

Discussion The storage of elastic energy in the tendon is a clever way for the kangaroo to get more "miles per gallon." Without such an energy storage system, most of the kangaroo's mechanical energy would be converted to an unrecoverable form of energy at the end of each hop. The tendons store some of the energy that would otherwise be lost and then release it to help the next jump. Since less mechanical energy is "lost" on each landing, the energy supplied by the kangaroo's muscles is less than it would otherwise be. Humans use a similar energy-saving mechanism when running (see Problem 103).

Practice Problem 6.12 Jumping with Joey

Suppose the kangaroo has a baby kangaroo (a *joey*) riding in her pouch. If the joey has grown to be one sixth the mass of its mother, how high can the kangaroo jump with the additional load? Assume that, without the joey, she can jump 2.8 m.

6.8   POWER

Sometimes the *rate* of energy conversion is important. When shopping for a sports car, you wouldn't ask the salesman how much work the engine can do. A tiny economy car like the Toyota Prius does more work than a Ferrari if the Prius is used for daily commuting while the Ferrari sits in the garage most of the time. But the Ferrari can do work *at a much faster rate* than the Prius can. In other words, it can change chemical energy in the gasoline into mechanical energy of the car at a much faster rate—it has a larger maximum power output. The higher power output enables the Ferrari to accelerate to high speeds much faster than the Prius. We give the name **power** (symbol P) to the rate of energy transfer. The average power is the amount of energy converted (ΔE) divided by the time the transfer takes (Δt):

Power: the *rate* of energy conversion

Average power:

$$P_{av} = \frac{\Delta E}{\Delta t} \qquad (6\text{-}26)$$

The SI unit of power, the joule per second, is given the name watt (1 W = 1 J/s), after James Watt (1736–1819), a Scottish inventor who greatly improved the efficiency of steam engines. Remember that the unit symbol W stands for *watt*, not *work*.

In the United States, the maximum power output of an electric motor or automobile engine is usually specified in horsepower, which is a non-SI unit of power (1 hp = 746 W).

The *kilowatt-hour* (kW·h) is a unit of energy, *not a unit of power*. One kilowatt-hour is the amount of energy transferred at a constant rate of 1 kW during a time interval of 1 h. The kilowatt-hour is commonly used by utility companies to measure the amount of electric energy used by consumers.

The work done by a force during a small time interval Δt is

$$W = F \, \Delta r \cos \theta \qquad (6\text{-}1)$$

The magnitude of the displacement is

$$\Delta r = v \, \Delta t$$

Hence, the power—the rate at which the force does work—can be found from the force and the velocity.

$$P = \frac{W}{\Delta t} = \frac{F \Delta r \cos \theta}{\Delta t} = F \frac{\Delta r}{\Delta t} \cos \theta = Fv \cos \theta$$

Instantaneous power (rate at which work is done):

$$P = Fv \cos \theta \qquad (6\text{-}27)$$

(θ is the angle between $\vec{\mathbf{F}}$ and $\vec{\mathbf{v}}$)

Example 6.13

Air Resistance on a Hill-Climbing Car

A 1000.0-kg car climbs a hill with a 4.0° incline at a constant 12.0 m/s (Fig. 6.34). (a) At what rate is the gravitational potential energy increasing? (b) If the mechanical power output of the engine is 20.0 kW, find the force of air resistance on the car. (Assume that air resistance is responsible for all of the energy dissipation.)

Strategy   (a) We can find the rate of gravitational potential energy increase in two ways. One is to find the potential energy change during a time interval Δt and divide it by the time interval, which is equivalent to using the definition of average power [Eq. (6-26)]. The other possibility is to use Eq. (6-27) to find the rate at which the gravitational force does work.

continued on next page

Example 6.13 continued

Figure 6.34

Car climbing a hill at constant speed.

(b) The car moves at constant speed, so its kinetic energy is not changing. Therefore, during any time interval, the work done by the engine (W_e) plus the (negative) work done by air resistance (W_a) is equal to the increase in the gravitational potential energy.

Given: car mass = 1000.0 kg; $v = 12.0$ m/s; 4.0° incline.
To find: (a) rate of potential energy change, $\Delta U/\Delta t$; (b) force due to air resistance, $\vec{F}_a$.

Solution (a) For a small change in elevation Δy, the change in potential energy is

$$\Delta U = mg\, \Delta y$$

The *rate* of potential energy change is

$$\frac{\Delta U}{\Delta t} = \frac{mg\, \Delta y}{\Delta t} = mg\, \frac{\Delta y}{\Delta t} = mgv_y$$

where $v_y = \Delta y/\Delta t$ is the y-component of the velocity. From Fig. 6.35, $v_y = v \sin \phi$, where $\phi = 4.0°$. Then,

$$\frac{\Delta U}{\Delta t} = mgv \sin \phi = 1000.0 \text{ kg} \times 9.80 \text{ m/s}^2 \times 12.0 \text{ m/s} \times \sin 4.0°$$
$$= 8200 \text{ W}$$

(b) During any time interval Δt, the (positive) work done by the engine plus the (negative) work done by air resistance must equal the increase in the gravitational potential energy:

$$W_{\text{total}} = W_e + W_a = \Delta U$$

Dividing each term by Δt, we find

$$\frac{W_e}{\Delta t} + \frac{W_a}{\Delta t} = \frac{\Delta U}{\Delta t} \quad \Rightarrow \quad P_e + P_a = \frac{\Delta U}{\Delta t}$$

where P_e and P_a represent the power output of the engine and the rate at which air resistance does (negative) work on the car, respectively. Then,

$$P_a = \frac{\Delta U}{\Delta t} - P_e = 8.2 \text{ kW} - 20.0 \text{ kW} = -11.8 \text{ kW}$$

So, of the 20.0 kJ of mechanical work that the engine does each second, 8.2 kJ goes into gravitational potential energy

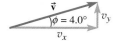

Figure 6.35

Resolving the velocity into x- and y-components.

and 11.8 kJ goes into pushing air out of the way and stirring it up in the process.

The direction of the force of air resistance $\vec{F}_a$ on the car is opposite to the car's velocity, so

$$P_a = F_a v \cos 180° = -F_a v$$

Solving for F_a,

$$F_a = -\frac{P_a}{v} = -\frac{-11\,800 \text{ W}}{12.0 \text{ m/s}} = 983 \text{ N}$$

Discussion We can check (a) by using Eq. (6-27) to find the rate at which the gravitational force does work: $P = Fv \cos \theta$, where $F = mg$. The angle θ is *not* the same as ϕ. In Eq. (6-27), θ is the angle between the force and velocity vectors, which is 94.0° (Fig. 6.36). Then,

$$P = mgv \cos 94.0°$$
$$= 1000.0 \text{ kg} \times 9.80 \text{ m/s}^2 \times 12.0 \text{ m/s} \times \cos 94.0°$$
$$= -8200 \text{ W}$$

Figure 6.36

The angle between the force and the velocity is $\theta = 94.0°$. (The angle is exaggerated for clarity.)

Gravity does work on the car at a rate of −8200 W, which means the potential energy is *increasing* at a rate of +8200 W.

We can also figure out what mechanical power the engine must supply to go 12.0 m/s on level ground. With no change in potential energy, all of the mechanical power output of the engine goes into stirring up the air, so $P_e + P_a = 0$. The magnitude of the force of air resistance is the same (983 N) since the speed is the same. Then air resistance dissipates energy at the same rate as before:

$$P_a = -F_a v = -983 \text{ N} \times 12.0 \text{ m/s} = -11.8 \text{ kW}$$

Therefore, $P_e = 11.8$ kW. On level ground, the gravitational potential energy isn't increasing, so the engine only needs to do enough work to counteract the tendency of air resistance to slow down the car.

In this example, we have assumed that all of the mechanical power output of the engine is delivered to the wheels to propel the car forward. In reality, some of the engine's power output is used to run auxiliary devices such as headlights, radios, and windshield wipers. Friction (in the moving parts of the engine, transmission, and drivetrain) also reduces the amount of power that is actually delivered to the wheels.

Practice Problem 6.13 Mechanical Power Output on Flat Ground or Going Downhill

What mechanical power must the engine supply (a) to drive on level ground at 12.0 m/s and (b) to go down a 4.0° incline at 12.0 m/s? (Since this is the same speed as in Example 6.13, the force of air resistance is the same.)

Master the Concepts

- Conservation law: a physical law phrased in terms of a quantity that does not change with time.

- The law of conservation of energy: the total energy of the universe is unchanged by any physical process.

- Work is an energy transfer due to the application of a force. The work done by a constant force $\vec{F}$ acting on an object during a displacement $\Delta\vec{r}$ is

$$W = F\,\Delta r\cos\theta \qquad (6\text{-}1)$$

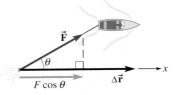

where θ is the angle between $\vec{F}$ and $\Delta\vec{r}$. If $\vec{F}$ or $\Delta\vec{r}$ is parallel to the x-axis,

$$W = F_x\,\Delta x \qquad (6\text{-}2)$$

- When several forces act on an object, the total work is the sum of the work done by each force individually.

- Translational kinetic energy is the energy associated with motion of the object as a whole. The translational kinetic energy of an object of mass m moving with speed v is

$$K = \tfrac{1}{2}mv^2 \qquad (6\text{-}6)$$

- The gravitational potential energy for an object of mass m in a *uniform* gravitational field is

$$U_{\text{grav}} = mgy \qquad (6\text{-}13)$$

where the +y-axis points up and we assign $U = 0$ to $y = 0$.

- The gravitational potential energy for two bodies of masses m_1 and m_2 whose centers are separated by a distance r is

$$U = -\frac{Gm_1m_2}{r} \qquad (6\text{-}14)$$

where we assign $U = 0$ to infinite separation ($r = \infty$).

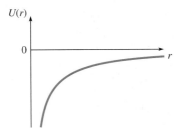

- There is no special significance to the sign of the potential energy. What matters is the sign of the potential

energy *change*. Only *changes* in potential energy enter our calculations.

- The work done by a variable force directed along the x-axis during a displacement Δx is the area under the $F_x(x)$ graph from x_i to x_f.

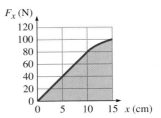

- Hooke's law: for many objects, the deformation is proportional to the magnitude of the force that causes the deformation. An ideal spring is massless and follows Hooke's law. The force exerted *by* the moveable end of an ideal spring when it is at position x is

$$F_x = -kx \qquad (6\text{-}19)$$

where the origin is chosen so the spring is relaxed at $x = 0$ and k is called the spring constant.

- If we assign $U = 0$ to the relaxed spring ($x = 0$), the elastic potential energy stored in an ideal spring of spring constant k is

$$U_{\text{elastic}} = \tfrac{1}{2}kx^2 \qquad (6\text{-}24)$$

- Mechanical energy is the sum of the kinetic and potential energies. The change in potential energy accounts for the work done by the forces associated with the potential energy. The work done by nonconservative forces is equal to the change in the mechanical energy:

$$W_{\text{nc}} = \Delta K + \Delta U = \Delta E_{\text{mech}} \qquad (6\text{-}12)$$

When nonconservative forces do no net work, the mechanical energy does not change.

$$\text{If } W_{\text{nc}} = 0,\ \Delta K + \Delta U = 0$$

- Average power is the average rate of energy conversion.

$$P_{\text{av}} = \frac{\Delta E}{\Delta t} \qquad (6\text{-}26)$$

The instantaneous rate at which a force $\vec{F}$ does work when the object it acts on moves with velocity $\vec{v}$ is

$$P = Fv\cos\theta \qquad (6\text{-}27)$$

where θ is the angle between $\vec{F}$ and $\vec{v}$.

- The SI unit of work and energy is the joule. $1\ \text{J} = 1\ \text{N·m}$. The SI unit of power is the watt. $1\ \text{W} = 1\ \text{J/s}$.

Conceptual Questions

1. An object moves in a circle. Is the total work done on the object by external forces necessarily zero? Explain.

2. You are walking to class with a backpack full of books. As you walk at constant speed on flat ground, does the force exerted on the backpack by your back and shoulders do any work? If so, is it positive or negative? Answer the same questions in two other situations: (1) you are walking down some steps at constant speed; (2) you start to run faster and faster on a level sidewalk to catch a bus.

3. Why do roads leading to the top of a mountain wind back and forth? [*Hint:* Think of the road as an inclined plane.]

4. A mango falls to the ground. During the fall, does the Earth's gravitational field do positive or negative work W_m on the mango? Does the mango's gravitational field do positive or negative work W_E on the Earth? Compare the signs and the magnitudes of W_m and W_E.

5. Can static friction do work? If so, give an example. [*Hint:* Static friction acts to prevent *relative* motion along the contact surface.]

6. In the design of a roller coaster, is it possible for any hill of the ride to be higher than the first one? If so, how?

7. When a ball is dropped to the floor from a height h, it strikes the ground and briefly undergoes a change of shape before rebounding to a maximum height less than h. Explain why it does not return to the same height h.

8. A gymnast is swinging in a vertical circle about a crossbar. In terms of energy conservation, explain why the speed of the gymnast's body is slowest at the top of the circle and fastest at the bottom.

9. A bicycle rider notices that he is approaching a steep hill. Explain, in terms of energy, why the bicyclist pedals hard to gain as much speed as possible on level road before reaching the hill.

10. You need to move a heavy crate by sliding it across a smooth floor. The coefficient of sliding friction is 0.2. You can either push the crate horizontally or pull the crate using an attached rope. When you pull on the rope, it makes a 30° angle with the floor. Which way should you choose to move the crate so that you do the least amount of work? How can you answer this question without knowing the weight of the crate or the displacement of the crate?

11. The main effort of running is the work done by the muscles to accelerate and decelerate the legs. When a foot strikes the ground, it is momentarily brought to rest while the remainder of the animal's body continues to move forward. When the foot is picked up, it is accelerated forward by one set of muscles in order to move ahead of the rest of the body. Then the foot is slowed down by a second set of muscles until it is brought to rest on the ground again. The muscles expend energy both when accelerating and when decelerating the leg. How are thoroughbred horses, deer, and greyhounds adapted so that they can run at great speed?

12. Explain why an ideal spring *must* exert forces of equal magnitude on the objects attached to each end, even if the spring itself has a nonzero acceleration. [*Hint:* Use one of Newton's laws of motion and remember that an ideal spring has zero mass.] Is the amount of work done by the spring on the two objects necessarily the same? Explain. If the answer is no, give an example to illustrate.

13. Zorba and Boris are at a water park. There are two water slides with straight slopes that start at the same height and end at the same height. Slide A has a more gradual slope than slide B. Boris says he likes slide B better because you reach a faster speed and he notes that he got to the bottom level in less time on slide B as measured with his stop watch. His brother Zorba says you reach the same speed with either slide. Who is correct and why? Both slides have negligible friction.

Multiple-Choice Questions

1. After getting on the Santa Monica Freeway, a sports car accelerates from 30 mi/h to 90 mi/h. Its kinetic energy
   (a) increases by a factor of $\sqrt{3}$.
   (b) increases by a factor of 3.
   (c) increases by a factor of 9.
   (d) increases by a factor that depends on the car's mass.

2. If a kangaroo on Earth can jump from a standing start so that its feet reach a height h above the surface, approximately how high can the same kangaroo jump from a standing start on the Moon's surface? $g_{\text{Moon}} \approx \frac{1}{6}g_{\text{Earth}}$. (Assume the kangaroo has an oxygen tank and pressure suit with negligible mass.)
   (a) h (b) $6h$ (c) $\frac{1}{6}h$
   (d) $36h$ (e) $\frac{1}{36}h$ (f) $\sqrt{6}h$

Questions 3–5. The orbit of Pluto is much more eccentric than the orbits of the planets. That is, instead of being nearly circular, the orbit is noticeably elliptical. The point in the orbit nearest the Sun is called the *perihelion* and the point farthest from the Sun is called the *aphelion*.

Answer choices for Questions 3–5:

    (a) its maximum value   (b) its minimum value
    (c) the same value as at every other point in the orbit

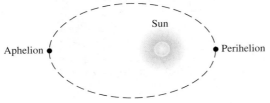

Multiple-Choice Questions 3–5

3. At perihelion, the gravitational potential energy of Pluto's orbit has

4. At perihelion, the kinetic energy of Pluto has

5. At perihelion, the mechanical energy of Pluto's orbit has

6. As Pluto moves from the perihelion to the aphelion, the work done by gravity on Pluto is

    (a) zero.   (b) positive.   (c) negative.

7. Two balls are thrown from the roof of a building with the same initial speed. One is thrown horizontally while the other is thrown at an angle of 20° above the horizontal. Which hits the ground with the greatest speed? Ignore air resistance.

    (a) The one thrown horizontally
    (b) The one thrown at 20°
    (c) They hit the ground with the same speed.
    (d) The answer cannot be determined with the given information.

8. A hiker descends from the South Rim of the Grand Canyon to the Colorado River. During this hike, the work done by gravity on the hiker is

    (a) positive and depends on the path taken.
    (b) negative and depends on the path taken.
    (c) positive and independent of the path taken.
    (d) negative and independent of the path taken.
    (e) zero.

Questions 9 and 10. A simple catapult, consisting of a leather pouch attached to rubber bands tied to two forks of a wooden Y, has a spring constant k and is used to shoot a pebble horizontally. When the catapult is stretched by a distance d, it gives a pebble of mass m a launch speed v. Answer choices for Questions 9 and 10:

    (a) $\sqrt{3}v$ (b) $3v$ (c) $3\sqrt{3}v$ (d) $9v$ (e) $27v$

9. What speed does the catapult give a pebble of mass m when stretched to a distance $3d$?

10. What speed does the catapult give a pebble of mass $m/3$ when stretched to a distance d?

11. A projectile is launched at an angle θ above the horizontal. Ignoring air resistance, what fraction of its initial kinetic energy does the projectile have at the top of its trajectory?

    (a) $\cos \theta$ (b) $\sin \theta$ (c) $\tan \theta$ (d) $\dfrac{1}{\tan \theta}$ (e) $\dfrac{1}{2}$
    (f) $\cos^2 \theta$ (g) $\sin^2 \theta$ (h) 0   (i) 1

Problems

    ⓒ   Combination conceptual/quantitative problem
    ⚕   Biological or medical application
    ✦   Challenging problem
    Blue # Detailed solution in the Student Solutions Manual
    ① ② Problems paired by concept
    〰   Text website interactive or tutorial

Section 6.2 Work Done by a Constant Force

1. How much work must Denise do to drag her basket of laundry of mass 5.0 kg a distance of 5.0 m along a floor, if the force she exerts is a constant 30.0 N at an angle of 60.0° with the horizontal?

2. A sled is dragged along a horizontal path at a constant speed of 1.5 m/s by a rope that is inclined at an angle of 30.0° with respect to the horizontal. The total weight of the sled is 470 N. The tension in the rope is 240 N. How much work is done by the rope on the sled in a time interval of 10.0 s?

3. Hilda holds a gardening book of weight 10 N at a height of 1.0 m above her patio for 50 s. How much work does she do *on the book* during that 50 s?

4. The tension in the horizontal towrope pulling a water-skier is 240 N while the skier moves due west a distance of 54 m. How much work does the towrope do on the water-skier?

5. A barge of mass 5.0×10^4 kg is pulled along the Erie Canal by two mules, walking along towpaths parallel to the canal on either side of it. The ropes harnessed to the mules make angles of 45° to the canal. Each mule is pulling on its rope with a force of 1.0 kN. How much work is done on the barge by both of these mules together as they pull the barge 150 m along the canal?

6. A 402-kg pile driver is raised 12 m above ground. (a) How much work must be done to raise the pile driver? (b) How much work

with the horizontal. Ignore air resistance. (a) Calculate the work done by gravity on the skier and the work done by the normal force on the skier. (b) If the slope is not frictionless so that the skier has a final velocity of 10.0 m/s, calculate the work done by gravity, the work done by the normal force, the work done by friction, the force of friction (assuming it is constant), and the coefficient of kinetic friction. (tutorial: water slide)

37. You are on the Moon and would like to send a probe into space so that it does not fall back to the surface of the Moon. What launch speed do you need?

38. A planet with a radius of 6.00×10^7 m has a gravitational field of magnitude 30.0 m/s^2 at the surface. What is the escape speed from the planet?

39. The escape speed from the surface of Planet Zoroaster is 12.0 km/s. The planet has no atmosphere. A meteor far away from the planet moves at speed 5.0 km/s on a collision course with Zoroaster. How fast is the meteor going when it hits the surface of the planet?

40. The escape speed from the surface of the Earth is 11.2 km/s. What would be the escape speed from another planet of the same density (mass per unit volume) as Earth but with a radius twice that of Earth?

41. A satellite is placed in a noncircular orbit about the Earth. The farthest point of its orbit (*apogee*) is 4 Earth radii from the center of the Earth, while its nearest point (*perigee*) is 2 Earth radii from the Earth's center. If we define the gravitational potential energy U to be zero for an infinite separation of Earth and satellite, find the ratio $U_{\text{perigee}}/U_{\text{apogee}}$.

42. What is the minimum speed with which a meteor strikes the top of the Earth's stratosphere (about 40 km above Earth's surface), assuming that the meteor begins as a bit of interplanetary debris far from Earth? Assume the drag force is negligible until the meteor reaches the stratosphere.

43. A projectile with mass of 500 kg is launched straight up from the Earth's surface with an initial speed v_i. What magnitude of v_i enables the projectile to just reach a maximum height of $5R_E$, measured from the *center* of the Earth? Ignore air friction as the projectile goes through the Earth's atmosphere.

44. The orbit of Halley's comet around the Sun is a long thin ellipse. At its aphelion (point farthest from the Sun), the comet is 5.3×10^{12} m from the Sun and moves with a speed of 10.0 km/s. What is the comet's speed at its perihelion (closest approach to the Sun) where its distance from the Sun is 8.9×10^{10} m?

45. Suppose a satellite is in a circular orbit 3.0 Earth radii above the surface of the Earth (4.0 Earth radii from the center of the Earth). By how much does it have to increase its speed in order to be able to escape Earth? [*Hint:* You need to calculate the orbital speed and the escape speed.]

46. An asteroid hits the Moon and ejects a large rock from its surface. The rock has enough speed to travel to a point between the Earth and the Moon where the gravitational forces on it from the Earth and the Moon are equal in magnitude and opposite in direction. At that point the rock has a very small velocity toward Earth. What is the speed of the rock when it encounters Earth's atmosphere at an altitude of 700 km above the surface?

Section 6.6 Work Done by Variable Forces: Hooke's Law

47. How much work is done on the bowstring of Example 6.9 to draw it back by 20.0 cm? [*Hint:* Rather than recalculate from scratch, use proportional reasoning.]

48. An ideal spring has a spring constant $k = 20.0$ N/m. What is the amount of work that must be done to stretch the spring 0.40 m from its relaxed length?

49. The force that must be exerted to drive a nail into a wall is roughly as shown in the graph. The first 1.2 cm are through soft drywall; then the nail enters the solid wooden stud. How much work must be done to hammer the nail a horizontal distance of 5.0 cm into the wall?

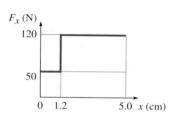

50. (a) If the length of the Achilles tendon increases 0.50 cm when the force exerted on it by the muscle increases from 3200 N to 4800 N, what is the "spring constant" of the tendon? (b) How much work is done by the muscle in stretching the tendon 0.50 cm as the force increases from 3200 N to 4800 N?

51. (a) If forces of magnitude 5.0 N applied to each end of a spring cause the spring to stretch 3.5 cm from its relaxed length, how far do forces of magnitude 7.0 N cause the same spring to stretch? (b) What is the spring constant of this spring? (c) How much work is done by the applied forces in stretching the spring 3.5 cm from its relaxed length? (tutorial: spring)

52. A block of wood is compressed 2.0 nm when inward forces of magnitude 120 N are applied to it on two opposite sides. (a) Assuming Hooke's law holds, what is the effective spring constant of the block? (b) Assuming Hooke's law still holds, how much is the same block compressed by inward forces of magnitude 480 N? (c) How much work is done by the applied forces during the compression of part (b)?

53. The length of a spring increases by 7.2 cm from its relaxed length when a mass of 1.4 kg is hanging in equilibrium from the spring. (a) What is the spring constant? (b) How much elastic potential energy is stored in the spring? (c) A different mass is suspended and the spring length increases by 12.2 cm from its relaxed length to its new equilibrium position. What is the second mass?

54. A spring fixed at one end is compressed from its relaxed position by a distance of 0.20 m. See the graph of the applied external force, F_x, versus the position, x, of the spring. (a) Find the work done by the external force in compressing the spring 0.20 m starting from its relaxed position. (b) Find the work done by the external force to compress the spring from 0.10 m to 0.20 m.

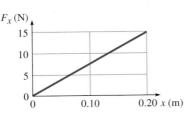

55. Rhonda keeps a 2.0-kg model airplane moving at constant speed in a horizontal circle at the end of a string of length 1.0 m. The tension in the string is 18 N. How much work does the string do on the plane during each revolution? (✦ tutorial: circular motion)

56. The graph shows the force exerted on an object versus the position of that object along the x-axis. The force has no components other than along the x-axis. What is the work done by the force on the object as the object is displaced from 0 to 3.0 m?

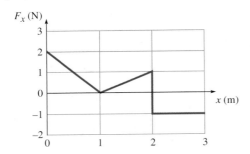

Section 6.7 Elastic Potential Energy

✦57. A kangaroo decides to see how high it can hop on *one leg*. Assuming the elastic energy stored in the tendon is the same as for Example 6.12, how high can it jump using a single leg?

58. When the spring on a toy gun is compressed by a distance x, it will shoot a rubber ball straight up to a height of h. Ignoring air resistance, how high will the gun shoot the same rubber ball if the spring is compressed by an amount $2x$? Assume $x \ll h$.

59. You shoot a 51-g pebble straight up with a catapult whose spring constant is 320 N/m. The catapult is initially stretched by 0.20 m. How high above the starting point does the pebble fly? Ignore air resistance.

✦60. A block (mass m) hangs from a spring (spring constant k). The block is released from rest a distance d above its *equilibrium* position. (a) What is the speed of the block as it passes through the equilibrium point? (b) What is the maximum distance below the equilibrium point that the block will reach?

61. A gymnast of mass 52 kg is jumping on a trampoline. She jumps so that her feet reach a maximum height of 2.5 m above the trampoline and, when she lands, her feet stretch the trampoline down 75 cm. How far does the trampoline stretch when she stands on it at rest? [*Hint:* Assume the trampoline obeys Hooke's law when it is stretched.]

62. Jorge is going to bungee jump from a bridge that is 55.0 m over the river below. The bungee cord has an unstretched length of 27.0 m. To be safe, the bungee cord should stop Jorge's fall when he is at least 2.00 m above the river. If Jorge has a mass of 75.0 kg, what is the minimum spring constant of the bungee cord? (✦ tutorial: spring scale)

63. A 2.0-kg block is released from rest and allowed to slide down a frictionless surface and into a spring. The far end of the spring is attached to a wall, as shown. The initial height of the block is 0.50 m above the lowest part of the slide and the spring constant is 450 N/m. (a) What is the block's speed when it is at a height of 0.25 m above the base of the slide? (b) How far is the spring compressed? (c) The spring sends the block back to the left. How high does the block rise?

Problems 63 and 105

Section 6.8 Power

64. Lars, of mass 82.4 kg, has been working out and can do work for about 2.0 min at the rate of 1.0 hp (746 W). How long will it take him to climb three flights of stairs, a vertical height of 12.0 m?

65. Show that 1 kilowatt-hour (kW·h) is equal to 3.6 MJ.

66. If a man has an average useful power output of 40.0 W, what minimum time would it take him to lift fifty 10.0-kg boxes to a height of 2.00 m?

67. In Section 6.2, Rosie lifts a trunk weighing 220 N up 4.0 m. If it take her 40 s to lift the trunk, at what average rate does she do work?

68. A bicycle and its rider together has a mass of 75 kg. What power output of the rider is required to maintain a constant speed of 4.0 m/s (about 9 mph) up a 5.0% grade (a road that rises 5.0 m for every 100 m along the pavement)? Assume that frictional losses of energy are negligible.

69. The power output of a cyclist moving at a constant speed of 6.0 m/s on a level road is 120 W. (a) What is the force exerted on the cyclist and the bicycle by the air? (b) By bending low over the handlebars, the cyclist reduces the air resistance to 18 N. If she maintains a power output of 120 W, what will her speed be?

✦70. A car with mass of 1000.0 kg accelerates from 0 m/s to 40.0 m/s in 10.0 s. Ignore air resistance. The engine has a 22% efficiency, which means that 22% of the energy released by the burning gasoline is converted into mechanical energy. (a) What is the average mechanical power output of the engine? (b) What volume of gasoline is consumed? Assume that the burning of 1.0 L of gasoline releases 46 MJ of energy.

71. A motorist driving a 1200-kg car on level ground accelerates from 20.0 m/s to 30.0 m/s in a time of 5.0 s. Neglecting friction and air resistance, determine the *average* mechanical power in watts the engine must supply during this time interval.

72. A 62-kg woman takes 6.0 s to run up a flight of stairs. The landing at the top of the stairs is 5.0 m above her starting place. (a) What is the woman's average power output while she is running? (b) Would that be equal to her average power *input*—the rate at which chemical energy in food or stored fat is used? Why or why not?

73. How many grams of carbohydrate does a person of mass 74 kg need to metabolize to climb five flights of stairs (15 m height increase)? Each gram of carbohydrate provides 17.6 kJ of energy. Assume 10.0% efficiency—that is, 10.0% of the available chemical energy in the carbohydrate is converted to mechanical energy. What happens to the other 90% of the energy?

74. An object moves in the positive x-direction under the influence of a force F_x. A graph of F_x versus v_x is shown. (a) What is the instantaneous power on the object when its velocity is 11 m/s? (b) What is the instantaneous power on the object when its velocity is 16 m/s?

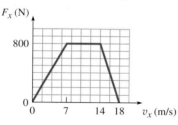

75. A top fuel drag racer with a mass of 500.0 kg completes a quarter-mile (402 m) drag race in a time of 4.2 s starting from rest. The car's final speed is 125 m/s. What is the engine's average power output? Ignore friction and air resistance.

76. (a) Calculate the change in potential energy of 1 kg of water as it passes over Niagara Falls (a vertical descent of 50 m). (b) At what rate is gravitational potential energy lost by the water of the Niagara River? The rate of flow is 5.5×10^6 kg/s. (c) If 10% of this energy can be converted into electric energy, how many households would the electricity supply? (An average household uses an average electrical power of about 1 kW.)

Comprehensive Problems

77. If a high jumper needs to make his center of gravity rise 1.2 m, how fast must he be able to sprint? Assume all of his kinetic energy can be transformed into potential energy. For an extended object, the gravitational potential energy is $U = mgh$, where h is the height of the center of gravity.

78. A pole-vaulter converts the kinetic energy of running to elastic potential energy in the pole, which is then converted to gravitational potential energy. If a pole-vaulter's center of gravity is 1.0 m above the ground while he sprints at 10.0 m/s, what is the maximum height of his center of gravity during the vault? For an extended object, the gravitational potential energy is $U = mgh$, where h is the height of the center of gravity. (In 1988, Sergei Bubka was the first pole-vaulter ever to clear 6 m.)

79. A hang glider moving at speed 9.5 m/s dives to an altitude 8.2 m lower. Ignoring drag, how fast is it then moving?

80. A car moving at 30 mi/h is stopped by jamming on the brakes and locking the wheels. The car skids 50 ft before coming to rest. How far would the car skid if it were initially moving at 60 mi/h? [*Hint:* You will not have to do any unit conversions if you set up the problem as a proportion.]

81. Prove that $U = -2K$ for any gravitational circular orbit. [*Hint:* Use Newton's second law to relate the gravitational force to the acceleration required to maintain uniform circular motion.]

82. A spring gun ($k = 28$ N/m) is used to shoot a 56-g ball horizontally. Initially the spring is compressed by 18 cm. The ball loses contact with the spring and leaves the gun when the spring is still compressed by 12 cm. What is the speed of the ball when it hits the ground, 1.4 m below the spring gun?

83. Two springs with equal spring constants k are connected first in series (one after the other) and then in parallel (side by side) with a weight hanging from the bottom of the combination. What is the effective spring constant of the two different arrangements? In other words, what would be the spring constant of a single spring that would behave exactly as (a) the series combination and (b) the parallel combination? Ignore the weight of the springs. [*Hint* for (a): *each* spring stretches an amount $x = F/k$, but only one spring exerts a force on the hanging object. *Hint* for (b): *each* spring exerts a force $F = kx$.]

(a)   (b)

84. A roller coaster car (mass = 988 kg including passengers) is about to roll down a track. The diameter of the circular loop is 20.0 m and the car starts out from rest 40.0 m above the lowest point of the track. Ignore friction and air resistance. (a) At what speed does the car reach the top of the loop?

(b) What is the force exerted on the car by the track at the top of the loop? (c) From what minimum height above the bottom of the loop can the car be released so that it does not lose contact with the track at the top of the loop?

◆85. A 4.0-kg block is released from rest at the top of a frictionless plane of length 8.0 m that is inclined at an angle of 15° to the horizontal. A cord is attached to the block and trails along behind it. When the block reaches a point 5.0 m along the incline from the top, someone grasps the cord and exerts a constant tension parallel to the incline. The tension is such that the block just comes to rest when it reaches the bottom of the incline. (The person's force is a nonconservative force.) What is this constant tension? Solve the problem twice, once using work and energy and again using Newton's laws and the equations for constant acceleration. Which method do you prefer?

◆86. The bungee jumper of Example 6.4 made a jump into the Gorge du Verdon in southern France from a platform 182 m above the bottom of the gorge. The jumper weighed 780 N and came within 68 m of the bottom of the gorge. The cord's unstretched length is 30.0 m. (a) Assuming that the bungee cord follows Hooke's law when it stretches, find its spring constant. [*Hint:* The cord does not begin to stretch until the jumper has fallen 30.0 m.] (b) At what speed is the jumper falling when he reaches a height of 92 m above the bottom of the gorge?

87. A spring with $k = 40.0$ N/m is at the base of a frictionless 30.0° inclined plane. A 0.50-kg object is pressed against the spring, compressing it 0.20 m from its equilibrium position. The object is then released. If the object is not attached to the spring, how far up the incline does it travel before coming to rest and then sliding back down?

88. In an adventure movie, a 62.5-kg stunt woman falls 8.10 m and lands in a huge air bag. Her speed just before she hit the air bag was 10.5 m/s. (a) What is the total work done on the stunt woman during the fall? (b) How much work is done by gravity on the stunt woman? (c) How much work is done by air resistance on the stunt woman? (d) Estimate the magnitude of the average force of air resistance by assuming it is constant throughout the fall.

◆89. When a 0.20-kg mass is suspended from a vertically hanging spring, it stretches the spring from its original length of 5.0 cm to a total length of 6.0 cm. The spring with the same mass attached is then placed on a horizontal frictionless surface. The mass is pulled so that the spring stretches to a *total* length of 10.0 cm; then the mass is released and it oscillates back and forth. What is the maximum speed of the mass as it oscillates?

90. Yosemite Falls in California is about 740 m high. (a) What average power would it take for a 70-kg person to hike up to the top of Yosemite Falls in 1.5 h? (b) The human body is about 25% efficient at converting chemical energy to mechanical energy. How much chemical energy is used in this hike? (c) One food Calorie is equal to 4.186×10^3 J. How many Calories of food energy would a person use in this hike?

◆91. A 1500-kg car coasts in neutral down a 2.0° hill. The car attains a terminal speed of 20.0 m/s. (a) How much power must the engine deliver to drive the car on a *level* road at 20.0 m/s? (b) If the maximum useful power that can be delivered by the engine is 40.0 kW, what is the steepest hill the car can climb at 20.0 m/s?

◆92. A spring used in an introductory physics laboratory stores 10.0 J of elastic potential energy when it is compressed 0.20 m. Suppose the spring is cut in half. When one of the halves is compressed by 0.20 m, how much potential energy is stored in it? [*Hint:* Does the half spring have the same *k* as the original uncut spring?]

◆93. An elevator can carry a maximum load of 1202 kg (including the mass of the elevator car). The elevator has an 801-kg counterweight that always moves with the same speed but in the *opposite direction* to the car. (a) What is the average power that must be delivered by the motor to carry the maximum load up 40.0 m in 60.0 s? (b) How would your answer be different if there were no counterweight?

94. (a) How much work does a major-league pitcher do on the baseball when he throws a 90.0 mi/h (40.2 m/s) fastball? The mass of a baseball is 153 g. (b) How many fastballs would a pitcher have to throw to "burn off" a 1520-Calorie meal? (1 Calorie = 1000 cal = 1 kcal.)

Assume that 80.0% of the chemical energy in the food is converted to thermal energy and only 20.0% becomes the kinetic energy of the fastballs.

95. The number of kilocalories per day required by a person resting under standard conditions is called the basal metabolic rate (BMR). (a) To generate 1 kcal, Jermaine's body needs approximately 0.010 mol of oxygen. If Jermaine's net intake of oxygen through breathing is 0.015 mol/min while he is resting, what is his BMR in kcal/day? (b) If Jermaine fasts for 24 h, how many pounds of fat does he lose? Assume that only fat is consumed. Each gram of fat consumed generates 9.3 kcal.

96. Tarzan is running along the ground and approaching a deep gully. A tree branch with a vine hangs over the gully. Tarzan must grab the vine and swing across the gully to the other side, where the ground surface is 1.7 m higher than the ground surface from which Tarzan starts. How fast does Tarzan have to be running to accomplish this feat?

97. Jane is running from the ivory hunters in the jungle. Cheetah throws a 7.0-m-long vine toward her. Jane leaps onto the vine with a speed of 4.0 m/s. When she catches the vine, it makes an angle of 20° with respect to the vertical. (a) When Jane is at her lowest point, she has moved downward a distance h from the height where she originally caught the vine. Show that h is given by $h = L - L \cos 20°$, where L is the length of the vine. (b) How fast is Jane moving when she is at the lowest point in her swing? (c) How high can Jane swing above the lowest point in her swing?

98. The escape speed from Earth is 11.2 km/s, but that is only the minimum speed needed to escape *Earth's* gravitational pull; it does not give the object enough energy to leave the solar system. What is the minimum speed for an object near the Earth's surface so that the object escapes both the Earth's and the Sun's gravitational pulls? Ignore drag due to the atmosphere and the gravitational forces due to the Moon and the other planets. Also ignore the rotation and the orbital motion of the Earth.

99. A skier starts from rest at the top of a frictionless slope of ice in the shape of a hemispherical dome with radius R and slides down the slope. At a certain height h, the normal force becomes zero and the skier leaves the surface of the ice. What is h in terms of R?

100. Two springs with spring constants k_1 and k_2 are connected in series. (a) What is the effective spring constant of the combination? (b) If a hanging object attached to the combination is displaced by 4.0 cm from the relaxed position, what is the potential energy stored in the spring for $k_1 = 5.0$ N/cm and $k_2 = 3.0$ N/cm? [See Problem 83(a).]

101. Two springs with spring constants k_1 and k_2 are connected in parallel. (a) What is the effective spring constant of the combination? (b) If a hanging object attached to the combination is displaced by 2.0 cm from the relaxed position, what is the potential energy stored

in the spring for $k_1 = 5.0$ N/cm and $k_2 = 3.0$ N/cm? [See Problem 83(b).]

102. A pendulum, consisting of a bob of mass M on a cord of length L, is interrupted in its swing by a peg a distance d below its point of suspension. (a) If the bob is to travel in a full circle of radius $(L - d)$ around the peg, what is the minimum possible speed it can have at the lowest point in its motion, just before it starts to go around? Ignore any decrease in the length of the string due to the peg's circumference. (b) From what minimum angle θ must the pendulum be released so that the bob attains the speed calculated in (a)?

103. Human feet and legs store elastic energy when walking or running. They are not nearly as efficient at doing so as kangaroo legs, but the effect is significant nonetheless. If not for the storage of elastic energy, a 70-kg man running at 4 m/s would lose about 100 J of mechanical energy each time he sets down a foot. Some of this energy is stored as elastic energy in the Achilles tendon and in the arch of the foot; the elastic energy is then converted back into the kinetic and gravitational potential energy of the leg, reducing the expenditure of metabolic energy. If the maximum tension in the Achilles tendon when the foot is set down is 4.7 kN and the tendon's spring constant is 350 kN/m, calculate how far the tendon stretches and how much elastic energy is stored in it.

104. The graph shows the tension in a rubber band as it is first stretched and then allowed to contract. As you stretch a rubber band, the tension force at a particular length (on the way to a maximum stretch) is larger than the force at that same length as you let the rubber band contract. That is why the graph shows two separate lines, one for stretching and one for contracting; the lines are not superimposed as you might have thought they would be. (a) Make a rough estimate of the total work done by the external force applied to the rubber band for the entire process. (b) If the rubber band obeyed Hooke's law, what would the answer to (a) have to be? (c) While the rubber band is stretched, is all of the work done on it accounted for by the increase in elastic potential energy? If not, what happens to the rest of it? [*Hint:* Take a rubber band and stretch it rapidly several times. Then hold it against your wrist or your lip.]

105. A 0.50-kg block, starting at rest, slides down a 30.0° incline with kinetic friction coefficient 0.25 (see the

figure with Problem 63). After sliding 85 cm down the incline, it slides across a frictionless horizontal surface and encounters a spring ($k = 35$ N/m). (a) What is the maximum compression of the spring? (b) After the compression of part (a), the spring rebounds and shoots the block back up the incline. How far along the incline does the block travel before coming to rest?

106. A wind turbine converts some of the kinetic energy of the wind into electric energy. Suppose that the blades of a small wind turbine have length $L = 4.0$ m. (a) When a 10 m/s (22 mi/h) wind blows head-on, what volume of air (in m^3) passes through the circular area swept out by the blades in 1.0 s? (b) What is the mass of this much air? Each cubic meter of air has a mass of 1.2 kg. (c) What is the translational kinetic energy of this mass of air? (d) If the turbine can convert 40% of this kinetic energy into electric energy, what is its electric power output? (e) What happens to the power output if the wind speed decreases to $\frac{1}{2}$ of its initial value? What can you conclude about electric power production by wind turbines?

107. Use dimensional analysis to show that the electric power output of a wind turbine is proportional to the *cube* of the wind speed. The relevant quantities on which the power can depend are the length L of the rotor blades, the density ρ of air (SI units kg/m^3), and the wind speed v.

108. Use this method to find how the speed with which animals of similar shape can run up a hill depends on the size of the animal. Let L represent some characteristic length, such as the height or diameter of the animal. Assume that the maximum rate at which the animal can do work is proportional to the animal's surface area: $P_{max} \propto L^2$. Set the maximum power output equal to the rate of increase of gravitational potential energy and determine how the speed v depends on L.

109. The potential energy of a particle constrained to move along the x-axis is shown in the graph. At $x = 0$, the particle is moving in the $+x$-direction with a kinetic energy of 200 J. Can this particle get into the region 3 cm $< x <$ 8 cm? Explain. If it can, what is its kinetic energy in that region? If it can't, what happens to it?

110. The potential energy of a particle constrained to move along the x-axis is shown in the graph. At $x = 0$, the particle is moving in the $+x$-direction with a kinetic energy of 400 J. Can this particle get into the region 3 cm $< x <$ 8 cm? Explain. If it can, what is its kinetic energy in that region? If it can't, what happens to it?

Answers to Practice Problems

6.1 −180 kJ

6.2 43 N; 4500 J; she pulls with a greater force but its component in the direction of the displacement is smaller.

6.3 $(2.5\, m)(1.50v)^2/(mv^2) = 5.6$

6.4 29 m/s

6.5 0.24

6.6 16.5 m/s

6.7 48 km/s

6.8 195 km/s

6.9 4.0 J

6.10 3.2 cm

6.11 9.8 m/s

6.12 2.4 m

6.13 (a) 11.8 kW (b) 3.6 kW

Answers to Checkpoints

6.2 The force is perpendicular to the displacement.

6.3 Kinetic energy is never negative. Work can be positive, negative, or zero, because kinetic energy can increase, decrease, or stay the same.

6.4 (a) The gravitational potential energy increases until it reaches its maximum value when the stone reaches its highest point above the ground. (b) The kinetic energy decreases as the potential energy increases. It is zero at the highest point. (c) The force of gravity does work on the stone throughout its motion.

6.5 The mechanical energy is the same throughout Mercury's orbit. The kinetic energy is greatest at the perihelion because the potential energy is smallest there.

6.7 The greatest elastic potential energy is at the maximum compression.

Linear Momentum

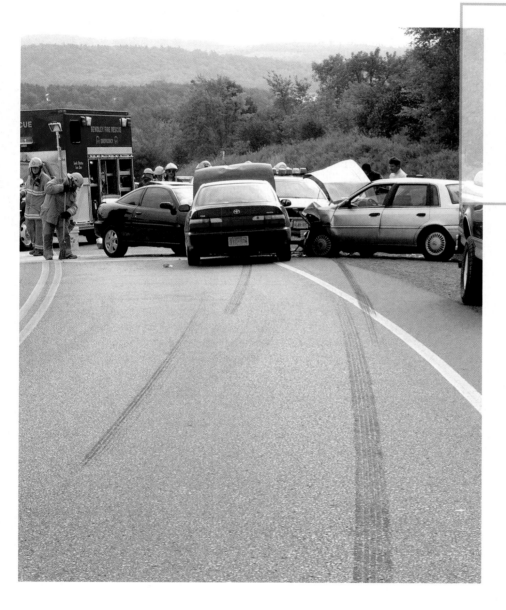

After a collision, an accident investigator measures the lengths of skid marks on the road. How can the investigator use this information to figure out the velocities of the vehicles immediately *before* the collision? (See p. 246 for the answer.)

Concepts & Skills to Review

- conservation laws (Section 6.1)
- Newton's third law of motion (Section 2.5)
- Newton's second law of motion (Section 3.3)
- velocity (Section 3.2)
- components of vectors (Section 2.3)
- vector subtraction (Section 3.1)
- kinetic energy (Section 6.3)

7.1   A CONSERVATION LAW FOR A VECTOR QUANTITY

In Chapter 3 we learned how to determine the acceleration of an object by finding the net force acting on it and applying Newton's second law of motion. If the forces happen to be constant, then the resulting constant acceleration enables us to calculate changes in velocity and position. Calculating velocity and position changes when the forces are not constant is much more difficult. In many cases, the forces cannot even be easily determined. Conservation of energy is one tool that enables us to draw conclusions about motion without knowing all the details of the forces acting. Recall, for example, how easily we can calculate the escape speed of a projectile using conservation of energy, without even knowing the path the object takes. Now imagine how difficult the same calculation would be using Newton's second law, with a gravitational force that changes magnitude and direction depending on the path taken.

In this chapter we develop another conservation law. Conservation laws are powerful tools. If a quantity is conserved, then no matter how complicated the situation, we can set the value of the conserved quantity at one time equal to its value at a later time. The "before-and-after" aspect of a conservation law enables us to draw conclusions about the results of a complicated set of interactions without knowing all of the details.

The new conserved quantity, *momentum*, is a vector quantity, in contrast to energy, which is a scalar. When momentum is conserved, both the magnitude and the direction of the momentum must be constant. Equivalently, the *x*- and *y*-components of momentum are constant. When we find the total momentum of more than one object, we must add the momentum vectors according to the procedure by which vectors are always added.

CONNECTION:

Conservation laws can involve scalars, such as energy, or vectors, such as momentum.

7.2   MOMENTUM

The word *momentum* is often heard in broadcasts of sporting events. A sports broadcaster might say, "The home team has won five consecutive games; they have the momentum in their favor." The team with "momentum" is hard to stop; they are moving forward on a winning streak. A football player, running for the goal line with a football tucked under his arm, has momentum; he is hard to stop. This use of the word *momentum* is closer to the physics usage. In physics we would agree that the runner has momentum, but we have a precise definition in mind.

In everyday use, momentum has something to do with mass as well as with velocity. Would you rather have a running child bump into you, or a football player running with the same velocity? The child has much less momentum than the football player, even though their velocities are the same.

Could a quantity combining mass and velocity be useful in physics? Imagine a collision between two spaceships (Fig. 7.1). Let the spaceships be so far from planets and stars that we can ignore gravitational interactions with celestial bodies. The spaceships exert forces on one another while they are in contact. According to Newton's third law, these forces are equal and opposite. The force on ship 2 exerted by ship 1 is equal and opposite to the force exerted on ship 1 by ship 2:

$$\vec{\mathbf{F}}_{21} = -\vec{\mathbf{F}}_{12}$$

$\vec{\mathbf{F}}_{21}$ is the force exerted *on* object 2 *by* object 1.

Figure 7.1 (a) Two spaceships about to collide. (b) During the collision, the spaceships exert forces on one another that are equal in magnitude and opposite in direction. (c) The velocities of the spaceships after the collision.

The changes in *velocities* of the two spaceships are *not* equal and opposite if the masses are different. Suppose a large spaceship (mass m_1) collides with a much smaller ship (mass $m_2 \ll m_1$). Assume for now that the forces are constant during the time interval Δt that the spaceships are in contact. Although the forces have the same magnitude, the magnitudes of the accelerations of the two ships are different because their masses are different. The ship with the larger mass has the smaller acceleration.

The acceleration of either spaceship causes its velocity to change by

$$\Delta \vec{\mathbf{v}} = \vec{\mathbf{a}} \, \Delta t = \frac{\vec{\mathbf{F}}}{m} \Delta t$$

The time interval Δt is the duration of the interaction between the two ships, so it must be the same for both ships.

Since the changes in velocity are inversely proportional to the masses, the changes in the *products* of mass and velocity are equal and opposite for the two bodies involved in the interaction:

$$m_1 \Delta \vec{\mathbf{v}}_1 = \vec{\mathbf{F}}_{12} \Delta t$$

$$m_2 \Delta \vec{\mathbf{v}}_2 = \vec{\mathbf{F}}_{21} \Delta t = (-\vec{\mathbf{F}}_{12}) \Delta t = -(m_1 \Delta \vec{\mathbf{v}}_1)$$

This is a useful insight, so we give the product of mass and velocity a name and symbol: **linear momentum** (symbol $\vec{\mathbf{p}}$, SI unit kg·m/s). Linear momentum (or just *momentum*) is a vector quantity having the same direction as the velocity.

Definition of linear momentum:

$$\vec{\mathbf{p}} = m\vec{\mathbf{v}} \qquad (7\text{-}1)$$

The collision of the two spaceships causes changes in their momenta that are equal in magnitude and opposite in direction:

$$\Delta \vec{\mathbf{p}}_2 = -\Delta \vec{\mathbf{p}}_1$$

In any interaction between two objects, momentum can be transferred from one object to the other. The momentum changes of the two objects are always equal and opposite, so the total momentum of the two objects is unchanged by the interaction. (By *total momentum* we mean the vector sum of the individual momenta of the objects.)

Example 7.1 gives some practice in finding the change in momentum of an object whose velocity changes. Remember that momentum is a vector quantity, so changes in momentum must be found by subtracting momentum vectors, not by subtracting the magnitudes of the momenta.

CONNECTION:

Newton's third law implies that during an interaction momentum is transferred from one body to another.

Example 7.1

Change of Momentum of a Moving Car

A car weighing 12 kN is driving due north at 30.0 m/s. After driving around a sharp curve, the car is moving east at 13.6 m/s. What is the change in momentum of the car?

Strategy   The definition of momentum is $\vec{\mathbf{p}} = m\vec{\mathbf{v}}$. We can start by finding the car's mass. There are two potential pitfalls:

1. momentum depends not on weight but on mass, and
2. momentum is a vector, so we must take its direction into consideration as well as its magnitude. To find the change in momentum, we need to do a *vector subtraction*.

Solution   The car's mass is

$$m = \frac{W}{g} = \frac{1.2 \times 10^4 \, \text{N}}{9.8 \, \text{m/s}^2} = 1220 \, \text{kg}$$

The car's initial velocity is

$$\vec{\mathbf{v}}_i = 30.0 \, \text{m/s, north}$$

The car's initial momentum is then

$$\vec{\mathbf{p}}_i = m\vec{\mathbf{v}}_i = 1220 \, \text{kg} \times 30.0 \, \text{m/s north}$$

$$= 3.66 \times 10^4 \, \text{kg·m/s north}$$

After the curve, the final velocity is

$$\vec{\mathbf{v}}_f = 13.6 \, \text{m/s, east}$$

The final momentum is

$$\vec{\mathbf{p}}_f = m\vec{\mathbf{v}}_f = 1220 \, \text{kg} \times 13.6 \, \text{m/s east}$$

$$= 1.66 \times 10^4 \, \text{kg·m/s east}$$

Momentum vectors are added and subtracted according to the same methods used for other vectors. To find the change in the momentum, we draw vector arrows representing the addition of $\vec{\mathbf{p}}_f$ and $-\vec{\mathbf{p}}_i$ (Fig. 7.2). Since *in this case* the three vectors in Fig. 7.2 form a right triangle, the magnitude of $\Delta\vec{\mathbf{p}}$ can be found from the Pythagorean theorem

$$|\Delta\vec{\mathbf{p}}| = \sqrt{p_i^2 + p_f^2}$$

$$= \sqrt{(3.66 \times 10^4 \, \text{kg·m/s})^2 + (1.66 \times 10^4 \, \text{kg·m/s})^2}$$

$$= 4.02 \times 10^4 \, \text{kg·m/s}$$

From the vector diagram, $\Delta\vec{\mathbf{p}}$ is directed at an angle θ east of south. Using trigonometry,

$$\tan \theta = \frac{\text{opposite}}{\text{adjacent}} = \frac{p_f}{p_i} = \frac{1.66 \times 10^4 \, \text{kg·m/s}}{3.66 \times 10^4 \, \text{kg·m/s}} = 0.454$$

$$\theta = \tan^{-1} 0.454 = 24.4°$$

Since the weight is given with two significant figures, we report the change in momentum of the car as 4.0×10^4 kg·m/s directed 24° east of south.

Discussion   As with displacements, velocities, accelerations, and forces, it is crucial to remember that momentum is a vector. When finding changes in momentum, we must find the difference between final and initial momentum *vectors*. If the initial and final momenta had not been perpendicular, we would have had to resolve the vectors into x- and y-components in order to subtract them.

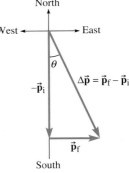

Figure 7.2

Vector subtraction to find the change in momentum.

Practice Problem 7.1   Falling Apple

(a) What is the momentum of an apple weighing 1.0 N just before it hits the ground, if it falls out of a tree from a height of 3.0 m? (b) The apple falls because of the gravitational interaction between the apple and the Earth. How much does this interaction change *Earth's* momentum? How much does it change Earth's velocity?

✓ CHECKPOINT 7.2

In Example 7.1, if the speed of the car had remained constant, would $\Delta\vec{\mathbf{p}}$ have been zero?

7.3   THE IMPULSE-MOMENTUM THEOREM

We found that the change in momentum of an object when a single force acts on it is equal to the product of the force acting on the object and the time interval during which the force acts:

$$\Delta\vec{\mathbf{p}} = \vec{\mathbf{F}} \, \Delta t$$

The product $\vec{\mathbf{F}}\,\Delta t$ is given the name **impulse**. Since the impulse is the product of a vector (the force) and a positive scalar (the time), impulse is a vector quantity having the same direction as that of the force. In words, $\Delta\vec{\mathbf{p}} = \vec{\mathbf{F}}\,\Delta t$ can be read as "*the change in momentum equals the impulse.*" The SI units of impulse are newton-seconds (N·s) and those of momentum are kilogram-meters per second (kg·m/s). These are equivalent units, as can be demonstrated using the definition of the newton (Problem 3).

If an object is involved in more than one interaction, then its change in momentum during any time interval is equal to the *total* impulse during that time interval. The total impulse is the vector sum of the impulses due to each force. The total impulse is also equal to the net force times the time interval:

$$\text{total impulse} = \vec{\mathbf{F}}_1\,\Delta t + \vec{\mathbf{F}}_2\,\Delta t + \cdots$$

$$= (\vec{\mathbf{F}}_1 + \vec{\mathbf{F}}_2 + \cdots)\,\Delta t = \sum\vec{\mathbf{F}}\,\Delta t$$

The total impulse on an object is equal to the change in the object's momentum during the same time interval. This relationship between total impulse and momentum change is called the impulse-momentum theorem and is especially useful in solving problems that involve collisions and impacts.

Impulse = $\vec{\mathbf{F}}\,\Delta t$

CONNECTION

Impulse is a momentum transfer due to a force; work is an energy transfer due to a force.

	Impulse	Work
Definition	$\vec{\mathbf{F}}\,\Delta t$	$\vec{\mathbf{F}}\cdot\Delta\vec{\mathbf{r}}$
Vector or Scalar?	Vector	Scalar*
Physical meaning	Momentum transfer	Energy transfer

*The scalar or dot product of two vectors is introduced in Section 6.2.

Impulse-Momentum Theorem

$$\Delta\vec{\mathbf{p}} = \sum\vec{\mathbf{F}}\,\Delta t \qquad (7\text{-}2)$$

Impulse When Forces Are Not Constant   Our discussion so far has assumed that the forces acting are constant or that Δt is very small so the change in $\vec{\mathbf{F}}$ is negligible. That is a rather unusual situation; the concept of momentum would be of limited use if it were applicable only when forces are constant. However, everything we have said still applies to situations where the forces are not constant, as long as we use the *average* force to calculate the impulse.

$$\text{impulse} = \vec{\mathbf{F}}_{av}\,\Delta t \qquad (7\text{-}3)$$

When the force is not constant, the impulse can be found using the average force.

Conceptual Example 7.2

Big Force–Short Time Versus Small Force–Long Time

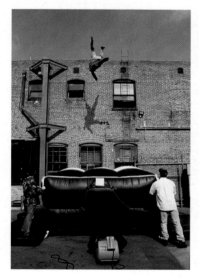

Which causes the larger change in momentum of an object, an average force of 5 N acting for 4 s or an average force of 2 N acting for 10 s? How might this principle be used when designing products to protect the human body from injury? Give an example.

Figure 7.3

Solution and Discussion   The change in momentum is equal to the impulse. The product of the force and the time interval gives the momentum change of the object. Over a period of 4 s, the 5-N force causes a momentum change of magnitude (5 N × 4 s) = 20 N·s, and the 2-N force acting for 10 s also causes a momentum change of magnitude (2 N × 10 s) = 20 N·s. The smaller force causes the same change in momentum because it acts for a longer time interval.

When designing products to protect the human body, one goal is to lengthen the time period during which a velocity change occurs. For example, when a movie stuntman falls from a great height, he lands on a large air bag (Fig. 7.3),

A stuntman lands safely in an air bag to break his fall. The air bag reduces the risk of injury in two ways. It changes the stuntman's momentum more gradually, so that forces of smaller magnitude act on his body. It also spreads these forces over a larger area so they are less likely to cause serious injury.

continued on next page

Example 7.2 continued

which changes his momentum much more gradually than if he were to fall onto concrete. The average force exerted by the air bag on the stuntman is much smaller than the average force exerted by concrete would be. Nets used under circus acrobats serve the same purpose. The net gives and dips downward when the acrobat falls into it, gradually reducing the speed of the fall over a longer time interval than if she fell directly onto the ground.

Practice Problem 7.2   Pole-Vaulter Landing on a Padded Surface

A pole-vaulter vaults over the bar and falls onto thick padding. He lands with a speed of 9.8 m/s; the padding then brings him to a stop in a time of 0.40 s. What is the average force on his body *due to the padding* during that time interval? Express your answer as a fraction or multiple of his weight. [*Hint:* The force due to the padding is not the only force acting on the vaulter during the 0.40-s interval.]

Application of momentum conservation to automotive design.

Designing a Safer Automobile   One automotive design change implemented to minimize injury on collision is the foam padding built into automobile dashboards (Fig. 7.4). Automobile bumpers have shock absorbers built in to lessen damage to the car body in small collisions. The structure of the car itself is often a single piece of metal with reinforced supports (*unibody* construction) so that the entire body can crumple and absorb the change in momentum more slowly than it would if it were made of separate sections of metal that would slide into or over each other or fall off the car. The safety glass in a windshield has two advantages. One is that it does not shatter and send sharp shards of glass into human tissue, but the other is that it distorts when struck by solid objects like human bones or a human head. The glass doesn't give much, but in a crash every little bit helps.

The use of seat belts plus the air bag is better than either alone. Without a seat belt, the body continues moving with the same speed the car had before the crash. The rapidly inflating air bag moves toward the body and the effective velocity is then the sum of the two velocities (air bag velocity + body velocity) when the two collide. The body flying into the air bag can be injured more than a restrained body making more gradual contact with the air bag. An adult should sit at least 12 in. from the air bag container to avoid injury from the deploying air bag itself. Small children should always be placed in the back seat, in proper car seats for their size, to ensure their safety.

Figure 7.4 Some safety features of the modern automobile. Many of these features serve to lengthen the time interval during which a momentum change occurs in a crash, thereby lessening the forces acting on the passengers.

Example 7.3

Collision Between an Automobile and a Tree

A car moving at 20.0 m/s (44.7 mi/h) crashes into a tree. Find the magnitude of the average force acting on a passenger of mass 65 kg in each of the following cases. (a) The passenger is not wearing a seat belt. He is brought to rest by a collision with the windshield and dashboard that lasts 3.0 ms. (b) The car is equipped with a passenger-side air bag. The force due to the air bag acts for 30 ms, bringing the passenger to rest.

Strategy From the impulse-momentum theorem, $\Delta\vec{\mathbf{p}} = \vec{\mathbf{F}}_{av}\,\Delta t$, where $\vec{\mathbf{F}}_{av}$ is the average force acting on the passenger and Δt is the time interval during which the force acts. The change in the passenger's momentum is the same in the two cases. What differs is the time interval during which the change occurs. It takes a larger force to change the momentum in a shorter time interval.

Solution The magnitude of the passenger's initial momentum is

$$|\vec{\mathbf{p}}_i| = |m\vec{\mathbf{v}}_i| = 65\text{ kg} \times 20.0\text{ m/s} = 1300\text{ kg·m/s}$$

His final momentum is zero, so the magnitude of the momentum change is

$$|\Delta\vec{\mathbf{p}}| = 1300\text{ kg·m/s}$$

This momentum change divided by the time interval gives the magnitude of the average force in each case.

(a) No seat belt: $|\vec{\mathbf{F}}_{av}| = \dfrac{|\Delta\vec{\mathbf{p}}|}{\Delta t} = \dfrac{1300\text{ kg·m/s}}{0.0030\text{ s}} = 4.3 \times 10^5\text{ N}$

(b) Air bag: $|\vec{\mathbf{F}}_{av}| = \dfrac{|\Delta\vec{\mathbf{p}}|}{\Delta t} = \dfrac{1300\text{ kg·m/s}}{0.030\text{ s}} = 4.3 \times 10^4\text{ N}$

Discussion The average forces required to bring the passenger to rest are inversely proportional to the time interval over which those forces act. It is a far happier situation to have the momentum change over as long a period as possible to make the forces smaller. Automotive safety engineers design cars to minimize the average forces on the passengers during sudden stops and collisions.

The air bag also spreads the force over a much larger area than impact with a hard surface like the windshield, further reducing the risk of injury.

Practice Problem 7.3   Catching a Fastball

A baseball catcher is catching a fastball that is thrown at 43 m/s (96 mi/h) by the pitcher. If the mass of the ball is 0.15 kg and if the catcher moves his mitt backward toward his body by 8.0 cm as the ball lands in the glove, what is the magnitude of the average force acting on the catcher's mitt? Estimate the time interval required for the catcher to move his hands.

PHYSICS AT HOME

Try playing catch with a friend [on the lawn] while using a raw egg or a water balloon as a ball. How do you move your hands to minimize the chance of breaking the egg or balloon when you catch it? What is likely to happen if you forget that the "ball" is an egg or balloon and catch it as you would a ball?

Graphical Calculation of Impulse

When a force is changing, how can we find the impulse? We've asked similar questions in previous chapters. For simplicity we consider components along the x-axis. Recall:

- displacement = $\Delta x = v_{av,x}\,\Delta t$ = area under $v_x(t)$ graph
- change in velocity = $\Delta v_x = a_{av,x}\,\Delta t$ = area under $a_x(t)$ graph

In both cases, the mathematical relationship is that of a rate of change. Velocity is the rate of change of position with time and acceleration is the rate of change of velocity with time. Now we have force as the rate of change of momentum with time. By analogy:

- impulse = $F_{av,x}\,\Delta t$ = area under $F_x(t)$ graph

So to find the impulse for a variable force, we find the area under the $F_x(t)$ graph. Then, if we wish to know the average force, we can divide the impulse by the time interval during which the force is applied.

CONNECTION:

See Sections 3.2, 3.3, and 6.6 to review how we used the area under a graph to find displacement, change in velocity, and work done by a force.

A "graph of $v_x(t)$" means the quantity v_x is plotted as a function of the variable t with v_x on the vertical axis and t on the horizontal axis.

Figure 7.5 (a) The area under the $F_x(t)$ graph for a variable force is the impulse. (b) The average force for a given time interval is the constant force that would produce the same impulse.

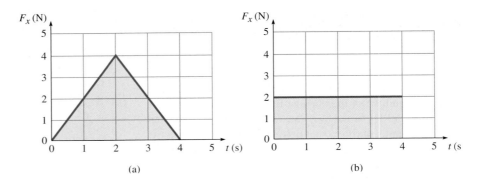

(a)   (b)

The variable force of Fig. 7.5a increases linearly from 0 to 4 N in a time of 2 s; then it decreases from 4 N to 0 N in 2 s. The area under the $F_x(t)$ graph is found from the triangular area

$$\text{area} = \tfrac{1}{2}\,\text{base} \times \text{height} = 2\text{ s} \times 4\text{ N} = 8\text{ N·s} = \text{impulse}$$

The average force during the 4-s time interval is

$$\text{average force} = \frac{\text{impulse}}{\text{time interval}} = \frac{8\text{ N·s}}{4\text{ s}} = 2\text{ N}$$

Figure 7.5b shows the average force over the 4-s time interval; the area under the curve (the impulse) is the same as in Fig. 7.5a.

Example 7.4

Hitting the Wall

An experimental robotic car of mass 10.2 kg moving at 1.2 m/s in the $+x$-direction crashes into a brick wall and rebounds. A force sensor on the car's bumper records the force that the wall exerts on the car as a function of time. These data are shown in graphical form in Fig. 7.6. (a) What is the maximum magnitude of the force exerted on the car? (b) What is the average force on the car during the collision? (c) At what speed does the car rebound from the wall?

Strategy The maximum force can be read directly from the graph. To solve parts (b) and (c) of this problem, we must

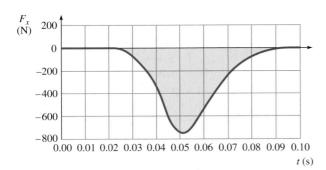

Figure 7.6
Force versus time for a car colliding with a wall.

find the impulse exerted on the car. Since impulse is the area under the $F_x(t)$ curve, we'll make an estimate of the area. The impulse is then equal to the average force times the time interval and also to the car's change in momentum. Once we find the change in momentum, we use it to find the car's final speed.

Given: $m = 10.2$ kg; $v_{ix} = 1.2$ m/s; graph of $F_x(t)$
To find: (a) F_{max}; (b) $F_{av,x}$; (c) v_{fx}

Solution (a) From Fig. 7.6, the maximum force is approximately 750 N in magnitude.

(b) Each division on the horizontal axis represents 0.01 s, and each vertical division represents 200 N. Then the area of each grid box represents $(200\text{ N} \times 0.01\text{ s}) = 2$ N·s. Counting the number of grid boxes between the $F_x(t)$ curve and the time axis, estimating fractions of boxes, yields about 10 boxes. Then the magnitude of the impulse is approximately

$$10\text{ boxes} \times 2\text{ N·s/box} = 20\text{ N·s}$$

The collision is underway when the force is nonzero. So the collision begins at about $t = 0.025$ s and ends at about $t = 0.095$ s. The duration of the collision is

$$\Delta t = 0.07\text{ s}$$

continued on next page

Example 7.4 continued

The magnitude of the average force is approximately

$$|F_{av,x}| = \frac{|\text{impulse}|}{\Delta t} = \frac{20 \text{ N}\cdot\text{s}}{0.07 \text{ s}} = 300 \text{ N}$$

(c) The impulse gives us the momentum change. The force exerted by the wall is in the $-x$-direction. Thus, the x-component of the impulse is negative. In the graph of F_x versus t, the area lies under the time axis and so is counted as negative. So, working with x-components,

$$\Delta p_x = mv_{fx} - mv_{ix} = F_{av,x} \Delta t = -20 \text{ N}\cdot\text{s}$$

Solving for v_{fx},

$$v_{fx} = \frac{\Delta p_x + mv_{ix}}{m} = \frac{\Delta p_x}{m} + v_{ix}$$

Substituting numerical values in this expression yields

$$v_{fx} = \frac{-20 \text{ N}\cdot\text{s}}{10.2 \text{ kg}} + 1.2 \text{ m/s} = -0.8 \text{ m/s}$$

The car rebounds at a speed of 0.8 m/s.

Discussion As a check, we compare the average force with the maximum force. The average force is a bit less than half of the maximum force. If the force were a linear function of time, the average would be exactly half the maximum. Here,

the average force is less than that because more time is spent at smaller values of force than at the larger values.

Practice Problem 7.4   Car-Van Collision

A car weighing 13.6 kN is moving at 10.0 m/s in the $+x$-direction when it collides head-on with a van weighing 33.0 kN. The horizontal force exerted on the car before, during, and after the collision is shown in Fig. 7.7. What is the car's velocity just after the collision?

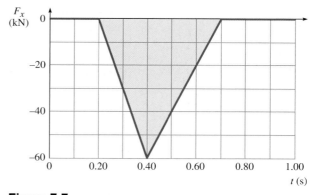

Figure 7.7

Varying force on a car during a car-van collision.

A Restatement of Newton's Second Law

We can use the relationship between impulse and momentum to find a new way to understand Newton's second law. Let's rewrite the impulse-momentum theorem this way:

$$\sum \vec{F}_{av} = \frac{\Delta \vec{p}}{\Delta t}$$

What happens if we let the time interval Δt get smaller and smaller, approaching zero? Then the average force is taken over a smaller and smaller time interval, approaching the instantaneous force:

$$\vec{F} = \lim_{\Delta t \to 0} \frac{\Delta \vec{p}}{\Delta t}$$

If more than one force acts, we must replace $\vec{F}$ with $\sum \vec{F}$. Then our restatement of Newton's second law becomes

Newton's Second Law

$$\sum \vec{F} = \lim_{\Delta t \to 0} \frac{\Delta \vec{p}}{\Delta t} \qquad (7\text{-}4)$$

CONNECTION:

Equation (7-4) is closer to Newton's original statement of his second law and is more general than $\sum \vec{F} = m\vec{a}$.

In words, *the net force is the rate of change of momentum.*

Equation (7-4) is *more general* than $\sum \vec{F} = m\vec{a}$, the form of Newton's second law used in Chapters 3 through 6, which holds only when mass is constant. One situation in which mass is not constant is the rocket engine. In a rocket engine, fuel combustion produces hot gases that are then expelled at high speeds (Fig. 7.8). The rocket's mass decreases as the exhaust gases are expelled.

Figure 7.8 The Space Shuttle is propelled upward as hot gases are exhausted downward at high speeds.

When mass is constant, then it can be factored out:

$$\sum \vec{\mathbf{F}} = \lim_{\Delta t \to 0} \frac{\Delta \vec{\mathbf{p}}}{\Delta t} = \lim_{\Delta t \to 0} \frac{\Delta (m\vec{\mathbf{v}})}{\Delta t} = m \lim_{\Delta t \to 0} \frac{\Delta \vec{\mathbf{v}}}{\Delta t} = m\vec{\mathbf{a}}$$

Thus, Eq. (7-4) reduces to the familiar form of Newton's second law from Chapters 3–6 when mass is constant.

7.4   CONSERVATION OF MOMENTUM

Consider two pucks that bump into one another after sliding along a frictionless table. Figure 7.9 shows what happens to the two pucks before, during, and after their interaction. If we think of the two pucks as constituting a single system, then the gravitational interactions with the Earth and the contact interactions with the table are *external* interactions—interactions with objects external to the system. The force of gravity on each object is balanced by the normal force on the same object and, thus, there is no net impulse up or down. Together, these forces produce a net external force of zero, so they leave the system's momentum unchanged. Since these two always cancel, we can ignore these external interactions and just focus on the interaction between the pucks. Therefore, we omit the normal and gravitational forces in Fig. 7.9.

Until contact is made, there is no interaction between the pucks (ignoring the small gravitational interaction between the two). During the collision, the pucks exert forces on each other. Force $\vec{\mathbf{F}}_{12}$ is the contact force acting on mass m_1 and force $\vec{\mathbf{F}}_{21}$ is the contact force acting on mass m_2. If we continue to regard the two pucks as parts of a single interacting system, then those forces are *internal* forces of this system. When they collide, some momentum is transferred from one puck to the other. The changes in momentum of the two are equal and opposite:

$$\Delta \vec{\mathbf{p}}_1 = -\Delta \vec{\mathbf{p}}_2$$

Since the change in momentum is the final momentum minus the initial momentum, we write:

$$\vec{\mathbf{p}}_{1f} - \vec{\mathbf{p}}_{1i} = -(\vec{\mathbf{p}}_{2f} - \vec{\mathbf{p}}_{2i})$$

Moving the initial momenta to the right side and the final momenta to the left:

$$\vec{\mathbf{p}}_{1f} + \vec{\mathbf{p}}_{2f} = \vec{\mathbf{p}}_{1i} + \vec{\mathbf{p}}_{2i} \qquad (7\text{-}5)$$

Equation (7-5) says the sum of the momenta of the pucks after the interaction is equal to the sum of the momenta before the interaction; or, more simply, the total momentum of the objects is unchanged by the collision. This isn't surprising since, if some momentum is just transferred from one to the other, the total hasn't changed. We say that momentum is *conserved* for this collision. The interaction between the pucks changes the momentum of each puck, but the total momentum of the system is unchanged.

Figure 7.9 Two sliding pucks with different masses before, during, and after collision.

In a system composed of more than two objects, interactions between objects inside the system do not change the total momentum of the system—they just transfer some momentum from one part of the system to another. Only external interactions can change the total momentum of the system. To summarize:

- The total momentum of a system is the vector sum of the momenta of each object in the system.
- External interactions can change the total momentum of a system.
- Internal interactions do not change the total momentum of a system.

In the absence of external interactions, momentum is conserved:

Law of Conservation of Linear Momentum

If the net external force acting on a system is zero, then the momentum of the system is conserved.

$$\text{If } \sum \vec{F}_{ext} = 0, \quad \vec{p}_i = \vec{p}_f \tag{7-6}$$

By definition, an *isolated*, or closed, system is subject to no external interactions; thus, *linear momentum is always conserved for an isolated system.* Remember that momentum is a vector quantity, so both the magnitude *and the direction* of the momentum at the beginning and end of the interaction must be the same. In component form, both p_x and p_y are unchanged by the interaction.

✓ CHECKPOINT 7.4

When is the momentum of a system *not* conserved?

Example 7.5

Adrift on a Raft

Diana is standing on a raft of mass 100.0 kg that is floating on a still lake. She decides to walk the length of the raft (Fig. 7.10). If Diana's mass is 55 kg and she walks with a velocity of 0.91 m/s *with respect to the shore*, how fast and in what direction does the raft move while Diana is walking?

Figure 7.10
Diana walking along a raft. Velocities $\vec{v}_D$ and $\vec{v}_r$ are measured with respect to the shore.

Assume the raft is stationary with respect to the shore before Diana starts walking.

Strategy Diana and the raft can be considered to be a single *isolated system*: as long as frictional forces on the raft due to the water and air are small enough to ignore, the net external force on the system is zero. Then the momentum of this system (raft + Diana) is conserved. We let the subscripts D stand for Diana and r for the raft and set the change in momentum of the system equal to zero.

Solution To walk forward, Diana must exert a backward force on the raft: the static frictional force between her feet and the raft. This is an internal interaction within the isolated system, so it cannot change the total momentum of the system. Only something acting from outside the system could do that. As Diana walks in one direction, she acquires some momentum. The rest of the system (the raft) must acquire an equal and opposite momentum, because the momentum of the isolated system (Diana + raft) is conserved, which means that the change in momentum of the system is zero.

continued on next page

Example 7.5 continued

Figure 7.10
Diana walking along a raft. Velocities $\vec{v}_D$ and $\vec{v}_r$ are measured with respect to the shore.

First we set the change in momentum of the system equal to zero:

$$\Delta\vec{p} = 0 = \Delta\vec{p}_D + \Delta\vec{p}_r$$

or

$$\Delta\vec{p}_D = -\Delta\vec{p}_r$$

This means that the momentum changes of Diana and of the raft are equal and opposite. Since momentum is the product of mass and velocity and the masses of the raft and Diana do not change,

$$m_D\,\Delta\vec{v}_D = -m_r\,\Delta\vec{v}_r$$

Solving for the change in velocity of the raft gives

$$\Delta\vec{v}_r = -\frac{m_D}{m_r}\,\Delta\vec{v}_D$$

Finally we substitute numerical values from the given information in the statement of the problem. Let Diana walk in the $+x$-direction.

$$\Delta\vec{v}_r = \frac{-55 \text{ kg} \times 0.91 \text{ m/s (in the } +x\text{-direction)}}{100.0 \text{ kg}}$$

$$= 0.50 \text{ m/s in the } -x\text{-direction}$$

The negative sign reverses the direction: $\Delta\vec{v}_r$ is in the $-x$-direction and has a magnitude of 0.50 m/s.

The raft moves in a direction opposite to Diana's motion to keep the momentum unchanged and thus conserved. Since the raft was originally stationary, this is the new velocity of the raft.

Discussion   In any momentum conservation problem there are two equivalent ways to proceed. In this example we set the momentum change of the system equal to zero. We could just as well write an equation that sets the initial total momentum equal to the final momentum of the system. The raft and Diana are initially at rest, so the initial momentum is zero:

$$0 = m_D\vec{v}_D + m_r\vec{v}_r$$

where $\vec{v}_D$ and $\vec{v}_r$ are the final velocities of Diana and the raft.

Practice Problem 7.5   Skaters Pushing Apart

Two skaters on in-line skates, Lisa and Bart, are initially at rest. They push apart and start moving in opposite directions. If Lisa's speed just after they push apart is 2.0 m/s and her mass is 85% of Bart's mass, how fast is Bart moving at that time?

Application of momentum conservation: recoil of a rifle

When a bullet is fired from a rifle, the system of rifle plus bullet must conserve momentum. Suppose the rifle is at rest before the bullet is fired. The momentum of the system is zero. When the bullet is fired, part of the system's mass breaks away and travels in one direction with a certain momentum. The rifle, which is the remaining mass of the system, moves in the exact opposite direction such that the total momentum of the system is still zero. The rifle has a much larger mass than the bullet, so it has a much smaller speed. The backward motion of the rifle is the *recoil* felt by anyone who has held a rifle against her shoulder and squeezed the trigger.

Application of momentum conservation: jets, rockets, and airplane wings

Jet engines and rockets operate by conservation of momentum. Hot combustion gases are forced out of nozzles at high speed by the engines. The increased backward momentum of the hot gases as they are expelled is accompanied by an increased forward momentum of the engines. Airplane wings generate lift by conservation of momentum. The main purpose of the wing is to deflect air downward, giving it a downward momentum component. (Exactly how the wing does this is the complicated part.) Since the wing pushes air downward, air pushes the wing upward.

Conceptual Example 7.6

Escape on Slippery Ice

A pilot parachutes from his disabled aircraft and lands on the frozen surface of a lake. There is no breeze blowing and the lake surface is too slippery to walk on. What can the pilot do to reach the shore?

Strategy and Solution Since the person in jeopardy is a pilot, he begins to think about how hot gases forced backward from a jet engine cause the plane to move forward. That gives him an idea: he bundles the parachute into a package and pushes it as hard as possible in a direction away from the nearest point of the shore. If friction is negligible, the net external force on the system of pilot plus parachute is zero and the total momentum of the system cannot change. The momentum of the parachute plus the momentum of the pilot must still equal zero. By conservation of momentum, the pilot begins sliding in the opposite direction and glides toward the shore.

Discussion If friction brings the pilot to rest before he reaches the shore, he can search his pockets and belt loops for other items to throw away. Once he reaches shore, he can tie one end of a rope to a tree and, holding onto the other end, venture back out onto the ice to retrieve any essential items. The rope provides him with an external force so he can get back to shore.

Practice Problem 7.6 Recoil of a Rifle

During an afternoon of target practice, you fire a Winchester .308 rifle of mass 3.8 kg. The bullets have a mass of 9.72 g and leave the rifle at a muzzle velocity of 860 m/s. If you are sloppy and fire a round when the butt of the rifle is not firmly up against your shoulder, at what speed does the rifle butt smash into your shoulder? (Ouch!)

PHYSICS AT HOME

In case you and a friend ever end up stuck in the middle of the ice, practice the technique the pilot used to escape to the lakeshore. Bring a heavy medicine ball out to the middle of the ice rink and face each other with your skates aligned parallel. Toss the ball to your friend. What happens to you? What happens to your friend when he catches the ball? Can you both be "saved" by tossing the ball back and forth? (The same technique works using in-line skates.)

7.5 CENTER OF MASS

We have seen that the momentum of an isolated system is conserved even though parts of the system may interact with other parts; internal interactions transfer momentum between parts of the system but do not change the total momentum of the system. We can define a point called the **center of mass** (CM) that serves as an average location of the system. In Section 7.6, we prove that the center of mass of an isolated system must move with constant velocity, regardless of how complicated the motions of parts of the system may be. Then we can treat the mass of the system as if it were all concentrated at the CM, like a point particle. The CM of an object is not necessarily located within the object; for some objects, such as a boomerang, the center of mass is located outside of the object itself (Fig. 7.11a).

What if a system is not isolated, but has external interactions? Again imagine all of the mass of the system concentrated into a single point particle located at the CM. The motion of this fictitious point particle is determined by Newton's second law, where the net force is the sum of all of the external forces acting on *any part* of the system. In the case of a complex system composed of many parts interacting with each other, the motion of the CM is considerably simpler than the motion of an arbitrary particle of the system (Fig. 7.11b,c).

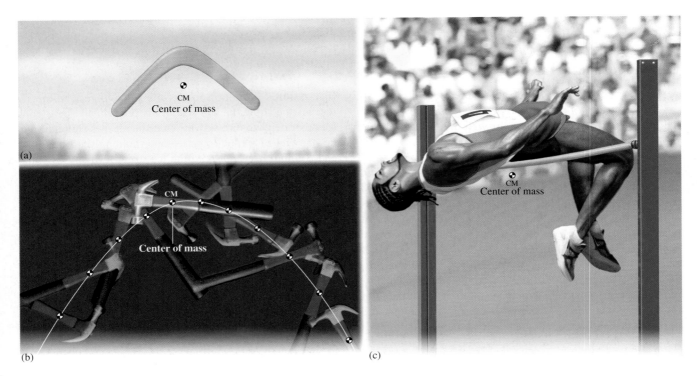

(a)

(b)

(c)

Figure 7.11 (a) The center of mass of a boomerang is a point outside of the boomerang. (b) The path followed by the center of mass when a hammer is tossed through the air. (c) British pole-vaulter Ben Challenger's center of mass actually passes *beneath* the bar as his body passes over the bar.

Location of Center of Mass   For a system composed of two particles, the center of mass lies somewhere on a line between the two particles. In Fig. 7.12, particles of masses m_1 and m_2 are located at positions x_1 and x_2, respectively. We define the location of the CM for these two particles as

$$x_{CM} = \frac{m_1 x_1 + m_2 x_2}{m_1 + m_2} \tag{7-7}$$

The CM is a *weighted average* of the positions of the two particles. Here we use the word *weighted* in its statistical sense. The position of a particle with more mass counts more—carries more *statistical* weight—than does the position of a particle with a smaller mass. We can rewrite Eq. (7-7) as a weighted average:

$$x_{CM} = \frac{m_1}{M} x_1 + \frac{m_2}{M} x_2 \tag{7-8}$$

Here $M = m_1 + m_2$ represents the total mass of the system. The statistical weight used for the location of each particle is the mass of that particle as a fraction of the total mass of the system.

Suppose masses m_1 and m_2 are equal. Then we expect the CM to be located midway between the two particles (Fig. 7.12a). If $m_1 = 2m_2$, as in Fig. 7.12b, then the CM is closer to the particle of mass m_1. Figure 7.12b shows that, in this case, the CM is twice as far from m_2 as from m_1.

For a system of N particles, at arbitrary locations in three-dimensional space, the definition of the CM is a generalization of Eq. (7-7).

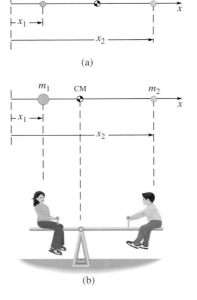

(a)

(b)

Figure 7.12 (a) Two particles of equal mass located at positions x_1 and x_2 from the origin. The CM is midway between the two. (b) Two particles of unequal mass. The CM is closer to the more massive particle. For two children balanced on a see-saw, the CM is at the fulcrum.

Definition of center of mass:

Vector form:
$$\vec{r}_{CM} = \frac{\sum m_i \vec{r}_i}{M} \tag{7-9}$$

Component form:
$$x_{CM} = \frac{\sum m_i x_i}{M} \qquad y_{CM} = \frac{\sum m_i y_i}{M} \qquad z_{CM} = \frac{\sum m_i z_i}{M}$$

where $i = 1, 2, 3, \ldots, N$ and $M = \sum m_i$

Remember that the symbol $\sum$ stands for *sum*. The shorthand notation $\sum m_i x_i$ is interpreted as

$$\sum m_i x_i = m_1 x_1 + m_2 x_2 + \cdots + m_N x_N$$

For particles in two-dimensional space, we use only two of these equations for the *x-y* plane and find the *x*- and *y*-components of the CM.

Example 7.7

Center of Mass of a Binary Star System

Due to the gravitational interaction between the two stars in a binary star system, each moves in a circular orbit around their CM. One star has a mass of 15.0×10^{30} kg; its center is located at $x = 1.0$ AU and $y = 5.0$ AU. The other has a mass of 3.0×10^{30} kg; its center is at $x = 4.0$ AU and $y = 2.0$ AU. Find the CM of the system composed of the two stars. (AU stands for *astronomical unit.* 1 AU = the average distance between the Earth and the Sun = 1.5×10^8 km.)

Strategy We treat the stars as point particles located at their centers. Since we are given *x*- and *y*-coordinates, the easiest way to proceed is to find the *x*- and *y*-coordinates of the CM. There is no particular advantage here in finding the position vector of the CM in terms of its length and direction.

Given: $m_1 = 15.0 \times 10^{30}$ kg $x_1 = 1.0$ AU $y_1 = 5.0$ AU
$\qquad\quad m_2 = 3.0 \times 10^{30}$ kg $x_2 = 4.0$ AU $y_2 = 2.0$ AU

To find: x_{CM}; y_{CM}

Solution The total mass of the system is the sum of the individual masses:

$$M = m_1 + m_2 = 15.0 \times 10^{30} \text{ kg} + 3.0 \times 10^{30} \text{ kg} = 18.0 \times 10^{30} \text{ kg}$$

For the *x*-position, we find

$$x_{CM} = \frac{m_1}{M} x_1 + \frac{m_2}{M} x_2$$

$$= \frac{15.0 \times 10^{30} \text{ kg}}{18.0 \times 10^{30} \text{ kg}} \times 1.0 \text{ AU} + \frac{3.0 \times 10^{30} \text{ kg}}{18.0 \times 10^{30} \text{ kg}} \times 4.0 \text{ AU}$$

$$= 1.5 \text{ AU}$$

and for the *y*-position, we find

$$y_{CM} = \frac{m_1}{M} y_1 + \frac{m_2}{M} y_2$$

$$= \frac{15.0}{18.0} \times 5.0 \text{ AU} + \frac{3.0}{18.0} \times 2.0 \text{ AU} = 4.5 \text{ AU}$$

Discussion In Fig. 7.13, we mark the position of the CM. As we expect for the case of two particles, it is located closer to the larger mass and on a line connecting the two. Once the CM position is found in a problem, check to be sure its location is reasonable. Suppose we had made an error in this example and found the CM to be at $x = 1.5$ AU and $y = 1.7$ AU. This is not a reasonable location for the CM since it is not along the line connecting the two and is closer to the less massive star; we then would go back to look for the error.

Figure 7.13

Finding the CM for the system of two stars.

Practice Problem 7.7   Three Balls with Unequal Masses

Three spherical objects are shown in Fig. 7.14. Their masses are $m_1 = m_3 = 1.0$ kg and $m_2 = 4.0$ kg. Find the location of the CM for the three objects.

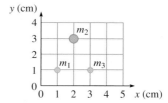

Figure 7.14

Three spheres located at *x*, *y* positions (1.0 cm, 1.0 cm), (2.0 cm, 3.0 cm), and (3.0 cm, 1.0 cm).

Using Symmetry to Locate the Center of Mass   Most objects we deal with in real life are not composed of a small set of point particles or spherically symmetrical objects. In Example 7.7, we use the location of the center of each star to find the CM. Due to spherical symmetry, the CM of either star (by itself) is at its geometric center. The same technique can be applied to other shapes with symmetry. A standard 2 by 4, which is an 8-ft-long uniform piece of lumber used in building 1.5 in. deep × 3.5 in. high, has its center of mass at its geometric center. By contrast, a "loaded" die does *not* have its CM at its geometric center, since a small metal plug has been inserted near one face to make the distribution of mass in the die asymmetrical. The definition of the CM [Eq. (7-9)] still holds as long as (x_i, y_i, z_i) are the coordinates of the CM of a part of the system with mass m_i.

7.6   MOTION OF THE CENTER OF MASS

Now that we know how to find the position of the CM of a system, we turn our attention to the motion of the CM. How is the velocity of the CM related to the velocities of the various parts of the system?

During a short time interval Δt, the displacement of the i-th particle is $\Delta \vec{\mathbf{r}}_i = \vec{\mathbf{v}}_i \, \Delta t$ and the displacement of the center of mass is $\Delta \vec{\mathbf{r}}_{CM} = \vec{\mathbf{v}}_{CM} \, \Delta t$. From the definition of the CM [Eq. (7-9)], the displacements must be related as follows:

$$\Delta \vec{\mathbf{r}}_{CM} = \frac{\sum m_i \Delta \vec{\mathbf{r}}_i}{M} \quad \Rightarrow \quad \vec{\mathbf{v}}_{CM} \, \Delta t = \frac{\sum m_i \vec{\mathbf{v}}_i \Delta t}{M}$$

Dividing both sides by Δt and multiplying by M yields

$$M\vec{\mathbf{v}}_{CM} = \sum m_i \vec{\mathbf{v}}_i \tag{7-10}$$

The right side of Eq. (7-10) is the sum of the momenta of the particles that constitute the system—the total momentum of the system $\vec{\mathbf{p}}$. Therefore,

$$\vec{\mathbf{p}} = M\vec{\mathbf{v}}_{CM} \tag{7-11}$$

For two-dimensional motion, Eq. (7-11) is equivalent to two component equations

$$p_x = Mv_{CM,x} \quad \text{and} \quad p_y = Mv_{CM,y} \tag{7-12}$$

In Section 7.4, we showed that, for an isolated system, the total linear momentum is conserved. In such a system, Eq. (7-11) implies that the CM must move with constant velocity regardless of the motions of the individual particles. On the other hand, what if the system is not isolated? If a net external force acts on a system, the CM does not move with constant velocity. Instead, it moves as if all the mass were concentrated there into a fictitious point particle with all the external forces acting on that point. The motion of the CM obeys the following statement of Newton's second law:

$$\sum \vec{\mathbf{F}}_{ext} = M\vec{\mathbf{a}}_{CM} \tag{7-13}$$

where M is the total mass of the system, $\sum \vec{\mathbf{F}}_{ext}$ is the net external force, and $\vec{\mathbf{a}}_{CM}$ is the acceleration of the CM. [Eq. (7-13) is proved in Problem 38.]

√ CHECKPOINT 7.6

Turn back to Fig. 7.11b. Why does the CM of the hammer move along a parabolic path?

Example 7.8

An Exploding Rocket

A model rocket is fired from the ground in a parabolic tra-jectory. At the top of the trajectory, a horizontal distance of 260 m from the launch point, an explosion occurs within the rocket, breaking it into two fragments. One fragment, hav-ing one third of the mass of the rocket, falls straight down to Earth as if it had been dropped from rest at that point. At what horizontal distance from the launch point does the other fragment land? Ignore air resistance. [*Hint:* The two fragments land simultaneously.]

Strategy Two different strategies can be used to solve this problem.

Strategy 1: We apply conservation of momentum to the explosion. The momentum of the rocket *just before* the explo-sion is equal to the total momentum of the two fragments *just after* the explosion. Why can momentum conservation be assumed here? There is an external force—gravity—acting on the system. External forces change momentum. However, the explosion takes place in a *very short time interval*. From the impulse-momentum theorem [Eq. (7-2)], the momentum change of the system is the force of gravity multiplied by the time interval. As long as the time interval considered is suffi-ciently short, the momentum change of the system can be ignored.

Strategy 2: The explosion is caused by an *internal* interaction between two parts of the rocket. The motion of the CM of the system is unaffected by internal interactions, so it continues in the same parabolic path. Just before the explosion, the rocket is at the top of its trajectory, so it has $p_y = 0$ (with the y-axis pointing up). Just after the explo-sion, one fragment is at rest. Then the other fragment must have $p_y = 0$; otherwise, conservation of momentum would be violated. Then both fragments have $v_y = 0$ just after the explosion. Ignoring air resistance, they land simulta-neously. At that same instant, the CM also reaches the ground.

Solution 1 First we make a sketch of the situation (Fig. 7.15). At the top of the trajectory, where the explosion occurs, $v_y = 0$; the rocket is moving in the x-direction. The initial momentum just before the explosion is entirely in the x-direction. If M is the mass of the rocket, then

$$p_{ix} = Mv_{ix}$$

Just after the explosion, one-third of the mass of the rocket is at rest; it then drops straight down under the influence of the gravitational force. This piece has zero momentum just after the explosion. To conserve momentum, the other two thirds of the rocket must have a momentum equal to the momentum just before the explosion.

$$p_{ix} = p_{1x} + p_{2x}$$
$$Mv_{ix} = 0 + (\tfrac{2}{3}M)\, v_{2x}$$

Solving for v_{2x}, we find

$$v_{2x} = \tfrac{3}{2}v_{ix}$$

The y-component of momentum must also be conserved:

$$p_{iy} = p_{1y} + p_{2y}$$

We know that both p_{iy} and p_{1y} are zero; therefore, p_{2y} is zero as well. Just after the explosion, both parts of the rocket have zero vertical components of velocity. Then both parts take the same time to fall to the ground as if the rocket had not exploded. With a horizontal velocity larger by a factor of $\tfrac{3}{2}$, the second piece of the rocket travels a horizontal distance from the explosion a factor of $\tfrac{3}{2}$ larger than 260 m (see Fig. 7.15). The distance from the launch point where this piece lands is

$$\Delta x = 260 \text{ m} + \tfrac{3}{2} \times 260 \text{ m} = 650 \text{ m}$$

Figure 7.15
Rocket motion after explosion.

continued on next page

Example 7.8 continued

Solution 2 The piece with mass $\frac{1}{3}M$ falls straight down and lands 260 m from the launch point. After the explosion, the CM continues to travel just as the rocket itself would have done if it had not broken apart. From the symmetry of the parabola, the CM touches the ground at a distance of 2×260 m = 520 m from the launch point. Since we know the location of the CM and that of one of the pieces, we can find where the second piece lands:

$$Mx_{CM} = \tfrac{1}{3}Mx_1 + \tfrac{2}{3}Mx_2$$

After canceling the common factor of M,

$$x_{CM} = \tfrac{1}{3}x_1 + \tfrac{2}{3}x_2$$

Solving for x_2 yields

$$x_2 = \frac{3x_{CM} - x_1}{2} = \frac{3 \times 520\text{ m} - 260\text{ m}}{2} = 650\text{ m}$$

which is the same answer that we found in Solution 1.

Discussion The insight that the motion of the CM is unaffected by internal interactions can be of enormous help.

Note, however, that solution 2 would not be so simple if the two fragments did not land simultaneously. As soon as one fragment (fragment 1) hits the ground, the external force on the system is no longer due exclusively to gravity, so the CM doesn't continue to follow the same parabolic path. The normal and frictional forces acting on fragment 1 affect its subsequent motion and the subsequent motion of the CM even though the motion of fragment 2 is unaffected.

Practice Problem 7.8   Diana and the Raft Revisited

In Example 7.5, Diana (mass 55 kg) walks at 0.91 m/s (relative to the water) on a raft of mass 100.0 kg. The raft moves in the opposite direction at 0.50 m/s. Suppose it takes her 3.0 s to walk from one end of the raft to the other. (a) How far does Diana walk (relative to the water)? (b) How far does the raft move while Diana is walking? (c) How far does the CM of Diana and the raft move during the 3.0 s?

7.7   COLLISIONS IN ONE DIMENSION

What Is a Collision? In the macroscopic world, a moving body bumps into another body that may be at rest or in motion. The two bodies exert forces on one another while they are in contact; as a result, their velocities change. In the microscopic and submicroscopic world, our picture of a collision is different. When atoms collide, they don't "touch" each other: the atom doesn't have a definite spatial boundary, so there are no surfaces to make "contact." However, the collision model is still useful for atoms and subatomic particles whenever there is an interaction in which the forces are strong over a short time interval, so that there is a clear "before collision" and a clear "after collision."

Analyzing Collisions Using Momentum Conservation We can often use conservation of momentum to analyze collisions even when external forces act on the colliding objects. If the net external force is small compared with the internal forces the colliding objects exert on each other during the collision, then the change in the total momentum of the two objects is small compared with the transfer of momentum from one object to the other. Then the total momentum after the collision is *approximately* the same as it was before the collision.

The same techniques that are used for collisions in the macroscopic world (car crashes, billiard ball collisions, baseball bats hitting balls) are also used in collisions in the microscopic world (gas molecules colliding with each other and with surfaces, radioactive decays of nuclei). First, we study collisions limited to motion along a line; later, we consider collisions limited to motion in a plane (in two dimensions).

Example 7.9

Collision in the Air

A krypton atom (mass 83.9 u) moving with a velocity of 0.80 km/s to the right and a water molecule (mass 18.0 u) moving with a velocity of 0.40 km/s to the left collide head-on. The water molecule has a velocity of 0.60 km/s to the right after

continued on next page

Example 7.9 continued

the collision. What is the velocity of the krypton atom after the collision? (The symbol "u" stands for the atomic mass unit.)

Strategy Since we know both initial velocities and one of the final velocities, we can find the second final velocity by applying momentum conservation. Let the subscript "1" refer to the krypton atom and let the subscript "2" refer to the water molecule. Let the x-axis point to the right. Figure 7.16 shows before and after pictures of the collision.

Solution Momentum conservation requires that the final momentum be equal to the initial momentum:

$$\vec{\mathbf{p}}_{1f} + \vec{\mathbf{p}}_{2f} = \vec{\mathbf{p}}_{1i} + \vec{\mathbf{p}}_{2i}$$

Now we substitute $\vec{\mathbf{p}} = m\vec{\mathbf{v}}$ for each momentum. It is easiest to work in terms of components. For simplicity we drop the "x" subscripts, remembering that all quantities refer to x-components:

$$m_1 v_{1f} + m_2 v_{2f} = m_1 v_{1i} + m_2 v_{2i}$$

Since $m_1/m_2 = 83.9/18.0 = 4.661$, we can substitute $m_1 = 4.661 m_2$:

$$4.661\, m_2 v_{1f} + m_2 v_{2f} = 4.661\, m_2 v_{1i} + m_2 v_{2i}$$

Before

After

Figure 7.16
Before and after snapshots of a collision.

The common factor m_2 cancels out. Solving for v_{1f},

$$v_{1f} = \frac{4.661 v_{1i} + v_{2i} - v_{2f}}{4.661}$$

$$= \frac{4.661 \times 0.80 \text{ km/s} + (-0.40 \text{ km/s}) - 0.60 \text{ km/s}}{4.661}$$

$$= 0.59 \text{ km/s}$$

After the collision, the krypton atom moves to the right with a speed of 0.59 km/s.

Discussion To check this result, we calculate the total momentum (x-component) before and after the collision:

$$m_1 v_{1i} + m_2 v_{2i} = (83.9 \text{ u})(0.80 \text{ km/s}) + (18.0 \text{ u})(-0.40 \text{ km/s})$$
$$= 60 \text{ u·km/s}$$

$$m_1 v_{1f} + m_2 v_{2f} = (83.9 \text{ u})(0.59 \text{ km/s}) + (18.0 \text{ u})(0.60 \text{ km/s})$$
$$= 60 \text{ u·km/s}$$

Momentum is conserved. There is no need to convert u to kg since we only need to compare these two values.

If we made the mistake of thinking of momentum as a scalar, we would get the wrong answer. The sum of the *magnitudes* of the momenta before the collision is *not* equal to the sum of the *magnitudes* of the momenta after the collision. Conservation of energy is perhaps easier to understand intuitively since energy is a scalar quantity. Converting kinetic energy to potential energy is analogous to moving money from a checking account to a savings account; the total amount of money is the same before and after. This sort of analogy does *not* work with momentum!

Practice Problem 7.9 Head-On Collision

A 5.0-kg ball is at rest when it is struck head-on by a 2.0-kg ball moving along a track at 10.0 m/s. If the 2.0-kg ball is at rest after the collision, what is the speed of the 5.0-kg ball after the collision?

Suppose we observe a bumper car traveling at speed v_i toward a second car that is at rest. The masses of the two cars are equal. When the first car hits the second, what happens?

Based on momentum considerations *alone*, there are many possible outcomes. One possibility is that the first car stops moving and the second car moves off with the same velocity that the first one had to begin with (Fig. 7.17a). This possibility satisfies conservation of momentum because the total momentum is the same before and after.

Another possibility is that the two cars stick together, moving away together (Fig. 7.17b). With what speed do they move after the collision? If the momentum is to be the same with twice as much mass moving, the speed must be half the initial speed of the first car. There are many other possibilities. Conservation of momentum doesn't tell us which of these outcomes actually happens, but if we know one car's velocity after the collision, we can use momentum conservation to determine the other car's velocity.

(a)

Before

After

(b)

Before

After

Figure 7.17 Two of the many possible outcomes of a collision between bumper cars of equal mass with one of them initially at rest.

Figure 7.18 Three successive photos of a racquetball during its collision with the floor ($t_1 < t_2 < t_3$).

Elastic and Inelastic Collisions

Collisions are often classified based on what happens to the kinetic energy of the colliding objects. A ball dropped from a height h does not rebound to the same height. The kinetic energy of the ball just after the collision with the floor or ground is less than it was just before the collision; the amount of the kinetic energy decrease depends on the makeup of the ball and the ground. A racquetball dropped onto a hard wooden floor may rebound nearly to its original height, but a watermelon rebounds very little or not at all. Why do some objects rebound much better than others?

Imagine a racquetball colliding with the floor (Fig. 7.18). The bottom of the ball is flattened. What makes the ball rebound from the floor? The forces holding the ball together are like springs; the kinetic energy of the ball has been transformed largely into potential energy stored in these springs. When the ball bounces back up, this energy is transformed back into kinetic energy. Then why does the watermelon not rebound? The watermelon, too, is deformed when it collides with the floor, but this deformation is not reversible. The kinetic energy of the watermelon is changed mostly into thermal energy rather than into potential energy.

A collision in which the *total* kinetic energy is the same before and after is called **elastic**. When the final kinetic energy is less than the initial kinetic energy, the collision is said to be **inelastic**. Collisions between macroscopic objects are generally inelastic to some degree, but sometimes the change in kinetic energy is so small that we treat them as elastic. When a collision results in two objects sticking together, the collision is **perfectly inelastic**. The decrease of kinetic energy in a perfectly inelastic collision is as large as *possible* (consistent with the conservation of momentum). Now that we have defined elastic and inelastic collisions, we can put together a problem-solving strategy for collision problems.

Problem-Solving Strategy for Collisions Involving Two Objects

1. Draw before and after diagrams of the collision.
2. Collect and organize information on the masses and velocities of the two objects before and after the collision. Express the velocities in component form (with correct algebraic signs).
3. Set the sum of the momenta of the two before the collision equal to the sum of the momenta after the collision. Write one equation for each direction:

$$m_1 v_{1ix} + m_2 v_{2ix} = m_1 v_{1fx} + m_2 v_{2fx}$$

$$m_1 v_{1iy} + m_2 v_{2iy} = m_1 v_{1fy} + m_2 v_{2fy}$$

4. If the collision is known to be perfectly inelastic, set the final velocities equal:

$$v_{1fx} = v_{2fx} \quad \text{and} \quad v_{1fy} = v_{2fy}$$

5. If the collision is known to be perfectly elastic, then set the final kinetic energy equal to the initial kinetic energy:

$$\tfrac{1}{2} m_1 v_{1i}^2 + \tfrac{1}{2} m_2 v_{2i}^2 = \tfrac{1}{2} m_1 v_{1f}^2 + \tfrac{1}{2} m_2 v_{2f}^2$$

6. Solve for the unknown quantities.

There is no *conservation law* for kinetic energy by itself. Total energy is always conserved, but that does not preclude some kinetic energy being transformed into another type of energy. The elastic collision is just a special kind of collision in which no kinetic energy is changed into other forms of energy. Momentum is conserved regardless of whether a collision is elastic or inelastic.

It can be proved (see Problem 56) that for *any* elastic collision between two objects, the relative speed is the same before and after the collision. (This fact is most useful in one-dimensional collisions; in two-dimensional collisions the *direction* of the relative velocity changes due to the collision.) Since the relative velocity is in the opposite direction after a one-dimensional collision—first the objects move together, then they move apart—we can write:

$$v_{2ix} - v_{1ix} = -(v_{2fx} - v_{1fx}) \tag{7-14}$$

assuming the objects move along the *x*-axis. For a one-dimensional elastic collision, Eq. (7-14) is a useful alternative to setting the final kinetic energy equal to the initial kinetic energy.

✓ CHECKPOINT 7.7

Is momentum conserved in a perfectly inelastic collision?

Collision at the Highway Entry Ramp

At a Route 3 highway on-ramp, a car of mass 1.50×10^3 kg is stopped at a stop sign, waiting for a break in traffic before merging with the cars on the highway. A pickup of mass 2.00×10^3 kg comes up from behind and hits the stopped car.

Assuming the collision is elastic, how fast was the pickup going just before the collision if the car is pushed straight ahead onto the highway at 20.0 m/s just after the collision?

continued on next page

Example 7.10 continued

Strategy Conservation of momentum provides one equation relating the initial and final velocities. That the collision is elastic provides another equation. With two unknown velocities, these two equations enable us to solve for both. Let "1" refer to the car stopped at the stop sign and "2" refer to the pickup. All motions are in one direction, which we call the x-axis. To simplify the notation, we drop the x subscripts and let all p's and v's refer to x-components. Figure 7.19 shows a before and after diagram for the collision.

Given: $m_1 = 1.50 \times 10^3$ kg; $m_2 = 2.00 \times 10^3$ kg; before the collision, $v_{1i} = 0$; after the collision, $v_{1f} = 20.0$ m/s
To find: v_{2i} (speed of the pickup just before the collision)

Solution From conservation of momentum,

$$m_1 \cancel{v}_{1i} + m_2 v_{2i} = m_1 v_{1f} + m_2 v_{2f} \qquad (1)$$

where we cross out the first term because $v_{1i} = 0$. The collision is elastic, so the relative velocity after the collision is equal and opposite to the relative velocity before the collision [Eq. (7-14)]:

$$v_{2i} - \cancel{v}_{1i} = -(v_{2f} - v_{1f}) \qquad (2)$$

We want to solve these two equations for v_{2i}, so we can eliminate v_{2f}. Multiplying Eq. (2) through by m_2 and rearranging yields

$$m_2 v_{2i} = m_2 v_{1f} - m_2 v_{2f} \qquad (3)$$

Adding Eqs. (1) and (3) gives

$$2m_2 v_{2i} = (m_1 + m_2) v_{1f} \qquad (4)$$

Finally, we solve Eq. (4) for v_{2i}:

$$v_{2i} = \frac{m_1 + m_2}{2m_2} v_{1f} = \frac{1500 \text{ kg} + 2000 \text{ kg}}{4000 \text{ kg}} \times 20.0 \text{ m/s} = 17.5 \text{ m/s}$$

Discussion To check this answer, first solve for v_{2f}. Then you can verify that momentum is conserved [Eq. (1)] and that the relative velocity changes sign [Eq. (2)]. You can also calculate the total kinetic energy before and after the collision and show they are equal, as they must be for an elastic collision. We leave these checks to you for practice.

The road exerts frictional forces on the vehicles, so the net external force on the vehicles was *not* zero during the collision. We still use conservation of momentum because during the short time interval of the collision, friction doesn't have time to change the system's momentum significantly.

Practice Problem 7.10   Perfectly Inelastic Collision Between the Cars

Instead of colliding elastically, suppose the two vehicles lock bumpers when they collide. With the same initial conditions ($v_{1i} = 0$ and $v_{2i} = 17.5$ m/s), find the speed at which the car would be pushed out onto the highway.

Before

After

Figure 7.19

Before and after diagrams of the collision (side view).

How are skid marks used to find car velocities just before the collision?

Suppose in Example 7.10 that the entry ramp speed limit is 20 mi/h (8.94 m/s). By measuring the length of the skid marks from the stop sign and estimating the coefficient of friction, the accident investigator can determine that the car was pushed onto the highway at a speed of 20.0 m/s. Witnesses confirm that the car was stopped before the collision. Then the investigator calculates the speed of the pickup just before the collision using conservation of momentum. The duration Δt of the collision is so short that we can ignore momentum changes due to external forces and treat the two vehicles as an isolated system. Finding that the pickup exceeded the speed limit, the investigator adds speeding to the charges against the driver of the pickup.

7.8 COLLISIONS IN TWO DIMENSIONS

Most collisions are not limited to motion in one dimension in the absence of a track or other device to constrain motion to a single line. In a two-dimensional collision, we use the same techniques we used for one-dimensional collisions, as long as we remember that momentum is a vector. (interactive: the virtual pool table.) To apply conservation of momentum, it is usually easiest to work with x- and y-components.

> **CONNECTION:**
>
> See the Problem-Solving Strategy in Section 7.7. The same strategy applies to collisions in two or three dimensions.

Example 7.11

Colliding Pucks on an Air Table

A small puck (mass $m_1 = 0.10$ kg) is sliding to the right with an initial speed of 8.0 m/s on an air table (Fig. 7.20a). An air table has many tiny holes through which air is blown; the resulting air cushion allows objects to slide with very little friction. The puck collides with a larger puck (mass $m_2 = 0.40$ kg), which is initially at rest. Figure 7.20b shows the outcome of the collision: the pucks move off at angles $\phi_1 = 60.0°$ above and $\phi_2 = 30.0°$ below the initial direction of motion of the small puck. (a) What are the final speeds of the pucks? (b) Is this an elastic collision or an inelastic collision? (c) If inelastic, what fraction of the initial kinetic energy is converted to other forms of energy in the collision?

Strategy The system of two pucks is an isolated system because the net external force is zero. Therefore, we can apply conservation of momentum. Since motions in two dimensions are involved, we treat the horizontal and vertical components of momentum separately.

Figure 7.20 shows the pucks before and after the collision. Now we collect information on the known quantities, writing velocities in component form.

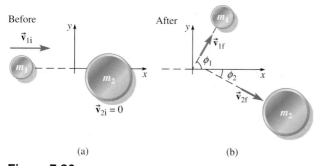

| Before | After |

$\vec{v}_{1i}$

m_1

m_2

$\vec{v}_{2i} = 0$

(a)

m_1

$\vec{v}_{1f}$

ϕ_1

ϕ_2

$\vec{v}_{2f}$

m_2

(b)

Figure 7.20

Snapshots in time, (a) before and (b) after a collision.

Masses: $m_1 = 0.10$ kg; $m_2 = 0.40$ kg

Before collision: $v_{1ix} = 8.0$ m/s; $v_{1iy} = v_{2ix} = v_{2iy} = 0$

After collision: $v_{1fx} = v_{1f} \cos \phi_1$; $v_{1fy} = v_{1f} \sin \phi_1$;
$v_{2fx} = v_{2f} \cos \phi_2$; $v_{2fy} = -v_{2f} \sin \phi_2$
($\phi_1 = 60.0°$ and $\phi_2 = 30.0°$)

To find: v_{1f} and v_{2f}; total kinetic energy before and after the collision

Solution (a) Working with components means that we set the total x-component of momentum before the collision equal to the total x-component of momentum after the collision. We treat the y-components in the same way. The initial momentum is in the x-direction only. Thus, the total momentum y-component after the collision must be zero.

First we set the x-component of the total momentum after the collision equal to the x-component of the total momentum before the collision:

$$p_{1fx} + p_{2fx} = p_{1ix} + p_{2ix}$$

Each momentum component is now rewritten using $p_x = mv_x$:

$$m_1 v_{1f} \cos \phi_1 + m_2 v_{2f} \cos \phi_2 = m_1 v_{1ix} + 0$$

Since $m_2 = 4m_1$,

$$m_1 v_{1f} \cos 60.0° + 4m_1 v_{2f} \cos 30.0° = m_1 v_{1ix}$$

After canceling the common factor m_1 and substituting numerical values for cos 60.0° and cos 30.0°, this reduces to

$$0.500 v_{1f} + 3.46 v_{2f} = 8.0 \text{ m/s} \qquad (1)$$

For conservation of the y-component of the momentum:

$$p_{1fy} + p_{2fy} = p_{1iy} + p_{2iy} = 0$$

continued on next page

Example 7.11 continued

The y-component of $\vec{\mathbf{p}}_{2f}$ is negative because the y-component of $\vec{\mathbf{v}}_{2f}$ is negative.

$$m_1 v_{1f} \sin \phi_1 + (-4m_1 v_{2f} \sin \phi_2) = 0$$

$$v_{1f} \sin 60.0° - 4v_{2f} \sin 30.0° = 0$$

We solve for v_{2f} in terms of v_{1f}:

$$v_{2f} = \frac{\sin 60.0°}{4 \sin 30.0°} v_{1f} = 0.433 v_{1f} \qquad (2)$$

Equations (1) and (2) contain two unknowns. To eliminate one unknown, we substitute $0.433 v_{1f}$ for v_{2f} in Eq. (1):

$$0.500 v_{1f} + 3.46(0.433 v_{1f}) = 2.00 v_{1f} = 8.0 \text{ m/s}$$

Solving this equation gives the value of v_{1f}:

$$v_{1f} = 4.0 \text{ m/s}$$

Then by substitution into Eq. (2), we find the value of v_{2f}:

$$v_{2f} = 0.433 v_{1f} = 1.73 \text{ m/s} \rightarrow 1.7 \text{ m/s}$$

(b) Now that we have the final speeds, we can compare the initial and final kinetic energies.

$$K_i = \tfrac{1}{2} m_1 v_{1i}^2$$

$$K_i = \tfrac{1}{2}(0.10 \text{ kg}) \times (8.0 \text{ m/s})^2 = 3.2 \text{ J}$$

and

$$K_f = \tfrac{1}{2} m_1 v_{1f}^2 + \tfrac{1}{2} m_2 v_{2f}^2$$
$$= \tfrac{1}{2}(0.10 \text{ kg}) \times (4.0 \text{ m/s})^2 + \tfrac{1}{2}(0.40 \text{ kg}) \times (1.73 \text{ m/s})^2$$
$$= 0.80 \text{ J} + 0.60 \text{ J} = 1.40 \text{ J}$$

The final kinetic energy is less than the initial kinetic energy, so the collision is inelastic.

(c) The amount of kinetic energy converted to other forms of energy (primarily internal energy of the pucks) is

$$3.2 \text{ J} - 1.40 \text{ J} = 1.8 \text{ J}$$

We divide by the initial kinetic energy to find the fraction of the initial kinetic energy converted to other forms:

$$\frac{1.8 \text{ J}}{3.2 \text{ J}} = 0.56$$

Less than half of the kinetic energy of the incident puck therefore survives the collision as the kinetic energies of the two pucks.

Discussion   Although a two-dimensional collision problem tends to require more complicated algebra than a one-dimensional problem, the physical principles are the same. As long as the net external force on the system is zero (or negligibly small), the total vector momentum must be conserved.

Practice Problem 7.11   Colliding Balls

A ball of mass m_1 moves at speed v_i along the $+x$-axis toward a second ball of mass m_2, which is initially at rest. The second ball has five times the mass of the first ball. After the collision between these two objects, m_1 moves along the $+y$-axis at a speed v_1, and m_2 moves at a speed $v_2 = \tfrac{1}{4} v_i$ at an angle of 36.9° below the $+x$-axis. Find v_1 in terms of v_i.

Conceptual Example 7.12

Eric at the Pool Table

Playing a game of pool, Eric is trying to decide whether to attempt a shot to sink the 4-ball in the pocket at corner B without *scratching* (sinking the cue ball "C" in corner A). He notices that the lines from the 4-ball to the two corner pockets happen to make a right angle (Fig. 7.21). The collision of the balls is nearly elastic. Assume Eric is an amateur player and does not know how to do fancy things, like putting sidespin on a ball. Should he attempt the shot?

Strategy   We assume a perfectly elastic collision between the balls. They have the same mass. The cue ball moves with an initial velocity $\vec{\mathbf{v}}_i$ and strikes the 4-ball, which is initially at rest. The 4-ball falls in pocket B if its velocity after the collision, $\vec{\mathbf{v}}_4$, points toward the pocket. Assuming it does, we use

conservation of momentum and kinetic energy to find the direction of the cue ball velocity, $\vec{\mathbf{v}}_c$, after the collision.

Solution   Conservation of momentum requires that

$$m\vec{\mathbf{v}}_i = m\vec{\mathbf{v}}_c + m\vec{\mathbf{v}}_4$$

or

$$\vec{\mathbf{v}}_i = \vec{\mathbf{v}}_c + \vec{\mathbf{v}}_4$$

This vector addition is shown graphically in Fig. 7.22a. Since the collision is elastic, the total kinetic energy doesn't change:

$$\tfrac{1}{2} m v_i^2 = \tfrac{1}{2} m v_c^2 + \tfrac{1}{2} m v_4^2$$

continued on next page

Conceptual Example 7.12 continued

Figure 7.21 Should Eric try to sink the 4-ball?

or

$$v_i^2 = v_c^2 + v_4^2$$

Since v_i, v_c, and v_4 are the sides of a triangle, this is a statement of the Pythagorean theorem—the triangle must be a *right* triangle with v_i as the hypotenuse (Fig. 7.22b). Therefore, the velocities of the 4-ball and the cue ball after the collision are perpendicular to each other.

Figure 7.22

(a) Graphical addition of velocity vectors as required by the conservation of momentum. (b) Since $v_i^2 = v_c^2 + v_4^2$, the three velocities form a right triangle.

If Eric sinks the 4-ball, the cue ball falls into pocket A. He shouldn't attempt this shot until he learns how to put some spin on the ball.

Discussion   Note that we did not resolve the velocities into *x*- and *y*-components. Doing so would have made the solution longer in this case.

We found that the two balls move at right angles after the collision. This result is true for any two-dimensional elastic collision between two objects of equal masses if one of them is initially at rest. In Example 7.11 the two pucks move at right angles after the collision, but the collision is inelastic—the masses are unequal.

Practice Problem 7.12   Finding the Speed Ratio

Suppose that the cue ball initially moves in the −*x*-direction. After the collision, the cue ball moves at 52.0° above the −*x*-axis and the 4-ball moves at 38.0° below the −*x*-axis. Find the ratio of the balls' speeds v_c/v_4 after the collision.

Master the Concepts

- Definition of linear momentum:

$$\vec{\mathbf{p}} = m\vec{\mathbf{v}} \tag{7-1}$$

- During an interaction, momentum is transferred from one body to another, but the total momentum of the two is unchanged.

$$\Delta\vec{\mathbf{p}}_2 = -\Delta\vec{\mathbf{p}}_1$$

- Impulse is the average force times the time interval.
- The total impulse equals the change in momentum:

$$\Delta\vec{\mathbf{p}} = \sum\vec{\mathbf{F}}\,\Delta t \tag{7-2}$$

continued on next page

- A conserved quantity is one that remains unchanged as time passes.
- Impulse is the area under a graph of force versus time.

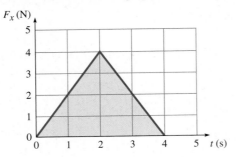

- The net force is the rate of change of momentum.

$$\sum \vec{F} = \lim_{\Delta t \to 0} \frac{\Delta \vec{p}}{\Delta t} \qquad (7\text{-}4)$$

- External interactions may change the total momentum of a system.
- Internal interactions do not change the total momentum of a system.
- Conservation of linear momentum: if the net external force acting on a system is zero, then the momentum of the system is conserved.
- The position of the CM of a system of N particles is

$$x_{CM} = \frac{m_1 x_1 + m_2 x_2 + \cdots + m_N x_N}{M}$$

and

$$y_{CM} = \frac{m_1 y_1 + m_2 y_2 + \cdots + m_N y_N}{M} \qquad (7\text{-}9)$$

where M is the total mass of the particles:

$$M = m_1 + m_2 + \cdots + m_N$$

- The total momentum of a system is equal to the total mass times the velocity of the center of mass:

$$\vec{p} = \vec{p}_1 + \vec{p}_2 + \cdots + \vec{p}_N = M\vec{v}_{CM} \qquad (7\text{-}11)$$

- No matter how complicated a system is, the CM moves as if all the mass of the system were concentrated to a point particle with all the external forces acting on it:

$$\sum \vec{F}_{ext} = M\vec{a}_{CM} \qquad (7\text{-}13)$$

- The CM of an isolated system moves at constant velocity.
- Conservation of momentum is used to solve problems involving collisions, explosions, and the like. Even when external forces are acting, the momentum of the system just before a collision is nearly equal to the momentum just after if the collision interaction is brief. The impulse, and, therefore, the change in momentum of the system, is small since the time interval is small.

Conceptual Questions

1. You are trapped on the second floor of a burning building. The stairway is impassable, but there is a balcony outside your window. Describe what might happen in the following situations. (a) You jump from the second-story balcony to the pavement below, landing stiff-legged on your feet. (b) You jump into a privet hedge, landing on your back and rolling to your feet. (c) You jump into a firefighters' net, landing on your back. What happens to the net as you land in it? What do the firefighters do to cushion your fall even more?

2. A force of 30 N is applied for 5 s to each of two bodies of different masses. (a) Which one has the greatest momentum change? (b) The greatest velocity change? (c) The greatest acceleration?

3. If you take a rifle and saw off part of the barrel, the muzzle speed (the speed at which bullets emerge from the barrel) will be smaller. Why?

4. A firecracker at rest explodes, sending fragments off in all directions. Initially the firecracker has zero momentum, but after the explosion the fragments flying off each have quite a lot of momentum. Hasn't momentum been created? If not, explain why not.

5. An astronaut in deep space is taking a space walk when the tether connecting him to his spaceship breaks. How can he get back to the ship? He doesn't have a rocket propulsion backpack, unfortunately, but he is carrying a big wrench.

6. An astronaut hits a golf ball on the surface of the Moon. Is the momentum of the ball conserved while it is in flight? Is there a *component* of its momentum that is conserved?

7. Which would be more effective: a hammer that collides *elastically* with a nail, or one that collides perfectly *inelastically*? Assume that the mass of the hammer is much larger than that of the nail.

8. Squid are the fastest swimmers among invertebrates. A cavity within the squid is filled with water. The *mantle*, a powerful muscle, squeezes the cavity and expels the water through a narrow opening (the *siphon*) at high speed. Using momentum conservation, explain how this propels the squid forward. How is the squid's swimming mechanism like a rocket engine?

9. In your own words, phrase each of Newton's three laws of motion as a statement about momentum.

10. Two objects with different masses have the same kinetic energy. Which has the larger magnitude of momentum?

11. A woman is 1.60 m tall. When standing straight, is her CM necessarily 0.80 m above the floor? Explain.

12. The momentum of a system can only be changed by an external force. What is the external force that changes the momentum of a bicycle (with its rider) as it speeds up, slows down, or changes direction? Is it true that changes in the bicycle's kinetic energy must come from an external force? Explain.

13. In an egg toss, two people try to toss a raw egg back and forth without breaking it as they move farther and farther apart. Discuss a strategy in terms of impulse and momentum for catching the egg without breaking it.

14. In the "executive toy," two balls are pulled back and then released. After the collision, two balls move away on the opposite side. Why do we never see three balls move away following this action, although with a lower velocity so that linear momentum is still conserved?

15. A baseball batting coach emphasizes the importance of "follow-through" when a batter is trying for a home run. The coach explains that the follow-through keeps the bat in contact with the ball for a longer time so the ball will travel a greater distance. Explain the reasoning behind this statement in terms of the impulse-momentum theorem.

16. Micah is standing on his frictionless skateboard facing a concrete wall. He wants to project himself backward by throwing small balls at the wall. His friend Jeremy says that Micah need not throw the balls against the wall, he just needs to throw the balls away from himself, but Micah says the balls need something to push against if they are to propel him backward. Who is right and why?

17. Mary and Daryl are new to the sport of rock climbing. Mary says she wants a stiff rope because a stiff rope is a strong rope. Daryl insists that a good climbing rope must have some stretch. Who is correct, and why?

Multiple-Choice Questions

1. A ball of mass m with initial speed v collides with another ball of mass M, initially at rest. After the collision the two balls stick together, moving with speed V. The ratio of the final speed V to the initial speed v is $V/v =$

   (a) $\dfrac{M}{M+m}$ (b) $\dfrac{M+m}{M}$

   (c) $\dfrac{m}{M+m}$ (d) $\dfrac{M+m}{m}$

   (e) $\sqrt{\dfrac{M}{M+m}}$ (f) $\sqrt{\dfrac{m}{M+m}}$

2. Two particles A and B of equal mass are located at some distance from each other. Particle A is at rest while B moves away from A at speed v. What happens to the center of mass of the system of two particles?

   (a) It does not move.
   (b) It moves with a speed v away from A.
   (c) It moves with a speed v toward A.
   (d) It moves with a speed $\frac{1}{2}v$ away from A.
   (e) It moves with a speed $\frac{1}{2}v$ toward A.

3. Two uniform spheres with equal mass per unit volume are in contact with one another. The mass of sphere A is five times that of sphere B. The center of mass of the system is

   (a) at the point where A and B touch.
   (b) inside sphere B somewhere on the line joining the centers of A and B.
   (c) inside sphere A somewhere on the line joining the centers.
   (d) at the center of sphere A.
   (e) outside of both spheres.

4. An object at rest suddenly explodes into three parts of equal mass. Two of the parts move away at right angles to each other and with equal speeds v. What is the velocity of the third part just after the explosion?

   (a) Direction of vector 1 and magnitude $2v$

   (b) Direction of vector 2 and magnitude $\sqrt{2}v$

   (c) Direction of vector 3 and magnitude $\dfrac{1}{\sqrt{2}}v$

   (d) Direction of vector 2 and magnitude $\dfrac{1}{\sqrt{2}}v$

   (e) Direction of vector 1 and magnitude $\frac{1}{2}v$

5. A 3.0-kg object is initially at rest. It then receives an impulse of magnitude 15 N·s. After the impulse, the object has
   (a) a speed of 45 m/s.
   (b) a momentum of magnitude 5.0 kg·m/s.
   (c) a speed of 7.5 m/s.
   (d) a momentum of magnitude 15 kg·m/s.

6. An object of mass m drops from rest a little above the Earth's surface for a time t. Ignore air resistance. After time t the magnitude of its momentum is
   (a) mgt^2
   (b) mgt
   (c) $mg\sqrt{t}$
   (d) $\sqrt{mgt}$
   (e) $\dfrac{mgt^2}{2}$

Multiple-Choice Questions 7–12 refer to a situation in which a golf ball is projected straight upward in the $+y$-direction. Ignore air resistance. The answer choices are found in the figure.

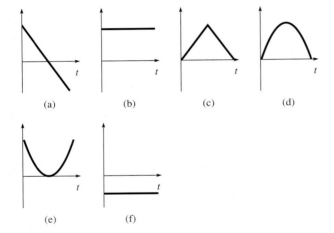

   (a)   (b)   (c)   (d)

   (e)   (f)

7. Which graph shows the acceleration a_y of the ball as a function of time?

8. Which graph shows the vertical position y of the ball as a function of time?

9. Which graph shows the momentum p_y of the ball as a function of time?

10. Which graph shows the kinetic energy of the ball as a function of time?

11. Which graph shows the potential energy of the ball as a function of time?

12. Which graph shows the total energy of the ball as a function of time?

Problems

  ◉ Combination conceptual/quantitative problem
  ▼ Biological or medical application
  ✦ Challenging problem

7.2 Momentum; 7.3 The Impulse-Momentum Theorem

1. Two cars, each of mass 1300 kg, are approaching each other on a head-on collision course. Each speedometer reads 19 m/s. What is the magnitude of the total momentum of the system?

2. What is the momentum of an automobile (weight = 9800 N) when it is moving at 35 m/s to the south?

3. Verify that the SI unit of impulse is the same as the SI unit of momentum.

4. A cue stick hits a cue ball with an average force of 24 N for a duration of 0.028 s. If the mass of the ball is 0.16 kg, how fast is it moving after being struck?

5. A system consists of three particles with these masses and velocities: mass 3.0 kg, moving north at 3.0 m/s; mass 4.0 kg, moving south at 5.0 m/s; and mass 7.0 kg, moving north at 2.0 m/s. What is the total momentum of the system?

6. A sports car traveling along a straight line increases its speed from 20.0 mi/h to 60.0 mi/h. (a) What is the ratio of the final to the initial magnitude of its momentum? (b) What is the ratio of the final to the initial kinetic energy?

7. A ball of mass 5.0 kg moving with a speed of 2.0 m/s in the $+x$-direction hits a wall and bounces back with the same speed in the $-x$-direction. What is the change of momentum of the ball?

8. An object of mass 3.0 kg is projected into the air at a 55° angle. It hits the ground 3.4 s later. What is its change in momentum while it is in the air? Ignore air resistance.

9. An object of mass 3.0 kg is allowed to fall from rest under the force of gravity for 3.4 s. What is the change in its momentum? Ignore air resistance.

10. What average force is necessary to bring a 50.0-kg sled from rest to a speed of 3.0 m/s in a period of 20.0 s? Assume frictionless ice.

11. For a safe re-entry into the Earth's atmosphere, the pilots of a space capsule must reduce their speed from 2.6×10^4 m/s to 1.1×10^4 m/s. The rocket engine produces a backward force on the capsule of 1.8×10^5 N. The mass of the capsule is 3800 kg. For how long must they fire their engine? [*Hint:* Ignore the change in mass of the capsule due to the expulsion of exhaust gases.]

12. A 0.15-kg baseball traveling in a horizontal direction with a speed of 20 m/s hits a bat and is popped straight up with a speed of 15 m/s. (a) What is the change in momentum (magnitude and direction) of the baseball? (b) If the bat was in contact with the ball for 50 ms, what was the average force of the bat on the ball?

13. An automobile traveling at a speed of 30.0 m/s applies its brakes and comes to a stop in 5.0 s. If the automobile has a mass of 1.0×10^3 kg, what is the average horizontal force exerted on it during braking? Assume the road is level.

14. A 3.0-kg body is initially moving northward at 15 m/s. Then a force of 15 N, toward the east, acts on it for 4.0 s. (a) At the end of the 4.0 s, what is the body's final velocity? (b) What is the change in momentum during the 4.0 s?

✦15. A boy of mass 60.0 kg is rescued from a hotel fire by leaping into a firefighters' net. The window from which he leapt was 8.0 m above the net. The firefighters lower their arms as he lands in the net so that he is brought to a complete stop in a time of 0.40 s. (a) What is his change in momentum during the 0.40-s interval? (b) What is the impulse on the net due to the boy during the interval? [*Hint:* Do not ignore gravity.] (c) What is the average force on the net due to the boy during the interval?

16. A 115-g ball is traveling to the left with a speed of 30 m/s when it is struck by a racket. The force on the ball, directed to the right and applied over 21 ms of contact time, is shown in the graph. What is the speed of the ball immediately after it leaves the racket? (🅦 tutorial: impulse)

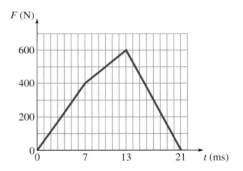

17. A pole-vaulter of mass 60.0 kg vaults to a height of 6.0 m before dropping to thick padding placed below to cushion her fall. (a) Find the speed with which she lands. (b) If the padding brings her to a stop in a time of 0.50 s, what is the average force on her body due to the padding during that time interval?

7.4 Conservation of Momentum

18. A rifle has a mass of 4.5 kg and it fires a bullet of mass 10.0 g at a muzzle speed of 820 m/s. What is the recoil speed of the rifle as the bullet leaves the gun barrel?

19. A 0.030-kg bullet is fired vertically at 200 m/s into a 0.15-kg baseball that is initially at rest. The bullet lodges in the baseball and, after the collision, the baseball/bullet rise to a height of 37 m. (a) What was the speed of the baseball/bullet right after the collision? (b) What

was the average force of air resistance while the baseball/bullet was rising?

20. A submarine of mass 2.5×10^6 kg and initially at rest fires a torpedo of mass 250 kg. The torpedo has an initial speed of 100.0 m/s. What is the initial recoil speed of the submarine? Neglect the drag force of the water.

21. A uranium nucleus (mass 238 u), initially at rest, undergoes radioactive decay. After an alpha particle (mass 4.0 u) is emitted, the remaining nucleus is thorium (mass 234 u). If the alpha particle is moving at 0.050 times the speed of light, what is the recoil speed of the thorium nucleus? (Note: "u" is a unit of mass; it is *not* necessary to convert it to kg.)

22. Dash is standing on his frictionless skateboard with three balls, each with a mass of 100 g, in his hands. The combined mass of Dash and his skateboard is 60 kg. How fast should dash throw the balls forward if he wants to move backward with a speed of 0.50 m/s? Do you think Dash can succeed? Explain.

23. A 58-kg astronaut is in space, far from any objects that would exert a significant gravitational force on him. He would like to move toward his spaceship, but his jet pack is not functioning. He throws a 720-g socket wrench with a velocity of 5.0 m/s in a direction away from the ship. After 0.50 s, he throws a 800-g spanner in the same direction with a speed of 8.0 m/s. After another 9.90 s, he throws a mallet with a speed of 6.0 m/s in the same direction. The mallet has a mass of 1200 g. How fast is the astronaut moving after he throws the mallet?

24. A man with a mass of 65 kg skis down a frictionless hill that is 5.0 m high. At the bottom of the hill the terrain levels out. As the man reaches the horizontal section, he grabs a 20-kg backpack and skis off a 2.0-m-high ledge. At what horizontal distance from the edge of the ledge does the man land?

✦25. A cannon on a railroad car is facing in a direction parallel to the tracks. It fires a 98-kg shell at a speed of 105 m/s (relative to the ground) at an angle of 60.0° above the horizontal. If the cannon plus car have a mass of 5.0×10^4 kg, what is the recoil speed of the car if it was at rest before the cannon was fired? [*Hint:* A component of a system's momentum along an axis is conserved if the net external force acting on the system has no component along that axis.]

105 m/s

60.0°

26. A marksman standing on a motionless railroad car fires a gun into the air at an angle of 30.0° from the horizontal. The bullet has a speed of 173 m/s (relative to the ground) and a mass of 0.010 kg. The man and car move to the left at a speed of 1.0×10^{-3} m/s after he shoots. What is the mass of the man and car? (See the hint in Problem 25.)

30.0°

7.5 Center of Mass; 7.6 Motion of the Center of Mass

27. Particle A is at the origin and has a mass of 30.0 g. Particle B has a mass of 10.0 g. Where must particle B be located if the coordinates of the CM are $(x, y) = (2.0$ cm, 5.0 cm)?

28. Particle A has a mass of 5.0 g and particle B has a mass of 1.0 g. Particle A is located at the origin and particle B is at the point $(x, y) = (25$ cm, 0). What is the location of the CM? (**ww** tutorial: center of mass)

29. The three bodies in the figure each have the same mass. If one of the bodies is moved 12 cm in the positive x-direction, by how much does the CM move?

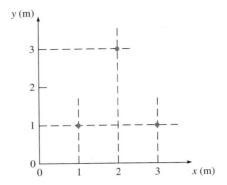

30. The positions of three particles, written as (x, y) coordinates, are: particle 1 (mass 4.0 kg) at (4.0 m, 0 m); particle 2 (mass 6.0 kg) at (2.0 m, 4.0 m); particle 3 (mass 3.0 kg) at (−1.0 m, −2.0 m). What is the location of the CM?

31. Belinda needs to find the CM of a sculpture she has made so that it will hang in a gallery correctly. The sculpture is all in one plane and consists of various shaped uniform objects with masses and sizes as shown. Where is the CM of this sculpture? Assume the thin rods connecting the larger pieces have no mass and place the reference frame origin at the top left corner of the sculpture.

32. Jane is sitting on a chair with her lower leg at a 30.0° angle with respect to the vertical, as shown. You need to develop a computer model of her leg to assist in some medical research. If you assume that her leg can be modeled as two uniform cylinders, one with mass $M = 20$ kg and length $L = 35$ cm and one with mass $m = 10$ kg and length $l = 40$ cm, where is the CM of her leg?

33. Find the *x*-coordinate of the CM of the composite object shown in the figure. The sphere, cylinder, and rectangular solid all have a uniform composition. Their masses and dimensions are: sphere: 200 g, diameter = 10 cm; cylinder: 450 g, length = 17 cm, radius = 5.0 cm; rectangular solid: 325 g, length in *x*-direction = 16 cm, height = 10 cm, depth = 12 cm.

34. Consider two falling bodies. Their masses are 3.0 kg and 4.0 kg. At time *t* = 0, the two are released from rest. What is the velocity of their CM at *t* = 10.0 s? Ignore air resistance.

35. Body A of mass 3 kg is moving in the +*x*-direction with a speed of 14 m/s. Body B of mass 4 kg is moving in the −*y*-direction with a speed of 7 m/s. What are the *x*- and *y*-components of the velocity of the CM of the two bodies?

36. If a particle of mass 5.0 kg is moving east at 10 m/s and a particle of mass 15 kg is moving west at 10 m/s, what is the velocity of the CM of the pair?

37. An object located at the origin and having mass *M* explodes into three pieces having masses *M*/4, *M*/3, and 5*M*/12. The pieces scatter on a horizontal frictionless *xy*-plane. The piece with mass *M*/4 flies away with velocity 5.0 m/s at 37° above the *x*-axis. The piece with mass *M*/3 has velocity 4.0 m/s directed at an angle of 45° above the −*x*-axis. (a) What are the velocity components of the third piece? (b) Describe the motion of the CM of the system after the explosion.

38. Prove Eq. (7-13) $\sum \vec{F}_{ext} = M\vec{a}_{CM}$. [*Hint:* Start with $\sum \vec{F}_{ext} = \lim_{\Delta t \to 0} (\Delta \vec{p}/\Delta t)$, where $\sum \vec{F}_{ext}$ is the net external force acting on a system and $\vec{p}$ is the total momentum of the system.]

7.7 Collisions in One Dimension

39. A helium atom (mass 4.00 u) moving at 618 m/s to the right collides with an oxygen molecule (mass 32.0 u) moving in the same direction at 412 m/s. After the collision, the oxygen molecule moves at 456 m/s to the right. What is the velocity of the helium atom after the collision?

40. A toy car with a mass of 120 g moves to the right with a speed of 0.75 m/s. A small child drops a 30.0-g piece of clay onto the car. The clay sticks to the car and the car continues to the right. What is the change in speed of the car? Consider the frictional force between the car and the ground to be negligible.

41. In the railroad freight yard, an empty freight car of mass *m* rolls along a straight level track at 1.0 m/s and collides with an initially stationary, fully loaded boxcar of mass 4.0*m*. The two cars couple together on collision. (a) What is the speed of the two cars after the collision? (b) Suppose instead that the two cars are at rest after the collision. With what speed was the loaded boxcar moving before the collision if the empty one was moving at 1.0 m/s? (tutorial: sticking collision)

42. A 0.020-kg bullet traveling at 200.0 m/s east hits a motionless 2.0-kg block and bounces off it, retracing its original path with a velocity of 100.0 m/s west. What is the final velocity of the block? Assume the block rests on a perfectly frictionless horizontal surface.

43. A block of wood of mass 0.95 kg is initially at rest. A bullet of mass 0.050 kg traveling at 100.0 m/s strikes the block and becomes embedded in it. With what speed do the block of wood and the bullet move just after the collision?

44. A 0.020-kg bullet is shot horizontally and collides with a 2.00-kg block of wood. The bullet embeds in the block and the block slides along a horizontal surface for 1.50 m. If the coefficient of kinetic friction between the block and surface is 0.400, what was the original speed of the bullet?

45. A 2.0-kg block is moving to the right at 1.0 m/s just before it strikes and sticks to a 1.0-kg block initially at rest. What is the total momentum of the two blocks after the collision?

46. A 75-kg man is at rest on ice skates. A 0.20-kg ball is thrown to him. The ball is moving horizontally at 25 m/s just before the man catches it. How fast is the man moving just after he catches the ball?

47. A BMW of mass 2.0×10^3 kg is traveling at 42 m/s. It approaches a 1.0×10^3 kg Volkswagen going 25 m/s in the same direction and strikes it in the rear. Neither driver applies the brakes. Neglect the relatively small frictional forces on the cars due to the road and due to air resistance. (a) If the collision slows the BMW down to 33 m/s, what is the speed of the VW after the collision? (b) During the collision, which car exerts a larger force on the other, or are the forces equal in magnitude? Explain.

48. A 100-g ball collides elastically with a 300-g ball that is at rest. If the 100-g ball was traveling in the positive *x*-direction at 5.00 m/s before the collision, what are the velocities of the two balls after the collision? (tutorial: elastic collision)

49. A projectile of 1.0-kg mass approaches a stationary body of 5.0 kg at 10.0 m/s and, after colliding, rebounds in the reverse direction along the same line with a speed of 5.0 m/s. What is the speed of the 5.0-kg body after the collision?

50. A 2.0-kg object is at rest on a perfectly frictionless surface when it is hit by a 3.0-kg object moving at 8.0 m/s. If the two objects are stuck together after the collision, what is the speed of the combination?

51. A spring of negligible mass is compressed between two blocks, A and B, which are at rest on a frictionless horizontal surface at a distance of 1.0 m from a wall on the left and 3.0 m from a wall on the right. The sizes of the blocks and spring are small. When the spring is released, block A moves toward the left wall and strikes it at the same instant that block B strikes the right wall. The mass of A is 0.60 kg. What is the mass of B?

52. Two identical gliders on an air track are held together by a piece of string, compressing a spring between the gliders. While they are moving to the right at a common speed of 0.50 m/s, someone holds a match under the string and burns it, letting the spring force the gliders apart. One glider is then observed to be moving to the right at 1.30 m/s. (a) What velocity does the other glider have? (b) Is the total kinetic energy of the two gliders after the collision greater than, less than, or equal to the total kinetic energy before the collision? If greater, where did the extra energy come from? If less, where did the "lost" energy go?

53. A 0.010-kg bullet traveling horizontally at 400.0 m/s strikes a 4.0-kg block of wood sitting at the edge of a table. The bullet is lodged into the wood. If the table height is 1.2 m, how far from the table does the block hit the floor?

54. Two objects with masses m_1 and m_2 approach each other with equal and opposite momenta so that the total momentum is zero. Show that, if the collision is elastic, the final *speed* of each object must be the same as its initial speed. (The final *velocity* of each object is *not* the same as its initial velocity, however.)

55. A 6.0-kg object is at rest on a perfectly frictionless surface when it is struck head-on by a 2.0-kg object moving at 10 m/s. If the collision is perfectly elastic, what is the speed of the 6.0-kg object after the collision? [*Hint:* You will need two equations.]

56. Use the result of Problem 54 to show that in *any* elastic collision between two objects, the relative speed of the two is the same before and after the collision. [*Hints:* Look at the collision in its CM *frame*—the reference frame in which the CM is at rest. The *relative* speed of two objects is the same in any inertial reference frame.]

7.8 Collisions in Two Dimensions

57. A firecracker is tossed straight up into the air. It explodes into three pieces of equal mass just as it reaches the highest point. Two pieces move off at 120 m/s at right angles to each other. How fast is the third piece moving?

58. Body A of mass M has an original velocity of 6.0 m/s in the +x-direction toward a stationary body (body B) of the same mass. After the collision, body A has velocity components of 1.0 m/s in the +x-direction and 2.0 m/s in the +y-direction. What is the magnitude of body B's velocity after the collision?

59. (a) With reference to Practice Problem 7.11, find the momentum change of the ball of mass m_1 during the collision. Give your answer in x- and y-component form; express the components in terms of m_1 and v_i. (b) Repeat for the ball of mass m_2. How are the momentum changes related?

60. A hockey puck moving at 0.45 m/s collides elastically with another puck that was at rest. The pucks have equal mass. The first puck is deflected 37° to the right and moves off at 0.36 m/s. Find the speed and direction of the second puck after the collision.

61. Puck 1 sliding along the x-axis strikes stationary puck 2 of the same mass. After the elastic collision, puck 1 moves off at speed v_{1f} in the direction 60.0° above the x-axis; puck 2 moves off at speed v_{2f} in the direction 30.0° below the x-axis. Find v_{2f} in terms of v_{1f}.

62. Block A, with a mass of 220 g, is traveling north on a frictionless surface with a speed of 5.0 m/s. Block B, with a mass of 300 g travels west on the same surface until it collides with A. After the collision, the blocks move off together with a velocity of 3.13 m/s at an angle of 42.5° to the north of west. What was B's speed just before the collision?

63. A projectile of mass 2.0 kg approaches a stationary target body at 5.0 m/s. The projectile is deflected through an angle of 60.0° and its speed after the collision is 3.0 m/s. What is the magnitude of the momentum of the target body after the collision?

64. A 1500-kg car moving east at 17 m/s collides with a 1800-kg car moving south at 15 m/s and the two cars stick together. (a) What is the velocity of the cars right after the collision? (b) How much kinetic energy was converted to another form during the collision?

65. A car with a mass of 1700 kg is traveling directly northeast (45° between north and east) at a speed of 14 m/s (31 mph), and collides with a smaller car with a mass of 1300 kg that is traveling directly south at a speed of 18 m/s (40 mph). The two cars stick together during the collision. With what speed and direction does the tangled mess of metal move right after the collision?

66. In a nuclear reactor, a neutron moving at speed v_i in the positive x-direction strikes a deuteron, which is at rest. The neutron is deflected by 90.0° and moves off with speed $v_i/\sqrt{3}$ in the positive y-direction. Find the x- and y-components of the deuteron's velocity after the collision. (The mass of the deuteron is twice the mass of the neutron.)

67. Two identical pucks are on an air table. Puck A has an initial velocity of 2.0 m/s in the +x-direction. Puck B is at rest. Puck A collides elastically with puck B and A moves off at 1.0 m/s at an angle of 60° above the x-axis. What is the speed and direction of puck B after the collision?

68. In a circus trapeze act, two acrobats actually fly through the air and grab on to one another, then together grab a

swinging bar. One acrobat, with a mass of 60 kg, is moving at 3.0 m/s at an angle of 10° above the horizontal and the other, with a mass of 80 kg, is approaching her with a speed of 2.0 m/s at an angle of 20° above the horizontal. What is the direction and speed of the acrobats right after they grab on to each other? Let the positive x-axis be in the horizontal direction and assume the first acrobat has positive velocity components in the positive x- and y-directions.

+69. Two African swallows fly toward one another, carrying coconuts. The first swallow is flying north horizontally with a speed of 20 m/s. The second swallow is flying at the same height as the first and in the opposite direction with a speed of 15 m/s. The mass of the first swallow is 0.270 kg and the mass of his coconut is 0.80 kg. The second swallow's mass is 0.220 kg and her coconut's mass is 0.70 kg. The swallows collide and lose their coconuts. Immediately after the collision, the 0.80-kg coconut travels 10° west of south with a speed of 13 m/s, and the 0.70-kg coconut moves 30° east of north with a speed of 14 m/s. The two birds are tangled up with one another and stop flapping their wings as they travel off together. What is the velocity of the birds immediately after the collision?

Comprehensive Problems

70. A sled of mass 5.0 kg is coasting along on a frictionless ice-covered lake at a constant speed of 1.0 m/s. A 1.0-kg book is dropped vertically onto the sled. At what speed does the sled move once the book is on it?

71. An automobile weighing 13.6 kN is moving at 17.0 m/s when it collides with a stopped car weighing 9.0 kN. If they lock bumpers and move off together, what is their speed just after the collision?

72. For a system of three particles moving along a line, an observer in a laboratory measures the following masses and velocities. What is the velocity of the CM of the system?

Mass (kg)	v_x (m/s)
3.0	+290
5.0	−120
2.0	+52

73. An intergalactic spaceship is traveling through space far from any planets or stars, where no human has gone before. The ship carries a crew of 30 people (of total mass 2.0×10^3 kg). If the speed of the spaceship is 1.0×10^5 m/s and its mass (excluding the crew) is 4.8×10^4 kg, what is the magnitude of the total momentum of the ship and the crew?

74. A baseball player pitches a fastball toward home plate at a speed of 41 m/s. The batter swings, connects with

the ball of mass 145 g, and hits it so that the ball leaves the bat with a speed of 37 m/s. Assume that the ball is moving horizontally just before and just after the collision with the bat. (a) What is the magnitude of the change in momentum of the ball? (b) What is the impulse delivered to the ball by the bat? (c) If the bat and ball are in contact for 3.0 ms, what is the magnitude of the average force exerted on the ball by the bat?

+75. A tennis ball of mass 0.060 kg is served. It strikes the ground with a velocity of 54 m/s (120 mi/h) at an angle of 22° below the horizontal. Just after the bounce it is moving at 53 m/s at an angle of 18° above the horizontal. If the interaction with the ground lasts 0.065 s, what average force did the ground exert on the ball?

76. A uniform rod of length 30.0 cm is bent into the shape of an inverted U. Each of the three sides is of length 10.0 cm. Find the location, in x- and y-coordinates, of the CM as measured from the origin.

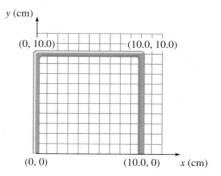

77. A child places 12 wooden blocks together, as shown in the figure. If each block has the same mass and density, where is the CM of these blocks? Each block is a cube with sides of 1.0 inch length. The origin of the coordinate system is at the center of the farthest block to the left.

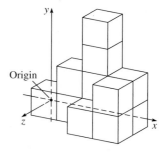

78. To contain some unruly demonstrators, the riot squad approaches with fire hoses. Suppose that the rate of flow of water through a fire hose is 24 kg/s and the stream of water from the hose moves at 17 m/s. What force is exerted by such a stream on a person in the crowd? Assume that the water comes to a dead stop against the demonstrator's chest.

79. An inexperienced catcher catches a 130 km/h fastball of mass 140 g within 1 ms, whereas an experienced catcher slightly retracts his hand during the catch, extending the

stopping time to 10 ms. What are the average forces imparted to the two gloved hands during the catches?

+80. A stationary 0.1-g fly encounters the windshield of a 1000-kg automobile traveling at 100 km/h. (a) What is the change in momentum of the car due to the fly? (b) What is the change of momentum of the fly due to the car? (c) Approximately how many flies does it take to reduce the car's speed by 1 km/h?

81. A 0.15-kg baseball is pitched with a speed of 35 m/s (78 mph). When the ball hits the catcher's glove, the glove moves back by 5.0 cm (2 in.) as it stops the ball. (a) What was the change in momentum of the baseball? (b) What impulse was applied to the baseball? (c) Assuming a constant acceleration of the ball, what was the average force applied by the catcher's glove?

+82. A projectile of mass 2.0 kg approaches a stationary target body at 8.0 m/s. The projectile is deflected through an angle of 90.0° and its speed after the collision is 6.0 m/s. What is the speed of the target body after the collision if the collision is perfectly elastic?

83. A radioactive nucleus is at rest when it spontaneously decays by emitting an electron and neutrino. The momentum of the electron is 8.20×10^{-19} kg·m/s and it is directed at right angles to that of the neutrino. The neutrino's momentum has magnitude 5.00×10^{-19} kg·m/s. (a) In what direction does the newly formed (daughter) nucleus recoil? (b) What is its momentum?

+84. A 60.0-kg woman stands at one end of a 120-kg raft that is 6.0 m long. The other end of the raft is 0.50 m from a pier. (a) The woman walks toward the pier until she gets to the other end of the raft and stops there. Now what is the distance between the raft and the pier? (b) In (a), how far did the woman walk (relative to the pier)?

85. A police officer is investigating the scene of an accident where two cars collided at an intersection. One car with a mass of 1100 kg moving west had collided with a 1300-kg car moving north. The two cars, stuck together, skid at an angle of 30° north of west for a distance of 17 m. The coefficient of kinetic friction between the tires and the road is 0.80. The speed limit for each car was 70 km/h. Was either car speeding?

+86. A jet plane is flying at 130 m/s relative to the ground. There is no wind. The engines take in 81 kg of air per second. Hot gas (burned fuel and air) is expelled from the engines at high speed. The engines provide a forward force on the plane of magnitude 6.0×10^4 N. At what

speed relative to the ground is the gas being expelled? [*Hint:* Look at the momentum change of the air taken in by the engines during a time interval Δt.] This calculation is approximate since we are ignoring the 3.0 kg of fuel consumed and expelled with the air each second.

87. Within cells, small organelles containing newly synthesized proteins are transported along microtubules by tiny molecular motors called kinesins. What force does a kinesin molecule need to deliver in order to accelerate an organelle with mass 0.01 pg (10^{-17} kg) from 0 to 1 μm/s within a time of 10 μs?

Problems 88 and 89

+88. The pendulum bobs in the figure are made of soft clay so that they stick together after impact. The mass of bob A is half that of bob B. Bob B is initially at rest. What is the ratio of the kinetic energy of the combined bobs, just after impact, to the kinetic energy of bob A just before impact?

+89. The pendulum bobs in the figure are made of soft clay so that they stick together after impact. The mass of bob A is half that of bob B. Bob B is initially at rest. If bob A is released from a height h above its lowest point, what is the maximum height attained by bobs A and B after the collision?

+90. A flat, circular metal disk of uniform thickness has a radius of 3.0 cm. A hole is drilled in the disk that is 1.5 cm in radius. The hole is tangent to one side of the disk. Where is the CM of the disk now that the hole has been drilled? [*Hint:* The original disk (before the hole is drilled) can be thought of as having two pieces—the disk with the hole plus the smaller disk of metal drilled out. Write an equation that expresses x_{CM} of the original disk in terms of the x_{CM}'s of the two pieces. Since the thickness is uniform, the mass of any piece is proportional to its area.]

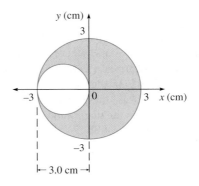

◆91. Two pendulum bobs have equal masses and lengths (5.1 m). Bob A is initially held horizontally while bob B hangs vertically at rest. Bob A is released and collides elastically with bob B. How fast is bob B moving immediately after the collision?

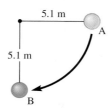

5.1 m

5.1 m

A

B

92. Two identical gliders, each with elastic bumpers and mass 0.10 kg, are on a horizontal air track. Friction is negligible. Glider 2 is stationary. Glider 1 moves toward glider 2 from the left with a speed of 0.20 m/s. They collide. After the collision, what are the velocities of glider 1 and glider 2?

◆93. A radium nucleus (mass 226 u) at rest decays into a radon nucleus (symbol Rn, mass 222 u) and an alpha particle (symbol α, mass 4 u). (a) Find the ratio of the speeds v_α/v_{Rn} after the decay. (b) Find the ratio of the magnitudes of the momenta p_α/p_{Rn}. (c) Find the ratio of the kinetic energies K_α/K_{Rn}. (Note: "u" is a unit of mass; it is *not* necessary to convert it to kg.)

Answers to Practice Problems

7.1 (a) 0.78 kg·m/s downward; (b) 0.78 kg·m/s toward the apple; 1.3×10^{-25} m/s

7.2 3.5 times his weight

7.3 1700 N; 0.0037 s

7.4 0.8 m/s in the $-x$-direction

7.5 1.7 m/s

7.6 2.2 m/s

7.7 (2.0 cm, 2.3 cm)

7.8 (a) 2.7 m; (b) 1.5 m in the other direction; (c) the CM does not move

7.9 4.0 m/s

7.10 10.0 m/s

7.11 0.751 v_i

7.12 0.781

Answers to Checkpoints

7.2 No, because the *direction* of the car's momentum would have changed.

7.4 When external forces act on a system, the momentum of the system is not conserved.

7.6 Despite the fact that the hammer is rotating, it is in free fall and its CM follows the same trajectory as a point particle in free fall.

7.7 Yes. Momentum is conserved in both elastic and inelastic collisions. In an inelastic collision, the initial and final *kinetic energies* are not equal.

Torque and Angular Momentum

In gymnastics, the iron cross is a notoriously difficult feat requiring incredible strength. Why does it require such great strength? (See p. 282 for the answer.)

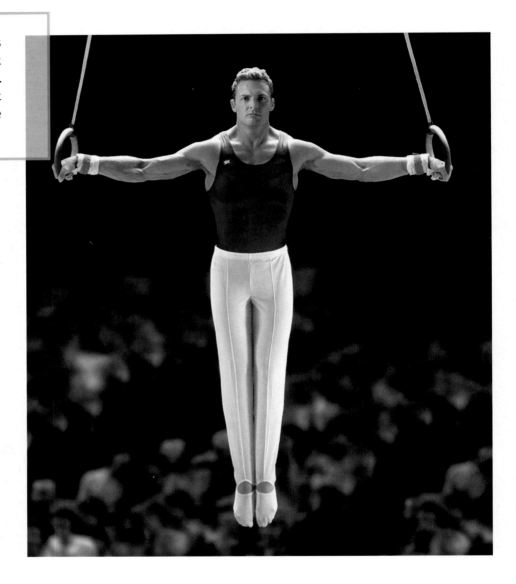

- translational equilibrium (Section 2.4)
- uniform circular motion and circular orbits (Sections 5.1 and 5.4)
- angular acceleration (Section 5.6)
- conservation of energy (Section 6.1)
- center of mass and its motion (Sections 7.5 and 7.6)
- rolling without slipping (Section 5.1)

Concepts & Skills to Review

8.1 ROTATIONAL KINETIC ENERGY AND ROTATIONAL INERTIA

When a rigid object is rotating about a fixed axis, it has kinetic energy because each particle other than those on the axis of rotation is moving in a circle around the axis. In principle, we can calculate the kinetic energy of rotation by summing the kinetic energy of each particle. To say the least, that sounds like a laborious task. We need a simpler way to express the rotational kinetic energy of such an object so that we don't have to calculate this sum over and over. Our simpler expression exploits the fact that the speed of each particle is proportional to the angular speed of rotation ω.

If a rigid object consists of N particles, the sum of the kinetic energies of the particles can be written mathematically using a subscript to label the mass and speed of each particle:

$$K_{\text{rot}} = \tfrac{1}{2}m_1 v_1^2 + \tfrac{1}{2}m_2 v_2^2 + \cdots + \tfrac{1}{2}m_N v_N^2 = \sum_{i=1}^{N} \tfrac{1}{2}m_i v_i^2$$

The speed of each particle is related to its distance from the axis of rotation. Particles that are farther from the axis move faster. In Section 5.1, we found that the speed of a particle moving in a circle is

$$v = r\omega \qquad (5\text{-}7)$$

where ω is the angular speed and r is the distance between the rotation axis and the particle (Fig. 8.1). By substitution, the rotational kinetic energy can be written

$$K_{\text{rot}} = \sum_{i=1}^{N} \tfrac{1}{2}m_i r_i^2 \omega^2$$

The entire object rotates at the same angular velocity ω, so the constants $\tfrac{1}{2}$ and ω^2 can be factored out of each term of the sum:

$$K_{\text{rot}} = \tfrac{1}{2}\left(\sum_{i=1}^{N} m_i r_i^2 \right) \omega^2$$

The quantity in the parentheses *cannot change* since the distance between each particle and the rotation axis stays the same if the object is rigid and doesn't change shape. However difficult it may be to compute the sum in the parentheses, we only need to do it *once* for any given mass distribution and axis of rotation.

Let's give the quantity in the brackets the symbol I. In Chapter 5, we found it useful to draw analogies between translational variables and their rotational equivalents. By using the symbol I, we can see that translational and rotational kinetic energy have similar forms: translational kinetic energy is

$$K_{\text{tr}} = \tfrac{1}{2}mv^2$$

and **rotational kinetic energy** is

Rotational kinetic energy:

$$K_{\text{rot}} = \tfrac{1}{2}I\omega^2 \qquad (8\text{-}1)$$

The symbol Σ stands for a sum. $\sum\limits_{i=1}^{N}$ means the sum for $i = 1, 2, \ldots, N$.

Figure 8.1 Four points on a spinning CD. Points at greater distances from the center are moving faster than points closer to the center.

Since $v = r\omega$ was used to derive Eq. (8-1), ω must be expressed in radians per unit time (normally rad/s).

The quantity I is called the **rotational inertia**:

Rotational inertia:

$$I = \sum_{i=1}^{N} m_i r_i^2 \qquad (8\text{-}2)$$

(SI unit: kg·m^2)

CONNECTION:

Rotational and translational kinetic energies have the same form: $\frac{1}{2}$ inertia × speed^2.

Comparing the expressions for translational and rotational kinetic energies, we see that angular speed ω takes the place of speed v and rotational inertia I takes the place of mass m. Mass is a measure of the inertia of an object, or, in other words, how difficult it is to change the object's velocity. Similarly, for a rigid rotating object, I is a measure of its rotational inertia—how hard it is to change its angular velocity. That is why the quantity I is called the rotational inertia; it is also sometimes called the **moment of inertia**.

When a problem requires you to find a rotational inertia, there are three principles to follow.

Finding the Rotational Inertia

1. If the object consists of a *small* number of particles, calculate the sum $I = \sum_{i=1}^{N} m_i r_i^2$ directly.

2. For symmetrical objects with simple geometric shapes, calculus can be used to perform the sum in Eq. (8-2). Table 8.1 lists the results of these calculations for the shapes most commonly encountered.

3. Since the rotational inertia is a sum, you can always mentally decompose the object into several parts, find the rotational inertia of each part, and then add them. This is an example of the *divide-and-conquer* problem-solving technique.

See the text website for more information on rotational inertia, including the parallel- and perpendicular-axis theorems.

Keep in mind that the rotational inertia of an object depends on the location of the rotation axis. For instance, imagine taking the hinges off the side of a door and putting them on the top so that the door swings about a horizontal axis like a cat flap door (Fig. 8.2b). The door now has a considerably larger rotational inertia than before the hinges were moved because the door's height is greater than its width. The door has the same mass as before, but its mass now lies on average much farther from the axis of rotation than that

Figure 8.2 The rotational inertia of a door depends on the rotation axis. (a) The door with hinges at the side has a smaller rotational inertia, $I = \frac{1}{3}Mw^2$, than (b) the rotational inertia, $I = \frac{1}{3}Mh^2$, of the same door with hinges at the top, because the door is taller than it is wide.

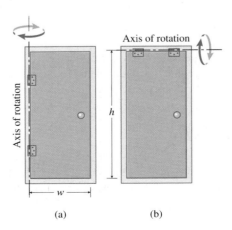

(a)   (b)

| Table 8.1 | Rotational Inertia for Uniform Objects with Various Geometrical Shapes |

Shape	Axis of Rotation	Rotational Inertia	Shape	Axis of Rotation	Rotational Inertia
Thin hollow cylindrical shell (or hoop)	Central axis of cylinder	MR^2	Solid sphere	Through center	$\frac{2}{5}MR^2$
Solid cylinder (or disk)	Central axis of cylinder	$\frac{1}{2}MR^2$	Thin hollow spherical shell	Through center	$\frac{2}{3}MR^2$
Hollow cylindrical shell or disk	Central axis of cylinder	$\frac{1}{2}M(a^2 + b^2)$	Thin rod (or rectangular plate)	Perpendicular to rod through end (or along edge of plate)	$\frac{1}{3}ML^2$
Rectangular plate	Perpendicular to plate through center	$\frac{1}{12}M(a^2 + b^2)$	Thin rod (or rectangular plate)	Perpendicular to rod through center (or parallel to edge of plate through center)	$\frac{1}{12}ML^2$

of the door in Fig. 8.2a. In applying Eq. (8-2) to find the rotational inertia of the door, the values of r_i range from 0 to the height of the door (h), whereas with the hinges in the normal position the values of r_i range from 0 only to the width of the door (w).

Figure 8.3 Hank Aaron choking up on the bat.

PHYSICS AT HOME

The change in rotational inertia of a rod as the rotation axis changes can be easily felt. Hold a baseball bat in the usual way, with your hands gripping the bottom of the bat. Swing the bat a few times. Now "choke up" on the bat—move your hands up the bat—and swing a few times. The bat is easier to swing because it now has a smaller rotational inertia. Children often choke up on a bat that is too massive for them. Even major league baseball players occasionally choke up on the bat when they want more control over their swing to place a hit in a certain spot (Fig. 8.3). On the other hand, choking up on the bat makes it impossible to hit a home run. To hit a long fly ball, you want the pitched baseball to encounter a bat that is swinging with a lot of rotational inertia.

✓ CHECKPOINT 8.1

According to Table 8.1, the rotational inertia of a uniform cylinder or disk about its central axis depends only on the mass and radius. Why does it not depend on the height of the cylinder (or thickness of the disk)?

Example 8.1

Rotational Inertia of a Barbell

A barbell consists of two plates, each a uniform disk of mass 20 kg and radius 15 cm, attached 20 cm from each end of a uniform rod of mass 10 kg, radius 1.25 cm, and length 2.20 m (Fig. 8.4). Find the rotational inertia of the barbell about two different axes of rotation: (a) axis a, the central axis of the bar, and (b) axis b, perpendicular to the bar and through its midpoint. Ignore the thickness of the disks and the holes in the disks.

Strategy   The rotational inertia of this composite object is the sum of the rotational inertias of the three parts (two disks and rod). Table 8.1 gives formulas for the rotational inertias of disks and rods, but *only for certain axes of rotation*. In particular, for axis b we have two disks rotating about an axis external to the disks, so none of the formulas in Table 8.1 apply; instead we'll return to the basic definition of rotational inertia [Eq. (8-2)] and make an approximation. Based on the distances between parts of the barbell and the two axes, we expect a smaller rotational inertia about axis a than about axis b. Let M and R be the mass and radius of each disk, and m, r, and L the mass, radius, and length of the rod, respectively.

Solution   (a) Each of the three component parts, the two disks and the rod, are solid cylinders rotating about their central axes. (The two formulas in Table 8.1 for thin rods are for axes *perpendicular* to the rod, so they are not useful here.) From Table 8.1,

$$I = \tfrac{1}{2}MR^2 + \tfrac{1}{2}MR^2 + \tfrac{1}{2}mr^2$$

$$= 2 \times [\tfrac{1}{2} \times 20 \text{ kg} \times (0.15 \text{ m})^2] + \tfrac{1}{2} \times 10 \text{ kg} \times (0.0125 \text{ m})^2$$

$$= 2 \times 0.225 \text{ kg·m}^2 + 0.00078 \text{ kg·m}^2 = 0.45 \text{ kg·m}^2$$

(b) Table 8.1 gives the rotational inertia of the rod about axis b as $\tfrac{1}{12}mL^2$. The center of each disk (assumed to have negligible thickness) is a distance $d = \tfrac{1}{2}(2.20 \text{ m} - 0.40 \text{ m}) = 0.90$ m from the midpoint of the rod. If we think of breaking a disk

into tiny pieces and applying Eq. (8-2), each of the distances r_i is at least $d = 0.90$ m (to the center) but no more than $\sqrt{d^2 + R^2} \approx 0.91$ m (to the edge). Therefore, to a good approximation, we can assume each disk to be a point mass at a distance d from the axis. Then

$$I = Md^2 + Md^2 + \tfrac{1}{12}mL^2$$

$$= 2 \times [20 \text{ kg} \times (0.90 \text{ m})^2] + \tfrac{1}{12} \times 10 \text{ kg} \times (2.20 \text{ m})^2$$

$$= 2 \times 16.2 \text{ kg·m}^2 + 4.03 \text{ kg·m}^2 = 36 \text{ kg·m}^2$$

As expected, the rotational inertia is much smaller about axis a than about axis b.

Discussion   The rod makes only a slight contribution to the rotational inertia about axis a because the radius of the rod is so much smaller than the radii of the disks, so its mass is on average much closer to the axis of rotation. The rod makes a more significant contribution to the rotational inertia about axis b because now the length, not radius, of the rod is relevant—its mass is distributed at distances from 0 to 1.10 m from the axis of rotation. Even if we account for the thickness of the disks, as long as their thicknesses are small relative to d, our estimate Md^2 of the contribution to I from each disk about axis b is still valid.

Practice Problem 8.1   Playground Merry-Go-Round

A playground merry-go-round is essentially a uniform disk that rotates about a vertical axis through its center (Fig. 8.5). Suppose the disk has a radius of 2.0 m and a mass of 160 kg; a child of mass 18.4 kg sits at the edge of the merry-go-round. What is the merry-go-round's rotational inertia, including the contribution due to the child? [*Hint:* Treat the child as a point mass at the edge of the disk.]

Figure 8.4

A barbell with two different rotation axes.

Figure 8.5

Child on a merry-go-round.

When applying conservation of energy to objects that rotate, the rotational kinetic energy is included in the mechanical energy. In Eq. (6-12),

$$W_{nc} = \Delta K + \Delta U = \Delta E_{mech} \qquad (6\text{-}12)$$

just as U stands for the sum of the elastic and gravitational potential energies, K stands for the sum of the translational and rotational kinetic energies:

$$K = K_{tr} + K_{rot}$$

Example 8.2

Atwood's Machine

Atwood's machine consists of a cord around a pulley of rotational inertia I, radius R, and mass M, with two blocks (masses m_1 and m_2) hanging from the ends of the cord as in Fig. 8.6. (Note that in Example 3.11 we analyzed Atwood's machine for the special case of a massless pulley; for a massless pulley $I = 0$.) Assume that the pulley is free to turn without friction and that the cord does not slip. Ignore air resistance. If the masses are released from rest, find how fast they are moving after they have moved a distance h (one up, the other down).

Strategy Ignoring both air resistance and friction means that no nonconservative forces act on the system; therefore, its mechanical energy is conserved:

$$\Delta U + \Delta K = 0$$

Gravitational potential energy is converted into the translational kinetic energies of the two blocks and the rotational kinetic energy of the pulley.

Solution For our convenience, we assume that $m_1 > m_2$. Mass m_1, therefore, moves down and m_2 moves up. After the masses have each moved a distance h, the changes in gravitational potential energy are

$$\Delta U_1 = -m_1 g h$$

$$\Delta U_2 = +m_2 g h$$

The mechanical energy of the system includes the kinetic energies of three objects: the two masses and the pulley. All start with zero kinetic energy, so

$$\Delta K = \tfrac{1}{2}(m_1 + m_2)v^2 + \tfrac{1}{2}I\omega^2$$

The speed v of the masses is the same since the cord's length is fixed. The speed v and the angular speed of the pulley ω are related if the cord does not slip: the tangential speed of the pulley must equal the speed at which the cord moves. The tangential speed of the pulley is its angular speed times its radius:

$$v = \omega R$$

After substituting v/R for ω, the energy conservation equation becomes

$$\Delta U + \Delta K = [-m_1 g h + m_2 g h] + \left[\tfrac{1}{2}(m_1 + m_2)v^2 + \tfrac{1}{2}I\left(\tfrac{v}{R}\right)^2\right] = 0$$

or

$$\left[\tfrac{1}{2}(m_1 + m_2) + \tfrac{1}{2}\tfrac{I}{R^2}\right]v^2 = (m_1 - m_2)gh$$

Solving this equation for v yields

$$v = \sqrt{\frac{2(m_1 - m_2)gh}{m_1 + m_2 + I/R^2}}$$

Discussion This answer is rich in information, in the sense that we can ask many "What if?" questions. Not only do these questions provide checks as to whether the answer is reasonable, they also enable us to perform thought experiments, which could then be checked by constructing an Atwood's machine and comparing the results.

For instance: What if m_1 is only slightly greater than m_2? Then the final speed v is small—as m_2 approaches m_1, v approaches 0. This makes intuitive sense: a small imbalance in weights produces a small acceleration. You should practice this kind of reasoning by making other such checks.

It is also enlightening to look at terms in an algebraic solution and connect them with physical interpretations. The quantity $(m_1 - m_2)g$ is the imbalance in the gravitational

Pulley
mass M

R M

$\vec{v}_2$

m_2

$\vec{v}_1$

h | Initial
position

m_1 h

Figure 8.6
Atwood's machine.

continued on next page

Example 8.2 continued

forces pulling on the two sides. The denominator $(m_1 + m_2 + I/R^2)$ is a measure of the total inertia of the system—the sum of the two masses plus an inertial contribution due to the pulley. The pulley's contribution is *not* simply equal to its mass. If, for example, the pulley is a uniform disk with $I = \frac{1}{2}MR^2$, the term I/R^2 would be equal to *half* the mass of the pulley.

The same principles used to analyze Atwood's machine have many applications in the real world. One such application is in elevators, where one of the hanging masses is the elevator and the other is the counterweight. Of course, the elevator and counterweight are not allowed to hang freely from a pulley—we must also consider the energy supplied by the motor.

Practice Problem 8.2   Modified Atwood's Machine

Figure 8.7 shows a modified form of Atwood's machine where one of the blocks slides on a table instead of hanging from the pulley. The blocks are released from rest. Find the speed of the blocks after they have moved a distance h in terms of m_1, m_2, I, R, and h. Ignore friction.

Figure 8.7
Modified Atwood's machine.

8.2   TORQUE

Suppose you place a bicycle upside down to repair it. First, you give one of the wheels a spin. If everything is working as it should, the wheel spins for quite a while; its angular acceleration is small. If the wheel doesn't spin for very long, then its angular velocity changes rapidly and the angular acceleration is large in magnitude; there must be excessive friction somewhere. Perhaps the brakes are rubbing on the rim or the bearings need to be repacked.

If we could eliminate *all* the frictional forces acting on the wheel, including air resistance, then we would expect the wheel to keep spinning without diminishing angular speed. In that case, its angular acceleration would be zero. The situation is reminiscent of Newton's first law: a body with no external interactions, or at least no net force acting on it, moves with constant velocity. We can state a "Newton's first law for rotation": a rotating body with no external interactions, and whose rotational inertia doesn't change, keeps rotating at constant angular velocity.

Of course, the hypothetical frictionless bicycle wheel does have external interactions. The Earth's gravitational field exerts a downward force and the axle exerts an upward force to keep the wheel from falling. Then is it true that, as long as there is no net external force, the angular acceleration is zero? No; it is easy to give the wheel an angular acceleration while keeping the net force zero. Imagine bringing the wheel to rest by pressing two hands against the tire on opposite sides. On one side, the motion of the rim of the tire is downward and the kinetic frictional force is upward (Fig. 8.8). On the other side, the tire moves upward and the frictional force is downward. In a similar way, we could apply equal and opposite forces to the opposite sides of a wheel at rest to make it start spinning. In either case, we exert equal magnitude forces, so that the net force is zero, and still give the wheel an angular acceleration.

Figure 8.8 A spinning bicycle wheel slowed to a stop by friction. Each hand exerts a normal force and a frictional force on the tire. The two normal forces add to zero and the two frictional forces add to zero.

The *radial* direction is directly toward or away from the axis of rotation. The *perpendicular* or *tangential* direction is perpendicular to both the radial direction and the axis of rotation; it is tangent to the circular path followed by a point as the object rotates.

Torque   A quantity related to force, called **torque**, plays the role in rotation that force itself plays in translation. A torque is not separate from a force; it is impossible to exert a torque without exerting a force. Torque is a measure of how effective a given force is at twisting or turning something. For something rotating about a fixed axis such as the bicycle wheel, a torque can *change* the rotational motion either by making it rotate faster or by slowing it down.

When stopping the bicycle wheel with two equal and opposite forces, as in Fig. 8.8, the net applied force is zero and, thus, the wheel is in translational equilibrium; but the net torque is not zero, so it is not in rotational equilibrium. Both forces tend to give the wheel the same sign of angular acceleration; they are both making the wheel slow down. The two torques are in fact equal, with the same sign.

(a) Maximum torque   (b) Zero torque   (c) Less torque

Figure 8.9 Torque on a bank vault door depends on the direction of the applied force. (a) Pushing perpendicularly gives the maximum torque. (b) Pushing radially inward with the same magnitude force gives zero torque. (c) The torque is proportional to the perpendicular component of the force ($F_\perp$).

Relationship Between Force and Torque   What determines the torque produced by a particular force? Imagine trying to push open a massive bank vault door. Certainly you would push as hard as you can; the torque is proportional to the magnitude of the force. It also matters where and in what direction the force is applied. For maximum effectiveness, you would push perpendicularly to the door (Fig. 8.9a). If you pushed radially, straight in toward the axis of rotation that passes through the hinges, the door wouldn't rotate, no matter how hard you push (Fig. 8.9b). A force acting in any other direction could be decomposed into radial and perpendicular components, with the radial component contributing nothing to the torque (Fig. 8.9c). Only the perpendicular component of the force ($F_\perp$) produces a torque.

The symbol $\perp$ stands for *perpendicular;* $\parallel$ stands for *parallel.*

Furthermore, *where* you apply the force is critical (Fig. 8.10). Instinctively, you would push at the outer edge, as far from the rotation axis as possible. If you pushed close to the axis, it would be difficult to open the door. Torque is proportional to the distance between the rotation axis and the **point of application** of the force (the point at which the force is applied).

To satisfy the requirements of the previous paragraphs, we define the magnitude of the torque as the product of the distance between the rotation axis and the point of application of the force (r) with the perpendicular component of the force ($F_\perp$):

Definition of torque:

$$\tau = \pm r F_\perp \qquad (8\text{-}3)$$

where r is the shortest distance between the rotation axis and the point of application of the force and $F_\perp$ is the perpendicular component of the force.

The symbol for torque is τ, the Greek letter tau. The SI unit of torque is the N·m. The SI unit of *energy,* the joule, is equivalent to N·m, but we do not write torque in joules. Even though both energy and torque can be written using the same SI base units, the two quantities have different meanings; torque is not a form of energy. To help maintain the distinction, the joule is used for energy but *not* for torque.

✓ CHECKPOINT 8.2

You are trying to loosen a nut, without success. Why might it help to switch to a wrench with a longer handle?

(a) Larger torque   (b) Smaller torque

Figure 8.10 Torques; the same force at different distances from the axis.

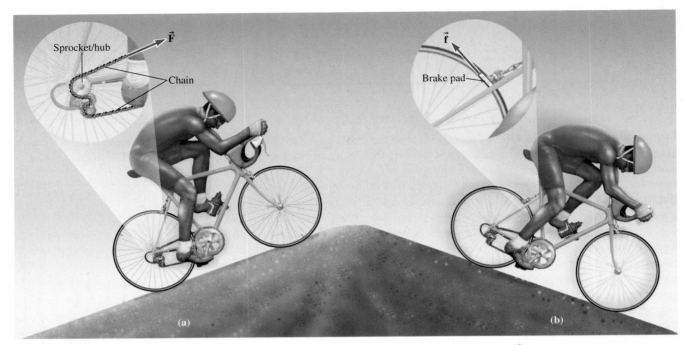

Figure 8.11 (a) When the cyclist climbs a hill, the top half of the chain exerts a large force $\vec{F}$ on the sprocket attached to the rear wheel. As viewed here, the torque about the axis of rotation (the axle) due to this force is clockwise. By convention, we call this a negative torque. (b) When the brakes are applied, the brake pads are pressed onto the rim, giving rise to frictional forces on the rim. As viewed here, the frictional force $\vec{f}$ causes a counterclockwise (positive) torque on the wheel about the axle.

In a more general treatment of torque, torque is a vector quantity defined as the cross product $\vec{\tau} = \vec{r} \times \vec{F}$. See Appendix A.8 for the definition of the cross product. For an object rotating about a fixed axis, Eq. (8-3) gives the component of $\vec{\tau}$ along the axis of rotation.

Sign Convention for Torque   The sign of the torque indicates the direction of the angular acceleration that torque would cause *by itself.* Recall from Section 5.1 that by convention a positive angular velocity ω means counterclockwise (CCW) rotation and a negative angular velocity ω means clockwise (CW) rotation. A positive angular acceleration α either increases the rate of CCW rotation (increases the magnitude of a positive ω) or decreases the rate of CW rotation (decreases the magnitude of a negative ω).

We use the same sign convention for torque. A force whose perpendicular component tends to cause rotation in the CCW direction gives rise to a positive torque; if it is the only torque acting, it would cause a positive angular acceleration α (Fig. 8.11). A force whose perpendicular component tends to cause rotation in the CW direction gives rise to a negative torque. The symbol $\pm$ in Eq. (8-3) reminds us to assign the appropriate algebraic sign each time we calculate a torque.

The sign of the torque is *not* determined by the sign of the angular velocity (in other words, whether the wheel is spinning CCW or CW); rather, it is determined by the sign of the angular *acceleration* the torque would cause if acting alone. To determine the sign of a torque, imagine which way the torque would make the object begin to spin if it is initially not rotating.

Example 8.3

A Spinning Bicycle Wheel

To stop a spinning bicycle wheel, suppose you push radially inward on opposite sides of the wheel, as shown in Fig. 8.8, with equal forces of magnitude 10.0 N. The radius of the wheel is 32 cm and the coefficient of kinetic friction between the tire and your hand is 0.75. The wheel is spinning in the CW sense. What is the net torque on the wheel?

continued on next page

Example 8.3 continued

Strategy The 10.0-N forces are directed radially toward the rotation axis, so they produce no torques themselves; only perpendicular components of forces give rise to torques. The forces of kinetic friction between the hands and the tire are tangent to the tire, so they do produce torques. The normal force applied to the tire is 10.0 N on each side; using the coefficient of friction, we can find the frictional forces.

Solution The frictional force exerted by each hand on the tire has magnitude

$$f = \mu_k N = 0.75 \times 10.0 \text{ N} = 7.5 \text{ N}$$

The frictional force is tangent to the wheel, so $f_\perp = f$. Then the magnitude of each torque is

$$|\tau| = rf_\perp = 0.32 \text{ m} \times 7.5 \text{ N} = 2.4 \text{ N·m}$$

The two torques have the same sign, since they are both tending to slow down the rotation of the wheel. Is the torque positive or negative? The angular velocity of the wheel is negative since it rotates CW. The angular acceleration has the opposite sign because the angular speed is decreasing. Since $\alpha > 0$, the net torque is also positive. Therefore,

$$\sum \tau = +4.8 \text{ N·m}$$

Discussion The trickiest part of calculating torques is determining the sign. To check, look at the frictional forces in Fig. 8.8. Imagine which way the forces would make the wheel begin to rotate if the wheel were not originally rotating. The frictional forces point in a direction that would tend to cause a CCW rotation, so the torques are positive.

Practice Problem 8.3   Disc Brakes

In the disc brakes that slow down a car, a pair of brake pads squeeze a spinning rotor; friction between the pads and the rotor provides the torque that slows down the car. If the normal force that each pad exerts on a rotor is 85 N and the coefficient of friction is 0.62, what is the frictional force on the rotor due to each of the pads? If this force acts 8.0 cm from the rotation axis, what is the magnitude of the torque on the rotor due to the pair of brake pads?

Lever Arms

There is another, completely equivalent, way to calculate torques that is often more convenient than finding the perpendicular component of the force. Figure 8.12 shows a force $\vec{F}$ acting at a distance r from an axis. The distance r is the length of a line perpendicular to the axis that runs from the axis to the force's point of application. The force makes an angle θ with that line. The torque is then

$$\tau = \pm rF_\perp = \pm r(F \sin \theta)$$

The factor $\sin \theta$ could be grouped with r instead of with F. Then $\tau = \pm(r \sin \theta)F$, or

$$\tau = \pm r_\perp F \tag{8-4}$$

The distance $r_\perp$ is called the **lever arm** (or **moment arm**). The magnitude of the torque is, therefore, the magnitude of the force times the lever arm.

Finding Torques Using the Lever Arm

1. Draw a line parallel to the force through the force's point of application; this line (dashed in Fig. 8.12) is called the force's **line of action**.

2. Draw a line from the rotation axis to the line of action. This line must be perpendicular to both the axis and the line of action. The distance from the axis to the line of action along this perpendicular line is the lever arm ($r_\perp$). If the line of action of the force goes through the rotation axis, the lever arm and the torque are both zero (see Fig. 8.9b).

3. The magnitude of the torque is the magnitude of the force times the lever arm:

$$\tau = \pm r_\perp F$$

4. Determine the algebraic sign of the torque as before.

Figure 8.12 Finding the magnitude of a torque using the lever arm.

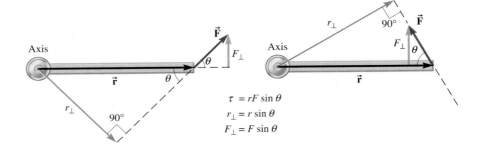

$$\tau = rF \sin \theta$$
$$r_\perp = r \sin \theta$$
$$F_\perp = F \sin \theta$$

Example 8.4

Screen Door Closer

An automatic screen door closer attaches to a door 47 cm away from the hinges and pulls on the door with a force of 25 N, making an angle of 15° with the door (Fig. 8.13). Find the magnitude of the torque exerted on the door due to this force about the rotation axis through the hinges using (a) the perpendicular component of the force and (b) the lever arm. (c) What is the sign of this torque as viewed from above?

Strategy For method (a), we must find the component of the 25-N force perpendicular to the radial direction. Then this component is multiplied by the length of the radial line. For method (b), we draw in the line of action of the force. Then the lever arm is the perpendicular distance from the line of action to the rotation axis. The torque is the magnitude of the force times the lever arm. We must be careful not to combine the two methods: the torque is *not* equal to the perpendicular force component times the lever arm. For (c), we determine whether this torque would tend to make the door rotate CCW or CW.

Solution (a) As shown in Fig. 8.14a, the radial component of the force ($F_\parallel$) passes through the rotation axis. The angle labeled 15° would actually be a bit larger than 15°, but since the thickness of the door is much less than 47 cm, we approximate it as 15°. The perpendicular component is

$$F_\perp = F \sin 15°$$

The magnitude of the torque is

$$|\tau| = rF_\perp = 0.47 \text{ m} \times 25 \text{ N} \times \sin 15° = 3.0 \text{ N·m}$$

(b) Figure 8.14b shows the line of action of the force, drawn parallel to the force and passing through the point of application. The lever arm is the perpendicular distance between the rotation axis and the line of action. The distance r is approximately 47 cm (again neglecting the thickness of the door). Then the lever arm is

$$r_\perp = r \sin 15°$$

and the magnitude of the torque is

$$|\tau| = r_\perp F = 0.47 \text{ m} \times \sin 15° \times 25 \text{ N} = 3.0 \text{ N·m}$$

Figure 8.13
Screen door with automatic closing mechanism.

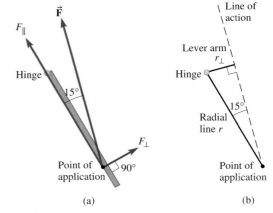

Figure 8.14
(a) Finding the perpendicular component of the force.
(b) Finding the lever arm.

(c) Using the top view of Fig. 8.13, the torque tends to close the door by making it rotate counterclockwise (assuming the door is initially at rest and no other torques act). The torque is therefore positive as viewed from above.

continued on next page

Example 8.4 continued

Discussion The most common mistake to make in either solution method would be to use cosine instead of sine (or, equivalently, to use the complementary angle 75° instead of 15°). A check is a good idea. If the automatic closer were more nearly parallel to the door, the angle would be less than 15°. The torque would be smaller because the force is more nearly pulling straight in toward the axis. Since the sine function gets smaller for angles closer to zero, the expression checks out correctly.

It might seem silly for a door closer to pull at such an angle that the perpendicular component is relatively small. The reason it's done that way is so the door closer does not get in the way. A closer that pulled in a perpendicular direction would stick straight out from the door. As discussed in Section 8.5, the situation is much the same in our bodies. In order to not inhibit the motion of our limbs, our tendons and muscles are nearly parallel to the bones. As a result, the forces they exert must be much larger than we might expect.

Practice Problem 8.4 Exercise Is Good for You

A person is lying on an exercise mat and lifts one leg at an angle of 30.0° from the horizontal with an 89-N (20-lb) weight attached to the ankle (Fig. 8.15). The distance between the ankle weight and the hip joint (which is the rotation axis for the leg) is 84 cm. What is the torque due to the ankle weight on the leg?

Figure 8.15
Exercise leg lifts.

Center of Gravity

We have seen that the torque produced by a force depends on the point of application of the force. What about gravity? The gravitational force on a body is not exerted at a single point, but is distributed throughout the volume of the body. When we talk of "the" force of gravity on something, we really mean the total force of gravity acting on each particle making up the system.

Fortunately, when we need to find the total torque due to the forces of gravity acting on an object, the total force of gravity can be considered to act at a single point. This point is called the **center of gravity**. The torque found this way is the same as finding all the torques due to the forces of gravity acting at every point in the body and adding them together. As you can verify in Problem 95, if the gravitational field is uniform in magnitude and direction, then the center of gravity of an object is located at the object's center of mass.

When calculating the torque due to gravity, consider the entire gravitational force to act at the center of gravity.

8.3 CALCULATING WORK DONE FROM THE TORQUE

Torques can do work, as anyone who has started a lawnmower with a pull cord can verify. Actually, it is the force that does the work, but in rotational problems it is often simpler to calculate the work done from the torque. Just as the work done by a constant force is the product of force and the parallel component of displacement, work done by a constant torque can also be calculated as the torque times the *angular* displacement.

Imagine a torque acting on a wheel that spins through an angular displacement $\Delta\theta$ while the torque is applied. The work done by the force that gives rise to the torque is the product of the perpendicular component of the force ($F_\perp$) with the arc length s through which the point of application of the force moves (Fig. 8.16). We use the perpendicular force component because that is the component parallel to the *displacement*, which is instantaneously tangent to the arc of the circle. Thus,

$$W = F_\perp s \qquad (8\text{-}5)$$

CONNECTION:

We're not introducing a different kind of work, just a different way to calculate work.

Figure 8.16 The work done by a torque is the product of the perpendicular force component $F_\perp$ and the arc length s.

To write the work in terms of torque, note that $\tau = rF_\perp$ and $s = r\Delta\theta$; then

$$W = F_\perp s = \frac{\tau}{r} \times r\Delta\theta = \tau\Delta\theta$$

$$W = \tau\Delta\theta \quad (\Delta\theta \text{ in radians}) \tag{8-6}$$

Work is indeed the product of torque and the angular displacement. If τ and $\Delta\theta$ have the same sign, the work done is positive; if they have opposite signs, the work done is negative. The *power* due to a constant torque—the rate at which work is done—is

$$P = \tau\omega \tag{8-7}$$

Example 8.5

Work Done on a Potter's Wheel

A potter's wheel is a heavy stone disk on which the pottery is shaped. Potter's wheels were once driven by the potter pushing on a foot treadle; today most potter's wheels are driven by electric motors. (a) If the potter's wheel is a uniform disk of mass 40.0 kg and diameter 0.50 m, how much work must be done by the motor to bring the wheel from rest to 80.0 rpm? (b) If the motor delivers a constant torque of 8.2 N·m during this time, through how many revolutions does the wheel turn in coming up to speed?

Strategy Work is an energy transfer. In this case, the motor is increasing the rotational kinetic energy of the potter's wheel. Thus, the work done by the motor is equal to the change in rotational kinetic energy of the wheel, ignoring frictional losses. In the expression for rotational kinetic energy, we must express ω in rad/s; we cannot substitute 80.0 rpm for ω. Once we know the work done, we use the torque to find the angular displacement.

Solution (a) The change in rotational kinetic energy of the wheel is

$$\Delta K = \tfrac{1}{2}I(\omega_f^2 - \omega_i^2) = \tfrac{1}{2}I\omega_f^2$$

Initially the wheel is at rest, so the initial angular velocity ω_i is zero. From Table 8.1, the rotational inertia of a uniform disk is

$$I = \tfrac{1}{2}MR^2$$

Substituting this for I,

$$\Delta K = \tfrac{1}{4}MR^2\omega_f^2$$

Before substituting numerical values, we convert 80.0 rpm to rad/s:

$$\omega_f = 80.0 \, \frac{\text{rev}}{\text{min}} \times 2\pi\frac{\text{rad}}{\text{rev}} \times \frac{1}{60}\frac{\text{min}}{\text{s}} = 8.38 \text{ rad/s}$$

Substituting the known values for mass and radius,

$$\Delta K = \tfrac{1}{4} \times 40.0 \text{ kg} \times (\tfrac{0.50}{2} \text{ m})^2 \times (8.38 \text{ rad/s})^2 = 43.9 \text{ J}$$

Therefore, the work done by the motor, rounded to two significant figures, is 44 J.

(b) The work done by a constant torque is

$$W = \tau\Delta\theta$$

Solving for the angular displacement $\Delta\theta$ gives

$$\Delta\theta = \frac{W}{\tau} = \frac{43.9 \text{ J}}{8.2 \text{ N·m}} = 5.35 \text{ rad}$$

Since 2π rad = 1 revolution,

$$\Delta\theta = 5.35 \text{ rad} \times \frac{1 \text{ rev}}{2\pi \text{ rad}} = 0.85 \text{ rev}$$

continued on next page

Example 8.5 continued

Discussion As always, work is an energy transfer. In this problem, the work done by the motor is the means by which the potter's wheel acquires its rotational kinetic energy. But work done by a torque does not *always* appear as a change in rotational kinetic energy. For instance, when you wind up a mechanical clock or a windup toy, the work done by the

45 N

27 N

Figure 8.17

Air conditioner belt and pulley.

torque you apply is stored as elastic potential energy in some sort of spring.

Practice Problem 8.5 **Work Done on an Air Conditioner**

A belt wraps around a pulley of radius 7.3 cm that drives the compressor of an automobile air conditioner. The tension in the belt on one side of the pulley is 45 N and on the other side of the pulley it is 27 N (Fig. 8.17). How much work is done by the belt on the compressor during one revolution of the pulley?

8.4 ROTATIONAL EQUILIBRIUM

In Chapter 2, we said that an object is in translational equilibrium when the net force acting on it is zero. It is quite possible for the net force acting to be zero, while the net torque is nonzero; the object would then have a nonzero angular acceleration. When designing a bridge or a new house, it would be unacceptable for any of the parts to have nonzero angular acceleration! Zero net force is sufficient to ensure *translational* equilibrium; if an object is also in *rotational* equilibrium, then the net torque acting on it must also be zero.

Conditions for equilibrium (both translational and rotational):

$$\sum \vec{F} = 0 \quad \text{and} \quad \sum \tau = 0 \tag{8-8}$$

Choosing an Axis of Rotation in Equilibrium Problems Before tackling equilibrium problems, we must resolve a conundrum: if something is not rotating, then where is the axis of rotation? How can we calculate torques without knowing where the axis of rotation is? In some cases, perhaps involving axles or hinges, there may be a clear axis about which the object would rotate if the balance of forces and torques is disturbed. In many cases, though, it is not clear what the rotation axis would be, and in general it depends on exactly how the equilibrium is upset. Fortunately, the axis can be chosen *arbitrarily* when calculating torques *in equilibrium problems.*

In equilibrium, the net torque about *any* rotation axis must be zero. Does that mean that we have to write down an infinite number of torque equations, one for each possible axis of rotation? Fortunately, no. Although the proof is complicated, it can be shown that if the net force acting on an object is zero and the net torque about one rotation axis is zero, then the net torque about every other axis parallel to that axis must also be zero. Therefore, one torque equation is all we need.

Since the torque can be calculated about any desired axis, a judicious choice can greatly simplify the solution of the problem. The best place to choose the axis is usually at the point of application of an unknown force so that the unknown force does not appear in the torque equation.

✓ CHECKPOINT 8.4

Is it possible for the net torque on an object to be zero and the net force nonzero? Is it possible for the net force to be zero and the net torque nonzero?

Problem-Solving Steps in Equilibrium Problems

- Identify an object or system in equilibrium. Draw a diagram showing all the forces acting on that object, each drawn at its point of application. Use the center of gravity as the point of application of any gravitational forces.
- To apply the force condition $\Sigma \vec{F} = 0$, choose a convenient coordinate system and resolve each force into its x- and y-components.
- To apply the torque condition $\Sigma \tau = 0$, choose a convenient rotation axis—generally one that passes through the point of application of an unknown force. Then find the torque due to each force. Use whichever method is easier: either the lever arm times the magnitude of the force or the distance times the perpendicular component of the force. Determine the direction of each torque; then either set the sum of all the torques (with their algebraic signs) equal to zero or set the magnitude of the CW torques equal to the magnitude of the CCW torques.
- Not all problems require all three equations (two force component equations and one torque equation). Sometimes it is easier to use more than one torque equation, with a different axis. Before diving in and writing down all the equations, think about which approach is the easiest and most direct.

Example 8.6

Carrying a 6 × 6 Beam

Two carpenters are carrying a uniform 6×6 beam. The beam is 8.00 ft (2.44 m) long and weighs 425 N (95.5 lb). One of the carpenters, being a bit stronger than the other, agrees to carry the beam 1.00 m in from the end; the other carries the beam at its opposite end. What is the upward force exerted on the beam by each carpenter?

Strategy The conditions for equilibrium are that the net external force equal zero and the net external torque equal zero:

$$\Sigma \vec{F} = 0 \quad \text{and} \quad \Sigma \tau = 0$$

Should we start with forces or with torques? In this problem, it is easiest to start with torques. If we choose the axis of rotation where one of the unknown forces acts, then that force has a lever arm of zero and its torque is zero. The torque equation can be solved for the other unknown force. Then with only one force still unknown, we set the sum of the y-components of the forces equal to zero.

Solution The first step is to draw a force diagram (Fig. 8.18). Each force is drawn at the point where it acts. Known distances are labeled.

We choose a rotation axis perpendicular to the xy-plane and passing through the point of application of $\vec{F}_2$. The simplest way to find the torques for this example is to multiply each force by its lever arm. The lever arm for $\vec{F}_1$ is

$$2.44 \text{ m} - 1.00 \text{ m} = 1.44 \text{ m}$$

and the magnitude of the torque due to this force is

$$|\tau| = F r_\perp = F_1 \times 1.44 \text{ m}$$

Since the beam is uniform, its center of gravity is at its midpoint. We imagine the entire gravitational force to act at this point. Then the lever arm for the gravitational force is

$$\tfrac{1}{2} \times 2.44 \text{ m} = 1.22 \text{ m}$$

and the torque due to gravity has magnitude

$$|\tau| = F r_\perp = 425 \text{ N} \times 1.22 \text{ m} = 518.5 \text{ N·m}$$

The torque due to $\vec{F}_1$ is negative since, if it were the only torque, it would make the beam start to rotate clockwise about our chosen axis of rotation. The torque due to gravity is positive since, if it were the only torque, it would make the beam start to rotate counterclockwise. Therefore,

$$\Sigma \tau = -F_1 \times 1.44 \text{ m} + 518.5 \text{ N·m} = 0$$

Figure 8.18 Diagram of the beam with rotation axis, forces, and distances shown.

continued on next page

Example 8.6 continued

Solving for F_1,

$$F_1 = \frac{518.5 \text{ N·m}}{1.44 \text{ m}} = 360 \text{ N}$$

Since another condition for equilibrium is that the net force be zero,

$$\sum F_y = F_1 + F_2 - mg = 0$$

Solving for F_2,

$$F_2 = 425 \text{ N} - 360 \text{ N} = 65 \text{ N}$$

Discussion A good way to check this result is to make sure that the net torque about a *different axis* is zero—for an object in equilibrium, the net torque about any axis must be zero. Suppose we choose an axis through the point of application of $\vec{F}_1$. Then the lever arm for $m\vec{g}$ is 1.22 m − 1.00 m = 0.22 m and the lever arm for $\vec{F}_2$ is 2.44 m − 1.00 m = 1.44 m. Setting the net torque equal to zero:

$$\sum \tau = -425 \text{ N} \times 0.22 \text{ m} + F_2 \times 1.44 \text{ m} = 0$$

Solving for F_2 gives

$$F_2 = \frac{425 \text{ N} \times 0.22 \text{ m}}{1.44 \text{ m}} = 65 \text{ N}$$

which agrees with the value calculated before. We could have used this second torque equation to find F_2 instead of setting $\sum F_y$ equal to zero.

Practice Problem 8.6 A Diving Board

A uniform diving board of length 5.0 m is supported at two points; one support is located 3.4 m from the end of the board and the second is at 4.6 m from the end (Fig. 8.19). The supports exert vertical forces on the diving board. A diver stands at the end of the board over the water. Determine the directions of the support forces. (tutorial: plank) [*Hint:* In this problem, consider torques about different rotation axes.]

Figure 8.19
Diving board.

The Cantilever A diving board is an example of a cantilever—a beam or pole that extends beyond its support. The forces exerted by the supports on a diving board are considerably larger than if the same board were supported at both ends (see Problem 32). The advantage is that the far end of the board is left free to vibrate; as it does, the support forces adjust themselves to keep the board from tipping over. The architect Frank Lloyd Wright was fond of using cantilever construction to open up the sides and corners of a building, allowing corner windows that give buildings a lighter and more spacious feel (Fig. 8.20).

Application of Rotational Equilibrium: cantilever building construction

Figure 8.20 The cantilevered master bedroom in the north wing of Wingspread by Frank Lloyd Wright juts well out over its brick foundation. The cypress trellis extending even farther beyond the bedroom balcony filters the natural light and serves to emphasize the free-floating nature of the structure with views of the landscape below.

Example 8.7

The Slipping Ladder

A 15.0-kg uniform ladder leans against a wall in the atrium of a large hotel (Fig. 8.21a). The ladder is 8.00 m long; it makes an angle $\theta = 60.0°$ with the floor. The coefficient of static friction between the floor and the ladder is $\mu_s = 0.45$. How far along the ladder can a 60.0-kg person climb before the ladder starts to slip? Assume that the wall is frictionless. (interactive: ladder and tutorial: ladder)

Strategy   Consider the ladder and the climber as a single system. Until the ladder starts to slip, this system is in equilibrium. Therefore, the net external force and the net external torque acting on the system are both equal to zero. Normal forces act on the ladder due to the wall ($\vec{\mathbf{N}}_w$) and the floor ($\vec{\mathbf{N}}_f$). A frictional force acts on the base of the ladder due to the floor ($\vec{\mathbf{f}}$), but no frictional force acts on the top of the ladder since the wall is frictionless. Gravitational forces act on the ladder and on the person climbing it. As the person ascends the ladder, the frictional force $\vec{\mathbf{f}}$ has to increase to keep the ladder in equilibrium. The ladder begins to slip when the frictional force required to maintain equilibrium is larger than its maximum possible value $\mu_s N_f$. The ladder is about to slip when $f = \mu_s N_f$.

$$\sum F_x = 0, \quad \sum F_y = 0, \quad \text{and} \sum \tau = 0$$

Solution   The first step is to make a careful drawing of the ladder and label all distances and forces (Fig. 8.21b). Instead of cluttering the diagram with numerical values, we use

$L \ (= 8.00 \text{ m})$ for the length of the ladder, d for the unknown distance from the bottom of the ladder to the point where the person stands, and $M \ (= 60.0 \text{ kg})$ and $m \ (= 15.0 \text{ kg})$ for the masses of the person and ladder, respectively. The weight of the ladder acts at the ladder's center of gravity, which is the ladder's midpoint since it is uniform.

Now we apply the conditions for equilibrium. Starting with $\sum F_x = 0$, we find

$$N_w - f = 0$$

where, if the climber is at the highest point possible, the frictional force must have its maximum possible magnitude:

$$f = \mu_s N_f$$

Combining these two equations, we obtain a relationship between the magnitudes of the two normal forces:

$$N_w = \mu_s N_f$$

Next we use the condition $\sum F_y = 0$, which gives

$$N_f - Mg - mg = 0$$

The only unknown quantity in this equation is N_f, so we can solve for it:

$$N_f = Mg + mg = (M + m)g$$

Now we can find the other normal force, N_w:

$$N_w = \mu_s N_f = \mu_s (M + m)g$$

(a)

(b)

Figure 8.21

(a) A ladder and (b) forces acting on the ladder.

continued on next page

Example 8.7 continued

At this point, we have expressions for the magnitudes of all the forces. We do not know the distance d, which is the goal of the problem. To find d we must set the net torque equal to zero.

First we choose a rotation axis. The most convenient choice is an axis perpendicular to the plane of Fig. 8.21 and passing through the bottom of the ladder. Since two of the five forces ($\vec{N}_f$ and $\vec{f}$) act at the bottom of the ladder, these two forces have zero lever arms and, thus, produce zero torque. Another reason why this is a convenient choice of axis is that the distance d is measured from the bottom of the ladder.

In this situation, with the forces either vertical or horizontal, it is probably easiest to use lever arms to find the torques. In three diagrams (Fig. 8.22), we first draw the line of action for each force; then the lever arm is the perpendicular distance between the axis and the line of action.

Using the usual convention that CCW torques are positive, the torque due to $\vec{N}_w$ is negative and the torques due to gravity are positive. The magnitude of each torque is the magnitude of the force times its lever arm:

$$\tau = F r_\perp$$

Setting the net torque equal to zero yields

$$-N_w L \sin\theta + mg\left(\tfrac{1}{2}L\cos\theta\right) + Mgd\cos\theta = 0$$

Now we solve for d algebraically.

$$\frac{-N_w L \sin\theta}{Mg\cos\theta} + \frac{\tfrac{1}{2}mgL\cos\theta}{Mg\cos\theta} + d = 0$$

$$d = \frac{N_w L \tan\theta}{Mg} - \frac{mL}{2M}$$

Substituting for N_w, we have

$$d = L\left(\frac{\mu_s(M+m)\tan\theta}{M} - \frac{m}{2M}\right)$$

$$= 8.00\ \text{m} \times \left(\frac{0.45 \times 75.0\ \text{kg} \times \tan 60.0°}{60.0\ \text{kg}} - \frac{15.0\ \text{kg}}{2 \times 60.0\ \text{kg}}\right)$$

$$= 6.8\ \text{m}$$

The person can climb 6.8 m up the ladder without having it slip. This is the distance *along the ladder*, not the height above the ground, which is

$$h = 6.8\ \text{m} \times \sin 60.0° = 5.9\ \text{m}$$

Discussion If the person goes any higher, then his weight produces a larger CCW torque about our chosen rotation axis. To stay in equilibrium, the total CW torque would have to get larger. The only force providing a CW torque is the normal force due to the wall, which pushes to the right. However, if this force were to get larger, the frictional force would have to get larger to keep the net horizontal force equal to zero. Since friction already has its maximum magnitude, there is no way for the ladder to be in equilibrium if the person climbs any higher.

Practice Problem 8.7 Another Ladder Leaning on a Wall

A uniform ladder of mass 10.0 kg and length 3.2 m leans against a frictionless wall with its base located 1.5 m from the wall. If the ladder is not to slip, what must be the minimum coefficient of static friction between the bottom of the ladder and the ground? Assume the wall is frictionless.

Figure 8.22

Finding the lever arm for each force.

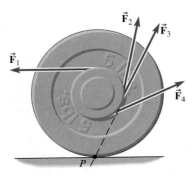

Figure 8.23 Forces $\vec{F}_1$ and $\vec{F}_2$ make the dumbbell roll to the left; $\vec{F}_4$ makes it roll to the right; $\vec{F}_3$ does not make it roll.

PHYSICS AT HOME

Take a dumbbell and wrap some string around the center of its axle. (An alternative: slide two spools of thread onto a pencil near its center with a small gap between the spools. Wrap some thread around the pencil between the two spools.) Place the dumbbell on a table (or on the floor). Unwind a short length of string and try pulling perpendicularly to the axle at different angles to the horizontal (Fig. 8.23). Depending on the direction of your pull, the dumbbell can roll in either direction. Try to find the angle at which the rolling changes direction; at this angle the dumbbell does not roll at all. (If using the pencil and spools of thread, pull gently and try to find the angle at which the whole thing *slides* along the table without any rotation.)

What is special about this angle? Since the dumbbell is in equilibrium when pulling at this angle, we can analyze the torques using any rotation axis we choose. A convenient choice is the axis that passes through point P, the point of contact with the table. Then the contact force between the table and the dumbbell acts at the rotation axis and its torque is zero. The torque due to gravity is also zero, since the line of action passes through point P. The dumbbell can only be in equilibrium if the torque due to the remaining force (the tension in the string) is zero. This torque is zero if the lever arm is zero, which means the line of action passes through point P.

Example 8.8

The Sign and the Breaking Cord

A uniform beam of weight 196 N and of length 1.00 m is attached to a hinge on the outside wall of a restaurant. A cord is attached at the center of the beam and is attached to the wall, making an angle of 30.0° with the beam (Fig. 8.24a). The cord keeps the beam perpendicular to the wall. If the breaking tension of the cord is 620 N, how large can the mass of the sign be without breaking the cord?

Strategy The beam is in equilibrium; both the net force and the net torque acting on it must be zero. To find the maximum weight of the sign, we let the tension in the cord have its maximum value of 620 N. We do not know the force exerted by the hinge on the beam, so we choose an axis of rotation through

the hinge. Then the force exerted by the hinge on the beam has a zero lever arm and does not enter the torque equation.

Before doing anything else, we draw a diagram showing each force acting on the beam and the chosen rotation axis. The FBD in previous chapters often placed all the force vectors starting from a single point. Now we draw each force vector starting at its point of application so that we can find the torque—either by finding the lever arm or by finding the perpendicular force component and the distance from the axis to the point of application.

Solution Figure 8.24b shows the forces acting on the beam; three of these contribute to the torque. The gravitational

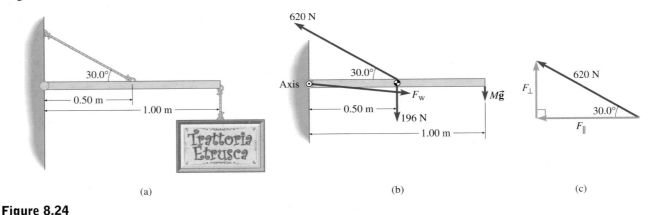

(a)   (b)   (c)

Figure 8.24

(a) A sign outside a restaurant. (b) Forces acting on the beam. (c) Finding the components of the tension in the cord.

continued on next page

Example 8.8 continued

force on the beam can be taken to act at the midpoint of the beam since it is uniform. The force due to the cord has a perpendicular component (Fig. 8.24c) of

$$F_\perp = 620 \text{ N} \times \sin 30.0° = 310 \text{ N}$$

The two gravitational forces tend to rotate the beam CW, while the tension in the cord tends to rotate it CCW. The net torque must be equal to zero:

$$-0.50 \text{ m} \times 196 \text{ N} - 1.00 \text{ m} \times Mg + 0.50 \text{ m} \times 310 \text{ N} = 0$$

or

$$1.00 \text{ m} \times Mg = 0.50 \text{ m} \times (310 \text{ N} - 196 \text{ N})$$

Now we solve for the unknown mass M:

$$M = \frac{0.50 \text{ m} \times (310 \text{ N} - 196 \text{ N})}{1.00 \text{ m} \times 9.80 \text{ N/kg}} = 5.8 \text{ kg}$$

Discussion   In this problem, we did not have to set the net force equal to zero. By placing the axis of rotation at the hinge, we eliminated two of the three unknowns from the torque equation: the horizontal and vertical components of the hinge force (or, equivalently, its magnitude and direction). If we wanted to find the hinge force as well, setting the net force equal to zero would be necessary.

Practice Problem 8.8   Hinge Forces

Find the vertical component of the force exerted by the hinge in two different ways: (a) setting the net force equal to zero and (b) using a torque equation about a different axis.

Distributed Forces

Gravity is not the only force that is distributed rather than acting at a point. Contact forces, including both the normal component and friction, are spread over the contact surface. Just as for gravity, we can consider the contact force to act at a single point, but the location of that point is often not at all obvious. For a book sitting on a horizontal table, it seems reasonable that the normal force effectively acts at the geometric center of the book cover that touches the table. It is less clear where that effective point is if the book is on an incline or is sliding. As Example 8.9 shows, when something is about to topple over, contact is about to be lost everywhere except at the corner around which the toppling object is about to rotate. That corner then must be the location of the contact forces.

Example 8.9

The Toppling File Cabinet

A file cabinet of height a and width b is on a ramp at angle θ (Fig. 8.25a). The file cabinet is filled with papers in such a way that its center of gravity is at its geometric center. Find the largest θ for which the file cabinet does not tip over. Assume the coefficient of static friction is large enough to prevent sliding. (![W] tutorial: file cabinet)

Strategy   Until the file cabinet begins to tip over, it is in equilibrium; the net force acting on it must be zero and the total torque about any axis must also be zero. We first draw a force diagram showing the three forces (gravity, normal, friction) acting on the file cabinet. The point of application of the two contact forces (normal, friction) must be at the lower edge of the file cabinet if it is on the steepest possible incline, just about to tip over. In that case, contact has been lost over the rest of the bottom surface of the file cabinet so that only the lower edge makes good contact with the ramp.

As in all equilibrium problems, a good choice of rotation axis makes the problem easier to solve. We know that, at the maximum angle, the contact forces act at the bottom edge of

the file cabinet. A good choice of rotation axis is along the bottom edge of the file cabinet, because then the normal and frictional forces have zero lever arm.

Solution   Figure 8.25b shows the forces acting on the file cabinet at the maximum angle θ. The gravitational force is drawn at the center of gravity. Instead of drawing a single

Figure 8.25

(a) File cabinet on an incline. (b) Forces acting on the file cabinet.

continued on next page

Example 8.9 continued

vector arrow for the gravitational force, we represent the gravitational force by its components parallel and perpendicular to the ramp. Then we find the lever arm for each of the components. The lever arm for the parallel component of the weight ($mg \sin \theta$) is $\frac{1}{2}a$ and the lever arm for the perpendicular component ($mg \cos \theta$) is $\frac{1}{2}b$. Setting the net torque equal to zero:

$$\sum \tau = -mg \cos \theta \times \tfrac{1}{2}b + mg \sin \theta \times \tfrac{1}{2}a = 0$$

After dividing out the common factors of $\frac{1}{2}mg$,

$$\cos \theta \times b = \sin \theta \times a$$

Solving for θ,

$$\theta = \tan^{-1} \frac{b}{a}$$

Discussion As a check, we can regard the normal and friction forces as two components of a single contact force. We can think of that contact force as acting at a single point—a "center of contact" analogous to the center of gravity. As the file cabinet is put on steeper and steeper surfaces, the effective point of application of the contact force moves toward the lower edge of the file cabinet (Fig. 8.26). If we take the rotation axis through the center of gravity so there is no gravitational torque, then the torque due to the contact force must be zero. The only

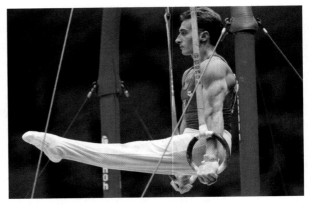

Figure 8.27
Yuri Chechi of Italy holds the pike position on the rings at the World Gymnastic Championships in Sabae, Japan.

way that can happen is if its lever arm is zero, which means that the contact force must point directly toward the center of gravity. If the angle θ has its maximum value, the contact force acts at the lower edge and $\tan \theta = b/a$. The file cabinet is about to tip when its center of gravity is directly above the lower edge. Any object supported only by contact forces can be in equilibrium only if the point of application of the total contact force is directly below the object's center of gravity.

Point of application of contact force

Conceptual Practice Problem 8.9 Gymnast Holding a Pike Position

Figure 8.27 shows a gymnast holding a pike position. What can you say about the location of the gymnast's center of gravity?

Figure 8.26
Contact force for various incline angles.

(a)   (b)

Figure 8.28 Location of the center of gravity when (a) standing and (b) reaching for the floor.

PHYSICS AT HOME

When a person stands up straight, the body's center of gravity lies directly above a point between the feet, about 3 cm in front of the ankle joint (see Fig. 8.28a). When a person bends over to touch her toes, the center of gravity lies outside the body (Fig. 8.28b). Note that the lower half of the body must move backward to keep the center of gravity from moving out in front of the toes, which would cause the person to fall over.

An interesting experiment can be done that illustrates what happens to your balance when you shift your center of gravity. Stand against a wall with the heels of your feet touching the wall and your back pressed against the wall. Then carefully try to bend over as if to touch your toes, without bending your knees. Can you do this without falling over? Explain.

8.5   EQUILIBRIUM IN THE HUMAN BODY

We can use the concepts of torque and equilibrium to understand some of how the musculoskeletal system of the human body works. A muscle has tendons at each end that connect it to two different bones across a joint (the flexible connection between the bones). When the muscle contracts, it pulls the tendons, which in turn pull on the bones. Thus, the muscle produces a pair of forces of equal magnitude, one acting on each of the two bones. The biceps muscle (Fig. 8.29) in the upper arm attaches the scapula to the forearm (radius) across the inside of the elbow joint. When the biceps contracts, the forearm is pulled toward the upper arm. The biceps is a *flexor* muscle; it moves one bone closer to another.

A muscle can pull but not push, so a flexor muscle such as the biceps cannot reverse its action to push the forearm away from the upper arm. The *extensor* muscles make bones move apart from each other. In the upper arm (Fig. 8.29), an extensor muscle—the triceps—connects the scapula and humerus to the ulna (a bone in the forearm parallel to the radius) across the outside of the elbow. Since the biceps and triceps connect to the forearm on opposite sides of the elbow joint, they tend to cause rotation about the joint in opposite directions. When the triceps contracts it pulls the forearm away from the upper arm. Using flexor and extensor muscles on opposite sides of the joint, the body can produce both positive and negative torques, although both muscles pull in the same direction.

Suppose the arm is held in a horizontal position. The deltoid muscle (the muscle shown in Fig. 8.30) exerts a force $\vec{F}_m$ on the humerus at an angle of about 15° above the horizontal. This force has to do two things. The vertical component (magnitude $F_m \sin 15° \approx 0.26 F_m$) supports the weight of the arm, while the horizontal component (magnitude $F_m \cos 15° \approx 0.97 F_m$) stabilizes the joint by pulling the humerus in against the shoulder (scapula). In Example 8.10, we estimate the magnitude of $\vec{F}_m$.

Application of Conditions for Equilibrium to the Human Body

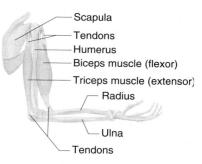

Figure 8.29 The biceps is a flexor muscle; the triceps is an extensor muscle.

Figure 8.30 Forces exerted on an outstretched arm by the deltoid muscle ($\vec{F}_m$), the scapula ($\vec{F}_s$), and gravity ($\vec{F}_g$).

Example 8.10

Force to Hold Arm Horizontal

A person is standing with his arm outstretched in a horizontal position. The weight of the arm is 30.0 N and its center of gravity is at the elbow joint, 27.5 cm from the shoulder joint (Fig. 8.30). The deltoid pulls on the upper arm at an angle of 15° above the horizontal and at a distance of 12 cm from the joint. What is the magnitude of the force exerted by the deltoid muscle on the arm?

Strategy   The arm is in equilibrium, so we can apply the conditions for equilibrium: $\Sigma \vec{F} = 0$ and $\Sigma \tau = 0$. When calculating torques, we choose the rotation axis at the shoulder joint because then the unknown force $\vec{F}_s$, which acts on the arm at the joint, has a zero lever arm and produces zero torque. With only one unknown in the torque equation, we can solve immediately for F_m. We do not need to apply the condition $\Sigma \vec{F} = 0$ unless we want to find $\vec{F}_s$.

Solution   The gravitational force is perpendicular to the line between its point of application and the rotation axis. Gravity produces a CW torque of magnitude

$$|\tau| = Fr = 30.0 \text{ N} \times 0.275 \text{ m} = 8.25 \text{ N·m}$$

For the torque due to $\vec{F}_m$, we find the component of $\vec{F}_m$ that is perpendicular to the line between its point of application and the rotation axis. Since this line is horizontal, we need the vertical component of $\vec{F}_m$, which is $F_m \sin 15°$. Then the magnitude of the CCW torque due to $\vec{F}_m$ is

$$|\tau| = F_\perp r = F_m \sin 15° \times 0.12 \text{ m}$$

The sum of these torques is zero. With the usual sign convention. (CCW is +),

$$F_m \sin 15° \times 0.12 \text{ m} - 8.25 \text{ N·m} = 0$$

continued on next page

Example 8.10 continued

Solving for F_m,

$$F_m = \frac{8.25 \text{ N·m}}{\sin 15° \times 0.12 \text{ m}} = 270 \text{ N}$$

Discussion   The force exerted by the muscle is much larger than the 30.0-N weight of the arm. The muscle must exert a larger force because the lever arm is small; the point of application is less than half as far from the joint as the center of gravity [0.12 m/(0.275 m) ≈ 4/9]. Also, the muscle cannot pull straight up on the arm; the vertical component of the muscle force is only about $\frac{1}{4}$ of the magnitude of the force. These two factors together make the weight supported (30.0 N) only $\frac{4}{9} \times \frac{1}{4} = \frac{1}{9}$ as large as the force exerted by the muscle.

Practice Problem 8.10   Holding a Juice Carton

Find the force exerted by the same person's deltoid muscle when holding a 1-L juice carton (weight 9.9 N) with the arm outstretched and parallel to the floor (as in Fig. 8.30). Assume that the juice carton is 60.0 cm from the shoulder.

Why does the iron cross require great strength?

The Iron Cross   When a gymnast does the iron cross (Fig. 8.31a), the primary muscles involved are the latissimus dorsi ("lats") and pectoralis major ("pecs"). Since the rings are supporting the gymnast's weight, they exert an upward force on the gymnast's arms. Thus, the task for the muscles is not to hold the arm up, but to pull it down. The lats pull on the humerus about 3.5 cm from the shoulder joint (Fig. 8.31b). The pecs pull on the humerus about 5.5 cm from the joint (Fig. 8.31c). The other ends of these two muscles connect to bone in many places, widely distributed over the back (lats) and chest (pecs). As a reasonable simplification, we can assume that these muscles pull at a 45° angle below the horizontal in the iron cross maneuver. We also assume that the two muscles exert equal forces, so we can replace the two with a single force acting at 4.5 cm from the joint.

To determine the force exerted, we look at the entire arm as a system in equilibrium. This time we can ignore the weight of the arm itself since the force exerted on the arm by the ring is much larger—half the gymnast's weight is supported by each ring. The ring exerts an upward force that acts on the hand about 60 cm from the shoulder joint (see Fig. 8.31d). Taking torques about the shoulder, in equilibrium we have

$$|\text{CW torque}| = |\text{CCW torque}|$$

$$F_m \times 0.045 \text{ m} \times \sin 45° = \tfrac{1}{2}W \times 0.60 \text{ m}$$

$$F_m = \frac{\tfrac{1}{2}W \times 0.60 \text{ m}}{0.045 \text{ m} \times \sin 45°} = 9.4W$$

Thus, the force exerted by the lats and pecs *on one side* of the gymnast's body is more than nine times his weight.

The structure of the human body makes large muscular forces necessary. Are there advantages to the structure? Due to the small lever arms, the muscle forces are much larger than they would otherwise be, but the human body has traded this for a wide range of movement of the bones. The biceps and triceps muscles can move the lower arms through almost 180° while they change their lengths by only a few centimeters. The muscles also remain nearly parallel to the bones. If the biceps and triceps muscles were attached to the lower arm much farther from the elbow, there would have to be a large flap of skin to allow them to move so far away from the bones. The arrangement of our bones and muscles favors a wide range of movement.

Another advantage of the body structure is that it tends to minimize the rotational inertia of our limbs. For example, the muscles that control the motion of the lower arm are contained mostly within the *upper* arm. This keeps the rotational inertia of the lower arms about the elbow smaller. It also keeps the rotational inertia of the entire arm about the shoulder smaller. Smaller rotational inertia means that the energy we have to expend to move our limbs around is smaller.

The biceps muscle with its tendons is almost parallel to the humerus. One interesting observation is that the tendon connects to the radius at different points in different people. In one person this point may be 5.0 cm from the elbow joint, while in another person whose arm is the same length it may be 5.5 cm from the elbow. Thus,

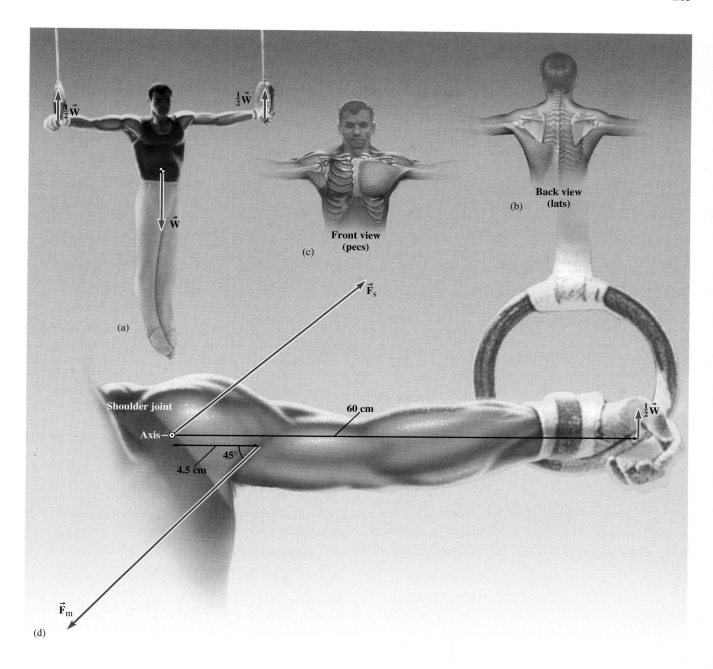

Figure 8.31 (a) Gymnast doing the iron cross. The principal muscles involved are (b) the "lats" and (c) the "pecs." (d) Simplified model of the forces acting on the arm of the gymnast.

some people are naturally stronger than others because of their internal structure. Chimpanzees have an advantage over humans because their biceps muscle has a longer lever arm. Do not make the mistake of arm wrestling with an adult chimp; challenge the chimp to a game of chess instead.

Application of Equilibrium Conditions: Heavy Lifting

When lifting an object from the floor, our first instinct is to bend over and pick it up. This is not a good way to lift something heavy. The spine is an ineffective lever and is susceptible to damage when a heavy object is lifted with bent waist. It is much better to squat down and use the powerful leg muscles to do the lifting instead of using our back muscles. Analyzing torques in a simplified model of the back can illustrate why.

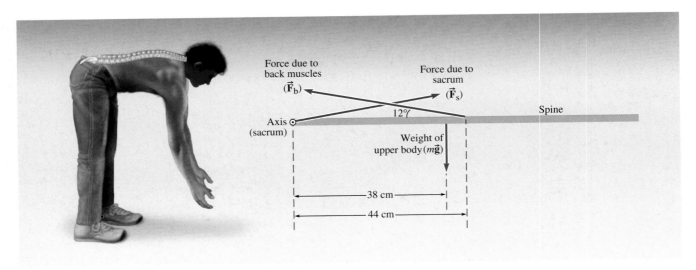

Figure 8.32 A simplified model of the human back when bent over.

Figure 8.33 A safer way to lift a heavy object.

The spine can be modeled as a rod with an axis at the tailbone (the sacrum). The sacrum exerts a force, marked $\vec{\mathbf{F}}_s$ in Fig. 8.32, when a person bends at the waist with the back horizontal. The forces due to the complicated set of back muscles can be replaced with a single equivalent force $\vec{\mathbf{F}}_b$ as shown. This equivalent force makes an angle of 12° with the spine and acts about 44 cm from the sacrum. The weight of the upper body, $m\vec{\mathbf{g}}$ in Fig. 8.32, is about 65% of total body weight; its center of gravity is about 38 cm from the sacrum. By placing an axis at the sacrum we can ignore the force $\vec{\mathbf{F}}_s$ in our torque equation. Since the vertical component of $\vec{\mathbf{F}}_b$ is $F_b \sin 12° \approx 0.21F_b$, only about $\frac{1}{5}$ the magnitude of the forces exerted by the back muscles is supporting the body weight. The much larger horizontal component is pressing the rod representing the spine into the sacrum.

If we put some numbers into this example, we can get an idea of the forces required for just supporting the upper body in this position. If the person's total weight is 710 N (160 lb), then the upper body weight is

$$mg = 0.65 \times 710 \text{ N}$$

Now we set the magnitude of the CCW torques about the axis equal to the magnitude of the CW torques:

$$F_b \times 0.44 \text{ m} \times \sin 12° = mg \times 0.38 \text{ m}$$

Substituting and solving,

$$F_b = \frac{0.65 \times 710 \text{ N} \times 0.38 \text{ m}}{0.44 \text{ m} \times \sin 12°} = 1920 \text{ N}$$

The muscular force that compresses the spine is the horizontal component of $\vec{\mathbf{F}}_b$:

$$F_b \cos 12° = 1900 \text{ N}$$

or about 430 lb. This is over four times the weight of the upper body.

Now if the person tries to lift something with his arms in this position, the lever arm for the weight of the load is even longer than for the weight of the upper body. The back muscles must supply a much larger force. The spine is now compressed with a dangerously large force. A cushioning disk called the lumbosacral disk, at the bottom of the spine, separates the last vertebra from the sacrum. This disk can be ruptured or deformed, causing great pain when the back is misused in such a fashion.

If, instead of bending over, we bend our knees and lower our body, keeping it vertically aligned as much as possible while lifting a load, the centers of gravity of the body and load are positioned more closely in a line above the sacrum, as in Fig. 8.33. Then the lever arms of these forces with respect to an axis through the sacrum are relatively small and the force on the lumbosacral disk is roughly equal to the upper body weight plus the weight being lifted.

8.6 ROTATIONAL FORM OF NEWTON'S SECOND LAW

The concepts of torque and rotational inertia can be used to formulate a "Newton's second law for rotation"—a law that fills the role of $\sum \vec{F} = m\vec{a}$ for rotation about a fixed axis:

Rotational form of Newton's second law:

$$\sum \tau = I\alpha \tag{8-9}$$

Thus, the angular acceleration of a rigid body is proportional to the net torque (more torque causes a larger α) and is inversely proportional to the rotational inertia (more inertia causes a smaller α). In rotational equilibrium, the angular acceleration must be zero; Eq. (8-9) then requires that the net torque be zero. We used $\sum \tau = 0$ as the condition for rotational equilibrium in Sections 8.4 and 8.5.

Equation (8-9) is proved in Problem 57. It is subject to an important restriction. Just as $\sum \vec{F} = m\vec{a}$ is valid only if the mass of the object is constant, $\sum \tau = I\alpha$ is valid only if the rotational inertia of the object is constant. For a *rigid* object rotating about a *fixed axis*, I cannot change, so Eq. (8-9) is always applicable.

Newton's second law for rotation explains why a tightrope walker carries a long pole to help maintain balance. Suppose the acrobat is about to topple over sideways. The pole has a large rotational inertia due to its length, so the angular acceleration of the system (acrobat plus pole) due to a small gravitational torque is much smaller than it would be without the pole. The smaller angular acceleration gives the acrobat more time to adjust his position and keep from falling.

CONNECTION:

In Newton's second law for *rotation*, net torque takes the place of net force, and rotational inertia takes the place of mass, and α takes the place of $\vec{a}$.

When calculating the net torque, remember to assign the correct algebraic sign to each torque before adding them.

The sum of the torques due to internal forces acting on a rigid object is always zero. Therefore, only *external* torques need be included in Eq. (8-9).

Example 8.11

The Grinding Wheel

A grinding wheel is a solid, uniform disk of mass 2.50 kg and radius 9.00 cm. Starting from rest, what constant torque must a motor supply so that the wheel attains a rotational speed of 126 rev/s in a time of 6.00 s?

Strategy Since the grinding wheel is a uniform disk, we can find its rotational inertia using Table 8.1. After converting the revolutions per second to radians per second, we can find the angular acceleration from the change in angular velocity over the given time interval. Once we have I and α, we can find the net torque from Newton's second law for rotation.

Solution The grinding wheel is a uniform disk, so its rotational inertia is

$$I = \tfrac{1}{2}mr^2$$

$$\tfrac{1}{2} \times 2.50 \text{ kg} \times (0.0900 \text{ m})^2 = 0.010125 \text{ kg·m}^2$$

A single rotation of the wheel is equivalent to 2π radians, so

$$\omega = 126 \frac{\text{rev}}{\text{s}} \times 2\pi \frac{\text{rad}}{\text{rev}}$$

The angular acceleration is

$$\alpha = \frac{\Delta \omega}{\Delta t}$$

continued on next page

Example 8.11 continued

Then the torque required is

$$\sum \tau = I\alpha = I\frac{\Delta\omega}{\Delta t}$$

$$= 0.010125 \text{ kg·m}^2 \times \frac{126 \text{ rev/s} \times 2\pi \text{ rad/rev}}{6.00 \text{ s}}$$

$$= 1.34 \text{ N·m}$$

If there are no other torques on the wheel, the motor must supply a constant torque of 1.34 N·m.

Discussion   We assumed that no other torques are exerted on the wheel. There is certain to be at least a small frictional

torque on the wheel with a sign opposite to the sign of the motor's torque. Then the motor would have to supply a torque larger than 1.34 N·m. The *net* torque would still be 1.34 N·m.

Practice Problem 8.11   **Another Approach**

Verify the answer to Example 8.11 by: (a) finding the angular displacement of the wheel using equations for constant α; (b) finding the change in rotational kinetic energy of the wheel; and (c) finding the torque from $W = \tau\Delta\theta$.

8.7   THE MOTION OF ROLLING OBJECTS

A rolling object combines translational motion of the center of mass with rotation about an axis that passes through the center of mass (see Section 5.1). For an object that is rolling without slipping, $v_{CM} = \omega R$. As a result, there is a specific relationship between the rolling object's translational and rotational kinetic energies. The total kinetic energy of a rolling object is the sum of its translational and rotational kinetic energies.

A wheel with mass M and radius R has a rotational inertia that is some pure number times MR^2; it couldn't be anything else and still have the right units. We can write the rotational inertia about an axis through the CM as $I_{CM} = \beta MR^2$ where β is a pure number that measures how far from the axis of rotation the mass is distributed. Larger β means the mass is, on average, farther from the axis. From Table 8.1, a hoop has $\beta = 1$; a disk, $\beta = \frac{1}{2}$; and a solid sphere, $\beta = \frac{2}{5}$.

Using $I_{CM} = \beta MR^2$ and $v_{CM} = \omega R$, the rotational kinetic energy for a rolling object can be written

$$K_{rot} = \frac{1}{2}I_{CM}\omega^2 = \frac{1}{2} \times \beta MR^2 \times \left(\frac{v_{CM}}{R}\right)^2 = \beta \times \frac{1}{2}Mv_{CM}^2$$

Since $\frac{1}{2}Mv_{CM}^2$ is the translational kinetic energy,

$$K_{rot} = \beta K_{tr} \tag{8-10}$$

This is convenient since β depends only on the shape, not on the mass or radius of the object. For a given shape rolling without slipping, the ratio of its rotational to translational kinetic energy is always the same (β).

The total kinetic energy can be written

$$K = K_{tr} + K_{rot}$$

$$K = \frac{1}{2}Mv_{CM}^2 + \frac{1}{2}I_{CM}\omega^2 \tag{8-11}$$

or in terms of β,

$$K = (1 + \beta)K_{tr}$$

$$K = (1 + \beta)\frac{1}{2}Mv_{CM}^2 \tag{8-12}$$

Thus, two objects of the same mass rolling at the same translational speed do *not* necessarily have the same kinetic energy. The object with the larger value of β has more rotational kinetic energy.

Conceptual Example 8.12

Hollow and Solid Rolling Balls

Starting from rest, two balls roll down a hill as in Fig. 8.34. One is solid, the other hollow. Which one is moving faster when it reaches the bottom of the hill? (tutorial: rolling)

Strategy and Solution   Energy conservation is the best way to approach this problem. As a ball rolls down the hill, its gravitational potential energy decreases as its kinetic energy increases by the same amount. The total kinetic energy is the sum of the translational and rotational contributions.

We do not know the mass or the radius of either ball and we cannot assume they are the same. Since both kinetic and potential energies are proportional to mass, mass does not affect the final speed. Also, the total kinetic energy does not depend on the radius of the ball [see Eq. (8-12)]. The final speeds of the two balls differ because different *fractions* of their total kinetic energies are translational.

One ball is a solid sphere and the other is approximately a spherical shell. The mass of a spherical shell is all concentrated on the surface of a sphere, while a solid sphere has its mass distributed throughout the sphere's volume. Therefore, the shell has a larger β than the solid sphere. When the shell rolls, it converts a bigger fraction of the lost potential energy into rotational kinetic energy; therefore, a smaller fraction becomes translational kinetic energy. The final speed of the solid sphere is larger since it puts a larger fraction of its kinetic energy into translational motion.

Figure 8.34
Rolling balls.

Discussion   We can make this conceptual question into a quantitative one: what is the ratio of the speeds of the two balls at the bottom of the hill?

Let the height of the hill be h. Then for a ball of mass M, the loss of gravitational potential energy is Mgh. This amount of gravitational potential energy is converted into translational and rotational kinetic energy:

$$Mgh = K_{tr} + K_{rot} = (1 + \beta)K_{tr} = (1 + \beta)\frac{Mv_{CM}^2}{2}$$

Mass cancels out, as expected. We can solve for the final speed in terms of g, h, and β. The final speed is independent of the ball's mass and radius.

$$v_{CM} = \sqrt{\frac{2gh}{1 + \beta}}$$

The ratio of the final speeds for two balls rolling down the same hill is, therefore,

$$\frac{v_1}{v_2} = \sqrt{\frac{1 + \beta_2}{1 + \beta_1}}$$

To evaluate the ratio, we look up the rotational inertias in Table 8.1. The solid sphere has $\beta = \frac{2}{5}$ and the spherical shell has $\beta = \frac{2}{3}$. Then

$$\frac{v_{solid}}{v_{hollow}} = \sqrt{\frac{1 + \frac{2}{3}}{1 + \frac{2}{5}}} \approx 1.091$$

The solid ball's final speed is, therefore, 9.1% faster than that of the hollow ball. This ratio depends neither on the masses of the balls, the radii of the balls, the height of the hill, nor the slope of the hill.

Practice Problem 8.12   Fraction of Kinetic Energy That Is Rotational Energy

What fraction of a rolling ball's kinetic energy is rotational kinetic energy? Answer both for a solid ball and a hollow one.

✓ CHECKPOINT 8.7

Give an example of how a marble can move so that $K_{tr} > 0$ and $K_{rot} = 0$; (b) $K_{tr} = 0$ and $K_{rot} > 0$; (c) $K_{rot} = \frac{2}{5}K_{tr}$.

Acceleration of Rolling Objects   What is the acceleration of a ball rolling down an incline? Figure 8.35 shows the forces acting on the ball. Static friction is the force that makes the ball rotate; if there were no friction, instead of rolling, the ball would just *slide* down the incline. This is true because friction is the only force acting that yields a

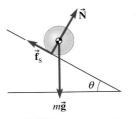

Figure 8.35 Forces acting on a ball rolling downhill.

nonzero torque about the rotation axis through the ball's center of mass. Gravity gives zero torque because it acts at the axis, so the lever arm is zero. The normal force points directly at the axis, so its lever arm is also zero.

The frictional force $\vec{f}$ provides a torque

$$\tau = rf$$

where r is the ball's radius. An analysis of the forces and torques combined with Newton's second law in both forms enables us to calculate the acceleration of the ball in Example 8.13.

Example 8.13

Acceleration of a Rolling Ball

Calculate the acceleration of a solid ball rolling down a slope inclined at an angle θ to the horizontal (Fig. 8.36a).

Strategy The net torque is related to the angular acceleration by $\sum \tau = I\alpha$, Newton's second law for rotation. Similarly, the net force acting on the ball gives the acceleration of the center of mass: $\sum \vec{F} = m\vec{a}_{CM}$. The axis of rotation is through the ball's CM. As already discussed, neither gravity nor the normal force produce a torque about this axis; the net torque is $\sum \tau = rf$, where f is the magnitude of the frictional force. One problem is that the force of friction is unknown. We must resist the temptation to assume that $f = \mu_s N$; there is no reason to assume that static friction has its maximum possible magnitude. We do know that the two accelerations, translational and rotational, are related. We know that v_{CM} and ω are proportional since r is constant. To stay proportional they must change in lock step; their rates of change, a_{CM} and α, are proportional to each other by the same factor of r. Thus, $a_{CM} = \alpha r$. This connection should enable us to eliminate f and solve for the acceleration. Since the speed of a ball after rolling a certain distance was found to be independent of the mass and radius of the ball in Example 8.12, we expect the same to be true of the acceleration.

Solution Since the net torque is

$$\sum \tau = rf$$

the angular acceleration is

$$\alpha = \frac{\sum \tau}{I} = \frac{rf}{I} \qquad (1)$$

where I is the ball's rotational inertia about its CM.

Figure 8.36b shows the forces along the incline acting on the ball. The acceleration of the CM is found from Newton's second law. The component of the net force acting along the incline (in the direction of the acceleration) is

$$\sum F_x = mg \sin \theta - f = ma_{CM} \qquad (2)$$

Because the ball is rolling without slipping, the acceleration of the CM and the angular acceleration are related by

$$a_{CM} = \alpha r$$

Now we try to eliminate the unknown frictional force f from the previous equations. Solving Eq. (1) for f gives

$$f = \frac{I\alpha}{r}$$

Substituting this into Eq. (2), we get

$$mg \sin \theta - \frac{I\alpha}{r} = ma_{CM}$$

Now to eliminate α, we can substitute $\alpha = a_{CM}/r$:

$$mg \sin \theta - \frac{Ia_{CM}}{r^2} = ma_{CM}$$

Solving for a_{CM},

$$a_{CM} = \frac{g \sin \theta}{1 + I/(mr^2)}$$

For a solid sphere, $I = \frac{2}{5}mr^2$, so

$$a_{CM} = \frac{g \sin \theta}{1 + \frac{2}{5}} = \frac{5}{7}g \sin \theta$$

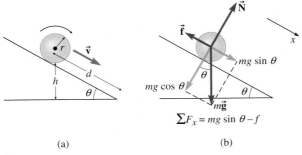

(a)   (b)

Figure 8.36

(a) A ball rolling downhill. (b) FBD for the ball, with the gravitational force resolved into components perpendicular and parallel to the incline.

continued on next page

Example 8.13 continued

Discussion The acceleration of an object *sliding* down an incline without friction is $a = g \sin \theta$. The acceleration of the rolling ball is smaller than $g \sin \theta$ due to the frictional force directed up the incline.

We can check the answer using the result of Example 8.12. The ball's acceleration is constant. If the ball starts from rest as in Fig. 8.36a, after it has rolled a distance d, its speed v is

$$v = \sqrt{2ad} = \sqrt{2\left(\frac{g \sin \theta}{1 + \beta}\right)d}$$

where $\beta = \frac{2}{5}$. The vertical drop during this time is $h = d \sin \theta$, so

$$v = \sqrt{\frac{2gh}{1 + \beta}}$$

Practice Problem 8.13 Acceleration of a Hollow Cylinder

Calculate the acceleration of a thin hollow cylindrical shell rolling down a slope inclined at an angle θ to the horizontal.

8.8 ANGULAR MOMENTUM

Newton's second law for translational motion can be written in two ways:

$$\sum \vec{F} = \lim_{\Delta t \to 0} \frac{\Delta \vec{p}}{\Delta t} \text{ (general form)} \quad \text{or} \quad \sum \vec{F} = m\vec{a} \text{ (constant mass)}$$

In Eq. (8-9) we wrote Newton's second law for rotation as $\sum \tau = I\alpha$, which applies only when I is constant—that is, for a rigid body rotating about a fixed axis. A more general form of Newton's second law for rotation uses the concept of **angular momentum** (symbol L).

> The net external torque acting on a system is equal to the rate of change of the angular momentum of the system.
>
> $$\sum \tau = \lim_{\Delta t \to 0} \frac{\Delta L}{\Delta t} \qquad (8\text{-}13)$$

CONNECTION:

Note the analogy with

$$\sum \vec{F} = \lim_{\Delta t \to 0} \frac{\Delta \vec{p}}{\Delta t}$$

The angular momentum of a rigid body rotating about a fixed axis is the rotational inertia times the angular velocity, which is analogous to the definition of linear momentum (mass times velocity):

> **Angular momentum:**
>
> $$L = I\omega \qquad (8\text{-}14)$$
>
> (rigid body, fixed axis)

CONNECTION:

Note the analogy with $\vec{p} = m\vec{v}$. See the Master the Concepts section for a complete table of these analogies.

Either Eq. (8-13) or Eq. (8-14) can be used to show that the SI units of angular momentum are $kg \cdot m^2/s$.

For a rigid body rotating around a fixed axis, angular momentum doesn't tell us anything new. The rotational inertia is constant for such a body since the distance r_i between every point on the object and the axis stays the same. Then any change in angular momentum must be due to a change in angular velocity ω:

$$\sum \tau = \lim_{\Delta t \to 0} \frac{\Delta L}{\Delta t} = \lim_{\Delta t \to 0} \frac{I\Delta \omega}{\Delta t} = I \lim_{\Delta t \to 0} \frac{\Delta \omega}{\Delta t} = I\alpha$$

Conservation of Angular Momentum However, Eq. (8-13) is *not* restricted to rigid objects or to fixed rotation axes. In particular, if the net external torque acting on a system is zero, then the angular momentum of the system cannot change. This is the **law of conservation of angular momentum**:

CONNECTION:

Another conservation law

⚠

Conservation of angular momentum:

$$\text{If } \sum \tau = 0, \; L_i = L_f \tag{8-15}$$

Here L_i and L_f represent the angular momentum of the system at two different times. Conservation of angular momentum is one of the most basic and fundamental laws of physics, along with the two other conservation laws we have studied so far (energy and linear momentum). For an isolated system, the total energy, total linear momentum, and total angular momentum of the system are each conserved. None of these quantities can change unless some external agent causes the change.

With conservation of energy, we add up the amounts of the different forms of energy (such as kinetic energy and gravitational potential energy) to find the *total* energy. The conservation law refers to the total energy. By contrast, linear momentum and angular momentum *cannot* be added to find the "total momentum." They are entirely different quantities, not two forms of the same quantity. They even have different dimensions, so it would be impossible to add them. Conservation of linear momentum and conservation of angular momentum are *separate* laws of physics.

Application of angular momentum: figure skater

Changing Rotational Inertia   In this section, we restrict our consideration to cases where the axis of rotation is fixed but where the rotational inertia is not necessarily constant. One familiar example of a changing rotational inertia occurs when a figure skater spins (Fig. 8.37). To start the spin, the skater glides along with her arms outstretched and then begins to rotate her body about a vertical axis by pushing against the ice with a skate. The push of the ice against the skate provides the external torque that gives the skater her initial angular momentum. Initially the skater's arms and the leg not in contact with the ice are extended away from her body. The mass of the arms and leg when extended contribute more to her rotational inertia than they do when held close to the body. As the skater spins, she pulls her arms and leg close and straightens her body to decrease her rotational inertia. As she does, her angular velocity increases dramatically in such a way that her angular momentum stays the same.

(a)   (b)

Figure 8.37 Figure skater Lucinda Ruh at the (a) beginning and (b) end of a spin. Her angular velocity is much higher in (b) than in (a).

✓ CHECKPOINT 8.8

If the skater then extends her arms and leg back to their initial configuration, does her angular velocity decrease back to its initial value, ignoring friction?

Many natural phenomena can be understood in terms of angular momentum. In a hurricane, circulating air is sucked inward by a low-pressure region at the center of the storm (the *eye*). As the air moves closer and closer to the axis of rotation, it circulates faster and faster. An even more dramatic example is the formation of a pulsar. Under certain conditions, a star can implode under its own gravity, forming a neutron star (a collection of tightly packed neutrons). If the Sun were to collapse into a neutron star, its radius would be only about 13 km. If a star is rotating before its collapse, then as its rotational inertia decreases dramatically, its angular velocity must increase to keep its angular momentum constant. Such rapidly rotating neutron stars are called pulsars because they emit regular pulses of x-rays, at the same frequency as their rotation, that can be detected when they reach Earth. Some pulsars rotate in only a few thousandths of a second per revolution.

Applications of angular momentum: hurricanes and pulsars

Example 8.14

Mouse on a Wheel

A 0.10-kg mouse is perched at point B on the rim of a 2.00-kg wagon wheel that rotates freely in a horizontal plane at 1.00 rev/s (Fig. 8.38). The mouse crawls to point A at the center. Assume the mass of the wheel is concentrated at the rim. What is the frequency of rotation in rev/s when the mouse arrives at point A?

Strategy Assuming that frictional torques are negligibly small, there is no external torque acting on the mouse/wheel system. Then the angular momentum of the mouse/wheel system must be conserved; it takes an external torque to change angular momentum. The mouse and wheel exert torques on one another, but these *internal* torques only transfer some angular momentum between the wheel and the mouse without changing the total angular momentum. We can think of the system as initially being a rigid body with rotational inertia I_i. When the mouse reaches the center, we think of the system as a rigid body with a different rotational

inertia I_f. The mouse changes the rotational inertia of the mouse/wheel system by moving from the outer rim, where its mass makes the maximum possible contribution to the rotational inertia, to the rotation axis, where its mass makes no contribution to the rotational inertia.

Solution Initially, all of the mass of the system is at a distance R from the rotation axis, where R is the radius of the wheel. Therefore,

$$I_i = (M + m)R^2$$

where M is the mass of the wheel and m is the mass of the mouse. After the mouse moves to the center of the wheel, its mass contributes nothing to the rotational inertia of the system:

$$I_f = MR^2$$

From conservation of angular momentum,

$$I_i\,\omega_i = I_f\,\omega_f$$

Substituting the rotational inertias and $\omega = 2\pi f$,

$$(M + m)R^2 \times 2\pi f_i = MR^2 \times 2\pi f_f$$

Factors of $2\pi R^2$ cancel from each side, leaving

$$(M + m)f_i = Mf_f$$

Solving for f_f,

$$f_f = \frac{M + m}{M} f_i = \frac{2.10\ \text{kg}}{2.00\ \text{kg}} (1.00\ \text{rev/s}) = 1.05\ \text{rev/s}$$

Figure 8.38
Mouse on a rotating wheel.

continued on next page

Example 8.14 continued

Discussion   Conservation laws are powerful tools. We do not need to know the details of what happens as the mouse crawls along the spoke from the outer edge of the wheel; we need only look at the initial and final conditions.

A common mistake in this sort of problem is to assume that the initial rotational kinetic energy is equal to the final rotational kinetic energy. This is not true because the mouse crawling in toward the center expends energy to do so. In other words, the mouse converts some internal energy into rotational kinetic energy.

Practice Problem 8.14   Change in Rotational Kinetic Energy

What is the percentage change in the rotational kinetic energy of the mouse/wheel system?

Angular Momentum in Planetary Orbits

Application of angular momentum: planetary orbits

Conservation of angular momentum applies to planets orbiting the Sun in elliptical orbits. Kepler's second law says that the orbital speed varies in such a way that the planet sweeps out area at a constant rate (Fig. 8.39a). In Problem 104, you can show that Kepler's second law is a direct result of conservation of angular momentum, where the angular momentum of the planet is calculated using an axis of rotation perpendicular to the plane of the orbit and passing through the Sun. When the planet is closer to the Sun, it moves faster; when it is farther away, it moves more slowly. Conservation of angular momentum can be used to relate the orbital speeds and radii at two different points in the orbit. The same applies to satellites and moons orbiting planets.

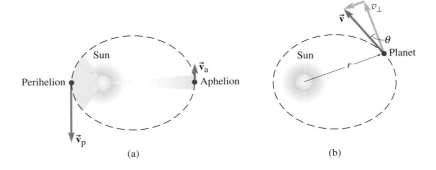

Figure 8.39 The planet's speed varies such that it sweeps out equal areas in equal time intervals. The eccentricity of the planetary orbit is exaggerated for clarity.

Example 8.15

Earth's Orbital Speed

At perihelion (closest approach to the Sun), Earth is 1.47×10^8 km from the Sun and its orbital speed is 30.3 km/s. What is Earth's orbital speed at aphelion (greatest distance from the Sun), when it is 1.52×10^8 km from the Sun? Note that at these two points Earth's velocity is perpendicular to a radial line from the Sun (see Fig. 8.39a).

Strategy   We take the axis of rotation through the Sun. Then the gravitational force on Earth points directly toward the axis; with zero lever arm, the torque is zero. With no other external forces acting on the Earth, the net external torque is zero. Earth's angular momentum about the rotation axis through the Sun must therefore be conserved. To find

Earth's rotational inertia, we treat it as a point particle since its radius is much less than its distance from the axis of rotation.

Solution   The rotational inertia of the Earth is

$$I = mr^2$$

where m is Earth's mass and r is its distance from the Sun. The angular velocity is

$$\omega = \frac{v_\perp}{r}$$

where $v_\perp$ is the component of the velocity perpendicular to a radial line from the Sun. At the two points under consideration,

continued on next page

Example 8.15 continued

$v_\perp = v$. As the distance from the Sun r varies, its speed v must vary to conserve angular momentum:

$$I_i \omega_i = I_f \omega_f$$

By substitution,

$$mr_i^2 \times \frac{v_i}{r_i} = mr_f^2 \times \frac{v_f}{r_f}$$

or

$$r_i v_i = r_f v_f \qquad (1)$$

Solving for v_f,

$$v_f = r_i/r_f \, v_i = \frac{1.47 \times 10^8 \text{ km}}{1.52 \times 10^8 \text{ km}} \times 30.3 \text{ km/s} = 29.3 \text{ km/s}$$

Discussion   Earth moves slower at a point farther from the Sun. This is what we expect from energy conservation. The potential energy is greater at aphelion than at perihelion.

Since the mechanical energy of the orbit is constant, the kinetic energy must be smaller at aphelion.

Equation (1) implies that the orbital speed and orbital radius are inversely proportional, but strictly speaking this equation only applies to the perihelion and aphelion. At a general point in the orbit, the *perpendicular component $v_\perp$* is inversely proportional to r (see Fig. 8.39b). The orbits of Earth and most of the other planets are nearly circular so that $\theta \approx 0°$ and $v_\perp \approx v$.

Practice Problem 8.15   Puck on a String

A puck on a frictionless, horizontal air table is attached to a string that passes down through a hole in the table. Initially the puck moves at 12 cm/s in a circle of radius 24 cm. If the string is pulled through the hole, reducing the radius of the puck's circular motion to 18 cm, what is the new speed of the puck?

8.9   THE VECTOR NATURE OF ANGULAR MOMENTUM

Until now we have treated torque and angular momentum as scalar quantities. Such a treatment is adequate in the cases we have considered so far. However, the law of conservation of angular momentum applies to *all* systems, including rotating objects whose axis of rotation changes direction. Torque and angular momentum are actually vector quantities. Angular momentum is conserved in *both magnitude and direction* in the absence of external torques.

An important special case is that of a symmetrical object rotating about an axis of symmetry, such as the spinning disk in Fig. 8.40. The magnitude of the angular momentum of such an object is $L = I\omega$. The direction of the angular momentum vector points along the axis of rotation. To choose between the two directions along the axis, a **right-hand rule** is used. Align your right hand so that, as you curl your fingers in toward your palm, your fingertips follow the object's rotation; then your thumb points in the direction of $\vec{L}$.

Figure 8.40 Right-hand rule for finding the direction of the angular momentum of a spinning disk.

Figure 8.41 Spinning like a top, the Earth maintains the direction of its angular momentum due to rotation as it revolves around the Sun (not to scale).

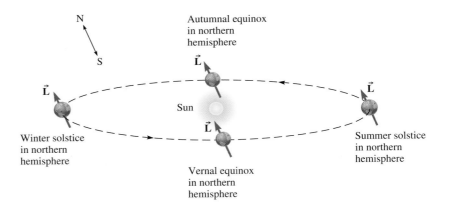

Application of angular momentum: the gyroscope

For rotation about a *fixed* axis, the net torque is also along the axis of rotation, in the direction of the *change* in angular momentum it causes. The sign convention we have used up to now for angular momentum and torque gives the sign of the *z-component of the vector quantity*, where the *z*-axis points toward the viewer (out of the page).

A disk with a large rotational inertia can be used as a *gyroscope*. When the gyroscope spins at a large angular velocity, it has a large angular momentum. It is then difficult to change the orientation of the gyroscope's rotation axis, because to do so requires changing its angular momentum. To change the direction of a large angular momentum requires a correspondingly large torque. Thus, a gyroscope can be used to maintain stability. Gyroscopes are used in guidance systems in airplanes, submarines, and space vehicles to maintain a constant direction in space.

The same principle explains the great stability of rifle bullets and spinning tops. A rifle bullet is made to spin as it passes through the rifle's barrel. The spinning bullet then keeps its correct orientation—nose first—as it travels through the air. Otherwise, a small torque due to air resistance could make the bullet turn around randomly, greatly increasing air resistance and undermining accuracy. A properly thrown football is made to spin for the same reasons. A spinning top can stay balanced for a long time, while the same top soon falls over if it is not spinning.

The Earth's rotation gives it a large angular momentum. As the Earth orbits the Sun, the axis of rotation stays in a fixed direction in space. The axis points nearly at Polaris (the North Star), so even as the Earth rotates around its axis, Polaris maintains its position in the northern sky. The fixed direction of the rotation axis gives us the regular progression of the seasons (Fig. 8.41).

A Classic Demonstration

A demonstration often done in physics classes is for a student to hold a spinning bicycle wheel while standing on a platform that is free to rotate. The wheel's rotation axis is initially horizontal (Fig. 8.42a). Then the student repositions the wheel so that its axis of rotation is vertical (Fig. 8.42b). As he repositions the wheel, the platform begins to rotate opposite to the wheel's rotation. If we assume *no* friction acts to resist rotation of the platform, then the platform continues to rotate as long as the wheel is held with its axis vertical. If the student returns the wheel to its original orientation, the rotation of the platform stops.

The platform is free to rotate about a vertical axis. As a result, once the student steps onto the platform, *the vertical component L_y of the angular momentum of the system* (student + platform + wheel) is conserved. The horizontal components of $\vec{L}$ are *not* conserved. The platform is not free to rotate about any horizontal axis since the floor can exert external torques to keep it from doing so. In vector language, we would say that only the vertical component of the external torque is zero, so only the vertical component of angular momentum is conserved.

Initially $L_y = 0$ since the student and the platform have zero angular momentum and the wheel's angular momentum is horizontal. When the wheel is repositioned so that it

Figure 8.42 A demonstration of angular momentum conservation.

(a)

(b)

Platform at rest

$\vec{L}_{\text{wheel}}$

$\vec{L}_{\text{wheel}}$

$\vec{L}_{\text{platform + student}}$

spins with an upward angular momentum ($L_y > 0$), the rest of the system (the student and the platform) must acquire an equal magnitude of downward angular momentum ($L_y < 0$) so that the vertical component of the total angular momentum is still zero. Thus, the platform and student rotate in the opposite sense from the rotation of the wheel. Since the platform and student have more rotational inertia than the wheel, they do not spin as fast as the wheel, but their vertical angular momentum is just as large.

The student and the wheel apply torques to each other to transfer angular momentum from one part of the system to the other. These torques are equal and opposite and they have both vertical and horizontal components. As the student lifts the wheel, he feels a strange twisting force that tends to rotate him about a horizontal axis. The platform prevents the horizontal rotation by exerting unequal normal forces on the student's feet. The horizontal component of the torque is so counterintuitive that, if the student is not expecting it, he can easily be thrown from the platform!

Master the Concepts

- The rotational kinetic energy of a rigid object with rotational inertia I and angular velocity ω is

$$K_{\text{rot}} = \tfrac{1}{2}I\omega^2 \qquad (8\text{-}1)$$

In this expression, ω must be measured in *radians* per unit time.

- Rotational inertia is a measure of how difficult it is to change an object's angular velocity. It is defined as:

$$I = \sum_{i=1}^{N} m_i r_i^2 \qquad (8\text{-}2)$$

where r_i is the perpendicular distance between a particle of mass m_i and the rotation axis. The rotational inertia depends on the location of the rotation axis.

- Torque measures the effectiveness of a force for twisting or turning an object. It can be calculated in two equivalent ways: either as the product of the perpendicular component of the force with the shortest distance between the rotation axis and the point of application of the force

$$\tau = \pm rF_{\perp} \qquad (8\text{-}3)$$

continued on next page

Master the Concepts continued

or as the product of the magnitude of the force with its lever arm (the perpendicular distance between the line of action of the force and the axis of rotation)

$$\tau = \pm r_\perp F \qquad (8\text{-}4)$$

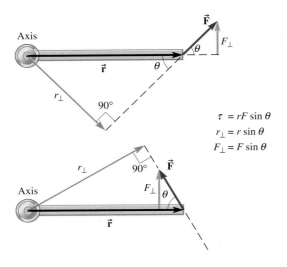

$$\tau = rF \sin \theta$$
$$r_\perp = r \sin \theta$$
$$F_\perp = F \sin \theta$$

- A force whose perpendicular component tends to cause rotation in the CCW direction gives rise to a positive torque; a force whose perpendicular component tends to cause rotation in the CW direction gives rise to a negative torque.
- The work done by a constant torque is the product of the torque and the angular displacement:

$$W = \tau \Delta \theta \quad (\Delta \theta \text{ in radians}) \qquad (8\text{-}6)$$

- The conditions for translational and rotational equilibrium are

$$\sum \vec{F} = 0 \text{ and } \sum \tau = 0 \qquad (8\text{-}8)$$

The rotation axis can be chosen *arbitrarily* when calculating torques in equilibrium problems. Generally, the best place to choose the axis is at the point of application of an unknown force so that the unknown force does not appear in the torque equation.

- Newton's second law for rotation is

$$\sum \tau = I\alpha \qquad (8\text{-}9)$$

where radian measure must be used for α. A more general form is

$$\sum \tau = \lim_{\Delta t \to 0} \frac{\Delta L}{\Delta t} \qquad (8\text{-}13)$$

where L is the angular momentum of the system.

- The total kinetic energy of a body that is rolling without slipping is the sum of the rotational kinetic energy about an axis through the CM and the translational kinetic energy:

$$K = \tfrac{1}{2}Mv_{CM}^2 + \tfrac{1}{2}I_{CM}\omega^2 \qquad (8\text{-}11)$$

- The angular momentum of a rigid body rotating about a fixed axis is the rotational inertia times the angular velocity:

$$L = I\omega \qquad (8\text{-}14)$$

- The law of conservation of angular momentum: if the net external torque acting on a system is zero, then the angular momentum of the system cannot change.

$$\text{If } \sum \tau = 0, \ L_i = L_f \qquad (8\text{-}15)$$

- This table summarizes the analogous quantities and equations in translational and rotational motion.

Translation	Rotation
m	I
$\vec{F}$	τ
$\vec{a}$	α
$\sum \vec{F} = m\vec{a}$	$\sum \tau = I\alpha$
Δx	$\Delta \theta$
$W = F_x \Delta x$	$W = \tau \Delta \theta$
$\vec{v}$	ω
$K = \tfrac{1}{2}mv^2$	$K = \tfrac{1}{2}I\omega^2$
$\vec{p} = m\vec{v}$	$L = I\omega$
$\sum \vec{F} = \lim_{\Delta t \to 0} \dfrac{\Delta \vec{p}}{\Delta t}$	$\sum \tau = \lim_{\Delta t \to 0} \dfrac{\Delta L}{\Delta t}$
If $\sum \vec{F} = 0$, $\vec{p}$ is conserved	If $\sum \tau = 0$, L is conserved

Conceptual Questions

1. In Fig. 8.2b, where should the doorknob be located to make the door easier to open?

2. Explain why it is easier to drive a wood screw using a screwdriver with a large diameter handle rather than one with a thin handle.

3. Why is it easier to push open a swinging door from near the edge away from the hinges rather than in the middle of the door?

4. A book measures 3 cm by 16 cm by 24 cm. About which of the axes shown in the figure is its rotational inertia smallest?

5. A body in equilibrium has only two forces acting on it. We found in Section 2.4 that the

Conceptual Question 4

forces must be equal in magnitude and opposite in direction in order to give a translational net force of zero. What else must be true of the two forces for the body to be in equilibrium? [*Hint:* Consider the lines of action of the forces.]

6. Why do many helicopters have a small propeller attached to the tail that rotates in a vertical plane? Why is this attached at the tail rather than somewhere else? [*Hint:* Most of the helicopter's mass is forward, in the cab.]

7. In the "Pinewood Derby," Cub Scouts construct cars and then race them down an incline. Some say that, everything else being equal (friction, drag coefficient, same wheels, etc.), a heavier car will win; others maintain that the weight of the car does not matter. Who is right? Explain. [*Hint:* Think about the fraction of the car's kinetic energy that is rotational.]

8. A large barrel lies on its side. In order to roll it across the floor, you apply a horizontal force, as shown in the figure. If the applied force points toward the axis of rotation, which runs down the center of the barrel through the center of mass, it produces zero torque about that axis. How then can this applied force make the barrel start to roll?

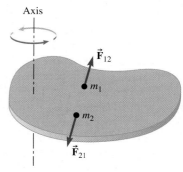

9. Animals that can run fast always have thin legs. Their leg muscles are concentrated close to the hip joint; only tendons extend into the lower leg. Using the concept of rotational inertia, explain how this helps them run fast.

10. Part (a) of the figure shows a simplified model of how the triceps muscle connects to the forearm. As the angle θ is changed, the tendon wraps around a nearly circular arc. Explain how this is much more effective than if the tendon is connected as in part (b) of the figure. [*Hint:* Look at the lever arm as θ changes.]

Question 10

11. Part (a) of the figure shows a simplified model of how the biceps muscle enables the forearm to support a load. What are the advantages of this arrangement as opposed to the alternative shown in part (b), where the flexor muscle is in the forearm instead of in the upper arm? Are the two equally effective when the forearm is

horizontal? What about for other angles between the upper arm and the forearm? Consider also the rotational inertia of the forearm about the elbow and of the entire arm about the shoulder.

Question 11

12. In Section 8.6, it was asserted that the sum of all the internal torques (that is, the torques due to internal forces) acting on a rigid object is zero. The figure shows two particles in a rigid object. The particles exert forces $\vec{\mathbf{F}}_{12}$ and $\vec{\mathbf{F}}_{21}$ on each other. These forces are directed along a line that joins the two particles. Explain why the torques due to these two forces must be equal and opposite even though the forces are applied at different points (and, therefore, possibly different distances from the axis).

13. A playground merry-go-round (Fig. 8.5) spins with negligible friction. A child moves from the center out to the rim of the merry-go-round platform. Let the system be the merry-go-round plus the child. Which of these quantities change: angular velocity of the system, rotational kinetic energy of the system, angular momentum of the system? Explain your answer.

14. The figure shows a balancing toy with weights extending on either side. The toy is extremely stable. It can be pushed quite far off center one way or the other but it does not fall over. Explain why it is so stable.

15. Explain why the posture taken by defensive football linemen makes them more difficult to push out of the way. Consider both the height of the center of gravity and the size of the support base (the area on the ground bounded

by the hands and feet touching the ground). In order to knock a person over, what has to happen to the center of gravity? Which do you think needs a more complex neurological system for maintaining balance: four legged animals or humans?

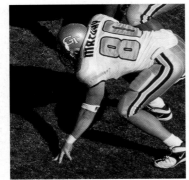

16. The center of gravity of the upper body of a bird is located below the hips; in a human, the center of gravity of the upper body is located well above the hips. Since the upper body is supported by the hips, are birds or humans more stable? Consider what happens if the upper body is displaced a little so that its center of gravity is not directly above or below the hips. In what direction does the torque due to gravity tend to make the upper body rotate about an axis through the hips?

17. An astronaut wants to remove a bolt from a satellite in orbit. He positions himself so that he is at rest with respect to the satellite, then pulls out a wrench and attempts to remove the bolt. What is wrong with his method? How can he remove the bolt?

18. Your door is hinged to close automatically after being opened. Where is the best place to put a wedge-shaped door stopper on a slippery floor in order to hold the door open? Should it be placed close to the hinge or far from it?

19. You are riding your bicycle and approaching a rather steep hill. Which gear should you use to go uphill, a low gear or a high gear? With a low gear the wheel rotates less than with a high gear for one rotation of the pedals.

20. One way to find the center of gravity of an irregular flat object is to suspend it from various points so that it is free to rotate. When the object hangs in

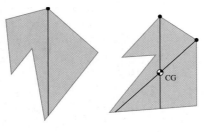

equilibrium, a vertical line is drawn downward from the support point. After drawing lines from several different support points, the center of gravity is the point where the lines all intersect. Explain how this works.

21. One of the effects of significant global warming would be the melting of part or all of the polar ice caps. This, in turn, would change the length of the day (the period of the Earth's rotation). Explain why. Would the day get longer or shorter?

Multiple-Choice Questions

1. A heavy box is resting on the floor. You would like to push the box to tip it over on its side, using the minimum force possible. Which of the force vectors in the diagram shows the correct location and direction of the force? The forces have equal horizontal components. Assume enough friction so that the box does not slide; instead it rotates about point P.

2. When both are expressed in terms of SI *base* units, torque has the same units as

   (a) angular acceleration   (b) angular momentum
   (c) force   (d) energy
   (e) rotational inertia   (f) angular velocity

Questions 3–4: A uniform solid cylinder rolls without slipping down an incline. At the bottom of the incline, the speed, v, of the cylinder is measured and the translational and rotational kinetic energies (K_{tr}, K_{rot}) are calculated. A hole is drilled through the cylinder along its axis and the experiment is repeated; at the bottom of the incline the cylinder now has speed v' and translational and rotational kinetic energies K'_{tr} and K'_{rot}.

3. How does the speed of the cylinder compare with its original value?

   (a) $v' < v$ (b) $v' = v$ (c) $v' > v$
   (d) Answer depends on the radius of the hole drilled.

4. How does the ratio of rotational to translational kinetic energy of the cylinder compare to its original value?

   (a) $\dfrac{K'_{rot}}{K'_{tr}} < \dfrac{K_{rot}}{K_{tr}}$ (b) $\dfrac{K'_{rot}}{K'_{tr}} = \dfrac{K_{rot}}{K_{tr}}$ (c) $\dfrac{K'_{rot}}{K'_{tr}} > \dfrac{K_{rot}}{K_{tr}}$

   (d) Answer depends on the radius of the hole drilled.

5. The SI units of angular momentum are

   (a) $\dfrac{\text{rad}}{\text{s}}$ (b) $\dfrac{\text{rad}}{\text{s}^2}$ (c) $\dfrac{\text{kg·m}}{\text{s}^2}$

   (d) $\dfrac{\text{kg·m}^2}{\text{s}^2}$ (e) $\dfrac{\text{kg·m}^2}{\text{s}}$ (f) $\dfrac{\text{kg·m}}{\text{s}}$

6. Which of the forces in the figure produces the largest magnitude torque about the rotation axis indicated?

(a) 1   (b) 2   (c) 3   (d) 4

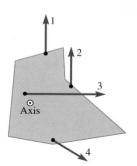

Multiple-Choice Questions 6–8

7. Which of the forces in the figure produces a CW torque about the rotation axis indicated?

(a) 3 only   (b) 4 only   (c) 1 and 2
(d) 1, 2, and 3   (e) 1, 2, and 4

8. Which pair of forces in the figure might produce equal magnitude torques with opposite signs?

(a) 2 and 3   (b) 2 and 4   (c) 1 and 2
(d) 1 and 3   (e) 1 and 4   (f) 3 and 4

9. A high diver in midair pulls her legs inward toward her chest in order to rotate faster. Doing so changes which of these quantities: her angular momentum L, her rotational inertia I, and her rotational kinetic energy K_{rot}?

(a) L only   (b) I only   (c) K_{rot} only
(d) L and I only   (e) I and K_{rot} only   (f) all three

10. A uniform bar of mass m is supported by a pivot at its top, about which the bar can swing like a pendulum. If a force F is applied perpendicularly to the lower end of the bar as in the diagram, how big must F be in order to hold the bar in equilibrium at an angle θ from the vertical?

(a) $2mg$ (b) $2mg \sin \theta$
(c) $(mg/2) \sin \theta$ (d) $2mg \cos \theta$
(e) $(mg/2) \cos \theta$ (f) $mg \sin \theta$

Problems

◉ Combination conceptual/quantitative problem
⚕ Biological or medical application
✦ Challenging problem
Blue # Detailed solution in the Student Solutions Manual
① ② Problems paired by concept
Ⓦ Text website interactive or tutorial

8.1 Rotational Kinetic Energy and Rotational Inertia

1. Verify that $\frac{1}{2}I\omega^2$ has dimensions of energy.

2. What is the rotational inertia of a solid iron disk of mass 49 kg, with a thickness of 5.00 cm and radius of 20.0 cm, about an axis through its center and perpendicular to it?

3. A bowling ball made for a child has half the radius of an adult bowling ball. They are made of the same material (and therefore have the same mass *per unit volume*). By what factor is the (a) mass and (b) rotational inertia of the child's ball reduced compared with the adult ball?

4. Find the rotational inertia of the system of point particles shown in the figure assuming the system rotates about the (a) x-axis, (b) y-axis, (c) z-axis. The z-axis is perpendicular to the xy-plane and points out of the page. Point particle A has a mass of 200 g and is located at $(x, y, z) = (-3.0\text{ cm}, 5.0\text{ cm}, 0)$, point particle B has a mass of 300 g and is at $(6.0\text{ cm}, 0, 0)$, and point particle C has a mass of 500 g and is at $(-5.0\text{ cm}, -4.0\text{ cm}, 0)$. (d) What are the x- and y-coordinates of the center of mass of the system?

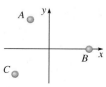

5. Four point masses of 3.0 kg each are arranged in a square on massless rods. The length of a side of the square is 0.50 m. What is the rotational inertia for rotation about an axis (a) passing through masses B and C? (b) passing through masses A and C? (c) passing through the center of the square and perpendicular to the plane of the square?

(a)   (b)   (c)

6. How much work is done by the motor in a CD player to make a CD spin, starting from rest? The CD has a diameter of 12.0 cm and a mass of 15.8 g. The laser scans at a constant tangential velocity of 1.20 m/s. Assume that the music is first detected at a radius of 20.0 mm from the center of the disk. Ignore the small circular hole at the CD's center.

7. Find the ratio of the rotational inertia of the Earth for rotation about its own axis to its rotational inertia for rotation about the Sun.

8. A bicycle has wheels of radius 0.32 m. Each wheel has a rotational inertia of 0.080 kg·m² about its axle. The total mass of the bicycle including the wheels and the rider is 79 kg. When coasting at constant speed, what fraction of the total kinetic energy of the bicycle (including rider) is the rotational kinetic energy of the wheels?

9. In many problems in previous chapters, cars and other objects that roll on wheels were considered to act as if they were sliding without friction. (a) Can the same assumption be made for a wheel rolling *by itself*? Explain your answer. (b) If a moving car of total mass 1300 kg has four wheels, each with rotational inertia of 0.705 kg·m² and radius of 35 cm, what fraction of the total kinetic energy is rotational?

10. A centrifuge has a rotational inertia of 6.5×10^{-3} kg·m². How much energy must be supplied to bring it from rest to 420 rad/s (4000 rpm)?

8.2 Torque

11. A mechanic turns a wrench using a force of 25 N at a distance of 16 cm from the rotation axis. The force is perpendicular to the wrench handle. What magnitude torque does she apply to the wrench?

12. The pull cord of a lawnmower engine is wound around a drum of radius 6.00 cm. While the cord is pulled with a force of 75 N to start the engine, what magnitude torque does the cord apply to the drum?

13. A child of mass 40.0 kg is sitting on a horizontal seesaw at a distance of 2.0 m from the supporting axis. What is the magnitude of the torque about the axis due to the weight of the child?

14. A 124-g mass is placed on one pan of a balance, at a point 25 cm from the support of the balance. What is the magnitude of the torque about the support exerted by the mass?

15. A uniform door weighs 50.0 N and is 1.0 m wide and 2.6 m high. What is the magnitude of the torque due to the door's own weight about a horizontal axis perpendicular to the door and passing through a corner?

16. A tower outside the Houses of Parliament in London has a famous clock commonly referred to as Big Ben, the name of its 13-ton chiming bell. The hour hand of each clock face is 2.7 m long and has a mass of 60.0 kg. Assume the hour hand to be a uniform rod attached at one end. (a) What is the torque on the clock mechanism due to the weight of one of the four hour hands when the clock strikes noon? The axis of rotation is perpendicular to a clock face and through the center of the clock. (b) What is the torque due to the weight of one hour hand about the same axis when the clock tolls 9:00 A.M.?

17. Any pair of equal and opposite forces acting on the same object is called a *couple*. Consider the couple in part (a) of the figure. The rotation axis is perpendicular to the page and passes through point *P*. (a) Show that the net torque due to this couple is equal to *Fd*, where *d* is the distance between the lines of action of the two forces. Because the distance *d* is independent of the location of the rotation axis, this shows that the torque is the same for any rotation axis. (b) Repeat for the couple in part (b) of the figure. Show that the torque is still

Fd if *d* is the *perpendicular* distance between the lines of action of the forces.

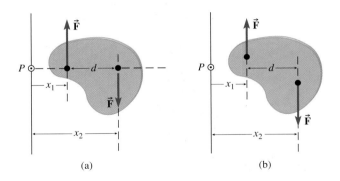

(a)   (b)

18. A 46.4-N force is applied to the outer edge of a door of width 1.26 m in such a way that it acts (a) perpendicular to the door, (b) at an angle of 43.0° with respect to the door surface, (c) so that the line of action of the force passes through the axis of the door hinges. Find the torque for these three cases.

19. A trap door, of length and width 1.65 m, is held open at an angle of 65.0° with respect to the floor. A rope is attached to the raised edge of the door and fastened to the wall behind the door in such a position that the rope pulls perpendicularly to the trap door. If the mass of the trap door is 16.8 kg, what is the torque exerted on the trap door by the rope? (🌀 tutorial: deck hatch)

20. A weightless rod, 10.0 m long, supports three weights as shown. Where is its center of gravity?

5.0 kg   15.0 kg   10.0 kg

0.0   5.0 m   10.0 m

21. A door weighing 300.0 N measures 2.00 m × 3.00 m and is of uniform density; that is, the mass is uniformly distributed throughout the volume. A doorknob is attached to the door as shown. Where is the center of gravity if the doorknob weighs 5.0 N and is located 0.25 m from the edge?

22. A plate of uniform thickness is shaped as shown. Where is the center of gravity? Assume the origin (0, 0) is

located at the lower left corner of the plate; the upper left corner is at $(0, s)$ and upper right corner is at (s, s).

8.3 Calculating Work Done from the Torque

23. A stone used to grind wheat into flour is turned through 12 revolutions by a constant force of 20.0 N applied to the rim of a 10.0-cm-radius shaft connected to the wheel. How much work is done on the stone during the 12 revolutions?

24. The radius of a wheel is 0.500 m. A rope is wound around the outer rim of the wheel. The rope is pulled with a force of magnitude 5.00 N, unwinding the rope and making the wheel spin CCW about its central axis. Ignore the mass of the rope. (a) How much rope unwinds while the wheel makes 1.00 revolution? (b) How much work is done by the rope on the wheel during this time? (c) What is the torque on the wheel due to the rope? (d) What is the angular displacement $\Delta\theta$, in radians, of the wheel during 1.00 revolution? (e) Show that the numerical value of the work done is equal to the product $\tau\Delta\theta$.

✦25. A flywheel of mass 182 kg has an effective radius of 0.62 m (assume the mass is concentrated along a circumference located at the effective radius of the flywheel). (a) How much work is done to bring this wheel from rest to a speed of 120 rpm in a time interval of 30.0 s? (b) What is the applied torque on the flywheel (assumed constant)?

✦26. A Ferris wheel rotates because a motor exerts a torque on the wheel. The radius of the London Eye, a huge observation wheel on the banks of the Thames, is 67.5 m and its mass is 1.90×10^6 kg. The cruising angular speed of the wheel is 3.50×10^{-3} rad/s. (a) How much work does the motor need to do to bring the stationary wheel up to cruising speed? [*Hint:* Treat the wheel as a hoop.] (b) What is the torque (assumed constant) the motor needs to provide to the wheel if it takes 20.0 s to reach the cruising angular speed?

8.4 Rotational Equilibrium

27. A rod is being used as a lever as shown. The fulcrum is 1.2 m from the load and 2.4 m from the applied force. If the load has a mass of 20.0 kg, what force must be applied to lift the load?

28. A weight of 1200 N rests on a lever at a point 0.50 m from a support. On the same side of the support, at a distance of 3.0 m from it, an upward force with magnitude F is applied. Ignore the weight of the board itself. If the system is in equilibrium, what is F?

29. A sculpture is 4.00 m tall and has its center of gravity located 1.80 m above the center of its base. The base is a square with a side of 1.10 m. To what angle θ can the sculpture be tipped before it falls over? (tutorial: filing cabinet)

30. A house painter is standing on a uniform, horizontal platform that is held in equilibrium by two cables attached to supports on the roof. The painter has a mass of 75 kg and the mass of the platform is 20.0 kg. The distance from the left end of the platform to where the painter is standing is $d = 2.0$ m and the total length of the platform is 5.0 m. (a) How large is the force exerted by the left-hand cable on the platform? (b) How large is the force exerted by the right-hand cable?

◉31. Four identical uniform metersticks are stacked on a table as shown. Where is the x-coordinate of the CM of the metersticks if the origin is chosen at the left end of the lowest stick? Why does the system balance?

32. A uniform diving board, of length 5.0 m and mass 55 kg, is supported at two points; one support is located 3.4 m from the end of the board and the second is at 4.6 m from the end (see Fig. 8.19). What are the forces acting on the board due to the two supports when a diver of mass 65 kg stands at the end of the board over the water? Assume that these forces are vertical. (tutorial: plank) [*Hint:* In this problem, consider using two different torque equations about different rotation axes. This may help you determine the directions of the two forces.]

✦33. A house painter stands 3.0 m above the ground on a 5.0-m-long ladder that leans against the wall at a point

4.7 m above the ground. The painter weighs 680 N and the ladder weighs 120 N. Assuming no friction between the house and the upper end of the ladder, find the force of friction that the driveway exerts on the bottom of the ladder. ([W] interactive: ladder; tutorial: ladder)

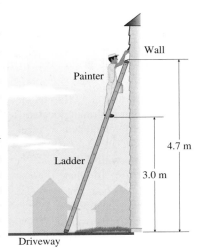

34. A mountain climber is rappelling down a vertical wall. The rope attaches to a buckle strapped to the climber's waist 15 cm to the right of his center of gravity. If the climber weighs 770 N, find (a) the tension in the rope and (b) the magnitude and direction of the contact force exerted by the wall on the climber's feet.

35. A sign is supported by a uniform horizontal boom of length 3.00 m and weight 80.0 N. A cable, inclined at an angle of 35° with the boom, is attached at a distance of 2.38 m from the hinge at the wall. The weight of the sign is 120.0 N. What is the tension in the cable and what are the horizontal and vertical forces F_x and F_y exerted on the boom by the hinge? Comment on the magnitude of F_y.

36. A boom of mass m supports a steel girder of weight W hanging from its end. One end of the boom is hinged at the floor; a cable attaches to the other end of the boom and pulls horizontally on it. The boom makes an angle θ with the horizontal. Find the tension in the cable as a function of m, W, θ, and g. Comment on the tension at $\theta = 0$ and $\theta = 90°$.

37. You are asked to hang a uniform beam and sign using a cable that has a breaking strength of 417 N. The store owner desires that it hang out over the sidewalk as shown. The sign has a weight of 200.0 N and the beam's weight is 50.0 N. The beam's length is 1.50 m and the sign's dimensions are 1.00 m horizontally × 0.80 m vertically. What is the minimum angle θ that you can have between the beam and cable?

38. Refer to Problem 37. You chose an angle θ of 33.8°. An 8.7-kg cat has climbed onto the beam and is walking from the wall toward the point where the cable meets the beam. How far can the cat walk before the cable breaks?

39. A man is doing push-ups. He has a mass of 68 kg and his center of gravity is located at a horizontal distance of 0.70 m from his palms and 1.00 m from his feet. Find the forces exerted by the floor on his palms and feet.

8.5 Equilibrium in the Human Body

40. Your friend balances a package with mass $m = 10$ kg on top of his head while standing. The mass of his upper body is $M = 55$ kg (about 65% of his total mass). Because the spine is vertical rather than horizontal, the force exerted by the sacrum on the spine ($\vec{F}_s$ in Fig 8.32) is directed approximately straight up and the force exerted by the back muscles ($\vec{F}_b$) is negligibly small. Find the magnitude of $\vec{F}_s$.

41. Find the tension in the Achilles tendon and the force that the tibia exerts on the ankle joint when a person who weighs 750 N supports himself on the ball of one foot. The normal force $N = 750$ N pushes up on the ball of the foot on one side of the ankle joint, while the Achilles tendon pulls up on the foot on the other side of the joint.

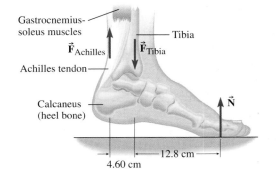

42. In the movie *Terminator*, Arnold Schwarzenegger lifts someone up by the neck and, with both arms fully extended and horizontal, holds the person off the ground. If the person being held weighs 700 N, is 60 cm from the shoulder joint, and Arnold has an anatomy analogous to that in Fig. 8.30, what force must *each* of the deltoid muscles exert to perform this task?

43. Find the force exerted by the biceps muscle in holding a 1-L milk carton (weight 9.9 N) with the forearm parallel to the floor. Assume that the hand is 35.0 cm from the elbow and that the upper arm is 30.0 cm long. The elbow is bent at a right angle and one tendon of the biceps is attached to the forearm at a position 5.00 cm from the elbow, while the other tendon is attached at 30.0 cm from the elbow. The weight of the forearm and empty hand is 18.0 N and the center of gravity of the forearm is at a distance of 16.5 cm from the elbow.

44. A person is doing leg lifts with 3.0-kg ankle weights. She is sitting in a chair with her legs bent at a right angle initially. The quadriceps muscles are attached to the patella via a tendon; the patella is connected to the tibia by the patellar tendon, which attaches to bone 10.0 cm below the knee joint. Assume that the tendon pulls at an angle of 20.0° *with respect to the lower leg*, regardless of the position of the lower leg. The lower leg has a mass of 5.0 kg and its center of gravity is 22 cm below the knee. The ankle weight is 41 cm from the knee. If the person lifts one leg, find the force exerted by the patellar tendon to hold the leg at an angle of (a) 30.0° and (b) 90.0° with respect to the vertical.

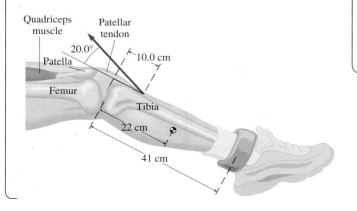

45. One day when your friend from Problem 40 is picking up a package, you notice that he bends at the waist to pick it up rather than keeping his back straight and bending his knees. You suspect that the lower back pain he complains about is caused by the large force on his lower vertebrae ($\vec{F}_s$ in Fig. 8.32) when he lifts objects in this way. Suppose that when the spine is horizontal, the back muscles exert a force $\vec{F}_b$ as in Fig. 8.32 (44 cm from the sacrum and at an angle of 12° to the horizontal). Assume that the CM of his upper body (including the arms) is at its geometric center, 38 cm from the sacrum. Find the horizontal component of $\vec{F}_s$ when your friend is holding a 10-kg package at a distance of 76 cm from his sacrum. Compare this with the magnitude of $\vec{F}_s$ found in Problem 40.

46. A man is trying to lift 60.0 kg off the floor by bending at the waist (see Fig. 8.32). Assume that the man's upper body weighs 455 N and the upper body's center of gravity is 38 cm from the sacrum (tailbone). (a) If, when bent over, the hands are a horizontal distance of 76 cm from the sacrum, what torque must be exerted by the erector spinae muscles to lift 60.0 kg off the floor? (The axis of rotation passes through the sacrum, as shown in Fig. 8.32.) (b) When bent over, the erector spinae muscles are a horizontal distance of 44 cm from the sacrum and act at a 12° angle above the horizontal. What force ($\vec{F}_b$ in Fig. 8.32) do the erector spinae muscles need to exert to lift the weight? (c) What is the component of this force that compresses the spinal column?

8.6 Rotational Form of Newton's Second Law

47. Verify that the units of the rotational form of Newton's second law [Eq. (8-9)] are consistent. In other words, show that the product of a rotational inertia expressed in kg·m^2 and an angular acceleration expressed in rad/s^2 is a torque expressed in N·m.

48. A spinning flywheel has rotational inertia $I = 400.0$ kg·m^2. Its angular velocity decreases from 20.0 rad/s to zero in 300.0 s due to friction. What is the frictional torque acting?

49. A turntable must spin at 33.3 rpm (3.49 rad/s) to play an old-fashioned vinyl record. How much torque must the motor deliver if the turntable is to reach its final angular speed in 2.0 revolutions, starting from rest? The turntable is a uniform disk of diameter 30.5 cm and mass 0.22 kg.

50. A lawn sprinkler has three spouts that spray water, each 15.0 cm long. As the water is sprayed, the sprinkler turns around in a circle. The sprinkler has a total rotational inertia of

9.20×10^{-2} kg·m^2. If the sprinkler starts from rest and takes 3.20 s to reach its final speed of 2.2 rev/s, what force does each spout exert on the sprinkler?

51. A chain pulls tangentially on a 40.6-kg uniform cylindrical gear with a tension of 72.5 N. The chain is attached along the outside radius of the gear at 0.650 m from the axis of rotation. Starting from rest, the gear takes 1.70 s to reach its rotational speed of 1.35 rev/s. What is the total frictional torque opposing the rotation of the gear?

52. Four masses are arranged as shown. They are connected by rigid, massless rods of lengths 0.75 m and 0.50 m. What torque must be applied to cause an angular acceleration of 0.75 rad/s^2 about the axis shown?

A 4.0 kg
B 3.0 kg
C 5.0 kg
D 2.0 kg

53. A bicycle wheel, of radius 0.30 m and mass 2 kg (concentrated on the rim), is rotating at 4.00 rev/s. After 50 s the wheel comes to a stop because of friction. What is the magnitude of the average torque due to frictional forces?

54. A playground merry-go-round (see Fig. 8.5), made in the shape of a solid disk, has a diameter of 2.50 m and a mass of 350.0 kg. Two children, each of mass 30.0 kg, sit on opposite sides at the edge of the platform. Approximate the children as point masses. (a) What torque is required to bring the merry-go-round from rest to 25 rpm in 20.0 s? (b) If two other bigger children are going to push on the merry-go-round rim to produce this acceleration, with what force magnitude must each child push? (tutorial: roundabout)

55. Two children standing on opposite sides of a merry-go-round (see Fig. 8.5) are trying to rotate it. They each push in opposite directions with forces of magnitude 10.0 N. (a) If the merry-go-round has a mass of 180 kg and a radius of 2.0 m, what is the angular acceleration of the merry-go-round? (Assume the merry-go-round is a uniform disk.) (b) How fast is the merry-go-round rotating after 4.0 s?

56. Refer to Atwood's machine (Example 8.2). (a) Assuming that the cord does not slip as it passes around the pulley, what is the relationship between the angular acceleration of the pulley (α) and the magnitude of the linear acceleration of the blocks (a)? (b) What is the net torque on the pulley about its axis of rotation in terms of the tensions T_1 and T_2 in the left and right sides of the cord? (c) Explain why the tensions cannot be equal if $m_1 \neq m_2$. (d) Apply Newton's second law to each of the blocks and Newton's second law for rotation to the pulley. Use these three equations to solve for a, T_1, and T_2. (e) Since the blocks move with constant acceleration, use the result of Example 8.2 along with the constant acceleration equation $v_{fy}^2 - v_{iy}^2 = 2a_y \Delta y$ to check your answer for a.

57. Derive the rotational form of Newton's second law as follows. Consider a rigid object that consists of a large number N of particles. Let F_i, m_i, and r_i represent the tangential component of the net force acting on the ith particle, the mass of that particle, and the particle's distance from the axis of rotation, respectively. (a) Use Newton's second law to find a_i, the particle's tangential acceleration. (b) Find the torque acting on this particle. (c) Replace a_i with an equivalent expression in terms of the angular acceleration α. (d) Sum the torques due to all the particles and show that

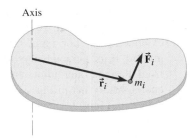

$$\sum_{i=1}^{N} \tau_i = I\alpha$$

8.7 The Motion of Rolling Objects

58. A solid sphere is rolling without slipping or sliding down a board that is tilted at an angle of 35° with respect to the horizontal. What is its acceleration?

59. A solid sphere is released from rest and allowed to roll down a board that has one end resting on the floor and is tilted at 30° with respect to the horizontal. If the sphere is released from a height of 60 cm above the floor, what is the sphere's speed when it reaches the lowest end of the board?

60. A hollow cylinder, a uniform solid sphere, and a uniform solid cylinder all have the same mass m. The three objects are rolling on a horizontal surface with identical translational speeds v. Find their total kinetic energies in terms of m and v and order them from smallest to largest.

61. A solid sphere of mass 0.600 kg rolls without slipping along a horizontal surface with a translational speed of 5.00 m/s. It comes to an incline that makes an angle of 30° with the horizontal surface. Ignoring energy losses due to friction, to what vertical height above the horizontal surface does the sphere rise on the incline?

62. A bucket of water with a mass of 2.0 kg is attached to a rope that is wound around a cylinder. The cylinder has a mass of 3.0 kg and is mounted horizontally on frictionless bearings. The bucket is released from rest. (a) Find its speed after it has fallen through a distance of 0.80 m. What are (b) the tension in the rope and (c) the acceleration of the bucket?

63. A 1.10-kg bucket is tied to a rope that is wrapped around a pole mounted horizontally on frictionless bearings. The cylindrical pole has a diameter of 0.340 m and a mass of 2.60 kg. When the

Problems 62 and 63

bucket is released from rest, how long will it take to fall to the bottom of the well, a distance of 17.0 m?

64. A uniform solid cylinder rolls without slipping down an incline. A hole is drilled through the cylinder along its axis. The radius of the hole is 0.50 times the (outer) radius of the cylinder. (a) Does the cylinder take more or less time to roll down the incline now that the hole has been drilled? Explain. (b) By what percentage does drilling the hole change the time for the cylinder to roll down the incline? (tutorial: rolling)

65. A solid sphere of radius R and mass M *slides* without friction down a loop-the-loop track. The sphere starts from rest at a height of h above the horizontal. Assume that the radius of the sphere is small compared to the radius r of the loop. (a) Find the minimum value of h in terms of r so that the sphere remains on the track all the way around the loop. (b) Find the minimum value of h if, instead, the sphere rolls without slipping on the track.

Problems 65 and 66

66. A hollow cylinder, of radius R and mass M, rolls without slipping down a loop-the-loop track of radius r. The cylinder starts from rest at a height h above the horizontal section of track. What is the minimum value of h so that the cylinder remains on the track all the way around the loop?

67. If the hollow cylinder of Problem 66 is replaced with a solid sphere, will the minimum value of h increase, decrease, or remain the same? Once you think you know the answer and can explain why, redo the calculation to find h.

68. The string in a yo-yo is wound around an axle of radius 0.500 cm. The yo-yo has both rotational and translational motion, like a rolling object, and has mass 0.200 kg and outer radius 2.00 cm. Starting from rest, it rotates and falls a distance of 1.00 m (the length of the string). Assume for simplicity that the yo-yo is a uniform circular disk and that the string is thin compared to the radius of the axle. (a) What is the speed of the yo-yo when it reaches the distance of 1.00 m? (b) How long does it take to fall? [*Hint:* The translational and rotational kinetic energies are related, but the yo-yo is *not* rolling on its outer radius.]

8.8 Angular Momentum

69. A turntable of mass 5.00 kg has a radius of 0.100 m and spins with a frequency of 0.550 rev/s. What is its angular momentum? Assume the turntable is a uniform disk.

70. Assume the Earth is a uniform solid sphere with radius of 6.37×10^6 m and mass of 5.97×10^{24} kg. Find the magnitude of the angular momentum of the Earth due to rotation about its axis.

71. The mass of a flywheel is 5.6×10^4 kg. This particular flywheel has its mass concentrated at the rim of the wheel. If the radius of the wheel is 2.6 m and it is rotating at 350 rpm, what is the magnitude of its angular momentum?

72. The angular momentum of a spinning wheel is 240 kg·m²/s. After application of a constant braking torque for 2.5 s, it slows and has a new angular momentum of 115 kg·m²/s. What is the torque applied?

73. How long would a braking torque of 4.00 N·m have to act to just stop a spinning wheel that has an initial angular momentum of 6.40 kg·m²/s?

74. A figure skater is spinning at a rate of 1.0 rev/s with her arms outstretched. She then draws her arms in to her chest, reducing her rotational inertia to 67% of its original value. What is her new rate of rotation?

75. A skater is initially spinning at a rate of 10.0 rad/s with a rotational inertia of 2.50 kg·m² when her arms are extended. What is her angular velocity after she pulls her arms in and reduces her rotational inertia to 1.60 kg·m²?

76. A uniform disk with a mass of 800 g and radius 17.0 cm is rotating on frictionless bearings with an angular speed of 18.0 Hz when Jill drops a 120-g clod of clay on a point 8.00 cm from the center of the disk, where it sticks. What is the new angular speed of the disk?

77. A spoked wheel with a radius of 40.0 cm and a mass of 2.00 kg is mounted horizontally on frictionless bearings. JiaJun puts his 0.500-kg guinea pig on the outer edge of the wheel. The guinea pig begins to run along the edge of the wheel with a speed of 20.0 cm/s with respect to the ground. What is the angular velocity of the wheel? Assume the spokes of the wheel have negligible mass.

78. A diver can change his rotational inertia by drawing his arms and legs close to his body in the tuck position. After he leaves the diving board (with some unknown angular velocity), he pulls himself into a ball as closely as possible and makes 2.00 complete rotations in 1.33 s. If his rotational inertia decreases by a factor of 3.00 when he goes from the straight to the tuck position, what was his angular velocity when he left the diving board?

79. The rotational inertia for a diver in a pike position is about 15.5 kg·m²; it is only 8.0 kg·m² in a tuck position. (a) If the diver gives himself an initial angular momentum of 106 kg·m²/s as he jumps off the board, how many turns can he make when jumping off a 10.0-m platform

(a)   (b)

Problem 79. (a) Mark Ruiz in the tuck position. (b) Gregory Louganis in the pike position.

in a tuck position? (b) How many in a pike position? [*Hint:* Gravity exerts no torque on the person as he falls; assume he is rotating throughout the 10.0-m dive.]

80. Consider the merry-go-round of Practice Problem 8.1. The child is initially standing on the ground when the merry-go-round is rotating at 0.75 rev/s. The child then steps on the merry-go-round. How fast is the merry-go-round rotating now? By how much did the rotational kinetic energy of the merry-go-round and child change?

8.9 The Vector Nature of Angular Momentum

Problems 81 and 82. A solid cylindrical disk is to be used as a stabilizer in a ship. By using a massive disk rotating in the hold of the ship, the captain knows that a large torque is required to tilt its angular momentum vector. The mass of the disk to be used is 1.00×10^5 kg and it has a radius of 2.00 m.

81. If the cylinder rotates at 300.0 rpm, what is the magnitude of the average torque required to tilt its axis by 60.0° in a time of 3.00 s? [*Hint:* Draw a vector diagram of the initial and final angular momenta.]

82. How should the disk be oriented to prevent rocking from side to side and from bow to stern? Does this orientation make it difficult to steer the ship? Explain.

Comprehensive Problems

83. The Moon's distance from Earth varies between 3.56×10^5 km at perigee and 4.07×10^5 km at apogee. What is the ratio of its orbital speed around Earth at perigee to that at apogee?

84. A ceiling fan has four blades, each with a mass of 0.35 kg and a length of 60 cm. Model each blade as a rod connected to the fan axle at one end. When the fan is turned on, it takes 4.35 s for the fan to reach its final angular speed of 1.8 rev/s. What torque was applied to the fan by the motor? Ignore torque due to the air.

85. The distance from the center of the breastbone to a man's hand, with the arm outstretched and horizontal to the floor, is 1.0 m. The man is holding a 10.0-kg dumbbell, oriented vertically, in his hand, with the arm horizontal. What is the torque due to this weight about a horizontal axis through the breastbone perpendicular to his chest?

86. A uniform rod of length L is free to pivot around an axis through its upper end. If it is released from rest when horizontal, at what speed is the lower end moving at its lowest point? [*Hint:* The gravitational potential energy change is determined by the change in height of the center of gravity.]

87. A gymnast is performing a giant swing on the high bar. In a simplified model of the giant swing, assume that the gymnast keeps his arms and body straight as he swings all the way around the upper bar. Assume also that the gymnast does no work during the

Problem 87. Notice that the angular speed is much greater at the bottom of the swing.

swing. With what angular speed should he be moving at the bottom of the giant swing in order to make it all the way around? The distance from the bar to his feet is 2.0 m and his center of gravity is 1.0 m from his feet.

88. The 12.2-m crane weighs 18 kN and is lifting a 67-kN load. The hoisting cable (tension T_1) passes over a pulley at the top of the crane and attaches to an electric winch in the cab. The pendant cable (tension T_2), which supports the crane, is fixed to the top of the crane. Find the tensions in the two cables and the force $\vec{F}_p$ at the pivot.

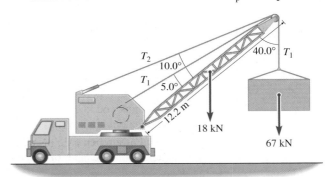

89. A collection of objects is set to rolling, without slipping, down a slope inclined at 30°. The objects are a solid sphere, a hollow sphere, a solid cylinder, and a hollow cylinder. A frictionless cube is also allowed to slide down the same incline. Which one gets to the bottom first? List the others in the order they arrive at the finish line.

90. A uniform cylinder with a radius of 15 cm has been attached to two cords and the cords are wound around it and hung from the ceiling. The cylinder is released from rest and the cords unwind as the cylinder descends. (a) What is the acceleration of the cylinder? (b) If the mass of the cylinder is 2.6 kg, what is the tension in each cord?

91. A modern sculpture has a large horizontal spring, with a spring constant of 275 N/m, that is attached to a 53.0-kg piece of uniform metal at its end and holds the metal at an angle of 50.0° above the horizontal direction. The other end of the metal is wedged into a corner as shown. By how much has the spring stretched?

50.0°

✦92. A painter (mass 61 kg) is walking along a trestle, consisting of a uniform plank (mass 20.0 kg, length 6.00 m) balanced on two sawhorses. Each sawhorse is placed 1.40 m from an end of the plank. A paint bucket (mass 4.0 kg, diameter 28 cm)

1.40 m   6.00 m   1.40 m   0.28 m

is placed as close as possible to the right-hand edge of the plank while still having the whole bucket in contact with the plank. (a) How close to the right-hand edge of the plank can the painter walk before tipping the plank and spilling the paint? (b) How close to the left-hand edge can the same painter walk before causing the plank to tip? [*Hint:* As the painter walks toward the right-hand edge of the plank and the plank starts to tip clockwise, what is the force acting upward on the plank from the left-hand sawhorse support?]

✦93. An experimental flywheel, used to store energy and replace an automobile engine, is a solid disk of mass 200.0 kg and radius 0.40 m. (a) What is its rotational inertia? (b) When driving at 22.4 m/s (50 mph), the fully energized flywheel is rotating at an angular speed of 3160 rad/s. What is the initial rotational kinetic energy of the flywheel? (c) If the total mass of the car is 1000.0 kg, find the ratio of the initial rotational kinetic energy of the flywheel to the translational kinetic energy of the car. (d) If the force of air resistance on the car is 670.0 N, how far can the car travel at a speed of 22.4 m/s (50 mph) with the initial stored energy? Ignore losses of mechanical energy due to means other than air resistance.

✦94. (a) Assume the Earth is a uniform solid sphere. Find the kinetic energy of the Earth due to its rotation about its axis. (b) Suppose we could somehow extract 1.0% of the Earth's rotational kinetic energy to use for other purposes. By how much would that change the length of the day? (c) For how many years would 1.0% of the Earth's rotational kinetic energy supply the world's energy usage (assume a constant 1.0×10^{21} J per year)?

95. A flat object in the xy-plane is free to rotate about the z-axis. The gravitational field is uniform in the $-y$-direction. Think of the object as a large number of particles with masses m_i located at coordinates (x_i, y_i), as in the figure. (a) Show that the torques on the particles about the z-axis can be written $\tau_i = -x_i m_i g$. (b) Show that if the center of gravity is located at (x_{CG}, y_{CG}), the total torque due to gravity on the object must be $\Sigma \tau_i = -x_{CG} M g$, where M is the total mass of the object. (c) Show that $x_{CG} = x_{CM}$. (This same line of reasoning can be applied to objects that are not flat and to other axes of rotation to show that $y_{CG} = y_{CM}$ and $z_{CG} = z_{CM}$.)

Axis of rotation
perpendicular to page

96. The operation of the Princeton Tokomak Fusion Test Reactor requires large bursts of energy. The power needed exceeds the amount that can be supplied by the utility company. Prior to pulsing the reactor, energy is stored in a giant flywheel of mass 7.27×10^5 kg and rotational inertia 4.55×10^6 kg·m². The flywheel rotates at a maximum angular speed of 386 rpm. When the stored energy is needed to operate the reactor, the flywheel is connected to an electrical generator, which converts some of the rotational kinetic energy into electric energy. (a) If the flywheel is a uniform disk, what is its radius? (b) If the flywheel is a hollow cylinder with its mass concentrated at the rim, what is its radius? (c) If the flywheel slows to 252 rpm in 5.00 s, what is the average power supplied by the flywheel during that time?

✦97. A box of mass 42 kg sits on top of a ladder. Ignoring the weight of the ladder, find the tension in the rope. Assume that the rope exerts horizontal forces on the ladder at each end. [*Hint:* Use a symmetry argument; then analyze the forces and torques on one side of the ladder.]

42 kg

Rope

h

0.50h

75°   75°

1.26 m

✦98. A person is trying to lift a ladder of mass 15 kg and length 8.0 m. The person is exerting a vertical force on the ladder at a point of contact 2.0 m from the center of gravity. The opposite end of the ladder rests on the floor. (a) When the ladder makes an angle of 60.0° with the floor, what is this vertical force? (b) A person tries to help by lifting the ladder at the point of contact with the floor. Does this help the person trying to lift the ladder? Explain.

99. A crustacean (*Hemisquilla ensigera*) rotates its anterior limb to strike a mollusk, intending to break it open. The limb reaches an angular velocity of 175 rad/s in 1.50 ms. We can approximate the limb as a thin rod rotating about an axis perpendicular to one end (the joint where the limb attaches to the crustacean). (a) If the mass of the limb is 28.0 g and the length is 3.80 cm, what is the rotational inertia of the limb about that axis? (b) If the extensor muscle is 3.00 mm from the joint and acts perpendicular to the limb, what is the muscular force required to achieve the blow?

100. A block of mass m_2 hangs from a rope. The rope wraps around a pulley of rotational inertia I and then attaches to a second block of mass m_1, which sits on a frictionless table. What is the acceleration of the blocks when they are released?

101. A 2.0-kg uniform flat disk is thrown into the air with a linear speed of 10.0 m/s. As it travels, the disk spins at 3.0 rev/s. If the radius of the disk is 10.0 cm, what is the magnitude of its angular momentum?

102. A hoop of 2.00-m circumference is rolling down an inclined plane of length 10.0 m in a time of 10.0 s. It started out from rest. (a) What is its angular velocity when it arrives at the bottom? (b) If the mass of the hoop, concentrated at the rim, is 1.50 kg, what is the angular momentum of the hoop when it reaches the bottom of the incline? (c) What force(s) supplied the net torque to change the hoop's angular momentum? Explain. [*Hint:* Use a rotation axis through the hoop's center.] (d) What is the magnitude of this force?

103. A large clock has a second hand with a mass of 0.10 kg concentrated at the tip of the pointer. (a) If the length of the second hand is 30.0 cm, what is its angular momentum? (b) The same clock has an hour hand with a mass of 0.20 kg concentrated at the tip of the pointer. If the hour hand has a length of 20.0 cm, what is its angular momentum?

104. A planet moves around the Sun in an elliptical orbit (see Fig. 8.39). (a) Show that the external torque acting on the planet about an axis through the Sun is zero. (b) Since the torque is zero, the planet's angular momentum is constant. Write an expression for the planet's angular momentum in terms of its mass m, its distance r from the Sun, and its angular velocity ω. (c) Given r and ω, how much area is swept out during a short time

Δt? [*Hint:* Think of the area as a fraction of the area of a *circle*, like a slice of pie; if Δt is short enough, the radius of the orbit during that time is nearly constant.] (d) Show that the area swept out per unit time is constant. You have just proved Kepler's second law!

105. A 68-kg woman stands straight with both feet flat on the floor. Her center of gravity is a horizontal distance of 3.0 cm in front of a line that connects her two ankle joints. The Achilles tendon attaches the calf muscle to the foot a distance of 4.4 cm behind the ankle joint. If the Achilles tendon is inclined at an angle of 81° with respect to the horizontal, find the force that each calf muscle needs to exert while she is standing. [*Hint:* Consider the equilibrium of the part of the body *above* the ankle joint.]

106. A merry-go-round (radius R, rotational inertia I_i) spins with negligible friction. Its initial angular velocity is ω_i. A child (mass m) on the merry-go-round moves from the center out to the rim. (a) Calculate the angular velocity after the child moves out to the rim. (b) Calculate the rotational kinetic energy and angular momentum of the system (merry-go-round + child) before and after.

107. Since humans are generally not symmetrically shaped, the height of our center of gravity is generally not half of our height. One way to determine the location of the center of gravity is shown in the diagram. A 2.2-m-long uniform plank is supported by two bathroom scales, one at either end. Initially the scales each read 100.0 N. A 1.60-m-tall student then lies on top of the plank, with the soles of his feet directly above scale B. Now scale A reads 394.0 N and scale B reads 541.0 N. (a) What is the student's weight? (b) How far is his center of gravity from the soles of his feet? (c) When standing, how far above the floor is his center of gravity, expressed as a fraction of his height?

Problem 107

108. A spool of thread of mass m rests on a plane inclined at angle θ. The end of the thread is tied as shown. The outer radius of the spool is R and the inner radius (where the thread is wound) is r. The rotational

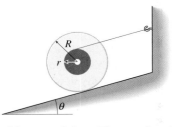

inertia of the spool is I. Give all answers in terms of m, θ, R, r, I, and g. (a) If there is no friction between the spool and the incline, describe the motion of the spool and calculate its acceleration. (b) If the coefficient of friction is large enough to keep the spool from slipping, calculate the magnitude and direction of the frictional force. (c) What is the minimum possible coefficient of friction to keep the spool from slipping in part (b)?

109. A bicycle travels up an incline at constant velocity. The magnitude of the frictional force due to the road on the rear wheel is $f = 3.8$ N. The upper section of chain pulls

on the sprocket wheel, which is attached to the rear wheel, with a force $\vec{F}_C$. The lower section of chain is slack. If the radius of the rear wheel is 6.0 times the radius of the sprocket wheel, what is the magnitude of the force $\vec{F}_C$ with which the chain pulls?

◆110. A circus roustabout is attaching the circus tent to the top of the main support post of length L when the post suddenly breaks at the base. The worker's weight is negligible relative to that of the uniform post. What is the speed with which the roustabout reaches the ground if (a) he jumps at the instant he hears the post crack or (b) if he clings to the post and rides to the ground with it? (c) Which is the safest course of action for the roustabout?

◆111. A student stands on a platform
Ⓒ that is free to rotate and holds two dumbbells, each at a distance of 65 cm from his central axis. Another student gives him a push and starts the system of student, dumbbells, and platform rotating at 0.50 rev/s. The student on the platform then pulls the dumbbells in close to his chest so that they are each 22 cm from his central axis. Each dumbbell has a mass of 1.00 kg and the rotational inertia of the student, platform, and dumbbells is initially 2.40 kg·m². Model each arm as a uniform rod of mass 3.00 kg with one end at the central axis; the length of the arm is initially 65 cm and then is reduced to 22 cm. What is his new rate of rotation?

▼112. A person places his hand palm downward on a scale and pushes down on the scale until it reads 96 N. The triceps muscle is responsible for this arm extension

force. Find the force exerted by the triceps muscle. The bottom of the triceps muscle is 2.5 cm to the left of the elbow joint and the palm is pushing at approximately 38 cm to the right of the elbow joint.

▼113. The posture of small animals may prevent them from being blown over by the wind. For example, with wind blow-

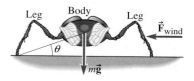

ing from the side, a small insect stands with bent legs; the more bent the legs, the lower the body and the smaller the angle θ. The wind exerts a force on the insect, which causes a torque about the point where the downwind feet touch. The torque due to the weight of the insect must be equal and opposite to keep the insect from being blown over. For example, the drag force on a blowfly due to a sideways wind is $F_{wind} = cAv^2$, where v is the velocity of the wind, A is the cross-sectional area on which the wind is blowing, and $c \approx 1.3$ N·s²·m⁻⁴. (a) If the blowfly has a cross-sectional side area of 0.10 cm², a mass of 0.070 g, and crouches such that $\theta = 30.0°$, what is the maximum wind speed in which the blowfly can stand? (Assume that the drag force acts at the center of gravity.) (b) How about if it stands such that $\theta = 80.0°$? (c) Compare to the maximum wind velocity that a dog can withstand, if the dog stands such that $\theta = 80.0°$, has a cross-sectional area of 0.030 m², and weighs 10.0 kg. (Assume the same value of c.)

◆114. (a) Redo Example 8.7 to find an algebraic solution for d in terms of M, m, μ_s, L, and θ. (b) Use this expression to show that placing the ladder at a larger angle θ (that is, more nearly vertical) enables the person to climb farther up the ladder without having it slip, all other things being equal. (c) Using the numerical values from Example 8.7, find the minimum angle θ that enables the person to climb all the way to the top of the ladder.

Answers to Practice Problems

8.1 390 kg·m²

8.2 $v = \sqrt{\dfrac{2m_2 gh}{m_1 + m_2 + I/R^2}}$

8.3 53 N; 8.4 N·m

8.4 −65 N·m

8.5 8.3 J

8.6 left support, downward; right support, upward

8.7 0.27

8.8 57 N, downward

8.9 It must lie in the same vertical plane as the two ropes holding up the rings. Otherwise, the gravitational force would have a nonzero lever arm with respect to a horizontal axis that passes through the contact points between his hands and the rings; thus, gravity would cause a net torque about that axis.

8.10 460 N

8.11 (a) 2380 rad; (b) 3.17 kJ; (c) 1.34 N·m

8.12 solid ball, $\frac{2}{7}$; hollow ball, $\frac{2}{5}$

8.13 $\frac{1}{2}g \sin \theta$

8.14 5% increase

8.15 16 cm/s

Answers to Checkpoints

8.1 Rotational inertia involves distances from masses to the rotation axis; distances *along* the rotation axis are irrelevant. Another way to see it: cut the cylinder or disk into a large number of thin disks with the same radius. Each thin disk has rotational inertia $I_i = \frac{1}{2}m_i R^2$. Now add up the rotational inertias of the thin disks: $I = \Sigma I_i = \Sigma \frac{1}{2}m_i R^2 = \frac{1}{2}R^2 \Sigma m_i = \frac{1}{2}MR^2$.

8.2 The longer handle lets you push at a greater distance from the rotation axis. Thus, you can exert a larger torque.

8.4 Yes in both cases. Torque depends not only on the magnitude and direction of the force but also on the point where the force is applied. Two forces that do not add to zero can produce torques that add to zero due to different lever arms. Then the net torque is zero and the net torque nonzero; the object is in rotational equilibrium but not in translational equilibrium. Similarly, two forces that add to zero can have different lever arms and produce torques that do not add to zero. In this case the net force is zero and the net torque is nonzero; the object is in translational equilibrium but not in rotational equilibrium.

8.7 (a) falling without spinning; (b) spinning about a fixed axis; (c) rolling without slipping along a surface

8.8 Yes. If friction is negligible, the external torque is zero so her angular momentum does not change. Extending her arms and leg makes her rotational inertia increase back to its initial value, so her angular velocity decreases to its initial value.

Review & Synthesis: Chapters 6–8

Review Exercises

1. A spring scale in a French market is calibrated to show the *mass* of vegetables in grams and kilograms. (a) If the marks on the scale are 1.0 mm apart for every 25 g, what maximum extension of the spring is required to measure up to 5.0 kg? (b) What is the spring constant of the spring? [*Hint:* Remember that the scale really measures *force.*]

2. Plot a graph of this data for a spring resting horizontally on a table. Use your graph to find (a) the spring constant and (b) the relaxed length of the spring.

Force (N)	0.200	0.450	0.800	1.500
Spring length (cm)	13.3	15.0	17.3	22.0

3. A pendulum consists of a bob of mass m attached to the end of a cord of length L. The pendulum is released from a point at a height of $L/2$ above the lowest point of the swing. What is the tension in the cord as the bob passes the lowest point?

4. How much energy is expended by an 80.0-kg person in climbing a vertical distance of 15 m? Assume that muscles have an efficiency of 22%; that is, the work done by the muscles to climb is 22% of the energy expended.

5. Ugonna stands at the top of an incline and pushes a 100-kg crate to get it started sliding down the incline. The crate slows to a halt after traveling 1.50 m along the incline. (a) If the initial speed of the crate was 2.00 m/s and the angle of inclination is 30.0°, how much energy was dissipated by friction? (b) What is the coefficient of sliding friction?

6. A packing carton slides down an inclined plane of angle 30.0° and of incline length 2.0 m. If the initial speed of the carton is 4.0 m/s directed down the incline, what is the speed at the bottom? Ignore friction.

7. A child's playground swing is supported by chains that are 4.0 m long. If the swing is 0.50 m above the ground and moving at 6.0 m/s when the chains are vertical, what is the maximum height of the swing?

8. A block slides down a plane that is inclined at an angle of 53° with respect to the horizontal. If the coefficient of kinetic friction is 0.70, what is the acceleration of the block?

9. Gerald wants to know how fast he can throw a ball, so he hangs a 2.30-kg target on a rope from a tree. He picks up a 0.50-kg ball of putty and throws it horizontally against the target. The putty sticks to the target and the putty and target swing up a vertical distance of 1.50 m from its original position. How fast did Gerald throw the ball of putty?

10. A hollow cylinder rolls without slipping or sliding along a horizontal surface toward an incline. If the cylinder's speed is 3.00 m/s at the base of the incline and the angle of inclination is 37.0°, how far along the incline does the cylinder travel before coming to a stop?

11. A grinding wheel, with a mass of 20.0 kg and a radius of 22.4 cm, is a uniform cylindrical disk. (a) Find the rotational inertia of the wheel about its central axis. (b) When the grinding wheel's motor is turned off, friction causes the wheel to slow from 1200 rpm to rest in 60.0 s. What torque must the motor provide to accelerate the wheel from rest to 1200 rpm in 4.00 s? Assume that the frictional torque is the same regardless of whether the motor is on or off.

12. An 11-kg bicycle is moving with a linear speed of 7.5 m/s. Each wheel can be modeled as a thin hoop with a mass of 1.3 kg and a diameter of 70 cm. The bicycle is stopped in 4.5 s by the action of brake pads that squeeze the wheels and slow them down. The coefficient of friction between the brake pads and a wheel is 0.90. There are four brake pads altogether; assume they apply equal magnitude normal forces on the wheels. What is the normal force applied to a wheel by one of the brake pads?

13. A 0.185-kg spherical steel ball is used in a pinball machine. The ramp is 2.05 m long and tilted at an angle of 5.00°. Just after a flipper hits the ball at the bottom of the ramp, the ball has an initial speed of 2.20 m/s. What is the speed of the ball when it reaches the top of the pinball machine?

14. A rotating star collapses under the influence of gravitational forces to form a pulsar. The radius of the star after collapse is 1.0×10^{-4} times the radius before collapse. There is no change in mass. In both cases, the mass of the star is uniformly distributed in a spherical shape. Find the ratios of the (a) angular momentum, (b) angular velocity, and (c) rotational kinetic energy of the star after collapse to the values before collapse. (d) If the period of the star's rotation before collapse is 1.0×10^{7} s, what is its period after collapse?

15. A 0.122-kg dart is fired from a gun with a speed of 132 m/s horizontally into a 5.00-kg wooden block. The block is attached to a spring with a spring constant of 8.56 N/m. The coefficient of kinetic friction between the block and the horizontal surface it is resting on is 0.630. After the dart embeds itself into the block, the block slides along the surface and compresses the spring. What is the maximum compression of the spring?

16. A 5.60-kg uniform door is 0.760 m wide by 2.030 m high, and is hung by two hinges, one at 0.280 m from the top and one at 0.280 m from the bottom of the door. If the vertical components of the forces on each of the two hinges are identical, find the vertical and horizontal force components acting on each hinge due to the door.

17. Consider the apparatus shown in the figure (not to scale). The pulley, which can be treated as a uniform disk, has a mass of 60.0 g and a radius of 3.00 cm. The spool also has a radius of 3.00 cm. The rotational inertia of the spool, axle, and paddles about their axis of rotation is 0.00140 kg·m². The block has a mass of 0.870 kg and is released from rest. After the block has fallen a distance of 2.50 m, it has a speed of 3.00 m/s. How much energy has been delivered to the fluid in the beaker?

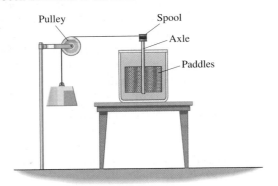

18. It is the bottom of the ninth inning at a baseball game. The score is tied and there is a runner on second base when the batter gets a hit. The 85-kg base runner rounds third base and is heading for home with a speed of 8.0 m/s. Just before he reaches home plate, he crashes into the opposing team's catcher, and the two players slide together along the base path toward home plate. The catcher has a mass of 95 kg and the coefficient of friction between the players and the dirt on the base path is 0.70. How far do the catcher and base runner slide?

19. Pendulum bob A has half the mass of pendulum bob B. Each bob is tied to a string that is 5.1 m long. When bob A is held with its string horizontal and then released, it swings down and, once bob A's string is vertical, it collides elastically with bob B. How high do the bobs rise after the collision?

20. During a game of marbles, the "shooter," a marble with three times the mass of the other marbles, has a speed of 3.2 m/s just before it hits one of the marbles. The other marble bounces off the shooter in an elastic collision at an angle of 40°, as shown, and the shooter moves off at an angle θ. Determine (a) the speed of the shooter after the collision, (b) the speed of the marble after the collision, and (c) the angle θ.

21. At the beginning of a scene in an action movie, the 78.0-kg star, Indianapolis Jones, will stand on a ledge 3.70 m above the ground and the 55.0-kg heroine, Georgia Smith, will stand on the ground. Jones will swing down on a rope, grab Smith around the waist, and continue swinging until they come to rest on another ledge on the other side of the set. At what height above the ground should the second ledge be placed? Assume that Jones and Smith remain nearly upright during the

swing so that their CMS are always the same distance above their feet.

22. A uniform disk is rotated about its symmetry axis. The disk goes from rest to an angular speed of 11 rad/s in a time of 0.20 s with a constant angular acceleration. The rotational inertia and radius of the disk are 1.5 kg·m² and 11.5 cm, respectively. (a) What is the angular acceleration during the 0.20-s interval? (b) What is the net torque on the disk during this time? (c) After the applied torque stops, a frictional torque remains. This torque has an associated angular acceleration of 9.8 rad/s². Through what total angle θ (starting from time $t = 0$) does the disk rotate before coming to rest? (d) What is the speed of a point halfway between the rim of the disk and its rotation axis 0.20 s after the applied torque is removed?

23. A block is released from rest and slides down an incline. The coefficient of sliding friction is 0.38 and the angle of inclination is 60.0°. Use energy considerations to find how fast the block is sliding after it has traveled a distance of 30.0 cm along the incline.

24. A uniform solid cylinder rolls without slipping or sliding down an incline. The angle of inclination is 60.0°. Use energy considerations to find the cylinder's speed after it has traveled a distance of 30.0 cm along the incline.

25. A block of mass 2.00 kg slides eastward along a frictionless surface with a speed of 2.70 m/s. A chunk of clay with a mass of 1.50 kg slides southward on the same surface with a speed of 3.20 m/s. The two objects collide and move off together. What is their velocity after the collision?

26. An ice-skater, with a mass of 60.0 kg, glides in a circle of radius 1.4 m with a tangential speed of 6.0 m/s. A second skater, with a mass of 30.0 kg, glides on the same circular path with a tangential speed of 2.0 m/s. At an instant of time, both skaters grab the ends of a lightweight, rigid set of rods, set at 90° to each other, that can freely rotate about a pole, fixed in place on the ice. (a) If each rod is 1.4 m long, what is the tangential speed of the skaters after they grab the rods? (b) What is the direction of the angular momentum before and after the skaters "collide" with the rods?

27. In a motor, a flywheel (solid disk of radius R and mass M) is rotating with angular velocity ω_i. When the clutch is released, a second disk (radius r and mass m) initially not rotating is brought into frictional contact with the flywheel. The two disks spin around the same axle with frictionless bearings. After a short time, friction between the two disks brings them to a common angular velocity. (a) Ignoring external influences, what is the final angular velocity?

(b) Does the total angular momentum of the two change? If so, account for the change. If not, explain why it does not. (c) Repeat (b) for the rotational kinetic energy.

28. A child's toy is made of a 12.0-cm-radius rotating wheel that picks up 1.00-g pieces of candy in a pocket at its lowest point, brings the candy to the top, then releases it. The frequency of rotation is 1.60 Hz. (a) How far from its starting point does the candy land? (b) What is the radial acceleration of the candy when it is on the wheel?

29. A Vulcan spaceship has a mass of 65 000 kg and a Romulan spaceship is twice as massive. Both have engines that generate the same total force of 9.5×10^6 N. (a) If each spaceship fires its engine for the same amount of time, starting from rest, which will have the greater kinetic energy? Which will have the greater momentum? (b) If each spaceship fires its engine for the same *distance*, which will have the greater kinetic energy? Which will have the greater momentum? (c) Calculate the energy and momentum of each spaceship in parts (a) and (b), ignoring any change in mass due to whatever is expelled by the engines. In part (a), assume that the engines are fired for 100 s. In part (b), assume that the engines are fired for 100 m.

30. Two blocks of masses m_1 and m_2, resting on frictionless inclined planes, are connected by a massless rope passing over an ideal pulley. Angle $\phi = 45.0°$ and angle $\theta = 36.9°$; mass m_1 is 6.00 kg and mass m_2 is 4.00 kg. (a) Using energy conservation, find how fast the blocks are moving after they travel 2.00 m along the inclines. (b) Now solve the same problem using Newton's second law. [Hint: First find the acceleration of each of the blocks. Then find how fast either block is moving after it travels 2.00 m along the incline with constant acceleration.]

31. A particle, constrained to move along the x-axis, has a total mechanical energy of −100 J. The potential energy of the particle is shown in the graph. At time $t = 0$, the particle is located at $x = 5.5$ cm and is moving to the left. (a) What is the particle's potential energy at $t = 0$? What is its kinetic energy at this time? (b) What are the particle's total, potential, and kinetic energies when it is at $x = 1$ cm and moving to the right? (c) What is the particle's kinetic energy when it is at $x = 3$ cm and moving to the left? (d) Describe the motion of this particle starting at $t = 0$.

32. You are mowing the lawn on a hill near your house when the lawnmower blade strikes a stone of mass 100 g and

sends it flying horizontally toward a window. The lawnmower blade can be modeled as a thin rod with a mass of 2.0 kg and a length of 50 cm rotating about its center. The stone impacts the blade near one end and is ejected with a velocity perpendicular to the rotation axis and the blade at the moment of collision. As a result of the impact, the blade slows from 60 rev/s to 55 rev/s. The window is 1.00 m in height, and its center is located 10.0 m away and at the same height as the lawnmower. (a) With what speed is the stone shot out by the mower? [Hint: The external force due to the lawnmower's drive shaft on the system (blade + stone) cannot be ignored during the collision, but the external *torque* about the shaft *can* be ignored. The angular momentum of the stone just after impact can be calculated from its tangential velocity and its distance from the rotation axis.] (b) Ignoring air resistance, will the stone hit the window?

33. A person on a bicycle (combined total mass 80.0 kg) starts from rest and coasts down a hill to the bottom 20.0 m below. Each wheel can be treated as a hoop with mass 1.5 kg and radius 40 cm. Ignore friction and air resistance. (a) Find the speed of the bike at the bottom. (b) Would the speed at the bottom be the same for a less massive rider? Explain.

34. Tarzan wants to swing on a vine across a river. He is standing on a ledge 3.00 m above the water's edge, and the river is 5.00 m wide. The vine is attached to a tree branch that is 8.00 m directly above the opposite edge of the river. Initially the vine makes a 60.0° angle with the vertical as he is holding it. He swings across starting from rest, but unfortunately the vine breaks when the vine is 20.0° from the vertical. (a) Assuming Tarzan weighs 900.0 N, what was the tension in the vine just before it broke? (b) Does he land safely on the other side of the river?

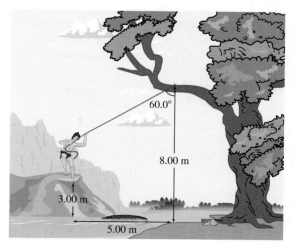

35. A boy of mass 60 kg is sledding down a 70-m slope starting from rest. The slope is angled at 15° below the horizontal. After going 20 m along the slope he passes his friend, who jumps on the sled. The friend has a mass of 50 kg and the coefficient of kinetic friction between the sled and the snow is 0.12. Ignoring the mass of the sled, find their speed at the bottom.

✦36. You want to throw a banana to a monkey hanging from a branch as shown in the figure. The banana has a mass of 200 g and the monkey has a mass of 3.00 kg. The monkey is startled and drops from the branch the moment you throw the banana. Ignore air resistance. (a) In what direction should you aim the banana so the monkey catches it in the air? (b) Explain why your answer to part (a) is the same for different values of the banana's launch speed. (c) If the monkey catches the banana at the point indicated in the figure, what was the banana's initial speed? (d) What is the horizontal distance d to the spot where the monkey lands?

1.67 m

3.33 m

3.00 m

2.00 m

d

MCAT Review

The section that follows includes MCAT exam material and is reprinted with permission of the Association of American Medical Colleges (AAMC).

1. A projectile with a mass of 0.2 kg and a horizontal speed of 2.0 m/s hits a recycle bin (which is free to move), then rebounds at 1.0 m/s back along the same path. What is the magnitude of the horizontal momentum the bin receives?

    A. 0.2 kg·m/s   B. 0.3 kg·m/s
    C. 0.5 kg·m/s   D. 0.6 kg·m/s

2. A vertically oriented spring is stretched by 0.15 m when a 100-g mass is suspended from it. What is the approximate spring constant of the spring?

    A. 0.015 N/m   B. 0.15 N/m
    C. 1.5 N/m   D. 6.5 N/m

3. When a downward force is applied at a point 0.60 m to the left of a fulcrum, equilibrium is obtained by placing a mass of 1.0×10^{-7} kg at a point 0.40 m to the right of the fulcrum. What is the magnitude of the downward force?

    A. 1.5×10^{-7} N   B. 6.5×10^{-7} N
    C. 9.8×10^{-7} N   D. 1.5×10^{-6} N

4. A 0.50-kg ball accelerates from rest at 10 m/s² for 2.0 s. It then collides with and sticks to a 1.0-kg ball that is initially at rest. After the collision, approximately how fast are the balls going?

    A. 3.3 m/s   B. 6.7 m/s
    C. 10.0 m/s   D. 15.0 m/s

5. A 1000-kg car requires 10,000 W of power to travel at 15 m/s on a level highway. How much extra power in watts is required for the car to climb a 10° hill at the same speed? (Use $g = 10$ m/s².)

    A. $1.0 \times 10^4 \times \sin 10°$ B. $1.5 \times 10^4 \times \sin 10°$
    C. $1.0 \times 10^5 \times \sin 10°$ D. $1.5 \times 10^5 \times \sin 10°$

6. A 90-kg patient walks the treadmill at a speed of 2 m/s, and $\theta_{in} = 30°$ for 10 min (600 s). What is the total work done by the patient on the treadmill? (Use $g = 10$ m/s².)

    A. 1.80 kJ   B. 18.0 kJ
    C. 0.54 MJ   D. 1.08 MJ

7. A 100-kg patient walks the treadmill at a speed of 3 m/s, and $\theta_{in} = 30°$ for 5 min (300 s). What is the mechanical power output of the patient in watts? (Use $g = 10$ m/s².)

    A. 300 W   B. 1500 W
    C. 3000 W   D. 7500 W

Read the paragraphs and then answer the following questions:

An exercise bike has the basic construction of a bicycle with a single heavy disk wheel. In addition to friction in the bearings and the transmission system, resistance to pedaling is provided by two narrow friction pads that push with equal force on each side of the wheel. The coefficient of kinetic friction between the pads and the wheel is 0.4, and the pads provide a total retarding force of 20 N tangential to the wheel. The pads are located at a position 0.3 m from the center of the wheel. The distance, recorded on the odometer, is considered to be the distance that a point on the wheel 0.3 m from the center moves. The pedals move in a circle of 0.15 m in radius and complete one revolution, while a transmission system allows the wheel to rotate twice.

In human metabolic processes, the ratio of energy released to volume of oxygen consumed averages 20 000 J/L. A cyclist with a basal metabolic rate of 85 W (rate of internal energy conversion while awake but inactive) pedals continuously for 20 min, registering 4800 m on the odometer. During this activity, the cyclist's average metabolic rate is 535 W. The cyclist's body converts the extra energy into mechanical work output with an efficiency of 20%.

8. What is the magnitude of the force pushing each friction pad onto the wheel?
   A. 10 N
   B. 25 N
   C. 40 N
   D. 50 N

9. Which of the following is closest to the radial acceleration of the part of the wheel that passes between the friction pads?
   A. 10 m/s^2
   B. 20 m/s^2
   C. 40 m/s^2
   D. 50 m/s^2

10. If the wheel has a kinetic energy of 30 J when the cyclist stops pedaling, how many rotations will it make before coming to rest?
    A. Less than 1
    B. Between 1 and 2
    C. Between 2 and 3
    D. Between 3 and 4

11. What is the difference between the average mechanical power output of the cyclist in the passage and the power dissipated by the wheel at the friction pads?
    A. 5 W
    B. 10 W
    C. 20 W
    D. 27 W

12. Which of the following actions would most likely increase the fraction of the cyclist's mechanical power output that is dissipated by the wheel at the friction pads?
    A. Reducing the force on the friction pads and pedaling at the same rate
    B. Maintaining the same force on the friction pads and pedaling at a slower rate
    C. Maintaining the same force on the friction pads and pedaling at a faster rate
    D. Increasing the force on the friction pads and pedaling at the same rate

13. Which of the following is the best estimate of the number of liters of oxygen the cyclist in the passage would consume in the 20 min of activity?
    A. 25 L
    B. 30 L
    C. 45 L
    D. 50 L

14. During a second workout, the cyclist reduces the force on the friction pads by 50%, then pedals for two times the previous distance in $\frac{1}{2}$ the previous time. How does the amount of energy dissipated by the pads in the second workout compare with energy dissipated in the first workout?
    A. One-eighth as much
    B. One-half as much
    C. Equal
    D. Two times as much

15. What is the ratio of the distance moved by a pedal to the distance moved by a point on the wheel located at a radius of 0.3 m in the same amount of time?
    A. 0.25
    B. 0.5
    C. 1
    D. 2

16. A cyclist's average metabolic rate during a workout is 500 W. If the cyclist wishes to expend at least 300 kcal (1 kcal = 4186 J) of energy, how long must the cyclist exercise at this rate?
    A. 0.6 min
    B. 3.6 min
    C. 36.0 min
    D. 41.9 min

17. If the friction pads are moved to a location 0.4 m from the center of the wheel, how does the amount of work done on the wheel, per revolution, change?
    A. It decreases by 25%
    B. It stays the same
    C. It increases by 33%
    D. It increases by 78%

CHAPTER

9

Fluids

A hippopotamus in Kruger National Park, South Africa, wants to feed on the vegetation growing on the bottom of a pond. When the hippo wades into the pond, it floats. How does a hippopotamus get its floating body to sink to the bottom of a pond? (See p. 329 for the answer.)

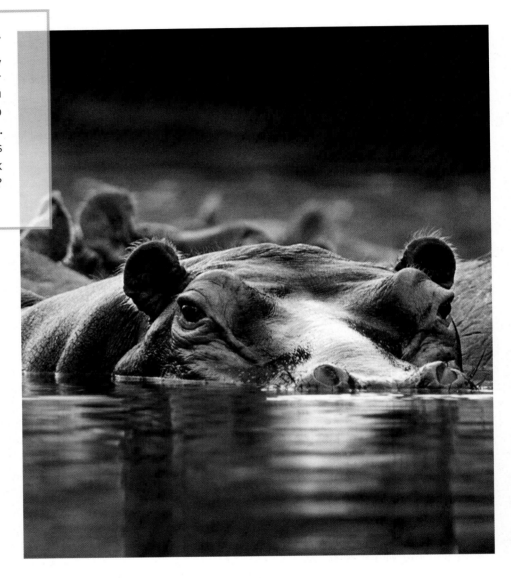

- conservation of energy (Chapter 6)
- force as rate of change of momentum (Section 7.3)
- conservation of momentum in collisions (Sections 7.7 and 7.8)
- equilibrium (Section 2.4)

9.1 STATES OF MATTER

Ordinary matter is usually classified into three familiar states or phases: solids, liquids, and gases. Solids tend to hold their shapes. Many solids are quite rigid; they are not easily deformed by external forces because forces due to neighboring atoms hold each atom in a particular position. Although the atoms vibrate around fixed equilibrium positions, they do not have enough energy to break the bonds with their neighbors. To bend an iron bar, for example, the arrangement of the atoms must be altered, which is not easy to do. A blacksmith heats iron in a forge to loosen the bonds between atoms so that he can bend the metal into the required shape.

In contrast to solids, liquids and gases do not hold their shapes. A liquid flows and takes the shape of its container and a gas expands to fill its container. **Fluids**—both liquids and gases—are easily deformed by external forces. This chapter deals mainly with properties that are common to both liquids and gases.

The atoms or molecules in a fluid do not have fixed positions, so a fluid does not have a definite shape. An applied force can easily make a fluid flow; for instance, the squeezing of the heart muscle exerts an applied force that pumps blood through the blood vessels of the body. However, this squeezing does not change the *volume* of the blood by much. In many situations we can think of liquids as **incompressible**—that is, as having a fixed volume that is impossible to change. The shape of the liquid can be changed by pouring it from a container of one shape into a container of a different shape, but the volume of the liquid remains the same.

In most liquids, the atoms or molecules are almost as closely packed as those in the solid phase of the same material. The intermolecular forces in a liquid are almost as strong as those in solids, but the molecules are not locked in fixed positions as they are in solids. That is why the volume of the liquid can remain nearly constant while the shape is easily changed. Water is one of the exceptions: in cold water, the molecules in the liquid phase are actually *more* closely packed than those in the solid phase (ice).

Gases, on the other hand, cannot be characterized by a definite volume nor by a definite shape. A gas expands to fill its container and can easily be compressed. The molecules in a gas are very far apart compared to the molecules in liquids and solids. The molecules are almost free of interactions with each other except when they collide.

Fluids (liquids and gases) are materials that flow.

Gases are much more compressible than liquids.

9.2 PRESSURE

Microscopic Origin of Pressure A **static** fluid does not flow; it is everywhere at rest. In the study of fluid statics (*hydrostatics*), we also assume that any solid object in contact with the fluid—whether a vessel containing the fluid or an object submerged in the fluid—is at rest. The atoms or molecules in a static fluid are not themselves static; they are continually moving. The motion of people bouncing up and down and bumping into each other in a mosh pit gives you a rough idea of the motion of the closely packed atoms or molecules in a liquid; in gases, the atoms or molecules are much farther apart than in liquids, so they travel greater distances between collisions.

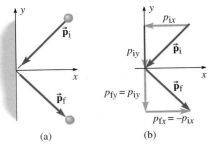

(a)   (b)

Figure 9.1 (a) A single fluid molecule bouncing off a container wall. (b) In this elastic collision, the y-component of the momentum is unchanged, while the x-component reverses direction.

Fluid pressure is caused by collisions of the fast-moving atoms or molecules of a fluid. When a single molecule hits a container wall and rebounds, its momentum changes due to the force exerted on it by the wall. Figure 9.1a shows a molecule of a fluid within a container making an elastic collision with one of the container walls. In this case, the y-component of momentum is unchanged, while the x-component reverses direction (Fig. 9.1b). The momentum change is in the $+x$-direction, which occurs because the wall exerts a force to the right on the molecule. By Newton's third law, the molecule exerts a force to the left on the wall during the collision. If we consider all the molecules colliding with this wall, *on average* they exert no force on the wall in the $\pm y$-direction, but all exert a force in the $-x$-direction. The frequent collisions of fluid molecules with the walls of the container cause a net force pushing outward on the walls.

PHYSICS AT HOME

Drop a very tiny speck of dust or lint into a container of water and push the speck below the surface. The motion of the speck—called *Brownian motion*—is easily observed as it is pushed and bumped about randomly by collisions with water molecules. The water molecules themselves move about randomly, but at much higher speeds than the speck of dust due to their much smaller mass.

The force due to a static fluid on a surface is always perpendicular to the surface.

Definition of Pressure A static fluid exerts a force on any surface with which it comes in contact; the direction of the force is perpendicular to the surface (Fig. 9.2). A static fluid *cannot* exert a force *parallel* to the surface. If it did, the surface would exert a force on the fluid parallel to the surface, by Newton's third law. This force would make the fluid flow along the surface, contradicting the premise that the fluid is static.

The *average pressure* of a fluid at points on a planar surface is

Definition of average pressure:

$$P_{av} = \frac{F}{A} \tag{9-1}$$

where F is the magnitude of the force acting perpendicularly to the surface and A is the area of the surface. By imagining a tiny surface at various points within the fluid and measuring the force that acts on it, we can define the pressure at any point within the fluid. In the limit of a small area A, $P = F/A$ is the **pressure P** of the fluid.

Pressure is a scalar quantity; it does not have a direction. The force acting on an object submerged in a fluid—or on some portion of the fluid itself—is a vector quantity; its direction is perpendicular to the contact surface. Pressure is defined as a scalar because, at a given location in the fluid, the magnitude of the force per unit area is the same for any orientation of the surface. The molecules in a static fluid are moving in random directions; there can be no preferred direction since that would constitute fluid flow. There is no reason that a surface would have a greater number of collisions, or collisions with more energetic molecules, for one particular surface orientation compared with any other orientation.

The SI unit for pressure is the newton per square meter (N/m^2), which is named the *pascal* (symbol Pa) after the French scientist Blaise Pascal (1623–1662). Another commonly used unit of pressure is the *atmosphere* (atm). One atmosphere is the *average* air pressure at sea level. The conversion factor between atmospheres and pascals is

$$1 \text{ atm} = 101.3 \text{ kPa}$$

Other units of pressure in common use are introduced in Section 9.5.

Figure 9.2 Forces due to a static fluid acting on the walls of the container and on a submerged object.

Example 9.1

Pressure due to Stiletto-Heeled Shoes

A young woman weighing 534 N (120 lb) walks to her bedroom while wearing tennis shoes. She then gets dressed for her evening date, putting on her new stiletto-heeled dress shoes. The area of the heel section of her tennis shoe is 60.0 cm^2 and the area of the heel of her dress shoe is 1.00 cm^2. For each pair of shoes, find the average pressure caused by the heel making contact with the floor when her entire weight is supported by one heel.

Strategy The average pressure is the force applied to the floor divided by the contact area. The force that the heel exerts on the floor is 534 N. To keep the units straight, we convert the areas from square centimeters to square meters.

Solution To convert the area of the tennis shoe heel and the dress shoe heel from cm^2 to m^2, we multiply by the conversion factor $\left(\dfrac{1 \text{ m}}{10^2 \text{ cm}}\right)^2$. For the tennis shoe heel:

$$A = 60.0 \text{ cm}^2 \times \left(\frac{1 \text{ m}}{10^2 \text{ cm}}\right)^2 = 6.00 \times 10^{-3} \text{ m}^2$$

For the dress shoe heel:

$$A = 1.00 \text{ cm}^2 \times \left(\frac{1 \text{ m}}{10^2 \text{ cm}}\right)^2 = 1.00 \times 10^{-4} \text{ m}^2$$

The average pressure is the woman's weight divided by the area of the heel. For the tennis shoe:

$$P = \frac{F}{A} = \frac{534 \text{ N}}{6.00 \times 10^{-3} \text{ m}^2} = 8.90 \times 10^4 \text{ N/m}^2 = 89.0 \text{ kPa}$$

For the stilettos:

$$P = \frac{534 \text{ N}}{1.00 \times 10^{-4} \text{ m}^2} = 5.34 \times 10^6 \text{ N/m}^2 = 5.34 \text{ MPa}$$

Discussion In atmospheres, these pressures are 0.879 atm and 52.7 atm, respectively. The pressure due to the dress shoe is 60 times the pressure due to the tennis shoe since the same force is spread over $\frac{1}{60}$ the area.

Practice Problem 9.1   Pressure from an Ordinary Dress Shoe Heel

Fortunately for floor manufacturers, and for women's feet, stiletto heels are out of fashion more often than they are in fashion. Suppose that a woman's dress shoes have heels that are each 4.0 cm^2 in area. Find the pressure on the floor, when the entire weight is on a single heel, for such a shoe worn by the same woman as in Example 9.1. Find the factor by which this pressure exceeds the pressure from the tennis shoe heel.

Atmospheric Pressure

On the surface of the Earth, we live at the bottom of an ocean of fluid called air. The forces exerted by air on our bodies and on surfaces of other objects may be surprisingly large: 1 atm is approximately 10 N/cm^2 of surface area, or nearly 15 lb/in^2. We are not crushed by this pressure because most of the fluids in our bodies are at approximately the same pressure as the air around us. As an analogy, consider a sealed bag of potato chips. Why is the bag not crushed by the air pushing in on all sides? Because the air inside the bag is at the same pressure and pushes out on the sides of the bag. The pressure of the fluids inside our cells matches the pressure of the surrounding fluids pushing in on the cell membranes, so the cells do not rupture.

By contrast, the blood pressure in the arteries is as much as 20 kPa higher than atmospheric pressure. The strong, elastic arterial walls are stretched by the pressure of the blood inside; the walls squeeze the arterial blood to keep its higher pressure from being transmitted to other fluids in the body.

Changing weather conditions cause variations of approximately 5% in the actual value of air pressure at sea level; 101.3 kPa (1 atm) is only the *average* value. Air pressure also decreases with increasing elevation. (In Section 9.4, we study the effect of gravity on fluid pressure in detail.) The average air pressure in Leadville, Colorado, the highest incorporated city in the United States (elevation 3100 m), is 70 kPa. Some Tibetans live at altitudes of over 5000 m, where the average air pressure is only half its value at sea level. In problems, please assume that the atmospheric pressure is 1 atm unless the problem states otherwise.

Figure 9.3 Forces acting on a cube of fluid.

Figure 9.4 Simplified diagram of a hydraulic lift. Notice that piston 1 has to move a great distance (d_1) to lift the truck a much smaller distance (d_2). In a real hydraulic lift, piston 1 is usually replaced by a pump that draws fluid from a reservoir and pushes it into the hydraulic system.

CONNECTION:

As for levers, systems of pulleys, and other simple machines, the hydraulic lift reduces the applied *force* needed to perform a task, but the *work* done is the same.

9.3 PASCAL'S PRINCIPLE

If the weight of a static fluid is negligible (as, for example, in a hydraulic system under high pressure), then the pressure must be the same everywhere in the fluid. Why? In Fig. 9.3, imagine the submerged cube to be composed of the same fluid as its surroundings. Ignoring the fluid's weight, the only forces acting on the cubical piece of fluid are those due to the surrounding fluid pushing inward. The forces pushing on each pair of opposite sides of the cube must be equal in magnitude, since the fluid inside the cube is in equilibrium. Therefore, the pressure must be the same on both sides. Since we can extend this argument to any size and shape piece of fluid, *the fluid pressure must be the same everywhere in a weightless, static fluid.*

More generally, when the weight of the fluid is *not* negligible, the pressure is not the same everywhere. In this case, analysis of the forces acting on a piece of fluid (see Conceptual Question 15) leads to a more general result called **Pascal's principle**.

Pascal's Principle

A *change in pressure* at any point in a confined fluid is transmitted everywhere throughout the fluid.

Applications of Pascal's Principle: Hydraulic Lifts, Brakes, and Controls When a truck needs to have its muffler replaced, it is lifted into the air by a mechanism called a hydraulic lift (Fig. 9.4). A force is exerted on a liquid by a piston with a relatively small area; the resulting increase in pressure is transmitted everywhere throughout the liquid. Then the truck is lifted by the fluid pressure on a piston of much larger area. The upward force on the truck is much larger than the force applied to the small piston. Pascal's principle has many other applications, such as the hydraulic brakes in cars and trucks and the hydraulic controls in airplanes.

To analyze the forces in the hydraulic lift, let force F_1 be applied to the small piston of area A_1, causing a pressure increase:

$$\Delta P = \frac{F_1}{A_1}$$

A truck is supported by a piston of much larger area A_2 on the other side of the lift. The increase in pressure due to the small piston is transmitted everywhere in the liquid. Ignoring the weight of the fluid (or assuming the two pistons to be at the same height), the force F_2 exerted by the fluid on the large piston is related to F_1 by

$$\frac{F_1}{A_1} = \frac{F_2}{A_2}$$

Since A_2 is larger than A_1, the force exerted on the large piston (F_2) is larger than the force applied to the small piston (F_1). We are not getting something for nothing; just as for the two-pulley systems discussed in Section 6.2, the advantage of the smaller force applied to the small piston is balanced by a greater distance it must be moved. The small piston has to move a long distance d_1 while the large piston moves a short distance d_2. Assuming the liquid to be incompressible, the volume of fluid displaced by each piston is the same, so

$$A_1 d_1 = A_2 d_2$$

The displacements of the pistons are inversely proportional to their areas, while the forces are directly proportional to the areas; then the product of force and displacement is the same:

$$\frac{F_1}{A_1} \times A_1 d_1 = \frac{F_2}{A_2} \times A_2 d_2 \quad \Rightarrow \quad F_1 d_1 = F_2 d_2$$

The work (force times displacement) done by moving the small piston equals the work done by the large piston in raising the truck.

Example 9.2

The Hydraulic Lift

In a hydraulic lift, if the radius of the smaller piston is 2.0 cm and the radius of the larger piston is 20.0 cm, what weight can the larger piston support when a force of 250 N is applied to the smaller piston?

Strategy According to Pascal's principle, the pressure increases the same amount at every point in the fluid. A natural way to work is in terms of proportions since the forces are proportional to the areas of the pistons.

Solution Since the pressure on the two pistons increases by the same amount,

$$\frac{F_1}{A_1} = \frac{F_2}{A_2}$$

Equivalently, the forces are proportional to the areas:

$$\frac{F_2}{F_1} = \frac{A_2}{A_1}$$

The ratio of the radii is $r_2/r_1 = 10$, so the ratio of the areas is $A_2/A_1 = (r_2/r_1)^2 = 100$. Then the weight that can be supported is

$$F_2 = 100F_1 = 25\,000 \text{ N} = 25 \text{ kN}$$

⚠ **Discussion** One common error in this sort of problem is to think of the area and the force as a *trade-off*—in other words, that the piston with the *large* area has the *small* force and vice versa. Since the pressures are the same, the force exerted by the fluid on either piston is proportional to the piston's area. We make the piston that lifts the truck large because we know the force on it will be large, *in direct proportion to* its area.

Practice Problem 9.2   Application of Pascal's Principle

Consider the hydraulic lift of Example 9.2. (a) What is the increase in pressure caused by the 250-N force on the small piston? (b) If the larger piston moves 5.0 cm, how far does the smaller piston move?

9.4   THE EFFECT OF GRAVITY ON FLUID PRESSURE

On a drive through the mountains or on a trip in a small plane, the feeling of our ears popping is evidence that pressure is not the same everywhere in a static fluid. Gravity makes fluid pressure increase as you move down and decrease as you move up. To understand more about this variation, we must first define the density of a fluid.

Density   The **density** of a substance is its mass per unit volume. The Greek letter ρ (rho) is used to represent density. The density of a uniform substance of mass m and volume V is

Density of a uniform substance: its mass divided by its volume.

$$\rho = \frac{m}{V} \qquad (9\text{-}2)$$

The SI units of density are kilograms per cubic meter: kg/m^3. For a nonuniform substance, Eq. (9-2) defines the **average density**.

Table 9.1 lists the densities of some common substances. Note that temperatures and pressures are specified in the table. For solids and liquids, density is only weakly dependent on temperature and pressure. On the other hand, gases are highly compressible, so even a relatively small change in temperature or pressure can change the density of a gas significantly.

Pressure Variation with Depth due to Gravity   Now, using the concept of density, we can find how pressure increases with depth due to gravity. Suppose we have a glass beaker containing a static liquid of uniform density ρ. Within this liquid, imagine a cylinder of liquid with cross-sectional area A and height d (Fig. 9.5a). The mass of the liquid in this cylinder is

$$m = \rho V$$

Table 9.1   Densities of Common Substances (at 0°C and 1 atm unless otherwise indicated)

Gases	Density (kg/m³)	Liquids	Density (kg/m³)	Solids	Density (kg/m³)
Hydrogen	0.090	Gasoline	680	Polystyrene	100
Helium	0.18	Ethanol	790	Cork	240
Steam (100°C)	0.60	Oil	800–900	Wood (pine)	350–550
Nitrogen	1.25	Water (0°C)	999.87	Wood (oak)	600–900
Air (20°C)	1.20	Water (3.98°C)	1000.00	Ice	917
Air (0°C)	1.29	Water (20°C)	1001.80	Wood (ebony)	1000–1300
Oxygen	1.43	Seawater	1025	Bone	1500–2000
Carbon dioxide	1.98	Blood (37°C)	1060	Concrete	2000
		Mercury	13 600	Quartz, granite	2700
				Aluminum	2702
				Iron, steel	7860
				Copper	8920
				Lead	11 300
				Gold	19 300
				Platinum	21 500

(a)

(b)

Figure 9.5 Applying Newton's second law to a cylinder of liquid tells us how pressure increases with increasing depth. (a) A cylinder of liquid of height d and area A. (b) Vertical forces on the cylinder of liquid.

where the volume of the cylinder is

$$V = Ad$$

The weight of the cylinder of liquid is therefore

$$mg = (\rho Ad)g$$

The vertical forces acting on this column of liquid are shown in Fig. 9.5b. The pressure at the top of the cylinder is P_1 and the pressure at the bottom is P_2. Since the liquid in the column is in equilibrium, the net vertical force acting on it must be zero by Newton's second law:

$$\sum F_y = P_2 A - P_1 A - \rho A dg = 0$$

Dividing by the common factor A and rearranging yields:

Pressure variation with depth in a static fluid with uniform density:

$$P_2 = P_1 + \rho g d \qquad (9\text{-}3)$$

where point 2 is a depth d below point 1

Since we can imagine a cylinder anywhere we choose within the liquid, Eq. (9-3) relates the pressure at any two points in a static liquid where point 2 is a depth d below point 1.

For gases, Eq. (9-3) can be applied as long as the depth d is small enough that changes in the density due to gravity are negligible. Since liquids are nearly incompressible, Eq. (9-3) holds to great depths in liquids.

For a liquid that is open to the atmosphere, suppose we take point 1 at the surface and point 2 a depth d below. Then $P_1 = P_{atm}$, so the pressure at a depth d below the surface is

Pressure at a depth d below the surface of a liquid open to the atmosphere:

$$P = P_{atm} + \rho g d \qquad (9\text{-}4)$$

✓ CHECKPOINT 9.4

Pressure in a static fluid depends on vertical position. Can it also depend on horizontal position? Explain.

Example 9.3

A Diver

A diver swims to a depth of 3.2 m in a freshwater lake. What is the increase in the force pushing in on her eardrum, compared to what it was at the lake surface? The area of the eardrum is 0.60 cm^2.

Strategy   We can find the increase in pressure at a depth of 3.2 m and then find the corresponding increase in force on the eardrum. If the force on the eardrum at the surface is $P_1 A$ and the force at a depth of 3.2 m is $P_2 A$, then the increase in the force is $(P_2 - P_1)A$.

Solution   The increase in pressure depends on the depth d and the density of water. From Table 9.1, the density of water is 1000 kg/m^3 to two significant figures for any reasonable temperature.

$$P_2 - P_1 = \rho g d$$
$$\Delta P = 1000 \text{ kg/m}^3 \times 9.8 \text{ m/s}^2 \times 3.2 \text{ m}$$
$$= 31.4 \text{ kPa}$$

The increase in force on the eardrum is

$$\Delta F = \Delta P \times A$$

where $A = 0.60 \text{ cm}^2 = 6.0 \times 10^{-5} \text{ m}^2$. Then

$$\Delta F = (3.14 \times 10^4 \text{ Pa}) \times (6.0 \times 10^{-5} \text{ m}^2)$$
$$= 1.9 \text{ N}$$

Discussion   A force also pushes *outward* on the eardrum due to the pressure inside the ear canal. If the diver descends rapidly so that the pressure inside the ear canal does not change, then a 1.9-N net force due to fluid pressure pushes inward on the eardrum. When the diver's ear "pops," the pressure inside the ear canal increases to equal the fluid pressure outside the eardrum, so that the net force due to fluid pressure on the eardrum is zero.

Practice Problem 9.3   Limits on Submarine Depth

A submarine is constructed so that it can safely withstand a pressure of 1.6×10^7 Pa. How deep may this submarine descend in the ocean if the average density of seawater is 1025 kg/m^3?

Conceptual Example 9.4

The Hydrostatic Paradox

Three vessels have different shapes, but the same base area and the same weight when empty (Fig. 9.6). The vessels are filled with water to the same level and then the air is pumped out. The top surface of the water is then at a low pressure that, for simplicity, we assume to be zero. (a) Are the water pressures at the bottom of each vessel the same? If not, which is largest and which is smallest? (b) If the three vessels containing water are weighed on a scale, do they give the same reading? If not, which weighs the most and which weighs the least? (c) If the water exerts the same downward force on the bottom of each vessel, is that force equal to the weight of water in the vessel? Is there a paradox here?

Figure 9.6
Three differently shaped vessels filled with water to same level.

[*Hint:* Think about the forces due to fluid pressure on the *sides* of the containers; do they have vertical components?]

continued on next page

Conceptual Example 9.4 continued

Solution and Discussion   (a) The water at the bottom of each vessel is the same depth d below the surface. Water at the surface of each vessel is at a pressure $P_{surface} = 0$. Therefore, the pressures at the bottom must be equal:

$$P = P_{surface} + \rho g d = \rho g d$$

(b) The weight of each filled vessel is equal to the weight of the vessel itself plus the weight of the water inside. The vessels themselves have equal weights, but vessel A holds more water than C, whereas vessel B holds less water than C. Vessel A weighs the most and vessel B weighs the least.

(c) Each container supports the water inside by exerting an upward force equal in magnitude to the weight of the water. By Newton's third law, the water exerts a downward force on the container of the same magnitude. Figure 9.7 shows the forces acting on each container due to the water. In vessel C, the horizontal forces on any two diametrically opposite points on the walls of the container are equal and opposite; thus, the net force on the container walls is zero. The force on the bottom is

$$F = PA = (\rho g d)(\pi r^2)$$

Figure 9.7
Forces exerted on the containers by the water.

The volume of water in the cylinder is $V = \pi r^2 d$, so

$$F = \rho g V = (\rho V)g = mg$$

The force on the bottom of vessel C is equal to the weight of the water, as expected. However, the force on the bottom of vessel A is less than the weight of the water in the container, while the force on the bottom of vessel B is greater than the weight of the water. Then how can the water be in equilibrium? In vessel A, the forces on the container walls have downward components as well as horizontal components. The horizontal components of the forces on any two diametrically opposite points are equal and opposite, so the horizontal components add to zero. The sum of the downward components of the forces on the walls and the downward force on the bottom of the container is equal to the weight of the water. Similarly, the forces on the walls of vessel B have upward components. In each case, the *total* force on the bottom *and sides* of the container due to the water is equal to the weight of the water.

Conceptual Practice Problem 9.4   Is Pressure Determined by Column Height?

Figure 9.8 shows a vessel with two points marked at the bottom of the water in the vessel. A narrow column of water is drawn above each point. (a) Is the pressure at point 2, P_2, the same as the pressure at point 1, P_1, even though the column of water above point 2 is not as tall? (b) Does $P = P_{atm} + \rho g d$ imply that $P_2 < P_1$? Explain.

Figure 9.8
Two different points on the bottom of an open vessel.

9.5   MEASURING PRESSURE

Many other units are used for pressure besides atmospheres and pascals. In the United States, the pressure in an automobile tire is measured in pounds per square inch (lb/in^2). Weather bureaus record atmospheric pressure in bars or millibars. In the United States, television weather reports and home barometers measure pressure in inches of mercury. One atmosphere is equal to approximately 1 bar (1000 millibars), 76 cm of mercury, or 29.9 in. of mercury. Blood pressure, the *difference* between the pressure in the blood and atmospheric pressure, is measured in millimeters of mercury (mm Hg), also called the torr. Inches or millimeters of mercury may seem like strange units for pressure: how can a force per unit area be equal to a *distance* (so many mm Hg)? There is an assumption inherent in using these pressure units that we can understand by studying the mercury manometer.

Manometer

A mercury manometer consists of a vertical U-shaped tube, containing some mercury, with one side typically open to the atmosphere and the other connected to a vessel containing a gas whose pressure we want to measure. Figure 9.9 shows the manometer before it is connected to such a vessel. When both sides of the manometer are open to the atmosphere, the mercury levels are the same.

Now we connect an inflated balloon to the left side of the U-tube (Fig. 9.10). If the gas in the balloon is at a higher pressure than the atmosphere, the gas pushes the mercury down on the left side and forces it up on the right side. The density of a gas is small compared to the density of mercury, so every point within the gas is assumed to be at the same pressure no matter what the depth. At point B, the mercury pushes on the gas with the same magnitude force with which the gas pushes on the mercury, so point B is at the same pressure as the gas. Since point B' is at the same height within the mercury as point B, the pressure at B' is the same as at B. Point C is at atmospheric pressure.

The pressure at B is

$$P_B = P_{B'} = P_C + \rho g d$$

where ρ is the density of mercury. The difference in the pressures on the two sides of the manometer is

$$\Delta P = P_B - P_C = \rho g d \qquad (9\text{-}5)$$

Thus, the difference in mercury levels d is a measure of the pressure *difference*— commonly reported in millimeters of mercury (mm Hg).

The pressure measured when one side of the manometer is open is the *difference* between atmospheric pressure and the gas pressure rather than the absolute pressure of the gas. This difference is called the **gauge pressure**, since it is what most gauges (not just manometers) measure:

Gauge pressure:

$$P_{\text{gauge}} = P_{\text{abs}} - P_{\text{atm}} \qquad (9\text{-}6)$$

Since the density of mercury is 13 600 kg/m³, 1.00 mm Hg can be converted to pascals by substituting $d = 1.00$ mm in Eq. (9-5):

$$1.00 \text{ mm Hg} = \rho g d = (13\,600 \text{ kg/m}^3)(9.80 \text{ m/s}^2)(0.00100 \text{ m}) = 133 \text{ Pa}$$

The liquid in a manometer may be something other than mercury, such as water or oil. Equation (9-5) still applies, as long as we use the correct density ρ of the liquid in the manometer.

Figure 9.9 A mercury manometer open on both sides. Points A and A' are both at atmospheric pressure. Any two points (such as B and B') at the same height within the fluid are at the same pressure: $P_B = P_{B'}$.

Figure 9.10 The manometer connected on one side to a container of gas at a pressure greater than atmospheric pressure.

Example 9.5

The Mercury Manometer

A manometer is attached to a container of gas to determine its pressure. Before the container is attached, both sides of the manometer are open to the atmosphere. After the container is attached, the mercury on the side attached to the gas container rises 12 cm above its previous level. (a) What is the gauge pressure of the gas in Pa? (b) What is the absolute pressure of the gas in Pa?

Strategy The mercury column is higher on the side connected to the container of gas, so we know that the pressure of the enclosed gas is lower than atmospheric pressure. We need to

find the *difference* in levels of the mercury columns on the two sides. Careful: It is *not* 12 cm! If one side went up by 12 cm, then the other side has gone down by 12 cm, since the same volume of mercury is contained in the manometer.

Solution (a) The difference in the mercury levels is 24 cm (Fig. 9.11). Since the mercury on the gas side went *up*, the absolute pressure of the gas is *lower* than atmospheric pressure. Therefore, the gauge pressure of the gas is *less than zero*. The gauge pressure in Pa is

$$P_{\text{gauge}} = \rho g d$$

continued on next page

Example 9.5 continued

where the "depth" is $d = -24$ cm (the mercury is 24 cm higher on the gas side). Then

$$P_{gauge} = 13\,600 \text{ kg/m}^3 \times 9.8 \text{ m/s}^2 \times (-0.24 \text{ m}) = -32 \text{ kPa}$$

Open to the atmosphere

Gas

12 cm

24 cm

12 cm

Hg

Figure 9.11

When a container of gas is attached to one side of the manometer, one side goes down 12 cm and the other side goes up 12 cm.

(b) The absolute pressure of the gas is

$$P = P_{gauge} + P_{atm}$$

$$= -32 \text{ kPa} + 101 \text{ kPa} = 69 \text{ kPa}$$

Discussion   As a check, the manometer tells us directly that the gauge pressure of the gas is −240 mm Hg. Converting to pascals gives

$$-240 \text{ mm Hg} \times 133 \text{ Pa/mm Hg} = -32 \text{ kPa}$$

Practice Problem 9.5   Column Heights in Manometer

A mercury manometer is connected to a container of gas. (a) The height of the mercury column on the side connected to the gas is 22.0 cm (measured from the bottom of the manometer). What is the height of the mercury column on the open side if the gauge pressure is measured to be 13.3 kPa? (b) If the gauge pressure of the gas doubles, what are the new heights of the two columns?

Barometer

A manometer can act as a **barometer**—a device to measure atmospheric pressure. Instead of attaching a container with a gas to one end of the manometer, attach a container and a vacuum pump. Pump the air out of the container to get as close to a vacuum—zero pressure—as possible. Then the atmosphere pushes down on one side and pushes the fluid up on the other side toward the evacuated container.

Figure 9.12 shows a barometer in which the vacuum is not created by a vacuum pump. The barometer was invented by Evangelista Torricelli (1608–1647), an assistant to Galileo, in the 1600s; in his honor, one millimeter of mercury is called one torr.

Vacuum ($P = 0$)

d

Atmospheric pressure

A B

Hg

Figure 9.12   A simple barometer. A tube, of length greater than 76 cm and closed at one end, is filled with mercury. The tube is then inverted into an open container of mercury. Some mercury flows down from the tube into the bowl. The space left at the top of the tube is nearly a vacuum because nothing is left but a negligible amount of mercury vapor. Points A and B are at the same level in the mercury and, therefore, are both at atmospheric pressure since the bowl is open to the air. The distance d from A to the top of the mercury column in the closed tube is a measure of the atmospheric pressure (often called *barometric pressure* because it is measured with a barometer).

When you next have a drink with a straw, insert the straw into the drink and place your finger over the upper opening of the straw so that no more air can enter the straw. Raise the lower end of the straw up out of your drink. Does the liquid in the straw flow back down into your glass? What do you suppose is holding the liquid in place? Make an FBD on your paper napkin.

Some air is trapped between your finger and the top of the liquid in the straw; that air exerts a downward force on the liquid of magnitude P_1A (Fig. 9.13). A downward gravitational force mg also acts on the liquid. The air at the bottom of the straw exerts an upward force on the liquid of magnitude $P_{atm}A$; this upward force is what holds the liquid in place. Because the liquid does not pour out of the straw, but instead is in equilibrium,

$$P_{atm}A = P_1A + mg$$

Thus, the pressure P_1 of the air trapped above the liquid must be less than atmospheric pressure.

How did P_1 become less than atmospheric pressure? As you pulled the straw up and out, the liquid in the straw falls a bit, expanding the volume available to the air trapped above the liquid. When a gas expands under conditions like this, its pressure decreases.

When you remove your finger from the top of the straw, air can get in at the top of the straw. Then the pressures above and below the liquid are equal, so the gravitational force pulls the liquid down and out of the straw.

Figure 9.13 Force acting on the liquid inside a straw.

Sphygmomanometer

Blood pressure is measured with a sphygmomanometer (Fig. 9.14). The oldest kind of sphygmomanometer consists of a mercury manometer on one side attached to a closed bag—the cuff. The cuff is wrapped around the upper arm at the level of the heart and is then pumped up with air. The manometer measures the gauge pressure of the air in the cuff.

At first, the pressure in the cuff is higher than the *systolic* pressure—the maximum pressure in the brachial artery that occurs when the heart contracts. The cuff pressure squeezes the artery closed and no blood flows into the forearm. A valve on the cuff is then opened to allow air to escape slowly. When the cuff pressure decreases to just below the systolic pressure, a little squirt of blood flows past the constriction in the artery with each heartbeat. The sound of turbulent blood flow past the constriction can be heard through the stethoscope.

As air continues to escape from the cuff, the sound of blood flowing through the constriction in the artery continues to be heard. When the pressure in the cuff reaches the *diastolic* pressure in the artery—the minimum pressure that occurs when the heart muscle is relaxed—there is no longer a constriction in the artery, so the pulsing sounds cease. The *gauge* pressures for a healthy heart are nominally around 120 mm Hg (systolic) and 80 mm Hg (diastolic).

Application of the manometer: measuring blood pressure

Figure 9.14 A sphygmomanometer being used to measure blood pressure.

9.6   THE BUOYANT FORCE

When an object is immersed in a fluid, the pressure on the lower surface of the object is higher than the pressure on the upper surface. The difference in pressures leads to an upward net force acting on the object due to the fluid pressure. If you try to push a beach ball underwater, you feel the effects of the buoyant force pushing the ball back up. It takes a rather large force to hold such an object completely underwater; the instant you let go, the object pops back up to the surface.

CONNECTION:

The buoyant force is not a new kind of force exerted by a fluid; it is the sum of forces due to fluid pressure.

(a)

(b)

Figure 9.15 (a) Forces due to fluid pressure on the top and bottom of an immersed rectangular solid. (b) The buoyant force is the sum of $\vec{F}_1$ and $\vec{F}_2$. Since $|\vec{F}_2| > |\vec{F}_1|$, the net force due to fluid pressure is upward.

Figure 9.16 Forces acting on a floating ice cube. The ice cube is in equilibrium, so $\vec{F}_B + m\vec{g} = 0$.

Consider a rectangular solid immersed in a fluid of uniform density ρ (Fig. 9.15a). For each vertical face (left, right, front, and back), there is a face of equal area opposite it. The forces on these two faces due to the fluid are equal in magnitude since the areas and the average pressures are the same. The directions are opposite, so the forces acting on the vertical faces cancel in pairs.

Let the top and bottom surfaces each have area A. The force on the lower face of the block is $F_2 = P_2A$; the force on the upper face is $F_1 = P_1A$. The total force on the block due to the fluid, called the **buoyant force** F_B, is upward since $F_2 > F_1$ (Fig. 9.15b).

$$\vec{F}_B = \vec{F}_1 + \vec{F}_2$$

$$F_B = (P_2 - P_1)A$$

Since $P_2 - P_1 = \rho g d$, the magnitude of the buoyant force can be written

Buoyant force:

$$F_B = \rho g d A = \rho g V \qquad (9\text{-}7)$$

where $V = Ad$ is the volume of the block.

Note that ρV is the mass of the volume V of the fluid that the block displaces. Thus, the buoyant force on the submerged block is equal to the weight of an equal volume of fluid, a result called **Archimedes' principle**.

Archimedes' Principle

A fluid exerts an upward buoyant force on a submerged object equal in magnitude to the weight of the volume of fluid displaced by the object.

Archimedes' principle applies to a submerged object of *any shape* even though we derived it for a rectangular block. Why? Imagine replacing an irregular submerged object with enough fluid to fill the object's place. This "piece" of fluid is in equilibrium, so the buoyant force must be equal to its weight. The buoyant force is the net force exerted on the "piece" of fluid by the surrounding fluid, which is identical to the buoyant force on the irregular object since the two have the same shape and surface area.

The same argument can be used to show that if an object is only partly submerged, the buoyant force is still equal to the weight of fluid displaced. Equation (9-7) applies as long as V is the part of the object's volume below the fluid surface rather than the entire volume of the object.

Net Force due to Gravity and Buoyancy   The net force due to gravity and buoyancy acting on an object totally or partially immersed in a fluid (Fig. 9.16) is

$$\vec{F} = m\vec{g} + \vec{F}_B$$

The force of gravity on an object of volume V_o and average density ρ_o is

$$W = mg = \rho_o g V_o$$

and the buoyant force is

$$F_B = \rho_f g V_f$$

where V_f and ρ_f are the volume of fluid displaced and the fluid density, respectively. Choosing up to be the $+y$-direction, the net force due to gravity and buoyancy is

$$F_y = \rho_f g V_f - \rho_o g V_o \qquad (9\text{-}8)$$

Here F_y can be positive or negative, depending on which density is larger. Imagine releasing a pebble and an air bubble underwater. The pebble's average density is greater than the density of water, so the net force on it is downward; the pebble sinks. An air bubble's average density is less than the density of water, so the net force is upward, causing the bubble to rise toward the surface of the water.

If the object is completely submerged, the volumes of the object and the displaced fluid are the same and

$$F_y = (\rho_f - \rho_o)gV$$

If $\rho_o < \rho_f$, the object floats with only part of its volume submerged. In equilibrium, the object displaces a volume of fluid whose weight is equal to the object's weight. At that point the gravitational force equals the buoyant force and the object floats. Setting $F_y = 0$ in Eq. (9-8) yields

$$\rho_f g V_f = \rho_o g V_o$$

which can be rearranged as:

$$\frac{V_f}{V_o} = \frac{\rho_o}{\rho_f}$$

On the left side of this equation is the fraction of the object's volume that is submerged; it is equal to the ratio of the density of the object to the density of the fluid.

Specific Gravity   This ratio of densities is called the **specific gravity** of the material when ρ_f is the density of water at 4°C. Specific gravity is without units because it is a ratio of two densities. Water at 4°C is chosen as the reference material because at that temperature, the density of water is a maximum (at atmospheric pressure). The gram was originally defined as the mass of one cubic centimeter of water at 4°C. Thus, water at 4°C has a density of 1 g/cm³ (1000 kg/m³). The specific gravity of seawater is 1.025, which means that seawater has a density of 1.025 g/cm³ (1025 kg/m³).

Specific gravity:

$$\text{S.G.} = \frac{\rho}{\rho_{\text{water}}} = \frac{\rho}{1000 \text{ kg/m}^3} \qquad (9\text{-}9)$$

Blood tests often include determination of the specific gravity of the blood—normally around 1.040 to 1.065. A reading that is too low may indicate anemia, since the presence of red blood cells increases the average density of the blood. Before taking blood from a donor, a drop of the blood is placed in a solution of known density. If the drop does not sink, it is not safe for the donor to give blood because the concentration of red blood cells is too low. Urinalysis also includes a specific gravity measurement (normally 1.015 to 1.030); too high a value indicates an abnormally high concentration of dissolved salts, which can signal a medical problem.

 Applications of specific gravity measurements in medicine

Freighters, aircraft carriers, and cruise ships float, although they are made from steel and other materials that are more dense than seawater. When a ship floats, the buoyant force acting on the ship is equal to the ship's weight. A ship is constructed so that it displaces a volume of seawater larger than the volume of the steel and other construction materials. The *average* density of the ship is its weight divided by its total volume. A large part of a ship's interior is filled with air. All of the "empty" space contributes to the total volume; the resulting average density is less than that of seawater, allowing the ship to float.

Application of Archimedes' principle: how a ship can float

 How can the hippo sink?

Now we can understand how a hippopotamus can sink to the bottom of a pond: it can expel some of the air in its body by exhaling. Exhalation increases the average density of the hippopotamus so that it is just slightly above the density of the water; thus, it sinks. (An armadillo does just the opposite: it swallows air, inflating its stomach and intestines, to increase the buoyant force for a swim across a large lake.) When the hippo needs to breathe, it swims back up to the surface.

Example 9.6

The Golden (?) Falcon

A small statue in the shape of a falcon has a weight of 24.1 N. The owner of the statue claims it is made of solid gold. When the statue is completely submerged in a container brimful of water, the weight of the water that spills over the top and into a bucket is 1.25 N. Find the density and specific gravity of the metal. Is the density consistent with the claim that the falcon is solid gold?

Strategy When the statue is completely submerged, it displaces a volume V of water equal to its own volume. The weight of the displaced water is equal to the buoyant force. Let $m_s g = 24.1$ N represent the weight of the statue (in terms of its mass m_s) and let $m_w g = 1.25$ N represent the weight of the water.

Solution The specific gravity of the statue is

$$\text{S.G.} = \frac{\rho_s}{\rho_w} = \frac{m_s/V}{m_w/V} = \frac{m_s}{m_w}$$

Rather than calculate the masses in kilograms, we recognize that a ratio of masses is equal to the ratio of the weights:

$$\text{S.G.} = \frac{m_s g}{m_w g} = \frac{24.1 \text{ N}}{1.25 \text{ N}} = 19.3$$

The density of the statue is

$$\rho_s = \text{S.G.} \times \rho_w = 19.3 \times 1000 \text{ kg/m}^3 = 1.93 \times 10^4 \text{ kg/m}^3$$

From Table 9.1, the statue has the correct density; it may *possibly* be gold.

Discussion According to legend, this method to determine the specific gravity of a solid was discovered by Archimedes in the third century B.C.E. King Hieron II asked Archimedes to find a way to check whether his crown was made of pure gold—without melting down the crown, of course! Archimedes came up with his method while he was taking a bath; he noticed the water level rising as he got in and connected the rising water level with the volume of water displaced by his body. In his excitement, he jumped out of the bath and ran naked through the streets of Siracusa (a city in Sicily) shouting "Eureka!"

Practice Problem 9.6   Identifying an Unknown Substance

An unknown solid substance has a weight of 142.0 N. The object is suspended from a scale and hung so that it is completely submerged in water (but not touching bottom). The scale reads 129.4 N. Find the specific gravity of the object and determine whether the substance could be anything listed in Table 9.1.

Example 9.7

Hidden Depths of an Iceberg

What percentage of a floating iceberg's volume is above water? The specific gravity of ice is 0.917 and the specific gravity of the surrounding seawater is 1.025.

Strategy The ratio of the density of ice to the density of seawater tells us the ratio of the volume of ice that is submerged in the seawater to the total volume of the iceberg. The rest of the ice is above the water.

Solution We could calculate the densities of seawater and of ice in SI units from their specific gravities, but that is unnecessary; the ratio of the specific gravities is equal to the ratio of the densities:

$$\frac{\text{S.G.}_{ice}}{\text{S.G.}_{seawater}} = \frac{\rho_{ice}/\rho_{water}}{\rho_{seawater}/\rho_{water}} = \frac{\rho_{ice}}{\rho_{seawater}}$$

The fraction of the iceberg's volume that is submerged is equal to the ratio of the densities of ice and seawater. Thus, the ratio of the volume submerged to the total volume of ice is

$$\frac{V_{submerged}}{V_{ice}} = \frac{\rho_{ice}}{\rho_{seawater}} = \frac{\text{S.G.}_{ice}}{\text{S.G.}_{seawater}}$$

$$= \frac{0.917}{1.025} = 0.895$$

89.5% of the ice is below the surface of the water, leaving only 10.5% above the surface.

Discussion An alternative solution does not depend on remembering that the ratio of the volumes is equal to the

continued on next page

Example 9.7 continued

ratio of the densities. The buoyant force is equal to the weight of a volume $V_{submerged}$ of water:

$$\text{buoyant force} = \rho_{seawater} V_{submerged} g$$

The weight of the iceberg is $mg = \rho_{ice} V_{ice} g$. From Newton's second law, the buoyant force must be equal in magnitude to the weight of the iceberg when it is floating in equilibrium:

$$\rho_{seawater} V_{submerged} g = \rho_{ice} V_{ice} g$$

or

$$\frac{V_{submerged}}{V_{ice}} = \frac{\rho_{ice}}{\rho_{seawater}}$$

The fact that ice floats is of great importance for the balance of nature. If ice were more dense than water, it would gradually fill up the ponds and lakes *from the bottom.* It would not form on top of lakes and remain there. The consequences for fish and other bottom dwellers of solidly frozen lakes would be catastrophic. The water below the surface layer of ice formed in winter remains just above freezing so that the fish are able to survive.

Practice Problem 9.7 Floating in Freshwater Versus Seawater

If the average density of a human being is 980 kg/m³, what fraction of a human body floats above water in a freshwater pond and what fraction floats above seawater in the ocean? The specific gravity of seawater is 1.025.

Conceptual Example 9.8

A Hovering Fish

How is it that a fish is able to hover almost motionless in one spot—until some attractive food is spotted and, with a flip of the tail, off it swims after the food? Fish have a thin-walled bladder, called a swim bladder, located under the spinal column. The swim bladder contains a mixture of oxygen and nitrogen obtained from the blood of the fish. How does the swim bladder help the fish keep the buoyant and gravitational forces balanced so that it can hover?

Solution and Discussion If the fish's average density is greater than that of the surrounding water, it will sink; if its average density is smaller than that of the water, it will rise. By varying the volume of the swim bladder, the fish is able to vary its overall volume and, thus, its average density. By adjusting its average density to match the density of the surrounding water, the fish can remain suspended in position. The fish can also adjust the volume of the bladder when it wants to rise or sink.

Conceptual Practice Problem 9.8 The Diving Beetle

A diving beetle traps a bubble of air under its wings. While under the water, the beetle uses the air in the bubble to breathe, gradually exchanging the oxygen for carbon dioxide. (a) What does the beetle do to the air bubble so that it can dive under the water? (b) Once under water, what does the beetle do so that it can rise to the surface? [*Hint:* Treat the beetle and the air bubble as a single system. How can the beetle change the buoyant force acting on the system?]

Buoyant Forces on Objects Immersed in a Gas Gases such as air are fluids and exert buoyant forces just as liquids do. The buoyant force due to air is often negligible if an object's average density is much larger than the density of air. To see a significant buoyant force in air, we must use an object with a small average density. A hot air balloon has an opening at the bottom and a burner for heating the air within (Fig. 9.17). Many molecules of the heated air escape through the opening, decreasing the balloon's average density. When the balloon is less dense on average than the surrounding air, it rises; at higher altitudes, the surrounding air becomes less and less dense. At some particular altitude, the buoyant force is equal in magnitude to the weight of the balloon. Then, by Newton's second law, the net force on the balloon is zero. The balloon is in *stable* equilibrium at this altitude: if the balloon rises a bit, it experiences a net force downward, while if the balloon sinks down a bit, it is pushed back upward.

Application of buoyant forces: hot air balloons

Figure 9.17 The buoyant force due to the outside air keeps these balloons aloft.

9.7   FLUID FLOW

Types of Fluid Flow   The study of *moving* fluids is a wonderfully complex subject. To illustrate some important ideas in less complex situations, we limit our study at first to fluids flowing under special conditions.

One difference between moving fluids and static fluids is that a moving fluid can exert a force *parallel* to any surface over or past which it flows; a static fluid cannot. Since the moving fluid exerts a force against a surface, the surface must also exert a force on the fluid. This **viscous force** opposes the flow of the fluid; it is the counterpart to the kinetic frictional force between solids. An external force must act on a viscous fluid (and thereby do work) to keep it flowing. Viscosity is considered in Section 9.9. Until then, we consider only nonviscous fluids—fluid flow where the viscous forces are negligibly small. We also ignore surface tension, which is considered in Section 9.11.

Fluid flow can be characterized as steady or unsteady. When the flow is **steady**, the velocity of the fluid *at any point* is constant in time. The velocity is not necessarily the same everywhere, but at any particular point, the velocity of the fluid passing that point remains constant in time. The density and pressure at any point in a steadily flowing fluid are also constant in time.

Steady flow is **laminar**. The fluid flows in neat layers so that each small portion of fluid that passes a particular point follows the same path as every other portion of fluid that passes the same point. The path that the fluid follows, starting from any point, is called a **streamline** (Fig. 9.18). The streamlines may curve and bend, but they cannot cross each other; if they did, the fluid would have to "decide" which way to go when it gets to such a point. The direction of the fluid velocity at any point must be tangent to the streamline passing through that point. Streamlines are a convenient way to depict fluid flow in a sketch.

Figure 9.18 A wind tunnel shows the streamlines in the flow of air past a car.

The Ideal Fluid   The special case that we consider first is the flow of an **ideal fluid**. An ideal fluid is incompressible, undergoes laminar flow, and has no viscosity. Under some conditions, real fluids can be modeled as (nearly) ideal, but not under all conditions.

The flow of an ideal fluid is governed by two principles: the continuity equation and Bernoulli's equation. The continuity equation is an expression of conservation of mass for an incompressible fluid: since no fluid is created or destroyed, the total mass of the fluid must be constant. Bernoulli's equation, discussed in Section 9.8, is a form of the energy conservation law applied to fluid flow. Together, these two equations enable us to predict the flow of an ideal fluid.

The Continuity Equation

We start by deriving the continuity equation, which relates the speed of flow to the cross-sectional area of the fluid. Suppose an incompressible fluid flows into a pipe of nonuniform cross-sectional area under conditions of steady flow. In Fig. 9.19, the fluid on the left moves at speed v_1. During a time Δt, the fluid travels a distance

$$x_1 = v_1\,\Delta t$$

If A_1 is the cross-sectional area of this section of pipe, then the mass of water moving past point 1 in time Δt is

$$\Delta m_1 = \rho V_1 = \rho A_1 x_1 = \rho A_1 v_1\,\Delta t$$

Figure 9.19 An incompressible fluid flowing horizontally through a nonuniform pipe.

Figure 9.20 Streamlines in a pipe of varying cross-sectional area. Streamlines are closer together where the fluid velocity is larger and farther apart where the velocity is smaller.

During this same time interval, the mass of fluid moving past point 2 is

$$\Delta m_2 = \rho V_2 = \rho A_2 x_2 = \rho A_2 v_2\, \Delta t$$

But, if the flow is steady, the mass passing through one section of pipe in time interval Δt must pass through any other section of the pipe in the same time interval. Therefore,

$$\Delta m_1 = \Delta m_2$$

or

$$\rho A_1 v_1\, \Delta t = \rho A_2 v_2\, \Delta t \qquad (9\text{-}10)$$

The quantity ρAv is the *mass flow rate* of the fluid:

Mass flow rate:

$$\frac{\Delta m}{\Delta t} = \rho Av \quad \text{(SI unit: kg/s)} \qquad (9\text{-}11)$$

Since the time intervals Δt are the same, Eq. (9-11) says that the mass flow rate past any two points is the same. Since the density of an incompressible fluid is constant, the volume flow rate past any two points must also be the same:

Volume flow rate:

$$\frac{\Delta V}{\Delta t} = Av \quad \text{(SI unit: m}^3\text{/s)} \qquad (9\text{-}12)$$

The **continuity equation** for an incompressible fluid equates the volume flow rates past two different points:

Continuity equation for incompressible fluid:

$$A_1 v_1 = A_2 v_2 \qquad (9\text{-}13)$$

The same volume of fluid that enters the pipe in a given time interval exits the pipe in the same time interval. Where the radius of the tube is large, the speed of the fluid is small; where the radius is small, the fluid speed is large. A familiar example is what happens when you use your thumb to partially block the end of a garden hose to make a jet of water. The water moves past your thumb, where the cross-sectional area is smaller, at a greater speed than it moves in the hose. Similarly, water traveling along a river speeds up, forming rapids, when the riverbed narrows or is partially blocked by rocks and boulders.

Streamlines are closer together where the fluid flows faster and farther apart where it flows more slowly (Fig. 9.20). Thus, streamlines help us visualize fluid flow. The fluid velocity at any point is tangent to a streamline through that point.

PHYSICS AT HOME

The continuity equation applies to an ideal fluid even if it is not flowing through a pipe. Turn on a faucet so that the water flows out in a moderate stream (Fig. 9.21). The falling water is in free fall, accelerated by gravity until it hits the sink below. As the water falls, its speed increases. The stream of water gradually narrows as it falls so that the product of speed and cross-sectional area is constant, as predicted by the continuity equation.

Figure 9.21 Demonstrating the continuity equation at a bathroom sink. Notice that the stream of water is narrower where the flow speed is faster.

Example 9.9

Speed of Blood Flow

The heart pumps blood into the aorta, which has an inner radius of 1.0 cm. The aorta feeds 32 major arteries. If blood in the aorta travels at a speed of 28 cm/s, at approximately what average speed does it travel in the arteries? Assume that blood can be treated as an ideal fluid and that the arteries each have an inner radius of 0.21 cm.

Strategy Since we have assumed blood to be an ideal fluid, we can apply the continuity equation. The main tube (the aorta) is connected to multiple tubes (the major arteries), so this problem seems to be more complicated than a single pipe with a constriction in it. What matters here is the total cross-sectional area into which the blood flows.

Solution We start by finding the cross-sectional area of the aorta

$$A_1 = \pi r^2_{aorta}$$

and then the total cross-sectional area of the arteries

$$A_2 = 32\pi r^2_{artery}$$

Now we apply the continuity equation and solve for the unknown speed.

$$A_1 v_1 = A_2 v_2$$

$$v_2 = v_1 \frac{A_1}{A_2} = 0.28 \text{ m/s} \times \frac{\pi \times (0.010 \text{ m})^2}{32\pi \times (0.0021 \text{ m})^2} = 0.20 \text{ m/s}$$

Discussion The blood flow slows in the arteries because the total cross-sectional area is greater than that of the aorta alone. From the arteries, the blood travels to the many capillaries of the body. Each capillary has a tiny cross-sectional area, but there are so many of them that the blood flow slows greatly once it reaches the capillaries—allowing time for the exchange of oxygen, carbon dioxide, and nutrients between the blood and the body tissues.

Practice Problem 9.9   Hosing Down a Wastebasket

A garden hose fills a 32-L wastebasket in 120 s. The opening at the end of the hose has a radius of 1.00 cm. (a) How fast is the water traveling as it leaves the hose? (b) How fast does the water travel if half the exit area is obstructed by placing a finger over the opening?

9.8   BERNOULLI'S EQUATION

The continuity equation relates the flow velocities of an ideal fluid at two different points, based on the change in cross-sectional area of the pipe. According to the continuity equation, the fluid must speed up as it enters a constriction (Fig. 9.22) and then slow down to its original speed when it leaves the constriction. Using energy ideas, we will show that the pressure of the fluid in the constriction (P_2) cannot be the same as the pressure before or after the constriction (P_1). For horizontal flow *the speed is higher where the pressure is lower.* This principle is often called the **Bernoulli effect**.

The Bernoulli effect: Fluid flows faster where the pressure is lower.

⚠️

The Bernoulli effect can seem counterintuitive at first; isn't rapidly moving fluid at *high* pressure? For instance, if you were hit with the fast-moving water out of a firehose, you would be knocked over easily. The force that knocks you over is indeed due to fluid pressure; you would justifiably conclude that the pressure was high. However, the pressure is not high *until you slow down the water* by getting in its way. The rapidly moving water in the jet is, in fact, approximately at atmospheric pressure (zero gauge pressure), but when you *stop* the water, its pressure increases dramatically.

Let's find the quantitative relationship between pressure changes and flow speed changes for an ideal fluid. In Fig. 9.23, the shaded volume of fluid flows to the right.

Figure 9.22 A small volume of fluid speeds up as it moves into a constriction (position A) and then slows down as it moves out of the constriction (position B).

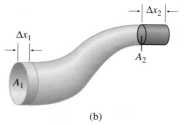

(a)

(b)

Figure 9.23 Applying conservation of energy to the flow of an ideal fluid. The shaded volume of fluid in (a) is flowing to the right; (b) shows the same volume of fluid a short time later.

If the left end moves a distance Δx_1, then the right end moves a distance Δx_2. Since the fluid is incompressible,

$$A_1 \Delta x_1 = A_2 \Delta x_2 = V$$

Work is done by the neighboring fluid during this flow. Fluid behind (to the left) pushes forward, doing positive work, while fluid ahead pushes backward, doing negative work. The total work done on the shaded volume by neighboring fluid is

$$W = P_1 A_1 \Delta x_1 - P_2 A_2 \Delta x_2 = (P_1 - P_2)V$$

Since no dissipative forces act on an ideal fluid, the work done is equal to the total change in kinetic and gravitational potential energy. The net effect of the displacement is to move a volume V of fluid from height y_1 to height y_2 and to change its speed from v_1 to v_2. The energy change is therefore

$$\Delta E = \Delta K + \Delta U = \tfrac{1}{2}m(v_2^2 - v_1^2) + mg(y_2 - y_1)$$

where the $+y$-direction is up. Substituting $m = \rho V$ and equating the work done on the fluid to the change in its energy yields

$$(P_1 - P_2)\,V = \tfrac{1}{2}\,\rho V(v_2^2 - v_1^2) + \rho V g(y_2 - y_1)$$

Dividing both sides by V and rearranging yields Bernoulli's equation, named after Swiss mathematician Daniel Bernoulli (1700–1782), but first derived by fellow Swiss mathematician Leonhard Euler (pronounced like *oiler*, 1707–1783).

CONNECTION:

Bernoulli's equation is a restatement of the principle of energy conservation applied to the flow of an ideal fluid.

> **Bernoulli's equation (for ideal fluid flow):**
>
> $$P_1 + \rho g y_1 + \tfrac{1}{2}\rho v_1^2 = P_2 + \rho g y_2 + \tfrac{1}{2}\rho v_2^2$$
>
> $$\text{(or } P + \rho g y + \tfrac{1}{2}\rho v^2 = \text{constant)} \qquad (9\text{-}14)$$

Bernoulli's equation relates the pressure, flow speed, and height at two points in an ideal fluid. Although we derived Bernoulli's equation in a relatively simple situation, it applies to the flow of any ideal fluid as long as points 1 and 2 are on the same streamline.

Each term in Bernoulli's equation has units of pressure, which in the SI system is Pa or N/m^2. Since a joule is a newton-meter, the pascal is also equal to a joule per cubic meter (J/m^3). Each term represents work or energy per unit volume. The pressure is the work done by the fluid on the fluid ahead of it per unit volume of flow. The kinetic energy per unit volume is $\frac{1}{2}\rho v^2$ and the gravitational potential energy per unit volume is ρgy. (Text website tutorial: energies)

√ CHECKPOINT 9.8

Discuss Bernoulli's equation in two special cases: (a) horizontal flow ($y_1 = y_2$) and (b) a static fluid ($v_1 = v_2 = 0$).

Example 9.10

Torricelli's Theorem

A barrel full of rainwater has a spigot near the bottom, at a depth of 0.80 m beneath the water surface. (a) When the spigot is directed horizontally (Fig. 9.24a) and is opened, how fast does the water come out? (b) If the opening points upward (Fig. 9.24b), how high does the resulting "fountain" go? (tutorial: waterfall)

Strategy   The water at the surface is at atmospheric pressure. The water emerging from the spigot is *also* at atmospheric pressure since it is in contact with the air. If the pressure of the emerging water were different than that of the air, the stream would expand or contract until the pressures were equal. We apply Bernoulli's equation to two points: point 1 at the water surface and point 2 in the emerging stream of water.

Solution   (a) Since $P_1 = P_2$, Bernoulli's equation is

$$\rho gy_1 + \tfrac{1}{2}\rho v_1^2 = \rho gy_2 + \tfrac{1}{2}\rho v_2^2$$

Point 1 is 0.80 m above point 2, so

$$y_1 - y_2 = 0.80 \text{ m}$$

(a)   (b)

Figure 9.24

Full barrel of rainwater with open spigot (a) horizontal and (b) upward.

The speed of the emerging water is v_2. What is v_1, the speed of the water at the surface? The water at the surface is moving slowly, since the barrel is draining. The continuity equation requires that

$$v_1 A_1 = v_2 A_2$$

Since the cross-sectional area of the spigot A_2 is much smaller than the area of the top of the barrel A_1, the speed of the water at the surface v_1 is negligibly small compared with v_2. Setting $v_1 = 0$, Bernoulli's equation reduces to

$$\rho gy_1 = \rho gy_2 + \tfrac{1}{2}\rho v_2^2$$

After dividing through by ρ, we solve for v_2:

$$g(y_1 - y_2) = \tfrac{1}{2}v_2^2$$

$$v_2 = \sqrt{2g(y_1 - y_2)} = 4.0 \text{ m/s}$$

(b) Now take point 2 to be at the top of the fountain. Then $v_2 = 0$ and Bernoulli's equation reduces to

$$\rho gy_1 = \rho gy_2$$

The "fountain" goes right back up to the top of the water in the barrel!

Discussion   The result of part (b) is called Torricelli's theorem. In reality, the fountain does not reach as high as the original water level; some energy is dissipated due to viscosity and air resistance.

Practice Problem 9.10   Fluid in Free Fall

Verify that the speed found in part (a) is the same as if the water just fell 0.80 m straight down. That shouldn't be too surprising since Bernoulli's equation is an expression of energy conservation.

Example 9.11

The Venturi Meter

A *Venturi meter* (Fig. 9.25) measures fluid speed in a pipe. A constriction (of cross-sectional area A_2) is put in a pipe of normal cross-sectional area A_1. Two vertical tubes, open to the atmosphere, rise from two points, one of which is in the constriction. The vertical tubes function like manometers, enabling the pressure to be determined. From this information the flow speed in the pipe can be determined.

Suppose that the pipe in question carries water, $A_1 = 2.0A_2$, and the fluid heights in the vertical tubes are $h_1 = 1.20$ m and $h_2 = 0.80$ m. (a) Find the ratio of the flow speeds v_2/v_1. (b) Find the gauge pressures P_1 and P_2. (c) Find the flow speed v_1 in the pipe.

Strategy Neither of the two flow speeds is given. We need more than Bernoulli's equation to solve this problem. Since we know the ratio of the areas, the continuity equation gives us the ratio of the speeds. The height of the water in the vertical tubes enables us to find the pressures at points 1 and 2. The fluid pressure at the bottom of each vertical tube is the same as the pressure of the moving fluid just beneath each tube—otherwise, water would flow into or out of the vertical tubes until the pressure equalized. The water in the vertical tubes is static, so the gauge pressure at the bottom is $P = \rho gd$. Once we have the ratio of the speeds and the pressures, we apply Bernoulli's equation.

Solution (a) From the continuity equation, the product of flow speed and area must be the same at points 1 and 2. Therefore,

$$\frac{v_2}{v_1} = \frac{A_1}{A_2} = 2.0$$

The water flows twice as fast in the constriction as in the rest of the pipe.

Figure 9.25
Venturi meter.

(b) The gauge pressures are:

$$P_1 = \rho gh_1 = 1000 \text{ kg/m}^3 \times 9.80 \text{ N/kg} \times 1.20 \text{ m} = 11.8 \text{ kPa}$$
$$P_2 = \rho gh_2 = 1000 \text{ kg/m}^3 \times 9.80 \text{ N/kg} \times 0.80 \text{ m} = 7.8 \text{ kPa}$$

(c) Now we apply Bernoulli's equation. We can use gauge pressures as long as we do so on both sides—in effect we are just subtracting atmospheric pressure from both sides of the equation:

$$P_1 + \rho gy_1 + \tfrac{1}{2}\rho v_1^2 = P_2 + \rho gy_2 + \tfrac{1}{2}\rho v_2^2$$

Since the tube is horizontal, $y_1 \approx y_2$ and we can ignore the small change in gravitational potential energy density ρgy. Then

$$P_1 + \tfrac{1}{2}\rho v_1^2 = P_2 + \tfrac{1}{2}\rho v_2^2$$

We are trying to find v_1, so we can eliminate v_2 by substituting $v_2 = 2.0v_1$:

$$P_1 + \tfrac{1}{2}\rho v_1^2 = P_2 + \tfrac{1}{2}\rho (2.0v_1)^2$$

Simplifying,

$$P_1 - P_2 = 1.5\rho v_1^2$$

$$v_1 = \sqrt{\frac{11\,800 \text{ Pa} - 7800 \text{ Pa}}{1.5 \times 1000 \text{ kg/m}^3}} = 1.6 \text{ m/s}$$

Discussion The assumption that $y_1 \approx y_2$ is fine as long as the pipe radius is small compared with the difference between the static water heights (40 cm). Otherwise, we would have to account for the different y values in Bernoulli's equation.

One subtle point: recall that we assumed that the fluid pressure at the bottom of the vertical tubes was the same as the pressure of the moving fluid just beneath. Does that contradict Bernoulli's equation? Since there is an abrupt change in fluid speed, shouldn't there be a significant difference in the pressures? No, because these points are *not on the same streamline*.

Practice Problem 9.11   Garden Hose

Water flows horizontally through a garden hose of radius 1.0 cm at a speed of 1.4 m/s. The water shoots horizontally out of a nozzle of radius 0.25 cm. What is the gauge pressure of the water inside the hose?

Application of Bernoulli's Principle: Arterial Flutter and Aneurisms Suppose an artery is narrowed due to buildup of plaque on its inner walls. The flow of blood through the constriction is similar to that shown in Fig. 9.22. Bernoulli's equation tells us that the pressure P_2 in the constriction is lower than the pressure elsewhere.

Figure 9.26 Streamlines showing the airflow past an airplane wing in a wind tunnel.

The arterial walls are elastic rather than rigid, so the lower pressure allows the arterial walls to contract a bit in the constriction. Now the flow velocity is even higher and the pressure even lower. Eventually the artery wall collapses, shutting off the flow of blood. Then the pressure builds up, reopens the artery, and allows blood to flow. The cycle of arterial flutter then begins again.

The opposite may happen where the arterial wall is weak. Blood pressure pushes the artery walls outward, forming a bulge called an aneurism. The lower flow speed in the bulge is accompanied by a higher blood pressure, which enlarges the aneurism even more (see Problem 88). Ultimately the artery may burst from the increased pressure.

Application of Bernoulli's Principle: Airplane Wings   How does an airplane wing generate lift? Figure 9.26 is a sketch of some streamlines for air flowing past an airplane wing in a wind tunnel. The streamlines bend, showing that the wing deflects air downward. By Newton's third law (or conservation of momentum), if the wing pushes downward on the air, the air also pushes upward on the wing. This upward force on the wing is lift. However, the situation is not as simple as air "bouncing" off the bottom of the wing—note that air passing above the wing is also deflected downward.

We can use Bernoulli's equation to get more insight into the generation of lift. (Bernoulli's equation applies in an approximate way to moving air. Even though air is not incompressible, for subsonic flight the density changes are small enough to be ignored.) If the air exerts a net upward force on the wing, the air pressure must be lower above the wing than beneath the wing. In Fig. 9.26, the streamlines above the wing are closer together than beneath the wing, showing that the flow speed above the wing is faster than it is beneath. This observation confirms that the pressure is lower above the wing, because where the pressure is lower, the flow speed is faster.

9.9   VISCOSITY

Bernoulli's equation ignores viscosity (fluid friction). According to Bernoulli's equation, an ideal fluid can continue to flow in a horizontal pipe at constant velocity on its own, just as a hockey puck would slide across frictionless ice at constant velocity without anything pushing it along. However, all real fluids have some viscosity; to maintain flow in a viscous fluid, we have to apply an external force since viscous forces oppose the flow of the fluid (Fig. 9.27). A *pressure difference* between the ends of the pipe must be maintained to keep a real liquid moving through a horizontal pipe. The pressure difference is important—in everything from blood flowing through arteries to oil pumped through a pipeline.

To visualize viscous flow in a tube of circular cross section, imagine the fluid to flow in cylindrical layers, or shells. If there were no viscosity, all the layers would move at the same speed (Fig. 9.28a). In viscous flow, the fluid speed depends on the distance from the tube walls (Fig. 9.28b). The fastest flow is at the center of the tube. Layers closer to the wall of the tube move more slowly. The outermost layer of fluid, which is in contact with the tube, does not move. Each layer of fluid exerts viscous forces on the

Figure 9.27 (a) To maintain viscous flow, a net force due to fluid pressure $(P_1 - P_2) A$ must be applied in the direction of flow to balance the viscous force F_v due to the pipe, which opposes flow. (b) The pressure in the fluid decreases from P_1 at the left end to P_2 at the right end.

(a) Fluid flow without viscosity

(b) Viscous flow

Figure 9.28 (a) In nonviscous flow through a tube, the flow speed is the same everywhere. (b) In viscous flow, the flow speed depends on distance from the tube wall. This simplified sketch shows layers of fluid each moving at a different speed, but in reality the flow speed increases continuously from zero for the outermost "layer" to a maximum speed at the center.

neighboring layers; these forces oppose the relative motion of the layers. The outermost layer exerts a viscous force on the tube.

A liquid is more viscous if the cohesive forces between molecules are stronger. The viscosity of a liquid decreases with increasing temperature because the molecules become less tightly bound. A decrease in the temperature of the human body is dangerous because the viscosity of the blood increases and the flow of blood through the body is hindered. Gases, on the other hand, have an increase in viscosity for an increase in temperature. At higher temperatures the gas molecules move faster and collide more often with each other.

The coefficient of viscosity (or simply the *viscosity*) of a fluid is written as the Greek letter eta (η) and has units of pascal-seconds (Pa·s) in SI. Other viscosity units in common use are the poise (pronounced *pwäz*, symbol P; 1 P = 0.1 Pa·s) and the centipoise (1 cP = 0.01 P = 0.001 Pa·s). Table 9.2 lists the viscosities of some common fluids.

Poiseuille's Law

The volume flow rate $\Delta V/\Delta t$ for laminar flow of a viscous fluid through a horizontal, cylindrical pipe depends on several factors. First of all, the volume flow rate is proportional to the *pressure drop per unit length* ($\Delta P/L$)—also called the pressure gradient. If a pressure drop ΔP maintains a certain flow rate in a pipe of length L, then a similar pipe of length $2L$ needs twice the pressure drop to maintain the same flow rate (ΔP across the first half and another ΔP across the second half). Thus, the flow rate ($\Delta V/\Delta t$) must be proportional to the pressure drop per unit length ($\Delta P/L$).

Next, the flow rate is inversely proportional to the viscosity of the fluid. The more viscous the fluid, the smaller the flow rate, if all other factors are equal.

The only other consideration is the radius of the pipe. In the nineteenth century, during a study of flow in blood vessels, French physician Jean-Léonard Marie Poiseuille (1799–1869) discovered that the flow rate is proportional to the *fourth power* of the pipe radius:

Poiseuille's Law (for Viscous Flow)

$$\frac{\Delta V}{\Delta t} = \frac{\pi}{8} \frac{\Delta P/L}{\eta} r^4 \qquad (9\text{-}15)$$

Table 9.2   Viscosities of Some Fluids

Substance	Temperature (°C)	Viscosity (Pa·s)
Gases		
Water vapor	100	1.3×10^{-5}
Air	0	1.7×10^{-5}
	20	1.8×10^{-5}
	30	1.9×10^{-5}
	100	2.2×10^{-5}
Liquids		
Acetone	30	0.30×10^{-3}
Methanol	30	0.51×10^{-3}
Ethanol	30	1.0×10^{-3}
Water	0	1.8×10^{-3}
	20	1.0×10^{-3}
	30	0.80×10^{-3}
	40	0.66×10^{-3}
	60	0.47×10^{-3}
	80	0.36×10^{-3}
	100	0.28×10^{-3}
Blood plasma	37	1.3×10^{-3}
Blood, whole	20	3.0×10^{-3}
	37	2.1×10^{-3}
Glycerin	20	0.83
	30	0.63
SAE 5W-30 motor oil	−30	≤ 6.6
	150	$\geq 2.9 \times 10^{-3}$

where $\Delta V / \Delta t$ is the volume flow rate, ΔP is the pressure difference between the ends of the pipe, r and L are the inner radius and length of the pipe, respectively, and η is the viscosity of the fluid. Poiseuille's name is pronounced *pwahzoy*, in a rough English approximation.

It isn't often that we encounter a *fourth-power* dependence. Why such a strong dependence on radius? First of all, if fluids are flowing through two different pipes at the *same speed*, the volume flow rates are proportional to radius squared (flow rate = speed multiplied by cross-sectional area). But, in viscous flow, the average flow speed is larger for wider pipes; fluid farther away from the walls can flow faster. It turns out that the average flow speed for a given pressure gradient is also proportional to radius squared, giving the overall fourth power dependence on the pipe radius of Poiseuille's law.

 Application of viscous flow: high blood pressure

The strong dependence of flow rate on radius is important in blood flow. A person with cardiovascular disease has arteries narrowed by plaque deposits. To maintain the necessary blood flow to keep the body functioning, the blood pressure increases. If the diameter of an artery narrows to $\frac{1}{2}$ of its original value due to plaque deposits, the blood flow rate would decrease to $\frac{1}{16}$ of its original value if the pressure drop across it were to stay the same. To compensate for some of this decrease in blood flow, the heart pumps harder, increasing the blood pressure. High blood pressure is not good either; it introduces its own set of health problems, not least of which is the increased demands placed on the heart muscle.

Example 9.12

Arterial Blockage

A cardiologist reports to her patient that the radius of the left anterior descending artery of the heart has narrowed by 10.0%. What percent increase in the blood pressure drop across the artery is required to maintain the normal blood flow through this artery?

Strategy We assume that the viscosity of the blood has not changed, nor has the length of the artery. To maintain normal blood flow, the volume flow rate must stay the same:

$$\frac{\Delta V_1}{\Delta t} = \frac{\Delta V_2}{\Delta t}$$

Solution If r_1 is the normal radius and r_2 is the actual radius, a 10.0% reduction in radius means $r_2 = 0.900 r_1$. Then, from Poiseuille's law,

$$\frac{\pi \Delta P_1 r_1^4}{8 \eta L} = \frac{\pi \Delta P_2 r_2^4}{8 \eta L}$$

$$r_1^4 \Delta P_1 = r_2^4 \Delta P_2$$

We solve for the ratio of the pressure drops:

$$\frac{\Delta P_2}{\Delta P_1} = \frac{r_1^4}{r_2^4} = \frac{1}{(0.900)^4} = 1.52$$

Discussion A factor of 1.52 means there is a 52% increase in the blood pressure difference across that artery. The increased pressure must be provided by the heart. If the normal pressure drop across the artery is 10 mm Hg, then it is now 15.2 mm Hg. The person's blood pressure either must increase by 5.2 mm Hg or there will be a reduction in blood flow through this artery. The heart is under greater strain as it works harder, attempting to maintain an adequate flow of blood.

Practice Problem 9.12   New Water Pipe

The town water supply is operating at nearly full capacity. The town board decides to replace the water main with a bigger one to increase capacity. If the maximum flow rate is to increase by a factor of 4.0, by what factor should they increase the radius of the water main?

Turbulence

When the fluid velocity at a given point changes, the flow is *unsteady*. **Turbulence** is an extreme example of unsteady flow (Fig. 9.29). In turbulent flow, swirling vortices—whirlpools of fluid—appear. The vortices are not stationary; they move with the fluid. The flow velocity at any point changes erratically; prediction of the direction or speed of fluid flow under turbulent conditions is difficult.

9.10   VISCOUS DRAG

When an object moves through a fluid, the fluid exerts a drag force on it. When the relative velocity between the object and the fluid is low enough for the flow around the object to be laminar, the drag force derives from viscosity and is called **viscous drag**.

Viscous drag: $F_D \propto v$
Turbulent drag: $F_D \propto v^2$

Figure 9.29 Turbulent flow of gas emerging from the nozzle of an aerosol can.

The viscous drag force is proportional to the speed of the object. For larger relative speeds, the flow becomes turbulent and the drag force is proportional to the square of the object's speed.

The viscous drag force depends also on the shape and size of the object. For a spherical object, the viscous drag force is given by Stokes's law:

Stokes's Law (viscous drag on a sphere)

$$F_D = 6\pi\eta r v \qquad (9\text{-}16)$$

where r is the radius of the sphere, η is the viscosity of the fluid, and v is the speed of the object with respect to the fluid.

✓ CHECKPOINT 9.10

Compare and contrast the viscous drag force with the kinetic frictional force.

An object's **terminal velocity** is the velocity that produces just the right drag force so that the net force is zero. An object falling at its terminal velocity has zero acceleration, so it continues moving at that constant velocity. Using Stokes's law, we can find the terminal velocity of a spherical object falling through a viscous fluid. When the object moves at terminal velocity, the net force acting on it is zero. If $\rho_o > \rho_f$, the object sinks; the terminal velocity is downward and the viscous drag force acts upward to oppose the motion. For an object, such as an air bubble in oil, that rises rather than sinks ($\rho_o < \rho_f$), the terminal velocity is *upward* and the drag force is *downward*.

Example 9.13

Falling Droplet

In an experiment to measure the electric charge of the electron, a fine mist of oil droplets is sprayed into the air and observed through a telescope as they fall. These droplets are so tiny that they soon reach their terminal velocity. If the radius of the droplets is 2.40 µm and the average density of the oil is 862 kg/m³, find the terminal speed of the droplets. The density of air is 1.20 kg/m³ and the viscosity of air is 1.8×10^{-5} Pa·s.

Strategy When the droplets fall at their terminal velocity, the net force on them is zero. We set the net force equal to zero and use Stokes's law for the drag force.

Solution We set the sum of the forces equal to zero when $v = v_t$.

$$\sum F_y = +F_D + F_B - W = 0$$

If m_{air} is the mass of displaced air, then

$$6\pi\eta r v_t + m_{air}g - m_{oil}g = 0$$

Solving for v_t,

$$v_t = \frac{g(m_{oil} - m_{air})}{6\pi\eta r}$$

$$= \frac{\frac{4}{3}\pi r^3 g(\rho_{oil} - \rho_{air})}{6\pi\eta r}$$

After dividing the numerator and denominator by πr, we substitute numerical values:

$$v_t = \frac{\frac{4}{3}(2.40 \times 10^{-6}\text{ m})^2 (9.80\text{ N/kg}) (862\text{ kg/m}^3 - 1.20\text{ kg/m}^3)}{6 \times 1.8 \times 10^{-5}\text{ Pa·s}}$$

$$= 6.0 \times 10^{-4}\text{ m/s} = 0.60\text{ mm/s}$$

Discussion We should check the units in the final expression:

$$\frac{\text{m}^2 \cdot (\text{N/kg}) \cdot \text{kg/m}^3}{\text{Pa·s}} = \frac{\text{N/m}}{\text{N/m}^2 \times \text{s}} = \text{m/s}$$

Stokes's law was applied in this way by Robert Millikan (1868–1953) in his experiments in 1909–1913 to measure the charge of the electron. Using an atomizer, Millikan produced a fine spray of oil droplets. The droplets picked up electric charge as they were sprayed through the atomizer. Millikan kept a droplet suspended without falling by applying an upward electric force. After removing the electric force, he measured the terminal speed of the droplet as it fell through the air. He calculated the mass of the droplet from the terminal speed and the density of the oil using Stokes's law.

continued on next page

Example 9.13 continued

By setting the magnitude of the electric force equal to the weight of a suspended droplet, Millikan calculated the electric charge of the droplet. He measured the charges of hundreds of different droplets and found that they were all multiples of the same quantity—the charge of an electron.

Practice Problem 9.13   Rising Bubble

Find the terminal velocity of an air bubble of 0.500 mm radius in a cup of vegetable oil. The specific gravity of the oil is 0.840 and the viscosity is 0.160 Pa·s. Assume the diameter of the bubble does not change as it rises.

PHYSICS AT HOME

A demonstration of terminal velocity can be done at home. Climb up a small stepladder, or lean over an upstairs balcony, and drop two objects at the same time: a coin and two or three nested cone-shaped paper coffee filters. You will see the effects of viscous drag on the coffee filters as they fall with a constant terminal velocity. Enlist the help of a friend so you can get a side view of the two objects falling. Why do the coffee filters work so well?

For small particles falling in a liquid, the terminal velocity is also called the *sedimentation velocity*. The sedimentation velocity is often small for two reasons. First, if the particle isn't much more dense than the fluid, then the vector sum of the gravitational and buoyant forces is small. Second, notice that the terminal velocity is proportional to r^2; viscous drag is most important for small particles. Thus, it can take a long time for the particles to sediment out of solution. Because the sedimentation velocity is proportional to g, it can be increased by the use of a centrifuge, a rotating container that creates artificial gravity of magnitude $g_{eff} = \omega^2 r$ [see Eq. (5-12) and Section 5.7]. Ultra-centrifuges are capable of rotating at 10^5 rev/min and produce artificial gravity approaching a million times g.

 Application of viscous drag: sedimentation velocity and the centrifuge

9.11   SURFACE TENSION

The surface of a liquid has special properties not associated with the interior of the liquid. The surface acts like a stretched membrane under tension. The **surface tension** (symbol γ, the Greek letter gamma) of a liquid is the force per unit *length* with which the surface pulls *on its edge*. The direction of the force is tangent to the surface at its edge. Surface tension is caused by the cohesive forces that pull the molecules toward each other.

The high surface tension of water enables water striders and other small insects to walk on the surface of a pond. The foot of the insect makes a small indentation in the water surface (Fig. 9.30); the deformation of the surface enables it to push upward on the foot as if the water surface were a thin sheet of rubber. Visually it looks similar to a person walking across the mat of a trampoline. Other small water creatures, such as mosquito larvae and planaria, hang from the surface of water, using surface tension to hold themselves up. In plants, surface tension aids in the transport of water from the roots to the leaves.

 Application of surface tension: how insects can walk on the surface of a pond

PHYSICS AT HOME

Place a needle (or a flat plastic-coated paper clip) gently on the surface of a glass of water. It may take some practice, but you should be able to get it to "float" on top of the water. Now add some detergent to the water and try again. The detergent reduces the surface tension of the water so it is unable to support the needle. Soaps and detergents are *surfactants*—substances that reduce the surface tension of a fluid. The reduced surface tension allows the water to spread out more, wetting more of a surface to be cleaned.

Figure 9.30 A water strider.

Figure 9.31 In the human lung, millions of tiny sacs called alveoli are inflated with each breath. Gas is exchanged between the air and the blood through the walls of the alveoli. The total surface area through which gas exchange takes place is about 80 m² —about 40 times the surface area of the body.

Application of surface tension: surfactant in the lungs

The high surface tension of water is a hindrance in the lungs. The exchange of oxygen and carbon dioxide between inspired air and the blood takes place in tiny sacs called *alveoli*, 0.05 to 0.15 mm in radius, at the end of the bronchial tubes (Fig. 9.31). If the mucus coating the alveoli had the same surface tension as other body fluids, the pressure difference between the inside and outside of the alveoli would not be great enough for them to expand and fill with air. The alveoli secrete a surfactant that decreases the surface tension in their mucous coating so they can inflate during inhalation.

Bubbles

In an underwater air bubble, the surface tension of the water surface tries to contract the bubble while the pressure of the enclosed air pushes outward on the surface. In equilibrium, the air pressure inside the bubble must be larger than the water pressure outside so that the net outward force due to pressure balances the inward force due to surface tension. The excess pressure $\Delta P = P_{in} - P_{out}$ depends both on the surface tension and the size of the bubble. In Problem 72, you can show that the excess pressure is

$$\Delta P = \frac{2\gamma}{r} \qquad (9\text{-}17)$$

Look closely at a glass of champagne and you can see strings of bubbles rising, originating from the same points in the liquid. Why don't bubbles spring up from random locations? A very small bubble would require an insupportably large excess pressure. The bubbles need some sort of nucleus—a small dust particle, for instance—on which to form so they can start out larger, with excess pressures that aren't so large. The strings of bubbles in the glass of champagne are showing where suitable nuclei have been "found."

Example 9.14

Lung Pressure

During inhalation the gauge pressure in the alveoli is about −400 Pa to allow air to flow in through the bronchial tubes. Suppose the mucous coating on an alveolus of initial radius 0.050 mm had the same surface tension as water (0.070 N/m). What lung pressure outside the alveoli would be required to begin to inflate the alveolus?

Strategy We model an alveolus as a sphere coated with mucus. Due to the surface tension of the mucus, the alveolus must have a lower pressure outside than inside, as for a bubble.

Solution The excess pressure is

$$\Delta P = \frac{2\gamma}{r} = \frac{2 \times 0.070 \text{ N/m}}{0.050 \times 10^{-3} \text{ m}} = 2.8 \text{ kPa}$$

continued on next page

Example 9.14 continued

Thus, the pressure inside the alveolus would be 2.8 kPa higher than the pressure outside. The gauge pressure inside is −400 Pa, so the gauge pressure outside would be

$$P_{\text{out}} = -0.4 \text{ kPa} - 2.8 \text{ kPa} = -3.2 \text{ kPa}$$

Discussion   The *actual* gauge pressure outside the alveoli is about −0.5 kPa rather than −3.2 kPa; then $\Delta P = P_{\text{in}} - P_{\text{out}} = -0.4 \text{ kPa} - (-0.5 \text{ kPa}) = 0.1 \text{ kPa}$ rather than 2.8 kPa. Here the surfactant comes to the rescue; by decreasing the surface tension in the mucus, it decreases ΔP to about 0.1 kPa and

allows the expansion of the alveoli to take place. For a newborn baby, the alveoli are initially collapsed, making the required pressure difference about 4 kPa. That first breath is as difficult an event as it is significant.

Practice Problem 9.14   Champagne Bubbles

A bubble in a glass of champagne is filled with CO_2. When it is 2.0 cm below the surface of the champagne, its radius is 0.50 mm. What is the gauge pressure inside the bubble? Assume that champagne has the same average density as water and a surface tension of 0.070 N/m.

Master the Concepts

- Fluids are materials that flow and include both liquids and gases. A liquid is nearly incompressible, whereas a gas expands to fill its container.

- Pressure is the perpendicular force per unit area that a fluid exerts on any surface with which it comes in contact ($P = F/A$). The SI unit of pressure is the pascal ($1 \text{ Pa} = 1 \text{ N/m}^2$).

- The average air pressure at sea level is 1 atm = 101.3 kPa.

- Pascal's principle: A change in pressure at any point in a confined fluid is transmitted everywhere throughout the fluid.

- The average density of a substance is the ratio of its mass to its volume

$$\rho = \frac{m}{V} \qquad (9\text{-}2)$$

- The specific gravity of a material is the ratio of its density to that of water at 4°C.

- Pressure variation with depth in a static fluid:

$$P_2 = P_1 + \rho g d \qquad (9\text{-}3)$$

where point 2 is a depth d below point 1.

- Instruments to measure pressure include the manometer and the barometer. The barometer measures the pressure of the atmosphere. The manometer measures a pressure difference.

- Gauge pressure is the amount by which the absolute pressure exceeds atmospheric pressure:

$$P_{\text{gauge}} = P_{\text{abs}} - P_{\text{atm}} \qquad (9\text{-}6)$$

- Archimedes' principle: a fluid exerts an upward buoyant force on a completely or partially submerged object equal in magnitude to the weight of the volume of fluid displaced by the object:

$$F_{\text{B}} = \rho g V \qquad (9\text{-}7)$$

where V is the volume of the part of the object that is submerged and ρ is the density of the fluid.

- In steady flow, the velocity of the fluid *at any point* is constant in time. In laminar flow, the fluid flows in neat layers so that each small portion of fluid that passes a particular point follows the same path as every other portion of fluid that passes the same point. The path that the fluid follows, starting from any point, is called a streamline. Laminar flow is steady. Turbulent flow is chaotic and unsteady. The viscous force opposes the flow of the fluid; it is the counterpart to the frictional force for solids.

- An ideal fluid exhibits laminar flow, has no viscosity, and is incompressible. The flow of an ideal fluid is governed by two principles: the continuity equation and Bernoulli's equation.

- The continuity equation states that the volume flow rate for an ideal fluid is constant:

$$\frac{\Delta V}{\Delta t} = A_1 v_1 = A_2 v_2 \qquad (9\text{-}12, 9\text{-}13)$$

- Bernoulli's equation relates pressure changes to changes in flow speed and height:

$$P_1 + \rho g y_1 + \tfrac{1}{2}\rho v_1^2 = P_2 + \rho g y_2 + \tfrac{1}{2}\rho v_2^2 \qquad (9\text{-}14)$$

continued on next page

Master the Concepts continued

- Poiseuille's law gives the volume flow rate $\Delta V/\Delta t$ for viscous flow in a horizontal pipe:

$$\frac{\Delta V}{\Delta t} = \frac{\pi}{8}\frac{\Delta P/L}{\eta}r^4 \qquad (9\text{-}15)$$

(a)

Direction of flow

$P_1 A$ $P_2 A$

$\vec{F}_v$

$\longrightarrow x$

(b) Pressure

P_1

P_2

$\longrightarrow x$

where ΔP is the pressure difference between the ends of the pipe, r and L are the inner radius and length of the pipe, respectively, and η is the viscosity of the fluid.

- Stokes's law gives the viscous drag force on a spherical object moving in a fluid:

$$F_D = 6\pi\eta rv \qquad (9\text{-}16)$$

- The surface tension γ (the Greek letter gamma) of a liquid is the force *per unit length* with which the surface pulls on its edge.

Conceptual Questions

1. Does a manometer (with one side open) measure absolute pressure or gauge pressure? How about a barometer? A tire pressure gauge? A sphygmomanometer?

2. A volunteer firefighter holds the end of a firehose as a strong jet of water emerges. (a) The hose exerts a large backward force on the firefighter. Explain the origin of this force. (b) If another firefighter steps on the hose, forming a constriction (a place where the area of the hose is smaller), the hose begins to pulsate wildly. Explain.

3. The weight of a boat is listed on specification sheets as its "displacement." Explain.

4. In tall buildings, the water supply system uses multiple pumping stations on different floors. At each station, water pumped up from below collects in a storage tank held at atmospheric pressure before it enters the pump. The storage tank supplies water to the floors below it. What are some of the reasons why these multiple pumping stations are used?

5. Can an astronaut on the Moon use a straw to drink from a normal drinking glass? How about if he pokes a straw through an otherwise sealed juice box? Explain.

6. It is commonly said that wood floats because it is "lighter than water" or that a stone sinks because it is "heavier than water." Are these accurate statements? If not, correct them.

7. Why must a blood pressure cuff be wrapped around the arm at the same vertical level as the heart?

8. A hot air balloon is floating in equilibrium with the surrounding air. (a) How does the pressure inside the balloon compare with the pressure outside? (b) How does the density of the air inside compare to the density outside?

9. When helium weather balloons are released, they are purposely underinflated. Why? [*Hint:* The balloons go to very high altitudes.]

10. Bernoulli's equation applies only to *steady flow*. Yet Bernoulli's equation allows the fluid velocity at one point to be different than the velocity at another point. For the fluid velocity to change, the fluid must be accelerated as it moves from one point to another. In what way is the flow *steady*, then?

11. Before getting an oil change, it is a good idea to drive a few miles to warm up the engine. Why?

12. Your ears "pop" when you change altitude quickly—such as during takeoff or landing in an airplane, or during a drive in the mountains. Curiously, if you are a passenger in a high-speed train, your ears sometimes pop as the speed of the train increases rapidly—even though there is little or no change in altitude. Explain.

13. It is easier to get a good draft in a chimney on a windy day than when the outside air is still, all other things being equal. Why?

14. Two soap bubbles of *different radii* are formed at the ends of a tube with a closed valve in the middle. What happens to the bubbles when the valve is opened? (If the alveoli in the lung did not have a surfactant that reduces surface tension in the smaller alveoli, the same thing would happen in the lung, with disastrous results!)

15. *Pascal's principle: proof by contradiction.* Points A and B are near each other at the same height in a fluid. Suppose $P_A > P_B$. (a) Can both v_A and v_B be zero? Explain. (b) Point C is just above point D in a static fluid. Suppose the pressure at C increases by an amount ΔP. What would happen if the pressure at D did not increase by the same amount?

16. What are the advantages of using hydraulic systems rather than mechanical systems to operate automobile brakes or the control surfaces of an airplane?

17. In any hydraulic system, it is important to "bleed" air out of the line. Why?

18. Is it possible for a skin diver to dive to any depth as long as his snorkel tube is sufficiently long? (A snorkel is a face mask with a breathing tube that sticks above the surface of the water.)

19. Is the buoyant force on a soap bubble greater than the weight of the bubble? If not, why do soap bubbles sometimes appear to float in air?

20. A plastic water bottle open at the top is three-fourths full of water and is placed on a scale. The bottle has an indentation for a label midway up the side and a strap has been placed around this indentation. If the strap is tightened, so the bottle is squeezed in at the middle and the water level is forced to rise, what happens to the reading on the scale? Is the water pressure at the bottom of the bottle the same?

Multiple-Choice Questions

1. A glass of ice water is filled to the brim with water; the ice cubes stick up above the water surface. After the ice melts, which is true?

   (a) The water level is below the top of the glass.
   (b) The water level is at the top of the glass but no water has spilled.
   (c) Some water has spilled over the sides of the glass.
   (d) Impossible to say without knowing the initial densities of the water and the ice.

2. A dam holding back the water in a reservoir exerts a horizontal force on the water. The magnitude of this force depends on

   (a) the maximum depth of the reservoir.
   (b) the depth of the water at the location of the dam.
   (c) the surface area of the reservoir.
   (d) both (a) and (b).
   (e) all three—(a), (b), and (c).

3. Bernoulli's equation applies to

   (a) any fluid.
   (b) an incompressible fluid, whether viscous or not.
   (c) an incompressible, nonviscous fluid, whether the flow is turbulent or not.
   (d) an incompressible, nonviscous, nonturbulent fluid.
   (e) a static fluid only.

Questions 4–5. Two spheres, A and B, fall through the same viscous fluid.

Answer choices for Questions 4 and 5:

   (a) A has the larger terminal velocity.
   (b) B has the larger terminal velocity.

   (c) A and B have the same terminal velocity.
   (d) Insufficient information is given to reach a conclusion.

4. A and B have the same radius; A has the larger mass. Which has the larger terminal velocity?

5. A and B have the same density; A has the larger radius. Which has the larger terminal velocity?

6. Bernoulli's equation is an expression of

   (a) conservation of mass.
   (b) conservation of energy.
   (c) conservation of momentum.
   (d) conservation of angular momentum.

7. The continuity equation is an expression of

   (a) conservation of mass.
   (b) conservation of energy.
   (c) conservation of momentum.
   (d) conservation of angular momentum.

8. What is the gauge pressure of the gas in the closed tube in the figure? (Take the atmospheric pressure to be 76 cm Hg.)

   (a) 20 cm Hg
   (b) −20 cm Hg
   (c) 96 cm Hg
   (d) 56 cm Hg
   (e) −96 cm Hg
   (f) −56 cm Hg

9. A manometer contains two different fluids of different densities. Both sides are open to the atmosphere. Which pair(s) of points in the figure have equal pressure?

   (a) $P_1 = P_5$
   (b) $P_2 = P_5$
   (c) $P_3 = P_4$
   (d) Both (a) and (c)
   (e) Both (b) and (c)

10. A Venturi meter is used to measure the flow speed of a *viscous* fluid. With reference to the figure, which is true?
    (a) $h_3 = h_1$ (b) $h_3 > h_1$
    (c) $h_3 < h_1$ (d) Insufficient information to determine

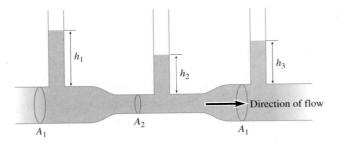

Problems

- ⊚ Combination conceptual/quantitative problem
- ⚕ Biological or medical application
- ✦ Challenging problem
- Blue # Detailed solution in the Student Solutions Manual
- ① ② Problems paired by concept
- ⓦ Text website interactive or tutorial

9.2 Pressure

1. Someone steps on your toe, exerting a force of 500 N on an area of 1.0 cm^2. What is the average pressure on that area in atm?

2. The pressure inside a bottle of champagne is 4.5 atm higher than the air pressure outside. The neck of the bottle has an inner radius of 1.0 cm. What is the frictional force on the cork due to the neck of the bottle?

3. What is the average pressure on the soles of the feet of a standing 90.0-kg person due to the contact force with the floor? Each foot has a surface area of 0.020 m^2.

⊚ 4. Atmospheric pressure is about 1.0×10^5 Pa on average. (a) What is the downward force of the air on a desktop with surface area 1.0 m^2? (b) Convert this force to pounds so you really understand how large it is. (c) Why does this huge force not crush the desk?

5. A 10-kg baby sits on a three-legged stool. The diameter of each of the stool's round feet is 2.0 cm. A 60-kg adult sits on a four-legged chair that has four circular feet, each with a diameter of 6.0 cm. Who applies the greater pressure to the floor and by how much?

6. A lid is put on a box that is 15 cm long, 13 cm wide, and 8.0 cm tall and the box is then evacuated until its inner pressure is 0.80×10^5 Pa. How much force is required to lift the lid (a) at sea level; (b) in Denver, on a day when the atmospheric pressure is 67.5 kPa ($\frac{2}{3}$ the value at sea level)?

9.3 Pascal's Principle

7. A container is filled with gas at a pressure of 4.0×10^5 Pa. The container is a cube, 0.10 m on a side, with one side facing south. What is the magnitude and direction of the force on the south side of the container due to the gas inside?

⚕ 8. A nurse applies a force of 4.40 N to the piston of a syringe. The piston has an area of $5.00 \times 10^{-5} \text{ m}^2$. What is the pressure increase in the fluid within the syringe?

9. A hydraulic lift is lifting a car that weighs 12 kN. The area of the piston supporting the car is A, the area of the other piston is a, and the ratio A/a is 100.0. How far must the small piston be pushed down to raise the car a distance of 1.0 cm? [*Hint:* Consider the work to be done.]

10. In a hydraulic lift, the radii of the pistons are 2.50 cm and 10.0 cm. A car weighing $W = 10.0$ kN is to be lifted by the force of the large piston. (a) What force F_a must be applied to the small piston? (b) When the small piston is pushed in by 10.0 cm, how far is the car lifted? (c) Find the mechanical advantage of the lift, which is the ratio W/F_a.

✦ 11. Depressing the brake pedal in a car pushes on a piston with cross-sectional area 3.0 cm^2. The piston applies pressure to the brake fluid, which is connected to two pistons, each with area 12.0 cm^2. Each of these pistons presses a brake pad against one side of a rotor attached to one of the rotating wheels. See the figure for this problem. (a) When the force applied by the brake pedal to the small piston is 7.5 N, what is the normal force applied to each side of the rotor? (b) If the coefficient of kinetic friction between a brake pad and the rotor is 0.80 and each pad is (on average) 12 cm from the rotation axis of the rotor, what is the torque on the rotor due to the two pads?

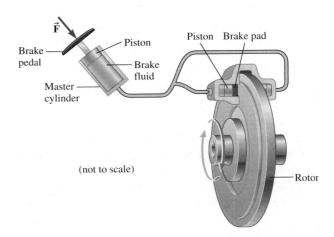

9.4 The Effect of Gravity on Fluid Pressure

12. At the surface of a freshwater lake the air pressure is 1.0 atm. At what depth under water in the lake is the water pressure 4.0 atm?

13. What is the pressure on a fish 10 m under the ocean surface?

14. How high can you suck water up a straw? The pressure in the lungs can be reduced to about 10 kPa below atmospheric pressure.

15. The density of platinum is 21 500 kg/m^3. Find the ratio of the volume of 1.00 kg of platinum to the volume of 1.00 kg of aluminum.

16. In the Netherlands, a dike holds back the sea from a town below sea level. The dike springs a leak 3.0 m below the water surface. If the area of the hole in the dike is 1.0 cm^2, what force must the Dutch boy exert to save the town?

17. A container has a large cylindrical lower part with a long thin cylindrical neck. The lower part of the container holds 12.5 m^3 of water and the surface area of the bottom of the container is 5.00 m^2. The height of the lower part of the container is 2.50 m and the neck contains a column of water 8.50 m high. The total volume of the column of water in the neck is 0.200 m^3. What is the magnitude of the force exerted by the water on the bottom of the container?

18. The maximum pressure most organisms can survive is about 1000 times atmospheric pressure. Only small, simple organisms such as tadpoles and bacteria can survive such high pressures. What then is the maximum depth at which these organisms can live under the sea (assuming that the density of seawater is 1025 kg/m^3)?

19. At the surface of a freshwater lake the pressure is 105 kPa. (a) What is the pressure increase in going 35.0 m below the surface? (b) What is the approximate pressure decrease in going 35 m above the surface? Air at 20°C has density of 1.20 kg/m^3.

9.5 Measuring Pressure

20. A woman's systolic blood pressure when resting is 160 mm Hg. What is this pressure in (a) Pa, (b) lb/in^2, (c) atm, (d) torr?

21. The gauge pressure of the air in an automobile tire is 32 lb/in^2. Convert this to (a) Pa, (b) torr, (c) atm.

22. An IV is connected to a patient's vein. The blood pressure in the vein has a gauge pressure of 12 mm Hg. At least how far above the vein must the IV bag be hung in order for fluid to flow into the vein? Assume the fluid in the IV has the same density as blood.

23. When a mercury manometer is connected to a gas main, the mercury stands 40.0 cm higher in the tube that is open to the air than in the tube connected to the gas main. A barometer at the same location reads 74.0 cm Hg. Determine the absolute pressure of the gas in cm Hg.

24. An experiment to determine the specific heat of a gas makes use of a water manometer attached to a flask. Initially the two columns of water are even. Atmospheric pressure is 1.0×10^5 Pa. After heating the gas, the water levels change to those shown. Find the change in pressure of the gas in Pa.

25. A manometer using oil (density 0.90 g/cm^3) as a fluid is connected to an air tank. Suddenly the pressure in the tank increases by 0.74 cm Hg. (a) By how much does the fluid level rise in the side of the manometer that is open to the atmosphere? (b) What would your answer be if the manometer used mercury instead?

26. Estimate the average blood pressure in a person's foot, if the foot is 1.37 m below the aorta, where the average blood pressure is 104 mm Hg. For the purposes of this estimate, assume the blood isn't flowing.

9.6 The Buoyant Force

27. A Canada goose floats with 25% of its volume below water. What is the average density of the goose?

28. A flat-bottomed barge, loaded with coal, has a mass of 3.0×10^5 kg. The barge is 20.0 m long and 10.0 m wide. It floats in fresh water. What is the depth of the barge below the waterline? (tutorial: boat)

29. (a) When ice floats in water at 0°C, what percent of its volume is submerged? (b) What is the specific gravity of ice?

30. (a) What is the density of an object that is 14% submerged when floating in water at 0°C? (b) What percentage of the object will be submerged if it is placed in ethanol at 0°C?

31. (a) What is the buoyant force on 0.90 kg of ice floating freely in liquid water? (b) What is the buoyant force on 0.90 kg of ice held completely submerged under water?

32. A block of birch wood floats in oil with 90.0% of its volume submerged. What is the density of the oil? The density of the birch is 0.67 g/cm^3.

33. When a block of ebony is placed in ethanol, what percentage of its volume is submerged?

34. A cylindrical disk has volume 8.97×10^{-3} m^3 and mass 8.16 kg. The disk is floating on the surface of some water with its flat surfaces horizontal. The area of each flat surface is 0.640 m^2. (a) What is the specific gravity of the disk? (b) How far below the water level is its bottom surface? (c) How far above the water level is its top surface?

35. An aluminum cylinder weighs 1.03 N. When this same cylinder is completely submerged in alcohol, the volume of the displaced alcohol is 3.90×10^{-5} m^3. If the cylinder is suspended from a scale while submerged in the alcohol, the scale reading is 0.730 N. What is the specific gravity of the alcohol? (tutorial: ball in beaker)

36. A fish uses a swim bladder to change its density so it is equal to that of water, enabling it to remain suspended under water. If a fish has an average density of 1080 kg/m^3 and mass 10.0 g with the bladder completely deflated, to what volume must the fish inflate the swim bladder in order to remain suspended in seawater of density 1060 kg/m^3?

37. While vacationing at the Outer Banks of North Carolina, you find an old coin that looks like it is made of gold. You know there were many shipwrecks here, so you take the coin home to check the possibility of it being gold. You suspend the coin from a spring scale and find that it has a weight in air of 1.75 oz (mass = 49.7 g). You then let the coin hang submerged in a glass of water and find that the scale reads 1.66 oz (mass = 47.1 g). Should you get excited about the possibility that this coin might really be gold?

38. The average density of a fish can be found by first weighing it in air and then finding the scale reading for the fish completely immersed in water and suspended from a scale. If a fish has weight 200.0 N in air and scale reading 15.0 N in water, what is the average density of the fish?

39. (a) A piece of balsa wood with density 0.50 g/cm^3 is released under water. What is its initial acceleration? (b) Repeat for a piece of maple with density 0.750 g/cm^3. (c) Repeat for a ping-pong ball with an average density of 0.125 g/cm^3.

40. A piece of metal is released under water. The volume of the metal is 50.0 cm^3 and its specific gravity is 5.0. What is its initial acceleration?

9.7 Fluid Flow; 9.8 Bernoulli's Equation

41. A garden hose of inner radius 1.0 cm carries water at 2.0 m/s. The nozzle at the end has radius 0.20 cm. How fast does the water move through the nozzle?

42. If the average volume flow of blood through the aorta is 8.5×10^{-5} m^3/s and the cross-sectional area of the aorta is 3.0×10^{-4} m^2, what is the average speed of blood in the aorta?

43. A nozzle of inner radius 1.00 mm is connected to a hose of inner radius 8.00 mm. The nozzle shoots out water moving at 25.0 m/s. (a) At what speed is the water in the hose moving? (b) What is the volume flow rate? (c) What is the mass flow rate?

44. Water entering a house flows with a speed of 0.20 m/s through a pipe of 1.0 cm inside radius. What is the speed of the water at a point where the pipe tapers to a radius of 2.5 mm?

45. A horizontal segment of pipe tapers from a cross-sectional area of 50.0 cm^2 to 0.500 cm^2. The pressure at the larger end of the pipe is 1.20×10^5 Pa and the speed is 0.040 m/s. What is the pressure at the narrow end of the segment?

46. In a tornado or hurricane, a roof may tear away from the house because of a difference in pressure between the air inside and the air outside. Suppose that air is blowing across the top of a 2000 ft^2 roof at 150 mph. What is the magnitude of the force on the roof?

47. Use Bernoulli's equation to estimate the upward force on an airplane's wing if the average flow speed of air is 190 m/s above the wing and 160 m/s below the wing. The density of the air is 1.3 kg/m^3 and the area of each wing surface is 28 m^2.

48. An airplane flies on a level path. There is a pressure difference of 500 Pa between the lower and upper surfaces of the wings. The area of each wing surface is about 100 m^2. The air moves below the wings at a speed of 80.5 m/s. Estimate (a) the weight of the plane and (b) the air speed above the wings.

49. A nozzle is connected to a horizontal hose. The nozzle shoots out water moving at 25 m/s. What is the gauge pressure of the water in the hose? Neglect viscosity and assume that the diameter of the nozzle is much smaller than the inner diameter of the hose.

50. Suppose air, with a density of 1.29 kg/m^3 is flowing into a Venturi meter. The narrow section of the pipe at point A has a diameter that is $\frac{1}{3}$ of the diameter of the larger section of the pipe at point B. The U-shaped tube is filled with *water* and the difference in height between the two sections of pipe is 1.75 cm. How fast is the air moving at point B?

51. A water tower supplies water through the plumbing in a house. A 2.54-cm-diameter faucet in the house can fill a cylindrical container with a diameter of 44 cm and a height of 52 cm in 12 s. How high above the faucet is the top of the water in the tower? (Assume that the diameter of the tower is so large compared to that of the faucet that the water at the top of the tower does not move.)

52. The volume flow rate of the water supplied by a well is 2.0×10^{-4} m^3/s. The well is 40.0 m deep. (a) What is the power output of the pump—in other words, at what rate does the well do work on the water? (b) Find the pressure difference the pump must maintain. (c) Can the pump be at the top of the well or must it be at the bottom? Explain.

9.9 Viscosity

53. Using Poiseuille's law [Eq. (9-15)], show that viscosity has SI units of pascal-seconds.

54. A viscous liquid is flowing steadily through a pipe of diameter D. Suppose you replace it by two parallel pipes, each of diameter $D/2$, but the same length as the original pipe. If the pressure difference between the ends of these two pipes is the same as for the original pipe, what is the total rate of flow in the two pipes compared to the original flow rate?

55. A hypodermic syringe is attached to a needle that has an internal radius of 0.300 mm and a length of 3.00 cm. The needle is filled with a solution of viscosity 2.00×10^{-3} Pa·s; it is injected into a vein at a gauge pressure of 16.0 mm Hg. Ignore the extra pressure required to accelerate the fluid from the syringe into the entrance of the needle. (a) What must the pressure of the fluid in the syringe be in order to inject the solution at a rate of 0.250 mL/s? (b) What force must be applied to the plunger, which has an area of 1.00 cm^2?

Problems 56–58. Four identical sections of pipe are connected in various ways to pumps that supply water at the pressures indicated in the figure (in units of 10^5 Pa). The water exits at the right at atmospheric pressure. Assume viscous flow.

56. If the *total* volume flow rates in systems A and C are the same and the flow speed in each of the pipes in C is 3.0 m/s, what is the flow speed in system A?

57. If the total volume flow rate in system B is 0.020 m^3/s, what is the total volume flow rate in system C?

58. If the total volume flow rates in systems A and B are the same, at what pressure does the pump supply water in system A?

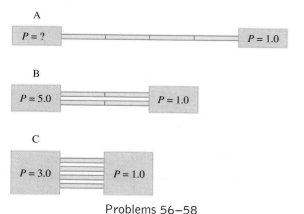

A

$P = ?$ $P = 1.0$

B

$P = 5.0$ $P = 1.0$

C

$P = 3.0$ $P = 1.0$

Problems 56–58

59. (a) What is the pressure difference required to make blood flow through an artery of inner radius 2.0 mm and length 0.20 m at a speed of 6.0 cm/s? (b) What is the pressure difference required to make blood flow at 0.60 mm/s through a capillary of radius 3.0 μm and

length 1.0 mm? (c) Compare both answers to your average blood pressure, about 100 torr.

60. (a) Since the flow rate is proportional to the pressure difference, show that Poiseuille's law can be written in the form $\Delta P = IR$, where I is the volume flow rate and R is a constant of proportionality called the fluid flow *resistance*. (Written this way, Poiseuille's law is analogous to *Ohm's law* for electric current to be studied in Chapter 18: $\Delta V = IR$, where ΔV is the potential drop across a conductor, I is the electric current flowing through the conductor, and R is the electrical resistance of the conductor.) (b) Find R in terms of the viscosity of the fluid and the length and radius of the pipe.

9.10 Viscous Drag

61. Two identical spheres are dropped into two different columns: one column contains a liquid of viscosity 0.5 Pa·s, while the other contains a liquid of the same density but unknown viscosity. The sedimentation velocity in the second tube is 20% higher than the sedimentation velocity in the first tube. What is the viscosity of the second liquid?

62. A sphere of radius 1.0 cm is dropped into a glass cylinder filled with a viscous liquid. The mass of the sphere is 12.0 g and the density of the liquid is 1200 kg/m^3. The sphere reaches a terminal speed of 0.15 m/s. What is the viscosity of the liquid?

63. A dinoflagellate takes 5.0 s to travel 1.0 mm. Approximate a dinoflagellate as a sphere of radius 35.0 μm (ignoring the flagellum). (a) What is the drag force on the dinoflagellate in seawater of viscosity 0.0010 Pa·s? (b) What is the power output of the flagellate?

64. An air bubble of 1.0-mm radius is rising in a container with vegetable oil of specific gravity 0.85 and viscosity 0.12 Pa·s. The container of oil and the air bubble are at 20°C. What is its terminal velocity?

65. This table gives the terminal speeds of various spheres falling through the same fluid. The spheres all have the same radius.

$m =$	8	12	16	20	24	28	(g)
$v_t =$	1.0	1.5	2.0	2.5	3.0	3.5	(cm/s)

Is the drag force primarily viscous or turbulent? Explain your reasoning.

66. This table gives the terminal speeds of various spheres falling through the same fluid. The spheres all have the same radius.

$m =$	5.0	11.3	20.0	31.3	45.0	80.0	(g)
$v_t =$	1.0	1.5	2.0	2.5	3.0	4.0	(cm/s)

Is the drag force primarily viscous or turbulent? Explain your reasoning.

67. *What keeps a cloud from falling?* A cumulus (fair-weather) cloud consists of tiny water droplets of average radius 5.0 μm. Find the terminal velocity for these droplets at 20°C, assuming viscous drag. (Besides the viscous drag force, there are also upward air currents called *thermals* that push the droplets upward. 🅦 tutorial: rain drop)

✦68. An aluminum sphere (specific gravity = 2.7) falling through water reaches a terminal speed of 5.0 cm/s. What is the terminal speed of an air bubble of the same radius rising through water? Assume viscous drag in both cases and ignore the possibility of changes in size or shape of the air bubble; the temperature is 20°C.

9.11 Surface Tension

69. An underwater air bubble has an excess inside pressure of 10 Pa. What is the excess pressure inside an air bubble with twice the radius?

70. Assume a water strider has a roughly circular foot of radius 0.02 mm. (a) What is the maximum possible upward force on the foot due to surface tension of the water? (b) What is the maximum mass of this water strider so that it can keep from breaking through the water surface? The strider has six legs.

✦71. The potential energy associated with surface tension is much like the elastic potential energy of a stretched spring or a balloon. Suppose we do work on a puddle of liquid, spreading it out through a distance of Δs along a line L perpendicular to the force. (a) What is the work done on the fluid surface in terms of γ, L, and Δs? (b) The work done is equal to the increase in surface energy of the fluid. Show that the increase in energy is proportional to the increase in area. (c) Show that we can think of γ as the surface energy per unit area. (d) Show that the SI units of surface tension can be expressed either as N/m (force per unit length) or J/m² (energy per unit area).

$\Delta A = L \, \Delta s$

✦72. A hollow hemispherical object is filled with air as in part (a) of the figure. (a) Show that the magnitude of the force due to fluid pressure on the curved surface of the hemisphere has magnitude $F = \pi r^2 P$, where r is the radius of the hemisphere and P is the pressure of the air. Ignore the weight of the air. [*Hint:* First find the force on the *flat* surface. What is the net force on the hemisphere due to the air?] (b) Consider an underwater air bubble to be divided into two hemispheres along the circumference as in part (b) of the figure. The upper

hemisphere of the water surface exerts a force of magnitude $2\pi r \gamma$ (circumference times force per unit length) on the lower hemisphere due to surface tension. Show that the air pressure inside the bubble must exceed the water pressure outside by $\Delta P = 2\gamma/r$.

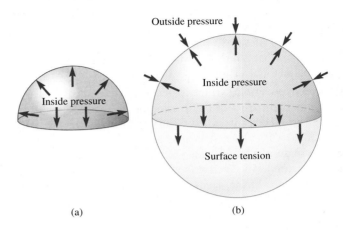

(a)   (b)

Comprehensive Problems

73. A wooden barrel full of water has a flat circular top of radius 25.0 cm with a small hole in it. A tube of height 8.00 m and inner radius 0.250 cm is suspended above the barrel with its lower end inserted snugly in the hole. Water is poured into the upper end of the tube until it is full. (a) What is the weight of the water in the tube? (b) What is the force with which the water in the barrel pushes up on the top of the barrel? (c) How can adding such a small weight of water lead to such a large force on the top of the barrel? (As a demonstration of the principle now named for him, Pascal astonished spectators by showing that the addition of a small amount of water to the tube could make the barrel burst.)

8.00 m

25.0 cm
(not to scale)

74. A block of aluminum that has dimensions 2.00 cm by 3.00 cm by 5.00 cm is suspended from a spring scale. (a) What is the weight of the block? (b) What is the scale reading when the block is submerged in oil with a density of 850 kg/m³?

75. A 85.0-kg canoe made of thin aluminum has the shape of half of a hollowed-out log with a radius of 0.475 m and a length of 3.23 m. (a) When this is placed in the water, what percentage of the volume of the canoe is below the waterline? (b) How much additional mass can be placed in this canoe before it begins to sink? (🅦 interactive: buoyancy)

76. Two identical beakers are filled to the brim and placed on balance scales. The base area of the beakers is large enough that any water that spills out of the beakers will fall onto the table the scales are resting on. A block of pine (density = 420 kg/m³) is placed in one of

the beakers. The block has a volume of 8.00 cm^3. Another block of the same size, but made of steel, is placed in the other beaker. How does the scale reading change in each case?

77. A very large vat of water has a hole 1.00 cm in diameter located a distance 1.80 m below the water level. (a) How fast does water exit the hole? (b) How would your answer differ if the vat were filled with gasoline? (c) How would your answer differ if the vat contained water, but was on the Moon, where the gravitational field strength is 1.6 N/kg?

78. A cube that is 4.00 cm on a side and of density 8.00×10^2 kg/m^3 is attached to one end of a spring. The other end of the spring is attached to the base of a beaker. When the beaker is filled with water until the entire cube is submerged, the spring is stretched by 1.00 cm. What is the spring constant?

79. You are hiking through a lush forest with some of your friends when you come to a large river that seems impossible to cross. However, one of your friends notices an old metal barrel sitting on the shore. The barrel is shaped like a cylinder and is 1.20 m high and 0.76 m in diameter. One of the circular ends of the barrel is open and the barrel is empty. When you put the barrel in the water with the open end facing up, you find that the barrel floats with 33% of it under water. You decide that you can use the barrel as a boat to cross the river, as long as you leave about 30 cm sticking above the water. How much extra mass can you put in this barrel to use it as a boat?

80. The deepest place in the ocean is the Marianas Trench in the western Pacific Ocean, which is over 11.0 km deep. On January 23, 1960, the research sub *Trieste* went to a depth of 10.915 km, nearly to the bottom of the trench. This still is the deepest dive on record. The density of seawater is 1025 kg/m^3. (a) What is the water pressure at that depth? (b) What was the force due to water pressure on a flat section of area 1.0 m^2 on the top of the sub's hull?

81. The pressure in a water pipe in the basement of an apartment house is 4.10×10^5 Pa, but on the seventh floor it is only 1.85×10^5 Pa. What is the height between the basement and the seventh floor? Assume the water is not flowing; no faucets are opened.

82. The body of a 90.0-kg person contains 0.020 m^3 of body fat. If the density of fat is 890 kg/m^3, what percentage of the person's body weight is composed of fat?

83. Near sea level, how high a hill must you ascend for the reading of a barometer you are carrying to drop by 1.0 cm Hg? Assume the temperature remains at 20°C as you climb. The reading of a barometer on an average day at sea level is 76.0 cm Hg. (tutorial: gauge)

84. A stone of weight W has specific gravity 2.50. (a) When the stone is suspended from a scale and submerged in water, what is the scale reading in terms of its weight in air? (b) What is the scale reading for the stone when it is submerged in oil (specific gravity = 0.90)?

85. If you watch water falling from a faucet, you will notice that the flow decreases in radius as the water falls. This can be explained by the equation of continuity, since the cross-sectional area of the water decreases as the speed increases. If the water flows with an initial velocity of 0.62 m/s and a diameter of 2.2 cm at the faucet opening, what is the diameter of the water flow after the water has fallen 30 cm?

86. The average speed of blood in the aorta is 0.3 m/s and the radius of the aorta is 1 cm. There are about 2×10^9 capillaries with an average radius of 6 μm. What is the approximate average speed of the blood flow in the capillaries?

87. If the cardiac output of a small dog is 4.1×10^{-3} m^3/s, the radius of its aorta is 0.50 cm, and the aorta length is 40.0 cm, determine the pressure drop across the aorta of the dog. Assume the viscosity of blood is 4.0×10^{-3} Pa·s.

88. In an aortic aneurysm, a bulge forms where the walls of the aorta are weakened. If blood flowing through the aorta (radius 1.0 cm) enters an aneurysm with a radius of 3.0 cm, how much on average is the blood pressure higher inside the aneurysm than the pressure in the unenlarged part of the aorta? The average flow rate through the aorta is 120 cm^3/s. Assume the blood is nonviscous and the patient is lying down so there is no change in height.

89. Scuba divers are admonished not to rise faster than their air bubbles when rising to the surface. This rule helps them avoid the rapid pressure changes that cause the bends. Air bubbles of 1.0 mm radius are rising from a scuba diver to the surface of the sea. Assume a water temperature of 20°C. (a) If the viscosity of the water is 1.0×10^{-3} Pa·s, what is the terminal velocity of the bubbles? (b) What is the largest rate of pressure change tolerable for the diver according to this rule?

90. A shallow well usually has the pump at the top of the well. (a) What is the deepest possible well for which a surface pump will work? [*Hint:* A pump maintains a pressure difference, keeping the outflow pressure higher than the intake pressure.] (b) Why is there not the same depth restriction on wells with the pump at the bottom?

91. A plastic beach ball has radius 20.0 cm and mass 0.10 kg, not including the air inside. (a) What is the weight of the beach ball including the air inside? Assume the air density is 1.3 kg/m^3 both inside and outside. (b) What is the buoyant force on the beach ball in air? The thickness of the plastic is about 2 mm—negligible compared to the radius of the ball. (c) The ball is thrown straight up in the air. At the top of its trajectory, what is its acceleration? [*Hint:* When $v = 0$, there is no drag force.]

92. A block of wood, with density 780 kg/m^3, has a cubic shape with sides 0.330 m long. A rope of negligible

mass is used to tie a piece of lead to the bottom of the wood. The lead pulls the wood into the water until it is just completely covered with water. What is the mass of the lead? [*Hint:* Don't forget to consider the buoyant force on both the wood and the lead.]

93. Are evenly spaced specific gravity markings on the cylinder of a hydrometer equal distances apart? In other words, is the depth d to which the cylinder is submerged linearly related to the density ρ of the fluid? To answer this question, assume that the cylinder has radius r and mass m. Find an expression for d in terms of ρ, r, and m and see if d is a linear function of ρ.

94. A hydrometer is an instrument for measuring the specific gravity of a liquid. For example, vintners use a hydrometer to determine the density changes as wine is fermented, and producers of maple sugar and maple syrup use the hydrometer to find how much sugar is in the collected sap. Markings along a stem are calibrated to indicate the specific gravity for the level at which the hydrometer floats in a liquid. The weighted base ensures that the hydrometer floats vertically. Suppose the hydrometer has a cylindrical stem of cross-sectional area 0.400 cm^2. The total volume of the bulb and stem is 8.80 cm^3 and the mass of the hydrometer is 4.80 g. (a) How far from the top of the cylinder should a mark be placed to indicate a specific gravity of 1.00? (b) When the hydrometer is placed in alcohol, it floats with 7.25 cm of stem above the surface. What is the specific gravity of the alcohol? (c) What is the lowest specific gravity that can be measured with this hydrometer?

Simple hydrometer
(Problems 93 and 94)

95. A house with its own well has a pump in the basement with an output pipe of inner radius 6.3 mm. Assume that the pump can maintain a gauge pressure of 410 kPa in the output pipe. A showerhead on the second floor (6.7 m above the pump's output pipe) has 36 holes, each of radius 0.33 mm. The shower is on "full blast" and no other faucet in the house is open. (a) Ignoring viscosity, with what speed does water leave the showerhead? (b) With what speed does water move through the output pipe of the pump?

96. To measure the airspeed of a plane, a device called a Pitot tube is used. A simplified model of the Pitot tube is a manometer with one side connected to a tube facing directly into the "wind" (stopping the air that hits it head-on) and the other side connected to a tube so that the "wind" blows across its openings. If the manometer uses mercury and the levels differ by 25 cm, what is the plane's airspeed? The density of air at the plane's altitude is 0.90 kg/m^3.

97. A U-shaped tube is partly filled with water and partly filled with a liquid that does not mix with water. Both sides of the tube are open to the atmosphere. What is the density of the liquid (in g/cm^3)?

98. Atmospheric pressure is equal to the weight of a vertical column of air, extending all the way up through the atmosphere, divided by the cross-sectional area of the column. (a) Explain why that must be true. [*Hint:* Apply Newton's second law to the column of air.] (b) If the air all the way up had a uniform density of 1.29 kg/m^3 (the density at sea level at 0°C), how high would the column of air be? (c) In reality, the density of air decreases with increasing altitude. Does that mean that the height found in (b) is a lower limit or an upper limit on the height of the atmosphere?

99. On a nice day when the temperature outside is 20°C, you take the elevator to the top of the Sears Tower in Chicago, which is 440 m tall. (a) How much less is the air pressure at the top than the air pressure at the bottom? Express your answer both in pascals and atm.

([W] tutorial: gauge) [*Hint:* The altitude change is small enough to treat the density of air as constant.] (b) How many pascals does the pressure decrease for every meter of altitude? (c) If the pressure gradient— the pressure decrease per meter of altitude—were uniform, at what altitude would the atmospheric pressure reach zero? (d) Atmospheric pressure does *not* decrease with a uniform gradient since the density of air decreases as you go up. Which is true: the pressure reaches zero at a *lower* altitude than your answer to (c), or the pressure is nonzero at that altitude and the atmosphere extends to a higher altitude? Explain.

100. A bug from South America known as *Rhodnius prolixus* extracts the blood of animals. Suppose *Rhodnius prolixus* extracts 0.30 cm^3 of blood in 25 min from a human arm through its feeding tube of length 0.20 mm and radius 5.0 μm. What is the absolute pressure at the bug's end of the feeding tube if the absolute pressure at the other end (in the human arm) is 105 kPa? Assume the viscosity of blood is 0.0013 Pa·s. [*Note:* Negative absolute pressures are possible in liquids in very slender tubes.]

101. The diameter of a certain artery has decreased by 25% due to arteriosclerosis. (a) If the same amount of blood flows through it per unit time as when it was unobstructed, by what percentage has the blood pressure difference between its ends increased? (b) If, instead, the pressure drop across the artery stays the same, by what factor does the blood flow rate through it decrease? (In reality we are likely to see a combination of some pressure increase with some reduction in flow.)

Answers to Practice Problems

9.1 1.3×10^6 N/m^2 = 1.3 MPa; the pressure is a factor of 15 greater than the pressure from the tennis shoe heel.
9.2 (a) 2.0×10^5 Pa; (b) 5.0 m
9.3 1.6 km

9.4 (a) Yes, $P_2 = P_1$. The column above point 2 is not as tall, but the pressure at the top of that column is *greater than* atmospheric pressure. (b) No, $P = P_{atm} + \rho g d$ gives the pressure at a depth d below a point where the pressure is P_{atm}.
9.5 (a) 32.0 cm; (b) 17.0 cm and 37.0 cm
9.6 S.G. = 11.3; could be lead
9.7 2% and 4%
9.8 (a) The beetle can squeeze the air bubble with its wings, compressing the air to reduce the bubble volume and decreasing the buoyant force. (b) When it is time to rise to the surface, the beetle relaxes the pressure on the bubble, allowing it to expand again.
9.9 (a) 0.85 m/s; (b) 1.7 m/s
9.10 $\sqrt{2gh}$ = 4.0 m/s
9.11 250 kPa
9.12 1.4
9.13 2.85 mm/s upward
9.14 480 Pa

Answers to Checkpoints

9.4 Pressure in a static fluid cannot depend on horizontal position. The net horizontal force on any part of the fluid must be zero—otherwise the horizontal acceleration would be nonzero and the fluid would begin to flow. The net vertical force *including the weight of the fluid* must also be zero, so pressure does depend on vertical position.

9.8 (a) For horizontal flow, Bernoulli's equation becomes $P_1 + \frac{1}{2} \rho v_1^2 = P_2 + \frac{1}{2} \rho v_2^2$; the pressure is lower where the flow speed is higher. (b) In a static fluid, Bernoulli's equation becomes $P_1 + \rho g y_1 = P_2 + \rho g y_2$. Letting $d = y_1 - y_2$, we have $P_2 - P_1 = \rho g y_1 - \rho g y_2 = \rho g d$, which is the pressure dependence with depth for a static fluid as discussed in Section 9.4.

9.10 Viscous drag and kinetic friction are both forces that oppose the motion of an object (relative to the surrounding fluid or relative to the surface on which the object slides, respectively). However, viscous drag depends strongly on the speed of the object ($F_D \propto v$), but kinetic friction does not.

Elasticity and Oscillations

Near the top of the 241-m-tall Hancock Tower in Boston, two steel boxes filled with lead are part of a system designed to reduce the swaying and twisting of the building caused by the wind. The mass of each box is nearly 300 000 kg (weight 300 tons). It might seem that adding a large mass to the *top* of the building would make it more "top heavy" and might *increase* the amount of swaying. Why is such a large mass used and how does it reduce the swaying of the building? (See p. 381 for the answer.)

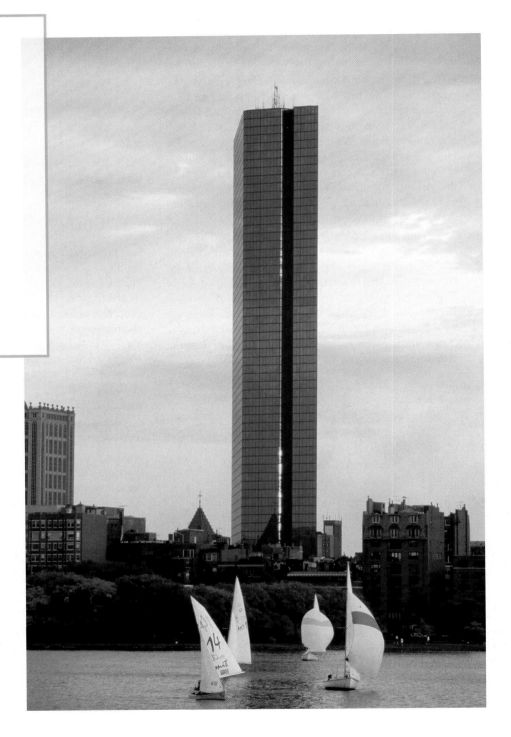

• Hooke's law (Section 6.6)
• graphical relationship of position, velocity, and acceleration (Sections 3.2 and 3.3)
• elastic potential energy (Section 6.7)

Concepts & Skills to Review

10.1 ELASTIC DEFORMATIONS OF SOLIDS

If the net force and the net torque on an object are zero, the object is in equilibrium—but that does not mean that the forces and torques have no effect. An object is deformed when contact forces are applied to it (Fig. 10.1). A **deformation** is a change in the size or shape of the object. Many solids are stiff enough that the deformation cannot be seen with the human eye; a microscope or other sensitive device is required to detect the change in size or shape.

When the contact forces are removed, an **elastic** object returns to its original shape and size. Many objects are elastic as long as the deforming forces are not too large. On the other hand, any object may be permanently deformed or even broken if the forces acting are too large. An automobile that collides with a tree at a low speed may not be damaged; but at a higher speed the car suffers a permanent deformation of the bodywork and the driver may suffer a broken bone.

CONNECTION:

The two topics of this chapter—elasticity and oscillations—may seem unrelated at first, but they are closely connected: many oscillations are caused by the kinds of elastic forces we study in Sections 10.1 through 10.4.

10.2 HOOKE'S LAW FOR TENSILE AND COMPRESSIVE FORCES

Suppose we stretch a wire by applying tensile forces of magnitude F to each end. The length of the wire increases from L to $L + \Delta L$. How does the elongation ΔL depend on the original length L? Conceptual Example 10.1 helps answer this question.

Figure 10.1 A tennis ball is flattened by the contact force exerted on it by the strings of the tennis racquet. Likewise, the strings of the racquet are deformed by the contact force exerted by the ball. The two forces are interaction partners.

Conceptual Example 10.1

Stretching Wires

If a given tensile force stretches a wire an amount ΔL, by how much would the same force stretch a wire twice as long but identical in thickness and composition?

Strategy and Solution   Think of the wire of length $2L$ as two wires of length L placed end-to-end (Fig. 10.2). Under the same tension, each of the two imagined wires stretches by an amount ΔL, so the total deformation of the long wire is $2\,\Delta L$.

Practice Problem 10.1   Cutting a Spring in Half

If a spring (spring constant k) is cut in half, what is the spring constant of each of the two newly formed springs?

Figure 10.2

Two identical wires are joined end-to-end and stretched by tensile forces. Each wire stretches an amount ΔL.

Strain: fractional length change

Stress and Strain   When stretched by the same tensile forces, the two wires in Conceptual Example 10.1 get longer by an amount proportional to their original lengths: $\Delta L \propto L$. In other words, the two wires have the same *fractional length change* $\Delta L / L$. The fractional length change is called the **strain**; it is a dimensionless measure of the degree of deformation.

$$\text{strain} = \frac{\Delta L}{L} \qquad (10\text{-}1)$$

Suppose we had wires of the same composition and length but different thicknesses. It would require larger tensile forces to stretch the thicker wire the same amount as the thinner one; a thick steel cable is harder to stretch than the same length of a thin strand of steel. In Conceptual Question 13, we conclude that the tensile force required is proportional to the cross-sectional area of the wire ($F \propto A$). Thus, the same applied force *per unit area* produces the same deformation on wires of the same length and composition. The force per unit area is called the **stress**:

Stress: force per unit cross-sectional area

$$\text{stress} = \frac{F}{A} \qquad (10\text{-}2)$$

The SI units of stress are the same as those of pressure: N/m^2 or Pa.

Hooke's Law   Suppose that a solid object of initial length L is subjected to tensile or compressive forces of magnitude F. As a result of the forces, the length of the object is changed by magnitude ΔL. According to Hooke's law, the deformation is proportional to the deforming forces as long as they are not too large:

$$F = k\Delta L \qquad (10\text{-}3)$$

In Eq. (10-3), k is a measure of the object's stiffness; it is analogous to the spring constant of a spring. This constant k depends on the length and cross-sectional area of the object. A larger cross-sectional area A makes k larger; a greater length L makes k smaller.

We can rewrite Hooke's law in terms of stress (F/A) and strain ($\Delta L/L$):

CONNECTION:

Hooke's law does not just apply to springs. The deformation of an object is often proportional to the forces applied to it.

Hooke's law: the strain is proportional to the stress

Hooke's Law

$$\text{stress} \propto \text{strain}$$
$$\frac{F}{A} = Y\frac{\Delta L}{L} \qquad (10\text{-}4)$$

Equation (10-4) still says that the length change (ΔL) is proportional to the magnitude of the deforming forces (F). Stress and strain account for the effects of length and cross-sectional area; the proportionality constant Y depends only on the inherent stiffness of the material from which the object is composed; it is independent of the length and cross-sectional area. Comparing Eqs. (10-3) and (10-4), the "spring constant" k for the object is

$$k = \frac{YA}{L} \qquad (10\text{-}5)$$

The constant of proportionality Y in Eqs. (10-4) and (10-5) is called the **elastic modulus** or **Young's modulus**; Y has the same units as those of stress (Pa or N/m^2), since strain is dimensionless. Young's modulus can be thought of as the inherent stiffness of a material; it measures the resistance of the material to elongation or compression. Material that is flexible and stretches easily (for example, rubber) has a *low* Young's modulus. A stiff material (such as steel) has a high Young's modulus; it takes a larger stress to produce the same strain. Table 10.1 gives Young's modulus for a variety of common materials.

Table 10.1 Approximate Values of Young's Modulus for Various Substances

Substance	Young's Modulus (10^9 Pa)	Substance	Young's Modulus (10^9 Pa)
Rubber	0.002–0.008	Wood, along the grain	10–15
Human cartilage	0.024	Brick	14–20
Human vertebra	0.088 (compression); 0.17 (tension)	Concrete	20–30 (compression)
		Marble	50–60
Collagen, in bone	0.6	Aluminum	70
Human tendon	0.6	Cast iron	100–120
Wood, across the grain	1	Copper	120
Nylon	2–6	Wrought iron	190
Spider silk	4	Steel	200
Human femur	9.4 (compression); 16 (tension)	Diamond	1200

√ CHECKPOINT 10.2

Which stretches more when put under the same tension: a steel wire 2.0 m long or a copper wire 1.0 m long with the same diameter? (See Table 10.1.)

Hooke's law holds up to a maximum stress called the *proportional limit.* For many materials, Young's modulus has the same value for tension and compression. Some composite materials, such as bone and concrete, have significantly different Young's moduli for tension and compression. The components of bone include fibers of collagen (a protein found in all connective tissue) that give it strength under tension and hydroxyapatite crystals (composed of calcium and phosphate) that give it strength under compression. The different properties of these two substances lead to different values of Young's modulus for tension and compression.

 Application of tensile and compressive forces: bone strength

Example 10.2

Compression of the Femur

A man whose weight is 0.80 kN is standing upright. By approximately how much is his femur (thighbone) shortened compared with when he is lying down? Assume that the compressive force on each femur is about half his weight (Fig. 10.3). The average cross-sectional area of the femur is 8.0 cm^2 and the length of the femur when lying down is 43.0 cm.

Strategy A change in length of the femur involves a strain. After finding the stress and looking up the Young's modulus, we can find the strain using Hooke's law. We assume that each femur supports *half* the man's weight.

Figure 10.3
Compression of the femur.

Solution The strain is proportional to the stress:

$$\frac{F}{A} = Y \frac{\Delta L}{L}$$

Solving this equation for ΔL gives

$$\Delta L = \frac{F/A}{Y} L$$

From Table 10.1, Young's modulus for a femur *in compression* is:

$$Y = 9.4 \times 10^9 \text{ Pa}$$

We need to convert the cross-sectional area to m^2 since 1 Pa = 1 N/m^2:

$$A = 8.0 \text{ cm}^2 \times \left(\frac{1 \text{ m}}{100 \text{ cm}}\right)^2 = 0.00080 \text{ m}^2$$

continued on next page

Example 10.2 continued

The force on each leg is 0.40 kN, or 4.0×10^2 N. The length change is then

$$\Delta L = \frac{F/A}{Y} L = \frac{(4.0 \times 10^2 \text{ N})/(0.00080 \text{ m}^2)}{9.4 \times 10^9 \text{ Pa}} \times 43.0 \text{ cm}$$

$$= 5.3 \times 10^{-5} \times 43.0 \text{ cm} = 0.0023 \text{ cm}$$

Discussion The strain—or fractional length change—is 5.3×10^{-5}. Since the strain is much smaller than 1, we are justified in not worrying about whether the length is

43.0 cm with or without the compressive load; we would calculate the same value of ΔL (to two significant figures) either way.

Practice Problem 10.2   Fractional Length Change of a Cable

A steel cable of diameter 3.0 cm supports a load of 2.0 kN. What is the fractional length increase of the cable compared to the length when there is no load if $Y = 2.0 \times 10^{11}$ Pa?

10.3 BEYOND HOOKE'S LAW

If the tensile or compressive stress exceeds the proportional limit, the strain is no longer proportional to the stress (Fig. 10.4). The solid still returns to its original length when the stress is removed as long as the stress does not exceed the *elastic limit*. If the stress exceeds the elastic limit, the material is permanently deformed. For still larger stresses, the solid fractures when the stress reaches the *breaking point*. The maximum stress that can be withstood without breaking is called the *ultimate strength*. The ultimate strength can be different for compression and tension; then we refer to the compressive strength or the tensile strength of the material.

A *ductile* material continues to stretch beyond its ultimate tensile strength without breaking; the stress then *decreases* from the ultimate strength (Fig. 10.4a). Examples of ductile solids are the relatively soft metals, such as gold, silver, copper, and lead. These metals can be pulled like taffy, becoming thinner and thinner until finally reaching the breaking point.

For a *brittle* substance, the ultimate strength and the breaking point are close together (Fig. 10.4b). Bone is an example of a brittle material; it fractures abruptly if the stress becomes too large (Fig. 10.4c). Under either tension or compression, its elastic limit, breaking point, and ultimate strength are approximately the same. Babies have

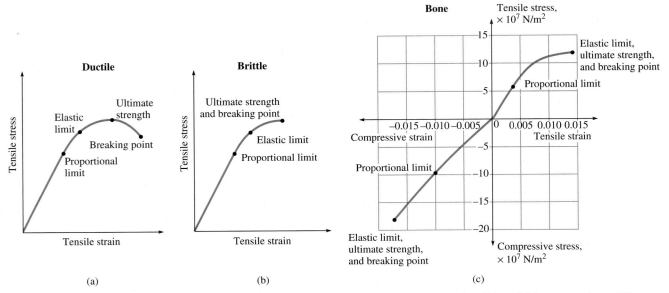

Figure 10.4 Stress-strain curves showing limits for (a) a ductile material, (b) a brittle material, and (c) compact bone. The elastic limit, ultimate strength, and breaking point are well separated for ductile materials, but close together for a brittle material.

Figure 10.5 In prestressed concrete, steel rods are stretched before the concrete is poured. After the concrete hardens, the frame holding the rods under tension is removed. The rods contract, compressing the concrete. Then, when the prestressed concrete is subject to a tensile force, the compression of the concrete is lessened but not eliminated so that the concrete itself is never subjected to a tensile stress.

more flexible bones than adults because they have built up less of the calcium compound hydroxyapatite. As people age, their bones become more brittle as the collagen fibers lose flexibility and their bones also become weaker as calcium gets reabsorbed (a condition called osteoporosis).

Like bone, reinforced concrete has one component for tensile strength and another for compressive strength. Reinforced concrete contains steel rods that provide tensile strength that concrete itself lacks (Fig. 10.5).

Human anatomy has special features for adapting to the compressive stress associated with standing upright. For example, the vertebrae in the spinal column gradually increase in size from the neck to the tailbone. Such an arrangement places the stronger vertebrae in the lower positions, where they must support more weight. The vertebrae are separated by fluid-filled disks, which have a cushioning effect by spreading out the compressive forces.

 Applications of elastic properties of materials: osteoporosis and reinforced concrete

 Application of compressive forces: the human vertebra

Example 10.3

Crane with Steel Cable

A crane is required to lift loads of up to 1.0×10^5 N (11 tons). (a) What is the minimum diameter of the steel cable that must be used? (b) If a cable of twice the minimum diameter is used and it is 8.0 m long when no load is present, how much longer is it when supporting a load of 1.0×10^5 N? (Data for steel: $Y = 2.0 \times 10^{11}$ Pa; proportional limit = 2.0×10^8 Pa; elastic limit = 3.0×10^8 Pa; tensile strength = 5.0×10^8 Pa.)

Strategy The data given for steel consists of four quantities that all have the same units. It would be easy to mix them up if we didn't understand what each one means. Young's modulus is the proportionality constant between stress and strain. That will be useful in part (b) where we find the elongation of the cable; the elongation is the strain times the original length. However, we should first check that the stress is less than the proportional limit before using Young's modulus to find the strain.

The elastic limit is the maximum stress so that no permanent deformation occurs; the tensile strength is the maximum

stress so that the cable does not break. We certainly don't want the cable to break, but it would be prudent to keep the stress under the elastic limit to give the cable a long useful life. Therefore, we choose a minimum diameter in (a) to keep the stress below the elastic limit.

Solution (a) We choose the minimum diameter to keep the stress less than the elastic limit:

$$\frac{F}{A} < \text{elastic limit} = 3.0 \times 10^8 \text{ Pa}$$

for $F = 1.0 \times 10^5$ N. Then

$$A > \frac{F}{\text{elastic limit}} = \frac{1.0 \times 10^5 \text{ N}}{3.0 \times 10^8 \text{ Pa}} = 3.33 \times 10^{-4} \text{ m}^2$$

The minimum cross-sectional area corresponds to the minimum diameter. The cross-sectional area of the cable is πr^2 or $\pi d^2/4$, so

$$d = \sqrt{\frac{4A}{\pi}} = \sqrt{\frac{4 \times 3.33 \times 10^{-4} \text{ m}^2}{\pi}} = 2.1 \text{ cm}$$

The minimum *diameter* is therefore 2.1 cm.

continued on next page

Example 10.3 continued

(b) If we double the diameter and keep the same load, the stress is reduced by a factor of four since the cross-sectional area is proportional to the square of the diameter. Therefore, the stress is

$$\frac{F}{A} = \frac{3.0 \times 10^8 \text{ Pa}}{4} = 7.5 \times 10^7 \text{ Pa}$$

The strain is then

$$\frac{\Delta L}{L} = \frac{F/A}{Y} = \frac{7.5 \times 10^7 \text{ Pa}}{2.0 \times 10^{11} \text{ Pa}} = 0.000375$$

The strain is the fractional length change. Then the length change is

$$\Delta L = 0.000375L = 0.000375 \times 8.0 \text{ m} = 0.0030 \text{ m} = 3.0 \text{ mm}$$

Discussion   By using a cable twice as thick as the minimum, we build in a safety factor. We don't want to be right at the edge of disaster! Since doubling the diameter of the cable increases the cross-sectional area of the cable by a factor of four, the maximum stress on the cable is one fourth of the elastic limit.

Practice Problem 10.3   Tuning a Harpsichord String

A harpsichord string is made of yellow brass (Young's modulus 9.0×10^{10} Pa, tensile strength 6.3×10^8 Pa). When tuned correctly, the tension in the string is 59.4 N, which is 93% of the maximum tension that the string can endure without breaking. What is the radius of the string?

The San Jacinto monument in Texas is the tallest stone column in the world.

Height Limits

What limits the height of a stone column? If the column is too tall, it could be crushed under its own weight. The maximum height of a column is limited since the compressive stress at the bottom cannot exceed the compressive strength of the material (see Problem 89). However, the maximum height at which a vertical column buckles is generally less than the height at which it would be crushed.

The bones of our limbs are hollow; the inside of the structural material is filled with marrow, which is structurally weak. A hollow bone is better able to resist fracture from bending and twisting forces than a solid bone with the same amount of structural material, although the hollow bone would buckle more easily under a compressive force along the central axis.

Figure 10.6 A column made from a rolled sheet of paper can support a book.

PHYSICS AT HOME

Challenge a friend to use a single sheet of 8.5 in. × 11 in. paper and two paper clips (or tape) to support a book at least 8 in. above a table. If your friend has no idea what to do, roll the sheet of paper into a narrow cylinder about 2.5 cm (an inch) in diameter; then fasten the cylinder at the top and bottom with paper clips (or with tape). Carefully place the book so that it is balanced on top of the cylinder (Fig. 10.6). If you have difficulty, try using thicker paper or a lighter book.

Use the same "apparatus" to get some insight into the buckling of columns. Try making the diameter of the paper cylinder twice as large. The walls of this column are thinner because there are fewer layers of the paper in the cylinder wall, although the same cross-sectional area *of paper* supports the book. If nothing happens, try again with a heavier book. You will likely see the walls crumple in on themselves as the cylinder buckles and the book falls to the table.

Why would the design of a giant's bones have to be different from a human's? If the giant's average density is the same as a human's, then his weight is larger by the same factor that his *volume* is larger. If the giant is five times as tall as a human, for instance, and has the same relative proportions, then his volume is $5^3 = 125$ times as large, since each of the three dimensions of any body part has increased by a factor of five. On the other hand, the cross-sectional area of a bone is proportional to the *square* of its radius. So while the leg bones must support 125 times as much weight, the maximum compressive force they can withstand has only increased by a factor of 25. The giant would need much thicker legs (in relation to their length) to support his increased weight. Similar analysis can be applied to the twisting and bending forces that are more likely to break bones than are compressive forces. The result is the same: the bones of a giant could not have human proportions.

Some science fiction or horror movies portray giant insects as greatly magnified versions of a normal insect. Such a giant insect's legs would collapse under the weight of the insect.

Application of compressive strength: size limitations on organisms

10.4   SHEAR AND VOLUME DEFORMATIONS

In this section we consider two other kinds of deformation. In each case we define a stress (force per unit area), a strain (dimensionless), and a modulus (the constant of proportionality between stress and strain).

Shear Deformation

Unlike tensile and compressive forces, which are perpendicular to two opposite surfaces of an object, a **shear deformation** is the result of a pair of equal and opposite forces that act *parallel* to two opposite surfaces (Fig. 10.7). The **shear stress** is the magnitude of the shear force divided by the area of the surface on which the force acts:

$$\text{shear stress} = \frac{\text{shear force}}{\text{area of surface}} = \frac{F}{A} \qquad (10\text{-}6)$$

Shear strain is the ratio of the relative displacement Δx to the separation L of the two surfaces:

$$\text{shear strain} = \frac{\text{displacement of surfaces}}{\text{separation of surfaces}} = \frac{\Delta x}{L} \qquad (10\text{-}7)$$

The shear strain is proportional to the shear stress as long as the stress is not too large. The constant of proportionality is the **shear modulus** S.

Figure 10.7 A book under shear stress. Shear forces produce the same kind of deformation in a solid block; the amount of the deformation is just smaller.

Hooke's Law for Shear Deformations

$$\text{shear stress} \propto \text{shear strain}$$

$$\frac{F}{A} = S\frac{\Delta x}{L} \qquad (10\text{-}8)$$

CONNECTION:

Hooke's law takes the same form for different kinds of stresses and strains. In each case, the strain is proportional to the stress.

The units of shear stress and the shear modulus are the same as for tensile or compressive stress and Young's modulus: Pa or N/m^2. The strain is once again dimensionless. Table 10.2 lists shear moduli for various materials.

An example of shear stress is the cutting action of a pair of scissors (or "shears") on a piece of paper. The forces acting on the paper from above and below are offset from each other and act parallel to the cross-sectional surfaces of the paper (Fig. 10.8).

Table 10.2	Shear and Bulk Moduli for Various Materials	
Material	**Shear Modulus S (10^9 Pa)**	**Bulk Modulus B (10^9 Pa)**
Gases		
Air (1)		0.00010
Air (2)		0.00014
Liquids		
Ethanol		0.9
Water		2.2
Mercury		25
Solids		
Cast iron	40–50	60–90
Marble		70
Aluminum	25–30	70
Copper	40–50	120–140
Steel	80–90	140–160
Diamond		620

(1) At 0°C and 1 atm; constant temperature expansion or compression
(2) At 0°C and 1 atm; no heat flow during expansion or compression

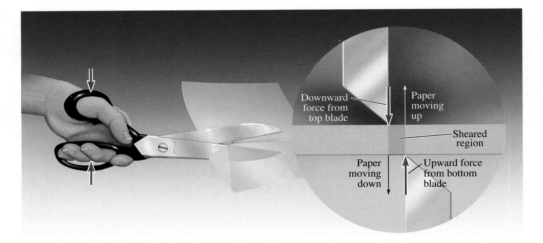

Figure 10.8 Scissors apply shear stress to a sheet of paper. The shear stress is the force exerted by a blade divided by the cross-sectional area of the paper—the thickness of the paper times the length of blade that is in contact with the paper.

Example 10.4

Cutting Paper

A sheet of paper of thickness 0.20 mm is cut with scissors that have blades of length 10.0 cm and width 0.20 cm. While cutting, the scissors blades each exert a force of 3.0 N on the paper; the length of each blade that makes contact with the paper is approximately 0.5 mm. What is the shear stress on the paper?

Strategy Shear stress is a force divided by an area. In this problem, identifying the correct area is tricky. The blades

push two *cross-sectional* paper surfaces in opposite directions so they are displaced with respect to one another. The shear stress is the force exerted by each blade divided by this cross-sectional area—the thickness of the paper times the length of blade *in contact with the paper*. (Compare Figs. 10.7 and 10.8.) The total length and the width of the blades are irrelevant.

continued on next page

Example 10.4 continued

Solution   The cross-sectional area is

$$A = \text{thickness} \times \text{contact length}$$

$$= 2.0 \times 10^{-4} \text{ m} \times 5 \times 10^{-4} \text{ m} = 1 \times 10^{-7} \text{ m}^2$$

The shear stress is

$$\frac{F}{A} = \frac{3.0 \text{ N}}{1 \times 10^{-7} \text{ m}^2} = 3 \times 10^7 \text{ N/m}^2$$

Discussion   To identify the correct area, remember that shear forces act *in the plane of* the surfaces that are displaced with respect to each other. By contrast, tensile and compressive forces are perpendicular to the area used to find tensile and compressive stresses.

Practice Problem 10.4   Shear Stress due to a Hole Punch

A hole punch has a diameter of 8.0 mm and presses onto ten sheets of paper with a force of 6.7 kN. If each sheet of paper is of thickness 0.20 mm, find the shear stress. [*Hint:* Be careful in deciding what area to use. Remember that a shear force acts *parallel* to the surface whose area is relevant.]

(a)

(b)

Figure 10.9 (a) An Olympic skier falls and his leg is subjected to a shear stress. (b) X-ray of a spiral fracture of the tibia.

When a bone is twisted, it is subjected to a shear stress. Shear stress is a more common cause of fracture than a compressive or tensile stress along the length of the bone. The twisting of a bone can result in a spiral fracture (Fig. 10.9).

Volume Deformation

As discussed in Chapter 9, a fluid exerts inward forces on an immersed solid object. These forces are perpendicular to the surfaces of the object. Since the fluid presses inward on all sides of the object (Fig. 10.10), the solid is compressed—its volume is reduced. The fluid pressure P is the force per unit surface area; it can be thought of as the **volume stress** on the solid object. Pressure has the same units as the other kinds of stress: N/m² or Pa.

$$\text{volume stress} = \text{pressure} = \frac{F}{A} = P$$

The resulting deformation of the object is characterized by the **volume strain**, which is the fractional change in volume:

$$\text{volume strain} = \frac{\text{change in volume}}{\text{original volume}} = \frac{\Delta V}{V} \qquad (10\text{-}9)$$

Unless the stress is too large, the stress and strain are proportional within a constant of proportionality called the **bulk modulus** B. A substance with a large bulk modulus is more difficult to compress than a substance with a small bulk modulus.

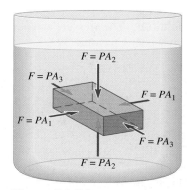

Figure 10.10 Forces on an object when submerged in a fluid.

An object at atmospheric pressure is already under volume stress: the air pressure already compresses the object slightly compared to what its volume would be in vacuum. For solids and liquids, the volume strain due to atmospheric pressure is, for most purposes, negligibly small (5×10^{-5} for water). Since we are usually concerned with the deformation due to a *change* in pressure ΔP from atmospheric pressure, we can write Hooke's law as:

Hooke's Law for Volume Deformation

$$\Delta P = -B\frac{\Delta V}{V} \qquad (10\text{-}10)$$

where V is the volume at atmospheric pressure. The negative sign in Eq. (10-10) allows the bulk modulus to be positive—an increase in the volume stress causes a *decrease* in volume, so ΔV is negative. Table 10.2 lists bulk moduli for various substances.

Unlike the stresses and strains discussed previously, volume stress can be applied to fluids (liquids and gases) as well as solids. The bulk moduli of liquids are generally not much less than those of solids, since the atoms in liquids are nearly as close together as those in solids. In Chapter 9 we assume that liquids are incompressible, which is often a good approximation since the bulk moduli of liquids are generally large. In gases, the atoms are much farther apart on average than in solids or liquids. Gases are much easier to compress than solids or liquids, so their bulk moduli are much smaller.

Example 10.5

Marble Statue Under Water

A marble statue of volume 1.5 m^3 is being transported by ship from Athens to Cyprus. The statue topples into the ocean when an earthquake-caused tidal wave sinks the ship; the statue ends up on the ocean floor, 1.0 km below the surface. Find the change in volume of the statue in cm^3 due to the pressure of the water. The density of seawater is 1025 kg/m^3.

Strategy   The water pressure is the volume stress; it is the force per unit area pressing inward and perpendicular to all the surfaces of the statue. The water pressure at a depth d is greater than the pressure at the water surface; we can find the pressure using the given density of seawater. Then, using the bulk modulus of marble given in Table 10.2, we find the change in volume from Hooke's law.

Solution   The pressure at a depth $d = 1.0$ km is larger than atmospheric pressure by

$$\Delta P = \rho g d$$
$$= 1025 \text{ kg/m}^3 \times 9.8 \text{ N/kg} \times 1000 \text{ m}$$
$$= 1.005 \times 10^7 \text{ Pa}$$

According to Table 10.2, the bulk modulus for marble is 70×10^9 Pa. This is the constant of proportionality between the volume stress (pressure increase) and the strain (fractional change in volume).

$$\Delta P = -B\frac{\Delta V}{V}$$

Solving for ΔV,

$$\Delta V = -\frac{\Delta P}{B}V = -\frac{1.005 \times 10^7 \text{ Pa}}{70 \times 10^9 \text{ Pa}} \times 1.5 \text{ m}^3$$
$$= -2.2 \times 10^{-4} \text{ m}^3 \times \left(\frac{100 \text{ cm}}{1 \text{ m}}\right)^3 = -220 \text{ cm}^3$$

The statue's volume decreases approximately 220 cm^3.

Discussion   The fractional decrease in volume is

$$\frac{1.005 \times 10^7 \text{ Pa}}{70 \times 10^9 \text{ Pa}} \approx \frac{1}{7000}$$

or a reduction of 0.014%.

In calculating the pressure increase, we assumed that the density of seawater is constant—the equation $\Delta P = \rho g d$ is derived for a constant fluid density ρ. Should we worry that our calculation of ΔP is wrong? The result of Practice Problem 10.5 shows that the density of seawater at a depth of 1.0 km is only about 0.43% greater than its density at the surface. The calculation of ΔP is inaccurate by less than 0.5%—negligible here since we only know the depth to two significant figures.

Practice Problem 10.5   Compression of Water

Show that a pressure increase of 1.0×10^7 Pa (100 atm) on 1 m^3 of seawater causes a 0.43% decrease in volume. The bulk modulus of seawater is 2.3×10^9 Pa.

Figure 10.11 (a) A point of *stable* equilibrium for a roller-coaster car. If the car is displaced slightly from its position at the bottom of the track, the net force pulls the car back toward the equilibrium point. (b) A point of *unstable* equilibrium for a roller-coaster car. If the car is displaced slightly from the very top of the track, the net force pushes the car *away from* the equilibrium point.

10.5 SIMPLE HARMONIC MOTION

Vibration, one of the most common kinds of motion, is repeated motion back and forth along the same path. Vibrations occur in the vicinity of a point of **stable equilibrium**. An equilibrium point is *stable* if the net force on an object when it is displaced a small distance from equilibrium points back toward the equilibrium point (Fig. 10.11). Such a force is called a **restoring force** since it tends to restore equilibrium. A special kind of vibratory motion—called **simple harmonic motion** (or **SHM**)—occurs whenever the restoring force is proportional to the displacement from equilibrium.

Figure 10.12 shows a graph of F_x versus x for some restoring force. We choose $x = 0$ at the equilibrium position. Since the graph is not linear, the resulting oscillations are not SHM—unless the amplitude is small. For small amplitudes, we can approximate the graph near equilibrium by a straight line tangent to the curve at the equilibrium point. For small amplitude oscillations, the restoring force is approximately linear, so the resulting oscillations are (approximately) SHM. The ideal spring is a favorite model of physicists because the restoring force it provides is proportional to the displacement from equilibrium.

Consider a relaxed ideal spring with spring constant k and zero mass. The spring is fixed at one end and attached at the other to an object of mass m (Fig. 10.13) that slides without friction. Since the normal force is equal and opposite to the weight of the object, the net force on the object is that due to the spring. When the spring is relaxed, the net force is zero; the object is in equilibrium.

If the object is now pulled to the right to the position $x = A$ and then released, the net force on the object is

$$F_x = -kx \qquad (10\text{-}11)$$

where the negative sign tells us that the spring force is opposite in direction to the displacement from equilibrium. At first the object is to the right of the equilibrium position and the spring pulls to the left. Notice that the force exerted by the spring is in the correct direction to restore the object to the equilibrium position; it always pushes or pulls back toward the equilibrium point.

Imagine taking a series of photos at equal time intervals as the object oscillates back and forth. In Fig. 10.14 the blue dots are the positions of the object at equal time intervals over one-half of a full cycle, from one endpoint to the other. (A full cycle would include the return trip.)

Energy Analysis in SHM Figure 10.14 suggests that the speed is greatest as the object passes through the equilibrium position. The object slows as it approaches the endpoints and gains speed as it approaches the equilibrium point. At the endpoints ($x = \pm A$), the body is instantaneously at rest before heading back in the other direction. Conservation of energy supports these observations. The total mechanical energy of the mass and spring is constant.

$$E = K + U = \text{constant}$$

Simple harmonic motion: vibratory motion that occurs when the restoring force is proportional to the displacement from equilibrium

CONNECTION:

As shown in Sections 10.2–10.4, Hooke's law applies to small deformations of many kinds of objects, not just springs. Thus, simple harmonic motion occurs in many situations as long as the vibrations are not too large.

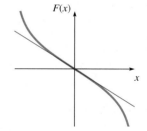

Figure 10.12 A nonlinear restoring force (red) can be approximated as a linear restoring force (blue) for small displacements.

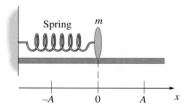

Figure 10.13 Spring in relaxed position. We choose the origin $x = 0$ at the object's equilibrium position.

Figure 10.14 Positions of an oscillating body at equal time intervals over half a period. The spring is omitted for clarity.

−A
Endpoint

0
Equilibrium position

A
Endpoint

x

CONNECTION:

Our study of SHM is based on familiar principles of energy conservation and Newton's second law, together with Hooke's law.

Amplitude: maximum displacement from equilibrium

where K is the kinetic energy and U is the elastic potential energy stored in the spring. As the object oscillates back and forth, energy is converted from potential to kinetic and back to potential in the half-cycle shown in Fig. 10.14. From Section 6.7, the elastic potential energy of the spring is

$$U = \tfrac{1}{2}kx^2 \qquad (6\text{-}24)$$

The speed at any point x can be found from the energy equation

$$E = \tfrac{1}{2}mv_x^2 + \tfrac{1}{2}kx^2 \qquad (10\text{-}12)$$

The maximum displacement of the body is the **amplitude** A. At the maximum displacement, where the motion changes direction, the velocity is zero. Since the kinetic energy is zero at $x = \pm A$, all the energy is elastic potential energy at the endpoints. Therefore, the total energy E at the endpoints is

$$E_{\text{total}} = \tfrac{1}{2}kA^2 \qquad (10\text{-}13)$$

and, since energy is conserved, this must be the total energy at any point in the object's motion. The maximum speed v_{m} occurs at $x = 0$ where all the energy is kinetic. Thus, at $x = 0$, the total energy equals the kinetic energy

$$E_{\text{total}} = \tfrac{1}{2}mv_{\text{m}}^2$$

and, from Eq. (10-13),

$$\tfrac{1}{2}mv_{\text{m}}^2 = \tfrac{1}{2}kA^2$$

Solving for v_{m} yields

$$v_{\text{m}} = \sqrt{\tfrac{k}{m}}\,A \qquad (10\text{-}14)$$

The maximum speed is proportional to the amplitude.

✓ CHECKPOINT 10.5

What is the displacement of an object in SHM when the kinetic and potential energies are equal?

Acceleration in SHM   The force on the object at any point x is given by Hooke's law; Newton's second law then gives the acceleration:

$$F_x = -kx = ma_x$$

Solving for the acceleration,

$$a_x(t) = -\frac{k}{m}x(t) \qquad (10\text{-}15)$$

Thus, the acceleration is a negative constant ($-k/m$) times the displacement; the acceleration and displacement are always in opposite directions. Whenever the acceleration is a negative constant times the displacement, the motion is SHM.

The acceleration has its maximum magnitude a_m, where the force is largest, which is at the maximum displacement $x = \pm A$:

$$a_m = \frac{k}{m} A \qquad (10\text{-}16)$$

> ⚠ In SHM, the acceleration changes with time. Equations derived for constant acceleration do not apply.

Example 10.6

Oscillating Model Rocket

A model rocket of 1.0-kg mass is attached to a horizontal spring with a spring constant of 6.0 N/cm. The spring is compressed by 18.0 cm and then released. The intent is to shoot the rocket horizontally, but the release mechanism fails to disengage, so the rocket starts to oscillate horizontally. Ignore friction and assume the spring to be ideal. (a) What is the amplitude of the oscillation? (b) What is the maximum speed? (c) What are the rocket's speed and acceleration when it is 12.0 cm from the equilibrium point?

Strategy   First, we sketch the situation (Fig. 10.15). Initially all of the energy is elastic potential energy and the kinetic energy is zero. The initial displacement must be the maximum displacement—or amplitude—of the oscillations since to get farther from equilibrium would require more elastic energy than the total energy available. The speed at any position can be found using energy conservation ($\frac{1}{2}kx^2 + \frac{1}{2}mv_x^2 = \frac{1}{2}kA^2$). The maximum speed occurs when all of the energy is kinetic. The acceleration can be found from Newton's second law.

Solution   (a) The amplitude of the oscillation is the maximum displacement, so $A = 18.0$ cm.

(b) From energy conservation, the maximum kinetic energy is equal to the maximum elastic potential energy:

$$K_m = \tfrac{1}{2}mv_m^2 = E = \tfrac{1}{2}kA^2$$

Solving for v_m,

$$v_m = \sqrt{\frac{k}{m}}\, A = \sqrt{\frac{6.0 \times 10^2 \text{ N/m}}{1.0 \text{ kg}}} \times 0.180 \text{ m} = 4.4 \text{ m/s}$$

(c) For the speed at a displacement of 0.120 m, we again use energy conservation.

$$\tfrac{1}{2}kx^2 + \tfrac{1}{2}mv^2 = \tfrac{1}{2}kA^2$$

Solving for v,

$$v = \sqrt{\frac{kA^2 - kx^2}{m}} = \sqrt{\frac{k}{m}\,(A^2 - x^2)}$$

$$= \sqrt{\frac{6.0 \times 10^2 \text{ N/m}}{1.0 \text{ kg}}\,[(0.180 \text{ m})^2 - (0.120 \text{ m})^2]} = 3.3 \text{ m/s}$$

From Newton's second law,

$$F_x = -kx = ma_x$$

At $x = \pm 0.120$ m,

$$a_x = -\frac{k}{m}x = \frac{6.0 \times 10^2 \text{ N/m}}{1.0 \text{ kg}} \times (\pm 0.120 \text{ m}) = \pm 72 \text{ m/s}^2$$

The magnitude of the acceleration is 72 m/s²; the direction is toward the equilibrium point.

Discussion   Note that at a given position (say $x = +0.120$ m), we can find the *speed* of the rocket, but the direction of the velocity can be either left or right; the rocket passes through each point (other than the endpoints) both on its way to the left and on its way to the right. By contrast, the *acceleration* at $x = +0.120$ m is always in the $-x$-direction, regardless of whether the rocket is moving to the left or to the right. If the rocket is moving to the right, then it is slowing down as it approaches $x = +A$; if it is moving to the left, then it is speeding up as it approaches $x = 0$.

Practice Problem 10.6   Maximum Acceleration of the Rocket

What is the maximum acceleration of the rocket in Example 10.6 and at what position(s) does it occur?

Spring is relaxed here

Figure 10.15
The model rocket before it is released.

−18.0 cm   0   x

10.6   THE PERIOD AND FREQUENCY FOR SHM

Definitions of Period and Frequency   SHM is *periodic* motion because the same motion repeats over and over—a particle goes back and forth over the same path in exactly the same way. Each time the particle repeats its original motion, we say that it has completed another cycle. To complete one cycle of motion, the particle must be at the same point *and heading in the same direction* as it was at the start of the cycle. The **period** T is the time taken by one complete cycle. The **frequency** f is the number of cycles per unit time:

$$f = \frac{1}{T} \qquad \text{(SI unit: Hz = cycles per second)} \qquad (5\text{-}8)$$

SHM is a special kind of periodic motion in which the restoring force is proportional to the displacement from equilibrium. Not all periodic vibrations are examples of simple harmonic motion since not all restoring forces are proportional to the displacement. Any restoring force can cause oscillatory motion. An electrocardiogram (Fig. 10.16) traces the periodic pattern of a beating heart, but the motion of the recorder needle is not simple harmonic motion. As we are about to show, in SHM the position is a *sinusoidal* function of time.

Circular Motion and SHM   To learn more about SHM, imagine setting up an experiment (Fig. 10.17). We attach an object to an ideal spring, move the object away from the equilibrium position, and then release it. The object vibrates back and forth in simple harmonic motion with amplitude A. At the same time a horizontal circular disk, of radius $r = A$ and with a pin projecting vertically up from its outer edge, is set into rotation with uniform circular motion. Both the pin and the object attached to the spring are illuminated so that shadows of the vibrating object and of the pin on the rotating disk are seen on a screen. The speed of the disk is adjusted until the shadows oscillate with the same period. We will show that the motion of the two shadows is identical, so the mathematical description of one can be used for the other.

To find the mathematical description of SHM, we analyze the uniform circular motion of the pin. Figure 10.17b shows the pin P moving counterclockwise around

CONNECTION:

The period and frequency are defined exactly as for uniform circular motion, which is another kind of periodic motion.

Period: time for one complete cycle

Figure 10.16 An electrocardiogram.

Most of the equations involving ω are correct only if ω is measured in *radians* per unit time (such as rad/s). Don't forget to put your calculator into radian mode.

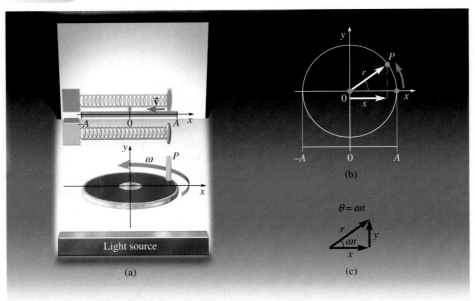

Figure 10.17 (a) An experiment to show the relation between uniform circular motion and SHM. (b) A pin P moving counterclockwise around a circle as a disk rotates with constant angular velocity ω. (c) Finding the x-component of the displacement.

a circle of radius A at a constant angular velocity ω in rad/s. For simplicity, let the pin start at $\theta = 0$ at time $t = 0$. The location of the pin at any time is then given by the angle θ:

$$\theta(t) = \omega t$$

The motion of the pin's shadow has the same x-component as the pin itself. Using a right triangle (Fig. 10.17c), we find that

$$x(t) = A \cos \theta = A \cos \omega t \qquad (10\text{-}17)$$

Since the pin moves in uniform circular motion, its acceleration is constant in *magnitude* but not in direction; the acceleration is toward the center of the circle. In Section 5.2, the magnitude of the radial acceleration is shown to be

$$a = \omega^2 r = \omega^2 A \qquad (5\text{-}12)$$

At any instant the direction of the acceleration vector is opposite to the direction of the displacement vector in Fig. 10.17b—that is, toward the center of the circle. Therefore,

$$a_x = -a \cos \theta = -\omega^2 A \cos \omega t \qquad (10\text{-}18)$$

Comparing Eqs. (10-17) and (10-18), we see that, at any time t,

$$a_x(t) = -\omega^2 x(t) \qquad (10\text{-}19)$$

In Eq. (10-15) we showed that in SHM the acceleration is proportional to the displacement:

$$a_x = -\frac{k}{m} x \qquad (10\text{-}15)$$

Comparing the right-hand sides of Eqs. (10-15) and (10-19), the motions of the two shadows are identical as long as

$$\omega = \sqrt{\frac{k}{m}} \qquad (10\text{-}20\text{a})$$

The position and acceleration of an object in SHM are sinusoidal functions of time [Eqs. (10-17) and (10-18)]. The sinusoidal functions are sine and cosine. In Problem 54, you can show that v_x is also a sinusoidal function of time.

The term *harmonic* in *simple harmonic motion* refers to a sinusoidal vibration; this usage is related to similar usage in music and acoustics. The sinusoidal functions are also called harmonic functions. In Chapter 12, we show that a complex vibration can be formed by combining harmonic vibrations at different frequencies, which is why the study of SHM is the basis for understanding more complex vibrations. The term *simple* in SHM means that the amplitude of the vibration is constant; we assume there is no energy dissipation to cause the vibration to die out.

Period and Frequency for an Ideal Mass-Spring System   Since the object in SHM and the pin in circular motion have the same frequency and period, the relationships between ω, f, and T still apply. Therefore, the frequency and period of a mass-spring system are

$$f = \frac{\omega}{2\pi} = \frac{1}{2\pi} \sqrt{\frac{k}{m}} \qquad (10\text{-}20\text{b})$$

and

$$T = \frac{1}{f} = 2\pi \sqrt{\frac{m}{k}} \qquad (10\text{-}20\text{c})$$

In the context of SHM, the quantity ω is called the **angular frequency**. Note that the angular frequency is determined by the mass and the spring constant but is independent of the amplitude.

With the identification of ω for a mass-spring system, we can write the maximum speed and acceleration from Eqs. (10-14) and (10-16):

$$v_m = \omega A \qquad\qquad\qquad (10\text{-}21)$$

$$a_m = \omega^2 A \qquad\qquad\qquad (10\text{-}22)$$

These expressions are more general than Eqs. (10-14) and (10-16)—they apply to any system in SHM, not just a mass-spring system.

To Find the Angular Frequency for Any Object in SHM

- Write down the restoring force as a function of the displacement from equilibrium. Since the restoring force is linear, it always takes the form $F = -kx$, where k is a constant.
- Use Newton's second law to relate the restoring force to the acceleration.
- Solve for ω using $a_x = -\omega^2 x$ [Eq. (10-19)].

A Vertical Mass and Spring

The mass and spring systems discussed so far oscillate horizontally. An oscillating mass on a vertical spring also exhibits SHM; the difference is that the equilibrium point is shifted downward by gravity. In our discussions, we assume ideal springs that obey Hooke's law and have a negligibly small mass of their own.

Suppose that an object of weight mg is hung from an ideal spring of spring constant k (Fig. 10.18). The object's equilibrium point is *not* the point at which the spring is relaxed. In equilibrium, the spring is stretched downward a distance d from its relaxed length so that the spring pulls up with a force equal to mg. Taking the $+y$-axis in the upward direction, the condition for equilibrium is

$$\sum F_y = +kd - mg = 0 \quad \text{(at equilibrium)} \qquad (10\text{-}23)$$

Let us take the origin ($y = 0$) at the equilibrium point. If the object is displaced vertically from the equilibrium point to a position y, the spring force becomes

$$F_{\text{spring},y} = k(d - y)$$

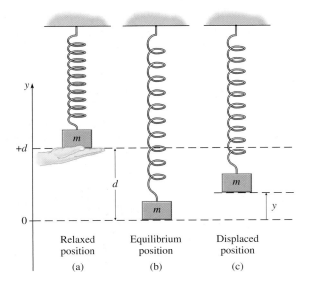

Figure 10.18 (a) A relaxed spring, of spring constant k, with mass m attached. (b) The same spring is extended to its equilibrium position, a distance d below the relaxed position, after mass m is allowed to hang freely. Note that we choose $y = 0$ at the equilibrium position, not at the relaxed position. (c) The spring is displaced from the equilibrium position.

If y is positive, the object is displaced upward and the spring force is less than kd. The y-component of the net force is then

$$\sum F_y = k(d-y) - mg = kd - ky - mg \quad \text{(at displacement } y \text{ from equilibrium)}$$

From Eq. (10-23), we know that $kd = mg$; therefore,

$$\sum F_y = -ky$$

The restoring force provided by the spring and gravity together is $-k$ times the displacement from equilibrium. Therefore, the vertical mass-spring exhibits SHM with the same period and frequency as if it were horizontal.

Example 10.7

A Vertical Spring

A spring with spring constant k is suspended vertically. A model goose of mass m is attached to the unstretched spring and then released so that the bird oscillates up and down. (Ignore friction and air resistance; assume an ideal massless spring.) Calculate the kinetic energy, the elastic potential energy, the gravitational potential energy, and the total mechanical energy at (a) the point of release and (b) the equilibrium point. Take the gravitational potential energy to be zero at the equilibrium point.

Strategy The bird oscillates in SHM about its equilibrium point $y = 0$ between two extreme positions $y = +A$ and $y = -A$ (Fig. 10.19). The amplitude A is equal to the distance the

spring is stretched at the equilibrium point; it can be found by setting the net force on the bird equal to zero. The total mechanical energy is the sum of the kinetic energy, the elastic potential energy, and the gravitational potential energy. We expect the total energy to be the same at the two points; since no dissipative forces act, mechanical energy is conserved.

Solution The equilibrium point is where the net force on the bird is zero:

$$\sum F_y = +kd - mg = 0 \quad \text{(10-23)}$$

In this equation, d is the extension of the spring at equilibrium. Since the bird is released where the spring is relaxed, d is also the amplitude of the oscillations:

$$A = d = \frac{mg}{k}$$

(a) At the point of release, $v = 0$ and the kinetic energy is zero. The elastic energy is also zero—the spring is unstretched. The gravitational potential energy is

$$U_g = mgy = mgA = \frac{(mg)^2}{k}$$

The total mechanical energy is the sum of the kinetic and potential (elastic + gravitational) energies,

$$E = K + U_e + U_g = \frac{(mg)^2}{k}$$

(b) At the equilibrium point, the bird moves with its maximum speed $v_m = \omega A$. The angular frequency is the same as for a horizontal spring: $\omega = \sqrt{k/m}$. Then the kinetic energy is

$$K = \tfrac{1}{2} m v_m^2 = \tfrac{1}{2} m \omega^2 A^2$$

Substituting $A = mg/k$ and $\omega^2 = k/m$,

$$K = \tfrac{1}{2} m \frac{k}{m} \frac{(mg)^2}{k^2} = \frac{1}{2} \frac{(mg)^2}{k}$$

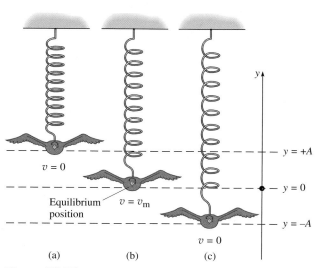

Figure 10.19

(a) The spring is unstretched before the model bird is released at position $y = +A$; (b) the model bird passes through the equilibrium position $y = 0$ with maximum speed; (c) the spring's maximum extension occurs when the bird is at $y = -A$.

In figure: $y = +A$, $v = 0$; Equilibrium position, $v = v_m$, $y = 0$; $y = -A$, $v = 0$; (a) (b) (c)

continued on next page

Example 10.7 continued

The spring is stretched a distance A, so the elastic energy is

$$U_e = \frac{1}{2}kA^2 = \frac{1}{2}k\frac{(mg)^2}{k^2} = \frac{1}{2}\frac{(mg)^2}{k}$$

The gravitational potential energy is zero at $y = 0$. Therefore, the total mechanical energy is

$$E = K + U_e + U_g = \frac{1}{2}\frac{(mg)^2}{k} + \frac{1}{2}\frac{(mg)^2}{k} + 0 = \frac{(mg)^2}{k}$$

which is the same as at $y = +A$.

Discussion   As the bird moves down from the release point toward the equilibrium point, gravitational potential energy is converted into elastic energy and kinetic energy. After the

bird passes the equilibrium point, both kinetic and gravitational energy are converted into elastic energy. At the lowest point in the motion, the gravitational potential energy has its lowest value, while the elastic potential energy has its greatest value. The *total* potential energy (gravitational plus elastic) has its minimum value at the equilibrium point since the kinetic energy is maximum there.

Practice Problem 10.7   Energy at Maximum Extension

Calculate the energies at the lowest point in the oscillations in Example 10.7.

10.7   GRAPHICAL ANALYSIS OF SHM

We have shown that the position of a particle moving in SHM along the x-axis is

$$x(t) = A \cos \omega t \tag{10-17}$$

Since the cosine function goes from -1 to $+1$, multiplying it by A gives us a displacement from $-A$ to $+A$. Figure 10.20a is a graph of the position as a function of time.

The velocity at any time is the slope of the $x(t)$ graph. Note that the maximum slope in Fig. 10.20a occurs when $x = 0$, which confirms what we already know from energy

Figure 10.20 Graphs of (a) position, (b) velocity, and (c) acceleration as functions of time for a particle in simple harmonic motion. Observe the interrelationships between the three graphs. The velocity graph is one-quarter cycle ahead of the position graph; that is, $v_x(t)$ reaches its positive maximum one-quarter period before $x(t)$ reaches its positive maximum. Likewise, the acceleration is one-quarter cycle ahead of the velocity and one-half cycle ahead of the position. (d) Kinetic energy as a function of time. (e) Potential energy as a function of time.

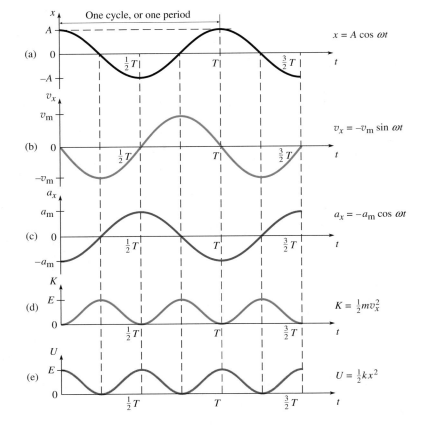

conservation: the velocity is maximum at the equilibrium point. Note also that the velocity is zero when the displacement is a maximum ($+A$ or $-A$). Figure 10.20b shows a graph of $v_x(t)$. The equation describing this graph is (see Problem 54):

$$v_x(t) = -v_m \sin \omega t = -\omega A \sin \omega t \qquad \text{(10-24)}$$

The acceleration is the slope of the $v_x(t)$ graph. Figure 10.20c is a graph of $a_x(t)$, which is described by the equation

$$a_x(t) = -a_m \cos \omega t = -\omega^2 A \cos \omega t \qquad \text{(10-18)}$$

Figures 10.20d,e show the kinetic and potential energies as functions of time, respectively. The total energy $E = K + U = \frac{1}{2}kA^2$ is constant.

We have written the position as a function of time in terms of the cosine function, but we can just as correctly use the sine function. The difference between the two is the initial position at time $t = 0$. If the position is at a maximum ($x = A$) at $t = 0$, $x(t)$ is a cosine function. If the position is at the equilibrium point ($x = 0$) at $t = 0$, $x(t)$ is a sine function. By analyzing the slopes of the graphs, you can show (Problem 50) that if the position as a function of time is

$$x(t) = A \sin \omega t \qquad \text{(10-25a)}$$

then the velocity and acceleration are

$$v_x(t) = v_m \cos \omega t \qquad \text{(10-25b)}$$

$$a_x(t) = -a_m \sin \omega t \qquad \text{(10-25c)}$$

√ CHECKPOINT 10.7

(a) When the displacement of an object in SHM is zero, what is its speed?
(b) When the speed is zero, what is the displacement?

Example 10.8

A Vibrating Loudspeaker Cone

A loudspeaker has a movable diaphragm (the *cone*) that vibrates back and forth to produce sound waves. The displacement of a loudspeaker cone playing a sinusoidal test tone is graphed in Fig. 10.21. Find (a) the amplitude of the motion, (b) the period of the motion, and (c) the frequency of the motion. (d) Write equations for $x(t)$ and $v_x(t)$.

Strategy The amplitude and period can be read directly from the graph. The frequency is the inverse of the period.

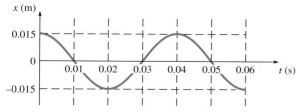

Figure 10.21
Horizontal displacement of a vibrating cone as a function of time.

Since $x(t)$ begins at the maximum displacement, it is described by a cosine function. By looking at the slope of $x(t)$, we can tell whether the velocity is a positive or negative sine function.

Solution (a) The amplitude is the maximum displacement shown on the graph: $A = 0.015$ m.

(b) The period is the time for one complete cycle. From the graph: $T = 0.040$ s.

(c) The frequency is the inverse of the period.

$$f = \frac{1}{T} = \frac{1}{0.040 \text{ s}} = 25 \text{ Hz}$$

(d) Since $x = +A$ at $t = 0$, we write $x(t)$ as a cosine function:

$$x(t) = A \cos \omega t$$

where $A = 0.015$ m and

$$\omega = 2\pi f = 160 \text{ rad/s}$$

continued on next page

Example 10.8 continued

Figure 10.21
Horizontal displacement of a vibrating cone as a function of time.

The slope of $x(t)$ is initially zero and then goes negative. Therefore, $v_x(t)$ is a negative sine function:

$$v_x(t) = -v_m \sin \omega t$$

where $\omega = 2\pi f = 160$ rad/s and

$$v_m = \omega A = 160 \text{ rad/s} \times 0.015 \text{ m} = 2.4 \text{ m/s}$$

Discussion   As a check, the velocity should be one-quarter cycle ahead of the position. If we imagine shifting the vertical axis to the right (ahead) by 0.01 s, the graph would have the shape of a negative sine function.

Practice Problem 10.8   Acceleration of the Speaker Cone

Sketch a graph and write an equation for $a_x(t)$.

10.8   THE PENDULUM

Simple Pendulum

When a pendulum swings back and forth, a string or thin rod constrains the bob to move along a circular arc. However, *for oscillations with small amplitude*, we assume that the bob moves *back and forth along the x-axis*; the vertical motion of the bob is negligible.

Since the weight of the bob has no x-component, the restoring force is the x-component of the force due to the string. We expect the restoring force to be proportional to the displacement for small oscillations. From Fig. 10.22,

$$\sum F_x = -T \sin \theta = -\frac{Tx}{L}$$

where L is the length of the string and $\sin \theta = x/L$. The y-component of the acceleration is negligibly small, so

$$\sum F_y = T \cos \theta - mg = ma_y \approx 0$$

Since $\cos \theta \approx 1$ for small θ, $T \approx mg$. Then

$$\sum F_x \approx -\frac{mgx}{L} = ma_x$$

Solving for a_x:

$$a_x = -\frac{g}{L}x$$

To identify the angular frequency, we recall that $a_x = -\omega^2 x$ [Eq. (10-19)]. Therefore, the angular frequency is

$$\omega = \sqrt{\frac{g}{L}} \tag{10-26a}$$

and the period is

$$T = \frac{2\pi}{\omega} = 2\pi\sqrt{\frac{L}{g}} \tag{10-26b}$$

Note that the period depends on L and g but not on the mass of the pendulum. (Text website tutorial: change in period)

Be careful not to confuse the *angular frequency* of the pendulum with its *angular velocity*. Even though the two have the same units (rad/s in SI) and are written with the same symbol (ω), for a pendulum they are *not* the same. When dealing with the pendulum, we use the symbol ω to stand for the *angular frequency* only. The angular frequency $\omega = 2\pi f$ of a given pendulum is constant, while the angular velocity (the rate of

Figure 10.22 (a) Forces on a pendulum bob. (b) Finding the x-component of the force due to the string.

change of θ) changes with time between zero (at the extremes) and its maximum magnitude (at the equilibrium point).

PHYSICS AT HOME

The relation between the period and the length of the pendulum is easily tested at home. Make a simple pendulum by tying a thin string to one end of a paper clip and sliding the clip over a coin. Some tape can be used to help hold the coin if it slips out of place. Holding the end of the string, let the coin swing through a small arc and note the time for the coin to make ten complete oscillations, starting from one extreme position and returning to the same position ten times. Divide the time by ten to get the period. (This gives a more accurate value than timing a single period.) Measure the length of the pendulum and test Eq. (10-26b).

Repeat the experiment by holding the string at a position closer to the coin, effectively shortening the length of the pendulum. What do you find? Is the period for the shorter pendulum longer, shorter, or the same as that measured for the longer pendulum?

The effect of a different mass on the period can also be tested by using two or three coins taped together, with the same length pendulum as used for the first measurement. Does a heavier coin affect the result?

Example 10.9

Grandfather Clock

A grandfather clock uses a pendulum with period 2.0 s to keep time. In one such clock, the pendulum bob has mass 150 g; the pendulum is set into oscillation by displacing it 33 mm to one side. (a) What is the length of the pendulum? (b) Does the initial displacement satisfy the small angle approximation?

Strategy   The period depends on the length of the pendulum and on the gravitational field strength g. It does not depend on the mass of the bob. It also does not depend on the initial displacement, as long as it is small compared to the length.

Solution   (a) Assuming small amplitudes, the period is

$$T = 2\pi \sqrt{\frac{L}{g}}$$

Solving for L,

$$L = \frac{T^2 g}{(2\pi)^2}$$

$$= \frac{(2.0 \text{ s})^2 \times 9.80 \text{ m/s}^2}{(2\pi)^2} = 0.99 \text{ m}$$

(b) The small angle approximation is valid if the maximum displacement is small compared to the length of the pendulum.

$$\frac{x}{L} = \frac{33 \text{ mm}}{990 \text{ mm}} = 0.033$$

Is that small enough? If $\sin \theta = x/L = 0.033$, then

$$\theta = \sin^{-1} 0.033 = 0.033006$$

Sin θ and θ differ by less than 0.02%. Since we only know T to two significant figures, the approximation is good.

Discussion   We should check that we didn't write the expression for the period "upside down," which is the most likely error we could make. Besides checking that the units work out, we know that a longer pendulum has a longer period, so L must go in the numerator. On the other hand, if g were larger, the restoring force would be larger and we would expect the period to shorten; thus, g belongs in the denominator.

Practice Problem 10.9   Pendulum on the Moon

A pendulum of length 0.99 m is taken to the Moon by an astronaut. The period of the pendulum is 4.9 s. What is the gravitational field strength on the surface of the Moon?

Large-Amplitude Motion of a Pendulum Is *Not* SHM   The period of a pendulum as just determined is valid only for small amplitudes. For larger amplitudes, the pendulum's motion is still periodic (though not SHM). Why would the period be any different for large amplitudes? Remember that we assumed the bob was moving horizontally back and forth along the x-axis. This simplification breaks down for large amplitudes.

For instance, if we pull the pendulum out horizontally ($\theta = 90°$), the tangential component of the weight is mg, but $F_x = 0$! Since we have overestimated F_x, we have underestimated the time for the bob to return to $x = 0$; thus, the period for large amplitudes is greater than $2\pi \sqrt{L/g}$. Another way of looking at it is in terms of the tangential force. The expression for the tangential component of the weight is correct even for large amplitudes. However, the distance the bob must move to return to equilibrium is larger than x. For instance, starting at $\theta = 90°$, the bob must move one quarter of the circumference, a distance $\frac{1}{4}(2\pi L) \approx 1.6L$, to return to equilibrium. Assuming linear motion along the x-axis would make the distance only L. With a longer distance to travel, the time is longer.

Physical Pendulum

Imagine that you have a simple pendulum of length L. Beside it you have a uniform metal bar of the same length, which is free to swing about an axis at one end. Would the two have the same period if they are set into oscillation?

For the simple pendulum, the bob is assumed to be a point mass; all the mass of the pendulum is at a distance L from the rotation axis. For the metal bar, however, the mass is uniformly distributed from the axis to a *maximum* distance L away from the axis. The center of mass is located at the midpoint, a distance $d = \frac{1}{2}L$ from the axis (Fig. 10.23). Since the mass is on average closer to the axis, the period is shorter than that of the simple pendulum.

Would this bar have a period equal to that of a simple pendulum of length $\frac{1}{2}L$? That is a good guess, since the center of mass of the bar is a distance $\frac{1}{2}L$ away from the rotation axis. Unfortunately, it isn't quite that easy. The gravitational force acts at the center of mass, but we *cannot* think of all the mass as being concentrated at that point—that would give the wrong rotational inertia. When set into oscillation, the bar, or any other rigid object free to rotate about a fixed axis, is called a **physical pendulum**. The period of a physical pendulum is

Axis

Axis

θ

L

Tension force

$m\vec{g}$

d

CM

L

θ

$m\vec{g}$

(a)   (b)

Figure 10.23 (a) A simple pendulum and (b) a physical pendulum.

$$T = 2\pi \sqrt{\frac{I}{mgd}} \tag{10-27}$$

where d is the distance from the rotation axis to the CM of the object and I is the rotational inertia about that axis. [See text website for a derivation of Eq. (10-27).]

For a uniform bar of length L, the CM is halfway down the bar:

$$d = \frac{1}{2}L$$

From Table 8.1, the rotational inertia of a uniform bar rotating about an axis through an endpoint is $I = \frac{1}{3}mL^2$. The period of oscillation is

$$T = 2\pi \sqrt{\frac{I}{mgd}} = 2\pi \sqrt{\frac{\frac{1}{3}mL^2}{(mg)\frac{1}{2}L}} = 2\pi \sqrt{\frac{2L}{3g}}$$

The bar has the same period as a simple pendulum of length $\frac{2}{3}L$.

Example 10.10

Comparison of Walking Frequencies and Speeds for Various Creatures

During a relaxed walking pace, an animal's leg can be thought of as a physical pendulum of length L that pivots about the hip. (a) What is the relaxed walking frequency for a cat ($L = 30$ cm), dog (60 cm), human (1 m), giraffe (2 m), and a mythological titan (10 m)? (b) Derive an equation that gives the walking speed (amount of ground covered per unit time) for a given walking frequency f. [*Hint:* Start by drawing a picture of the leg position at the start of the swing (leg back) and the end of the swing (leg forward) and assume a comfortable angle of about 30° between these two positions. To how many steps does a complete period of the pendulum correspond?] (c) Find the walking speed for each of the animals listed in part (a).

continued on next page

Example 10.10 continued

Strategy We have to use an idealized model of the leg, since we don't know the exact location of the center of mass or the rotational inertia. The simple pendulum is not a good model, since it would assume all the mass of the leg at the foot! A much better model is to think of the leg as a uniform cylinder pivoting about one end.

Solution (a) For a uniform cylinder, the center of mass is a distance $d = \frac{1}{2}L$ from the pivot and the rotational inertia about an axis at one end is $I = \frac{1}{3}mL^2$. Then the period is

$$T = 2\pi\sqrt{\frac{I}{mgd}} = 2\pi\sqrt{\frac{\frac{1}{3}mL^2}{(mg)\frac{1}{2}L}} = 2\pi\sqrt{\frac{2L}{3g}}$$

and the frequency f is

$$f = \frac{1}{T} = \frac{1}{2\pi}\sqrt{\frac{3g}{2L}} \approx 0.2\sqrt{\frac{g}{L}}$$

Substituting the numerical values of L for each animal, we find the frequencies to be 1 Hz (cat), 0.8 Hz (dog), 0.6 Hz (human), 0.4 Hz (giraffe), and 0.2 Hz (titan).

(b) One period of the "pendulum" corresponds to two steps. In Fig. 10.24a, the right leg is about to step forward. The step occurs as the pendulum swings forward through half a cycle. In Fig. 10.24b, the right foot is about to touch the ground; in Fig. 10.24c, the right foot touches the ground and now the left leg is about to step forward. During this step, the right foot stays in place on the ground, but the right leg is swinging backward relative to the hip joint. During each

step, the distance covered is approximately the length of a 30° arc of radius L, which is one twelfth the circumference of a circle of radius L. So during one period, the distance walked is

$$D = 2 \times \frac{1}{12} \times 2\pi L = \frac{\pi}{3}L \approx L$$

and the walking speed is

$$v = \frac{D}{T} = Lf = 0.2\sqrt{gL}$$

(c) The speeds are 0.3 m/s (cat), 0.5 m/s (dog), 0.6 m/s (human), 0.9 m/s (giraffe), and 2 m/s (titan).

Discussion You may be more familiar with walking speeds in mi/h. Converting the units, 0.6 m/s ≈ 1.3 mi/h, which is just about right for a leisurely walk. A brisk walk is about 3 mi/h for most people; to go much faster than that, you need to jog or run.

The solution says that longer legs walk faster, but the frequency of the steps is lower. You can verify that by walking beside a friend who is much taller or much shorter than you, or by taking your dog for a walk.

Practice Problem 10.10 Walking Speed for a Human

A more realistic model of a human leg of length 1.0 m has the center of mass 0.45 m from the hip and a rotational inertia of $\frac{1}{6}mL^2$. What is the walking speed predicted by this model?

(a)   (b)   (c)

Figure 10.24 The forward motion of a leg during walking is similar to the swing of a physical pendulum. From (a) to (b), the right leg swings forward like a pendulum. In (c), the right foot is on the ground and the left leg is about to swing forward.

Figure 10.25 Graphs of $x(t)$ for a mass-spring system with increasing amounts of damping. In (c) the damping is sufficient to prevent oscillations from occurring.

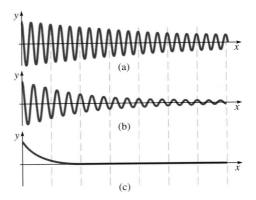

Application of damped oscillation: shock absorbers in a car

Spring

Holes in the piston

Viscous oil

Figure 10.26 A shock absorber.

10.9 DAMPED OSCILLATIONS

In SHM, we assume that no dissipative forces such as friction or viscous drag exist. Since the mechanical energy is constant, the oscillations continue forever with constant amplitude. SHM is a simplified model. The oscillations of a swinging pendulum or a vibrating tuning fork gradually die out as energy is dissipated. The amplitude of each cycle is a little smaller than that of the previous cycle (Fig. 10.25a). This kind of motion is called **damped oscillation**, where the word *damped* is used in the sense of *extinguished* or *restrained*. For a small amount of damping, oscillations occur at approximately the same frequency as if there were no damping. A greater degree of damping lowers the frequency slightly (Fig. 10.25b). Even more damping prevents oscillations from occurring at all (Fig. 10.25c).

Damping is not always a disadvantage. The suspension system of a car includes shock absorbers that cause the vibration of the body—a mass connected to the chassis by springs—to be quickly damped. The shock absorbers reduce the discomfort that passengers would otherwise experience due to the bouncing of an automobile as it travels along a bumpy road. Figure 10.26 shows how a shock absorber works. In order to compress or expand the shock absorber, a viscous oil must flow through the holes in the piston. The viscous force dissipates energy regardless of which direction the piston moves. The shock absorber enables the spring to smoothly return to its equilibrium length without oscillating up and down (Fig. 10.25c). When the oil leaks out of the shock absorber, the damping is insufficient to prevent oscillations. After hitting a bump, the body of the car oscillates up and down (Fig. 10.25b).

10.10 FORCED OSCILLATIONS AND RESONANCE

When damping forces are present, the only way to keep the amplitude of oscillations from diminishing is to replace the dissipated energy from some other source. When a child is being pushed on a swing, the parent replaces the energy dissipated with a small push. In order to keep the amplitude of the motion constant, the parent gives a little push once per cycle, adding just enough energy each time to compensate for the energy dissipated in one cycle. The frequency of the *driving force* (the parent's push) matches the *natural frequency* of the system (the frequency at which it would oscillate on its own).

Forced oscillations (or driven oscillations) occur when a periodic external driving force acts on a system that can oscillate. The frequency of the driving force does not have to match the natural frequency of the system. Ultimately, the system oscillates at the driving frequency, even if it is far from the natural frequency. However, the amplitude of the oscillations is generally quite small unless the driving frequency f is close to the natural frequency f_0 (Fig. 10.27). When the driving frequency is equal to the natural frequency of the system, the amplitude of the motion is a maximum. This condition is called **resonance**.

At resonance, the driving force is always in the same direction as the object's velocity. Since the driving force is always doing positive work, the energy of the oscillator builds up until the energy dissipated balances the energy added by the driving force. For an oscillator with little damping, this requires a large amplitude. When the driving and natural frequencies differ, the driving force and velocity are no longer synchronized; sometimes they are in the same direction and sometimes in opposite directions. The driving force is not at resonance, so it sometimes does negative work. The net work done by the driving force decreases as the driving frequency moves away from resonance. Therefore, the oscillator's energy and amplitude are smaller than at resonance.

Applications of Resonance   Large-amplitude vibrations due to resonance can be dangerous in some situations. Materials can be stressed past their elastic limits, causing permanent deformation or breaking. In 1940, the wind set the Tacoma Narrows Bridge in Washington state into vibration with increasing amplitude. Turbulence in the air as it flowed across the bridge caused the air pressure to fluctuate with a frequency matching one of the bridge's resonant frequencies. As the amplitude of the oscillations grew, the bridge was closed; soon after, the bridge collapsed (Fig. 10.28). Engineers now design bridges with much higher resonant frequencies so the wind cannot cause resonant vibrations.

In the nineteenth century, bridges were sometimes set into resonant vibration when the cadence of marching soldiers matched a resonant frequency of the bridge. After the collapse of several bridges due to resonance, soldiers were told to break step when crossing a bridge to eliminate the danger of their cadence setting the bridge into resonance.

Tall buildings sway back and forth at a particular resonant frequency determined by the structure. The vibration pattern is similar to what you see if you hold one end of a ruler to the edge of a desk and then pluck the other end. Engineers have many methods to reduce the amplitude of the swaying. One of the simplest and most widely used is the tuned mass damper (TMD). Building engineers attach a damped mass-spring system to the structure at a point where its vibration amplitude is largest—near the top. In the Hancock Tower, each of the 300 000-kg boxes is attached to the building frame with springs and shock absorbers and can slide back and forth, riding on a thin layer of oil that covers a 9-m-long steel plate. The resonant frequency of the TMD is matched to the resonant frequency of the swaying building. When the swaying of the building drives the TMD into oscillation, energy is dissipated in the shock absorbers. The TMD in the Hancock Tower reduces the amplitude of its swaying by about 50%.

Figure 10.27 Two resonance curves for an oscillator with natural frequency f_0. The amplitude of the driving force is constant. In the red graph, the oscillator has one fourth as much damping as in the blue graph.

Applications of resonance: vibration of bridges and buildings

How is the swaying of a tall building reduced?

(a)

(b)

Figure 10.28 (a) The Tacoma Narrows Bridge begins to vibrate. (b) Ultimately the vibrations caused the bridge to collapse.

Master the Concepts

- A deformation is a change in the size or shape of an object.
- When deforming forces are removed, an *elastic* object returns to its original shape and size.
- Hooke's law, in a generalized form, says that the deformation of a material (measured by the strain) is proportional to the magnitude of the forces causing the deformation (measured by the stress). The definitions of stress and strain are as given in the following table.

Type of Deformation

	Tensile or Compressive	Shear	Volume
Stress	Force per unit cross-sectional area F/A	Shear force divided by the parallel area of the surface on which it acts F/A	Pressure P
Strain	Fractional length change $\Delta L/L$	Ratio of the relative displacement Δx to the separation L of the two parallel surfaces $\Delta x/L$	Fractional volume change $\Delta V/V$
Constant of proportionality	Young's modulus Y	Shear modulus S	Bulk modulus B

- If the tensile or compressive stress exceeds the *proportional limit*, the strain is no longer proportional to the stress. The solid still returns to its original length when the stress is removed as long as the stress does not exceed the *elastic limit*. If the stress exceeds the elastic limit, the material is permanently deformed. For larger stresses yet, the solid fractures when the stress reaches the *breaking point*. The maximum stress that can be withstood without breaking is called the *ultimate strength*.
- Vibrations occur in the vicinity of a point of stable equilibrium. An equilibrium point is *stable* if the net force on an object when it is displaced from equilibrium points back toward the equilibrium point. Such a force is called a restoring force since it tends to restore equilibrium.
- Simple harmonic motion is periodic motion that occurs whenever the restoring force is proportional to the displacement from equilibrium. In SHM, the position, velocity, and acceleration as functions of time are sinusoidal (i.e., sine or cosine functions). Any oscillatory motion is approximately SHM if the amplitude is small, because for small oscillations the restoring force is approximately linear.
- The period T is the time taken by one complete cycle of oscillation. The frequency f is the number of cycles per unit time:

$$f = \frac{1}{T} \qquad (5\text{-}8)$$

The angular frequency is measured in radians per unit time:

$$\omega = 2\pi f \qquad (5\text{-}9)$$

- The maximum velocity and acceleration in SHM are

$$v_m = \omega A \quad \text{and} \quad a_m = \omega^2 A \qquad (10\text{-}21, 10\text{-}22)$$

where ω is the angular frequency. The acceleration is proportional to and in the opposite direction from the displacement:

$$a_x(t) = -\omega^2 x(t) \qquad (10\text{-}19)$$

- The equations that describe SHM are

If $x = A$ at $t = 0$,   If $x = 0$ at $t = 0$,

$x = A \cos \omega t$ $x = A \sin \omega t$

$v_x = -v_m \sin \omega t$ $v_x = v_m \cos \omega t$

$a_x = -a_m \cos \omega t$ $a_x = -a_m \sin \omega t$

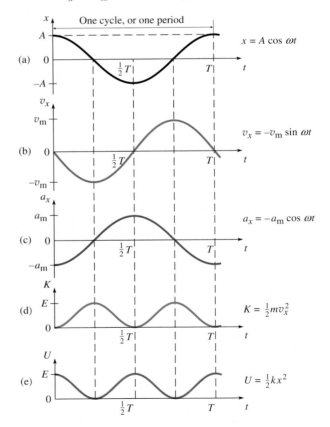

In either case, the velocity is one-quarter cycle ahead of the position and the acceleration is one-quarter cycle ahead of the velocity.

- The period of oscillation for a mass-spring system is

$$T = 2\pi \sqrt{\frac{m}{k}} \qquad (10\text{-}20c)$$

continued on next page

Master the Concepts continued

For a simple pendulum it is

$$T = 2\pi\sqrt{\frac{L}{g}} \qquad \text{(10-26b)}$$

and for a physical pendulum it is

$$T = 2\pi\sqrt{\frac{I}{mgd}} \qquad \text{(10-27)}$$

- In the absence of dissipative forces, the total mechanical energy of a simple harmonic oscillator is constant and proportional to the square of the amplitude:

$$E = \tfrac{1}{2}kA^2 \qquad \text{(10-13)}$$

where the potential energy has been chosen to be zero at the equilibrium point. At any point, the sum of the kinetic and potential energies is constant:

$$E = \tfrac{1}{2}mv_x^2 + \tfrac{1}{2}kx^2 = \tfrac{1}{2}kA^2 \qquad \text{(10-12)}$$

Conceptual Questions

1. Young's modulus for diamond is about 20 times as large as that of glass. Does that tell you which is stronger? If not, what does it tell you?

2. A grandfather clock is running too fast. To fix it, should the pendulum be lengthened or shortened? Explain.

3. A karate student hits downward on a stack of concrete blocks supported at both ends. A block breaks. Explain where it starts to break first, at the bottom or at the top. (The block experiences shear, compressive, and tensile stresses. Recall that concrete has much less tensile strength than compressive strength. Which part of the block is stretched and which is compressed when the block bends in the middle?)

4. A cylindrical steel bar is compressed by the application of forces of magnitude F at each end. What magnitude forces would be required to compress by the same amount (a) a steel bar of the same cross-sectional area but one half the length? (b) a steel bar of the same length but one half the radius?

5. The columns built by the ancient Greeks and Romans to support temples and other structures are tapered; they are thicker at the bottom than at the top. This certainly has an aesthetic purpose, but is there an engineering purpose as well? What might it be?

6. Explain how the period of a mass-spring system can be independent of amplitude, even though the distance traveled during each cycle is proportional to the amplitude.

7. In a reciprocating saw, a *Scotch yoke* converts the rotation of the motor into the back-and-forth motion of the blade. The Scotch yoke is a mechanical device used to convert oscillatory motion to circular motion or *vice versa*. A wheel with a fixed knob rotates at constant angular velocity; the knob is constrained within a vertical slot causing the saw blade to move left and right without moving up and down. Is the motion of the saw blade SHM? Explain.

8. A mass hanging vertically from a spring and a simple pendulum both have a period of oscillation of 1 s on Earth. An astronaut takes the two devices to another planet where the gravitational field is stronger than that of Earth. For each of the two systems, state whether the period is now longer than 1 s, shorter than 1 s, or equal to 1 s. Explain your reasoning.

9. A bungee jumper leaps from a bridge and comes to a stop a few centimeters above the surface of the water below. At that lowest point, is the tension in the bungee cord equal to the jumper's weight? Explain why or why not.

10. Does it take more force to break a longer rope or a shorter rope? Assume the ropes are identical except for their lengths and are ideal—there are no weak points. Does it take more *energy* to break the long rope or the short rope? Explain.

11. A pilot is performing vertical loop-the-loops over the ocean at noon. The plane speeds up as it approaches the bottom of the circular loop and slows as it approaches the top of the loop. An observer in a helicopter is watching the shadow of the plane on the surface of the water. Does the shadow exhibit SHM? Explain.

12. Are you more likely to find steel rods in a horizontal concrete beam or in a vertical concrete column? Is concrete more in need of reinforcement under tensile or compressive stress?

13. Suppose that it takes tensile forces of magnitude F to produce a given strain $\Delta L/L$ in a steel wire of cross-sectional area A. If you had two such wires side by side and stretched them simultaneously, what magnitude tensile forces would be required to produce the same strain? By thinking of a thick wire as two (or more) thinner

wires side by side, explain why the force to produce a given strain must be proportional to the cross-sectional area. Thus, the strain depends on the stress—the force per unit area.

14. Think of a crystalline solid as a set of atoms connected by ideal springs. When a wire is stretched, how is the elongation of the wire related to the elongation of each of the interatomic springs? Use your answer to explain why a given tensile stress produces an elongation of the wire proportional to the wire's initial length—or, equivalently, that a given stress produces the same strain in wires of different lengths.

15. What are the advantages of using the concepts of stress and strain to describe deformations?

16. An old highway is built out of concrete blocks of equal length. A car traveling on this highway feels a little bump at the joint between blocks. The passengers in the car feel that the ride is uncomfortable at a speed of 45 mi/h, but much smoother at speeds either lower or higher than that. Explain.

17. The period of oscillation of a simple pendulum does not depend on the mass of the bob. By contrast, the period of a mass-spring system does depend on mass. Explain the apparent contradiction. [*Hint:* What provides the restoring force in each case? How does the restoring force depend on mass?]

18. A mass connected to an ideal spring is oscillating without friction on a horizontal surface. Sketch graphs of the kinetic energy, potential energy, and total energy as functions of time for one complete cycle.

Multiple-Choice Questions

Questions 1–4. A body is suspended vertically from an ideal spring. The spring is initially in its relaxed position. The body is then released and oscillates about the equilibrium position. Answer choices for Questions 1–4:

   (a) The spring is relaxed.
   (b) The body is at the equilibrium point.
   (c) The spring is at its maximum extension.
   (d) The spring is somewhere between the equilibrium point and maximum extension.

1. The acceleration is greatest in magnitude and is directed upward when:

2. The speed of the body is greatest when:

3. The acceleration of the body is zero when:

4. The acceleration is greatest in magnitude and is directed downward when:

5. Two simple pendulums, A and B, have the same length, but the mass of A is twice the mass of B. Their vibrational amplitudes are equal. Their periods are T_A and T_B, respectively, and their energies are E_A and E_B. Choose the correct statement.

   (a) $T_A = T_B$ and $E_A > E_B$ (b) $T_A > T_B$ and $E_A > E_B$
   (c) $T_A > T_B$ and $E_A < E_B$ (d) $T_A = T_B$ and $E_A < E_B$

6. A force F applied to each end of a steel wire (length L, diameter d) stretches it by 1.0 mm. How much does F stretch another steel wire, of length $2L$ and diameter $2d$?

   (a) 0.50 mm   (b) 1.0 mm   (c) 2.0 mm
   (d) 4.0 mm   (e) 0.25 mm

7. A stiff material is characterized by

   (a) high ultimate strength.
   (b) high breaking strength.
   (c) high Young's modulus.
   (d) high proportional limit.

8. A brittle material is characterized by

   (a) high breaking strength and low Young's modulus.
   (b) low breaking strength and high Young's modulus.
   (c) high breaking strength and high Young's modulus.
   (d) low breaking strength and low Young's modulus.

9. Which pair of quantities can be expressed in the same units?

   (a) stress and strain
   (b) Young's modulus and strain
   (c) Young's modulus and stress
   (d) ultimate strength and strain

10. Two wires have the same diameter and length. One is made of copper, the other brass. The wires are connected together end to end. When the free ends are pulled in opposite directions, the two wires *must* have the same

   (a) stress.   (b) strain.   (c) ultimate strength.
   (d) elongation.   (e) Young's modulus.

Questions 11–20. See the graph of $v_x(t)$ for an object in SHM. Answer choices for each question:

   (a) 1 s, 2 s, 3 s   (b) 5 s, 6 s, 7 s   (c) 0 s, 1 s, 7 s, 8 s
   (d) 3 s, 4 s, 5 s   (e) 0 s, 4 s, 8 s   (f) 2 s, 6 s
   (g) 3 s, 5 s   (h) 1 s, 3 s   (i) 5 s, 7 s
   (j) 3 s, 7 s   (k) 1 s, 5 s

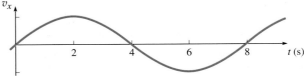

Multiple-Choice Questions 11–20

11. When is the kinetic energy maximum?

12. When is the kinetic energy zero?

13. When is the potential energy maximum?

14. When is the potential energy minimum?

15. When is the object at the equilibrium point?

16. When does the acceleration have its maximum magnitude?

17. Which answer specifies times when the net force is in the +x-direction?

18. Which answer specifies times when the object is on the −x-side of the equilibrium point ($x < 0$)?

19. Which answer specifies times when the object is moving away from the equilibrium point?

20. Which answer specifies times when the potential energy is decreasing?

Problems

⊙   Combination conceptual/quantitative problem

☤   Biological or medical application

✦   Challenging problem

Blue #   Detailed solution in the Student Solutions Manual

① ② Problems paired by concept

Ⓦ Text website interactive or tutorial

10.2 Hooke's Law for Tensile and Compressive Forces

1. A steel beam is placed vertically in the basement of a building to keep the floor above from sagging. The load on the beam is 5.8×10^4 N, the length of the beam is 2.5 m, and the cross-sectional area of the beam is 7.5×10^{-3} m². Find the vertical compression of the beam.

2. A 91-kg man's thighbone has a relaxed length of 0.50 m, a cross-sectional area of 7.0×10^{-4} m², and a Young's modulus of 1.1×10^{10} N/m². By how much does the thighbone compress when the man is standing on both feet?

3. A brass wire with Young's modulus of 9.2×10^{10} Pa is 2.0 m long and has a cross-sectional area of 5.0 mm². If a weight of 5.0 kN is hung from the wire, by how much does it stretch?

4. A wire of length 5.00 m with a cross-sectional area of 0.100 cm² stretches by 6.50 mm when a load of 1.00 kN is hung from it. What is the Young's modulus for this wire?

5. Two steel wires (of the same length and different radii) are connected together, end to end, and tied to a wall. An applied force stretches the combination by 1.0 mm. How far does the *midpoint* move?

6. Abductin is an elastic protein found in scallops, with a Young's modulus of 4.0×10^6 N/m². It is used as an inner hinge ligament, with a cross-sectional area of 0.78 mm² and a relaxed length of 1.0 mm. When the muscles in the shell relax, the shell opens. This increases efficiency as the muscles do not need to exert any force to open the shell, only to close it. If the muscles must exert a force of 1.5 N to keep the shell closed, by how much is the abductin ligament compressed?

7. A 0.50-m-long guitar string, of cross-sectional area 1.0×10^{-6} m², has Young's modulus $Y = 2.0 \times 10^9$ N/m². By how much must you stretch the string to obtain a tension of 20 N?

8. It takes a flea 1.0×10^{-3} s to reach a peak speed of 0.74 m/s. (a) If the mass of the flea is 0.45×10^{-6} kg, what is the average power required? (b) Insect muscle has a maximum output of 60 W/kg. If 20% of the flea's weight is muscle, can the muscle provide the power needed? (c) The flea has a resilin pad at the base of the hind leg that compresses when the flea bends its leg to jump. If we assume the pad is a cube with a side of 6.0×10^{-5} m, and the pad compresses fully, what is the energy stored in the compression of the pads of the two hind legs? The Young's modulus for resilin is 1.7×10^6 N/m². (d) Does this provide enough power for the jump?

10.3 Beyond Hooke's Law

9. Using the stress-strain graph for bone (Fig. 10.4c), calculate Young's moduli for tension and for compression. Consider only small stresses.

10. An acrobat of mass 55 kg is going to hang by her teeth from a steel wire and she does not want the wire to stretch beyond its elastic limit. The elastic limit for the wire is 2.5×10^8 Pa. What is the minimum diameter the wire should have to support her?

11. A hair breaks under a tension of 1.2 N. What is the diameter of the hair? The tensile strength is 2.0×10^8 Pa.

12. The ratio of the tensile (or compressive) strength to the density of a material is a measure of how strong the material is "pound for pound." (a) Compare tendon (tensile strength 80.0 MPa, density 1100 kg/m³) with steel (tensile strength 0.50 GPa, density 7700 kg/m³): which is stronger "pound for pound" under tension? (b) Compare bone (compressive strength 160 MPa, density 1600 kg/m³) with concrete (compressive strength 0.40 GPa, density 2700 kg/m³): which is stronger "pound for pound" under compression?

13. What is the maximum load that could be suspended from a copper wire of length 1.0 m and radius 1.0 mm without permanently deforming the wire? Copper has an elastic limit of 2.0×10^8 Pa and a tensile strength of 4.0×10^8 Pa.

14. What is the maximum load that could be suspended from a copper wire of length 1.0 m and radius 1.0 mm

without breaking the wire? Copper has an elastic limit of 2.0×10^8 Pa and a tensile strength of 4.0×10^8 Pa.

15. The leg bone (femur) breaks under a compressive force of about 5×10^4 N for a human and 10×10^4 N for a horse. The human femur has a compressive strength of 1.6×10^8 Pa, while the horse femur has a compressive strength of 1.4×10^8 Pa. What is the effective cross-sectional area of the femur in a human and in a horse? (*Note:* Since the center of the femur contains bone marrow, which has essentially no compressive strength, the effective cross-sectional area is about 80% of the total cross-sectional area.)

16. The maximum strain of a steel wire with Young's modulus 2.0×10^{11} N/m^2, just before breaking, is 0.20%. What is the stress at its breaking point, assuming that strain is proportional to stress up to the breaking point?

17. A marble column with a cross-sectional area of 25 cm^2 supports a load of 7.0×10^4 N. The marble has a Young's modulus of 6.0×10^{10} Pa and a compressive strength of 2.0×10^8 Pa. (a) What is the stress in the column? (b) What is the strain in the column? (c) If the column is 2.0 m high, how much is its length changed by supporting the load? (d) What is the maximum weight the column can support?

18. A copper wire of length 3.0 m is observed to stretch by 2.1 mm when a weight of 120 N is hung from one end. (a) What is the diameter of the wire and what is the tensile stress in the wire? (b) If the tensile strength of copper is 4.0×10^8 N/m^2, what is the maximum weight that may be hung from this wire?

10.4 Shear and Volume Deformations

19. A sphere of copper is subjected to 100 MPa of pressure. The copper has a bulk modulus of 130 GPa. By what fraction does the volume of the sphere change? By what fraction does the radius of the sphere change?

20. By what percentage does the density of water increase at a depth of 1.0 km below the surface?

21. Atmospheric pressure on Venus is about 90 times that on Earth. A steel sphere with a bulk modulus of 160 GPa has a volume of 1.00 cm^3 on Earth. If it were put in a pressure chamber and the pressure were increased to that of Venus (9.12 MPa), how would its volume change?

22. How would the volume of 1.00 cm^3 of aluminum on Earth change if it were placed in a vacuum chamber and the pressure changed to that of the Moon (less than 10^{-9} Pa)?

23. Two steel plates are fastened together using four bolts. The bolts each have a shear modulus of 8.0×10^{10} Pa and a shear strength of 6.0×10^8 Pa. The radius of each bolt is 1.0 cm. Normally, the bolts clamp the two plates together and the frictional forces between the plates keep them from sliding. If the bolts are loose, then the frictional forces are small and the bolts themselves

would be subject to a large shear stress. What is the maximum shearing force F on the plates that the four bolts can withstand?

24. An anchor, made of cast iron of bulk modulus 60.0×10^9 Pa and of volume 0.230 m^3, is lowered over the side of the ship to the bottom of the harbor where the pressure is greater than sea level pressure by 1.75×10^6 Pa. Find the change in the volume of the anchor.

25. The upper surface of a cube of gelatin, 5.0 cm on a side, is displaced 0.64 cm by a tangential force. If the shear modulus of the gelatin is 940 Pa, what is the magnitude of the tangential force?

26. A large sponge has forces of magnitude 12 N applied in opposite directions to two opposite faces of area 42 cm^2 (see Fig. 10.7 for a similar situation). The thickness of the sponge (L) is 2.0 cm. The deformation angle (γ) is 8.0°. (a) What is Δx? (b) What is the shear modulus of the sponge?

10.5 Simple Harmonic Motion;
10.6 The Period and Frequency for SHM

27. The period of oscillation of a spring-and-mass system is 0.50 s and the amplitude is 5.0 cm. What is the magnitude of the acceleration at the point of maximum extension of the spring?

28. A sewing machine needle moves with a rapid vibratory motion, rather like SHM, as it sews a seam. Suppose the needle moves 8.4 mm from its highest to its lowest position and it makes 24 stitches in 9.0 s. What is the maximum needle speed?

29. The prong of a tuning fork moves back and forth when it is set into vibration. The distance the prong moves between its extreme positions is 2.24 mm. If the frequency of the tuning fork is 440.0 Hz, what are the maximum velocity and the maximum acceleration of the prong? Assume SHM.

30. The period of oscillation of an object in an ideal spring-and-mass system is 0.50 s and the amplitude is 5.0 cm. What is the speed at the equilibrium point?

31. Show that the equation $a = -\omega^2 x$ is consistent for units, and that $\sqrt{k/m}$ has the same units as ω.

32. A 170-g object on a spring oscillates left to right on a frictionless surface with a frequency of 3.00 Hz and an amplitude of 12.0 cm. (a) What is the spring constant? (b) If the object starts at $x = 12.0$ cm at $t = 0$ and the equilibrium point is at $x = 0$, what equation describes its position as a function of time?

33. The air pressure variations in a sound wave cause the eardrum to vibrate. (a) For a given vibration amplitude,

are the maximum velocity and acceleration of the eardrum greatest for high-frequency sounds or low-frequency sounds? (b) Find the maximum velocity and acceleration of the eardrum for vibrations of amplitude 1.0×10^{-8} m at a frequency of 20.0 Hz. (c) Repeat (b) for the same amplitude but a frequency of 20.0 kHz.

34. Show that, for SHM, the maximum displacement, velocity, and acceleration are related by $v_m^2 = a_m A$.

35. An empty cart, tied between two ideal springs, oscillates with $\omega = 10.0$ rad/s. A load is placed in the cart, making the total mass 4.0 times what it was before. What is the new value of ω?

36. A cart with mass m is attached between two ideal springs, each with the same spring constant k. Assume that the cart can oscillate without friction. (a) When the cart is displaced by a small distance x from its equilibrium position, what force magnitude acts on the cart? (b) What is the angular frequency, in terms of m, x, and k, for this cart? (tutorial: cart between springs)

Problems 35 and 36

37. In a playground, a wooden horse is attached to the ground by a stiff spring. When a 24-kg child sits on the horse, the spring compresses by 28 cm. With the child sitting on the horse, the spring oscillates up and down with a frequency of 0.88 Hz. What is the oscillation frequency of the spring when no one is sitting on the horse?

38. A small bird's wings can undergo a maximum displacement amplitude of 5.0 cm (distance from the tip of the wing to the horizontal). If the maximum acceleration of the wings is 12 m/s², and we assume the wings are undergoing simple harmonic motion when beating, what is the oscillation frequency of the wing tips?

39. Equipment to be used in airplanes or spacecraft is often subjected to a shake test to be sure it can withstand the vibrations that may be encountered during flight. A radio receiver of mass 5.24 kg is set on a platform that vibrates in SHM at 120 Hz and with a maximum acceleration of 98 m/s² (= $10g$). Find the radio's (a) maximum displacement, (b) maximum speed, and (c) the maximum net force exerted on it.

40. In an aviation test lab, pilots are subjected to vertical oscillations on a shaking rig to see how well they can recognize objects in times of severe airplane vibration. The frequency can be varied from 0.02 to 40.0 Hz and the amplitude can be set as high as 2 m for low frequencies. What are the maximum velocity and acceleration to which the pilot is subjected if the frequency is set at 25.0 Hz and the amplitude at 1.00 mm?

41. The diaphragm of a speaker has a mass of 50.0 g and responds to a signal of frequency 2.0 kHz by moving back and forth with an amplitude of 1.8×10^{-4} m at that frequency. (a) What is the maximum force acting on the diaphragm? (b) What is the mechanical energy of the diaphragm?

42. An ideal spring has a spring constant $k = 25$ N/m. The spring is suspended vertically. A 1.0-kg body is attached to the unstretched spring and released. It then performs oscillations. (a) What is the magnitude of the acceleration of the body when the extension of the spring is a maximum? (b) What is the maximum extension of the spring?

43. An ideal spring with a spring constant of 15 N/m is suspended vertically. A body of mass 0.60 kg is attached to the unstretched spring and released. (a) What is the extension of the spring when the speed is a maximum? (b) What is the maximum speed?

44. A 0.50-kg object, suspended from an ideal spring of spring constant 25 N/m, is oscillating vertically. How much change of kinetic energy occurs while the object moves from the equilibrium position to a point 5.0 cm lower?

45. A small rowboat has a mass of 47 kg. When a 92-kg person gets into the boat, the boat floats 8.0 cm lower in the water. If the boat is then pushed slightly deeper in the water, it will bob up and down with simple harmonic motion (neglecting any friction). What will be the period of oscillation for the boat as it bobs around its equilibrium position?

46. A baby jumper consists of a cloth seat suspended by an elastic cord from the lintel of an open doorway. The unstretched length of the cord is 1.2 m and the cord stretches by 0.20 m when a baby of mass 6.8 kg is placed into the seat. The mother then pulls the seat down by 8.0 cm and releases it. (a) What is the period of the motion? (b) What is the maximum speed of the baby?

10.7 Graphical Analysis of SHM

47. The displacement of an object in SHM is given by $y(t) = (8.0 \text{ cm}) \sin [(1.57 \text{ rad/s})t]$. What is the frequency of the oscillations?

48. A body is suspended vertically from an ideal spring of spring constant 2.5 N/m. The spring is initially in its relaxed position. The body is then released and oscillates about its equilibrium position. The motion is described by

$$y = (4.0 \text{ cm}) \sin [(0.70 \text{ rad/s})t]$$

What is the maximum kinetic energy of the body?

49. An object of mass 306 g is attached to the base of a spring, with spring constant 25 N/m, that is hanging from the ceiling. A pen is attached to the back of the object, so that it can write on a paper placed behind the mass-spring system. Ignore friction. (a) Describe the pattern traced on the paper if the object is held at the

point where the spring is relaxed and then released at $t = 0$. (b) The experiment is repeated, but now the paper moves to the left at constant speed as the pen writes on it. Sketch the pattern traced on the paper. Imagine that the paper is long enough that it doesn't run out for several oscillations.

50. (a) Sketch a graph of $x(t) = A \sin \omega t$ (the position of an object in SHM that is at the equilibrium point at $t = 0$). (b) By analyzing the slope of the graph of $x(t)$, sketch a graph of $v_x(t)$. Is $v_x(t)$ a sine or cosine function? (c) By analyzing the slope of the graph of $v_x(t)$, sketch $a_x(t)$. (d) Verify that $v_x(t)$ is $\frac{1}{4}$ cycle ahead of $x(t)$ and that $a_x(t)$ is $\frac{1}{4}$ cycle ahead of $v_x(t)$. (tutorial: sinusoids)

51. A mass-and-spring system oscillates with amplitude A and angular frequency ω. (a) What is the *average* speed during one complete cycle of oscillation? (b) What is the maximum speed? (c) Find the ratio of the average speed to the maximum speed. (d) Sketch a graph of $v_x(t)$, and refer to it to explain why this ratio is greater than $\frac{1}{2}$.

52. A ball is dropped from a height h onto the floor and keeps bouncing. No energy is dissipated, so the ball regains the original height h after each bounce. Sketch the graph for $y(t)$ and list several features of the graph that indicate that this motion is *not* SHM.

53. A 230.0-g object on a spring oscillates left to right on a frictionless surface with a frequency of 2.00 Hz. Its position as a function of time is given by $x = (8.00 \text{ cm}) \sin \omega t$. (a) Sketch a graph of the elastic potential energy as a function of time. (b) The object's velocity is given by $v_x = \omega (8.00 \text{ cm}) \cos \omega t$. Graph the system's kinetic energy as a function of time. (c) Graph the sum of the kinetic energy and the potential energy as a function of time. (d) Describe qualitatively how your answers would change if the surface weren't frictionless.

54. (a) Given that the position of an object is $x(t) = A \cos \omega t$, show that $v_x(t) = -\omega A \sin \omega t$. [*Hint:* Draw the velocity vector for point P in Fig. 10.17b and then find its x-component.] (b) Verify that the expressions for $x(t)$ and $v_x(t)$ are consistent with energy conservation. [*Hint:* Use the trigonometric identity $\sin^2 \omega t + \cos^2 \omega t = 1$.]

10.8 The Pendulum

55. What is the period of a pendulum consisting of a 6.0-kg mass oscillating on a 4.0-m-long string?

56. A pendulum of length 75 cm and mass 2.5 kg swings with a mechanical energy of 0.015 J. What is the amplitude?

57. A 0.50-kg mass is suspended from a string, forming a pendulum. The period of this pendulum is 1.5 s when the amplitude is 1.0 cm. The mass of the pendulum is now reduced to 0.25 kg. What is the period of oscillation now, when the amplitude is 2.0 cm? (tutorial: change in period)

58. A bob of mass m is suspended from a string of length L, forming a pendulum. The period of this pendulum is 2.0 s. If the pendulum bob is replaced with one of mass $\frac{1}{3}m$ and the length of the pendulum is increased to $2L$, what is the period of oscillation?

59. A pendulum (mass m, unknown length) moves according to $x = A \sin \omega t$. (a) Write the equation for $v_x(t)$ and sketch one cycle of the $v_x(t)$ graph. (b) What is the maximum kinetic energy?

60. A clock has a pendulum that performs one full swing every 1.0 s (back *and* forth). The object at the end of the pendulum weighs 10.0 N. What is the length of the pendulum?

61. A pendulum of length L_1 has a period $T_1 = 0.950$ s. The length of the pendulum is adjusted to a new value L_2 such that $T_2 = 1.00$ s. What is the ratio L_2/L_1?

62. A pendulum clock has a period of 0.650 s on Earth. It is taken to another planet and found to have a period of 0.862 s. The change in the pendulum's length is negligible. (a) Is the gravitational field strength on the other planet greater than or less than that on Earth? (b) Find the gravitational field strength on the other planet.

63. A grandfather clock is constructed so that it has a simple pendulum that swings from one side to the other, a distance of 20.0 mm, in 1.00 s. What is the maximum speed of the pendulum bob? Use two different methods. First, assume SHM and use the relationship between amplitude and maximum speed. Second, use energy conservation.

64. Christy has a grandfather clock with a pendulum that is 1.000 m long. (a) If the pendulum is modeled as a simple pendulum, what would be the period? (b) Christy observes the actual period of the clock, and finds that it is 1.00% faster than that for a simple pendulum that is 1.000 m long. If Christy models the pendulum as two objects, a 1.000-m uniform thin rod and a point mass located 1.000 m from the axis of rotation, what percentage of the total mass of the pendulum is in the uniform thin rod?

65. A pendulum of length 120 cm swings with an amplitude of 2.0 cm. Its mechanical energy is 5.0 mJ. What is the mechanical energy of the same pendulum when it swings with an amplitude of 3.0 cm?

66. A thin circular hoop is suspended from a knife edge. Its rotational inertia about the rotation axis (along the knife) is $I = 2mr^2$. Show that it oscillates with the same frequency as a simple pendulum of length equal to the diameter of the hoop.

10.9 Damped Oscillations

67. (a) What is the energy of a pendulum ($L = 1.0$ m, $m = 0.50$ kg) oscillating with an amplitude of 5.0 cm? (b) The pendulum's energy loss (due to damping) is replaced in a

clock by allowing a 2.0-kg mass to drop 1.0 m in 1 week. What average percentage of the pendulum's energy is lost during one cycle?

68. The amplitude of oscillation of a pendulum decreases by a factor of 20.0 in 120 s. By what factor has its energy decreased in that time?

69. Because of dissipative forces, the amplitude of an oscillator decreases 5.00% in 10 cycles. By what percentage does its *energy* decrease in ten cycles?

Comprehensive Problems

70. Four people sit in a car. The masses of the people are 45 kg, 52 kg, 67 kg, and 61 kg. The car's mass is 1020 kg. When the car drives over a bump, its springs cause an oscillation with a frequency of 2.00 Hz. What would the frequency be if only the 45-kg person were present?

71. A pendulum passes $x = 0$ with a speed of 0.50 m/s; it swings out to $A = 0.20$ m. What is the period T of the pendulum? (Assume the amplitude is small.)

72. What is the length of a simple pendulum whose horizontal position is described by

$$x = (4.00 \text{ cm}) \cos [(3.14 \text{ rad/s}) \, t]?$$

What assumption do you make when answering this question?

73. Martin caught a fish and wanted to know how much it weighed, but he didn't have a scale. He did, however, have a stopwatch, a spring, and a 4.90-N weight. He attached the weight to the spring and found that the spring would oscillate 20 times in 65 s. Next he hung the fish on the spring and found that it took 220 s for the spring to oscillate 20 times. (a) Before answering part (b), determine if the fish weighs more or less than 4.90 N. (b) What is the weight of the fish?

74. A naval aviator had to eject from her plane before it crashed at sea. She is rescued from the water by helicopter and dangles from a cable that is 45 m long while being carried back to the aircraft carrier. What is the period of her vibration as she swings back and forth while the helicopter hovers over her ship?

75. An object of mass m is hung from the base of an ideal spring that is suspended from the ceiling. The spring has a spring constant k. The object is pulled down a distance D from equilibrium and released. Later, the same system is set oscillating by pulling the object down a distance $2D$ from equilibrium and then releasing it. (a) How do the period and frequency of oscillation change when the initial displacement is increased from D to $2D$? (b) How does the total energy of oscillation change when the initial displacement is increased from D to $2D$? Give the answer as a numerical ratio. (c) The mass-spring system is set into oscillation a third time. This time the object is pulled down a distance of

$2D$ and then given a push downward some more, so that it has an initial speed v_i downward. How do the period and frequency of oscillation compare to those you found in part (a)? (d) How does the total energy compare to when the object was released from rest at a displacement $2D$?

76. A spider's web can undergo SHM when a fly lands on it and displaces the web. For simplicity, assume that a web obeys Hooke's law (which it does not really as it deforms permanently when displaced). If the web is initially horizontal, and a fly landing on the web is in equilibrium when it displaces the web by 0.030 mm, what is the frequency of oscillation when the fly lands?

77. A mass-spring system oscillates so that the position of the mass is described by $x = -10 \cos (1.57t)$, where x is in cm when t is in seconds. Make a plot that has a dot for the position of the mass at $t = 0$, $t = 0.2$ s, $t = 0.4$ s, . . . , $t = 4$ s. The time interval between each dot should be 0.2 s. From your plot, tell where the mass is moving fastest and where slowest. How do you know?

78. A hedge trimmer has a blade that moves back and forth with a frequency of 28 Hz. The blade motion is converted from the rotation provided by the electric motor to an oscillatory motion by means of a Scotch yoke (see Conceptual Question 7). The blade moves 2.4 cm during each stroke. Assuming that the blade moves with SHM, what are the maximum speed and maximum acceleration of the blade?

79. The simple pendulum can be thought of as a special case of the physical pendulum where all of the mass is at a distance L from the rotation axis. For a simple pendulum of mass m and length L, show that the expression for the period of a physical pendulum (Eq. 10-27) reduces to the expression for the period of a simple pendulum (Eq. 10-26b).

80. Luke is trying to catch a pesky animal that keeps eating vegetables from his garden. He is building a trap and needs to use a spring to close the door to his trap. He has a spring in his garage and he wants to determine the spring constant of the spring. To do this, he hangs the spring from the ceiling and measures that it is 20.0 cm long. Then he hangs a 1.10-kg brick on the end of the spring and it stretches to 31.0 cm. (a) What is the spring constant of the spring? (b) Luke now pulls the brick 5.00 cm from the equilibrium position to watch it oscillate. What is the maximum speed of the brick? (c) When the displacement is 2.50 cm from the equilibrium position, what is the speed of the brick? (d) How long will it take for the brick to oscillate five times?

81. A 4.0-N body is suspended vertically from an ideal spring of spring constant 250 N/m. The spring is initially in its relaxed position. Write an equation to describe the motion of the body if it is released at $t = 0$. [*Hint:* Let $y = 0$ at the equilibrium point and take $+y =$ up.]

82. Show, using dimensional analysis, that the frequency f at which a mass-spring system oscillates radical is independent of the amplitude A and proportional to $\sqrt{k/m}$. [*Hint:* Start by assuming that f does depend on A (to some power).]

83. A horizontal spring with spring constant of 9.82 N/m is attached to a block with a mass of 1.24 kg that sits on a frictionless surface. When the block is 0.345 m from its equilibrium position, it has a speed of 0.543 m/s. (a) What is the maximum displacement of the block from the equilibrium position? (b) What is the maximum speed of the block? (c) When the block is 0.200 m from the equilibrium position, what is its speed?

84. A steel piano wire ($Y = 2.0 \times 10^{11}$ Pa) has a diameter of 0.80 mm. At one end it is wrapped around a tuning pin of diameter 8.0 mm. The length of the wire (not including the wire wrapped around the tuning pin) is 66 cm. Initially, the tension in the wire is 381 N. To tune the wire, the tension must be increased to 402 N. Through what angle must the tuning pin be turned?

85. When the tension is 402 N, what is the tensile stress in the piano wire in Problem 84? How does that compare to the elastic limit of steel piano wire (8.26×10^8 Pa)?

86. A tightrope walker who weighs 640 N walks along a steel cable. When he is halfway across, the cable makes an angle of 0.040 rad below the horizontal. (a) What is the strain in the cable? Assume the cable is horizontal with a tension of 80 N before he steps onto it. Ignore the weight of the cable itself. (b) What is the tension in the cable when the tightrope walker is standing at the midpoint? (c) What is the cross-sectional area of the cable? (d) Has the cable been stretched beyond its elastic limit (2.5×10^8 Pa)?

Problem 86 (the 0.040-rad angles are greatly exaggerated).

87. A gibbon, hanging onto a horizontal tree branch with one arm, swings with a small amplitude. The gibbon's CM is 0.40 m from the branch and its rotational inertia divided by its mass is $I/m = 0.25$ m². Estimate the frequency of oscillation.

88. In Problem 8.41, we found that the force of the tibia (shinbone) on the ankle joint for a person (of weight 750 N) standing on the ball of one foot was 2800 N. The ankle joint therefore pushes upward on the bottom of the tibia with a force of 2800 N, while the top end of the tibia must feel a net downward force of approximately 2800 N (ignoring the weight of the tibia itself). The tibia has a length of 0.40 m, an average inner diameter of 1.3 cm, and an average outer diameter of 2.5 cm. (The central core of the bone contains marrow that has negligible compressive strength.) (a) Find the average cross-sectional area of the tibia. (b) Find the compressive stress in the tibia. (c) Find the change in length for the tibia due to the compressive forces.

89. The maximum height of a cylindrical column is limited by the compressive strength of the material; if the compressive stress at the bottom were to exceed the compressive strength of the material, the column would be crushed under its own weight. (a) For a cylindrical column of height h and radius r, made of material of density ρ, calculate the compressive stress at the bottom of the column. (b) Since the answer to part (a) is independent of the radius r, there is an absolute limit to the height of a cylindrical column, regardless of how wide it is. For marble, which has a density of 2.7×10^3 kg/m³ and a compressive strength of 2.0×10^8 Pa, find the maximum height of a cylindrical column. (c) Is this limit a practical concern in the construction of marble columns? Might it limit the height of a beanstalk?

90. A bungee jumper leaps from a bridge and undergoes a series of oscillations. Assume $g = 9.78$ m/s². (a) If a 60.0-kg jumper uses a bungee cord that has an unstretched length of 33.0 m and she jumps from a height of 50.0 m above a river, coming to rest just a few centimeters above the water surface on the first downward descent, what is the period of the oscillations? Assume the bungee cord follows Hooke's law. (b) The next jumper in line has a mass of 80.0 kg. Should he jump using the same cord? Explain.

91. Spider silk has a Young's modulus of 4.0×10^9 N/m^2 and can withstand stresses up to 1.4×10^9 N/m^2. A single web strand has a cross-sectional area of 1.0×10^{-11} m^2, and a web is made up of 50 radial strands. A bug lands in the center of a horizontal web so that the web stretches downward. (a) If the maximum stress is exerted on each strand, what angle θ does the web make with the horizontal? (b) What does the mass of a bug have to be in order to exert this maximum stress on the web? (c) If the web is 0.10 m in radius, how far down does the web extend?

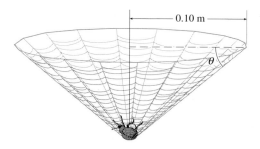

0.10 m

θ

92. What is the period of a pendulum formed by placing a horizontal axis (a) through the end of a meterstick (100-cm mark)? (b) through the 75-cm mark? (c) through the 60-cm mark?

93. The motion of a simple pendulum is approximately SHM only if the amplitude is small. Consider a simple pendulum that is released from a horizontal position ($\theta_i = 90°$ in Fig. 10.22). (a) Using conservation of energy, find the speed of the pendulum bob at the bottom of its swing. Express your answer in terms of the mass m and the length L of the pendulum. Do *not* assume SHM. (b) Assuming (incorrectly, for such a large amplitude) that the motion *is* SHM, determine the maximum speed of the pendulum. Based on your answers, is the period of a pendulum for large amplitudes larger or smaller than that given by Eq. (10-26b)?

94. The gravitational potential energy of a pendulum is $U = mgy$. (a) Taking $y = 0$ at the lowest point, show that $y = L(1 - \cos \theta)$, where θ is the angle the string makes with the vertical. (b) If θ is small, $(1 - \cos \theta) \approx \frac{1}{2}\theta^2$ and $\theta \approx x/L$ (Appendix A.7). Show that the potential energy can be written $U \approx \frac{1}{2}kx^2$ and find the value of k (the equivalent of the spring constant for the pendulum).

95. A pendulum is made from a uniform rod of mass m_1 and a small block of mass m_2 attached at the lower end. (a) If the length of the pendulum is L and the oscillations are small, find the period of the oscillations in terms of m_1, m_2, L, and g. (b) Check your answer to part (a) in the two special cases $m_1 \gg m_2$ and $m_1 \ll m_2$.

96. Resilin is a rubber-like protein that helps insects to fly more efficiently. The resilin, attached from the wing to the body, is relaxed when the wing is down and is extended when the wing is up. As the wing is brought up, some elastic energy is stored in the resilin. The wing is then brought back down with little muscular energy, since the

potential energy in the resilin is converted back into kinetic energy. Resilin has a Young's modulus of 1.7×10^6 N/m^2. (a) If an insect wing has resilin with a relaxed length of 1.0 cm and with a cross-sectional area of 1.0 mm^2, how much force must the wings exert to extend the resilin to 4.0 cm? (b) How much energy is stored in the resilin?

Answers to Practice Problems

10.1 $2k$ (When the original spring is stretched an amount L, each of the half-springs stretches only $\frac{1}{2}L$. Each of the newly formed springs stretches half as far as the original spring for a given applied force.)

10.2 1.4×10^{-5}

10.3 0.18 mm

10.4 1.3×10^8 Pa

10.5 $-\dfrac{\Delta P}{B} = -\dfrac{1.0 \times 10^7 \text{ Pa}}{2.3 \times 10^9 \text{ Pa}} = -0.0043 = \dfrac{\Delta V}{V}$

and $\Delta V = -0.43\% \times V$

10.6 110 m/s^2 at $x = \pm A$

10.7 $K = 0$, $U_e = 2(mg)^2/k$, $U_g = -(mg)^2/k$, $E = (mg)^2/k$

10.8

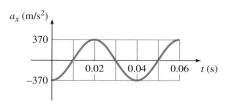

$a_x(t) = -a_m \cos \omega t$, where $\omega = 160$ rad/s and $a_m = 370$ m/s^2.

10.9 1.6 m/s^2 (about 1/6 that of the Earth)

10.10 0.82 m/s or 1.8 mi/h

Answers to Checkpoints

10.2 The two wires are under the same stress (same tensile force and same cross-sectional area). Young's modulus for steel is about $\frac{5}{3}$ times that for copper, so the *strain* for the steel wire is $\frac{3}{5}$ the strain of the copper wire. However, the strain is the *fractional* length change. The steel wire is twice as long, so its length change is $2 \times (3/5)$ times the length change of the copper wire. The steel wire stretches more.

10.5 When the kinetic and potential energies are equal, each is half of the total energy. When $U = \frac{1}{2}kx^2 = \frac{1}{2}E_{\text{total}} = \frac{1}{2}(\frac{1}{2}kA^2)$, $x = \pm A/\sqrt{2}$.

10.7 (a) When the displacement is zero, the potential energy has its minimum value. From conservation of energy, the kinetic energy then has its maximum value. Therefore, the speed has its maximum magnitude ($v = \pm v_m$), as shown in Fig. 10.20. (b) When the speed is zero, the kinetic energy is minimum and the potential energy is maximum. Therefore, the displacement has its maximum magnitude ($x = \pm A$).

Waves

On January 17, 1995, a terrible earthquake struck the Hanshin region of Japan, killing over 6400 people and injuring about 40 000 others. Some 200 000 homes and buildings were damaged, causing the evacuation to shelters of 320 000 people. The heaviest damage occurred in the city of Kobe, including the buckling and collapse of an elevated highway. However, geologists found that the point of origin of the earthquake was 15–20 km below the northern tip of Awaji Island, about 20 km southwest of Kobe. How did the earthquake cause great devastation at locations many kilometers away? (See p. 393 for the answer.)

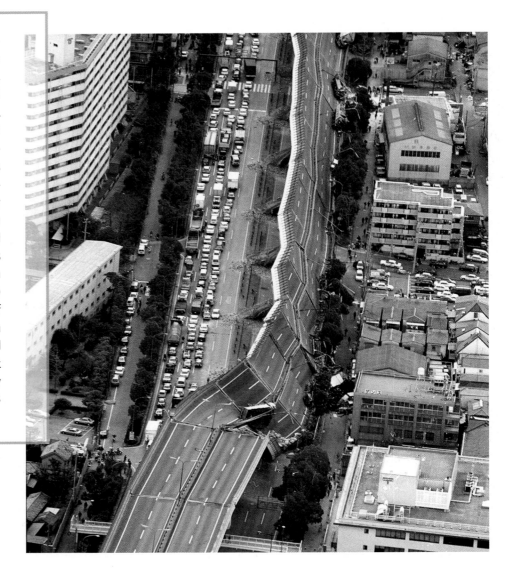

- period, frequency, angular frequency (Section 10.6)
- position, velocity, acceleration, and energy in simple harmonic motion (Section 10.5)
- resonance (Section 10.10)
- graphical analysis of SHM (Section 10.7)

Concepts & Skills to Review

11.1   WAVES AND ENERGY TRANSPORT

Basic Models: Particles and Waves   Physicists use only a few basic models to describe the physical world. One such model is the particle: a pointlike object with no inner structure and with certain characteristics such as mass and electric charge. Another basic model is the **wave**. Water waves are familiar examples. When a pebble is dropped into a pond, it disturbs the surface of the water. Ripples on the surface of the pond travel away from the spot where the pebble landed.

Examples of Waves   Any wave is characterized as some sort of "disturbance" that travels away from its source. In Chapters 11 and 12, we concentrate on mechanical waves traveling through a material medium, such as water waves, sound waves, and the seismic waves caused by earthquakes. Particles in the medium are disturbed from their equilibrium positions as the wave passes, returning to their equilibrium positions after the wave has passed. In Chapter 22, we discuss electromagnetic waves such as radio waves and light waves, in which the disturbance consists of oscillating electromagnetic fields. Two of our five human senses are wave detectors: the ear is sensitive to the tiny fluctuations in air pressure caused by compressional waves in air (sound) and the eye is sensitive to electromagnetic waves in a certain frequency range (light).

Energy Transport by a Wave

Suppose we drop a pebble into a still pond. The kinetic energy of the pebble just before it hits the pond is partly converted into the energy carried off by the water wave. That waves carry energy is clear to anyone who has been surfing or swimming in the ocean. Speaking of surfing, information on the Internet is carried by waves of various sorts: electrical waves in wires, microwaves between Earth and communications satellites, light waves in optical fibers. Microwaves in ovens carry energy from their source to the food; the electromagnetic energy of the microwaves is absorbed by water molecules in the food and appears as thermal energy. Electromagnetic waves from the Sun bring the energy that fuels the growth of green plants. Seismic waves carry energy released by an earthquake to other parts of the Earth, sometimes with devastating results.

Seismic waves travel away from the *focus* of an earthquake (the point of origin) both through the Earth (*body waves*) and along the Earth's crust (*surface waves*), transporting vibrations and energy. However, the material through which the waves travel is *not* transported. Most earthquake damage is caused by seismic waves rather than caused by fault movement. In the Hanshin earthquake, damage to buildings was caused by seismic waves at distances over 100 km from the *epicenter* (the point on the surface directly above the focus), but the motion of the vibrating particles in the ground never moved more than about 1.5 m.

The sound of thunder travels for miles in all directions, but none of the air molecules zapped by lightning travels more than a meter or so during the few seconds that it takes the sound to reach our ears. A wave can transmit energy from one point to another without transporting any matter between the two points (Fig. 11.1).

CONNECTION:

In wave motion, energy is transferred from one oscillating particle to another. Energy is conserved overall, but the energy of any one oscillating particle can change. Mechanical waves carry the same kinds of energy as a simple harmonic oscillator: kinetic energy and potential energy.

How can an earthquake cause damage far from the epicenter?

(a)   (b)

Figure 11.1 Two different ways to transfer energy. (a) When a baseball pitcher throws a ball to the catcher, the ball carries energy with it. The pitcher gives the ball kinetic energy; the catcher receives the energy when the ball hits his hand and his hand recoils. (b) Suppose instead that they hold a rope stretched between them. If the pitcher suddenly moves his hand up and down quickly, a wave pulse travels along the rope until it reaches the catcher's hand. Once again, the pitcher sends the energy and the catcher receives it when the rope makes his hand recoil. However, in this case the pitcher is still holding his end of the rope; it never leaves his hand. Energy is transferred *without any matter moving from the pitcher to the catcher.*

> **PHYSICS AT HOME**
>
> Stretch a heavy rope between yourself and a friend and test out the transfer of energy from one to the other by sending wave pulses down the rope. Can you feel the energy transfer when the pulse arrives?

> **PHYSICS AT HOME**
>
> Observe carefully what happens when you snap your fingers. You start by pressing your thumb against your fingers and then sideways, the thumb in one direction and the fingers in the opposite direction. Initially friction keeps them from moving sideways, but suddenly they slip, releasing the built-up energy.
>
> Similarly, the rocks on two sides of a fault line are pressed together and sideways. Friction keeps them from moving sideways as elastic (or strain) energy builds up. Then suddenly they slip, releasing a tremendous amount of energy largely in the form of seismic waves that carry vibrations far from the focus of the earthquake.

Intensity

For a wave that travels in a three-dimensional medium (such as sound waves or seismic waves traveling through the Earth), the **intensity** (symbol I, SI unit W/m^2) is a measure of the *average power per unit area* carried by the wave past a surface perpendicular to the wave's direction of propagation.

$$I = P/A$$

For example, if a sound wave's intensity is a fairly loud $I = 10^{-5}$ W/m^2 when it reaches the eardrum and the area of the eardrum is $A = 10^{-4}$ m^2, then the power delivered to the eardrum is $P = IA = 10^{-9}$ W (assuming that all the energy incident on the eardrum is absorbed). The energy absorbed by the eardrum at this rate in *one hour* would be

$$10^{-9} \text{ W} \times 3600 \text{ s} \approx 4 \text{ } \mu\text{J}$$

The human ear is a very sensitive detector indeed.

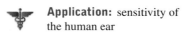 **Application:** sensitivity of the human ear

Intensity and Distance from the Wave Source   For most waves, the intensity decreases as the distance from the source increases. Some of the energy can be absorbed (dissipated) by the wave medium. The amount of energy absorbed depends on the

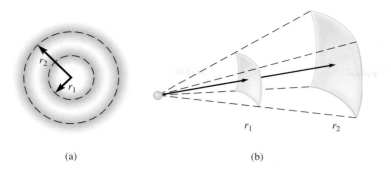

Figure 11.2 (a) A point source of sound radiating energy uniformly in all directions. (b) The intensity at a distance r_2 is smaller than the intensity at a distance r_1 since the same power is spread out over a greater area.

(a)   (b)

medium. Air absorbs relatively little sound energy, which is why we can hear sounds generated far away.

Another reason that intensity decreases with distance is that, as the wave spreads out, the energy gets spread over a larger and larger area. Consider a point source emitting a wave uniformly in all directions—an *isotropic* source (Fig. 11.2). The average power (energy per unit time) emitted is constant. Imagine a sphere surrounding the source; the rate at which energy passes through the surface of the sphere is the same no matter what the radius. The surface area of a sphere is $4\pi r^2$, so as the wave moves farther from the source, the energy spreads out over a larger and larger area. Thus, the power per unit area (intensity) decreases with distance. Assuming that no energy is absorbed by the medium and there are no obstacles to reflect or absorb sound,

$$I = \frac{\text{power}}{\text{area}} = \frac{P}{4\pi r^2} \qquad (11\text{-}1)$$

(point source emitting uniformly in all directions; no reflection or absorption)

Therefore, if energy absorption by the medium can be ignored, the intensity of the sound is inversely proportional to the square of the distance from the source. This "inverse square law" is the result of a conserved quantity (here, energy) radiating uniformly from a point source in three-dimensional space.

✓ CHECKPOINT 11.1

A siren in a fire tower 20 m high generates a sound wave with intensity 0.090 W/m^2 at a point on the ground below the tower. What is the intensity of the sound wave 2.0 km from the tower? Assume the siren is an isotropic source.

11.2 TRANSVERSE AND LONGITUDINAL WAVES

A Slinky toy can be used to demonstrate two different kinds of wave. In a **transverse** wave, the motion of particles in the medium is perpendicular to the direction of propagation of the wave. To send a transverse wave down a Slinky, wiggle the end of the Slinky back and forth in a direction perpendicular to the length of the Slinky (Fig. 11.3a). In a **longitudinal** wave, the motion of particles in the medium is along the same line as the direction of propagation of the wave. To send a longitudinal wave down the Slinky, jiggle the end in and out along its length to alternately stretch and compress the coils (Fig. 11.3b). A red dot painted on one coil of the Slinky helps illustrate the difference. In a transverse wave, the dot moves back and forth about a fixed position with its motion perpendicular to the direction of propagation of the wave; in a longitudinal wave, the

Direction of
hand motion

Direction of
hand motion

(a)

Compression   Compression

Rarefaction   Rarefaction   Rarefaction

(b)

Figure 11.3 (a) Transverse and (b) longitudinal waves on a Slinky.

dot also moves back and forth about a fixed position but along the direction of propagation of the wave. In both cases, the wave itself moves from one end of the Slinky to the other while the dot is moving about its fixed position.

PHYSICS AT HOME

Ask a friend to sit at a table and hold one end of a long, loose spring (or a Slinky). With the spring supported by the table surface, grasp the other end and stretch the spring. Figure out how to move your hand to send transverse and longitudinal waves down the spring.

The Slinky—or any long spring—is a better approximation to solid materials than the stretched rope. In solids both types of waves can exist; a transverse wave results from a shear disturbance and a longitudinal wave from a compressional disturbance. Therefore, seismic body waves can be either longitudinal or transverse (Fig. 11.4).

Fluids can be compressed, but, because they flow, they do not sustain shear stresses. Therefore, longitudinal waves travel through fluids but transverse waves do not. However, gravity or surface tension can provide the transverse restoring force that allows a transverse wave to travel *along the surface* of a liquid.

A sound wave is longitudinal; each small volume of air vibrates back and forth along the direction of travel of the wave. Molecules are compressed together in some places and more thinly spaced (*rarefied*) in others; the air has regions of higher and lower density called **compressions** and **rarefactions** (see Fig. 11.3b).

P waves

Motion of
rock particles

Direction of
wave propagation

(a)

S waves

Motion of
rock particles

Direction of
wave propagation

(b)

Surface waves

Motion of
rock particles

Direction of
wave propagation

(c)

Figure 11.4 Three types of seismic waves. (a) Longitudinal body waves (*P waves*) are the fastest seismic waves (typically 4–8 km/s). They are similar to sound waves in air: particles in the Earth's interior are pushed together and pulled apart in the same direction that the wave propagates. (b) Transverse body waves (*S waves*) travel more slowly—typically 2–5 km/s. In an S wave, particles in the Earth's interior vibrate at right angles to the direction that the wave travels. By measuring the time between the first arrivals of these two types of waves at different detection stations, geologists are able to determine the point of origin of the earthquake. (c) In a surface wave, the motion of the ground combines longitudinal and transverse components.

Waves That Combine Transverse and Longitudinal Motion

Not all seismic waves are purely transverse or purely longitudinal. In a surface wave, the ground near the surface rolls approximately in a circle. Thus, the motion of the ground has components both parallel and perpendicular to the direction of propagation. The transverse component can either be up and down (as shown in Fig. 11.4c) or side to side. The motion of the ground is greatest at the surface.

Ocean waves are similar to the surface seismic wave shown in Fig. 11.4c. Deep underwater, the wave is mostly longitudinal (Fig. 11.5); as the wave passes, water moves back and forth along the direction of propagation of the wave. Higher up, the wave has both transverse and longitudinal components; water moves in an oval as the wave passes. Water near the surface moves approximately in a circle. The air above the surface presents little resistance, so water swells upward more easily there and then is pulled back downward by gravity (or, for small amplitudes, by surface tension). When the wave gets close to shore, the crest often collapses or *breaks*; the motion of the water particles is then much more complex.

When a guitar string is plucked *gently*, the wave on the string is almost purely transverse; stretching of the string is negligible. When it is plucked more forcefully, the resulting wave is a combination of transverse and longitudinal waves. At any instant, the string is stretched more in some places than in others; a point on the string has longitudinal motion as well as transverse motion.

Direction of
wave propagation

Figure 11.5 The motion of water in an ocean wave combines transverse and longitudinal motion.

11.3   SPEED OF TRANSVERSE WAVES ON A STRING

The speed of a mechanical wave depends on properties of the wave medium. What properties of a string determine the speed of a transverse wave moving along it? Suppose that a string of length L and mass m is under tension F. In Problem 56, you can show that $\sqrt{FL/m}$ is the only combination of those three quantities with the correct units for speed. There could be a dimensionless constant multiplier, but a derivation using more advanced mathematics shows that the constant is 1; the speed of a transverse wave on a string is

$$v = \sqrt{\frac{FL}{m}} \qquad (11\text{-}2)$$

We can rewrite Eq. (11-2) in another form. Length and mass are not independent; for a given string composition and diameter (say, a yellow brass string of 0.030 in. diameter), the mass of the string is proportional to its length. By defining the **linear mass density** (mass per unit length) of the string to be

$$\mu = \frac{m}{L} \qquad (11\text{-}3)$$

the speed of a transverse wave on a string can be written

$$v = \sqrt{\frac{F}{\mu}} \qquad (11\text{-}4)$$

An advantage of Eq. (11-4) over Eq. (11-2) is that it shows clearly that the wave speed depends on *local* properties of the medium; it does not depend on how much of the medium there is. The wave speed in the vicinity of some point P, for instance, does not depend on how long the string is; only properties of the string in the immediate vicinity of point P can determine how fast the wave travels past that point.

Note that as tension increases, wave speed increases; as mass density increases, wave speed decreases. A somewhat more general way to think about it, applicable to other waves as well, is:

> More restoring force makes faster waves; more inertia makes slower waves.

The wave speed is not the same as the speed of a particle in the wave medium.

The speed at which a wave propagates is not the same as the speed at which a particle in the medium moves. Suppose a horizontal string is stretched along the x-axis and a transverse pulse in the y-direction is sent down the string. The speed of propagation of the wave v is the speed at which the *pattern* or disturbance moves along the string (in the x-direction); for a uniform string, the wave speed is constant. A point on the string vibrates up and down in the $\pm y$-direction with a *different* speed that is *not* constant.

Example 11.1

A Piñata

A string of length 2.0 m has a mass of 125 mg. The string is attached to the ceiling and a piñata of mass 4.0 kg hangs from the other end. A child whacks the piñata sideways with a stick; as a result, a transverse pulse travels up the string toward the ceiling. At what speed does the pulse travel?

4.0 kg

Strategy   We start with a diagram of the situation (see the figure). The piñata puts the string under tension. The tension in the string is equal to the weight of the piñata because the weight of the string itself is negligible in comparison. The mass and length of the string are given, so the linear mass density can be found. Then we can find the wave speed.

Solution   The speed of a transverse wave on a string is given by Eq. (11-4):

$$v = \sqrt{\frac{F}{\mu}}$$

where F is the tension in the string and μ is the linear mass density of the string. The tension is equal to the weight hanging on the string:

$$F = Mg$$

The linear mass density of the string is mass per unit length ($\mu = m/L$). Substituting the tension and mass density, we have

$$v = \sqrt{\frac{F}{m/L}} = \sqrt{\frac{(Mg)L}{m}}$$

$$= \sqrt{\frac{4.0 \text{ kg} \times 9.8 \text{ m/s}^2 \times 2.0 \text{ m}}{125 \times 10^{-6} \text{ kg}}} = 790 \text{ m/s}$$

Discussion   The *weight* of the string (mg) is negligible in comparison with the weight hanging from the end of the string (Mg). That is not always the case, as can be seen in Practice Problem 11.1.

Practice Problem 11.1   Initial Velocity of Another Wave Pulse Traveling on a String

A string of length 10.0 m has a linear mass density of 25 g/m. The string is fixed at the top and has an object of mass 0.200 kg hanging from the bottom. (a) What is the *initial* wave speed of a pulse sent up the string from the bottom? (b) What is the speed of the pulse as it approaches the top of the string? [*Hint:* Does the weight of the string itself affect the tension in either case?]

11.4   PERIODIC WAVES

Application of periodic waves: the difference between musical sound and noise

A **periodic** wave repeats the same pattern over and over, each repeating section transporting the energy that was used to generate it. A periodic water wave can be produced by steadily dropping a series of pebbles into the water; a periodic wave on a cord can be produced by taking one end of the cord and moving it up and down, over and over, in a repeating pattern. As the wave propagates along the cord, every point on the cord oscillates with the same up and down pattern, though with a time delay that depends on the wave speed. Whereas musical sounds are often periodic waves, noise is *aperiodic*.

(a)   (b)

Figure 11.6 (a) Periodic sound wave pattern produced by singing the vowel "ah." (b) Aperiodic sound wave pattern produced by hissing the consonant "s." (The microphone generates an electrical signal proportional to the pressure variations of the sound wave. This signal is displayed as a function of time on the screen.)

The human voice makes a periodic sound wave when a vowel is sung at a steady pitch (constant frequency); most of the consonant sounds are aperiodic (Fig. 11.6).

Period, Frequency, Wavelength, and Amplitude   At any given point in space, a periodic wave repeats itself after a time T called the **period**. The inverse of the period is the **frequency** f.

$$f = \frac{1}{T} \quad \text{(SI unit Hz = s}^{-1}\text{)} \tag{5-8}$$

The frequency tells how often the pattern of motion repeats itself at any single point. For instance, if the frequency is 20 Hz, then there are 20 repetitions, or cycles, per second. Each cycle takes a time $T = 1/f = 0.05$ s. The angular frequency is $\omega = 2\pi f$ and is measured in rad/s.

During one period T, a periodic wave traveling at speed v moves a distance vT. In Fig. 11.7, note that, at any instant, points separated by a distance vT along the direction of propagation of a wave move "in sync" with each other. Thus, vT is the *repetition distance* of the wave, just as the period is the *repetition time*. This distance is called the **wavelength** (symbol λ, the Greek letter lambda).

$$\lambda = vT \tag{11-5}$$

Combining this relation and the expression for frequency, we obtain

$$v = \frac{\lambda}{T} = f\lambda \tag{11-6}$$

Equations (11-5) and (11-6) are true for all periodic waves, no matter how the wave is produced or what the shape of the wave.

> ## ✓ CHECKPOINT 11.4
>
> A seismic wave travels at 4.0 km/s and has a wavelength of 20 km. How long does it take a rock particle to complete one cycle of oscillation?

The maximum displacement of any particle from its equilibrium position is the **amplitude** A of the wave. For a sinusoidal wave traveling along a stretched string in the x-direction, the amplitude A is the maximum displacement of a particle in the positive or negative y-direction. For surface water waves, the amplitude is the height of a crest (a high point) above or the depth of a trough (a low point) below the undisturbed water level.

Harmonic Waves   **Harmonic waves** are a special kind of periodic wave in which the disturbance is sinusoidal (either a sine or cosine function). In a harmonic transverse wave on a string, for instance, every point on the string moves in SHM with the same amplitude and angular frequency, although different points reach their maximum displacements at different times. The maximum speed and maximum

CONNECTION:

The terminology for periodic waves is similar to that used for uniform circular motion (Chapter 5) and for simple harmonic motion (Chapter 10).

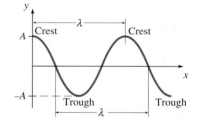

Figure 11.7 Snapshot graph of a sinusoidal wave moving with speed v in the x-direction. The graph shows the displacement y of particles in the wave medium as a function of x, their position along the direction of wave propagation, at one particular time t. The amplitude A and the wavelength λ are shown.

acceleration of a point on the string depend on both the angular frequency and the amplitude of the wave:

$$v_m = \omega A \tag{10-21}$$

$$a_m = \omega^2 A \tag{10-22}$$

Intensity and Amplitude   Since the total energy of an object moving in SHM is proportional to the amplitude squared (Section 10.5), the total energy of a harmonic wave is proportional to the square of its amplitude. Intensity is the rate at which a wave transports energy per unit area perpendicular to the direction of propagation. The intensity of a harmonic wave is proportional to its total energy and, therefore, is proportional to the square of the amplitude. That turns out to be a general result not limited to harmonic waves:

> The intensity of a wave is proportional to the square of its amplitude.

11.5   MATHEMATICAL DESCRIPTION OF A WAVE

A wave is represented mathematically by a variation in some quantity (such as pressure or displacement) that is described as a function of both position and time. For a transverse wave on a guitar string, the function specifies the displacement of each point on the string from its equilibrium position. If the string is oriented along the x-axis and the displacement of any point on the string is in the $\pm y$-direction, then the wave is described by a function of two variables: $y(x, t)$.

Traveling Waves   Consider a long stretched string along the x-axis. One end of the string (at $x = 0$) is moved by an external agent according to some function $y = h(t)$; as a result, a transverse wave is produced that travels in the $+x$-direction with wave speed v. If the wave retains the same shape as it moves down the string, then the motion of any point x on the string copies the motion of the left end after a time delay x/v (the time it takes the wave to travel a distance x at speed v—see Fig. 11.8). Thus, $y(x, t) = h(t - x/v)$. Even though the function that describes the wave has two variables (x and t), these variables must occur in the particular combination $(t - x/v)$ in order to describe a wave that retains its form as it propagates in the $+x$-direction. For a wave moving in the $-x$-direction, the variables would occur in the combination $(t + x/v)$. A wave that retains its shape as it moves in a single direction is called a *traveling wave*.

Harmonic Traveling Waves   Suppose the motion of the left end of the string is described by $y = A \cos \omega t$. By substituting $(t - x/v)$ for t, we obtain the function that describes the motion of *any* point $x > 0$:

$$y(x, t) = A \cos \left[\omega(t - x/v) \right]$$

⚠ In Eq. (10-21), v_m is the maximum speed at which a point on the string moves in the $\pm y$-direction. v_m is not the same as v, the speed of wave propagation in the $\pm x$-direction (see Section 11.3).

✋ The notation $y(x, t)$ means that y is a *function* of x and t: the value of y depends on the values of x and t in such a way that only one value of y (the dependent variable) corresponds to a particular choice of x and t (the independent variables).

$+x$-direction: $y(x, t) = h(t - x/v)$
$-x$-direction: $y(x, t) = h(t + x/v)$
To understand the notation $h(t - x/v)$, imagine that you have a computer program that calculates the function $h(t)$: you type in the value of t and the program returns the corresponding value of h. To find $h(t - x/v)$, you calculate $t - x/v$ and type *that* value in as input to the same computer program.

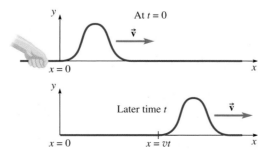

Figure 11.8 A wave pulse, with the same shape, at successive times. The motion of the point x repeats the motion of the point $x = 0$ with a time delay $\Delta t = x/v$.

To simplify the writing, we introduce a constant called the **wavenumber** (symbol k, SI unit rad/m):

$$k = \frac{\omega}{v} = \frac{2\pi f}{v} = \frac{2\pi}{\lambda} \qquad (11\text{-}7)$$

Then the equation for the harmonic wave can be written

$$y(x, t) = A \cos(\omega t - kx) \qquad (11\text{-}8)$$

The argument of the sine or cosine function, $(\omega t \pm kx)$, is called the **phase** of the wave at x and t. Phase is measured in units of angle (usually radians). The phase of a wave at a given point and instant of time tells us how far along that point is in the repeating pattern of its motion. Since a sine or cosine function repeats every 2π radians, the motions of two different points x_1 and x_2 that differ in phase by an integer times 2π are exactly the same; the points move "in sync" or *in phase* with each other. The distance between the two points is an integral number of wavelengths:

If

$$k(x_2 - x_1) = 2\pi n \quad \text{(where } n \text{ is any integer)}$$

then

$$x_2 - x_1 = \frac{2\pi n}{k} = \frac{2\pi n}{2\pi/\lambda} = n\lambda$$

> **CONNECTION:**
>
> Note the analogy between ω and k. $\omega = 2\pi/T$, where T is the repeat *time*; $k = 2\pi/\lambda$, where λ is the repeat *distance*. ω is measured in radians per *second*; k is measured in radians per *meter*. (tutorial: sine wave)

Example 11.2

A Traveling Wave on a String

A wave on a string is described by $y(x, t) = a \sin(bt + cx)$, where a, b, and c are positive constants. (a) Does this wave retain its shape as it travels? (b) In what direction does the wave travel? (c) What is the wave speed?

Strategy We try to manipulate the function to see if it can be written as a function of either $(t - x/v)$ or $(t + x/v)$ as in the general harmonic wave equation $y(x, t) = A \cos \omega(t - x/v)$. The wave speed v does not appear explicitly in the function as written, but it may be some combination of the other constants in the function.

Solution The coefficient of t in our equation should be the constant that represents ω. Factoring out that constant, we have

$$y(x, t) = a \sin b\left(t + \frac{cx}{b}\right) = a \sin b\left(t + \frac{x}{b/c}\right)$$

Now we see that $y(x, t)$ is a function of $t + x/v$, where $v = b/c$:

$$y(x, t) = a \sin b\left(t + \frac{x}{v}\right) \text{ where } v = \frac{b}{c}$$

Therefore: (a) yes, the wave retains its shape since it is a function of $(t + x/v)$; (b) it travels in the $-x$-direction since the t and x/v terms have the same sign; and (c) the wave speed is b/c.

Discussion Before being completely satisfied with this solution, it is a good idea to check that b/c has the right units for wave speed. The two terms bt and cx that are added together must have the same units. In SI, the argument of a sine function is measured in radians. Then b is measured in rad/s and c is measured in rad/m. Then the units of b/c are (rad/s)/(rad/m) = m/s, which is correct for wave speed.

Practice Problem 11.2 Another Traveling Wave on a String

A wave on a string is described by

$$y(x, t) = (0.0050 \text{ m}) \sin[(4.0 \text{ rad/s})t - (0.50 \text{ rad/m})x]$$

(a) Does this wave retain its shape as it travels? (b) In what direction does the wave travel? (c) What is the wave speed?

11.6 GRAPHING WAVES

To graph a one-dimensional wave $y(x, t)$, only one of the two independent variables (x, t) can be plotted. The other must be "frozen"; it is treated as a constant. If x is held constant, then one particular point (determined by the value of x) is singled out; the graph shows the motion of *that point* as a function of time (Fig. 11.9a). If instead t is held constant and y is plotted as a function of x, then the graph is like a snapshot—an instantaneous picture of what the wave looks like *at that particular instant* (Fig. 11.9b).

Figure 11.9 Two graphs of a harmonic wave on a string described by the equation $y(x, t) = A \sin(\omega t - kx)$. (a) The vertical displacement y of a particular point on the string ($x = 0$) as a function of time t. (b) The vertical displacement y as a function of horizontal position x at a single instant of time ($t = 0$).

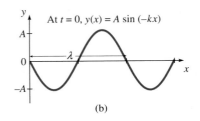

Example 11.3

A Transverse Harmonic Wave

A transverse harmonic wave travels in the $+x$-direction on a string at a speed of 5.0 m/s. Figure 11.10 shows a graph of $y(t)$ for the point $x = 0$. (a) What is the period of the wave? (b) What is the wavelength? (c) What is the amplitude? (d) Write the function $y(x, t)$ that describes the wave. (e) Sketch a graph of $y(x)$ at $t = 0$.

Strategy Since the graph uses time as the independent variable, the period can be read from the graph as the time for one cycle. The wavelength is the distance traveled by the wave during one period. The amplitude can be read from the graph as the maximum displacement. These are all the constants needed to write the function $y(x, t)$. We do have to think about the direction of travel and whether to write sine or cosine.

Solution (a) The period T is the time for one cycle. From the graph, $T = 2.0$ s.

(b) The wavelength λ is the distance traveled by the wave at speed $v = 5.0$ m/s during one period:

$$\lambda = vT = 5.0 \text{ m/s} \times 2.0 \text{ s} = 10 \text{ m}$$

(c) The amplitude A is the maximum displacement from equilibrium. From the graph, $A = 0.030$ m.

(d) Figure 11.10 is a sine function. The motion of the point $x = 0$ is

$$y(t) = A \sin\left(2\pi \frac{t}{T}\right)$$

Figure 11.10

Graph of a transverse harmonic wave.

Since the wave moves in the $+x$-direction, a point at $x > 0$ duplicates the motion of $x = 0$ with a time delay of $\Delta t = x/v$ (the time for the wave to travel a distance x). Then

$$y(x, t) = A \sin\left(2\pi \frac{t - x/v}{T}\right)$$

where $v = 5.0$ m/s and $T = 2.0$ s.

(e) Substituting $t = 0$,

$$y(x) = A \sin\left(-2\pi \frac{x}{vT}\right)$$

Substituting $vT = \lambda$ and using the identity $\sin(-\theta) = -\sin\theta$ (Appendix A.7), we have

$$y(x, t = 0) = -A \sin\left(2\pi \frac{x}{\lambda}\right)$$

A graph of this function is an inverted sine function with amplitude $A = 0.030$ m and wavelength

$$\lambda = vT = 5.0 \text{ m/s} \times 2.0 \text{ s} = 10 \text{ m}$$

Discussion Figure 11.10 shows that the point $x = 0$ is initially at $y = 0$ and then moves up (in the $+y$-direction) until it reaches the crest (maximum y) at $t = 0.50$ s. Imagine the graph in (e) to represent the first frame (at $t = 0$) of a movie of the wave. Since the wave moves to the right, the sinusoidal pattern shifts a little to the right in each successive frame. The point $x = 0$ moves up until it reaches the crest when the wave has traveled 2.5 m to the right. Since the wave speed is 5.0 m/s, the point $x = 0$ reaches the crest at $t = (2.5 \text{ m})/(5.0 \text{ m/s}) = 0.50$ s.

continued on next page

Example 11.3 continued

Practice Problem 11.3   Another Harmonic Transverse Wave

A wave is described by $y(x, t) = (1.2 \text{ cm}) \sin (10.0\pi t + 2.5\pi x)$, where x is in meters and t is in seconds. (a) Sketch a graph of $y(t)$ at $x = 0$. (b) Sketch a graph of $y(x)$ at $t = 0$. (c) What is the period of the wave? (d) What is the wavelength? (e) What is the amplitude? (f) What is the speed of the wave? (g) In what direction does the wave move?

11.7   PRINCIPLE OF SUPERPOSITION

Suppose two waves of the same type pass through the same region of space. Do the waves affect each other? If the amplitudes of the waves are large enough, then particles in the medium are displaced far enough from their equilibrium positions that Hooke's law (restoring force $\propto$ displacement) no longer holds; in that case, the waves *do* affect each other. However, for small amplitudes, the waves can pass through each other and emerge *unchanged*. More generally, when the amplitudes are not too large, the principle of superposition applies:

Principle of Superposition

When two or more waves overlap, the net disturbance at any point is the sum of the individual disturbances due to each wave.

Figure 11.11 illustrates the superposition principle for two wave pulses traveling toward one another on a string. The wave pulses pass right through one another without affecting one another; once they have separated, their shapes and heights are the same as before the overlap (Fig. 11.11a). The principle of superposition enables us to distinguish two voices speaking in the same room at the same time; the sound waves pass through each other unaffected.

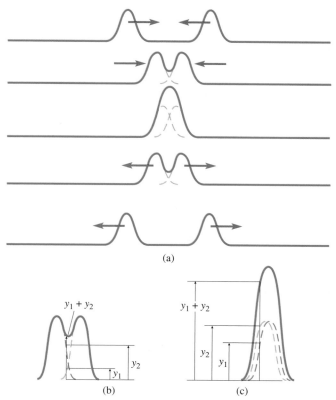

Figure 11.11 (a) Two identical wave pulses traveling toward and through each other. (b), (c) Applying the superposition principle at two different times; in each case, the dashed lines are the separate wave pulses and the solid line is the sum. If one of the pulses (acting alone) would produce a displacement y_1 at a certain point and the other would produce a displacement y_2 at the same point, the result when the two overlap is a displacement of $y_1 + y_2$.

Example 11.4

Superposition of Two Wave Pulses

Two identical wave pulses travel at 0.5 m/s toward each other on a long cord (Fig. 11.12). Sketch the shape of the cord at $t = 1.0$, 1.5, and 2.0 s.

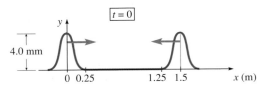

Figure 11.12

Two wave pulses at $t = 0$.

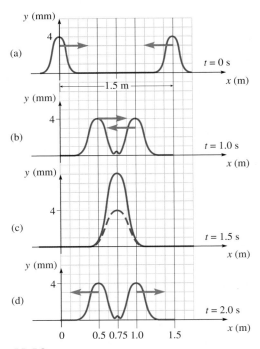

Figure 11.13

Wave positions at times $t = 0$, 1.0, 1.5, and 2.0 s.

Strategy We start by sketching the two pulses in their new positions at each time given. Wherever they overlap, we apply superposition by adding the individual displacements at each point to find the net displacement of the cord at that point.

Solution Using graph paper, we draw the wave pulses at $t = 0$ (Fig. 11.13a). At $t = 1.0$ s, each pulse has moved 0.5 m toward the other. The leading edges of the pulses are just starting to overlap (Fig. 11.13b). At $t = 1.5$ s, each pulse has moved another 0.25 m; the crests overlap exactly. By adding the displacements point by point, we see that the string has the shape of a single pulse twice as high as either of the individual pulses (Fig. 11.13c). At $t = 2.0$ s, the pulses have each moved another 0.25 m (Fig. 11.13d).

Discussion When the two pulses exactly overlap, the displacement of points on the string is larger than for corresponding points on a single pulse because we add displacements *in the same direction* ($y > 0$ for both). However, superposition does not *always* produce larger displacements (see Practice Problem 11.4).

Practice Problem 11.4   Superposition of Two Opposite Wave Pulses

Repeat Example 11.4, except now let the pulse on the right be inverted (Fig. 11.14). [*Hint:* Points on the string below the x-axis have negative displacements ($y < 0$).]

Figure 11.14

Wave pulses for Practice Problem 11.4.

11.8   REFLECTION AND REFRACTION

Reflection

At an abrupt boundary between one medium and another, **reflection** occurs; a reflected wave carrying some of the energy of the incident wave travels backward from the boundary. A sound wave in air, for instance, reflects when it reaches a wall.

A reflected wave can be inverted. Let's look at an extreme example: a string tied to a wall. If you send a wave pulse down the string, the reflected pulse is inverted (Fig. 11.15). By the principle of superposition, the shape of the string *at any point* is the sum of the incident and reflected waves, even at the fixed point at the end. The only way the end can stay in place is if the reflected wave is an upside down version of the incident wave. Another way to understand the inversion is by considering the force exerted on the string by the wall. When an upward pulse reaches the fixed end, the force exerted by the string on the wall has an upward component. By Newton's third law, the wall exerts a force on the string with a downward component. This downward force produces a downward reflected pulse.

Now, instead of tying the string to the wall, tie it to another string with an enormous linear mass density—so large that its motion is too small to measure. The original string doesn't know the difference; it just knows that one end is fixed in place. The second string with the huge density has a much slower wave speed than the first string. Now make the mass density of the second string not huge, but still greater than the first string. The greater inertia inhibits the motion of the boundary point and causes the reflected wave to be inverted. In general, when a transverse wave on a string reflects from a boundary with a region of slower wave speed, the reflected wave is inverted. On the other hand, when such a wave reflects from a boundary with a region of *faster* wave speed, the reflected wave is *not* inverted.

Change in Wavelength at a Boundary

When there is an abrupt change in wave medium, an incident wave splits up at the boundary; part is reflected and part is transmitted past the boundary into the other medium. The frequencies of both the reflected and transmitted waves are the same as the frequency of the incident wave. To understand why, think of a wave incident on the knot between two different strings. Both the reflected and the transmitted waves are generated by the up-and-down motion of the knot; the knot vibrates at the frequency dictated by the incident wave. However, if the wave speed changes at the boundary, *the wavelength of the transmitted wave is not the same* as the wavelength of the incident and reflected waves. Since $v = \lambda f$ and the frequencies are the same,

$$f = \frac{v_1}{\lambda_1} = \frac{v_2}{\lambda_2} \qquad (11\text{-}9)$$

Equation (11-9) applies to any kind of wave and is of particular importance in the study of optics.

Figure 11.15 Snapshots of the reflection of a wave pulse from a fixed end. The reflected pulse is upside down.

When a wave passes from one medium into another, the frequency of the transmitted wave is the same as that of the incident wave.

Example 11.5

Wavelength in Air and Under Water

A horn near the beach emits a 440-Hz sound wave. (a) What is the wavelength of the sound wave in air? The speed of sound in air is 340 m/s. (b) What is the wavelength of the sound wave in seawater? The speed of sound in seawater is 1520 m/s.

Strategy   The *frequency* of the sound wave in water is the same as in air. The wavelengths depend on both the frequency and the speed of sound in the medium. Sound travels faster in solids and liquids than in gases; during one period, the wave travels farther in water than it does in air, so the wavelength is longer in water.

Solution   (a) The wavelength in air is related to the speed of sound in air and the frequency:

$$\lambda_{\text{air}} = v_{\text{air}} T = \frac{v_{\text{air}}}{f}$$

Substituting numerical values,

$$\lambda_{\text{air}} = \frac{340 \text{ m/s}}{440 \text{ Hz}} = 0.77 \text{ m}$$

(b) The wave in the water has the *same frequency*, but the speed of sound is different:

$$\lambda_{\text{water}} = \frac{v_{\text{water}}}{f} = \frac{1520 \text{ m/s}}{440 \text{ Hz}} = 3.5 \text{ m}$$

Discussion   The wavelength in water is longer, as expected. As a quick check, the ratio of the wavelengths should be equal to the ratio of the wave speeds:

$$\frac{0.77 \text{ m}}{3.5 \text{ m}} = 0.22; \qquad \frac{340 \text{ m/s}}{1520 \text{ m/s}} = 0.22$$

continued on next page

Example 11.5 continued

Practice Problem 11.5   Working on the Railroad

A railroad worker, driving in spikes, misses the spike and hits the iron rail; a sound wave travels through the air and through the rail. (We ignore the *transverse* wave that also travels in the rail.) The wavelength of the sound in air is 0.548 m. The speed of sound in air is 340 m/s; the speed of sound in iron is 5300 m/s. (a) What is the frequency of the wave? (b) What is the wavelength of the sound wave in the rail?

Refraction

Application of refraction: why ocean waves approach shore nearly head-on

Figure 11.16 Wave crests for a seismic wave incident on a boundary between two different kinds of rock. Not only does the wavelength (distance between wave crests) change at the boundary, the wave also refracts (changes its direction of propagation). The reflected wave is omitted for clarity.

A transmitted wave not only has a different wavelength than the incident wave; it also travels in a different direction unless the incident wave's direction of propagation is along the *normal* (the direction perpendicular to the boundary). This change in propagation direction is called **refraction**. If the change in wave speed is gradual, then the change in direction is gradual as well. The speed of ocean waves depends on the depth of the water; the waves are slower in shallower water. As waves approach the shore, they gradually slow down; as a result, they gradually bend until they reach shore nearly head-on. A *sudden* change in wave speed, such as when a seismic wave is incident on a boundary between different kinds of rock, causes a sudden refraction (Fig. 11.16).

Application of Reflection and Refraction: Seismology   Understanding the propagation of seismic waves, including reflection and refraction due to boundaries between geological features, is an essential part of the effort to reduce damage from future earthquakes. Scientists create small seismic waves with a large vibrator, then use seismographs to record ground vibrations at various locations. The goal is to produce a seismic hazard map so that preventative measures can be targeted to areas with the highest risk of earthquake damage.

11.9   INTERFERENCE AND DIFFRACTION

Interference

The principle of superposition leads to dramatic effects when applied to coherent waves. Two waves are **coherent** if they have the *same frequency* and they maintain a *fixed phase relationship* with one another. One way to obtain coherent waves is to get them from the same source. Such is the case, for example, if one *monophonic* amplifier sends the same signal to two speakers. Should some fluctuation occur in the amplifier driving the speakers, the same fluctuation occurs in both speakers at the same time and they maintain their coherence. Waves are **incoherent** if the phase relationship between them varies randomly. (As defined here, *coherent* and *incoherent* are idealized extremes. In reality, two waves do not have to have either perfect correlation between their phases or no correlation at all.)

Suppose coherent waves with amplitudes A_1 and A_2 pass through the same point in space. If the waves are *in phase* at that point—that is, the phase difference is any *even* integral multiple of π rad—then the two waves consistently reach their maxima at exactly the same instants of time (Fig. 11.17a). The superposition of the waves that are in phase with one another is called **constructive interference**; the amplitude of the combined waves is the sum of the amplitudes of the two individual waves ($A_1 + A_2$).

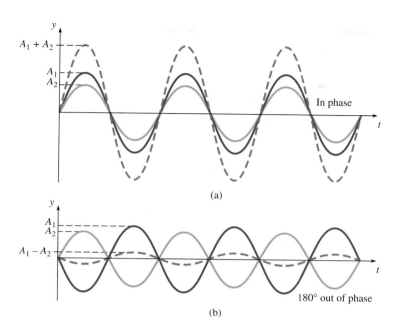

Figure 11.17 Coherent waves
(a) in phase and (b) 180° out of
phase. (One wave is drawn with
a lighter line to distinguish it
from the other.) The dashed
curve is the superposition of the
two waves.

Two waves that are *180° out of phase* at a given point have a phase difference of π rad, 3π rad, 5π rad, and so on. The waves are half a cycle apart; when one reaches its maximum, the other reaches its minimum (Fig. 11.17b). The superposition of waves that are 180° out of phase is called **destructive interference**—the amplitude of the combined waves is the *difference* of the amplitudes of the two individual waves ($|A_1 - A_2|$). For any other fixed phase relationship between the two waves, the superposition has an amplitude between $A_1 + A_2$ and $|A_1 - A_2|$.

Suppose two coherent waves start out in phase with one another. In Fig. 11.18, two rods vibrate up and down in step with one another to generate circular waves on the surface of the water. If the two waves travel the same distance to reach a point on the water surface, they arrive *in phase* and interfere constructively. At points where the distances are different, the phase difference is proportional to the path difference. One wavelength of path difference corresponds to a phase difference of 2π radians (one full cycle), so

Figure 11.18 Overhead snapshot of two coherent surface water waves. The two waves travel different distances d_1 and d_2 to reach a point P. The phase difference between the waves at point P is $k(d_1 - d_2)$.

$$\frac{d_1 - d_2}{\lambda} = \frac{\text{phase difference}}{2\pi \text{ rad}} \qquad \text{(11-10)}$$

Thus, the phase difference is

$$\text{phase difference} = \frac{2\pi \text{ rad}}{\lambda} \times (d_1 - d_2) = k(d_1 - d_2) \qquad \text{(11-11)}$$

If the path difference $d_1 - d_2$ is an integral number of wavelengths, then the phase difference is an even integral multiple of π rad and constructive interference occurs at point P. If the path difference is $\frac{1}{2}\lambda, \frac{3}{2}\lambda, \frac{5}{2}\lambda, \ldots$, then the phase difference is an odd integral multiple of π rad and destructive interference occurs at point P. If the phase difference is not an integral multiple of π, the amplitude has a value between the maximum and minimum possible values.

When two coherent waves are interfering and have a phase difference = $n\pi$, the interference is constructive for even n and the interference is destructive for odd n.

Intensity Effects for Interfering Waves

When coherent waves interfere, the *amplitudes* add (for constructive interference) or subtract (for destructive interference)—see Example 11.6. However, since intensity is proportional to amplitude *squared*, we cannot simply add or subtract the *intensities* of coherent waves when they interfere. *Incoherent* waves, on the other hand, have no fixed phase relationship; interference effects are averaged out due to the rapidly varying phase difference. In the superposition of incoherent waves, the total intensity is the sum of the individual intensities.

Why don't we see and hear interference effects all the time? Light from ordinary sources—incandescent bulbs, fluorescent bulbs, or the Sun—is incoherent because it is generated by large numbers of independent atomic sources. A single source of sound normally contains many different frequencies, so a point of constructive interference for one frequency is not a point of constructive interference for other frequencies. Furthermore, in most situations there are many different sound waves that reach our ears after traveling different paths due to the reflection of sound from walls, ceilings, chairs, and so forth.

Example 11.6

Intensity of Interfering Waves

Two coherent waves interfere. The intensity of one of them (alone) is 9.0 times the intensity of the other. What is the ratio of the maximum possible intensity to the minimum possible intensity of the resulting wave?

Strategy   The intensity is *not* the sum or difference of the individual intensities because the waves are coherent. Since the waves maintain a fixed phase relationship, the principle of superposition tells us that the maximum and minimum *amplitudes* of the interfering waves are the sum and difference of the *individual amplitudes*. Intensity is proportional to amplitude squared, so we find the ratio of the amplitudes and then add or subtract them.

Solution   The intensities of the two individual waves are related by $I_1 = 9.0 I_2$ or $I_1/I_2 = 9.0$. Since intensity is proportional to amplitude squared,

$$\frac{A_1}{A_2} = \sqrt{\frac{I_1}{I_2}} = 3.0$$

Thus, $A_1 = 3.0 A_2$. The maximum possible amplitude for the superposition occurs if the waves are in phase:

$$A_{max} = A_1 + A_2 = 4.0 A_2$$

The minimum possible amplitude for the superposition occurs if the waves are 180° out of phase:

$$A_{min} = |A_1 - A_2| = 2.0 A_2$$

The ratio of the maximum to minimum intensity is

$$\frac{I_{max}}{I_{min}} = \left(\frac{A_{max}}{A_{min}}\right)^2 = \left(\frac{4.0}{2.0}\right)^2 = 4.0$$

Discussion   Had we added and subtracted the *intensities* instead of the amplitudes, we would have found a ratio of $10/8 = 1.25$ between the maximum and minimum intensities. We must be careful to add or subtract the *amplitudes* of the interfering waves instead of the intensities themselves when the waves are coherent.

Practice Problem 11.6   Two More Coherent Waves

Repeat Example 11.6, but change the ratio of the individual intensities to 4.0 (instead of 9.0).

Diffraction

Diffraction is the spreading of a wave around an obstacle in its path (Fig. 11.19). The amount of diffraction depends on the relative size of the obstacle and the wavelength of the waves. Diffraction enables you to hear around a corner but not to see around a corner. Sound waves, with typical wavelengths in air of around 1 m, diffract around the corner much more than do light waves with much smaller wavelengths (less than 1 μm). We will study interference and diffraction of electromagnetic waves (including light) in detail in Chapter 25.

Figure 11.19 Water waves incident from the right on a gap in a breakwater (Three Fathoms Cove, Hong Kong). Notice the shape of the wave crests to the left of the gap.

11.10 STANDING WAVES

Standing waves occur when a wave is reflected at a boundary and the reflected wave interferes with the incident wave so that the wave appears not to propagate. Suppose that a harmonic wave on a string, coming from the right, hits a boundary where the string is fixed. The equation of the incident wave is

$$y(x, t) = A \sin (\omega t + kx)$$

The + sign is chosen in the phase because the wave travels to the left.

The reflected wave travels to the right, so $+kx$ is replaced with $-kx$; and the reflected wave is inverted, so $+A$ is replaced with $-A$. Then the reflected wave is described by

$$y(x, t) = -A \sin (\omega t - kx)$$

Applying the principle of superposition, the motion of the string is described by

$$y(x, t) = A \, [\sin (\omega t + kx) - \sin (\omega t - kx)]$$

This can be rewritten in a form that shows the motion of the string more clearly. Using the trigonometric identity (Appendix A.7),

$$\sin \alpha - \sin \beta = 2 \cos \left[\tfrac{1}{2}(\alpha + \beta)\right] \sin \left[\tfrac{1}{2}(\alpha - \beta)\right]$$

where

$$\alpha = \omega t + kx \quad \text{and} \quad \beta = \omega t - kx$$

we have

$$y(x, t) = 2A \cos \omega t \sin kx$$

Notice that t and x are separated. Every point moves in SHM with the same frequency. However, in contrast to a *traveling* harmonic wave, every point reaches its maximum distance from equilibrium *simultaneously*. In addition, different points move with different amplitudes; the amplitude at any point x is $2A \sin kx$.

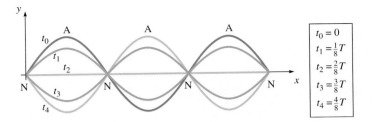

Figure 11.20 A standing wave at various times: $t = 0, \frac{1}{8}T,$ $\frac{2}{8}T, \frac{3}{8}T,$ and $\frac{4}{8}T$, where T is the period.

Node–node distance is $\frac{1}{2}\lambda$.
Node–antinode distance is $\frac{1}{4}\lambda$.

Figure 11.20 shows the string at time intervals of $\frac{1}{8}T$, where T is the period. What you actually see when looking at a standing wave is a blur of moving string, with points that never move (**nodes**, labeled "N") halfway between points of maximum amplitude (**antinodes**, labeled "A"). The nodes are the points where $\sin kx = 0$. Since $\sin n\pi = 0$ ($n = 0, 1, 2, \ldots$), the nodes are located at $x = n\pi/k = n\lambda/2$. Thus, the distance between two adjacent nodes is $\frac{1}{2}\lambda$. The antinodes occur where $\sin kx = \pm 1$, which is exactly halfway between a pair of nodes. So the nodes and antinodes alternate, with one quarter of a wavelength between a node and the neighboring antinode.

So far we have ignored what happens at the other end of the string. If the other end is fixed, then it is a node. The string thus has two or more nodes, with one at each end. The distance between each pair of nodes is $\frac{1}{2}\lambda$, so

$$n(\lambda/2) = L \qquad\qquad \text{(11-12a)}$$

where L is the length of the string and $n = 1, 2, 3, \ldots$. The possible wavelengths for standing waves on a string are

There is no need to memorize Eqs. (11-12) and (11-13). Start with a sketch like Fig. 11.21, find the wavelengths, and then use $v = f\lambda$ to find the frequencies.

$$\lambda_n = \frac{2L}{n} \quad (n = 1, 2, 3, \ldots) \qquad\qquad \text{(11-12b)}$$

The frequencies are

$$f_n = \frac{v}{\lambda_n} = \frac{nv}{2L} \quad (n = 1, 2, 3, \ldots) \qquad\qquad \text{(11-13)}$$

The lowest frequency standing wave ($n = 1$) is called the **fundamental**. Notice that the higher frequency standing waves are all integral multiples of the fundamental; the set of standing wave frequencies makes an evenly spaced set:

$$f_1, 2f_1, 3f_1, 4f_1, \ldots, nf_1, \ldots$$

These frequencies are called the *natural frequencies* or *resonant frequencies* of the string. *Resonance* occurs when a system is driven at one of its natural frequencies; the resulting vibrations are large in amplitude compared to when the driving frequency is not close to any of the natural frequencies.

CONNECTION:

An ideal mass-spring system has a single resonant frequency (Section 10.10), but extended objects generally have many different resonant frequencies.

 CHECKPOINT 11.10

A standing wave on a string 1.0 m long has four nodes, not including the nodes at the two fixed ends. What is the wavelength?

Figure 11.21 shows the first four standing wave patterns on a string. The two ends are always nodes since they are fixed in place. Notice that each successive pattern has one more node and one more antinode than the previous one. The fundamental has the fewest possible number of nodes (2) and antinodes (1).

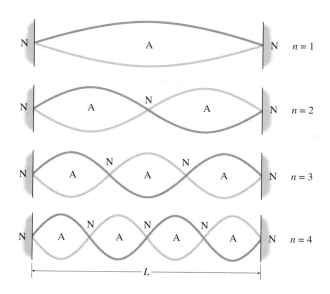

Figure 11.21 Four standing wave patterns for a string fixed at both ends. "N" marks the locations of the nodes and "A" marks the locations of the antinodes. In each case, the node-to-node distance is $\frac{1}{2}\lambda$ and n such "loops" fit into the length L of the string, so $n(\lambda/2) = L$.

Example 11.7

Wavelength of a Standing Wave

A string is attached to a vibrator driven at 1.20×10^2 Hz. A weight hangs from the other end of the string; the weight is adjusted until a standing wave is formed (Fig. 11.22). What is the wavelength of the standing wave on the string?

Strategy The measured distance of 42 cm encompasses six "loops"—that is, six segments of string between one node and the next. Each of the loops represents a length of $\frac{1}{2}\lambda$.

Solution The length of one loop is

$$42 \text{ cm} \times \tfrac{1}{6} = 7.0 \text{ cm}$$

Since the length of one loop is $\frac{1}{2}\lambda$, the wavelength is 14 cm.

Discussion This string is *not* fixed at both ends. The left end is connected to a moving vibrator, so it is not a node. The right end wraps around a pulley; it may not be easy to determine precisely where the "end" is. For this case, it is

Figure 11.22

Measuring distance between nodes for a standing wave.

more accurate to measure the distance between two actual nodes rather than to assume that the ends are nodes.

Practice Problem 11.7   Standing Wave with Seven Loops

The vibrator frequency is increased until there are seven loops within the 42-cm length. What is the new standing wave frequency for this string (assuming the same tension)?

Resonance is responsible for much of the structural damage caused by seismic waves. If the frequency at which the ground vibrates is close to a resonant frequency of a structure, the vibration of the structure builds up to a large amplitude. Thus, to construct a building that can survive an earthquake, it is not enough to make it stronger. Either the building must be designed so it is isolated from ground vibrations, or a damping mechanism—something like a shock absorber—must be incorporated to dissipate energy and reduce the amplitude of the vibrations. Damping is b ecoming increasingly common in large buildings since it is just as effective and much less expensive than isolation.

Large sections of the Hanshin expressway vibrated in a twisting motion due to ground vibrations near a resonant frequency. The road now has rubber base isolators instead of steel bearings connecting the roadway to the concrete piers. Part of their function is to act like shock absorbers.

Application of resonance: damage caused by earthquakes

Master the Concepts

- An isotropic source radiates sound uniformly in all directions. Assuming that no energy is absorbed by the medium and there are no obstacles to reflect or absorb sound, the intensity I at a distance r from an isotropic source is

$$I = \frac{\text{power}}{\text{area}} = \frac{P}{4\pi r^2} \qquad \text{(11-1)}$$

- In a transverse wave, the motion of particles in the medium is perpendicular to the direction of propagation of the wave. In a longitudinal wave, the motion of particles in the medium is along the same line as the direction of propagation of the wave.

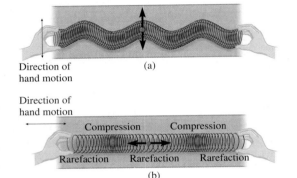

Direction of hand motion   (a)

Direction of hand motion

(b)

- The speed of a mechanical wave depends on properties of the wave medium. More restoring force makes faster waves; more inertia makes slower waves.
- The speed of a transverse wave on a string is

$$v = \sqrt{\frac{F}{\mu}} \qquad \text{(11-4)}$$

where

$$\mu = m/L \qquad \text{(11-3)}$$

- A periodic wave repeats the same pattern over and over. Harmonic waves are a special kind of periodic wave characterized by a sinusoidal function (either a sine or cosine function).
- If a periodic wave has period T and travels at speed v, the repetition distance of the wave is the wavelength:

$$\lambda = vT \qquad \text{(11-5)}$$

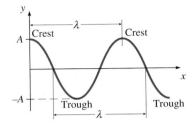

- The principle of superposition: When two or more waves overlap, the net disturbance at any point is the sum of the individual disturbances due to each wave.
- A harmonic traveling wave can be described by

$$y(x, t) = A \cos (\omega t - kx) \qquad \text{(11-8)}$$

The argument of the sinusoidal function, $(\omega t \pm kx)$, is called the phase of the wave at x and t. The constant k is the wave number

$$k = \frac{\omega}{v} = \frac{2\pi f}{v} = \frac{2\pi}{\lambda} \qquad \text{(11-7)}$$

- Reflection occurs at a boundary between different wave media. Some energy may be transmitted into the new medium and the rest is reflected. The wave transmitted past the boundary is refracted (propagates in a different direction).
- Coherent waves have the *same frequency* and maintain a *fixed phase relationship* with one another. Coherent waves that are in phase with one another interfere constructively; those that are 180° out of phase interfere destructively.
- Diffraction occurs when a wave bends around an obstacle in its path.
- In a standing wave on a string, every point moves in SHM with the same frequency. Nodes are points of zero amplitude; antinodes are points of maximum amplitude. The distance between two adjacent nodes is $\frac{1}{2}\lambda$.

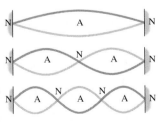

Conceptual Questions

1. The piano strings that vibrate with the lowest frequencies consist of a steel wire around which a thick coil of copper wire is wrapped. Only the inner steel wire is under tension. What is the purpose of the copper coil?

2. Is the vibration of a string in a piano, guitar, or violin a *sound* wave? Explain.

3. The wavelength of the fundamental standing wave on a cello string depends on which of these quantities: length of the string, mass per unit length of the string, or tension? The wavelength of the *sound wave* resulting from the string's vibration depends on which of the same three quantities?

4. If the length of a guitar string is decreased while the tension remains constant, what happens to each of these

quantities? (a) the wavelength of the fundamental, (b) the frequency of the fundamental, (c) the time for a pulse to travel the length of the string, (d) the maximum velocity of a point on the string (assuming the amplitude is the same both times), (e) the maximum acceleration of a point on the string (assuming the amplitude is the same both times).

5. Why is it possible to understand the words spoken by two people at the same time?

6. A cello player can change the frequency of the sound produced by her instrument by (a) increasing the tension in the string, (b) pressing her finger on the string at different places along the fingerboard, or (c) bowing a different string. Explain how each of these methods affects the frequency.

7. Why is a transverse wave sometimes called a shear wave?

8. The drawing shows a complex wave moving to the right along a cord. Draw the shape of the cord an instant later and determine which parts of the cord are moving upward and which are moving downward. Indicate the directions on your drawing with arrows.

9. When an earthquake occurs, the S waves (transverse waves) are not detected on the opposite side of the Earth while the P waves (longitudinal waves) are. How does this provide evidence that the Earth's solid core is surrounded by liquid?

10. Simple ear-protection devices use materials that reflect or absorb sound before it reaches the ears. A newer technology, sometimes called *noise cancellation*, uses a microphone to produce an electrical signal that mimics the noise. The signal is modified electronically, then fed to the speakers in a pair of headphones. The speakers emit sound waves that *cancel* the noise. On what principle is this technology based? What kind of modification is made to the electrical signal?

11. When connecting speakers to a stereo, it is important to connect them with the correct polarity so that, if the same electrical signal is sent, they both move in the same direction. If the wires going to one speaker are reversed, the listener hears a noticeably weaker bass (low frequencies). Explain what causes this and why low frequencies are affected more than high frequencies.

Multiple-Choice Questions

1. Standing waves are produced by the superposition of two waves with
   (a) the same amplitude, frequency, and direction of propagation.
   (b) the same amplitude and frequency, and opposite propagation directions.
   (c) the same amplitude and direction of propagation, but different frequencies.
   (d) the same amplitude, different frequencies, and opposite directions of propagation.

2. A transverse wave travels on a string of mass m, length L, and tension F. Which statement here is correct?
   (a) The energy of the wave is proportional to the square root of the wave amplitude.
   (b) The speed of a moving point on the string is the same as the wave speed.
   (c) The wave speed is determined by the values of m, L, and F.
   (d) The wavelength of the wave is proportional to L.

3. A transverse wave on a string is described by $y(x, t) = A \cos (\omega t + kx)$. It arrives at the point $x = 0$ where the string is fixed in place. Which function describes the reflected wave?
   (a) $A \cos (\omega t + kx)$ (b) $A \cos (\omega t - kx)$
   (c) $- A \sin (\omega t + kx)$ (d) $- A \cos (\omega t - kx)$
   (e) $A \sin (\omega t + kx)$

4. A violin string of length L is fixed at both ends. Which one of these is *not* a wavelength of a standing wave on the string?
   (a) L (b) $2L$ (c) $L/2$ (d) $L/3$ (e) $2L/3$ (f) $3L/2$

5. The speed of waves in a stretched string depends on which one of the following?
   (a) The tension in the string
   (b) The amplitude of the waves
   (c) The wavelength of the waves
   (d) The gravitational field strength

6. The higher the frequency of a wave,
   (a) the smaller its speed.
   (b) the shorter its wavelength.
   (c) the greater its amplitude.
   (d) the longer its period.

7. In a transverse wave, the individual particles of the medium
   (a) move in circles.   (b) move in ellipses.
   (c) move parallel to the direction of the wave's travel.
   (d) move perpendicularly to the direction of the wave's travel.

8. Which is the only one of these properties of a wave that could be changed without changing any of the others?
   (a) amplitude   (b) wavelength
   (c) speed   (d) frequency

9. Two successive transverse pulses, one caused by a brief displacement to the right and the other by a brief displacement to the left, are sent down a Slinky that is fastened at the far end. At the point where the first reflected pulse meets the second advancing pulse, the deflection (compared with that of a single pulse) is
   (a) quadrupled.   (b) doubled.
   (c) canceled.   (d) halved.

10. The intensity of an isotropic sound wave is
    (a) directly proportional to the distance from the source.
    (b) inversely proportional to the distance from the source.
    (c) directly proportional to the square of the distance from the source.
    (d) inversely proportional to the square of the distance from the source.
    (e) none of the above.

Problems

   ⓒ   Combination conceptual/quantitative problem
   ☤   Biological or medical application
   ✦   Challenging problem
Blue #   Detailed solution in the Student Solutions Manual
 ① ② Problems paired by concept
   Text website interactive or tutorial

11.1 Waves and Energy Transport

1. The intensity of sunlight that reaches Earth's atmosphere is 1400 W/m^2. What is the intensity of the sunlight that reaches Jupiter? Jupiter is 5.2 times as far from the Sun as Earth. [*Hint:* Treat the Sun as an isotropic source of light waves.]

2. Michelle is enjoying a picnic across the valley from a cliff. She is playing music on her radio (assume it to be an isotropic source) and notices an echo from the cliff. She claps her hands and the echo takes 1.5 s to return. (a) Given that the speed of sound in air is 343 m/s on that day, how far away is the cliff? (b) If the intensity of the music 1.0 m from the radio is 1.0×10^{-5} W/m^2, what is the intensity of the music arriving at the cliff?

3. The intensity of the sound wave from a jet airplane as it is taking off is 1.0×10^2 W/m^2 at a distance of 5.0 m. What is the intensity of the sound wave that reaches the ears of a person standing at a distance of 120 m from the runway? Assume that the sound wave radiates from the airplane equally in all directions.

4. At what rate in watts does the jet airplane in Problem 3 radiate energy in the form of sound waves?

5. The Sun emits electromagnetic waves (including light) equally in all directions. The intensity of the waves at Earth's upper atmosphere is 1.4 kW/m^2. At what rate does the Sun emit electromagnetic waves? (In other words, what is the power output?)

11.3 Speed of Transverse Waves on a String

6. (a) What is the speed of propagation of the pulse shown in the figure? (b) At what average speed does the point at $x = 2.0$ m move during this time interval?

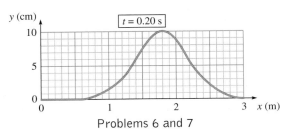

Problems 6 and 7

7. (a) What is the position of the peak of the pulse shown in the figure with Problem 6 at $t = 3.00$ s? (b) When does the peak of the pulse arrive at $x = 4.00$ m?

8. When the tension in a cord is 75 N, the wave speed is 140 m/s. What is the linear mass density of the cord?

9. A metal guitar string has a linear mass density of $\mu = 3.20$ g/m. What is the speed of transverse waves on this string when its tension is 90.0 N?

10. Two strings, each 15.0 m long, are stretched side by side. One string has a mass of 78.0 g and a tension of 180.0 N. The second string has a mass of 58.0 g and a tension of 160.0 N. A pulse is generated at one end of each string simultaneously. On which string will the pulse move faster? Once the faster pulse reaches the far end of its string, how much additional time will the slower pulse require to reach the end of its string?

11. A uniform string of length 10.0 m and weight 0.25 N is attached to the ceiling. A weight of 1.00 kN hangs from its lower end. The lower end of the string is suddenly displaced horizontally. How long does it take the resulting wave pulse to travel to the upper end? [*Hint:* Is the weight of the string negligible in comparison with that of the hanging mass?]

11.4 Periodic Waves

12. What is the speed of a wave whose frequency and wavelength are 500.0 Hz and 0.500 m, respectively?

13. What is the wavelength of a wave whose speed and period are 75.0 m/s and 5.00 ms, respectively?

14. What is the frequency of a wave whose speed and wavelength are 120 m/s and 30.0 cm, respectively?

15. The speed of sound in air at room temperature is 340 m/s. (a) What is the frequency of a sound wave in air with wavelength 1.0 m? (b) What is the frequency of a radio wave with the same wavelength? (Radio waves are electromagnetic waves that travel at 3.0×10^8 m/s in air or in vacuum.)

16. Light visible to humans consists of electromagnetic waves with wavelengths (in air) in the range 400–700 nm (4.0×10^{-7} m to 7.0×10^{-7} m). The speed of light in air is 3.0×10^8 m/s. What are the frequencies of electromagnetic waves that are visible?

17. A fisherman notices a buoy bobbing up and down in the water in ripples produced by waves from a passing speedboat. These waves travel at 2.5 m/s and have a wavelength of 7.5 m. At what frequency does the buoy bob up and down?

11.5 Mathematical Description of a Wave

18. You are swimming in the ocean as water waves with wavelength 9.6 m pass by. What is the closest distance that another swimmer could be so that his motion is exactly opposite yours (he goes up when you go down)?

19. What is the speed of the wave represented by $y(x, t) = A \sin (kx - \omega t)$, where $k = 6.0$ rad/cm and $\omega = 5.0$ rad/s?

20. The equation of a wave is

$$y(x, t) = (3.5 \text{ cm}) \sin \left\{ \frac{\pi}{3.0 \text{ cm}} [x - (66 \text{ cm/s})t] \right\}$$

Find (a) the amplitude and (b) the wavelength of this wave.

✦21. A wave on a string has equation

$$y(x, t) = (4.0 \text{ mm}) \sin (\omega t - kx)$$

where $\omega = 6.0 \times 10^2$ rad/s and $k = 6.0$ rad/m. (a) What is the amplitude of the wave? (b) What is the wavelength? (c) What is the period? (d) What is the wave speed? (e) In which direction does the wave travel?

◉22. A transverse wave on a string is described by the equation $y(x, t) = (2.20 \text{ cm}) \sin [(130 \text{ rad/s})t + (15 \text{ rad/m})x]$. (a) What is the maximum transverse speed of a point on the string? (b) What is the maximum transverse acceleration of a point on the string? (c) How fast does the wave move along the string? (d) Why is your answer to (c) different from the answer to (a)?

23. Write an equation for a sine wave with amplitude 0.120 m, wavelength 0.300 m, and wave speed 6.40 m/s traveling in the −x-direction.

✦24. Write the equation for a transverse sinusoidal wave with a maximum amplitude of 2.50 cm and an angular frequency of 2.90 rad/s that is moving along the positive x-direction with a wave speed that is 5.00 times as fast as the maximum speed of a point on the string. Assume that at time $t = 0$, the point $x = 0$ is at $y = 0$ and then moves in the −y-direction in the next instant of time.

11.6 Graphing Waves

25. A sine wave is traveling to the right on a cord. The lighter line in the figure represents the shape of the cord at time $t = 0$; the darker line represents the shape of the cord at time $t = 0.10$ s. (Note that the horizontal and vertical scales are different.) What are (a) the amplitude and (b) the wavelength of the wave? (c) What is the speed of the wave? What are (d) the frequency and (e) the period of the wave?

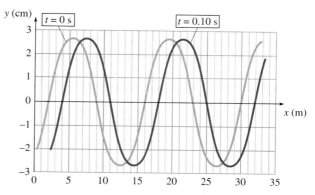

26. (a) Plot a graph for

$$y(x, t) = (4.0 \text{ cm}) \sin [(378 \text{ rad/s})t - (314 \text{ rad/cm})x]$$

versus x at $t = 0$ and at $t = \frac{1}{480}$ s. From the plots determine the amplitude, wavelength, and speed of the wave. (b) For the same function, plot a graph of $y(x, t)$ versus t at $x = 0$ and find the period of the vibration. Show that $\lambda = vT$.

27. For a transverse wave on a string described by

$$y(x, t) = (0.0050 \text{ m}) \cos [(4.0\pi \text{ rad/s})t - (1.0\pi \text{ rad/m})x]$$

find the maximum speed and the maximum acceleration of a point on the string. Plot graphs for one cycle of displacement y versus t, velocity v_y versus t, and acceleration a_y versus t at the point $x = 0$.

28. A transverse wave on a string is described by

$$y(x, t) = (1.2 \text{ mm}) \sin [(2.0\pi \text{ rad/s})t - (0.50\pi \text{ rad/m})x]$$

Plot the displacement y and the velocity v_y versus t for one complete cycle of the point $x = 0$ on the string.

29. (a) Sketch graphs of y versus x for the function

$$y(x, t) = (0.80 \text{ mm}) \sin (kx - \omega t)$$

for the times $t = 0$, 0.96 s, and 1.92 s. Make all three graphs of the same axes, using a solid line for the first, a dashed line for the second, and a dotted line for the third. Use the values $k = \pi/(5.0 \text{ cm})$ and $\omega = (\pi/6.0)$ rad/s. (b) Repeat part (a) for the function

$$y(x, t) = (0.50 \text{ mm}) \sin (kx + \omega t)$$

(c) Which function represents a wave traveling in the −x-direction and which represents a wave traveling in the +x-direction?

✦30. The drawing shows a snapshot of a transverse wave traveling along a string at 10.0 m/s. The equation for the wave is $y(x, t) = A \cos (\omega t + kx)$. (a) Is the wave moving to the right or to the left? (b) What are the numerical values of A, ω, and k? (c) At what times could this snapshot have been taken? (Give the three smallest nonnegative possibilities.)

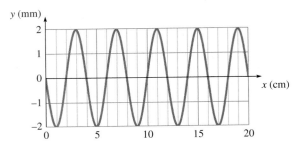

11.7 Principle of Superposition

31. Two pulses on a cord at time $t = 0$ are moving toward each other; the speed of each pulse is 40 cm/s. Sketch the shape of the cord at 0.15, 0.25, and 0.30 s.

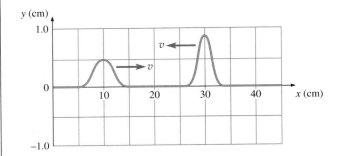

32. Two pulses on a cord at time $t = 0$ are moving toward one another; the speed of each pulse is 2.5 m/s. Sketch the shape of the cord at 0.60, 0.80, and 0.90 s.

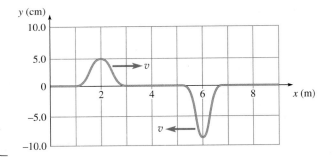

33. Using graph paper, sketch two identical sine waves of amplitude 4.0 cm that differ in phase by (a) $\pi/3$ rad (60°) and (b) $\pi/2$ rad (90°). Find the amplitude of the superposition of the two waves in each case.

34. Two traveling sine waves, identical except for a phase difference ϕ, add so that their superposition produces another traveling wave with the same amplitude as the two component waves. What is the phase difference between the two waves?

35. A traveling sine wave is the result of the superposition of two other sine waves with equal amplitudes,

wavelengths, and frequencies. The two component waves each have amplitude 5.00 cm. If the superposition wave has amplitude 6.69 cm, what is the phase difference ϕ between the component waves? [*Hint:* Let $y_1 = A \sin (\omega t + kx)$ and $y_2 = A \sin (\omega t + kx - \phi)$. Make use of the trigonometric identity (Appendix A.7) for $\sin \alpha + \sin \beta$ when finding $y = y_1 + y_2$ and identify the new amplitude in terms of the original amplitude.]

11.8 Reflection and Refraction

36. Light of wavelength 0.500 μm (in air) enters the water in a swimming pool. The speed of light in water is 0.750 times the speed in air. What is the wavelength of the light in water?

Problems 37–38. The pulse of the figure travels to the right on a string whose ends at $x = 0$ and $x = 4.0$ m are both fixed in place. Imagine a reflected pulse that begins to move onto the string at an endpoint at the same time the incident pulse reaches that endpoint. The superposition of the incident and reflected pulses gives the shape of the string.

37. When does the string first look completely flat for $t > 0$?

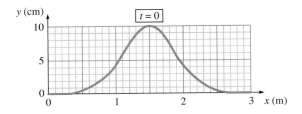

Problems 37, 38, 76, and 77

38. When is the first time for $t > 0$ that the string looks exactly as it does at $t = 0$?

11.9 Interference and Diffraction

39. Two waves with identical frequency but different amplitudes $A_1 = 5.0$ cm and $A_2 = 3.0$ cm, occupy the same region of space (are superimposed). (a) At what phase difference does the resulting wave have the largest amplitude? What is the amplitude of the resulting wave in that case? (b) At what phase difference does the resulting wave have the smallest amplitude and what is its amplitude? (c) What is the ratio of the largest and smallest amplitudes?

40. Two waves with identical frequency but different amplitudes $A_1 = 6.0$ cm and $A_2 = 3.0$ cm, occupy the same

region of space (i.e., are superimposed). (a) At what phase difference will the resulting wave have the highest intensity? What is the amplitude of the resulting wave in that case? (b) At what phase difference will the resulting wave have the lowest intensity and what will its amplitude be? (c) What is the ratio of the two intensities?

41. A sound wave with intensity 25 mW/m^2 interferes constructively with a sound wave that has an intensity of 15 mW/m^2. What is the intensity of the superposition of the two? (![W] tutorial: superposition)

42. A sound wave with intensity 25 mW/m^2 interferes destructively with a sound wave that has an intensity of 28 mW/m^2. What is the intensity of the superposition of the two?

43. Two coherent sound waves have intensities of 0.040 W/m^2 and 0.090 W/m^2 where you are listening. (a) If the waves interfere constructively, what is the intensity that you hear? (b) What if they interfere destructively? (c) If they were incoherent, what would be the intensity? [*Hint:* If your answers are correct, then (c) is the average of (a) and (b).]

◆44. While testing speakers for a concert, Tomás sets up two speakers to produce sound waves at the same frequency, which is between 100 Hz and 150 Hz. The two speakers vibrate in phase with one another. He notices that when he listens at certain locations, the sound is very soft (a minimum intensity compared to nearby points). One such point is 25.8 m from one speaker and 37.1 m from the other. What are the possible frequencies of the sound waves coming from the speakers? (The speed of sound in air is 343 m/s.)

11.10 Standing Waves

45. In order to decrease the fundamental frequency of a guitar string by 4.0%, by what percentage should you reduce the tension?

46. The tension in a guitar string is increased by 15%. What happens to the fundamental frequency of the string?

47. A standing wave has wavenumber 2.0×10^2 rad/m. What is the distance between two adjacent nodes?

48. A harpsichord string of length 1.50 m and linear mass density 25.0 mg/m vibrates at a (fundamental) frequency of 450.0 Hz. (a) What is the speed of the transverse string waves? (b) What is the tension? (c) What are the wavelength and frequency of the sound wave in air produced by vibration of the string? (The speed of sound in air at room temperature is 340 m/s.)

49. A cord of length 1.5 m is fixed at both ends. Its mass per unit length is 1.2 g/m and the tension is 12 N. (a) What is the frequency of the fundamental oscillation? (b) What tension is required if the $n = 3$ mode has a frequency of 0.50 kHz?

50. Tension is maintained in a string by attaching one end to a wall and by hanging a 2.20-kg object from the other end of the string after it passes over a pulley that is 2.00 m from the wall. The string has a mass per unit length of 3.55 mg/m. What is the fundamental frequency of this string?

51. A guitar's E-string has length 65 cm and is stretched to a tension of 82 N. It vibrates at a fundamental frequency of 329.63 Hz. Determine the mass per unit length of the string.

52. A string 2.0 m long is held fixed at both ends. If a sharp blow is applied to the string at its center, it takes 0.050 s for the pulse to travel to the ends of the string and return to the middle. What is the fundamental frequency of oscillation for this string?

53. A 1.6-m-long string fixed at both ends vibrates at resonant frequencies of 780 Hz and 1040 Hz, with no other resonant frequency between these values. (a) What is the fundamental frequency of this string? (b) When the tension in the string is 1200 N, what is the total mass of the string?

54. A certain string has a mass per unit length of 0.120 g/m. It is attached to a vibrating device and weight similar to that shown in Figure 11.22. The vibrator oscillates at a constant frequency of 110 Hz. How heavy should the weight be in order to produce standing waves in a string of length 42 cm?

◆55. The longest "string" (a thick metal wire) on a particular piano is 2.0 m long and has a tension of 300.0 N. It vibrates with a fundamental frequency of 27.5 Hz. What is the total mass of the wire?

◆56. Suppose that a string of length L and mass m is under tension F. (a) Show that $\sqrt{FL/m}$ has units of speed. (b) Show that there is no other combination of L, m, and F with units of speed. [*Hint:* Of the dimensions of the three quantities L, m, and F, only F includes time.] Thus, the speed of transverse waves on the string can only be some dimensionless constant times $\sqrt{FL/m}$.

Comprehensive Problems

57. The speed of waves on a lake depends on frequency. For waves of frequency 1.0 Hz, the wave speed is 1.56 m/s; for 2.0-Hz waves, the speed is 0.78 m/s. The 2.0-Hz waves from a speedboat's wake reach you 120 s after the 1.0-Hz waves generated by the same boat. How far away is the boat?

58. A transverse wave on a string is described by

    $$y(x, t) = (1.2 \text{ cm}) \sin [(0.50\pi \text{ rad/s})t - (1.00\pi \text{ rad/m})x]$$

    Find the maximum velocity and the maximum acceleration of a point on the string. Plot graphs for displacement y versus t, velocity v_y versus t, and acceleration a_y versus t at $x = 0$.

59. What is the wavelength of the radio waves transmitted by an FM station at 90 MHz? (Radio waves travel at 3.0×10^8 m/s.)

60. A longitudinal wave has a wavelength of 10 cm and an amplitude of 5.0 cm and travels in the y-direction. The wave speed in this medium is 80 cm/s. (a) Describe the

motion of a particle in the medium as the wave travels through the medium. (b) How would your answer differ if the wave were transverse instead?

61. An underground explosion sends out both transverse (S waves) and longitudinal (P waves) mechanical wave pulses (seismic waves) through the crust of the Earth. Suppose the speed of transverse waves is 8.0 km/s and that of longitudinal waves is 10.0 km/s. On one occasion, both waves follow the same path from a source to a detector (a seismograph); the longitudinal pulse arrives 2.0 s before the transverse pulse. What is the distance between the source and the detector?

62. The graph shows ground vibrations recorded by a seismograph 180 km from the focus of a small earthquake. It took the waves 30.0 s to travel from their source to the seismograph. Estimate the wavelength.

63. When the string of a guitar is pressed against a fret, the shortened string vibrates at a frequency 5.95% higher than when the previous fret is pressed. If the length of the part of the string that is free to vibrate is 64.8 cm, how far from one end of the string are the first three frets located?

64. A guitar string has a fundamental frequency of 300.0 Hz. (a) What are the next three lowest standing wave frequencies? (b) If you press a finger *lightly* against the string at its midpoint so that both sides of the string can still vibrate, you create a node at the midpoint. What are the lowest four standing wave frequencies now? (c) If you press *hard* at the same point, only one side of the string can vibrate. What are the lowest four standing wave frequencies?

65. A sign is hanging from a single metal wire, as shown in part (a) of the drawing. The shop owner notices that the wire vibrates at a fundamental resonance frequency of 660 Hz, which irritates his customers. In an attempt to fix the problem, the shop owner cuts the wire in half and hangs the sign from the two halves, as shown in part (b). Assuming the tension in the two wires to be the same, what is the new fundamental frequency of each wire?

66. (a) Write an equation for a surface seismic wave moving along the −x-axis with amplitude 2.0 cm, period 4.0 s, and wavelength 4.0 km. Assume the wave is harmonic, x is measured in m, and t is measured in s. (b) What is the maximum speed of the ground as the wave moves by? (c) What is the wave speed?

67. The formula for the speed of transverse waves on a spring is the same as for a string. (a) A spring is stretched to a length much greater than its relaxed length. Explain why the tension in the spring is approximately proportional to the length. (b) A wave takes 4.00 s to travel from one end of such a spring to the other. Then the length is increased 10.0%. Now how long does a wave take to travel the length of the spring? [*Hint:* Is the mass per unit length constant?]

68. Deep-water waves are *dispersive* (their wave speed depends on the wavelength). The restoring force is provided by gravity. Using dimensional analysis, find out how the speed of deep-water waves depends on wavelength λ, assuming that λ and g are the only relevant quantities. (Mass density does not enter into the expression because the restoring force, arising from the weight of the water, is itself proportional to the mass density.)

69. In contrast to deep-water waves, shallow ripples on the surface of a pond are due to surface tension. The surface tension γ of water characterizes the restoring force; the mass density ρ of water characterizes the water's inertia. Use dimensional analysis to determine whether the surface waves are *dispersive* (the wave speed depends on the wavelength) or *nondispersive* (their wave speed is independent of wavelength). [*Hint:* Start by assuming that the wave speed is determined by γ, ρ, and the wavelength λ.]

70. A seismic wave is described by the equation

$$y(x, t) = (7.00 \text{ cm}) \cos [(6.00\pi \text{ rad/cm})x + (20.0\pi \text{ rad/s})t]$$

The wave travels through a uniform medium in the x-direction. (a) Is this wave moving right (+x-direction) or left (−x-direction)? (b) How far from their equilibrium positions do the particles in the medium move? (c) What is the frequency of this wave? (d) What is the wavelength of this wave? (e) What is the wave speed? (f) Describe the motion of a particle that is at $y = 7.00$ cm and $x = 0$ when $t = 0$. (g) Is this wave transverse or longitudinal?

71. The drawing shows a snapshot of a transverse wave moving to the left on a string. The wave speed is 10.0 m/s. At the instant the snapshot is taken, (a) in what direction is point A moving? (b) In what direction is point B moving? (c) At which of these points is the speed of the string segment (not the wave speed) larger? Explain.

72. Consider a point just to the left of point A in the drawing with Problem 71. Plot the position of that point and the velocity of that point as a function of time as the wave passes the point.

73. Two speakers spaced a distance 1.5 m apart emit coherent sound waves at a frequency of 680 Hz in all directions. The waves start out in phase with each other. A listener walks in a circle of radius greater than one meter centered

on the midpoint of the two speakers. At how many points does the listener observe destructive interference? The listener and the speakers are all in the same horizontal plane and the speed of sound is 340 m/s. [*Hint:* Start with a diagram; then determine the *maximum* path difference between the two waves at points on the circle.] Experiments like this must be done in a special room so that reflections are negligible.

◆74. (a) Use a graphing calculator or computer graphing program to plot y versus x for the function

$$y(x, t) = (5.0 \text{ cm}) \, [\sin (kx - \omega t) + \sin (kx + \omega t)]$$

for the times $t = 0$, 1.0 s, and 2.0 s. Use the values $k = \pi / (5.0 \text{ cm})$ and $\omega = (\pi / 6.0)$ rad/s. (b) Is this a traveling wave? If not, what kind of wave is it?

◆75 Show that the amplitudes of the graphs you made in Problem 74 satisfy the equation $A' = 2A \cos (\omega t)$, where A' is the amplitude of the wave you plotted and A is 5.0 cm, the amplitude of the waves that were added together.

Problems 76–77. The pulse of Problems 37–38 travels on a string that has fixed ends.

◆76. The pulse travels on a string whose ends at $x = 0$ and $x = 4.0$ m are both fixed in place. Sketch the shape of the string at $t = 2.2$ s.

◆77. The pulse travels on a string whose ends at $x = 0$ and $x = 4.0$ m are both fixed in place. Sketch the shape of the string at $t = 1.6$ s.

Answers to Practice Problems

11.1 (a) 8.9 m/s; (b) 13 m/s

11.2 (a) Yes, the traveling wave retains its shape; (b) it travels in the +x-direction because the t and x/v terms have *opposite* signs; (c) the wave speed is 8.0 m/s.

11.3

(a)

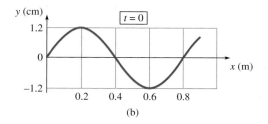

(b)

(c) $T = 0.200$ s; (d) $\lambda = 0.80$ m; (e) $A = 1.2$ cm; (f) $v = 4.0$ m/s; (g) the wave travels in the $-x$-direction because the signs of the terms containing x and t are the same.

11.4

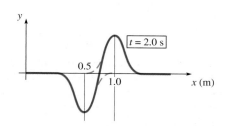

11.5 (a) 620 Hz; (b) 8.5 m

11.6 9.0

11.7 140 Hz

Answers to Checkpoints

11.1 For an isotropic source, $I \propto 1/r^2$. At a distance 10^2 times as far from the tower, the intensity is $10^{-4} \times 0.090 \text{ W/m}^2 = 9.0 \text{ } \mu\text{W/m}^2$.

11.4 The period T is the time for one cycle. During one period, the wave travels 20 km at a speed of 4.0 km/s. Then the period is (20 km)/(4.0 km/s) = 5.0 s.

11.10 The nodes are evenly spaced, so the nodes are at $x = 0$, 20 cm, 40 cm, 60 cm, 80 cm, and 100 cm. The distance between nodes is half the wavelength, so the wavelength is 40 cm.

JENNIFER
WEILL MEDICAL COLLEGE/CORNELL
B11

06/03/04 12:57:48
P80   6MHz   E721

GE

CN0
8cm
DR66
G 48

CRL 8.8mm   6W6D
CRL 11.6mm   7W2D

MI<0.4

Congratulations! You're expecting twins!

Ultrasonic imaging of the fetus is an increasingly important part of prenatal care. Could an image of the fetus be produced just as well using sound in the audible range rather than ultrasound? Why is ultrasound used rather than some other imaging technology, such as x-rays? Are there other medical applications of ultrasound? (See p. 445 for the answer.)

12.1   SOUND WAVES

When a guitar string is plucked, a transverse wave travels along the string. The wave on the string is not what we hear, of course, since the string has no direct connection to our eardrums. The vibration of the string is transmitted through the bridge to the body of the guitar, which in turn transmits the vibration to the air—a sound wave. A transverse wave on a guitar string is not a sound wave, though it does *cause* a sound wave.

In the absence of a sound wave, molecules in the air dart around in random directions. On average, they are uniformly distributed and the pressure is the same everywhere (ignoring the insignificant variation of pressure due to small changes in altitude). In a sound wave, the uniform distribution of molecules is disturbed. A loudspeaker produces pressure fluctuations that travel through the air in all directions (Fig. 12.1). In some regions (*compressions*), the molecules are bunched together and the pressure is higher than the average pressure. In other regions (*rarefactions*), the molecules are spread out and the pressure is lower than average. The sound wave can be described mathematically by the gauge pressure p (the difference between the pressure at a given point and the average pressure in the surroundings) as a function of position and time (Fig. 12.2a).

The speaker cone produces these pressure variations by displacing molecules in the air from their uniform distribution (Fig. 12.2b). When the cone moves to the left of its equilibrium position, air spreads into a region of lower pressure (rarefaction).

Application: how a guitar creates a sound wave

Application: how a loudspeaker generates a sound wave

Figure 12.1 The vibrating speaker cones in this boombox create alternating regions of high and low pressure in the air. Air nearby is affected by a net force due to the nonuniform air pressure; as a result, variations in pressure travel in all directions away from the speakers. This traveling disturbance is a sound wave.

When the cone moves to the right, air is squeezed together into a region of higher pressure (compression).

Thus, the regions of higher and lower pressure are formed when molecules are displaced from a uniform distribution. A sound wave can be described equally well by the displacement *s* of an *element* of the air—a region of air that can be considered to move together as a unit (Fig. 12.2c). An element is much smaller than the wavelength of the wave, but still large enough to contain many molecules. For a sinusoidal wave, elements at points of maximum or minimum pressure have zero displacement, while the neighboring elements move in toward them (a compression) or away from them (a rarefaction). Conversely, where the gauge pressure is zero, the displacement of an element has its maximum magnitude.

If the pressure is higher on one side than on the other, the net force pushes air toward the side with lower pressure. The uneven distribution of pressure results in air molecules being pushed toward rarefactions and away from compressions, as shown by the force arrows in Fig. 12.2b. Note that the directions of these force arrows, pointing opposite to the displacement arrows in a corresponding region, are such that where there is a compression at a given instant, there will later be a rarefaction, and *vice versa*; the pressure at a given point fluctuates above and below the average pressure.

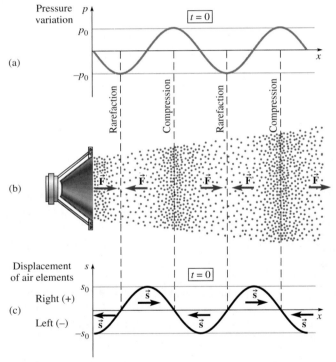

Figure 12.2 A sound wave generated by a loudspeaker. (a) Graph of the pressure variation *p* of the air as a function of position *x*. Pressure is high where air is squeezed together and low where it is more spread out. (b) Elements of the air are displaced from their equilibrium positions. Since the pressure is not uniform, air elements experience a net force due to air pressure; the force arrows indicate the direction of this net force. The force is always directed away from a compression (higher pressure) and toward a rarefaction. (c) Graph of the displacement *s* of an air element from its equilibrium position *x* as a function of *x*; the arrows indicate the directions of the displacements in each region. Air elements are displaced leftward or rightward toward compressions and away from rarefactions. Elements at the center of each compression or rarefaction are at their equilibrium positions ($s = 0$).

Frequencies of Sound Waves

The human ear responds to sound waves within a limited range of frequencies. We generally consider the **audible range** to extend from 20 Hz to 20 kHz. Very few people can actually hear sounds over that entire range. Even for a person with excellent hearing, the sensitivity of the ear declines rapidly below 100 Hz and above 10 kHz. The terms **infrasound** and **ultrasound** are used to describe sound waves with frequencies below 20 Hz and above 20 kHz, respectively.

The audible ranges for animals can be quite different. Dogs can hear frequencies as high as 50 kHz, which is why we can make a dog whistle that is inaudible to humans. Dolphins make use of frequencies as high as 250 kHz. Elephants communicate over long distances (up to 4 km) using sounds with fundamental frequencies as low as 14 Hz. A rhinoceros uses frequencies down to 10 Hz. Such low-frequency sounds cannot be heard by humans, but the vibrations can be felt and the sounds can be recorded using special equipment.

12.2   THE SPEED OF SOUND WAVES

For string waves, the restoring force is characterized by the tension in the string F and the inertia is characterized by the linear mass density μ (mass per unit length). The speed of transverse waves on a string is

$$v = \sqrt{\frac{F}{\mu}} \qquad (11\text{-}4)$$

For sound waves in a fluid, the restoring force is characterized by the bulk modulus B, defined in Section 10.4 as the constant of proportionality between an increase in pressure and the fractional volume change:

$$\Delta P = -B \frac{\Delta V}{V} \qquad (10\text{-}10)$$

The inertia of the fluid is characterized by its mass density ρ. Following our dictum "more restoring force makes faster waves; more inertia makes slower waves," we expect the speed of sound to be faster in a medium with a larger bulk modulus (harder to compress means more restoring force) and slower in a medium with a larger density. By analogy with Eq. (11-4), we might *guess* that

$$v = \sqrt{\frac{\text{a measure of the restoring force}}{\text{a measure of the inertia}}} = \sqrt{\frac{B}{\rho}} \quad \text{(in fluids)} \qquad (12\text{-}1)$$

This guess turns out to be correct; Eq. (12-1) is the correct expression for the speed of sound in fluids.

Temperature Dependence of the Speed of Sound in a Gas   The bulk modulus B of an ideal gas turns out to be directly proportional to the density ρ and to T, the *absolute temperature* ($B \propto \rho T$). As a result, the speed of sound in an ideal gas is proportional to the square root of the absolute temperature, but is independent of pressure and density (at a fixed temperature):

$$v = \sqrt{\frac{B}{\rho}} \propto \sqrt{\frac{\rho T}{\rho}} \propto \sqrt{T} \qquad \text{(ideal gas)}$$

The SI unit of absolute temperature is the kelvin (symbol K). To find absolute temperature in kelvins, add 273.15 to the temperature in degrees Celsius:

$$T \text{ (in K)} = T_C \text{ (in °C)} + 273.15 \qquad (12\text{-}2)$$

Since $v \propto \sqrt{T}$, the speed of sound in an ideal gas at any absolute temperature T can be found if it is known at one temperature:

$$v = v_0 \sqrt{\frac{T}{T_0}} \qquad (12\text{-}3)$$

CONNECTION:

Just as for transverse waves on a string, the speed of sound waves is determined by a balance between two characteristics of the wave medium: the restoring force and the inertia.

More restoring force $\Rightarrow$ faster waves; more inertia $\Rightarrow$ slower waves.

Table 12.1 Speed of Sound in Various Materials (at 0°C and 1 atm unless otherwise noted)

Medium	Speed (m/s)	Medium	Speed (m/s)
Carbon dioxide	259	Blood (37°C)	1570
Air	331	Muscle (37°C)	1580
Nitrogen	334	Lead	1322
Air (20°C)	343	Concrete	3100
Helium	972	Copper	3560
Hydrogen	1284	Bone (37°C)	4000
Mercury (25°C)	1450	Pyrex glass	5640
Fat (37°C)	1450	Aluminum	5100
Water (25°C)	1493	Steel	5790
Seawater (25°C)	1533	Granite	6500

where the speed of sound is v_0 at absolute temperature T_0. For example, the speed of sound in air at 0°C (or 273 K) is 331 m/s. At room temperature (20°C, or 293 K), the speed of sound in air is

$$v = 331 \text{ m/s} \times \sqrt{\frac{293 \text{ K}}{273 \text{ K}}} = 343 \text{ m/s}$$

An *approximate* formula that can be used for the speed of sound in air is

$$v = (331 + 0.606 T_C) \text{ m/s} \qquad (12\text{-}4)$$

where T_C is air temperature *in degrees Celsius* (see Problem 8). The speed of sound in air increases 0.606 m/s for each degree Celsius increase in temperature. Equation (12-4) gives speeds accurate to better than 1% all the way from −66°C to +89°C.

Speed of Sound in a Solid   The speed of sound in a *solid* depends on the Young's modulus Y and the shear modulus S. For sound waves traveling along the length of a thin solid rod, the speed is approximately

$$v = \sqrt{\frac{Y}{\rho}} \qquad \text{(thin solid rod)} \qquad (12\text{-}5)$$

Table 12.1 gives the speed of sound in various materials.

Conceptual Example 12.1

Speed of Sound in Hydrogen and Mercury

From Table 12.1, the speed of sound in hydrogen gas at 0°C is almost as large as the speed of sound in mercury, even though the density of mercury is 150 000 times larger than the density of hydrogen. How is that possible? Shouldn't the speed in mercury be much smaller, since it has so much more inertia?

Solution and Discussion   The speed of sound depends on *two* characteristics of the medium: the restoring force (measured by the bulk modulus) and the inertia (measured by the density). The bulk modulus of mercury is much larger than the bulk modulus of hydrogen. The bulk modulus is a measure of

how hard it is to compress a material. Liquids (such as mercury) are much more difficult to compress than are gases. Thus, the restoring forces in mercury are much larger than those in hydrogen; this allows sound to travel a bit faster in mercury than it does in hydrogen gas.

Conceptual Practice Problem 12.1   Speed of Sound in Solids versus Liquids

Why does sound generally travel faster in a solid than in a liquid?

12.3 AMPLITUDE AND INTENSITY OF SOUND WAVES

Since there are two ways to describe a sound wave—pressure and displacement—the amplitude of a sound wave can take one of two forms: the pressure amplitude p_0 or the displacement amplitude s_0. The pressure amplitude p_0 is the maximum pressure fluctuation above or below the equilibrium pressure, the displacement amplitude s_0 is the maximum displacement of an element of the medium from its equilibrium position. The pressure amplitude is proportional to the displacement amplitude. For a harmonic sound wave at angular frequency ω, an advanced analysis shows that

$$p_0 = \omega v \rho s_0 \qquad (12\text{-}6)$$

where v is the speed of sound and ρ is the mass density of the medium.

Is a larger amplitude sound wave perceived as *louder*? Yes, all other things being equal. However, the relationship between our perception of loudness and the amplitude of a sound wave is complex. Loudness is a subjective aspect of how sound is perceived; it has to do with how the ear responds to sound and how the brain interprets signals from the ear. Perceived loudness turns out to be *roughly* proportional to the logarithm of the amplitude. If the amplitude of a sound wave doubles repeatedly, the perceived loudness does not double; it increases by a series of roughly equal steps.

Discussions of loudness are more often phrased in terms of intensity rather than amplitude since we are interested in how much energy the sound wave carries. The intensity of a sinusoidal sound wave is

$$I = \frac{p_0^2}{2\rho v} \qquad (12\text{-}7)$$

where ρ is the mass density of the medium and v is the speed of sound in that medium. The most important thing to remember is that *intensity is proportional to amplitude squared*, which is true for all waves, not just sound. It is closely related to the fact that energy in SHM is proportional to amplitude squared [see Eq. (10-13)].

Intensity $\propto$ (Amplitude)^2
Intensity is the average power per unit area carried by a wave (see Section 11.1).

Example 12.2

The Brown Creeper

The song of the Brown Creeper (*Certhia americana*) is very high in frequency—as high as 8 kHz. Many people who have lost some of their high-frequency hearing can't hear it at all. Suppose that you are out in the woods and hear the song. If the intensity of the song at your position is 1.4×10^{-8} W/m^2 and the frequency is 6.0 kHz, what are the pressure and displacement amplitudes? (Assume the temperature is 20°C.)

Strategy The displacement and pressure amplitudes are related through Eq. (12-6); the pressure amplitude is related to the

intensity through Eq. (12-7). These relationships can be used to solve for both pressure amplitude, p_0, and displacement amplitude, s_0. The density of air at 20°C is $\rho = 1.20$ kg/m^3 (see Table 9.1). The speed of sound in air at 20°C is $v = 343$ m/s. We need to multiply the frequency by 2π to get the angular frequency ω.

Solution Intensity and pressure amplitude are related by

$$I = \frac{p_0^2}{2\rho v} \qquad (12\text{-}7)$$

Solving for p_0,

$$p_0 = \sqrt{2I\rho v}$$

$$= \sqrt{2 \times 1.4 \times 10^{-8} \text{ W/m}^2 \times 1.20 \text{ kg/m}^3 \times 343 \text{ m/s}}$$

$$= 3.4 \times 10^{-3} \text{ Pa}$$

The pressure and displacement amplitudes are related by

$$p_0 = \omega v \rho s_0 \qquad (12\text{-}6)$$

continued on next page

Example 12.2 continued

Substituting in Eq. (12-7) yields

$$I = \frac{(\omega v \rho s_0)^2}{2\rho v}$$

Solving for s_0,

$$s_0 = \sqrt{\frac{2I}{\rho \omega^2 v}} = \sqrt{\frac{2 \times 1.4 \times 10^{-8}\ \text{W/m}^2}{1.20\ \text{kg/m}^3 \times (2\pi \times 6000\ \text{Hz})^2 \times 343\ \text{m/s}}}$$

$$= 2.2 \times 10^{-10}\ \text{m}$$

Discussion This problem illustrates how sensitive the human ear is. The pressure amplitude is a fluctuation of one part in 30 million in the air pressure. Since the pressure amplitude is 3.4×10^{-3} Pa, the maximum force on the eardrum would be about

$$F_{\text{max}} = 3.4 \times 10^{-3}\ \text{N/m}^2 \times 10^{-4}\ \text{m}^2 \approx 3 \times 10^{-7}\ \text{N}$$

which is about the weight of a large amoeba. The displacement amplitude is about the size of an atom.

Practice Problem 12.2   Pressure and Intensity at an Outdoor Concert

At a distance of 5.0 m from the stage at an outdoor rock concert, the sound intensity is 1.0×10^{-4} W/m^2. Estimate the intensity and pressure amplitude at a distance of 25 m if there were no speakers other than those on stage. Explain the assumptions you make.

Decibels

Since the perception of loudness by the human ear is roughly proportional to the logarithm of the intensity, it is also roughly proportional to the logarithm of the amplitude (since $\log x^2 = 2 \log x$). An intensity of $I_0 = 10^{-12}$ W/m^2 is about the lowest intensity sound wave that can be heard under ideal conditions by a person with excellent hearing; it is therefore called the **threshold of hearing**. The threshold of hearing is used as a reference intensity in the definition of the intensity level.

A sound intensity I is compared to the reference level I_0 by taking the ratio of the two intensities. Suppose a sound has an intensity of 10^{-5} W/m^2; the ratio is

$$\frac{I}{I_0} = \frac{10^{-5}\ \text{W/m}^2}{10^{-12}\ \text{W/m}^2} = 10^7$$

so the intensity is 10^7 times that of the hearing threshold. The power to which 10 is raised is the **sound intensity level** β in units of bels (after Alexander Graham Bell). A ratio of 10^7 indicates a sound intensity of 7 bels or, as it is more commonly stated, 70 decibels (dB). Since $\log_{10}(10^x) = x$, the sound intensity level in decibels is

$$\beta = (10\ \text{dB}) \log_{10} \frac{I}{I_0} \tag{12-8}$$

The notation $\log_{10}$ stands for the base-10 logarithm. See Appendix A.3 for a review of the properties of logarithms.

An intensity level of 0 dB corresponds to the threshold of hearing ($I = 10^{-12}$ W/m^2). Although the intensity level is really a pure number, the "units" (dB) remind us what the number means.

Table 12.2 gives the pressure amplitudes, intensities, and intensity levels for a wide range of sounds. Notice that, even for sounds that are quite loud, the pressure fluctuations due to sound waves are small compared to the "background" atmospheric pressure.

✓ CHECKPOINT 12.3

Why doesn't Table 12.2 include a column listing the *displacement* amplitudes of the sound waves?

Table 12.2   Pressure Amplitudes, Intensities, and Intensity Levels of a Wide Range of Sounds in Air at 20°C

Sound	Pressure Amplitude (atm)	Pressure Amplitude (Pa)	Intensity (W/m²)	Intensity Level (dB)
Threshold of hearing	3×10^{-10}	3×10^{-5}	10^{-12}	0
Leaves rustling	1×10^{-9}	1×10^{-4}	10^{-11}	10
Whisper (1 m away)	3×10^{-9}	3×10^{-4}	10^{-10}	20
Library background noise	1×10^{-8}	0.001	10^{-9}	30
Living room background noise	3×10^{-8}	0.003	10^{-8}	40
Office or classroom	1×10^{-7}	0.01	10^{-7}	50
Normal conversation at 1 m	3×10^{-7}	0.03	10^{-6}	60
Inside a moving car, light traffic	1×10^{-6}	0.1	10^{-5}	70
City street (heavy traffic)	3×10^{-6}	0.3	10^{-4}	80
Shout (at 1 m); or inside a subway train; risk of hearing damage if exposure lasts several hours	1×10^{-5}	1	10^{-3}	90
Car without muffler at 1 m	3×10^{-5}	3	10^{-2}	100
Construction site	1×10^{-4}	10	10^{-1}	110
Indoor rock concert; threshold of pain; hearing damage occurs rapidly	3×10^{-4}	30	1	120
Jet engine at 30 m	1×10^{-3}	100	10	130

Example 12.3

Decibels from a Jackhammer

The sound intensity 5 m from a jackhammer is 4.20×10^{-2} W/m². What is the sound intensity level in decibels? (Use the usual reference level of $I_0 = 1.00 \times 10^{-12}$ W/m².)

Strategy We are given the intensity in W/m² and asked for the intensity level in dB. First we find the ratio of the given intensity to the reference level. Then we take the logarithm of the result (to get the level in bels) and multiply by 10 (to convert from bels to dB).

Solution The ratio of the intensity to the reference level is

$$\frac{I}{I_0} = \frac{4.20 \times 10^{-2} \text{ W/m}^2}{1.00 \times 10^{-12} \text{ W/m}^2} = 4.20 \times 10^{10}$$

The intensity level in bels is

$$\log_{10} \frac{I}{I_0} = \log_{10} 4.20 \times 10^{10} = 10.6 \text{ bels}$$

The intensity level in decibels is

$$\beta = 10.6 \text{ bels} \times (10 \text{ dB/bel}) = 106 \text{ dB}$$

Discussion As a quick check, 100 dB corresponds to $I = 10^{-2}$ W/m² and 110 dB corresponds to $I = 10^{-1}$ W/m²; since the intensity is between 10^{-2} W/m² and 10^{-1} W/m², the intensity level must be between 100 dB and 110 dB.

Practice Problem 12.3 **Consequences of a Hole in the Muffler**

When rust creates a hole in the muffler of a car, the sound intensity level inside the car is 26 dB higher than when the muffler was intact. By what factor does the intensity increase?

As we saw in Section 11.9, when two sounds are coming from different sources, the waves are incoherent. If we know the intensity of each wave alone at a certain point, then the intensity due to the two waves together at that point is the sum of the two intensities:

$$I = I_1 + I_2 \quad \text{(incoherent waves)}$$

 This is *not* true for two coherent waves, where the total intensity depends on the phase relationship between the waves. Since there is no fixed phase relationship between two incoherent waves, on average there is neither constructive nor destructive interference. The total power per unit area is the sum of the power per unit area of each wave.

Example 12.4

The Sound Intensity Level of Two Lathes

A metal lathe in a workshop produces a 90.0-dB sound intensity level at a distance of 1 m. What is the intensity level when a second identical lathe starts operating? Assume the listener is at the same distance from both lathes.

Strategy   The noise is coming from two different machines and, thus, they are incoherent sources. We *cannot* add 90.0 dB to 90.0 dB to get 180.0 dB, which would be a senseless result—two lathes are not going to drown out a jet engine at close range (see Table 12.2). Instead, what doubles is the *intensity*. We must work in terms of intensity rather than intensity level.

Solution   First find the intensity due to one lathe:

$$\beta = 90.0 \text{ dB} = (10 \text{ dB}) \log_{10} \frac{I}{I_0}$$

$$\log_{10} \frac{I}{I_0} = 9.00, \quad \text{so} \quad \frac{I}{I_0} = 1.00 \times 10^9$$

We could solve for I numerically but it is not necessary. With two machines operating, the intensity doubles, so

$$\frac{I'}{I_0} = 2.00 \times 10^9$$

and the new intensity level is

$$\beta' = (10 \text{ dB}) \log_{10} \frac{I'}{I_0} = (10 \text{ dB}) \log_{10} (2.00 \times 10^9) = 93.0 \text{ dB}$$

Discussion   The new intensity level is just 3 dB higher than the original one, even though the intensity is twice as big. This turns out to be a general result: a 3-dB increase represents a doubling of the intensity.

Practice Problem 12.4   Intensity Change for an Increment of 5 dB

The maximum recommended exposure time to a sound level of 90 dB is 8 h. For every increase of 5.0 dB in sound level up to 120 dB, the exposure time should be reduced by a factor of 2. (At 120 dB, damage occurs almost immediately; there is no safe exposure time.) What factor of intensity change does an intensity level increment of 5.0 dB represent?

 Sound intensity level is useful because it roughly approximates the way we perceive loudness (since it is a logarithmic function of intensity). Equal increments in intensity level roughly correspond to equal increases in loudness. Two useful rules of thumb: every time the intensity increases by a *factor* of 10, the intensity level *adds* 10 dB; since $\log_{10} 2 = 0.30$, adding 3.0 dB to the intensity level *doubles* the intensity (see Problem 17). In Example 12.4, when both lathes are running at the same time, the intensity is twice as big as for one lathe, but the two do not sound twice as loud as one. Intensity *level* is a better guide to loudness; two lathes produce a level 3 dB higher than one lathe.

Decibels can also be used in a relative sense; instead of comparing an intensity to I_0, we can compare two intensities directly. Suppose we have two intensities I_1 and I_2 and two corresponding intensity levels β_1 and β_2. Then

$$\beta_2 - \beta_1 = 10 \text{ dB} \left(\log_{10} \frac{I_2}{I_0} - \log_{10} \frac{I_1}{I_0} \right)$$

Since $\log x - \log y = \log \frac{x}{y}$ [see Appendix A.3, Eq. (A-21)],

$$\beta_2 - \beta_1 = (10 \text{ dB}) \log_{10} \frac{I_2/I_0}{I_1/I_0} = (10 \text{ dB}) \log_{10} \frac{I_2}{I_1} \quad \text{(12-9)}$$

Example 12.5

Variation of Intensity Level with Distance

At a distance of 30 m from a jet engine, the sound intensity level is 130 dB. Serious, permanent hearing damage occurs rapidly at intensity levels this high, which is why you see airport personnel using hearing protection out on the runway. Assume the engine is an isotropic source of sound and ignore reflections and absorption. At what distance is the intensity level 110 dB—still quite loud but below the threshold of pain?

Strategy The intensity level drops 20 dB. According to the rule of thumb, each 10-dB change represents a factor of 10 in intensity. Therefore, we must find the distance at which the intensity is 2 factors of 10 smaller—that is, $\frac{1}{100}$ the original intensity. The intensity is proportional to $1/r^2$ since we assume an isotropic source [see Eq. (11-1)].

Solution We set up a ratio between the intensities and the inverse square of the distances:

$$\frac{I_1}{I_2} = \left(\frac{r_2}{r_1}\right)^2$$

From the rule of thumb, we know that $I_2 = \frac{1}{100} I_1$. Then

$$\frac{r_2}{r_1} = \sqrt{\frac{I_1}{I_2}} = \sqrt{100} = 10$$

$$r_2 = 10r_1 = 300 \text{ m}$$

Discussion It is not necessary to use the rule of thumb. Let $\beta_1 = 130$ dB and $\beta_2 = 110$ dB. Then

$$\beta_2 - \beta_1 = -20 \text{ dB} = (10 \text{ dB}) \log_{10} \frac{I_2}{I_1}$$

From this, we find that

$$\log_{10} \frac{I_2}{I_1} = -2 \quad \text{or} \quad \frac{I_2}{I_1} = \frac{1}{100}$$

We can only consider 300 m an estimate. The jet engine may not radiate sound equally in all directions; it might be louder in front than on the side. Sound is partly absorbed and partly reflected by the runway, by the plane, and by any nearby objects. The air itself absorbs some of the sound energy—that is, some of the energy of the wave is dissipated.

Practice Problem 12.5 A Plane as Quiet as a Library

At what distance from the jet engine would the intensity level be comparable to the background noise level of a library (30 dB)? Is your answer realistic?

12.4 STANDING SOUND WAVES

Pipe Open at Both Ends

Recall (Section 11.8) that a transverse wave on a string is reflected from a fixed end. A string fixed at both ends reflects the wave at each end. A standing wave on a string is caused by the superposition of two waves traveling in opposite directions. Standing *sound* waves are also caused by reflections at boundaries. Standing wave patterns for sound waves can be more complex, since sound is a three-dimensional wave. However, the air inside a pipe open at both ends gives rise to standing waves closely analogous to those on a string, as long as the pipe's diameter is small compared with its length. Such a pipe is an excellent model of some organ pipes and flutes.

If the pipe is open at both ends, then the pipe has the same boundary condition at each end. At each open end, the column of air inside the pipe communicates with the outside air, so the pressure at the ends can't deviate much from atmospheric pressure. The open ends are therefore *pressure nodes* (Fig. 12.3). They are also *displacement*

Open ends are pressure nodes and displacement antinodes.

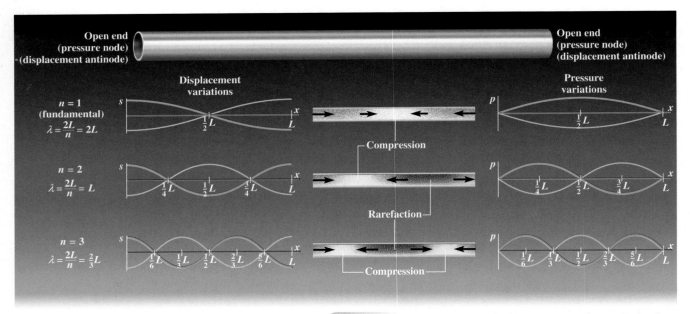

Figure 12.3 Standing waves in a pipe open at both ends. (Although the *graphs* show air displacement *s* on the vertical axis and *x* on the horizontal, remember that the displacements are in the ±*x*-direction, as illustrated by the black vector arrows.)

CONNECTION:

The same sketch used to find wavelengths of standing waves for a string fixed at both ends can be used to find the wavelengths for a pipe open at both ends. (The wave speeds are different, however, so a string and pipe of the same length do not have the same standing wave *frequencies*.)

antinodes—elements of air vibrate back and forth with maximum amplitude at the ends. Since nodes and antinodes alternate with equal spacing (λ/4), the wavelengths of standing sound waves in a pipe open at both ends are the same as for a string fixed at both ends (compare Fig. 12.3 with Fig. 11.21), regardless of whether you consider the pressure or the displacement description.

Standing sound waves (thin pipe open at both ends):

$$\lambda_n = \frac{2L}{n} \tag{11-12}$$

$$f_n = \frac{v}{\lambda_n} = n\frac{v}{2L} = nf_1 \tag{11-13}$$

where $n = 1, 2, 3, \ldots$

Pipe Closed at One End

Some organ pipes are *closed at one end* and open at the other (Fig. 12.4). The closed end is a pressure *antinode*; the air at the closed end meets a rigid surface, so there is no restriction on how far the pressure can deviate from atmospheric pressure. The closed

Figure 12.4 Some organ pipes are open at the top; others are closed. A pipe closed at one end has a fundamental wavelength twice as large and therefore a fundamental frequency half as large as a pipe of the same length that is open at both ends, assuming the pipes are thin. (For musicians: the pitch of the pipe closed at one end sounds an octave lower than the other, since the interval of an octave corresponds to a factor of 2 in frequency.)

Figure 12.5 Standing waves in a pipe closed at one end.

end is also a *displacement node* since the air near it cannot move beyond that rigid surface. Some wind instruments are effectively pipes closed at one end. The reed of a clarinet admits only brief puffs of air into the instrument; the rest of the time the reed closes off that end of the pipe. The pressure at the reed end fluctuates above and below atmospheric pressure. The reed end is a pressure antinode and a displacement node.

Closed ends are pressure antinodes and displacement nodes.

   The wavelengths and frequencies of the standing waves can be found using either the pressure or displacement descriptions of the wave. Using displacement, the fundamental has a node at the closed end, an antinode at the open end, and no other nodes or antinodes (Fig. 12.5). The distance from a node to the nearest antinode is always $\frac{1}{4}\lambda$, so for the fundamental

$$L = \tfrac{1}{4}\lambda \quad \text{or} \quad \lambda = 4L$$

which is twice as large as the wavelength ($2L$) of the fundamental in a pipe of the same length open at both ends. Two thin organ pipes of the same length, one open at both ends and one closed at one end, do not have the same fundamental wavelength (see Fig. 12.4).

   What are the other standing wave frequencies? The next standing wave mode is found by adding one node and one antinode. Then the length of the pipe is 3 quarter-cycles: $L = \frac{3}{4}\lambda$ or $\lambda = \frac{4}{3}L$. This is $\frac{1}{3}$ the wavelength of the fundamental and the frequency is 3 times that of the fundamental. Adding one more node and one more antinode, the wavelength is $\frac{4}{5}L$. Continuing the pattern, we find that the wavelengths and frequencies for standing waves are

Standing sound waves (thin pipe closed at one end):

$$\lambda_n = \frac{4L}{n} \tag{12-10a}$$

$$f_n = \frac{v}{\lambda_n} = n\frac{v}{4L} = nf_1 \tag{12-10b}$$

where $n = 1, 3, 5, 7, \ldots$

Note that the standing wave frequencies for a pipe closed at one end are only *odd* multiples of the fundamental. The "missing" standing wave patterns for even values of n require a clarinet to have many more keys and levers than a flute (Fig. 12.6). What the keys do is effectively shorten the length of the pipe, making the standing wave frequencies higher.

Figure 12.6 A flute can be modeled as a pipe open at both ends, while a clarinet can be modeled as a pipe closed at one end. Although the instruments are similar in length, the clarinet can play tones nearly an octave lower than the flute can. (a) The flute's open blow hole serves as one of its open "ends." If a flute's fundamental frequency is f_1 with no keys pressed, the next highest frequency possible without using any keys is $2f_1$—the flutist overblows, exciting the next highest standing wave frequency rather than the fundamental. The flute needs enough keys to fill in all the notes with frequencies between f_1 and $2f_1$. (b) The clarinet can be modeled as a pipe open at one end and closed at the other. The mouthpiece end with its vibrating reed is more like a closed end (pressure antinode) than an open end (pressure node). For a clarinet, if the fundamental frequency is f_1 with no keys pressed, the next highest frequency possible without using any keys is $3f_1$. The clarinet must have more keys because it has to accommodate all the notes with frequencies between f_1 and $3f_1$.

✓ CHECKPOINT 12.4

Why can't a pipe of length L closed at one end support a standing wave with wavelength $2L$?

Example 12.6

A Demonstration of Resonance

A thin hollow tube of length 1.00 m is inserted vertically into a tall container of water (Fig. 12.7). A tuning fork ($f = 520.0$ Hz) is struck and held near the top of the tube as the tube is slowly pulled up and out of the water. At certain distances (L) between the top of the tube and the water surface, the otherwise faint sound of the tuning fork is greatly amplified. At what values of L does this occur? The temperature of the air in the tube is 18°C.

Strategy Sound waves in the air inside the tube reflect from the water surface. Thus, we have an air column of

Figure 12.7

Experimental setup for Example 12.6.

variable length L, closed at one end by the water surface and open at the other end. The sound is amplified due to resonance; when the frequency of the tuning fork matches one of the natural frequencies of the air column, a large-amplitude standing wave builds up in the column. For standing waves in a column of air, the wavelength and frequency are related by the speed of sound in air. We start by finding the speed of sound in air from the temperature given. Then we can find the wavelength of the sound waves emanating from the tuning fork. Last, we find the column lengths that support standing waves of that wavelength.

Solution The speed of sound in air at 18°C is

$$v = (331 + 0.606 \times 18) \text{ m/s} = 342 \text{ m/s}$$

With the speed of sound and the frequency known, we can find the wavelength. The wavelength is the distance traveled by a wave during one period:

$$\lambda = vT = \frac{v}{f}$$

$$\lambda = \frac{342 \text{ m/s}}{520.0 \text{ Hz}} = 0.6577 \text{ m} = 65.77 \text{ cm}$$

continued on next page

Example 12.6 continued

The first possible resonance for a tube closed at one end occurs when there is a pressure node at the open end, a pressure antinode at the closed end, and no other pressure nodes or antinodes. Therefore,

$$L_1 = \tfrac{1}{4}\lambda = \tfrac{1}{4} \times 65.77 \text{ cm} = 16.4 \text{ cm}$$

To reach other resonances, the tube must be pulled out to accommodate additional pressure nodes and antinodes. To add one node and one antinode, the additional distance is $\tfrac{1}{2}\lambda$ = 32.9 cm. The resonances occur at intervals of 32.9 cm:

$$L_2 = 16.4 \text{ cm} + 32.9 \text{ cm} = 49.3 \text{ cm}$$

$$L_3 = 49.3 \text{ cm} + 32.9 \text{ cm} = 82.2 \text{ cm}$$

The next one would require a tube longer than 1.00 m, so there are three values of L that produce resonance in this tube.

Discussion As a check, we can sketch the standing wave pattern for the third resonance (Figs. 12.8a,b). There are 5 quarter-wavelengths in the length of the column, so

$$L_3 = \tfrac{5}{4}\lambda = \tfrac{5}{4} \times 65.77 \text{ cm} = 82.2 \text{ cm}$$

At the open end of the tube, the node for pressure and the antinode for maximum displacement is actually a little *above* the opening. For this reason it is best to measure the distance between two successive resonances to find an accurate value

for a half-wavelength rather than measuring the distance for the first possible resonance, the shortest distance between the opening and the water surface, and setting it equal to a quarter-wavelength.

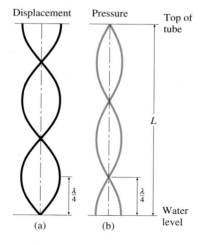

Figure 12.8

(a) Standing wave pattern, showing *displacement* nodes and antinodes, for the third resonance. (b) Standing wave pattern, showing *pressure* nodes and antinodes, for the third resonance.

Practice Problem 12.6   A Roundabout Way to Measure Temperature

A tuning fork of frequency 440.0 Hz is held above the hollow tube in Example 12.6. If the distance ΔL that the tube is moved between resonances is 39.3 cm, what is the temperature of the air inside the tube?

Problem-Solving Strategy for Standing Waves

There is no need to memorize equations for standing wave frequencies and wavelengths. Just sketch the standing wave patterns as in Figs. 12.3 and 12.5. Make sure that nodes and antinodes alternate and that the boundary conditions at the ends are correct. Then determine the wavelengths by setting the distance between a node and antinode equal to $\tfrac{1}{4}\lambda$. Once the wavelengths are known, the frequencies are found from $v = f\lambda$.

PHYSICS AT HOME

You can set up a resonance in an empty water bottle by blowing horizontally across the top of the bottle. Once you have heard one resonance, add varying amounts of water to raise the level within and listen for other resonances. The resonant sound is noticeably louder than the nonresonant sounds. Notice that the longer the air column within the bottle, the lower the pitch heard.

12.5   TIMBRE

The sound produced by the vibration of a tuning fork is nearly a pure sinusoid at a single frequency. In contrast, most musical instruments produce complex sounds that are the superposition of many different frequencies. The standing wave on a string or in a column of air is almost always the superposition of many standing wave patterns at

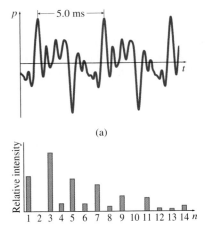

(a)

(b)

Figure 12.9 (a) A graph of the sound wave produced by a clarinet. (b) A bar graph showing the relative intensities of the harmonics, often called the *spectrum*. The frequency of each harmonic is nf_1, where $f_1 = 200$ Hz. Notice that *odd* multiples of the fundamental dominate the spectrum. A simple pipe closed at one end would show *only* odd multiples in its spectrum. (Data courtesy of P. D. Krasicky, Cornell University.)

different frequencies. The lowest frequency in a complex sound wave is called the fundamental; the rest of the frequencies are called **overtones**. All the overtones of a periodic sound wave have frequencies that are integral multiples of the fundamental; the fundamental and the overtones are then called **harmonics**.

Middle C played on an oboe does not sound the same as middle C played on a trumpet, even though the fundamental frequency is the same, largely because the two instruments produce overtones with different relative amplitudes. What is different about the two sounds is the **tone quality**, or **timbre** (pronounced "tamber").

Any periodic wave, no matter how complicated, can be decomposed into a set of harmonics, each of which is a simple sinusoid. The characteristic wave form for a note played on a clarinet, for example, can be decomposed into its harmonic series (Fig. 12.9). This process is called harmonic analysis, or Fourier analysis, in honor of the French mathematician, Jean Baptiste Joseph Fourier (1768–1830), who developed mathematical methods for analyzing periodic functions. Although the spectrum of a periodic wave consists only of members of a harmonic sequence, not all members of the sequence need be present, not even the fundamental (Fig. 12.10).

The opposite of harmonic analysis is harmonic synthesis: combining various harmonics to produce a complex wave. Electronic synthesizers can mimic the sounds of various instruments. Realistic-sounding synthesizers must also allow the adjustment of other parameters such as the attack and decay of the sound.

Figure 12.10 Complex wave form (bottom wave) composed by superposition of three sinusoidal waves (three upper waves). A wave with three harmonic components having frequencies of 110, 165, and 220 Hz repeats at a frequency of 55 Hz because each of these three frequencies is an integral multiple of 55 Hz. Even though the fundamental is missing—there is no harmonic component at 55 Hz—the ear is clever enough to "reconstruct" a 55-Hz tone. That's why you can listen to and recognize music on an inexpensive radio whose speaker may reproduce only a small range of frequencies.

12.6 THE HUMAN EAR

Figure 12.11 shows the structure of the human ear. The human ear has an external part or *pinna* that acts something like a funnel, collecting sound waves and concentrating them at the opening of the auditory canal. The pinna is better at collecting sound coming from in front than from behind, which helps with localization. Resonance in the *auditory canal* (see Problem 56) boosts the ear's sensitivity in the 2- to 5-kHz frequency range—a crucial range for understanding speech.

At the end of the auditory canal, the eardrum (*tympanum*) vibrates in response to the incident sound wave. The region just beyond the eardrum is called the middle ear. The vibrations of the eardrum are transmitted through three tiny bones of the middle ear (the *auditory ossicles*) to the *oval window* of the *cochlea*, a tapered spiral-shaped organ filled with fluid. The oval window is a membrane that is in contact with the fluid in the cochlea. The ossicles act as levers; the force exerted by the "stirrup" on the oval window is 1.5 to 2.0 times the force the eardrum exerts on the "hammer." The area of the oval window is one-twentieth that of the eardrum, so there is an overall amplification in pressure by a factor of 30 to 40. The ossicles protect the ear from damage: in response to a loud sound, a muscle pulls the stirrup away from the oval window. At the same time, another muscle increases the eardrum tension. These two changes make the ear temporarily less sensitive. It takes a few milliseconds for the muscles to respond in this way, so they provide no protection against *sudden* loud sounds.

The *cochlear partition* runs most of the length of the cochlea, separating it into two chambers (the *scala vestibuli* and the *scala tympani*). Vibration of the oval window sends a compressional wave down the fluid in the scala vestibuli, around the end of the partition, and back up the scala tympani to the *round window*. This wave sets the *basilar membrane*, located on the cochlear partition, into vibration. The basilar membrane is thinnest and under greatest tension near the oval and round windows; it gradually increases in thickness and decreases in tension toward its other end. High-frequency waves cause the membrane to vibrate with maximum amplitude near its thin, high-tension end; low-frequency

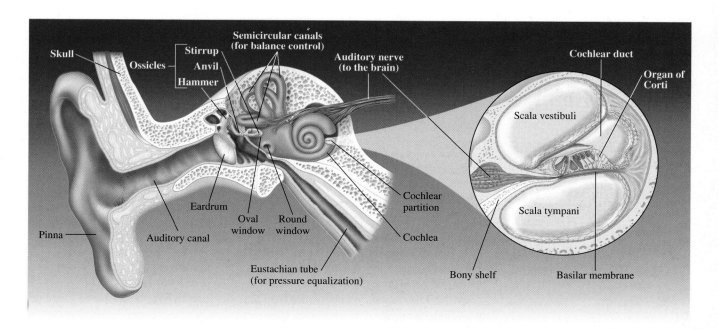

Figure 12.11 Structure of the human ear with a cross section of the cochlea.

waves cause maximum amplitude vibrations near its thicker, lower-tension end. The location of the maximum amplitude vibrations is one way the ear determines frequency; for low-frequency sounds (up to about 1 kHz), the ear sends periodic nerve signals to the brain at the frequency of the sound wave. For complex sounds, which consist of the superposition of many different frequencies (see Section 12.5), the ear performs a spectral analysis—it decomposes the complex sound into its constituent frequencies.

Located on the basilar membrane is the sensory organ (the *organ of Corti*). Rows of hair cells on the basilar membrane excite neurons when they bend in response to vibration. These neurons send electrical signals to the brain.

Loudness

Although loudness is most closely correlated to intensity level, it also depends on frequency (as well as other factors). In other words, the sensitivity of the ear is frequency-dependent. Figure 12.12 shows a set of *curves of equal loudness* for a typical person. Each curve shows the intensity levels at which sounds of different frequencies are perceived to be equally loud.

Pitch

Pitch is the perception of frequency. If you sing or play up and down a scale, it is the pitch that is rising and falling. Although pitch is the aspect of sound perception most closely tied to a single physical quantity, frequency, our sense of pitch is affected to a small extent by other factors such as intensity and timbre (Section 12.5).

Our sense of pitch is a *logarithmic* function of frequency, just as loudness is approximately a logarithmic function of intensity. If you start at the lowest note on the piano (which has a fundamental frequency of 27.5 Hz) and play a chromatic scale—every

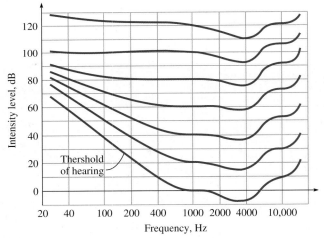

Figure 12.12 Curves of equal loudness. The curves show that the ear is most sensitive to frequencies between 3 kHz and 4 kHz, partly due to resonance in the auditory canal. The ear's sensitivity falls off rapidly below 800 Hz and above 10 kHz. At any given frequency between 800 Hz and 10 kHz, the curves are approximately evenly spaced: equal steps in intensity level produce equal steps in loudness, which is why intensity level is often used as an approximate measure of loudness. In this frequency range, 1 dB is about the smallest change in intensity level that is perceptible as a change in loudness. The threshold of hearing is shown by the lowest curve in the set; a person with excellent hearing cannot hear sounds with intensity levels below this curve. The threshold of hearing is at an intensity level of 0 dB only in the vicinity of 1 kHz.

white and black key in turn—all the way to the highest note (4190 Hz), you hear a series of equal steps in pitch. The frequencies do *not* increase in equal steps; the fundamental frequency of each note is 5.95% higher than the previous note. Under ideal conditions, most people can sense frequency changes as small as 0.3%. A trained musician can sense a frequency change of 0.1% or so.

Localization

How can you tell where a sound comes from? The ear has several different tools it uses to localize sounds:

- The principal method for high-frequency sounds (> 4 kHz) is the difference in intensity sensed by the two ears. The head casts a "sound shadow," so a sound coming from the right has a larger intensity at the right ear than at the left ear.
- The shape of the pinna makes it slightly preferential to sounds coming from the front. This helps with front-back localization for high-frequency sounds.
- For lower-frequency sounds, both the difference in arrival time and the phase difference between the waves arriving at the two ears are used for localization.

12.7 BEATS

When two sound waves are close in frequency (within about 15 Hz of one another), the superposition of the two produces a pulsation that we call **beats**. Beats can be produced by any kind of wave; they are a general result of the principle of superposition when applied to two waves of nearly the same frequency.

Beats are caused by the slow change in the phase difference between the two waves. Suppose that at one instant ($t = 0$ in Fig. 12.13), the two waves are in phase with one another and interfere constructively. The amplitude of the superposition is the sum of the amplitudes of the two waves shown in Fig. 12.13a. However, since the frequencies are different, the waves do not *stay* in phase. The higher-frequency wave has a shorter cycle, so it gets ahead of the other one. The phase difference between the two steadily increases; as it does, the amplitude of the superposition decreases. At a later time ($t = 5T_0$), the phase difference reaches 180°; now the waves are half a cycle out of phase and interfere destructively (Fig. 12.13b). Now the amplitude of the superposition is minimum—the difference

CONNECTION:

When two waves with different frequencies are superimposed, constructive interference alternates with destructive interference, causing *beats*.

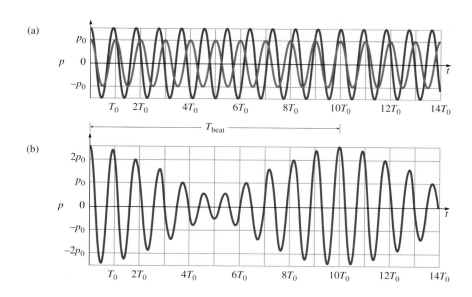

Figure 12.13 (a) Graph (red) of a sound wave with frequency $f_1 = 1/T_0$ and amplitude p_0. Graph (blue) of a second sound wave with frequency $f_2 = 1.1f_1$ and amplitude $1.5p_0$. (b) The superposition of the two has maximum amplitude $2.5p_0$ and minimum amplitude $0.5p_0$.

between the amplitudes of the two waves. As the phase difference continues to increase, the amplitude increases until constructive interference occurs again ($t = 10T_0$). The ear perceives the amplitude (and intensity) cycling from large to small to large to small as a pulsation—a repeating alternation of increasing and decreasing loudness.

At what frequency do the beats occur? It depends on how far apart the frequencies of the two waves are. We can measure the time between beats T_{beat} as the time to go from constructive interference to the next occurrence of constructive interference. During that time, each wave must go through a whole number of cycles, with one of them going through one more cycle than the other. Since frequency (f) is the number of cycles per second, the number of cycles a wave goes through during a time T_{beat} is fT_{beat}. (To illustrate: in Fig. 12.13, $T_{beat} = 10T_0$. During that time, wave 1 goes through $f_1 T_{beat} = 10$ cycles, while wave 2 goes through $f_2 T_{beat} = 1.1/T_0 \times 10T_0 = 11$ cycles.) If $f_2 > f_1$, then wave 2 goes through one cycle more than wave 1:

$$f_2 T_{beat} - f_1 T_{beat} = (\Delta f)T_{beat} = 1$$

The beat frequency f_{beat} is $1/T_{beat}$:

$$f_{beat} = 1/T_{beat} = \Delta f \qquad (12\text{-}11)$$

Thus, we obtain the remarkably simple result that the beat frequency is the difference between the frequencies of the two waves. If the difference in frequencies exceeds roughly 15 Hz, then the ear no longer perceives the beats; instead, we hear two tones at different pitches.

✓ CHECKPOINT 12.7

(a) At what time(s) in Fig. 12.13 do the two waves interfere constructively?
(b) At what time(s) do they interfere destructively?

Application of beats: tuning a piano

Piano tuners listen for beats as they tune. The tuner sounds two strings and listens for the beats. The beat frequency indicates whether the interval is correct or not. If the two strings are played by the same key, they are tuned to the same fundamental frequency, so the beat frequency should be (nearly) zero. If the two strings belong to two different notes, the beat frequency is nonzero. In this case the tuner listens to beats between two *overtones* that are close in frequency.

Example 12.7

The Piano Tuner

A piano tuner strikes his tuning fork ($f = 523.3$ Hz) and strikes a key on the piano at the same time. The two have nearly the same frequency; he hears 3.0 beats per second. As he tightens the piano string, he hears the beat frequency gradually decrease to 2.0 beats per second when the two sound together. (a) What was the frequency of the piano string before it was tightened? (b) By what percentage did the tension increase?

Strategy   The beat frequency is the difference between the two frequencies; we only have to determine which is higher. The wavelength of the string is determined by its length, which does not change. The increase in tension increases the speed of waves on the string, which in turn increases the frequency.

Solution   (a) Since the piano tuner heard 3.0 beats per second, the difference in the two frequencies was 3.0 Hz:

$$\Delta f = 3.0 \text{ Hz}$$

Is the piano string's frequency 3.0 Hz higher or 3.0 Hz lower than the tuning fork's frequency? As the tension increases gradually, the beat frequency decreases, which means that the frequency of the piano string is getting *closer* to the frequency

continued on next page

Example 12.7 continued

of the tuning fork. Therefore, the string frequency must be 3.0 Hz *lower* than the tuning fork frequency:

$$f_{string} = 523.3 \text{ Hz} - 3.0 \text{ Hz} = 520.3 \text{ Hz}$$

(b) The tension (F) is related to the speed of the wave on the string (v) and the mass per unit length (μ) by

$$v = \sqrt{\frac{F}{\mu}} \qquad (11\text{-}4)$$

The mass per unit length does not change, so $v \propto \sqrt{F}$. The speed of the wave on the string is related to its wavelength and frequency by

$$v = \lambda f$$

⚠ The wavelength λ in this expression is the wavelength of the transverse wave on the string, *not* the wavelength of the sound wave in air. Since λ does not change, $v \propto f$. Therefore, $f \propto \sqrt{F}$ or

$$F \propto f^2$$

This means that the ratio of the tension F to the original tension F_0 is equal to the ratio of the frequencies squared:

$$\frac{F}{F_0} = \left(\frac{f}{f_0}\right)^2 = \left(\frac{521.3 \text{ Hz}}{520.3 \text{ Hz}}\right)^2 = 1.004$$

The tension was increased 0.4%.

Discussion We needed to find whether the original frequency was too high or too low. As the beat frequency decreases, the frequency of the string is getting closer to the frequency of the tuning fork. Tightening the string makes the string's frequency increase; since increasing the string's frequency brings it closer to the tuning fork's frequency, we know that the original frequency of the string was lower than the frequency of the tuning fork. Had an increase in tension *increased* the beat frequency instead, we would know that the original frequency was already too high; the tension would have to be relaxed to tune the string.

Practice Problem 12.7   Tuning a Violin

A tuning fork with a frequency of 440.0 Hz produces 4.0 beats per second when sounded together with a violin string of nearly the same frequency. What is the frequency of the string if a slight increase in tension increases the beat frequency?

12.8   THE DOPPLER EFFECT

A police car races by, its sirens screaming. As it passes, we hear the pitch change from higher to lower. The frequency change is called the **Doppler effect**, after the Austrian physicist Johann Christian Andreas Doppler (1803–1853). The observed frequency is different from the frequency transmitted by the source when the source or the observer are in motion relative to the wave medium.

We consider only the motion of the source and observer directly toward or away from one another in the reference frame in which the wave medium is at rest. Velocities of the source and observer are expressed as components along the direction of propagation of the sound wave (from source to observer). A positive component means the velocity is in the direction of propagation of the wave, but a negative component means the velocity is opposite the direction of propagation.

Moving Source

First we consider a moving source. A source emits a sound wave at frequency f_s, which means that wave crests (regions of maximum amplitude, indicated by circles in Fig. 12.14) leave the source spaced by a time interval $T_s = 1/f_s$. If the source is moving at velocity v_s toward a stationary observer on the right, Fig. 12.14a shows that the wavelength—the distance between crests—is smaller in front of the source and larger behind the source. In Fig. 12.14b, at the instant that crest 6 is emitted, crest 5 has traveled outward a distance vT_s from point 5, where v is the speed of sound. During the same time interval, the source has advanced a distance v_sT_s. The wavelength λ, measured by the observer on the right is the distance between crests 5 and 6:

$$\lambda = vT_s - v_sT_s$$

Figure 12.14 (a) A speedboat is moving to the right at speed v_s (exaggerated for clarity) while it blows its siren. The siren emits wave crests at positions 1, 2, 3, 4, 5, and 6; each wave crest moves outward in all directions, from the point at which it was emitted, at speed v. (b) Wave crest 6 is emitted a time T_s after wave crest 5 is emitted. During that time, wave crest 5 moves a distance vT_s and the boat moves a distance v_sT_s. The wavelength is the distance between wave crests: $\lambda = vT_s - v_sT_s$.

The frequency at which the crests arrive at the observer is the *observed* wave frequency f_o. The observed period T_o between the arrival of two crests is the time it takes sound to travel a distance $(v - v_s)T_s$:

$$T_o = \frac{\lambda}{v} = \frac{(v - v_s)T_s}{v}$$

The observed frequency is

$$f_o = \frac{1}{T_o} = \frac{v}{v - v_s} \times \frac{1}{T_s}$$

Dividing numerator and denominator by v and substituting $f_s = 1/T_s$ yields

Doppler effect (moving source):

$$f_o = \left(\frac{1}{1 - v_s/v}\right)f_s \qquad (12\text{-}12)$$

$v_s > 0$ for a source moving in the direction of the wave

Since the denominator $1 - v_s/v$ is less than 1, the observed frequency is higher than the source frequency when the source moves in the same direction as the wave (toward the observer). If the source instead moves *away* from the observer, the correct observed frequency is given by Eq. (12-12) as long as we make v_s negative (the source moves opposite the direction of the wave). With v_s negative, $1 - v_s/v$ is *greater* than 1, so the observed frequency is *less* than the source frequency.

Moving Observer

Now we consider motion of the observer. A stationary source emits a sound wave at frequency f_s and wavelength $\lambda = v/f_s$, where v is the speed of sound. A stationary observer would measure the arrival of wave crests spaced by a time interval $T_s = 1/f_s$. An observer

Figure 12.15 An observer moving at speed v_o (exaggerated for clarity) away from a stationary sound source. The observed frequency is lower than the source frequency.

moving away from the source at velocity v_o would observe a longer time interval between crests. Just as crest 1 reaches the observer, the next (crest 2) is a distance λ away. Crest 2 catches up with the observer at a time T_o later when the distance the wave crest travels toward the observer is equal to the distance the observer travels away from the wave crest plus the wavelength (Fig. 12.15):

$$vT_o = v_o T_o + \lambda \quad \text{or} \quad (v - v_o)T_o = \lambda = v/f_s$$

Solving for T_o,

$$T_o = \frac{v/f_s}{v - v_o}$$

The observed frequency is

$$f_o = \frac{1}{T_o} = \frac{v - v_o}{v} f_s$$

Dividing numerator and denominator by v yields

Doppler effect (moving observer):

$$f_o = (1 - v_o/v)f_s \qquad (12\text{-}13)$$

$v_o > 0$ for an observer moving in the direction of the wave

An observer moving away from the source measures a frequency lower than f_s. An observer moving *toward* the source moves opposite to the direction of the wave; in that case, v_o is negative and the observed frequency is *higher* than f_s.

✓ CHECKPOINT 12.8

(a) Does the motion of the source of a sound wave affect the wavelength?
(b) Does the motion of the observer affect the wavelength?

Example 12.8

Train Whistle and Doppler Shift

A monorail train approaches a platform at a speed of 10.0 m/s while it blows its whistle. A musician with perfect pitch standing on the platform hears the whistle as "middle C," a frequency of 261 Hz. There is no wind and the temperature is a chilly 0°C. What is the observed frequency of the whistle when the train is at rest?

Strategy In this case, the source—the whistle—is moving and the observer is stationary. The source is moving *toward*

the observer, so v_s is *positive*. With the source approaching the observer, the observed frequency is higher than the source frequency. When the train is at rest, there is no Doppler shift; the observed frequency then is equal to the source frequency.

Solution For a moving source, the source (f_s) and observed (f_o) frequencies are related by

$$f_o = \left(\frac{1}{1 - v_s/v} \right) f_s$$

continued on next page

Example 12.8 continued

where $v = 331$ m/s (the speed of sound in air at 0°C), $v_s = +10.0$ m/s, and $f_o = 261$ Hz. Solving for f_s,

$$f_s = (1 - v_s/v)f_o$$

$$= \left(1 - \frac{10.0 \text{ m/s}}{331 \text{ m/s}}\right) \times 261 \text{ Hz}$$

$$= 253 \text{ Hz}$$

The source frequency is less than the observed frequency, as expected. The observed frequency when the train is at rest is equal to the source frequency: 253 Hz.

Discussion   When the train is moving toward the platform, the distance between source and observer is decreasing. Wave crests emitted later take *less time* to reach the observer than if the train were at rest, so the time between arrivals of wave crests is smaller than if the train were stationary. When the distance between source and observer is decreasing, the observed frequency is higher than the source frequency; when the distance is increasing, the observed frequency is lower than the source frequency.

Practice Problem 12.8   A Sports Car Racing By

Justine is gardening in her front yard when a Mazda Miata races by at 32.0 m/s (71.6 mi/h). If she hears the sound of the Miata's engine at 220.0 Hz as it approaches her, what frequency does she hear after it passes? Assume the temperature is 20°C and there is no wind.

Motion of Both Source and Observer

If both source and observer are moving, we combine the two Doppler shifts (see Conceptual Question 10) to obtain

$$f_o = \left(\frac{1 - v_o/v}{1 - v_s/v}\right)f_s = \left(\frac{v - v_o}{v - v_s}\right)f_s \qquad (12\text{-}14)$$

 Remember that the signs of v_o and v_s are positive for motion in the direction of propagation of the wave and negative for motion opposite the direction of propagation.

Example 12.9

Determining Speed from Horn Frequency

Two cars, with equal ground speeds, are moving in opposite directions away from each other on a straight highway. One driver blows a horn with a frequency of 111 Hz; the other measures the frequency as 105 Hz. If the speed of sound is 338 m/s and there is no wind, what is the ground speed of each car?

Strategy   A sound wave travels from source to observer. The source moves opposite the direction of the wave, so v_s is negative. The observer moves in the direction of the wave, so v_o is positive. The speeds are the same, so $v_s = -v_o$.

Solution   With both the source and observer moving, the frequencies are related by

$$f_o = \left(\frac{1 - v_o/v}{1 - v_s/v}\right)f_s$$

To simplify the algebra, we let $\alpha = v_o/v = -v_s/v$. Then

$$f_o = \left(\frac{1 - \alpha}{1 + \alpha}\right)f_s$$

Now we solve for α:

$$(1 + \alpha)\frac{f_o}{f_s} = 1 - \alpha$$

$$\alpha = \frac{1 - f_o/f_s}{1 + f_o/f_s} = \frac{1 - (105 \text{ Hz})/(111 \text{ Hz})}{1 + (105 \text{ Hz})/(111 \text{ Hz})} = 0.02778$$

Now we can find v_o:

$$v_o = \alpha v = 0.02778 \times 338 \text{ m/s} = 9.4 \text{ m/s}$$

The speed of each car is 9.4 m/s.

Discussion   Quick check on the algebra: substituting $v = 338$ m/s, $f_s = 111$ Hz, $v_o = 9.4$ m/s, and $v_s = -9.4$ m/s directly into Eq. (12-14),

$$f_o = \frac{1 - (9.4 \text{ m/s})/(338 \text{ m/s})}{1 - (-9.4 \text{ m/s})/(338 \text{ m/s})} \times 111 \text{ Hz} = 105 \text{ Hz}$$

Practice Problem 12.9   Finding Speed from the Doppler Shift

A car is driving due west at 15 m/s and sounds its horn with a frequency of 260.0 Hz. A passenger in a car heading east away from the first car hears the horn at a frequency of 230.0 Hz. How fast is the second car traveling? The speed of sound is 350 m/s.

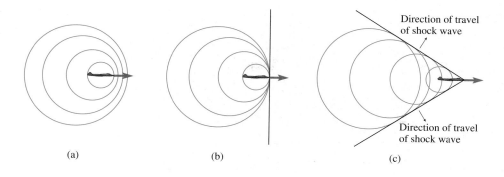

(a)   (b)   (c)

Figure 12.16 (a) Wave crests for a plane moving slower than sound. (b) A plane moving at the speed of sound; the wave crests pile up on each other since the plane moves to the right as fast as the wave crests. (c) Shock wave for a supersonic plane. The wave crests pile up along the cone indicated by the black lines.

Shock Waves

Let's examine two interesting special cases of the Doppler formula [Eq. (12-14)]. First, what if the observer moves away from the source at the speed of sound ($v_o = v$)? The Doppler-shifted frequency would be zero according to Eq. (12-14). What does that mean? If the observer moves away from the source with a speed equal to (or greater than) the wave speed, the wave crests *never reach the observer.*

Second, what if the source moves toward the observer at a speed approaching the speed of sound ($v_s \rightarrow v$)? Then Eq. (12-14) gives an observed frequency that increases without bound ($f_o \rightarrow \infty$). Figure 12.16 helps us understand what that means. For a plane moving slower than sound, the wave crests in front of it are closer together due to the plane's motion (Fig. 12.16a). An observer to the right would measure a frequency higher than the source frequency. As the plane's speed increases, the wave crests in front of it get closer and closer together and the observed frequency increases. For a plane moving at the speed of sound (Fig. 12.16b), the wave crests pile up on top of each other; they move to the right at the same speed as the plane, so they can't get ahead of it. An observer to the right would measure a wavelength of zero—zero distance between wave crests—and therefore an infinite frequency.

What happens if the source moves at a speed *greater than* the speed of sound? Figure 12.16c shows that the wave crests pile up on top of one another to form cone-shaped *shock waves*, which travel outward in the direction indicated. There are two principal shock waves formed, one starting at the nose of the plane and one at the tail (Fig. 12.17). The sound of a shock wave is referred to as a *sonic boom.*

Figure 12.17 A bullet moving through air faster than sound. Notice the two principal shock waves starting at either end of the bullet.

Application of shock waves: supersonic flight

See text website for more information about supersonic flight.

PHYSICS AT HOME

You can make a visible shock wave by trailing your finger along the surface of the water in a sink or tub. If your finger pushes the water faster than water waves travel, water piles up in front of your finger and forms a V-shaped shock wave. See if you can approximate the case of a plane moving at the speed of sound with rounded waves moving outward from your finger (Fig. 12.16b) instead of a V-shaped wave. The next time you are in a boat, notice the V-shaped bow wave that extends from the prow of the boat when you are moving faster than the speed of water waves.

12.9 ECHOLOCATION AND MEDICAL IMAGING

Bats, dolphins, whales, and some birds use *echolocation* to locate prey and to "see" their environment. To find their way around in the darkness of caves, oilbirds of northern South America and cave swiftlets of Borneo and East Asia emit sound waves and listen for the echoes. The time it takes for the echoes to return tells them how far they are from an obstacle or cave wall. Differences between the echoes that reach the two sides of the head provide information on the direction from which the echo comes.

Application of echolocation by bats and dolphins

The sounds used by oilbirds and cave swiftlets for echolocation are audible to humans, but dolphins, whales, and most bats use ultrasound (20 to 200 kHz) instead. Bats and dolphins can also determine an object's velocity by sensing the Doppler shift between the emitted and reflected waves—a clear advantage in locating prey that are darting around to avoid being eaten. Some horseshoe bats can detect frequency differences as small as 0.1 Hz.

Prey are not completely helpless. Moths, lacewings, and praying mantises have primitive ears containing a few nerve cells to detect the ultrasound emitted by a nearby bat. A group of moths fluttering about at some distance from a cave may, for no apparent reason, fold their wings and drop suddenly to the ground. Folding their wings both reduces the amount of reflected sound and helps them drop quickly to the ground to evade the swooping bat. The moths' bodies are furry rather than smooth to help absorb some of the sound waves and thus reduce the intensity of reflected sound.

When the tiger moth detects the ultrasound from a bat, it emits its own ultrasound by flexing a part of its exoskeleton. The extra sounds mixed in with the echoes tend to confuse the bat, perhaps encouraging it to hunt elsewhere.

Application of echolocation:
sonar and radar

Echolocation is a useful navigational tool for seafarers. To find the depth of water below a ship, a *sonar* (**so**und **na**vigation and **r**anging) device sends out ultrasonic pulses (Fig. 12.18). The time delay Δt between an emitted ultrasonic pulse and the return of its reflection is used to determine the distance to the seafloor. Seismic P waves—sound waves traveling through the Earth—generated by explosions or air guns are used to study the interior structure of Earth and to find oil beneath the surface.

Radar is a form of echolocation that uses electromagnetic waves instead of sound waves, but otherwise the concept is similar. Weather forecasting relies on *Doppler radar* to show not only the location of a storm, but also the wind velocity.

 ### Medical Applications of Ultrasound

Millions of expectant parents see their unborn child for the first time when the mother has an ultrasonic examination. Ultrasonic imaging uses a pulse-echo technique similar to that used by bats and in sonar. Pulses of ultrasound are reflected at boundaries between different types of tissue.

Figure 12.18 A ship with a sonar device to locate the depth of the seafloor; an ultrasound pulse, sent out from the ship by a transmitter, is reflected from the seafloor and detected by a receiver on the ship.

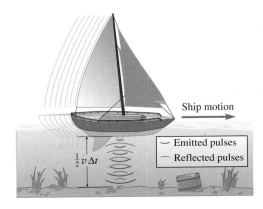

In the early stages of pregnancy (tenth to fourteenth weeks), the scan is used to verify that the fetus is alive and to check for twins. The length of the fetus is measured to help determine the due date more accurately. Some abnormalities can be discovered even at this early stage. For example, some chromosomal abnormalities can be detected by measuring the thickness of the skin at the back of the neck. After the eighteenth week, the fetus can be examined in even more detail. The major organs are examined to be sure they are developing normally. After the thirtieth week, the flow of blood in the umbilical cord is checked to ensure that oxygen and nutrients reach the fetus. The position of the placenta is also checked.

Why are sound waves used rather than, say, electromagnetic waves such as x-rays? X-ray radiation is damaging to tissue—especially to rapidly growing fetal tissue. After decades of use, ultrasound has no known adverse effects. In addition, ultrasound images are captured in real time, so they are available immediately and can show movement. A third reason is that regular x-rays detect the amount of radiation that passes through tissue, but cannot resolve details at different depths, and so cannot produce an image of a "slice" of the abdomen; a more complicated and expensive diagnostic tool such as a CAT scan (computer-assisted tomography) would be required to resolve details at different depths. Fourth, some kinds of tissue are not detected well by x-rays but are clearly resolved in ultrasound.

Why is ultrasound used rather than sound waves of audible frequencies or lower? Sound waves with high frequencies have small wavelengths. Waves with small wavelengths diffract less around the same obstacle than do waves with larger wavelengths (see Section 11.9). Too much diffraction would obscure details in the image. As a rough rule of thumb, the wavelength is a lower limit on the smallest detail that can be resolved. The frequencies used in imaging are typically in the range 1 to 15 MHz, which means that the wavelengths in human tissue are in the range 0.1 to 1.5 mm. As a comparison, if sound waves at 15 kHz were used, the wavelength inside the body would be 10 cm. Higher frequencies give better resolution but at the expense of less penetration; sound waves are absorbed within a distance of about 500λ in tissue.

The medical applications of ultrasonic imaging are not limited to prenatal care. Ultrasound is also used to examine organs such as the heart, liver, gallbladder, kidneys, bladder, breasts, and eyes, and to locate tumors. It can be used to diagnose various heart conditions and to assess damage after a heart attack (Fig. 12.19). Ultrasound can show movement, so it is used to assess heart valve function and to monitor blood flow in large blood vessels. Because ultrasound provides real-time images, it is sometimes used to guide procedures such as biopsies, in which a needle is used to take a sample from an organ or tumor for testing.

Doppler ultrasound is a technique that is used to examine blood flow. It can help reveal blockages to blood flow, show the formation of plaque in arteries, and provide detailed information on the heartbeat of the fetus during labor and delivery. The Doppler-shifted reflections interfere with the emitted ultrasound, producing beats. The beat frequency is proportional to the speed of the reflecting object (see Problem 52).

Why is ultrasound used to image the fetus?

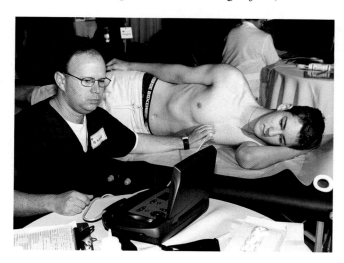

Figure 12.19 Ultrasonic imaging is used to diagnose heart disease.

Master the Concepts

- A sound wave can be described either by the gauge pressure p, which measures the pressure fluctuations above and below the ambient atmospheric pressure, or by the displacement s of each point in the medium from its undisturbed position.

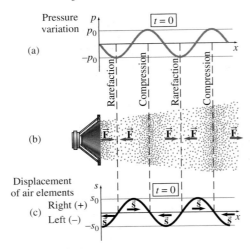

- Humans with excellent hearing can hear frequencies from 20 Hz to 20 kHz. The terms infrasound and ultrasound are used to describe sound waves with frequencies below 20 Hz and above 20 kHz, respectively.

- The speed of sound in a fluid is

$$v = \sqrt{\frac{B}{\rho}} \qquad (12\text{-}1)$$

- The speed of sound in an ideal gas at any absolute temperature T can be found if it is known at one temperature:

$$v = v_0 \sqrt{\frac{T}{T_0}} \qquad (12\text{-}3)$$

where the speed of sound at absolute temperature T_0 is v_0.

- The speed of sound in air at 0°C (or 273 K) is 331 m/s.

- For sound waves traveling along the length of a thin solid rod, the speed is approximately

$$v = \sqrt{\frac{Y}{\rho}} \quad \text{(thin solid rod)} \qquad (12\text{-}5)$$

- The pressure amplitude of a sound wave is proportional to the displacement amplitude. For a harmonic sound wave at angular frequency ω,

$$p_0 = \omega v \rho s_0 \qquad (12\text{-}6)$$

where v is the speed of sound and ρ is the mass density of the medium.

- The intensity of a sound wave is related to the pressure amplitude as follows:

$$I = \frac{p_0^2}{2\rho v} \qquad (12\text{-}7)$$

where ρ is the mass density of the medium and v is the speed of sound in that medium. The most important thing to remember is that *intensity is proportional to amplitude squared*, which is true for all waves, not just sound.

- Sound intensity level in decibels is

$$\beta = (10 \text{ dB}) \log_{10} \frac{I}{I_0} \qquad (12\text{-}8)$$

where $I_0 = 10^{-12}$ W/m^2. Sound intensity level is useful since it roughly corresponds to the way we perceive loudness. Equal increments in intensity level roughly correspond to equal increases in loudness.

- In a standing sound wave in a thin pipe, an open end is a pressure node and a displacement antinode; a closed end is a pressure antinode and a displacement node.

For a pipe open at both ends,

$$\lambda_n = \frac{2L}{n} \qquad (11\text{-}12)$$

$$f_n = n\frac{v}{2L} = nf_1 \qquad (11\text{-}13)$$

where $n = 1, 2, 3, \dots$.

For a pipe closed at one end,

$$\lambda_n = \frac{4L}{n} \qquad (12\text{-}10a)$$

$$f_n = n\frac{v}{4L} = nf_1 \qquad (12\text{-}10b)$$

where $n = 1, 3, 5, 7, \dots$.

- When two sound waves are close in frequency, the superposition of the two produces a pulsation called *beats*.

$$f_{\text{beat}} = \Delta f \qquad (12\text{-}11)$$

- Doppler effect: if v_s and v_o are the velocities of the source and observer, the observed frequency is

$$f_o = \left(\frac{1 - v_o/v}{1 - v_s/v}\right) f_s \qquad (12\text{-}14)$$

where v_s and v_o are positive in the direction of propagation of the wave and the wave medium is at rest.

Conceptual Questions

1. Explain why the pitch of a bassoon is more sensitive to a change in air temperature than the pitch of a cello. (That's why wind players keep blowing air through the instrument to keep it in tune.)

2. On a warm day, a piano is tuned to match an organ in an auditorium. Will the piano still be in tune with the organ the next morning, when the room is cold? If not, will the organ be higher or lower in pitch than the piano? (Assume that the piano's tuning doesn't change. Why is that a reasonable assumption?)

3. Many real estate agents have an ultrasonic rangefinder that enables them to quickly and easily measure the dimensions of a room. The device is held to one wall and reads the distance to the opposite wall. How does it work?

4. For high-frequency sounds, the ear's principal method of localization is the difference in intensity sensed by the two ears. Why can't the ear reliably use this method for low-frequency sounds? Doesn't the head cast a "sound shadow" regardless of the frequency? Explain. [*Hint:* Consider diffraction of sound waves around the head.]

5. For low-frequency sounds, the ear uses the phase difference between the sound waves arriving at the two ears to determine direction. Why can't the ear reliably use phase difference for high-frequency sounds? Explain.

6. A sign along the road in Tompkins County reads, "State Law: Noise Limit, 90 decibels." If you were subjected to such a noise level for an extended period of time, would you need to worry about your hearing being affected?

7. Why is it that your own voice sounds strange to you when you hear it played back on a tape recorder, but your friends all agree that it is just what your voice sounds like? [*Hint:* Consider the media through which the sound wave travels when you usually hear your own voice.]

8. What is the purpose of the gel that is spread over the skin before an ultrasonic imaging procedure? [*Hint:* The speed of sound in the gel is similar to the speed in the body, while the speed in air is much slower. What happens to a wave at an abrupt change in wave speed?]

9. A stereo system whose amplifier can produce 60 W per channel is replaced by one rated 120 W per channel. Would you expect the new stereo to be able to play twice as loudly as the old one? Explain.

10. A moving source emits a sound wave that is heard by a moving observer. Imagine a thin wall at rest between the source and observer. The wall completely absorbs the sound and instantaneously emits an *identical* sound wave. Use this scenario to explain why we can combine the Doppler shifts due to motion of the source and observer as in Eq. (12-14). [*Hint:* What is the net effect of this imaginary wall?]

11. Explain why the displacement of air elements at condensations and rarefactions is zero.

12. Why is the speed of sound in solids generally much faster than the speed of sound in air?

13. If the pressure amplitude of a sound wave is doubled, what happens to the displacement amplitude, the intensity, and the intensity level?

14. The source and observer of a sound wave are both at rest with respect to the ground. The wind blows in the direction from source to observer. Is the observed frequency Doppler-shifted? Explain.

15. Many brass instruments have valves that increase the total length of the pipe from mouthpiece to bell. When a valve is depressed, is the fundamental frequency raised or lowered? What happens to the pitch?

16. When the viola section of an orchestra with six members plays together, is the sound 6 times as loud as when a single viola plays? Explain. Is the intensity 6 times what it would be for a single viola? [*Hint:* The six sound waves are not coherent.]

17. The fundamental frequency of the highest note on the piano is 4.186 kHz. Most musical instruments do not go that high; only a few singers can produce sounds with fundamental frequencies higher than around 1 kHz. Yet a good-quality stereo system must reproduce frequencies up to at least 16 to 18 kHz. Explain.

Multiple-Choice Questions

1. An organ pipe is closed at one end. Several standing wave patterns are sketched in the drawing. Which one is not a possible standing wave pattern for this pipe?

2. Of the standing wave patterns sketched in the drawing, which shows the lowest frequency standing wave for an organ pipe closed at one end? (tutorial: standing waves)

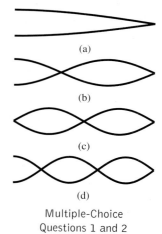

(a)

(b)

(c)

(d)

Multiple-Choice
Questions 1 and 2

3. The speed of sound in water is 4.3 times the speed of sound in air. A whistle on land produces a sound wave with a frequency f_0. When this sound wave enters the water, its frequency becomes
   (a) $4.3f_0$
   (b) f_0
   (c) $\dfrac{f_0}{4.3}$
   (d) not enough information given

4. The intensity of a sound wave is directly proportional to
   (a) the frequency.
   (b) the amplitude.
   (c) the square of the amplitude.
   (d) the square of the speed of sound.
   (e) none of the above.

5. The fundamental frequency of a pipe closed at one end is f_1. How many nodes are present in a standing wave of frequency $9f_1$?
   (a) 4   (b) 5   (c) 6   (d) 8   (e) 9   (f) 10

6. The length of a pipe closed at one end is L. In the standing wave whose frequency is 7 times the fundamental frequency, what is the closest distance between nodes?
   (a) $\frac{1}{14}L$ (b) $\frac{1}{7}L$ (c) $\frac{2}{7}L$ (d) $\frac{4}{7}L$ (e) $\frac{8}{7}L$
   (f) none of the above

7. The three lowest resonant frequencies of a system are 50 Hz, 150 Hz, and 250 Hz. The system could be
   (a) a tube of air closed at both ends.
   (b) a tube of air open at one end.
   (c) a tube of air open at both ends.
   (d) a vibrating string with fixed ends.

8. A source of sound with frequency 620 Hz is placed on a moving platform that approaches a physics student at speed v; the student hears sound with a frequency f_1. Then the source of sound is held stationary while the student approaches it at the same speed v; the student hears sound with a frequency f_2. Choose the correct statement.
   (a) $f_1 = f_2$; both are greater than 620 Hz.
   (b) $f_1 = f_2$; both are less than 620 Hz.
   (c) $f_1 > f_2 > 620$ Hz.
   (d) $f_2 > f_1 > 620$ Hz.

9. A moving van and a small car are traveling in the same direction on a two-lane road. The van is moving at twice the speed of the car and overtakes the car. The driver of the car sounds his horn, frequency = 440 Hz, to signal the van that it is safe to return to the lane. Which is the correct statement?
   (a) The car driver and van driver both hear the horn frequency as 440 Hz.
   (b) The car driver hears 440 Hz, but the van driver hears a lower frequency.
   (c) The car driver hears 440 Hz, but the van driver hears a higher frequency.
   (d) Both drivers hear the same frequency and it is lower than 440 Hz.

10. A trombone and a bassoon play notes of equal loudness with the same fundamental frequency. The two sounds differ primarily in
    (a) pitch.
    (b) intensity level.
    (c) amplitude.
    (d) timbre.
    (e) wavelength.

Problems

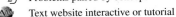
Combination conceptual/quantitative problem
Biological or medical application
Challenging problem
Blue #   Detailed solution in the Student Solutions Manual
(1   2)   Problems paired by concept
Text website interactive or tutorial

Note: Assume a temperature of 20.0°C in all problems unless otherwise indicated.

12.2 The Speed of Sound Waves

1. Bats emit ultrasonic waves with a frequency as high as 1.0×10^5 Hz. What is the wavelength of such a wave in air of temperature 15°C?

2. Dolphins emit ultrasonic waves with a frequency as high as 2.5×10^5 Hz. What is the wavelength of such a wave in seawater at 25°C?

3. At a baseball game, a spectator is 60.0 m away from the batter. How long does it take the sound of the bat connecting with the ball to travel to the spectator's ears? The air temperature is 27.0°C.

4. A lightning flash is seen in the sky and 8.2 s later the boom of the thunder is heard. The temperature of the air is 12°C. (a) What is the speed of sound at that temperature? [*Hint:* Light is an electromagnetic wave that travels at a speed of 3.00×10^8 m/s.] (b) How far away is the lightning strike?

5. During a thunderstorm, you can easily estimate your distance from a lightning strike. Count the number of seconds that elapse from when you see the flash of lightning to when you hear the thunder. The rule of thumb is that 5 s elapse for each mile of distance. Verify that this rule of thumb is (approximately) correct. (One mile is 1.6 km and light travels at a speed of 3×10^8 m/s.)

6. A copper alloy has a Young's modulus of 1.1×10^{11} Pa and a density of 8.92×10^3 kg/m^3. What is the speed of sound in a thin rod made from this alloy? Compare your result with that given in Table 12.1.

7. Find the speed of sound in mercury, which has a bulk modulus of 2.8×10^{10} Pa and a density of 1.36×10^4 kg/m^3.

8. Derive Eq. (12-4) as: (a) Starting with Eq. (12-3), substitute $T = T_C + 273.15$. (b) Apply the binomial approximation to the square root (see Appendix A.5) and simplify.

9. (a) Show that since the bulk modulus has SI units N/m^2 and mass density has SI units kg/m^3, Eq. (12-1) gives the speed of sound in m/s. Thus, the equation is dimensionally consistent. (b) Show that no other combination of B and ρ can give dimensions of speed. Thus, Eq. (12-1) *must* be correct except for the possibility of a dimensionless constant.

10. Stan and Ollie are standing next to a train track. Stan puts his ear to the steel track to hear the train coming. He hears the sound of the train whistle through the track 2.1 s before Ollie hears it through the air. How far away is the train?

12.3 Amplitude and Intensity of Sound Waves

11. A sound wave with an intensity level of 80.0 dB is incident on an eardrum of area 0.600×10^{-4} m^2. How much energy is absorbed by the eardrum in 3.0 min?

12. The sound level 25 m from a loudspeaker is 71 dB. What is the rate at which sound energy is produced by the loudspeaker, assuming it to be an isotropic source?

13. In a factory, three machines produce noise with intensity levels of 85 dB, 90 dB, and 93 dB. When all three are running, what is the intensity level? How does this compare to running just the loudest machine?

14. At the race track, one race car starts its engine with a resulting intensity level of 98.0 dB at point P. Then seven more cars start their engines. If the other seven cars each produce the same intensity level at point P as the first car, what is the new intensity level with all eight cars running?

15. (a) What is the pressure amplitude of a sound wave with an intensity level of 120.0 dB in air? (b) What force does this exert on an eardrum of area 0.550×10^{-4} m^2?

16. An intensity level change of +1.00 dB corresponds to what percentage change in intensity?

17. (a) Show that if $I_2 = 10.0I_1$, then $\beta_2 = \beta_1 + 10.0$ dB. (A factor of 10 increase in intensity corresponds to a 10.0-dB increase in intensity level.) (b) Show that if $I_2 = 2.0I_1$, then $\beta_2 = \beta_1 + 3.0$ dB. (A factor of 2 increase in intensity corresponds to a 3.0-dB increase in intensity level. tutorial: decibels)

18. At a rock concert, the engineer decides that the music isn't loud enough. He turns up the amplifiers so that the amplitude of the sound, where you're sitting, increases by 50.0%. (a) By what percentage does the intensity increase? (b) How does the intensity level (in dB) change?

12.4 Standing Sound Waves

19. Humans can hear sounds with frequencies up to about 20.0 kHz, but dogs can hear frequencies up to about 40.0 kHz. Dog whistles are made to emit sounds that dogs can hear but humans cannot. If the part of a dog whistle that actually produces the high frequency is made of a tube open at both ends, what is the longest possible length for the tube?

20. (a) What should be the length of an organ pipe, closed at one end, if the fundamental frequency is to be 261.5 Hz? (b) What is the fundamental frequency of the organ pipe of part (a) if the temperature drops to 0.0°C?

21. Repeat Problem 20 for an organ pipe that is open at both ends.

22. An organ pipe that is open at both ends has a fundamental frequency of 382 Hz at 0.0°C. What is the fundamental frequency for this pipe at 20.0°C?

23. What is the length of the organ pipe in Problem 22?

24. A certain pipe has resonant frequencies of 234 Hz, 390 Hz, and 546 Hz, with no other resonant frequencies between these values. (a) Is this a pipe open at both ends or closed at one end? (b) What is the fundamental frequency of this pipe? (c) How long is this pipe?

25. In an experiment to measure the speed of sound in air, standing waves are set up in a narrow pipe open at both ends using a speaker driven at 702 Hz. The length of the pipe is 2.0 m. What is the air temperature inside the pipe (assumed reasonably near room temperature, 20°C to 35°C)? [*Hint:* The standing wave is not necessarily the fundamental.]

26. When a tuning fork is held over the open end of a very thin tube, as in Fig. 12.7, the smallest value of L that produces resonance is found to be 30.0 cm. (a) What is the wavelength of the sound? [*Hint:* Assume that the displacement antinode is at the open end of the tube.] (b) What is the next larger value of L that will produce resonance with the same tuning fork? (c) If the frequency of the tuning fork is 282 Hz, what is the speed of sound in the tube?

27. Two tuning forks, A and B, excite the next-to-lowest resonant frequency in two air columns of the same length, but A's column is closed at one end and B's column is open at both ends. What is the ratio of A's frequency to B's frequency?

28. How long a pipe is needed to make a tuba whose lowest note is low C (frequency 130.8 Hz)? Assume that a tuba is a long straight pipe open at both ends.

29. An aluminum rod, 1.0 m long, is held lightly in the middle. One end is struck head-on with a rubber mallet so that a longitudinal pulse—a sound wave—travels down the rod. The fundamental frequency of the longitudinal vibration is 2.55 kHz. (a) Describe the location of the node(s) and antinode(s) for the fundamental mode of vibration. Use either displacement or pressure nodes and antinodes. (b) Calculate the speed of sound in aluminum from the information given in the problem. (c) The vibration of the rod produces a sound wave in air that can be heard. What is the wavelength of the sound wave in the air? Take the speed of sound in air to be 334 m/s. (d) Do the two ends of the rod vibrate longitudinally in phase or out of phase with each other? That is, at any given instant, do they move in the same direction or in opposite directions?

12.7 Beats

30. A violin is tuned by adjusting the tension in the strings. Brian's A string is tuned to a slightly lower frequency than Jennifer's, which is correctly tuned to 440.0 Hz. (a) What is the frequency of Brian's string if beats of 2.0 Hz are heard when the two bow the strings together? (b) Does Brian need to tighten or loosen his A string to get in tune with Jennifer? Explain.

31. A piano tuner sounds two strings simultaneously. One has been previously tuned to vibrate at 293.0 Hz. The tuner hears 3.0 beats per second. The tuner increases the tension on the as-yet untuned string, and now when they are played together the beat frequency is 1.0 s^{-1}. (a) What was the original frequency of the untuned string? (b) By what percentage did the tuner increase the tension on that string?

32. An auditorium has organ pipes at the front and at the rear of the hall. Two identical pipes, one at the front and one at the back, have fundamental frequencies of 264.0 Hz at 20.0°C. During a performance, the organ pipes at the back of the hall are at 25.0°C, while those at the front are still at 20.0°C. What is the beat frequency when the two pipes sound simultaneously?

33. A musician plays a string on a guitar that has a fundamental frequency of 330.0 Hz. The string is 65.5 cm long and has a mass of 0.300 g. (a) What is the tension in the string? (b) At what speed do the waves travel on the string? (c) While the guitar string is still being plucked, another musician plays a slide whistle that is closed at one end and open at the other. He starts at a very high frequency and slowly lowers the frequency until beats, with a frequency of 5 Hz, are heard with the guitar. What is the fundamental frequency of the slide whistle with the slide in this position? (d) How long is the open tube in the slide whistle for this frequency?

34. A cello string has a fundamental frequency of 65.40 Hz. What beat frequency is heard when this cello string is bowed at the same time as a violin string with frequency of 196.0 Hz? [*Hint:* The beats occur between the third harmonic of the cello string and the fundamental of the violin.]

12.8 The Doppler Effect

35. An ambulance traveling at 44 m/s approaches a car heading in the same direction at a speed of 28 m/s. The ambulance driver has a siren sounding at 550 Hz. At what frequency does the driver of the car hear the siren?

36. At a factory, a noon whistle is sounding with a frequency of 500 Hz. As a car traveling at 85 km/h approaches the factory, the driver hears the whistle at frequency f_i. After driving past the factory, the driver hears frequency f_f. What is the change in frequency $f_f - f_i$ heard by the driver?

37. In parts of the midwestern United States, sirens sound when a severe storm that may produce a tornado is approaching. Mandy is walking at a speed of 1.56 m/s directly toward one siren and directly away from another siren when they both begin to sound with a frequency of 698 Hz. What beat frequency does Mandy hear? (tutorial: Doppler effect)

38. A source of sound waves of frequency 1.0 kHz is traveling through the air at 0.50 times the speed of sound. (a) Find the frequency of the sound received by a stationary observer if the source moves toward her. (b) Repeat if the source moves away from her instead.

39. A source of sound waves of frequency 1.0 kHz is stationary. An observer is traveling at 0.50 times the speed of sound. (a) What is the observed frequency if the observer moves toward the source? (b) Repeat if the observer moves away from the source instead.

40. A child swinging on a swing set hears the sound of a whistle that is being blown directly in front of her. At the bottom of her swing when she is moving toward the whistle, she hears a higher pitch, and at the bottom of her swing when she is moving away from the swing she hears a lower pitch. The higher pitch has a frequency that is 5.0% higher than the lower pitch. What is the speed of the child at the bottom of the swing?

41. A source and an observer are *each* traveling at 0.50 times the speed of sound. The source emits sound waves at 1.0 kHz. Find the observed frequency if (a) the source and observer are moving *toward* each other; (b) the source and observer are moving *away* from each other; (c) the source and observer are moving in the same direction.

42. Blood flow rates can be found by measuring the Doppler shift in frequency of ultrasound reflected by red blood cells (known as *angiodynography*). If the speed of the red blood cells is v, the speed of sound in blood is u, the ultrasound source emits waves of frequency f, and we assume that the blood cells are moving directly toward the ultrasound source, show that the frequency f_r of reflected waves detected by the apparatus is given by

$$f_r = f \frac{1 + v/u}{1 - v/u}$$

[*Hint:* There are *two* Doppler shifts. A red blood cell first acts as a moving observer; then it acts as a moving source when it reradiates the reflected sound at the same frequency that it received.]

43. Show that for a moving source, the fractional shift in observed frequency is equal to v_s/v, the source's speed as a fraction of the speed of sound. [*Hint:* Use the binomial approximation from Appendix A.5.]

44. The pitch of the sound from a race car engine drops the musical interval of a fourth when it passes the spectators. This means the frequency of the sound after passing is 0.75 times what it was before. How fast is the race car moving?

12.9 Echolocation and Medical Imaging

45. A ship is lost in a dense fog in a Norwegian fjord that is 1.80 km wide. The air temperature is 5.0°C. The captain fires a pistol and hears the first echo after 4.0 s. (a) How

far from one side of the fjord is the ship? (b) How long after the first echo does the captain hear the second echo?

46. A ship mapping the depth of the ocean emits a sound of 38 kHz. The sound travels to the ocean floor and returns 0.68 s later. (a) How deep is the water at that location? (b) What is the wavelength of the wave in water? (c) What is the wavelength of the reflected wave as it travels into the air, where the speed of sound is 350 m/s?

47. A boat is using sonar to detect the bottom of a freshwater lake. If the echo from a sonar signal is heard 0.540 s after it is emitted, how deep is the lake? Assume the temperature of the lake is uniform and at 25°C.

48. A geological survey ship mapping the floor of the ocean sends sound pulses down from the surface and measures the time taken for the echo to return. How deep is the ocean at a point where the echo time (down and back) is 7.07 s? The temperature of the seawater is 25°C.

49. A bat emits chirping sounds of frequency 82.0 kHz while hunting for moths to eat. If the bat is flying toward the moth at a speed of 4.40 m/s and the moth is flying away from the bat at 1.20 m/s, what is the frequency of the sound wave reflected from the moth as observed by the bat? Assume it is a cool night with a temperature of 10.0°C. [*Hint:* There are two Doppler shifts. Think of the moth as a receiver, which then becomes a source as it "retransmits" the reflected wave.]

50. The bat of Problem 49 emits a chirp that lasts for 2.0 ms and then is silent while it listens for the echo. If the beginning of the echo returns just after the outgoing chirp is finished, how close to the moth is the bat? [*Hint:* Is the change in distance between the two significant during a 2.0-ms time interval?]

51. Doppler ultrasound is used to measure the speed of blood flow (see Problem 42). The reflected sound interferes with the emitted sound, producing beats. If the speed of red blood cells is 0.10 m/s, the ultrasound frequency used is 5.0 MHz, and the speed of sound in blood is 1570 m/s, what is the beat frequency?

52. (a) In Problem 42, find the beat frequency between the outgoing and reflected sound waves. (b) Show that the beat frequency is proportional to the speed of the blood cell if $v \ll u$. [*Hint:* Use the binomial approximation from Appendix A.5.]

Comprehensive Problems

53. A 30.0-cm-long string has a mass of 0.230 g and is vibrating at its next-to-lowest natural frequency f_2. The tension in the string is 7.00 N. (a) What is f_2? (b) What are the frequency and wavelength of the sound in the surrounding air if the speed of sound is 350 m/s?

54. Kyle is climbing a sailboat mast and is 5.00 m above the surface of the ocean, while his friend Rob is scuba diving below the boat. Kyle shouts to someone on another boat and Rob hears him shout 0.0210 s later. The ocean

temperature is 25°C and the air is at 20°C. How deep is Rob below the boat?

55. What are the four lowest standing wave frequencies for an organ pipe that is 4.80 m long and closed at one end?

56. The length of the auditory canal in humans averages about 2.5 cm. What are the lowest three standing wave frequencies for a pipe of this length open at one end? What effect might resonance have on the sensitivity of the ear at various frequencies? (Refer to Fig. 12.12. Note that frequencies critical to speech recognition are in the range 2 to 5 kHz.)

57. Some bats determine their distance to an object by detecting the difference in intensity between echoes.(a) If intensity falls off at a rate that is inversely proportional to the distance squared, show that the echo intensity is inversely proportional to the fourth power of distance. (b) The bat was originally 0.60 m from one object and 1.10 m from another. After flying closer, it is now 0.50 m from the first and at 1.00 m from the second object. What is the percentage increase in the intensity of the echo from each object?

58. The Vespertilionidae family of bats detect the distance to an object by timing how long it takes for an emitted signal to reflect off the object and return. Typically they emit sound pulses 3 ms long and 70 ms apart while cruising. (a) If an echo is heard 60 ms later ($v_{sound} = 331$ m/s), how far away is the object? (b) When an object is only 30 cm away, how long will it be before the echo is heard? (c) Will the bat be able to detect this echo?

59. At what frequency f does a sound wave in air have a wavelength of 15 cm, about half the diameter of the human head? Some methods of localization work well only for frequencies below f, while others work well only above f. (See Conceptual Questions 4 and 5.)

60. Horseshoe bats use the Doppler effect to determine their location. A Horseshoe bat flies toward a wall at a speed of 15 m/s while emitting a sound of frequency 35 kHz. What is the beat frequency between the emission frequency and the echo?

61. According to a treasure map, a treasure lies at a depth of 40.0 fathoms on the ocean floor due east from the lighthouse. The treasure hunters use sonar to find where the depth is 40.0 fathoms as they head east from the lighthouse. What is the elapsed time between an emitted pulse and the return of its echo at the correct depth if the water temperature is 25°C? [*Hint:* One fathom is 1.83 m.]

62. When playing *fortissimo* (very loudly), a trumpet emits sound energy at a rate of 0.800 W out of a bell (opening) of diameter 12.7 cm. (a) What is the sound intensity level right in front of the trumpet? (b) If the trumpet radiates sound waves uniformly in all directions, what is the sound intensity level at a distance of 10.0 m?

63. One cold and windy winter day, Zach notices a humming sound coming from his chimney when the chimney is open at the top and closed at the bottom. He opens the chimney at the bottom and notices that the sound

changes. He goes over to the piano to try to match the note that the chimney is producing with the bottom open. He finds that the "C" three octaves below middle "C" matches the chimney's fundamental frequency. Zach knows that the frequency of middle "C" is 261.6 Hz, and each lower octave is $\frac{1}{2}$ of the frequency of the octave above. From this information, Zach finds the height of the chimney and the fundamental frequency of the note that was produced when the chimney was *closed* at the bottom. Assuming that the speed of sound in the cold air is 330 m/s, reproduce Zach's calculations to find (a) the height of the chimney and (b) the fundamental frequency of the chimney when it is *closed* at the bottom.

64. A periodic wave is composed of the superposition of three sine waves whose frequencies are 36, 60, and 84 Hz. The speed of the wave is 180 m/s. What is the wavelength of the wave? [*Hint:* The 36 Hz is not necessarily the fundamental frequency.]

65. Analysis of the periodic sound wave produced by a violin's G string includes three frequencies: 392, 588, and 980 Hz. What is the fundamental frequency? [*Hint:* The wave on the string is the superposition of several different standing wave patterns.]

66. Your friend needs advice on her newest "acoustic sculpture." She attaches one end of a steel wire, of diameter 4.00 mm and density 7860 kg/m^3, to a wall. After passing over a pulley, located 1.00 m from the wall, the other end of the wire is attached to a hanging weight. Below the horizontal length of wire she places a 1.50-m-long hollow tube, open at one end and closed at the other. Once the sculpture is in place, air will blow through the tube, creating a sound. Your friend wants this sound to cause the steel wire to oscillate at the same resonant frequency as the tube. What weight (in newtons) should she hang from the wire if the temperature is 18.0°C?

67. A sound wave arriving at your ear is transferred to the fluid in the cochlea. If the intensity in the fluid is 0.80 times that in air and the frequency is the same as for the wave in air, what will be the ratio of the pressure amplitude of the wave in air to that in the fluid? Approximate the fluid as having the same values of density and speed of sound as water.

68. In this problem, you will estimate the smallest kinetic energy of vibration that the human ear can detect. Suppose that a harmonic sound wave at the threshold of hearing ($I = 1.0 \times 10^{-12}$ W/m^2) is incident on the eardrum. The speed of sound is 340 m/s and the density of air is 1.3 kg/m^3. (a) What is the maximum speed of an element of air in the sound wave? [*Hint:* See Eq. (10-21).] (b) Assume the eardrum vibrates with displacement s_0 at angular frequency ω; its maximum speed is then equal to the maximum speed of an air element. The mass of the eardrum is approximately 0.1 g. What is the *average* kinetic energy of the eardrum? (c) The average kinetic energy of the eardrum due to collisions with air

molecules *in the absence of a sound wave* is about 10^{-20} J. Compare your answer with (b) and discuss.

69. During a rehearsal, all eight members of the first violin section of an orchestra play a very soft passage. The sound intensity level at a certain point in the concert hall is 38.0 dB. What is the sound intensity level at the same point if only one of the violinists plays the same passage? [*Hint:* When playing together, the violins are *incoherent* sources of sound.]

Answers to Practice Problems

12.1 Although solids usually have somewhat higher densities than liquids, they have *much* higher bulk moduli—they are much stiffer. The greater restoring forces in solids cause sound waves to travel faster.

12.2 Assumptions: Treat the stage as a point source; ignore reflection and absorption of waves. 4.0×10^{-6} W/m^2, 0.057 Pa.

12.3 400

12.4 a factor of 3.2

12.5 3000 km. No; it is not realistic to ignore absorption and reflection over such a great distance.

12.6 24°C

12.7 444.0 Hz

12.8 182.5 Hz

12.9 27 m/s

Answers to Checkpoints

12.3 The relationship between pressure and displacement amplitudes depends on the frequency and, therefore, does not have a unique value for a given pressure amplitude and intensity.

12.4 A pipe of length L closed at one end has a node at one end and an antinode at the other. The wavelength can be $2L$ only if both ends are nodes (or both are antinodes), because the distance between two successive nodes (or two successive antinodes) is $\frac{1}{2}\lambda$.

12.7 (a) Constructive interference means the two waves are *in phase*, which occurs at $t = 0$ and $t = 10T_0$. At those times, the superposition of the waves has its maximum amplitude. (b) Destructive interference means the two waves are *out of phase*, which occurs at $t = 5T_0$. At this time, the superposition has its minimum amplitude. Destructive interference would next occur at $t = 15T_0$ (not shown on the graph).

12.8 (a) The motion of the source does affect the wavelength: λ is shorter in front of the source and longer behind it (see Fig. 12.14). (b) The motion of the observer does not affect the wavelength, which is the instantaneous distance between two wave crests (see Fig. 12.15).

Review & Synthesis: Chapters 9–12

Review Exercises

1. (a) Which has more buoyant force acting on it in water, 1.0 kg of lead or 1.0 kg of aluminum? Explain. (b) Which has more buoyant force acting on it, 1.0 kg of steel that is sinking to the bottom of a lake or 1.0 kg of wood with a density of 500 kg/m^3 that is floating on the lake? Explain. (c) Once you have answered the qualitative questions, find the quantitative answers to parts (a) and (b).

2. A solid piece of plastic, with a density of 890 kg/m^3, is placed in oil with a density of 830 kg/m^3 and the plastic sinks (A). Then the plastic is placed in water and it floats (B). (a) What percentage of the plastic is submerged in the water? (b) Finally, the same oil in which the plastic sinks is poured over the plastic and the water. Will less (C) or more (D) of the plastic be submerged in the water compared to B? Explain. (c) Calculate the percentage of the plastic submerged in the water in figure C.

    A   B   C   D

3. Water enters an apartment building 0.90 m below the street level with a gauge pressure of 52.0 kPa through the main pipe with a 5.00-cm radius. A second-story bathroom has a faucet with a 1.20-cm radius that is located 4.20 m above the street. How fast is the water moving through the main pipe?

4. To escape a burning building, Arnold has to jump from a third-story window that is about 10 m above the ground. Arnold is worried about breaking his leg. The largest bone in Arnold's leg is the femur, which has a minimum cross-sectional area of about 5×10^{-4} m and a maximum ultimate strength for compression of about 1.70×10^8 N/m^2. Arnold has a mass of 82 kg. (a) If Arnold lands on the ground with his legs stiff, then his femur can compress only about 5 mm. What will happen to Arnold's femur? (b) Suppose instead of landing on the ground, Arnold lands in deep snow so his legs can move about 30 cm between the time they first hit the snow and the time he comes to a complete stop. What will happen to Arnold's femur in this case?

5. A 5.0-kg block of wood is attached to a spring with a spring constant of 150 N/m. The block is free to slide on a horizontal frictionless surface once the spring is stretched and released. A 1.0-kg block of wood rests on top of the first block. The coefficient of static friction between the two blocks of wood is 0.45. What is the maximum speed that this set of blocks can have as it oscillates if the top block of wood is not to slip?

6. A child swinging on a swing set hears the sound of a whistle that is being blown directly in front of her. At the bottom of her swing when she is moving toward the whistle, she hears a higher pitch, and at the bottom of her swing when she is moving away from the whistle she hears a lower pitch. The higher pitch has a frequency that is 4.0% higher than the lower pitch. How high is the child swinging?

7. Consider the following equations for two different traveling waves:

   I. $y(x, t) = (1.50 \text{ cm}) \sin [(4.00 \text{ cm}^{-1})x + (6.00 \text{ s}^{-1})t]$

   II. $y(x, t) = (4.50 \text{ cm}) \sin [(3.00 \text{ cm}^{-1})x - (3.00 \text{ s}^{-1})t]$

   (a) Which wave has the fastest wave speed? What is that speed? (b) Which wave has the longest wavelength? What is that wavelength? (c) Which wave has the fastest maximum speed of a point in the medium? What is that speed? (d) Which wave is moving in the positive x-direction?

8. A Foucault pendulum has an object with a mass of 15.0 kg hung by a 14.0-m-long thin wire. (a) What is the oscillation frequency of this pendulum? (b) If the pendulum has a maximum oscillation angle of 6.10°, what is the maximum speed of this pendulum? (c) What is the maximum tension in the wire? (d) If the wire has a mass of 10.0 g, what is the fundamental frequency of the wire when it is at maximum tension?

9. The lowest frequency string on a guitar is 65.5 cm long and is tuned to 82 Hz. (a) If the string has a mass of 3.31 g, what is the tension in the string? (b) By fingering the guitar at the fifth fret, you shorten the vibrating length of the string, thereby changing the fundamental frequency of this string to match that of the next-highest-frequency string on the guitar, 110 Hz. How long is the lowest frequency string when it is fingered at the fifth fret?

10. Two children are playing with a tin-can telephone. The children are 12 m apart, the string connecting their tin cans has a linear mass density of 1.3 g/m, and it is stretched with a tension of 8.0 N. One child decides to pluck the string. How long does it take for the wave pulse to travel from one child to the other?

11. A sound wave with a frequency of 400.0 Hz is incident upon a set of stairs. The reflected waves from the vertical surfaces of adjacent steps cancel each other. What is the minimum tread depth of a step for this to occur?

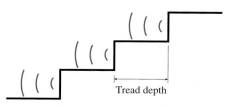

Tread depth

12. Akiko rides her bike toward a brick wall with a speed of 7.00 m/s while blowing a whistle that is emitting sound

with a frequency of 512.0 Hz. (a) What is the frequency of the sound that is reflected from the wall as heard by Haruki, who is standing still? (b) Junichi is walking away from the wall at a speed of 2.00 m/s. What is the frequency of the sound reflected from the wall that Junichi hears?

13. A siren has a circle of 25 equally sized, evenly spaced holes near the rim of a disk free to rotate about its center. Air is blown toward the plane of the disk as it rotates with a frequency of 60.0 Hz. What is the frequency and wavelength of the sound produced?

14. A stretched string has a fundamental frequency of 847 Hz. What is the fundamental frequency if the tension is tripled?

15. The average adult has about 5 L of blood and a healthy adult heart pumps blood at a rate of about 80 cm^3/s. Estimate how long it takes for medicine delivered intravenously to travel throughout a person's body.

16. A sound wave of frequency 1231 Hz travels through air directly toward a wall, then through the wall out into air again. If the initial speed of the sound wave is 341 m/s and its speed in the wall is 620 m/s, what are (a) the initial wavelength of the sound, (b) the wavelength of the sound in the wall, and (c) the wavelength of the sound when it exits the wall on the other side?

17. A speedboat is traveling at 20.1 m/s toward another boat moving in the opposite direction with a speed of 15.6 m/s. The speedboat pilot sounds his horn, which has a frequency of 312 Hz. What is the frequency heard by a passenger in the oncoming boat?

18. A glass tube is closed at one end and has a diaphragm covering the other end. The tube is filled with gas and some sawdust has been scattered along inside the tube. When the diaphragm is driven at a frequency of 1457 Hz, the sawdust forms small piles 20 cm apart. (a) What is the speed of the sound in the gas? (b) Do the piles of sawdust represent nodes or antinodes in the sound wave? Explain.

19. A section of pipe with an internal diameter of 10.0 cm tapers to an inner diameter of 6.00 cm as it rises through a height of 1.70 m at an angle of 60.0° with respect to the horizontal. The pipe carries water and its higher end is open to air. (a) If the speed of the water at the lower point is 15.0 cm/s, what are the pressure at the lower end and the speed of the water as it exits the pipe? (b) If the higher end of the pipe is 0.300 m above ground, at what horizontal distance from the pipe outlet does the water land?

20. When a standing wave is produced in a string fixed at both ends, the string oscillates so fast that it looks like a blur. You want to photograph the string when it is at positions A, B, and C shown in the figure. The tension in the string is 2.00 N and its mass per unit length is 0.200 g/m. The string's length is 0.720 m. Assume that you take your first picture when the string is in position A and let that be time $t = 0$. What are the first two times after $t = 0$ at which you can photograph the string in each of the positions A, B, and C?

21. The A string on a guitar has length 64.0 cm and fundamental frequency 110.0 Hz. The string's tension is 133 N. It is vibrating in its fundamental standing wave mode with a maximum displacement from equilibrium of 2.30 mm. The air temperature is 20.0°C.

   (a) What is the wavelength of the fundamental mode of vibration?

   (b) What is the wave speed on the string?

   (c) What is the linear mass density of the string?

   (d) What is the maximum speed of any point on the oscillating string?

   (e) The string transmits vibrations through the bridge to the body of the instrument and then to the air. What is the frequency of the sound wave in air?

   (f) What is the wavelength of the sound wave in air?

22. At a grocery store, a spring scale (spring constant = 450 N/m) hangs near the produce section. The spring hangs vertically with a 0.250-kg pan suspended from its lower end. Jenna drops a 2.20-kg bag of oranges from a height of 30.0 cm above the pan. The pan and oranges start oscillating vertically in SHM.

   (a) What is the velocity of the pan immediately after the oranges land on the pan? Assume a perfectly inelastic collision.

   (b) How far is the new equilibrium point of the pan (with oranges) below its position before the oranges were dropped on it?

   (c) What is the amplitude of the oscillations?

   (d) What is the frequency of the oscillations?

23. A spherical balloon with a radius of 12.0 cm is filled with helium. The bottom of the balloon is attached to a 2.30 m length of ribbon that is anchored to the ground. The balloon alone has a mass of 2.80×10^{-3} kg. Ignore the mass of the ribbon.

   (a) What is tension in the ribbon?

   (b) After the balloon is displaced slightly to the side from its equilibrium position, it oscillates back and forth like an inverted pendulum. What is the period of oscillation? Ignore friction and air resistance.

24. An atomizer is a device that delivers a fine mist of some liquid such as perfume by blowing air horizontally over the top of a tube immersed in the liquid. Suppose a perfume with density 800 kg/m³ has a 3.0-cm tube extending vertically from the top of the liquid. What minimum speed does air flow over the top of the tube when the liquid just reaches the top of the tube?

25. A tetherball set has a ball with mass 0.411 kg and a nylon string with diameter 2.50 mm, Young's modulus 4.00×10^9 Pa, and density 1150 kg/m³. The nylon string has a length of 2.200 m when the ball is at rest (hanging straight down). While playing tetherball, Monty hits the ball around the pole so it moves in a horizontal circle with the string at an angle of 65.0° to the pole. (a) How much does the string stretch compared with when the ball is at rest? (b) What is the ball's kinetic energy? (c) How long would it take a transverse wave pulse to travel the length of the string from the ball to the top of the pole?

+26. A harpsichord string is made of yellow brass (Young's modulus 9.0×10^{10} Pa, tensile strength 6.3×10^8 Pa, mass density 8500 kg/m³). When tuned correctly, the tension in the string is 59.4 N, which is 93% of the maximum tension that the string can endure without breaking. The length of the string that is free to vibrate is 9.4 cm. What is the fundamental frequency?

MCAT Review

The section that follows includes MCAT exam material and is reprinted with permission of the Association of American Medical Colleges (AAMC).

1. What is the volume of a brick that weighs 30 N in air and 20 N when completely submerged in water? (Note: The density of water is 1000 kg/m³ and let g be 10 m/s².)

  A. 1×10^{-3} m³   B. 5×10^{-3} m³

  C. 1×10^{-2} m³   D. 5×10^{-2} m³

2. The expansion of a particular cable when subjected to a tensile stress obeys $F = k\Delta L$, where F is the tension, $k = 5.0 \times 10^6$ N/m, and ΔL is the expansion. How far will a 100-m section of cable expand when placed under 5000 N of tension?

  A. 10^{-3} m   B. 10^{-2} m

  C. 10^{-1} m   D. 10 m

3. SL, the sound level in decibels, is defined as SL = $10 \log_{10}(I/I_0)$, where $I_0 = 1.0 \times 10^{-12}$ W/m² (the minimum sound intensity audible to humans). A fire siren has a sound level of about 100 dB. What is the intensity I of the fire siren?

  A. 1.0×10^{-22} W/m²   B. 1.0×10^{-10} W/m²

  C. 1.0×10^{-8} W/m²   D. 1.0×10^{-2} W/m²

4. Suppose that 2 cm of a liquid with a specific gravity of 0.5 is added to a 4-cm column of water. How does the new gauge pressure at the base of the column, P_n, compare with the original pressure, P_i?

  A. $P_n = \frac{3}{4}P_i$ B. $P_n = P_i$

  C. $P_n = \frac{5}{4}P_i$ D. $P_n = \frac{3}{2}P_i$

5. Consecutive resonances occur at wavelengths of 8 m and 4.8 m in an organ pipe closed at one end. What is the length of the organ pipe? (Note: Resonances occur at $L = n\lambda/4$, where L is the pipe length, λ is the wavelength, and $n = 1, 3, 5, \ldots$.)

  A. 3.2 m   B. 4.8 m

  C. 6.0 m   D. 8.0 m

6. Two mechanical waves of the same frequency pass through the same medium. The amplitude of wave A is 3 units, and the amplitude of wave B is 5 units. Which of the following describes the range of amplitudes possible when the two waves pass through the medium simultaneously?

  A. Always 4 units

  B. Between 2 and 8 units

  C. Between 3 and 5 units

  D. Between 5 and 8 units

7. A simple pendulum is swinging with an amplitude of 10°. As the bob of the pendulum swings through one oscillation, its linear acceleration

  A. remains constant in magnitude and direction.

  B. remains constant in magnitude but changes direction.

  C. changes in magnitude but remains constant in direction.

  D. changes in magnitude and direction.

8. In a simplified model of the blood flow, the velocity of blood flow through a coronary artery is inversely proportional to the fourth power of the radius of the artery. What is the ratio of kinetic energy of the blood in an artery of 2 cm radius to the kinetic energy of the same volume of blood in an artery 1 cm in radius?

  A. $1:2^4$ B. $1:4^4$

  C. $2^4:1$ D. $2^4:1$

Read the paragraph and then answer the following questions:

Three balls with the same volume of 1.0×10^{-6} m³ are in an open tank of water that has a density (ρ) equal to 1.0×10^3 kg/m³. The balls are in the water at different levels. Ball 1 floats in water with a part of it above the surface, ball 2 is completely submerged in the water, and ball 3 rests on the bottom of the tank. Any movement of the water obeys Bernoulli's equation:

$$P_1 + \frac{1}{2}\rho v_1^2 + \rho g y_1 = P_2 + \frac{1}{2}\rho v_2^2 + \rho g y_2$$

where P_1 and P_2 are the pressures at elevations y_1 and y_2, and v_1 and v_2 are the speeds of the water. (Note: Unless otherwise noted, the water and the balls are stationary.)

9. The buoyant forces B_1, B_2, and B_3 exerted by water on the balls are related by which of the following?

   A. $B_1 < B_2 < B_3$

   B. $B_1 < B_2 = B_3$

   C. $B_1 = B_2 > B_3$

   D. $B_1 > B_2 > B_3$

10. The densities of the balls ρ_1, ρ_2, and ρ_3 are related by which of the following?

    A. $\rho_1 < \rho_2 < \rho_3$ B. $\rho_1 < \rho_2 = \rho_3$

    C. $\rho_1 = \rho_2 < \rho_3$ D. $\rho_1 = \rho_2 > \rho_3$

11. Assume that the density of ball 3 is 7.8×10^3 kg/m^3. Ignoring atmospheric pressure, what is the supporting force exerted by the bottom of the tank on ball 3?

    A. 1.0×10^{-2} N   B. 6.7×10^{-2} N

    C. 7.6×10^{-2} N   D. 8.8×10^{-2} N

12. Assume that the density of ball 1 is 8.0×10^2 kg/m^3. Ignoring atmospheric pressure, what fraction of ball 1 is above the surface of the water?

    A. $\frac{4}{5}$ B. $\frac{3}{4}$ C. $\frac{1}{4}$ D. $\frac{1}{5}$

13. Ball 2 is in the water 20 cm above ball 3. What is the approximate difference in pressure between the two balls?

    A. 2×10^2 N/m^2 B. 5×10^2 N/m^2

    C. 2×10^3 N/m^2 D. 5×10^3 N/m^2

14. If ball 3 is a hollow, iron ball and atmospheric pressure can be ignored, what should be the volume of the hollow portion of ball 3 such that the force exerted by it on the bottom of the tank is 0? (Note: Density of iron is 7.8×10^3 kg/m^3.)

    A. 0.13×10^{-6} m^3 B. 0.78×10^{-6} m^3

    C. 0.87×10^{-6} m^3 D. 1.15×10^{-6} m^3

CHAPTER

13

Temperature and the Ideal Gas

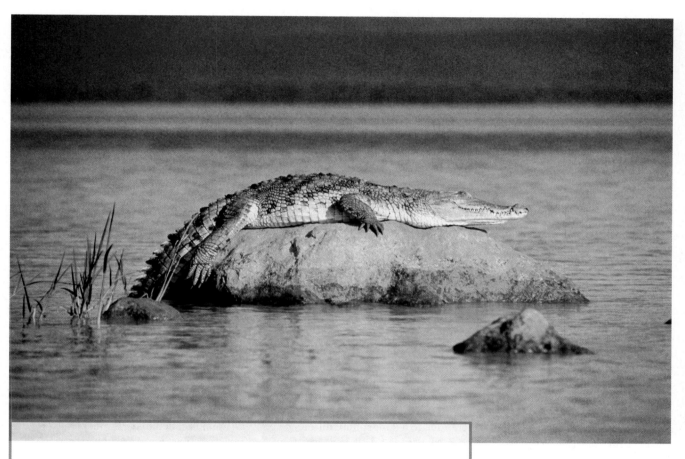

A crocodile basks on a rock in Lake Baringo (Kenya) to get warm.

In warm-blooded or homeothermic (constant temperature) animals, body temperature is carefully regulated. The hypothalamus, located in the brain, acts as the master thermostat to keep body temperature constant to within a fraction of a degree Celsius in a healthy animal. If the body temperature starts to deviate much from the desired constant level, the hypothalamus causes changes in blood flow and initiates other processes, such as shivering or perspiration, to bring the temperature back to normal. What evolutionary advantage does a constant body temperature give the warm-blooded animals (birds and mammals) over the cold-blooded (such as reptiles and insects)? What are the disadvantages? (See p. 476 for the answer.)

- energy conservation (Chapter 6)
- momentum conservation (Section 7.4)
- collisions (Sections 7.7 and 7.8)

13.1 TEMPERATURE AND THERMAL EQUILIBRIUM

The measurement of **temperature** is part of everyday life. We measure the temperature of the air outdoors to decide how to dress when going outside; a thermostat measures the air temperature indoors to control heating and cooling systems to keep our homes and offices comfortable. Regulation of oven temperature is important in baking. When we feel ill, we measure our body temperature to see if we have a fever. Despite how matter-of-fact it may seem, temperature is a subtle concept. Although our subjective sensations of hot and cold are related to temperature, they can easily mislead, as the next Physics at Home demonstrates.

Figure 13.1 It is easy to trick our sense of temperature.

PHYSICS AT HOME

Try an experiment described by the philosopher John Locke in 1690. Fill one container with water that is hot (but not too hot to touch); fill a second container with lukewarm water; and fill a third container with cold water. Put one hand in the hot water and one in the cold water (Fig. 13.1) for about 10 to 20 s. Then plunge both hands into the container of lukewarm water. Although both hands are now immersed in water that is at a single temperature, the hand that had been in the hot water feels cool while the hand that had been in the cold water feels warm. This demonstration shows that we cannot trust our subjective senses to measure temperature.

The definition of temperature is based on the concept of **thermal equilibrium**. Suppose two objects or systems are allowed to exchange energy. The net flow of energy is always from the object at the higher temperature to the object at the lower temperature. As energy flows, the temperatures of the two objects approach one another. When the temperatures are the same, there is no longer any net flow of energy; the objects are now said to be in thermal equilibrium. Thus, *temperature is a quantity that determines when objects are in thermal equilibrium.* (The objects do *not* necessarily have the same *energy* when in thermal equilibrium.) The energy that flows between two objects or systems due to a temperature difference between them is called **heat**. In Chapter 14 we discuss heat in detail. If heat can flow between two objects or systems, the objects or systems are said to be in **thermal contact**.

Heat: energy in transit due to a temperature difference. Heat flows spontaneously from the hotter object to the colder object.

To measure the temperature of an object, we put a thermometer into thermal contact with the object. Temperature measurement relies on the **zeroth law of thermodynamics**.

Zeroth Law of Thermodynamics

If two objects are each in thermal equilibrium with a third object, then the two are in thermal equilibrium with one another.

Without the zeroth law, it would be impossible to define temperature, since different thermometers could give different results. The rather odd name *zeroth* law of thermodynamics came about because this law was formulated historically *after* the first, second, and third laws of thermodynamics and yet it is so fundamental that it should come *before* the others. **Thermodynamics**, the subject of Chapters 13 to 15, concerns temperature, heat flow, and the internal energy of systems.

13.2 TEMPERATURE SCALES

Thermometers measure temperature by exploiting some property of matter that is temperature-dependent. The familiar liquid-in-glass thermometer relies on thermal expansion: the mercury or alcohol expands as its temperature rises (or contracts as its temperature drops) and we read the temperature on a calibrated scale. Since some materials expand more than others, these thermometers must be calibrated on a scale using some easily reproducible phenomenon, such as the melting point of ice or the boiling point of water. The assignment of temperatures to these phenomena is arbitrary.

The most commonly used temperature scale in the world is the Celsius scale. On the Celsius scale, 0°C is the freezing temperature of water at $P = 1$ atm (the *ice point*) and 100°C is the boiling temperature of water at $P = 1$ atm (the *steam point*).

In the United States, the Fahrenheit scale is still commonly used (Fig. 13.2). At 1 atm, the ice point is 32°F and the steam point is 212°F, so the difference between the steam and ice points is 180°F. The size of the Fahrenheit degree interval is therefore smaller than the Celsius degree interval: a temperature difference of 1°C is equivalent to a difference of 1.8°F:

$$\Delta T_F = \Delta T_C \times 1.8 \frac{°F}{°C} \tag{13-1}$$

Since the two scales also have an offset (0°C is not the same temperature as 0°F), conversion between the two is:

$$T_F = (1.8°F/°C)\, T_C + 32°F \tag{13-2a}$$

$$T_C = \frac{T_F - 32°F}{1.8°F/°C} \tag{13-2b}$$

The SI unit of temperature is the **kelvin** (symbol K, *without* a degree sign). The kelvin has the same degree size as the Celsius scale; that is, a temperature *difference* of 1°C is the same as a difference of 1 K. However, 0 K represents *absolute zero*—there are no temperatures below 0 K. The ice point is 273.15 K, so temperature in °C (T_C) and temperature in kelvins (T) are related.

$$T_C = T - 273.15 \tag{13-3}$$

Equation (13-3) is the definition of the Celsius scale in terms of the kelvin. Table 13.1 shows some temperatures in kelvins, °C, and °F.

⚠️ The freezing and boiling temperatures of water depend on the pressure.

Figure 13.2 The Fahrenheit and Celsius temperature scales.

Table 13.1 Some Reference Temperatures in K, °C, and °F

	K	°C	°F		K	°C	°F
Absolute zero	0	−273.15	−459.67	Water boils	373.15	100.00	212.0
Lowest transient temperature achieved (laser cooling)	10^{-9}			Campfire	1 000	700	1 300
				Gold melts	1 337	1 064	1 947
Intergalactic space	3	−270	−454	Lightbulb filament	3 000	2 700	4 900
Helium boils	4.2	−269	−452	Surface of Sun; iron welding arc	6 300	6 000	11 000
Nitrogen boils	77	−196	−321				
Carbon dioxide freezes ("dry ice")	195	−78	−108	Center of Earth	16 000	15 700	28 300
				Lightning channel	30 000	30 000	50 000
Mercury freezes	234	−39	−38	Center of Sun	10^7	10^7	10^7
Ice melts/water freezes	273.15	0	32.0	Interior of neutron star	10^9	10^9	10^9
Human body temperature	310	37	98.6				

Example 13.1

A Sick Friend

A friend suffering from the flu has a fever; her body temperature is 38.6°C. What is her temperature in (a) K and (b) °F?

Strategy   (a) Kelvins and °C differ only by a shift of the zero point. Converting from °C to K requires only the addition of 273.15 K since 0°C (the ice point) corresponds to 273.15 K. (b) The °F is a different size than the °C, as well as having a different zero. In the Celsius scale, the zero is at the ice point. First multiply by 1.8°F/°C to find how many °F above the ice point. Then add 32°F (the Fahrenheit temperature of the ice point).

Solution   (a) The temperature is 38.6 K *above* the ice point of 273.15 K. Therefore, the kelvin temperature is

$$T = 38.6 \text{ K} + 273.15 \text{ K} = 311.8 \text{ K}$$

(b) First find how many °F above the ice point:

$$\Delta T_F = 38.6°\text{C} \times (1.8°\text{F/°C}) = 69.5°\text{F}$$

The ice point is 32°F, so

$$T_F = 32.0°\text{F} + 69.5°\text{F} = 101.5°\text{F}$$

Discussion   The answer is reasonable since 98.6°F is normal body temperature.

Practice Problem 13.1   Normal Body Temperatures with Two Scales

Convert the normal human body temperature (98.6°F) to degrees Celsius and kelvins.

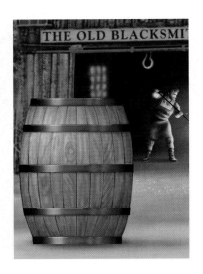

13.3   THERMAL EXPANSION OF SOLIDS AND LIQUIDS

Most objects expand as their temperature increases. Long before the cause of thermal expansion was understood, the phenomenon was put to practical use. For example, the cooper (barrel maker) heated iron hoops red hot to make them expand before fitting them around the wooden staves of a barrel. The iron hoops contracted as they cooled, pulling the staves tightly together to make a leak-tight barrel.

Linear Expansion

If the length of a wire, rod, or pipe is L_0 at temperature T_0 (Fig. 13.3), then

$$\frac{\Delta L}{L_0} = \alpha \Delta T \tag{13-4}$$

where $\Delta L = L - L_0$ and $\Delta T = T - T_0$. The length at temperature T is

$$L = L_0 + \Delta L = (1 + \alpha \Delta T) L_0 \tag{13-5}$$

The constant of proportionality α is called the **coefficient of linear expansion** of the substance. It plays a role in thermal expansion similar to that of the elastic modulus in tensile stress. If T is measured in kelvins or in degrees Celsius, then α has units of K^{-1} or $°\text{C}^{-1}$. Since only the *change* in temperature is involved in Eq. (13-4), either Celsius or Kelvin temperatures can be used to find ΔT; a temperature change of 1K is the same as a temperature change of 1°C.

As is true for the elastic modulus, the coefficient of linear expansion has different values for different solids and also depends to some extent on the starting temperature of the object. Table 13.2 lists the coefficients for various solids.

✓ CHECKPOINT 13.3

A steel tower is 150.00 m tall at 40°C. How much shorter is it at −10°C?

CONNECTION:

Recall that the fractional length change (strain) caused by a tensile or compressive stress is proportional to the stress that caused it [Hooke's law, Eq. (10-4)]. Similarly, the fractional length change caused by a temperature change is proportional to the temperature change, as long as the temperature change is not too great.

Table 13.2 Coefficients of Linear Expansion α for Solids
(at $T = 20°C$ unless otherwise indicated)

Material	$\alpha \, (10^{-6} \, K^{-1})$
Glass (Vycor)	0.75
Brick	1.0
Glass (Pyrex)	3.25
Granite	8
Glass, most types	9.4
Cement or concrete	12
Iron or steel	12
Copper	16
Silver	18
Brass	19
Aluminum	23
Lead	29
Ice (at 0°C)	51

Figure 13.4 is a graph of the relative length of a steel girder as a function of temperature over a *wide* range of temperatures. The curvature of this graph shows that the thermal expansion of the girder is in general *not* proportional to the temperature change. However, over a *limited* temperature range, the curve can be approximated by a straight line; the slope of the tangent line is the coefficient α at the temperature T_0. For small temperature changes near T_0, the change in length of the girder can be treated as being proportional to the temperature change with only a small error.

Applications of Thermal Expansion: Expansion Joints in Bridges and Buildings Allowances must be made in building sidewalks, roads, bridges, and buildings to leave space for expansion in hot weather. Old subway tracks have small spaces left between rail sections to prevent the rails from pushing into each other and causing the track to bow. A train riding on such tracks is subject to a noticeable amount of "clickety-clack" as it goes over these small expansion breaks in the tracks. Expansion joints are easily observed in bridges (Fig. 13.5). Concrete roads and sidewalks have joints between sections. Homeowners sometimes build their own sidewalks without realizing the necessity for such joints; these sidewalks begin to crack almost immediately!

Allowances must also be made for contraction in cold weather. If an object is not free to expand or contract, then as the temperature changes it is subjected to *thermal stress* as its environment exerts forces on it to prevent the thermal expansion or contraction that would otherwise occur.

Figure 13.3 Expansion of a solid rod with increasing temperature.

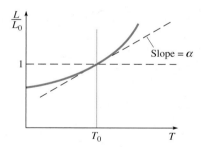

Figure 13.4 The relative length of a steel girder as a function of temperature. The dashed tangent line shows what Eq. (13-4) predicts for small temperature changes in the vicinity of T_0. The slope of this tangent line is the value of α at $T = T_0$.

Figure 13.5 Expansion joints permit the roadbed of a bridge to expand and contract as the temperature changes.

Example 13.2

Expanding Rods

Two metal rods, one aluminum and one brass, are each clamped at one end (Fig. 13.6). At 0.0°C, the rods are each 50.0 cm long and are separated by 0.024 cm at their unfastened ends. At what temperature will the rods just come into contact? (Assume that the base to which the rods are clamped undergoes a negligibly small thermal expansion.)

Strategy   Two rods of different materials expand by different amounts. The sum of the two expansions ($\Delta L_{br} + \Delta L_{Al}$) must equal the space between the rods. After finding ΔT, we add it to $T_0 = 0.0$°C to obtain the temperature at which the two rods touch.

Known: $L_0 = 50.0$ cm, $T_0 = 0.0$°C for both
Look up: $\alpha_{br} = 19 \times 10^{-6}$ K^{-1}; $\alpha_{Al} = 23 \times 10^{-6}$ K^{-1}
Requirement: $\Delta L_{br} + \Delta L_{Al} = 0.024$ cm
Find: $T_f = T_0 + \Delta T$

Solution   The brass rod expands by

$$\Delta L_{br} = (\alpha_{br} \Delta T)L_0$$

and the aluminum rod by

$$\Delta L_{Al} = (\alpha_{Al} \Delta T)L_0$$

The sum of the two expansions is known:

$$\Delta L_{br} + \Delta L_{Al} = 0.024 \text{ cm}$$

Since both the initial lengths and the temperature changes are the same,

$$(\alpha_{br} + \alpha_{Al}) \Delta T \times L_0 = 0.024 \text{ cm}$$

Solving for ΔT,

$$\Delta T = \frac{0.024 \text{ cm}}{(\alpha_{br} + \alpha_{Al})L_0}$$
$$= \frac{0.024 \text{ cm}}{(19 \times 10^{-6} \text{ K}^{-1} + 23 \times 10^{-6} \text{ K}^{-1}) \times 50.0 \text{ cm}}$$
$$= 11.4\text{°C}$$

The temperature at which the two touch is

$$T_f = T_0 + \Delta T = 0.0\text{°C} + 11.4\text{°C} \rightarrow 11\text{°C}$$

Discussion   As a check on the solution, we can find how much each individual rod expands and then add the two amounts:

$$\Delta L_{Al} = \alpha_{Al} \Delta T L_0$$
$$= 23 \times 10^{-6} \text{ K}^{-1} \times 11.4 \text{ K} \times 50.0 \text{ cm} = 0.013 \text{ cm}$$

$$\Delta L_{br} = \alpha_{br} \Delta T L_0$$
$$= 19 \times 10^{-6} \text{ K}^{-1} \times 11.4 \text{ K} \times 50.0 \text{ cm} = 0.011 \text{ cm}$$

$$\text{total expansion} = 0.013 \text{ cm} + 0.011 \text{ cm} = 0.024 \text{ cm}$$

which is correct.

Practice Problem 13.2   Expansion of a Wall

The outer wall of a building is constructed from concrete blocks. If the wall is 5.00 m long at 20.0°C, how much longer is the wall on a hot day (30.0°C)? How much shorter is it on a cold day (−5.0°C)?

0.024 cm
50.0 cm — 50.0 cm
Brass   Aluminum
$T_0 = 0.0$°C

Figure 13.6
Two clamped rods.

Differential Expansion

When two strips made of different metals are joined together and then heated, one expands more than the other (unless they have the same coefficient of expansion). This differential expansion can be put to practical use: the joined strips bend into a curve, allowing one strip to expand more than the other.

Application of differential expansion: bimetallic strip in a thermostat

The bimetallic strip (Fig. 13.7) is made by joining a material with a lower coefficient of expansion, such as steel, and one of a higher coefficient of expansion, such as brass. Unequal expansions or contractions of the two materials force the bimetallic strip to bend. In Fig. 13.7, the brass expands more than the steel when the bimetallic strip is heated. As the strip is cooled, the brass contracts more than the steel.

The bimetallic strip is used in many wall thermostats. The bending of the bimetallic strip closes or opens an electrical switch in the thermostat that turns the furnace or air conditioner on or off. Inexpensive oven thermometers also use a bimetallic strip wound into a spiral coil; the coil winds tighter or unwinds as the temperature changes.

Bimetallic strip

Brass

Steel

Cold   Room temperature   Hot

Figure 13.7 A bimetallic strip bends when its temperature changes; brass expands and contracts more than steel for the same temperature change.

Area Expansion

As you might suspect, *each dimension* of an object expands when the object's temperature increases. For instance, a pipe expands not only in length, but also in radius. An isotropic substance expands uniformly in all directions, causing changes in area and volume that leave the *shape* of the object unchanged. In Problem 25, you can show that, for small temperature changes, the area of any flat surface of a solid changes in proportion to the temperature change:

$$\frac{\Delta A}{A_0} = 2\alpha\Delta T \qquad (13\text{-}6)$$

The factor of two in Eq. (13-6) arises because the surface expands in two perpendicular directions.

Volume Expansion

The fractional change in volume of a solid or liquid is also proportional to the temperature change as long as the temperature change is not too large:

$$\frac{\Delta V}{V_0} = \beta\Delta T \qquad (13\text{-}7)$$

The coefficient of volume expansion, β, is the fractional change in volume per unit temperature change. For solids, the coefficient of volume expansion is three times the coefficient of linear expansion (as shown in Problem 26):

$$\beta = 3\alpha \qquad (13\text{-}8)$$

The factor of three in Eq. (13-8) arises because the object expands in three-dimensional space. For liquids, the volume expansion coefficient is the only one given in tables. Since liquids do not necessarily retain the same shape as they expand, the quantity that is uniquely defined is the change in volume. Table 13.3 provides values of β for some common liquids and gases.

A hollow cavity in a solid expands exactly as if it were filled—the interior of a steel gasoline container expands when its temperature increases just as if it were a solid steel block. The steel wall of the can does *not* expand inward to make the cavity smaller.

CONNECTION:

Compare Eq. (10-10). There, the fractional volume change is proportional to the *pressure* change; here it is proportional to the *temperature* change.

Table 13.3	Coefficients of Volume Expansion β for Liquids and Gases (at $T = 20°C$ unless otherwise indicated)
Material	$\beta(10^{-6}\ \mathbf{K^{-1}})$
Liquids	
Water (at 0°C)*	−68
Mercury	182
Water (at 20°C)	207
Gasoline	950
Ethyl alcohol	1120
Benzene	1240
Gases	
Air (and most other gases) at 1 atm	3340

*Below 3.98°C, water *contracts* with increasing temperature.

Application of volume expansion: thermometers

In an ordinary alcohol-in-glass or mercury-in-glass thermometer, it is not just the liquid that expands as temperature rises. The reading of the thermometer is determined by the difference in the volume expansion of the liquid and that of the interior of the glass. The calibration of an accurate thermometer must account for the expansion of the glass. Comparison of Tables 13.2 and 13.3 shows that, as is usually the case, the liquid expands much more than the glass for a given temperature change.

Example 13.3

Hollow Cylinder Full of Water

A hollow copper cylinder is filled to the brim with water at 20.0°C. If the water and the container are heated to a temperature of 91°C, what percentage of the water spills over the top of the container?

Strategy The volume expansion coefficient for water is greater than that for copper, so the water expands more than the interior of the cylinder. The cavity expands just as if it were solid copper. Since the problem does not specify the initial volume, we call it V_0. We need to find out how much a volume V_0 of water expands and how much a volume V_0 of copper expands; the difference is the water volume that spills over the top of the container.

Known: Initial copper cylinder interior volume = initial water volume = V_0
Initial temperature = T_0 = 20.0°C
Final temperature = 91°C; ΔT = 71°C
Look up: $\alpha_{Cu} = 16 \times 10^{-6}$ °C^{-1}; $\beta_{H_2O} = 207 \times 10^{-6}$ °C^{-1}
Find: $\Delta V_{H_2O} - \Delta V_{Cu}$ as a percentage of V_0

Solution The volume expansion of the interior of the copper cylinder is

$$\Delta V_{Cu} = \beta_{Cu} \Delta T V_0$$

where $\beta_{Cu} = 3\alpha_{Cu}$. The volume expansion of the water is

$$\Delta V_{H_2O} = \beta_{H_2O} \Delta T V_0$$

The amount of water that spills is

$$\Delta V_{H_2O} - \Delta V_{Cu} = \beta_{H_2O} \Delta T V_0 - \beta_{Cu} \Delta T V_0$$
$$= (\beta_{H_2O} - \beta_{Cu}) \Delta T V_0$$
$$= (207 \times 10^{-6} \text{ °C}^{-1} - 3 \times 16 \times 10^{-6} \text{ °C}^{-1})$$
$$\times 71\text{°C} \times V_0$$
$$= 0.011 V_0$$

The percentage of water that spills is therefore 1.1%.

Discussion As a check, we can find the change in volume of the copper container and of the water and find the difference.

$$\Delta V_{Cu} = \beta_{Cu} \Delta T V_0 = 3 \times 16 \times 10^{-6} \text{ °C}^{-1} \times 71\text{°C} \times V_0 = 0.0034 V_0$$
$$\Delta V_{H_2O} = \beta_{H_2O} \Delta T V_0 = 207 \times 10^{-6} \text{ °C}^{-1} \times 71\text{°C} \times V_0 = 0.0147 V_0$$
volume of water that spills = $0.0147 V_0 - 0.0034 V_0 = 0.0113 V_0$

which again shows that 1.1% spills.

Practice Problem 13.3 Overflowing Gas Can

A driver fills an 18.9-L steel gasoline can with gasoline at 15.0°C right up to the top. He forgets to replace the cap and leaves the can in the back of his truck. The temperature climbs to 30.0°C by 1 P.M. How much gasoline spills out of the can?

13.4 MOLECULAR PICTURE OF A GAS

Number Density As we saw in Chapter 9, the densities of liquids are generally not much less than the densities of solids. Gases are *much* less dense than liquids and solids because the molecules are, on average, much farther apart. The mass density—mass per unit volume—of a substance depends on the mass m of a single molecule and the number of molecules N packed into a given volume V of space (Fig. 13.8). The number of molecules per unit volume, N/V, is called the **number density** to distinguish it from mass density. In SI units, number density is written as the number of molecules per cubic meter, usually written simply as m^{-3} (read "per cubic meter"). If a gas has a total mass M, occupies a volume V, and each molecule has a mass m, then the number of gas molecules is

$$N = \frac{M}{m}$$ (13-9)

(a)   (b)

Figure 13.8 These two gases have the same mass per unit volume but different number densities. The red arrows represent the molecular velocities. In (a), there are a larger number of molecules in a given volume, but the mass of each molecule in (b) is greater.

and the average number density is

$$\frac{N}{V} = \frac{M}{mV} = \frac{\rho}{m} \qquad (13\text{-}10)$$

where $\rho = M/V$ is the mass density.

Moles   It is common to express the amount of a substance in units of **moles** (abbreviated mol). The mole is an SI base unit and is defined as follows: one mole of anything contains the same number of units as there are atoms in 12 *grams* (not kilograms) of carbon-12. This number is called **Avogadro's number** and has the value

 The abbreviation "mol" stands for moles, *not* molecules.

$$N_A = 6.022 \times 10^{23} \text{ mol}^{-1} \quad \text{(Avogadro's number)}$$

Avogadro's number is written with units, mol^{-1}, to show that this is the number *per mole*. The number of moles, n, is therefore given by

$$\text{number of moles} = \frac{\text{total number}}{\text{number per mole}}$$

$$n = \frac{N}{N_A} \qquad (13\text{-}11)$$

Molecular Mass and Molar Mass   The mass of a molecule is often expressed in units other than kg. The most common is the **atomic mass unit** (symbol u). By definition, one atom of carbon-12 has a mass of 12 u (exactly). Using Avogadro's number, the relationship between atomic mass units and kilograms can be calculated (see Problem 27):

$$1 \text{ u} = 1.66 \times 10^{-27} \text{ kg} \qquad (13\text{-}12)$$

The proton, neutron, and hydrogen atom all have masses within 1% of 1 u—which is why the atomic mass unit is so convenient. More precise values are 1.007 u for the proton, 1.009 u for the neutron, and 1.008 u for the hydrogen atom. The mass of an atom is *approximately* equal to the number of nucleons (neutrons plus protons)—the *atomic mass number*—times 1 u.

Instead of the mass of one molecule, tables commonly list the **molar mass**—the mass of the substance *per mole*. For an element with several isotopes (such as carbon-12, carbon-13, and carbon-14), the molar mass is averaged according to the naturally occurring abundance of each isotope. The atomic mass unit is chosen so that the mass of a molecule in "u" is numerically the same as the molar mass in g/mol. For example, the molar mass of O_2 is 32.0 g/mol and the mass of one molecule is 32.0 u.

The mass of a molecule is very nearly equal to the sum of the masses of its constituent atoms. The molar mass of a molecule is therefore equal to the sum of the molar masses of the atoms. For example, the molar mass of carbon is 12.0 g/mol and the molar mass of (atomic) oxygen is 16.0 g/mol; therefore, the molar mass of carbon dioxide (CO_2) is $(12.0 + 2 \times 16.0)$ g/mol = 44.0 g/mol.

✓ CHECKPOINT 13.4

(a) What is the mass (in u) of a CO_2 molecule? (b) What is the mass (in g) of 3.00 mol of CO_2?

Example 13.4

A Helium Balloon

A helium balloon of volume 0.010 m^3 contains 0.40 mol of He gas. (a) Find the number of atoms, the number density, and the mass density. (b) Estimate the average distance between He atoms.

Strategy   The number of moles tells us the number of atoms as a fraction of Avogadro's number. Once we have the number of atoms, N, the next quantity we are asked to find is N/V. To find the mass density, we can look up the atomic mass of helium in the periodic table. The mass per atom times the number density (atoms per m^3) equals the mass density (mass per m^3). To find the average distance between atoms, imagine a simplified picture in which each atom is at the center of a spherical volume equal to the total volume of the gas divided by the number of atoms. In this approximation, the average distance between atoms is equal to the diameter of each sphere.

Solution   (a) The number of atoms is

$$N = nN_A$$
$$= 0.40 \text{ mol} \times 6.022 \times 10^{23} \text{ atoms/mol}$$
$$= 2.4 \times 10^{23} \text{ atoms}$$

Figure 13.9
Simplified model in which equally spaced helium atoms sit at the centers of spherical volumes of space.

The number density is

$$\frac{N}{V} = \frac{2.4 \times 10^{23} \text{ atoms}}{0.010 \text{ m}^3} = 2.4 \times 10^{25} \text{ atoms/m}^3$$

The mass of a helium atom is 4.00 u. Then the mass in kg of a helium atom is

$$m = 4.00 \text{ u} \times 1.66 \times 10^{-27} \text{ kg/u} = 6.64 \times 10^{-27} \text{ kg}$$

and the mass density of the gas is

$$\rho = \frac{M}{V} = m \times \frac{N}{V}$$
$$= 6.64 \times 10^{-27} \text{ kg} \times 2.4 \times 10^{25} \text{ m}^{-3} = 0.16 \text{ kg/m}^3$$

(b) We assume that each atom is at the center of a sphere of radius r (Fig. 13.9). The volume of the sphere is

$$\frac{V}{N} = \frac{1}{N/V} = \frac{1}{2.4 \times 10^{25} \text{ atoms/m}^3} = 4.2 \times 10^{-26} \text{ m}^3 \text{ per atom}$$

Then

$$\frac{V}{N} = \frac{4}{3}\pi r^3 \approx 4r^3 \quad (\text{since } \pi \approx 3)$$

Solving for r,

$$r \approx \left(\frac{V}{4N}\right)^{1/3} = 2.2 \times 10^{-9} \text{ m} = 2.2 \text{ nm}$$

The average distance between atoms is $d = 2r \approx 4$ nm (since this is an estimate).

Discussion   For comparison, in *liquid* helium the average distance between atoms is about 0.4 nm, so in the gas the average separation is about ten times larger.

Practice Problem 13.4   Number Density for Water

The mass density of liquid water is 1000.0 kg/m^3. Find the number density.

13.5   ABSOLUTE TEMPERATURE AND THE IDEAL GAS LAW

We have examined the thermal expansion of solids and liquids. What about gases? Is the volume expansion of a gas proportional to the temperature change? We must be careful; since gases are easily compressed, we must also specify what happens to the pressure. The French scientist Jacques Charles (1746–1823) found experimentally that, if the pressure of a gas is held constant, the change in temperature is indeed proportional to the change in volume (Fig. 13.10a).

Charles's law: $\Delta V \propto \Delta T$ (for constant P)

According to Charles's law, a graph of V versus T for a gas held at constant pressure is a straight line, but the line does not necessarily pass through the origin (Fig. 13.10b).

However, if we graph V versus T (at constant P) for various gases, something interesting happens. If we extrapolate the straight line to where it reaches $V = 0$, the

(a)

(b)

(c)

(d)

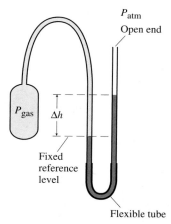

Figure 13.10 (a) Apparatus to verify Charles's law. The pressure of the enclosed gas is held constant by the fixed quantity of mercury resting on top of it and atmospheric pressure pushing down on the mercury. If the temperature of the gas is changed, it expands or contracts, moving the mercury column above it. (b) Charles's law: for a gas held at constant pressure, changes in temperature are proportional to changes in volume. (c) Volume versus temperature graphs for various gas samples, each at a constant pressure, are extrapolated to $V = 0$. The graphs intersect the temperature axis at the same temperature, T_{limit}, even though the gases may differ in composition and mass. (d) An absolute temperature scale sets $T_{limit} = 0$.

Figure 13.11 A constant volume gas thermometer. A dilute gas is contained in the vessel on the left, which is connected to a mercury manometer. The right side can be moved up or down to keep the mercury level on the left at a fixed level, so the volume of gas is kept constant. Then the manometer is used to measure the pressure of the gas: $P_{gas} = P_{atm} + \rho g \Delta h$.

Absolute zero: the lower limit of attainable temperatures.

temperature at that point is the *same* regardless of what gas we use, how many moles of gas are present, or what the pressure of the gas is (Fig. 13.10c). (One reason we have to extrapolate is that all gases become liquids or solids before they reach $V = 0$.) This temperature, $-273.15°C$ or $-459.67°F$, is called **absolute zero**—the lower limit of attainable temperatures. In kelvins—an *absolute* temperature scale—absolute zero is defined as 0 K (Fig. 13.10d). As long as it is understood that an absolute temperature scale is to be used, then Charles's law can be written

$$V \propto T \quad \text{(for constant } P\text{)}$$

PHYSICS AT HOME

Take an empty 2-L soda bottle, cap it tightly, and put it in the freezer. Check it an hour later; what has happened? Estimate the percentage change in the volume of the air inside and compare with the percentage change in absolute temperature (if you don't have a thermometer handy, a typical freezer temperature is about $-10°C$).

Thermal expansion of a gas can be used to measure temperature. Gas thermometers are universal: it does not matter what gas is used or how many moles of gas are present, as long as the number density is sufficiently low. Gas thermometers give absolute temperature in a natural way and they are extremely accurate and reproducible. The main disadvantage of gas thermometers is that they are much less convenient to use than most other thermometers, so they are mainly used to calibrate other thermometers.

A thermometer based on Charles's law would be called a *constant pressure gas thermometer*. More common is the *constant volume gas thermometer* (Fig. 13.11), which is based on Gay-Lussac's law:

$$P \propto T \quad \text{(for constant } V\text{)}$$

Here we keep the volume of the gas constant, measure the pressure and use that to indicate the temperature. (It is much easier to keep the volume constant and measure the pressure than to do the opposite.)

Both Charles's law and Gay-Lussac's law are valid only for a **dilute** gas—a gas where the number density is low enough (and, therefore, the average distance between gas molecules is large enough) that interactions between the molecules are negligible except when they collide. Two other experimentally discovered laws that apply to dilute gases are Boyle's law and Avogadro's law. Boyle's law states that the pressure of a gas is inversely proportional to its volume at constant temperature:

$$P \propto \frac{1}{V} \quad \text{(for constant } T\text{)}$$

Avogadro's law states that the volume occupied by a gas at a given temperature and pressure is proportional to the number of gas molecules N:

$$V \propto N \quad \text{(constant } P, T\text{)}$$

(A constant number of gas molecules was assumed in the statements of Boyle's, Gay-Lussac's, and Charles's laws.)

One equation combines all four of these gas laws—the **ideal gas law**:

Ideal Gas Law (Microscopic Form)

$$PV = NkT \quad (N = \text{number of molecules}) \tag{13-13}$$

In the ideal gas law, T stands for *absolute* temperature (in K) and P stands for *absolute* (not gauge) pressure.

The constant of proportionality is a universal quantity known as **Boltzmann's constant** (symbol k); its value is

$$k = 1.38 \times 10^{-23} \text{ J/K} \tag{13-14}$$

The macroscopic form of the ideal gas law is written in terms of n, the number of *moles* of the gas, in place of N, the number of molecules. Substituting

$$N = nN_A$$

into the microscopic form yields

$$PV = nN_A kT$$

The product of N_A and k is called the **universal gas constant**:

$$R = N_A k = 8.31 \frac{\text{J/K}}{\text{mol}} \tag{13-15}$$

Then the ideal gas law in macroscopic form is written

Ideal Gas Law (Macroscopic Form)

$$PV = nRT \quad (n = \text{number of moles}) \tag{13-16}$$

Many problems deal with the changing pressure, volume, and temperature in a gas with a constant number of molecules (and a constant number of moles). In such problems, it is often easiest to write the ideal gas law as follows:

$$\frac{P_1 V_1}{T_1} = \frac{P_2 V_2}{T_2}$$

✓ CHECKPOINT 13.5

Two containers with the same volume are filled with two different gases. The pressure of the two gases is the same. (a) Must their temperatures be the same? Explain. (b) If their temperatures are the same, must they have the same number density? The same mass density?

Example 13.5

Temperature of the Air in a Tire

Before starting out on a long drive, you check the air in your tires to make sure they are properly inflated. The pressure gauge reads 31.0 lb/in² (214 kPa), and the temperature is 15°C. After a few hours of highway driving, you stop and check the pressure again. Now the gauge reads 35.0 lb/in² (241 kPa). What is the temperature of the air in the tires now?

Strategy We treat the air in the tire as an ideal gas. We must work with absolute temperatures and absolute pressures when using the ideal gas law. The pressure gauge reads *gauge* pressure; to get absolute pressure we add 1 atm = 101 kPa. We don't know the number of molecules inside the tire or the volume, but we can reasonably assume that neither changes. The number is constant as long as the tire does not leak. The volume may actually change a bit as the tire warms up and expands, but this change is small. Since N and V are constant, we can rewrite the ideal gas law as a proportionality between P and T.

Solution First convert the initial and final gauge pressures to absolute pressures:

$$P_i = 214 \text{ kPa} + 101 \text{ kPa} = 315 \text{ kPa}$$

$$P_f = 241 \text{ kPa} + 101 \text{ kPa} = 342 \text{ kPa}$$

Now convert the initial temperature to an absolute temperature:

$$T_i = 15°C + 273 \text{ K} = 288 \text{ K}$$

According to the ideal gas law, pressure is proportional to temperature, so

$$\frac{T_f}{T_i} = \frac{P_f}{P_i} = \frac{342 \text{ kPa}}{315 \text{ kPa}}$$

Then

$$T_f = \frac{P_f}{P_i} T_i = \frac{342}{315} \times 288 \text{ K} = 313 \text{ K}$$

Now convert back to °C:

$$313 \text{ K} - 273 \text{ K} = 40°C$$

Discussion The final answer of 40°C seems reasonable since, after a long drive, the tires are noticeably warm, but not hot enough to burn your hand.

💡 It is often most convenient to work with the ideal gas law by setting up a proportion. In this problem, we did not know the volume or the number of molecules, so we had no choice. In essence, what we used was Gay-Lussac's law. Starting with the ideal gas law, we can "rederive" Gay-Lussac's law or Charles's law or any other proportionality inherent in the ideal gas law.

Practice Problem 13.5   Air Pressure in the Tire After the Temperature Decreases

Suppose you now (unwisely) decide to bleed air from the tires, since the manufacturer suggests keeping the pressure between 28 lb/in² and 32 lb/in². (The manufacturer's specification refers to when the tires are "cold.") If you let out enough air so that the pressure returns to 31 lb/in², what percentage of the air molecules did you let out of the tires? What is the gauge pressure after the tires cool back down to 15°C?

PHYSICS AT HOME

The next time you take a car trip, check the tire pressure with a gauge just before the trip and then again after an hour or more of highway driving. Calculate the temperature of the air in the tires from the two pressure readings and the initial temperature. Feel the tire with your hand to see if your calculation is reasonable.

Example 13.6

Scuba Diver

A scuba diver needs air delivered at a pressure equal to the pressure of the surrounding water—the pressure in the lungs must match the water pressure on the diver's body to prevent the lungs from collapsing. Since the pressure in the air tank is much higher, a regulator delivers air to the diver at the appropriate pressure. The compressed air in a diver's tank lasts 80 min at the water's surface. About how long does the same tank last at a depth of 30 m under water? (Assume that the volume of air breathed per minute does not change and ignore the small quantity of air left in the tank when it is "empty.")

Strategy   The compressed air in the *tank* is at a pressure much higher than the pressure at which the diver breathes, whether at the surface or at 30 m depth. The constant quantity is N, the number of gas molecules in the tank. We also assume that the temperature of the gas remains the same; it may change slightly, but much less than the pressure or volume.

Solution   Since N and T are constant,

$$PV = \text{constant}$$

or

$$P \propto 1/V$$

The pressure at the surface is (approximately) 1 atm, while the pressure at 30 m under water is

$$P = 1\ \text{atm} + \rho g h$$

$$\rho g h = 1000\ \text{kg/m}^3 \times 9.8\ \text{m/s}^2 \times 30\ \text{m} = 294\ \text{kPa} \approx 3\ \text{atm}$$

Therefore, at a depth of 30 m,

$$P \approx 4\ \text{atm}$$

To match the pressure of the surrounding water, the pressure of the compressed air is four times larger at a depth of 30 m; then the volume of air is one fourth what it was at the surface. The diver breathes the same volume per minute, so the tank will last one fourth as long—20 min.

Discussion   To do the same thing a bit more formally, we could write:

$$P_i V_i = P_f V_f$$

After setting $P_i = 1$ atm and $P_f = 4$ atm, we find that $V_f / V_i = \frac{1}{4}$.

In this problem, the only numerical values given (indirectly) were the initial and final pressures. Assuming that N and T remain constant, we then can find the ratio of the final and initial volumes. Whenever there *seems* to be insufficient numerical information given in a problem, think in terms of ratios and look for constants that cancel out.

Practice Problem 13.6   Pressure in the Air Tank After the Temperature Increases

A tank of compressed air is at an absolute pressure of 580 kPa at a temperature of 300.0 K. The temperature increases to 330.0 K. What is the pressure in the tank now?

Problem-Solving Tips for the Ideal Gas Law

- In most problems, some change occurs; decide which of the four quantities (P, V, N or n, and T) remain constant during the change.
- Use the microscopic form if the problem deals with the number of molecules and the macroscopic form if the problem deals with the number of moles.
- Use subscripts (i and f) to distinguish initial and final values.
- Work in terms of ratios so that constant factors cancel out.
- Write out the units when doing calculations.
- Remember that P stands for *absolute* pressure (not gauge pressure) and T stands for *absolute* temperature (in kelvins, not °C or °F).

13.6 KINETIC THEORY OF THE IDEAL GAS

In a gas, the interaction between two molecules weakens rapidly as the distance between the molecules increases. In a dilute gas, the average distance between gas molecules is large enough that we can ignore interactions between the molecules except when they collide. In addition, the volume of space occupied by the molecules themselves is a small fraction of the total volume of the gas—the gas is mostly "empty space." The **ideal gas** is a simplified model of a dilute gas in which we think of the molecules as pointlike particles that move *independently* in free space with no interactions except for elastic collisions.

This simplified model is a good approximation for many gases under ordinary conditions. Many properties of gases can be understood from this model; the microscopic theory based on it is called the **kinetic theory** of the ideal gas.

Microscopic Basis of Pressure

The force that a gas exerts on a surface is due to collisions that the gas molecules make with that surface. For instance, think of the air inside an automobile tire. Whenever an air molecule collides with the inner tire surface, the tire exerts an inward force to turn the air molecule around and return it to the bulk of the gas. By Newton's third law, the gas molecule exerts an outward force on the tire surface. The net force per unit area on the inside of the tire due to all the collisions of the many air molecules is equal to the air pressure in the tire. The pressure depends on three things: how many molecules there are, how often each one collides with the wall, and the momentum transfer due to each collision.

We want to find out how the pressure of an ideal gas is determined by the motions of the gas molecules. To simplify the discussion, consider a gas contained in a box of length L and side area A (Fig. 13.12a)—the result does not depend on the shape of the container. Figure 13.12b shows a gas molecule about to collide with the rightmost wall of the container. For simplicity, we assume that the collision is elastic; a more advanced analysis shows that the result is correct even though not all collisions are elastic.

For an elastic collision, the x-component of the molecule's momentum is reversed in direction since the wall is much more massive than the molecule. Since the gas exerts only an outward force on the wall (a static fluid exerts no tangential force on a boundary), the y- and z-components of the molecule's momentum are unchanged. Thus, the molecule's momentum change is $\Delta p_x = 2m|v_x|$.

When does this molecule next collide with the same wall? Ignoring for now collisions with other molecules, its x-component of velocity never changes magnitude—only the sign of v_x changes when it reverses direction (Fig. 13.12c). The time it takes the molecule to travel the length L of the container and hit the other wall is $L/|v_x|$. Then the round-trip time is

$$\Delta t = 2\frac{L}{|v_x|}$$

CONNECTION:

We are using the principle that force is the rate of change of momentum (Newton's second law) to draw a conclusion about pressure in a gas.

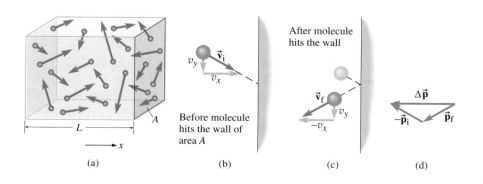

(a) (b) (c) (d)

Figure 13.12 (a) Gas molecules confined to a container of length L and area A. (b) A molecule is about to collide with the wall of area A. (c) After an elastic collision, v_x has changed sign, while v_y and v_z are unchanged. (d) The change in momentum due to the collision has magnitude $2|p_x|$ and is perpendicular to the wall.

The *average* force exerted by the molecule on the wall is the change in momentum (Fig. 13.12d) divided by the time for one complete round-trip:

$$F_{\text{av},x} = \frac{\Delta p_x}{\Delta t} = \frac{2m|v_x|}{2L/|v_x|} = \frac{m|v_x|^2}{L} = \frac{mv_x^2}{L}$$

The total force on the wall is the sum of the forces due to each molecule in the gas. If there are N molecules in the gas, we can simply multiply N by the *average* force due to one molecule to get the total force on the wall. To represent such an average, we use angle brackets $\langle\ \rangle$; the quantity inside the brackets is averaged over all the molecules in the gas.

$$F = N \langle F_{\text{av}} \rangle = \frac{Nm}{L} \langle v_x^2 \rangle$$

The pressure is then

$$P = \frac{F}{A} = \frac{Nm}{AL} \langle v_x^2 \rangle$$

The volume of the box is $V = AL$, so

$$P = \frac{Nm}{V} \langle v_x^2 \rangle \tag{13-17}$$

which is true regardless of the shape of the container enclosing the gas. Since we end up averaging over all the molecules in the gas, the simplifying assumption about no collisions with other molecules does not affect the result.

The product $m\langle v_x^2 \rangle$ suggests kinetic energy. It certainly makes sense that if the average kinetic energy of the gas molecules is larger, the pressure is higher. The average translational kinetic energy of a molecule in the gas is $\langle K_{\text{tr}} \rangle = \frac{1}{2} m \langle v^2 \rangle$. For any gas molecule, $v^2 = v_x^2 + v_y^2 + v_z^2$, since velocity is a vector quantity. The gas as a whole is at rest, so there is no preferred direction of motion. Then the average value of v_x^2 must be the same as the averages of v_y^2 and v_z^2, so

$$\langle v_x^2 \rangle = \tfrac{1}{3} \langle v^2 \rangle$$

Therefore,

$$m\langle v_x^2 \rangle = \tfrac{1}{3} m\langle v^2 \rangle = \tfrac{2}{3} \langle K_{\text{tr}} \rangle$$

The pressure of an ideal gas is proportional to the average translational kinetic energy of its molecules and to the number of molecules per unit volume.

Substituting this into Eq. (13-17), the pressure is

$$P = \frac{2}{3} \frac{N\langle K_{\text{tr}} \rangle}{V} = \frac{2}{3} \frac{N}{V} \langle K_{\text{tr}} \rangle \tag{13-18}$$

Equation (13-18) is written with the variables grouped in two different ways to give two different insights. The first grouping says that pressure is proportional to the kinetic energy density (the kinetic energy per unit volume). The second says that pressure is proportional to the product of the number density N/V and the average molecular kinetic energy. The pressure of a gas increases if either the gas molecules are packed closer together or if the molecules have more kinetic energy.

Note that $\langle K_{\text{tr}} \rangle$ is the average *translational* kinetic energy of a gas molecule and v is the CM speed of a molecule. A gas molecule with more than one atom (such as N_2), has vibrational and rotational kinetic energy *in addition to* its translational kinetic energy K_{tr}, but Eq. (13-18) still holds.

What about the assumption that the gas molecules never collide with each other? It certainly is *not* true that the same molecule returns to collide with the same wall at a fixed time interval and has the same v_x each time it returns! However, the derivation really only relies on average quantities. In a gas at equilibrium, an average quantity like $\langle v_x^2 \rangle$ remains unchanged even though any one particular molecule changes its velocity components as a result of each collision.

Temperature and Translational Kinetic Energy

The temperature of an ideal gas has a direct physical interpretation that we can now bring to light. We found that in an ideal gas, the pressure, volume, and number of molecules are related to the average translational kinetic energy of the gas molecules:

$$P = \frac{2}{3}\frac{N}{V}\langle K_{tr}\rangle \qquad (13\text{-}18)$$

Solving for the average kinetic energy,

$$\langle K_{tr}\rangle = \frac{3}{2}\frac{PV}{N} \qquad (13\text{-}19)$$

The ideal gas law relates P, V, and N to the temperature:

$$PV = NkT \qquad (13\text{-}13)$$

By rearranging the ideal gas law, we find that P, V, and N occur in the same combination as in Eq. (13-19):

$$\frac{PV}{N} = kT$$

Then by substituting kT for $(PV)/N$ in Eq. (13-19), we find that

$$\langle K_{tr}\rangle = \tfrac{3}{2}kT \qquad (13\text{-}20)$$

Therefore, *the absolute temperature of an ideal gas is proportional to the average translational kinetic energy of the gas molecules.* Temperature then is a way to describe the average translational kinetic energy of the gas molecules. At higher temperatures, the gas molecules have (on average) greater kinetic energy.

✓ CHECKPOINT 13.6

At what temperature in °C would molecules of O_2 have twice the average translational kinetic energy that molecules of H_2 have at 20°C?

RMS Speed The speed of a gas molecule that has the average kinetic energy is called the **rms** (root mean square) **speed**. The rms speed is *not* the same as the average speed. Instead, the rms speed is the square *root* of the *mean* (average) of the speed *squared*. Since

$$\langle K_{tr}\rangle = \tfrac{1}{2}m\langle v^2\rangle = \tfrac{1}{2}mv_{rms}^2 \qquad (13\text{-}21)$$

the rms speed is

$$v_{rms} = \sqrt{\langle v^2\rangle}$$

Squaring before averaging emphasizes the effect of the faster-moving molecules, so the rms speed is a bit higher than the average speed—about 9% higher as it turns out.

Since the average kinetic energy of molecules in an ideal gas depends only on temperature, Eq. (13-21) implies that more massive molecules move more slowly on average than lighter ones at the same temperature. If two different gases are placed in a single chamber so that they reach equilibrium and are at the same temperature, their molecules must have the same average translational kinetic energies. If one gas has molecules of larger mass, its molecules must move with a slower average velocity than those of the gas with the lighter mass molecules. In Problem 74, you can show that

$$v_{rms} = \sqrt{\frac{3kT}{m}} \qquad (13\text{-}22)$$

where k is Boltzmann's constant and m is the mass of a molecule. Therefore, at a given temperature, the rms speed is inversely proportional to the square root of the mass of the molecule.

Example 13.7

O₂ Molecules at Room Temperature

Find the average translational kinetic energy and the rms speed of the O_2 molecules in air at room temperature (20°C).

Strategy   The average translational kinetic energy depends only on temperature. We must remember to use absolute temperature. The rms speed is the speed of a molecule that has the average kinetic energy.

Solution   The absolute temperature is

$$20°C + 273 \text{ K} = 293 \text{ K}$$

Therefore, the average translational kinetic energy is

$$\langle K_{tr} \rangle = \tfrac{3}{2} kT$$
$$= 1.50 \times 1.38 \times 10^{-23} \text{ J/K} \times 293 \text{ K}$$
$$= 6.07 \times 10^{-21} \text{ J}$$

From the periodic table, we find the atomic mass of oxygen to be 16.0 u; the molecular mass of O_2 is twice that (32.0 u). First we convert that to kg:

$$32.0 \text{ u} \times 1.66 \times 10^{-27} \text{ kg/u} = 5.31 \times 10^{-26} \text{ kg}$$

The rms speed is the speed of a molecule with the average kinetic energy:

$$\langle K_{tr} \rangle = \tfrac{1}{2} m v_{rms}^2$$

$$v_{rms} = \sqrt{\frac{2\langle K_{tr} \rangle}{m}} = \sqrt{\frac{2 \times 6.07 \times 10^{-21} \text{ J}}{5.31 \times 10^{-26} \text{ kg}}} = 478 \text{ m/s}$$

Discussion   How can we decide if the result is reasonable, since we have no first-hand experience watching molecules bounce around? Recall from Chapter 12 that the speed of sound in air at room temperature is 343 m/s. Since sound waves in air propagate by the collisions that occur between air molecules, the speed of sound must be of the same order of magnitude as the average speeds of the molecules.

Practice Problem 13.7   CO₂ Molecules at Room Temperature

Find the average translational kinetic energy and the rms speed of the CO_2 molecules in air at room temperature (20°C).

Maxwell-Boltzmann Distribution

So far we have considered only the *average* kinetic energy and *rms* speed of a molecule. Sometimes we may want to know more: how many molecules have speeds in a certain range? The distribution of speeds is called the **Maxwell-Boltzmann distribution**. The distribution for oxygen at two different temperatures is shown in Fig. 13.13. The interpretation of the graphs is that the number of gas molecules having speeds between any two values v_1 and v_2 is proportional to the area under the curve between v_1 and v_2. In Fig. 13.13, the shaded areas represent the number of oxygen molecules having speeds

Figure 13.13 The probability distribution of kinetic energies in oxygen at two temperatures: −10°C (263 K) and +30°C (303 K). The area under either curve for any range of speeds is proportional to the number of molecules whose speeds lie in that range. Despite the relatively small difference in rms speeds (453 m/s at 263 K and 486 m/s at 303 K), the fraction of molecules in the high-speed tail is quite different.

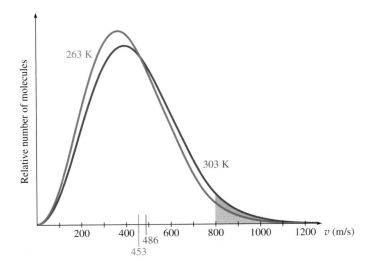

above 800 m/s at the two selected temperatures. A relatively small temperature change has a significant effect on the number of gas molecules with high speeds.

Any given molecule changes its kinetic energy often—at each collision, which means billions of times per second. However, the total number of gas molecules in a given kinetic energy range in the gas stays the same, as long as the temperature is constant. In fact, it is the frequent collisions that maintain the stability of the Maxwell-Boltzmann distribution. The collisions keep the kinetic energy distributed among the gas molecules *in the most disordered way possible*, which is the Maxwell-Boltzmann distribution.

Application of the Maxwell-Boltzmann Distribution: Composition of Planetary Atmospheres The Maxwell-Boltzmann distribution helps us understand planetary atmospheres. Why does Earth's atmosphere contain nitrogen, oxygen, and water vapor, among other gases, but not hydrogen or helium, which are by far the most common elements in the universe? Molecules in the upper atmosphere that are moving faster than the *escape speed* (see Example 6.8) have enough kinetic energy to escape from the planetary atmosphere to outer space. Those that are heading away from the planet's surface will escape if they avoid colliding with another molecule. The high-energy tail of the Maxwell-Boltzmann distribution does not get depleted by molecules that escape. Other molecules will get boosted to those high kinetic energies as a result of collisions; these replacements will in turn also escape. Thus, the atmosphere gradually leaks away.

How fast the atmosphere leaks away depends on how far the rms speed is from the escape speed. If the rms speed is too small compared with the escape speed, the time for all the gas molecules to escape is so long that the gas is present in the atmosphere indefinitely. This is the case for nitrogen, oxygen, and water vapor in Earth's atmosphere. On the other hand, since hydrogen and helium are much less massive, their rms speeds are higher. Though only a tiny fraction of the molecules are above the escape speed, the fraction is sufficient for these gases to escape quickly from Earth's atmosphere (Fig. 13.14). The Moon is often said to lack an atmosphere. The Moon's low escape speed (2400 m/s) allows most gases to escape, but it does have an atmosphere about 1 cm tall composed of krypton (a gas with molecular mass 83.8 u, about 2.6 times that of oxygen).

Figure 13.14 Maxwell-Boltzmann distributions for oxygen and hydrogen at $T = 300$ K. Escape speed from Earth is 11 200 m/s (not shown on the graph).

CONNECTION:

The basic principle behind escape speed is conservation of energy (Sec. 6.5). At the escape speed, an atom or molecule has just enough kinetic energy to escape the planet's gravitational pull.

13.7 TEMPERATURE AND REACTION RATES

What we have learned about the distribution of kinetic energies and its relationship to temperature has a great relevance to the dependence of chemical reaction rates on temperature. Imagine a mixture of two gases, N_2 and O_2, which can react to form nitric oxide (NO):

$$N_2 + O_2 \rightarrow 2NO$$

In order for the reaction to occur, a molecule of nitrogen must collide with a molecule of oxygen. But the reaction does not occur every time such a collision takes place. The reactant molecules must possess enough kinetic energy to initiate the reaction, because the reaction involves the rearrangement of chemical bonds between atoms. Some chemical bonds must be broken before new ones form; the energy to break these bonds must come from the energy of the reactants. The minimum kinetic energy of the reactant molecules that allows the reaction to proceed is called the **activation energy** (E_a).

If a molecule of N_2 collides with one of O_2, but their total kinetic energy is less than the activation energy, then the two just bounce off one another. Some energy may be transferred from one molecule to the other, or converted between translational, rotational, and vibrational energy, but we are still left with one molecule of N_2 and one of O_2.

Now we begin to see why, with few exceptions, rates of reaction increase with temperature. At higher temperatures, the average kinetic energy of the reactants is higher and therefore a greater fraction of the collisions have total kinetic energies exceeding

 Note that energy must be *supplied* to break a bond. *Forming* a bond *releases* energy.

the activation energy. If the activation energy is much greater than the average translational kinetic energy of the reactants,

$$E_a \gg \tfrac{3}{2} kT \qquad (13\text{-}23)$$

then the only candidates for reaction are molecules far off in the exponentially decaying, high-energy tail of the Maxwell-Boltzmann distribution. In this situation, a small increase in temperature can have a dramatic effect on the reaction rate: the reaction rate depends *exponentially* on temperature.

$$\text{reaction rate} \propto e^{-E_a/(kT)} \qquad (13\text{-}24)$$

Although we have discussed reactions in terms of gases, the same general principles apply to reactions in liquid solutions. The temperature determines what fraction of the collisions have enough energy to react, so reaction rates are temperature-dependent whether the reaction occurs in a gas mixture or a liquid solution.

Example 13.8

Increase in Reaction Rate with Temperature Increase

The activation energy for the reaction $N_2O \rightarrow N_2 + O$ is 4.0×10^{-19} J. By what percentage does the reaction rate increase if the temperature is increased from 700.0 K to 707.0 K (a 1% increase in absolute temperature)?

Strategy   We should first check that $E_a \gg \tfrac{3}{2} kT$; otherwise, Eq. (13-24) does not apply. Assuming that checks out, we can set up a ratio of the reaction rates at the two temperatures.

Solution   Start by calculating $E_a/(kT_1)$, where $T_1 = 700.0$ K:

$$\frac{E_a}{kT_1} = \frac{4.0 \times 10^{-19} \text{ J}}{1.38 \times 10^{-23} \text{ J/K} \times 700.0 \text{ K}} = 41.41$$

So E_a is about 41 times kT, or about 28 times $\tfrac{3}{2} kT$. The activation energy is much greater than the average kinetic energy; thus, only a small fraction of the collisions might cause a reaction to occur.

At $T_2 = 707.0$ K,

$$\frac{E_a}{kT_2} = \frac{4.0 \times 10^{-19} \text{ J}}{1.38 \times 10^{-23} \text{ J/K} \times 707.0 \text{ K}} = \frac{41.41}{1.01} = 41.00$$

The ratio of the reaction rates is

$$\frac{\text{new rate}}{\text{old rate}} = \frac{e^{-41.00}}{e^{-41.41}} = e^{-(41.00 - 41.41)} = e^{0.41} = 1.5$$

The reaction rate at 707.0 K is 1.5 times the rate at 700.0 K—a 50% increase in reaction rate for a 1% increase in temperature!

Discussion   Normally we might suspect an error when a 1% change in one quantity causes a 50% change in another! However, this problem illustrates the dramatic effect of an *exponential* dependence. Reaction rates can be *extremely* sensitive to small temperature changes.

Practice Problem 13.8   Decrease in Reaction Rate for Lower Temperature

What is the percentage decrease in the rate of the same reaction if the temperature is lowered from 700.0 K to 699.0 K?

What are the evolutionary advantages of warm-blooded versus cold-blooded animals?

At the beginning of this chapter, we asked about the necessity for temperature regulation in warm-blooded animals (Fig. 13.15). The temperature dependence of chemical reaction rates has a profound effect on biological functions. If our internal temperatures varied, we would have a varying metabolic rate, becoming sluggish in cold weather.

Application: Temperature and Metabolism   By maintaining a constant body temperature higher than that of the environment, warm-blooded animals are able to tolerate a wider range of environmental temperatures than cold-blooded animals (such as

Figure 13.15 Warm-blooded animals use different strategies to maintain a constant body temperature. (a) The fur of an Arctic fox serves as a layer of insulation to help it stay warm. (b) Dogs pant and (c) people sweat when their bodies are in danger of overheating. In cases (b) and (c), the evaporation of water has a cooling effect on the body.

reptiles and insects). Temperature fluctuation in the environment is much more severe on land than in water; thus, land animals are more likely to be homeothermic than aquatic animals. Keeping muscles at their optimal temperatures contributes to the much larger effort required to move around on land or in the air as opposed to moving through water. Keeping the muscles and vital organs warm allows the high level of aerobic metabolism needed to sustain intense physical activity.

Cold-blooded animals depend on the environment for temperature regulation; thus, we see a snake lying on a rock heated by the Sun in an attempt to keep warm. As a snake's blood temperature goes down in cold weather, the snake becomes inactive and lethargic. Most insects are inactive below 10°C and many cannot survive the cold of winter.

However, if environmental conditions become too extreme, it may be difficult for homeotherms to maintain ideal body temperature. Hypothermia occurs when the central core of the body becomes too cold; bodily processes slow and eventually cease. People caught outside in blizzards are urged to stay awake and to keep moving; the energy produced by exercise may be up to 20 times that produced by the resting body and can compensate for heat loss in extreme cold.

Warm-blooded animals must consume much more food than cold-blooded animals of a similar size; metabolic processes in warm-blooded animals act like a furnace to keep the body warm. A human must consume about 1500 kcal of food energy per day just to keep warm when resting at 20°C; an alligator of similar body weight needs only 60 kcal/day at rest at 20°C.

13.8 DIFFUSION

Mean Free Path   How far does a gas molecule move, on average, between collisions? The mean (average) length of the path traveled by a gas molecule as a free particle (no interactions with other particles) is called the **mean free path** (Λ, the Greek capital

Figure 13.16 Successive straight-line paths traveled by a molecule between collisions.

lambda). The mean free path depends on two things: how large the molecules are and how many of them occupy a given volume. A detailed calculation yields

Mean free path:

$$\Lambda = \frac{1}{\sqrt{2}\ \pi d^2\ (N/V)}$$ (13-25)

Typically the mean free path is much larger than the average distance between neighboring molecules. Nitrogen molecules in air at room temperature have mean free paths of about 0.1 μm, which is about 25 times the average distance between molecules. Each molecule collides an average of 5×10^9 times per second. (For more information on mean free path, see text website.)

Diffusion

A gas molecule moves in a straight line between collisions—the effect of gravity on the velocity of the molecule is negligible during a time interval of only 0.2 ns. At each collision, both the speed and direction of the molecule's motion change. The mean free path tells us the *average* length of the molecule's straight line paths between collisions. The result is that a given molecule follows a *random walk* trajectory (Fig. 13.16).

After an elapsed time *t*, how far on average has a molecule moved from its initial position? The answer to this question is relevant when we consider **diffusion**. Someone across the room opens a bottle of perfume: how long until the scent reaches you? As gas molecules diffuse into the air, the frequent collisions are what determine how long it takes the scent to travel across the room (assuming, as we do here, that there are no air currents). When there is a difference in concentrations between different points in a gas, the random thermal motion of the molecules tends to even out the concentrations (other things being equal). The net flow from regions of high concentration (near the perfume bottle) to regions of lower concentration (across the room) is diffusion.

Consider a molecule of perfume in the air. It has a mean free path Λ. After a large number of collisions *N*, it has traveled a total *distance N*Λ. However, its displacement from its original position is much less than that, since at each collision it changes direction. It can be shown using statistical analysis of the random walk that the rms magnitude of its displacement after *N* collisions is proportional to $\sqrt{N}$. Since the number of collisions is proportional to the elapsed time, the rms displacement is proportional to $\sqrt{t}$.

The root mean squared displacement in one direction is

$$x_{\mathrm{rms}} = \sqrt{2Dt}$$ (13-26)

where *D* is a diffusion constant such as those given in Table 13.4. The diffusion constant *D* depends on the molecule or atom that is diffusing and the medium through which it is moving.

Application: diffusion of oxygen through cell membranes

Diffusion is crucial in biological processes such as the transport of oxygen. Oxygen molecules diffuse from the air in the lungs through the walls of the alveoli and then through the walls of the capillaries to oxygenate the blood. The oxygen is then carried by hemoglobin in the blood to various parts of the body, where it again diffuses through capillary walls into intercellular fluids and then through cell membranes into cells. Diffusion is a slow process over long distances but can be quite effective over short distances—which is why cell membranes must be thin and capillaries must have small diameters. Evolution has seen to it that the capillaries of animals of widely different sizes are all about the same size—as small as possible while still allowing blood cells to flow through them.

Table 13.4   Diffusion Constants at 1 atm and 20°C

Diffusing Molecule	Medium	D (m²/s)
DNA	Water	1.3×10^{-12}
Oxygen	Tissue (cell membrane)	1.8×10^{-11}
Hemoglobin	Water	6.9×10^{-11}
Sucrose ($C_{12}H_{22}O_{11}$)	Water	5.0×10^{-10}
Glucose ($C_6H_{12}O_6$)	Water	6.7×10^{-10}
Oxygen	Water	1.0×10^{-9}
Oxygen	Air	1.8×10^{-5}
Hydrogen	Air	6.4×10^{-5}

Example 13.9

Diffusion Time for Oxygen into Capillaries

How long on average does it take an oxygen molecule in an alveolus to diffuse into the blood? Assume for simplicity that the diffusion constant for oxygen passing through the two membranes (alveolus and capillary walls) is the same: 1.8×10^{-11} m²/s. The total thickness of the two membranes is 1.2×10^{-8} m.

Strategy   Take the x-direction to be through the membranes. Then we want to know how much time elapses until $x_{rms} = 1.2 \times 10^{-8}$ m.

Solution   Solving Eq. (13-26) for t yields

$$t = \frac{x_{rms}^2}{2D}$$

Now substitute $x_{rms} = 1.2 \times 10^{-8}$ m and $D = 1.8 \times 10^{-11}$ m²/s:

$$t = \frac{(1.2 \times 10^{-8} \text{ m})^2}{2 \times 1.8 \times 10^{-11} \text{ m}^2/\text{s}} = 4.0 \times 10^{-6} \text{ s}$$

Discussion   The time is proportional to the *square* of the membrane thickness. It would take four times as long for an oxygen molecule to diffuse through a membrane twice as thick. The rapid increase of diffusion time with distance is a principal reason why evolution has favored thin membranes over thicker ones.

Practice Problem 13.9   Time for Oxygen to Get Halfway Through the Membrane

How long on average does it take an oxygen molecule to get *halfway* through the alveolus and capillary wall?

Master the Concepts

- Temperature is a quantity that determines when objects are in thermal equilibrium. The flow of energy that occurs between two objects or systems due to a temperature difference between them is called heat flow. If heat can flow between two objects or systems, the objects or systems are said to be in thermal contact. When two systems in thermal contact have the same temperature, there is no net flow of heat between them; the objects are said to be in thermal equilibrium.

- Zeroth law of thermodynamics: if two objects are each in thermal equilibrium with a third object, then the two are in thermal equilibrium with one another.

- The SI unit of temperature is the kelvin (symbol K, *without* a degree sign). The kelvin scale is an absolute temperature scale, which means that $T = 0$ is set to absolute zero.

continued on next page

Master the Concepts continued

- Temperature in °C (T_C) and temperature in kelvins (T) are related by

$$T_C = T - 273.15 \qquad (13\text{-}3)$$

- As long as the temperature change is not too great, the fractional length change of a solid is proportional to the temperature change:

$$\frac{\Delta L}{L_0} = \alpha \Delta T \qquad (13\text{-}4)$$

The constant of proportionality, α, is called the coefficient of linear expansion of the substance.

- The fractional change in volume of a solid or liquid is also proportional to the temperature change as long as the temperature change is not too large:

$$\frac{\Delta V}{V_0} = \beta \Delta T \qquad (13\text{-}7)$$

For solids, the coefficient of volume expansion is three times the coefficient of linear expansion: $\beta = 3\alpha$.

- The mole is an SI base unit and is defined as: one mole of anything contains the same number of units as there are atoms in 12 *grams* (not kilograms) of carbon-12. This number is called Avogadro's number and has the value

$$N_A = 6.022 \times 10^{23}\ \text{mol}^{-1}$$

- The mass of an atom or molecule is often expressed in the atomic mass unit (symbol u). By definition, one atom of carbon-12 has a mass of 12 u (exactly).

$$1\ \text{u} = 1.66 \times 10^{-27}\ \text{kg} \qquad (13\text{-}12)$$

The atomic mass unit is chosen so that the mass of an atom or molecule in "u" is numerically the same as the molar mass in g/mol.

- In an ideal gas, the molecules move independently in free space with no interactions except when two molecules collide. The ideal gas is a useful model for many real gases, provided that the gas is sufficiently dilute. The ideal gas law:

$$\text{microscopic form: } PV = NkT \qquad (13\text{-}13)$$

$$\text{macroscopic form: } PV = nRT \qquad (13\text{-}16)$$

where Boltzmann's constant and the universal gas constant are

$$k = 1.38 \times 10^{-23}\ \text{J/K} \qquad (13\text{-}14)$$

$$R = N_A k = 8.31\ \frac{\text{J/K}}{\text{mol}} \qquad (13\text{-}15)$$

- The pressure of an ideal gas is proportional to the average translational kinetic energy of the molecules:

$$P = \frac{2}{3} \frac{N}{V} \langle K_{tr} \rangle \qquad (13\text{-}18)$$

- The average translational kinetic energy of the molecules is proportional to the absolute temperature:

$$\langle K_{tr} \rangle = \frac{3}{2} kT \qquad (13\text{-}20)$$

- The speed of a gas molecule that has the average kinetic energy is called the rms speed:

$$\langle K_{tr} \rangle = \frac{1}{2} m v_{rms}^2 \qquad (13\text{-}21)$$

- The distribution of molecular speeds in an ideal gas is called the Maxwell-Boltzmann distribution.

- If the activation energy for a chemical reaction is much greater than the average kinetic energy of the reactants, the reaction rate depends *exponentially* on temperature:

$$\text{reaction rate} \propto e^{-E_a/(kT)} \qquad (13\text{-}24)$$

- The mean free path (Λ) is the average length of the path traveled by a gas molecule as a free particle (no interactions with other particles) between collisions:

$$\Lambda = \frac{1}{\sqrt{2}\ \pi d^2\ (N/V)} \qquad (13\text{-}25)$$

- The root mean square displacement of a diffusing molecule along the x-axis is

$$x_{rms} = \sqrt{2Dt} \qquad (13\text{-}26)$$

where D is a diffusion constant.

Conceptual Questions

1. Explain why it would be impossible to uniquely define the temperature of an object if the zeroth law of thermodynamics were violated?

2. Why do we call the temperature 0 K "absolute zero"? How is 0 K fundamentally different from 0°C or 0°F?

3. Under what special circumstances can kelvins or Celsius degrees be used interchangeably?

4. What happens to a hole in a flat metal plate when the plate expands on being heated? Does the hole get larger or smaller?

5. Why would silver and brass probably not be a good choice of metals for a bimetallic strip (leaving aside the question of the cost of silver)? (See Table 13.2.)

6. One way to loosen the lid on a glass jar is to run it under hot water. How does that work?

7. Why must we use absolute temperature (temperature in kelvins) in the ideal gas law ($PV = NkT$)? Explain how using the Celsius scale would give nonsensical results.

8. Natural gas is sold by volume. In the United States, the price charged is usually per cubic foot. Given the price per cubic foot, what other information would you need in order to calculate the price per mole?

9. What are the SI units of mass density and number density? If two different gases have the same number density, do they have the same mass density?

10. Suppose we have two tanks, one containing helium gas and the other nitrogen gas. The two gases are at the same temperature and pressure. Which has the higher number density (or are they equal)? Which has the higher mass density (or are they equal)?

11. The mass of an aluminum atom is 27.0 u. What is the mass of *one mole* of aluminum atoms? (No calculation required!)

12. A ping-pong ball that has been dented during hard play can often be restored by placing it in hot water. Explain why this works.

13. Why does a helium weather balloon expand as it rises into the air? Assume the temperature remains constant.

14. Explain why there is almost no hydrogen (H_2) or helium (He) in Earth's atmosphere, yet both are present in Jupiter's atmosphere. [*Hint:* Escape velocity from Earth is 11.2 km/s and escape velocity from Jupiter is 60 km/s.]

15. Explain how it is possible that more than half of the molecules in an ideal gas have kinetic energies less than the average kinetic energy. Shouldn't half have less and half have more?

16. In air under ordinary conditions (room temperature and atmospheric pressure), the average intermolecular distance is about 4 nm and the mean free path is about 0.1 μm. The diameter of a nitrogen molecule is about 0.3 nm. Explain how the mean free path can be so much larger than the average distance between molecules.

17. In air under ordinary conditions (room temperature and atmospheric pressure), the average intermolecular distance is about 4 nm and the mean free path is about 0.1 μm. The diameter of a nitrogen molecule is about 0.3 nm. Which two distances should we compare to decide that air is dilute and can be treated as an ideal gas? Explain.

18. In air under ordinary conditions (room temperature and atmospheric pressure), the average intermolecular distance is about 4 nm and the mean free path is about 0.1 μm. The diameter of a nitrogen molecule is about 0.3 nm. What would it mean if the intermolecular distance and the molecular diameter were about the same? In that case, would it make sense to speak of a mean free path? Explain.

19. Explain how an automobile airbag protects the passenger from injury. Why would the airbag be ineffective if the gas pressure inside is too low when the passenger comes into contact with it? What about if it is too high?

20. It takes longer to hard-boil an egg in Mexico City (2200 m above sea level) than it does in Amsterdam (parts of which are below sea level). Why? [*Hint:* At higher altitudes, water boils at less than 100°C.]

Multiple-Choice Questions

1. In a mixed gas such as air, the rms speeds of different molecules are
   (a) independent of molecular mass.
   (b) proportional to molecular mass.
   (c) inversely proportional to molecular mass.
   (d) proportional to $\sqrt{\text{molecular mass}}$.
   (e) inversely proportional to $\sqrt{\text{molecular mass}}$.

2. The average kinetic energy of the molecules in an ideal gas increases with the volume remaining constant. Which of these statements *must* be true?
   (a) The pressure increases and the temperature stays the same.
   (b) The number density decreases.
   (c) The temperature increases and the pressure stays the same.
   (d) Both the pressure and the temperature increase.

3. Which of these will increase the average kinetic energy of the molecules in an ideal gas?
   (a) reduce the volume, keeping P and N constant
   (b) increase the volume, keeping P and N constant
   (c) reduce the volume, keeping T and N constant
   (d) increase the pressure, keeping T and V constant
   (e) increase N, keeping V and T constant

4. The absolute temperature of an ideal gas is directly proportional to
   (a) the number of molecules in the sample.
   (b) the average momentum of a molecule of the gas.
   (c) the average translational kinetic energy of the gas.
   (d) the diffusion constant of the gas.

5. The rms speed is the
   (a) speed at which all the gas molecules move.
   (b) speed of a molecule with the average kinetic energy.
   (c) average speed of the gas molecules.
   (d) maximum speed of the gas molecules.

6. What are the most favorable conditions for real gases to approach ideal behavior?
   (a) high temperature and high pressure
   (b) low temperature and high pressure
   (c) low temperature and low pressure
   (d) high temperature and low pressure

7. An ideal gas has the volume V_0. If the temperature and the pressure are each tripled during a process, the new volume is
   (a) V_0.
   (b) $9V_0$.
   (c) $3V_0$.
   (d) $0.33V_0$.

8. The average kinetic energy of a gas molecule can be found from which of these quantities?
   (a) pressure only
   (b) number of molecules only
   (c) temperature only
   (d) pressure and temperature are both required

9. If the temperature of an ideal gas is doubled and the pressure is held constant, the rms speed of the molecules
   (a) remains unchanged.
   (b) is 2 times the original speed.
   (c) is $\sqrt{2}$ times the original speed.
   (d) is 4 times the original speed.

10. A metal box is heated until each of its sides has expanded by 0.1%. By what percent has the *volume* of the box changed?
    (a) −0.3%   (b) −0.2%   (c) +0.1%
    (d) +0.2%   (e) +0.3%

Problems

13.2 Temperature Scales

1. On a warm summer day, the air temperature is 84°F. Express this temperature in (a) °C and (b) kelvins. (tutorial: sun's temperature)

2. The temperature at which liquid nitrogen boils (at atmospheric pressure) is 77 K. Express this temperature in (a) °C and (b) °F.

3. (a) At what temperature (if any) does the numerical value of Celsius degrees equal the numerical value of Fahrenheit degrees? (b) At what temperature (if any) does the numerical value of kelvins equal the numerical value of Fahrenheit degrees?

4. A room air conditioner causes a temperature change of −6.0°C. (a) What is the temperature change in kelvins? (b) What is the temperature change in °F?

5. Aliens from the planet Jeenkah have based their temperature scale on the boiling and freezing temperatures of ethyl alcohol. These temperatures are 78°C and −114°C, respectively. The people of Jeenkah have six digits on each hand, so they use a base-12 number system and have decided to have 144°J between the freezing and boiling temperatures of ethyl alcohol. They set the freezing point to 0°J. How would you convert from °J to °C?

13.3 Thermal Expansion of Solids and Liquids

6. A 2.4-m length of copper pipe extends directly from a hot-water heater in a basement to a faucet on the first floor of a house. If the faucet isn't fixed in place, how much will it rise when the pipe is heated from 20.0°C to 90.0°C. Ignore any increase in the size of the faucet itself or of the water heater.

7. Two 35.0-cm metal rods, one made of copper and one made of aluminum, are placed end to end, touching each other. One end is fixed, so that it cannot move. The rods are heated from 0.0°C to 150°C. How far does the other end of the system of rods move?

8. Steel railroad tracks of length 18.30 m are laid at 10.0°C. How much space should be left between the track sections if they are to just touch when the temperature is 50.0°C?

9. A highway is made of concrete slabs that are 15 m long at 20.0°C. (a) If the temperature range at the location of the highway is from −20.0°C to +40.0°C, what size expansion gap should be left (at 20.0°C) to prevent buckling of the highway? (b) How large are the gaps at −20.0°C?

10. A lead rod and a common glass rod both have the same length when at 20.0°C. The lead rod is heated to 50.0°C. To what temperature must the glass rod be heated so that they are again at the same length?

11. The coefficient of linear expansion of brass is 1.9×10^{-5} °C^{-1}. At 20.0°C, a hole in a sheet of brass has an area of 1.00 mm^2. How much larger is the area of the hole at 30.0°C? (🕸 tutorial: loop around the equator)

12. Aluminum rivets used in airplane construction are made slightly too large for the rivet holes to be sure of a tight fit. The rivets are cooled with dry ice (−78.5°C) before they are driven into the holes. If the holes have a diameter of 0.6350 cm at 20.5°C, what should be the diameter of the rivets at 20.5°C if they are to just fit when cooled to the temperature of dry ice?

13. A temperature change ΔT causes a volume change ΔV but has no effect on the mass of an object. (a) Show that the change in density $\Delta \rho$ is given by $\Delta \rho = -\beta \rho \Delta T$. (b) Find the fractional change in density ($\Delta \rho / \rho$) of a brass sphere when the temperature changes from 32°C to −10.0°C.

14. A cylindrical brass container with a base of 75.0 cm^2 and height of 20.0 cm is filled to the brim with water when the system is at 25.0°C. How much water overflows when the temperature of the water and the container is raised to 95.0°C?

15. An ordinary drinking glass is filled to the brim with water (268.4 mL) at 2.0°C and placed on the sunny pool deck for a swimmer to enjoy. If the temperature of the water rises to 32.0°C before the swimmer reaches for the glass, how much water will have spilled over the top of the glass? Assume the glass does not expand.

16. Consider the situation described in Problem 15. (a) Take into account the expansion of the glass and calculate how much water will spill out of the glass. Compare your answer with the case where the expansion of the glass was not considered. (b) By what percentage has the answer changed when the expansion of the glass is considered?

17. A steel sphere with radius 1.0010 cm at 22.0°C must slip through a brass ring that has an internal radius of 1.0000 cm at the same temperature. To what temperature must the brass ring be heated so that the sphere, still at 22.0°C, can just slip through?

18. A long, narrow steel rod of length 2.5000 m at 25°C is oscillating as a pendulum about a horizontal axis through one end. If the temperature changes to 0°C, what will be the fractional change in its period?

19. The George Washington Bridge crosses the Hudson River between New York and New Jersey. The span of the steel bridge is about 1.6 km. If the temperature can vary from a low of −15°F in winter to a high of 105°F in summer, by how much might the length of the span change over an entire year?

20. A square brass plate, 8.00 cm on a side, has a hole cut into its center of area 4.90874 cm^2 (at 20.0°C). The hole in the plate is to slide over a cylindrical steel shaft of cross-sectional area 4.91000 cm^2 (also at 20.0°C). To what temperature must the brass plate be heated so that it can just slide over the steel cylinder (which remains at 20.0°C)? [*Hint:* The steel cylinder is not heated so it does not expand; only the brass plate is heated.]

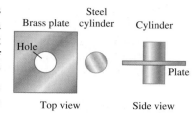

Brass plate   Steel cylinder   Cylinder

Hole

Plate

Top view   Side view

21. A copper washer is to be fit in place over a steel bolt. Both pieces of metal are at 20.0°C. If the diameter of the bolt is 1.0000 cm and the inner diameter of the washer is 0.9980 cm, to what temperature must the washer be raised so it will fit over the bolt? Only the copper washer is heated.

0.9980 cm

1.0000 cm

22. Repeat Problem 21, but now the copper washer and the steel bolt are both raised to the same temperature. At what temperature will the washer fit on the bolt?

◆23. A steel rule is calibrated for measuring lengths at 20.00°C. The rule is used to measure the length of a Vycor glass brick; when both are at 20.00°C, the brick is found to be 25.00 cm long. If the rule and the brick are both at 80.00°C, what would be the length of the brick as measured by the rule?

24. The fuselage of an Airbus A340 has a circumference of 17.72 m on the ground. The circumference increases by 26 cm when it is in flight. Part of this increase is due to the pressure difference between the inside and outside of the plane and part is due to the increase in the temperature due to air drag while it is flying along at 950 km/h. Suppose we wanted to heat a full-size model of the airbus made of aluminum to cause the same increase in circumference without changing the pressure. What would be the increase in temperature needed?

◆25. A flat square of side s_0 at temperature T_0 expands by Δs in both length and width when the temperature increases by ΔT. The original area is $s_0^2 = A_0$ and the final area is $(s_0 + \Delta s)^2 = A$. Show that if $\Delta s \ll s_0$,

$$\frac{\Delta A}{A_0} = 2\alpha \Delta T \qquad (13\text{-}6)$$

(Although we derive this relation for a square plate, it applies to a flat area of any shape.)

26. The volume of a solid cube with side s_0 at temperature T_0 is $V_0 = s_0^3$. Show that if $\Delta s \ll s_0$, the change in volume ΔV due to a change in temperature ΔT is given by

$$\frac{\Delta V}{V_0} = 3\alpha\Delta T \qquad (13\text{-}7, 8)$$

and therefore that $\beta = 3\alpha$. (Although we derive this relation for a cube, it applies to a solid of any shape.)

13.4 Molecular Picture of a Gas

27. Use the definition that 1 mol of ^{12}C (carbon-12) atoms has a mass of exactly 12 g, along with Avogadro's number, to derive the conversion between atomic mass units and kg.

28. Find the molar mass of ammonia (NH_3).

29. Find the mass (in kg) of one molecule of CO_2.

30. The mass of 1 mol of ^{13}C (carbon-13) is 13.003 g. (a) What is the mass in u of one ^{13}C atom? (b) What is the mass in kilograms of one ^{13}C atom?

31. Estimate the number of H_2O molecules in a human body of mass 80.2 kg. Assume that, on average, water makes up about 62% of the mass of a human body.

32. The mass density of diamond (a crystalline form of carbon) is 3500 kg/m^3. How many carbon atoms per cm^3 are there?

33. How many hydrogen atoms are present in 684.6 g of sucrose ($C_{12}H_{22}O_{11}$)?

34. How many moles of He are in 13 g of He?

35. The principal component of natural gas is methane (CH_4). How many moles of CH_4 are present in 144.36 g of methane?

36. What is the mass of one gold atom in kilograms?

37. Air at room temperature and atmospheric pressure has a mass density of 1.2 kg/m^3. The average molecular mass of air is 29.0 u. How many molecules are in 1.0 cm^3 of air?

38. At 0.0°C and 1.00 atm, 1.00 mol of a gas occupies a volume of 0.0224 m^3. (a) What is the number density? (b) Estimate the average distance between the molecules. (c) If the gas is nitrogen (N_2), the principal component of air, what is the total mass and mass density?

39. Sand is composed of SiO_2. Find the order of magnitude of the number of silicon (Si) atoms in a grain of sand. Approximate the sand grain as a sphere of diameter 0.5 mm and an SiO_2 molecule as a sphere of diameter 0.5 nm.

13.5 Absolute Temperature and the Ideal Gas Law

40. A flight attendant wants to change the temperature of the air in the cabin from 18°C to 24°C without changing the number of moles of air per m^3. What fractional change in pressure would be required?

41. A cylinder in a car engine takes $V_i = 4.50 \times 10^{-2}$ m^3 of air into the chamber at 30°C and at atmospheric pressure. The piston then compresses the air to one-ninth of the original volume (0.111 V_i) and to 20.0 times the original pressure (20.0 P_i). What is the new temperature of the air?

42. A tire with an inner volume of 0.0250 m^3 is filled with air at a gauge pressure of 36.0 psi. If the tire valve is opened to the atmosphere, what volume *outside of the tire* does the escaping air occupy? Some air remains within the tire occupying the original volume, but now that remaining air is at atmospheric pressure. Assume the temperature of the air does not change.

43. Verify, using the ideal gas law, the assertion in Problem 38 that 1.00 mol of a gas at 0.0°C and 1.00 atm occupies a volume of 0.0224 m^3.

44. Verify that the SI units of PV (pressure times volume) are joules.

45. Incandescent lightbulbs are filled with an inert gas to lengthen the filament life. With the current off (at $T = 20.0$°C), the gas inside a lightbulb has a pressure of 115 kPa. When the bulb is burning, the temperature rises to 70.0°C. What is the pressure at the higher temperature?

46. What fraction of the air molecules in a house must be pushed outside while the furnace raises the inside temperature from 16.0°C to 20.0°C? The pressure does not change since the house is not 100% airtight.

47. What is the mass density of air at $P = 1.0$ atm and $T =$ (a) −10°C and (b) 30°C? The average molecular mass of air is approximately 29 u.

48. A constant volume gas thermometer containing helium is immersed in boiling ammonia (−33°C) and the pressure is read once equilibrium is reached. The thermometer is then moved to a bath of boiling water (100.0°C). After the manometer was adjusted to keep the volume of helium constant, by what factor was the pressure multiplied?

49. A hydrogen balloon at Earth's surface has a volume of 5.0 m^3 on a day when the temperature is 27°C and the pressure is 1.00×10^5 N/m^2. The balloon rises and expands as the pressure drops. What would the volume of the same number of moles of hydrogen be at an altitude of 40 km where the pressure is 0.33×10^3 N/m^2 and the temperature is −13°C?

50. An ideal gas that occupies 1.2 m^3 at a pressure of 1.0×10^5 Pa and a temperature of 27°C is compressed to a volume of 0.60 m^3 and heated to a temperature of 227°C. What is the new pressure?

51. A diver rises quickly to the surface from a 5.0-m depth. If she did not exhale the gas from her lungs before rising, by what factor would her lungs expand? Assume the temperature to be constant and the pressure in the lungs to match the pressure outside the diver's body. The density of seawater is 1.03×10^3 kg/m^3.

52. In intergalactic space, there is an average of about one hydrogen atom per cm^3 and the temperature is 3 K. What is the absolute pressure?

53. A tank of compressed air of volume $1.0 \, m^3$ is pressurized to 20.0 atm at $T = 273$ K. A valve is opened and air is released until the pressure in the tank is 15.0 atm. How many air molecules were released?

54. A mass of 0.532 kg of molecular oxygen is contained in a cylinder at a pressure of 1.0×10^5 Pa and a temperature of 0.0°C. What volume does the gas occupy?

55. A bubble rises from the bottom of a lake of depth 80.0 m, where the temperature is 4°C. The water temperature at the surface is 18°C. If the bubble's initial diameter is 1.00 mm, what is its diameter when it reaches the surface? (Ignore the surface tension of water. Assume the bubble warms as it rises to the same temperature as the water and retains a spherical shape. Assume $P_{atm} = 1.0$ atm.)

56. A bubble with a volume of $1.00 \, cm^3$ forms at the bottom of a lake that is 20.0 m deep. The temperature at the bottom of the lake is 10.0°C. The bubble rises to the surface where the water temperature is 25.0°C. Assume that the bubble is small enough that its temperature always matches that of its surroundings. What is the volume of the bubble just before it breaks the surface of the water? Ignore surface tension.

57. A scuba diver has an air tank with a volume of $0.010 \, m^3$. The air in the tank is initially at a pressure of 1.0×10^7 Pa. Assuming that the diver breathes 0.500 L/s of air, find how long the tank will last at depths of (a) 2.0 m and (b) 20.0 m. (Make the same assumptions as in Example 13.6.)

58. An emphysema patient is breathing pure O_2 through a face mask. The cylinder of O_2 contains $0.60 \, ft^3$ of O_2 gas at a pressure of 2200 lb/in^2. (a) What volume would the oxygen occupy at atmospheric pressure (and the same temperature)? (b) If the patient takes in 8 L/min of O_2 at atmospheric pressure, how long will the cylinder last?

59. Consider the expansion of an ideal gas at constant pressure. The initial temperature is T_0 and the initial volume is V_0. (a) Show that $\Delta V/V_0 = \beta \Delta T$, where $\beta = 1/T_0$. (b) Compare the coefficient of volume expansion β for an ideal gas at 20°C to the values for liquids and gases listed in Table 13.3.

13.6 Kinetic Theory of the Ideal Gas

60. What is the temperature of an ideal gas whose molecules have an average translational kinetic energy of 3.20×10^{-20} J?

61. What is the total translational kinetic energy of the gas molecules of 0.420 mol of air at atmospheric pressure that occupies a volume of 1.00 L ($0.00100 \, m^3$)?

62. What is the kinetic energy per unit volume in an ideal gas at (a) $P = 1.00$ atm and (b) $P = 300.0$ atm?

63. Show that, for an ideal gas,

$$P = \tfrac{1}{3} \rho v_{rms}^2$$

where P is the pressure, ρ is the mass density, and v_{rms} is the rms speed of the gas molecules.

64. Estimate the percentage of the O_2 molecules in air at 0.0°C and 1.00 atm that are moving faster than the speed of sound in air at that temperature (see Fig. 13.13).

65. What is the total internal kinetic energy of 1.0 mol of an ideal gas at 0.0°C and 1.00 atm?

66. If 2.0 mol of nitrogen gas (N_2) are placed in a cubic box, 25 cm on each side, at 1.6 atm of pressure, what is the rms speed of the nitrogen molecules?

67. There are two identical containers of gas at the same temperature and pressure, one containing argon and the other neon. What is the ratio of the rms speed of the argon atoms to that of the neon atoms? The atomic mass of argon is twice that of neon. (⬤ tutorial: RMS speed)

68. A smoke particle has a mass of 1.38×10^{-17} kg and it is randomly moving about in thermal equilibrium with room temperature air at 27°C. What is the rms speed of the particle?

69. Find the rms speed in air at 0.0°C and 1.00 atm of (a) the N_2 molecules, (b) the O_2 molecules, and (c) the CO_2 molecules.

70. What are the rms speeds of helium atoms, and nitrogen, hydrogen, and oxygen molecules at 25°C?

71. If the upper atmosphere of Jupiter has a temperature of 160 K and the escape speed is 60 km/s, would an astronaut expect to find much hydrogen there?

72. A sealed cylinder contains a sample of ideal gas at a pressure of 2.0 atm. The rms speed of the molecules is v_0. If the rms speed is then reduced to 0.90 v_0, what is the pressure of the gas?

73. What is the temperature of an ideal gas whose molecules in random motion have an average translational kinetic energy of 4.60×10^{-20} J?

74. Show that the rms speed of a molecule in an ideal gas at absolute temperature T is given by

$$v_{rms} = \sqrt{\frac{3kT}{m}} \qquad (13\text{-}22)$$

where k is Boltzmann's constant and m is the mass of a molecule.

75. Show that the rms speed of a molecule in an ideal gas at absolute temperature T is given by

$$v_{rms} = \sqrt{\frac{3RT}{M}}$$

where M is the *molar mass*—the mass of the gas per mole.

13.7 Temperature and Reaction Rates

76. The reaction rate for the hydrolysis of benzoyl-l-arginine amide by trypsin at 10.0°C is 1.878 times faster than that at 5.0°C. Assuming that the reaction rate is exponential as in Eq. (13-24), what is the activation energy?

77. The reaction rate for the prepupal development of male *Drosophila* is temperature-dependent. Assuming that the reaction rate is exponential as in Eq. (13-24), the activation energy for this development is then 2.81×10^{-19} J. A *Drosophila* is originally at 10.00°C and its temperature is increasing. If the rate of development has increased 3.5%, how much has its temperature increased?

78. At high altitudes, water boils at a temperature lower than 100.0°C due to the lower air pressure. A rule of thumb states that the time to hard-boil an egg doubles for every 10.0°C drop in temperature. What activation energy does this rule imply for the chemical reactions that occur when the egg is cooked?

13.8 Diffusion

79. Estimate the mean free path of a N_2 molecule in air at (a) sea level ($P \approx 100$ kPa and $T \approx 290$ K), (b) the top of Mt. Everest (altitude = 8.8 km, $P \approx 50$ kPa, and $T \approx 230$ K), and (c) an altitude of 30 km ($P \approx 1$ kPa and $T \approx 230$ K). For simplicity, assume that air is pure nitrogen gas. The diameter of a N_2 molecule is approximately 0.3 nm.

80. About how long will it take a perfume molecule to diffuse a distance of 5.00 m in one direction in a room if the diffusion constant is 1.00×10^{-5} m²/s? Assume that the air is perfectly still—there are no air currents.

81. Estimate the time it takes a sucrose molecule to move 5.00 mm in one direction by diffusion in water. Assume there are no currents in the water.

82. Your friend is 3.0 m away from you in a room. There are no significant air currents. She opens a bottle of perfume and you first smell it 20 s later. How long would it have taken for you to smell it if she had been 6.0 m away instead? (tutorial: diffusion)

Comprehensive Problems

83. The driver from Practice Problem 13.3 fills his 18.9-L steel gasoline can in the morning when the temperature of the can and the gasoline is 15.0°C and the pressure is 1.0 atm, but this time he remembers to replace the tightly fitting cap after filling the can. Assume that the can is completely full of gasoline (no air space) and that the cap does not leak. The temperature climbs to 30.0°C. Ignoring the expansion of the steel can, what would be the pressure of the heated gasoline? The bulk modulus for gasoline is 1.00×10^9 N/m².

84. An iron bridge girder ($Y = 2.0 \times 10^{11}$ N/m²) is constrained between two rock faces whose spacing doesn't change. At 20.0°C the girder is relaxed. How large a stress develops in the iron if the sun heats the girder to 40.0°C?

85. Consider the sphere and ring of Problem 17. What must the final temperature be if both the ring and the sphere are heated to the same final temperature?

86. Agnes Pockels (1862–1935) was able to determine Avogadro's number using only a few household chemicals, in particular oleic acid, whose formula is $C_{18}H_{34}O_2$. (a) What is the molar mass of this acid? (b) The mass of one drop of oleic acid is 2.3×10^{-5} g and the volume is 2.6×10^{-5} cm³. How many moles of oleic acid are there in one drop? (c) Now all Pockels needed was to find the number of molecules of oleic acid. Luckily, when oleic acid is spread out on water, it lines up in a layer one molecule thick. If the base of the molecule of oleic acid is a square of side d, the height of the molecule is known to be $7d$. Pockels spread out one drop of oleic acid on some water, and measured the area to be 70.0 cm². Using the volume and the area of oleic acid, what is d? (d) If we assume that this film is one molecule thick, how many molecules of oleic acid are there in the drop? (e) What value does this give you for Avogadro's number?

87. A certain acid has a molecular mass of 63 u. By mass, it consists of 1.6% hydrogen, 22.2% nitrogen, and 76.2% oxygen. What is the chemical formula for this acid?

88. These data are from a constant-volume gas thermometer experiment. The volume of the gas was kept constant, while the temperature was changed. The resulting pressure was measured. Plot the data on a pressure versus temperature diagram. Based on these data, estimate the value of absolute zero in Celsius.

T (°C)	P (atm)
0	1.00
20	1.07
100	1.37
−33	0.88
−196	0.28

89. Given that our body temperature is 98.6°F, (a) what is the average kinetic energy of the molecules in the air in our lungs? (b) If our temperature has increased to 100.0°F, by what percentage has the kinetic energy of the molecules increased?

90. The volume of air taken in by a warm-blooded vertebrate in the Andes mountains is 210 L/day at standard temperature and pressure (i.e., 0°C and 1 atm). If the air in the lungs is at 39°C, under a pressure of 450 mm Hg, and we assume that the vertebrate takes in an average volume of 100 cm³ per breath at the temperature and

pressure of its lungs, how many breaths does this vertebrate take per day?

91. As a Boeing 747 gains altitude, the passenger cabin is pressurized. However, the cabin is not pressurized fully to atmospheric (1.01×10^5 Pa), as it would be at sea level, but rather pressurized to 7.62×10^4 Pa. Suppose a 747 takes off from sea level when the temperature in the airplane is 25.0°C and the pressure is 1.01×10^5 Pa. (a) If the cabin temperature remains at 25.0°C, what is the percentage change in the number of moles of air in the cabin? (b) If instead, the number of moles of air in the cabin does not change, what would the temperature be?

92. An iron cannonball of radius 0.08 m has a cavity of radius 0.05 m that is to be filled with gunpowder. If the measurements were made at a temperature of 22°C, how much extra volume of gunpowder, if any, will be required to fill 500 cannonballs when the temperature is 30°C?

93. Ten students take a test and get the following scores: 83, 62, 81, 77, 68, 92, 88, 83, 72, and 75. What are the average value, the rms value, and the most probable value, respectively, of these test scores?

94. A hand pump is being used to inflate a bicycle tire that has a gauge pressure of 40.0 psi. If the pump is a cylinder of length 18.0 in. with a cross-sectional area of 3.00 in.^{2}, how far down must the piston be pushed before air will flow into the tire?

95. An ideal gas in a constant-volume gas thermometer (Fig. 13.11) is held at a volume of 0.500 L. As the temperature of the gas is increased by 20.0°C, the mercury level on the right side of the manometer must rise by 8.00 mm in order to keep the gas volume constant. (a) What is the slope of a graph of P versus T for this gas (in mm Hg/°C)? (b) How many moles of gas are present?

96. A cylinder with an interior cross-sectional area of 70.0 cm^2 has a moveable piston of mass 5.40 kg at the top that can move up and down without friction. The cylinder contains 2.25×10^{-3} mol of an ideal gas at 23.0°C. (a) What is the volume of the gas when the piston is in equilibrium? Assume the air pressure outside the cylinder is 1.00 atm. (b) By what factor does the volume change if the gas temperature is raised to 223.0°C and the piston moves until it is again in equilibrium?

97. Estimate the average distance between air molecules at 0.0°C and 1.00 atm.

98. If you wanted to make a scale model of air at 0.0°C and 1.00 atm, using ping-pong balls (diameter, 3.75 cm) to represent the N$_2$ molecules (diameter, 0.30 nm), (a) how far apart on average should the ping-pong balls be at any instant? (b) How far would a ping-pong ball travel on average before colliding with another?

99. For divers going to great depths, the composition of the air in the tank must be modified. The ideal composition is to have approximately the same number of O$_2$ molecules per unit volume as in surface air (to avoid oxygen poisoning), and to use helium instead of nitrogen for the remainder of the gas (to avoid nitrogen narcosis, which results from nitrogen dissolving in the bloodstream). Of the molecules in dry surface air, 78% are N$_2$, 21% are O$_2$, and 1% are Ar. (a) How many O$_2$ molecules per m^3 are there in surface air at 20.0°C and 1.00 atm? (b) For a diver going to a depth of 100.0 m, what percentage of the gas molecules in the tank should be O$_2$? (Assume that the density of seawater is 1025 kg/m^3 and the temperature is 20.0°C.)

100. Show that, in two gases at the same temperature, the rms speeds are inversely proportional to the square root of the molecular masses:

$$\frac{(v_{\mathrm{rms}})_1}{(v_{\mathrm{rms}})_2} = \sqrt{\frac{m_2}{m_1}}$$

101. The SR-71 Blackbird reconnaissance aircraft is primarily made of titanium and typically flies at speeds above Mach 3. In flight, the length of the SR-71 increases by about 0.20 m from its takeoff length of 32.70 m. The average coefficient of linear expansion for titanium over the temperature range experienced by the SR-71 is 10.1×10^{-6} K^{-1}. What is the approximate temperature of the SR-71 while it is in flight if it started at 20°C?

102. In plants, water diffuses out through small openings known as stomatal pores. If $D = 2.4 \times 10^{-5}$ m^2/s for water vapor in air, and the length of the pores is 2.5×10^{-5} m, how long does it take for a water molecule to diffuse out through the pore?

103. The alveoli (see Section 13.8) have an average radius of 0.125 mm and are approximately spherical. If the pressure in the sacs is 1.00×10^5 Pa, and the temperature is 310 K (average body temperature), how many air molecules are in an alveolus?

104. A 10.0-L vessel contains 12 g of N$_2$ gas at 20°C. (a) Estimate the nearest-neighbor distance. (b) Is the gas dilute? [*Hint:* Compare the nearest-neighbor distance to the diameter of an N$_2$ molecule, about 0.3 nm.]

105. During hibernation, an animal's metabolism slows down, and its body temperature lowers. For example, a California ground squirrel's body temperature lowers from 40.0°C to 10.0°C during hibernation. If we assume that the air in the squirrel's lungs is 75.0% N$_2$ and 25.0% O$_2$, by how much will the rms speed of the air molecules in the lungs have decreased during hibernation?

106. A steel ring of inner diameter 7.00000 cm at 20.0°C is to be heated and placed over a brass shaft of outer diameter 7.00200 cm at 20.0°C. (a) To what

temperature must the ring be heated to fit over the shaft? The shaft remains at 20.0°C. (b) Once the ring is on the shaft and has cooled to 20.0°C, to what temperature must the ring plus shaft combination be cooled to allow the ring to slide off the shaft again?

107. The inner tube of a Pyrex glass mercury thermometer has a diameter of 0.120 mm. The bulb at the bottom of the thermometer contains 0.200 cm³ of mercury. How far will the thread of mercury move for a change of 1.00°C? Remember to take into account the expansion of the glass. (tutorial: thermometer)

108. A wine barrel has a diameter at its widest point of 134.460 cm at a temperature of 20.0°C. A circular iron band, of diameter 134.448 cm, is to be placed around the barrel at the widest spot. The iron band is 5.00 cm wide and 0.500 cm thick. (a) To what temperature must the band be heated to be able to fit it over the barrel? (b) Once the band is in place and cools to 20.0°C, what will be the tension in the band?

109. A 12.0-cm cylindrical chamber has an 8.00-cm-diameter piston attached to one end. The piston is connected to an ideal spring as shown. Initially, the gas inside the chamber is at atmospheric pressure and 20.0°C and the spring is not compressed. When a total of 6.50×10^{-2} mol of gas is added to the chamber at 20.0°C, the spring compresses a distance of $\Delta x = 5.40$ cm. What is the spring constant of the spring?

110. A bimetallic strip is made from metals with expansion coefficients α_1 and α_2 (with $\alpha_2 > \alpha_1$). The thickness of each layer is s. At some temperature T_0, the bimetallic strip is relaxed and straight. (a) Show that, at temperature $T_0 + \Delta T$, the radius of curvature of the strip is

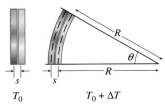

$$R \approx \frac{s}{(\alpha_2 - \alpha_1)\Delta T}$$

[*Hint:* At T_0, the lengths of the two layers are the same. At temperature $T_0 + \Delta T$, the layers form circular arcs of radii R and $R + s$, which subtend the same angle θ. Assume a small ΔT so that $\alpha\Delta T \ll 1$ (for either α).] (b) If the layers are made of iron and brass, with $s = 0.1$ mm, what is R for $\Delta T = 20.0$°C?

Answers to Practice Problems

13.1 37.0°C; 310.2 K

13.2 0.60 mm longer; 1.5 mm shorter

13.3 0.26 L

13.4 3.34×10^{28} molecules/m³

13.5 7.9% of the air molecules; 189 kPa (27 lb/in²)

13.6 640 kPa

13.7 $\langle K_{tr} \rangle = 6.07 \times 10^{-21}$ J (same as O₂) and $v_{rms} = 408$ m/s (lower than that of O₂ since the CO₂ molecule is more massive)

13.8 6% decrease

13.9 1.0×10^{-6} s

Answers to Checkpoints

13.3 From Table 13.2, $\alpha = 12 \times 10^{-6}$ K⁻¹. The temperature change is −50°C = −50 K and the fractional length change is $\Delta L/L_0 = \alpha\Delta T = -6.0 \times 10^{-4}$. Then $\Delta L = -6.0 \times 10^{-4} \times 150.00$ m = −0.090 m. The tower is 9.0 cm shorter.

13.4 (a) The molar mass is 44.0 g/mol, so one CO₂ molecule has a mass of 44.0 u. (b) 3.00 mol of CO₂ have a mass of (3.00 mol) × (44.0 g/mol) = 132 g.

13.5 (a) The temperatures do not have to be the same, because they could have different numbers of molecules (N) or moles (n). (b) If the temperatures are the same, then they have the same number of molecules, so they have the same number density N/V. They would have the same mass density only if their molar masses are the same.

13.6 The average translational kinetic energy of an ideal gas depends only on *absolute* temperature. The H₂ is at 20°C = 293 K, so to have twice the translational kinetic energy, the O₂ must be at 2 × 293 K = 586 K = 313°C.

Heat

The weather forecast predicts a late spring hard freeze one night; the temperature is to fall several degrees below 0°C and the apple crop is in danger of being ruined. To protect the tender buds, farmers rush out and spray the trees with water. How does that protect the buds? (See p. 500 for the answer.)

Concepts & Skills to Review

- energy conservation (Chapter 6)
- thermal equilibrium (Section 13.1)
- absolute temperature and the ideal gas law (Section 13.5)
- kinetic theory of the ideal gas (Section 13.6)

14.1   INTERNAL ENERGY

From Section 13.6, the average translational kinetic energy $\langle K_{\mathrm{tr}} \rangle$ of the molecules of an ideal gas is proportional to the absolute temperature of the gas:

$$\langle K_{\mathrm{tr}} \rangle = \tfrac{3}{2} kT \tag{13-20}$$

The molecules move about in random directions even though, on a macroscopic scale, the gas is neither moving nor rotating. Equation (13-20) also gives the average translational kinetic energy of the random motion of molecules in liquids, solids, and nonideal gases except at very low temperatures. This random microscopic kinetic energy is *part* of what we call the **internal energy** of the system:

Definition of Internal Energy

The internal energy of a system is the total energy of all of the molecules in the system *except* for the macroscopic kinetic energy (kinetic energy associated with macroscopic translation or rotation) and the external potential energy (energy due to external interactions).

CONNECTION:

We've used the idea of a *system* before, for instance when finding the net external force on a system or the momentum change of a system.

A **system** is whatever we define it to be: one object or a group of objects. Everything that is not part of the system is considered to be external to the system, or in other words, in the surroundings of the system.

Internal energy includes

- Translational and rotational kinetic energy of molecules *due to their individual random motions.*
- Vibrational energy—both kinetic and potential—of molecules and of atoms within molecules due to random vibrations about their equilibrium points.
- Potential energy due to interactions between the atoms and molecules of the system.
- Chemical and nuclear energy—the kinetic and potential energy associated with the binding of atoms to form molecules, the binding of electrons to nuclei to form atoms, and the binding of protons and neutrons to form nuclei.

Internal energy does *not* include

CONNECTION:

Revisit Table 6.1 for an overview of the forms of energy discussed in this book.

- The kinetic energy of the molecules due to translation, rotation, or vibration of the whole system or of a macroscopic part of the system.
- Potential energy due to interactions of the molecules of the system with something outside of the system (such as a gravitational field due to something outside of the system).

Example 14.1

Dissipation of Energy by Friction

A block of mass 10.0 kg starts at point *A* at a height of 2.0 m above the horizontal and slides down a frictionless incline (Fig. 14.1). It then continues sliding along the horizontal surface of a table that has friction. The block comes to rest at point *C*, a distance of 1.0 m along the table surface. How much has the internal energy of the system (block + table) increased?

continued on next page

Example 14.1 continued

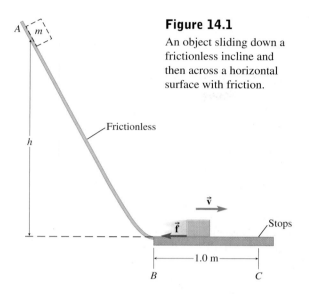

Figure 14.1

An object sliding down a frictionless incline and then across a horizontal surface with friction.

Strategy   Gravitational potential energy is converted to macroscopic translational kinetic energy as the block's speed increases. Friction then converts this macroscopic kinetic energy into internal energy—some of it in the block and some in the table. Since total energy is conserved, the increase in internal energy is equal to the decrease in gravitational potential energy:

> decrease in PE from A to B = increase in KE from A to B
>
> = decrease in KE from B to C
>
> = increase in internal energy from B to C

Solution   The initial potential energy (taking $U_g = 0$ at the horizontal surface) is

$$U_g = mgh = 10.0 \text{ kg} \times 9.8 \text{ m/s}^2 \times 2.0 \text{ m} = 200 \text{ J}$$

The final potential energy is zero. The initial and final translational kinetic energies of the block are both zero. Neglecting the small transfer of energy to the air, the increase in the internal energy of the block and table is 200 J.

Discussion   We do not know how much of this internal energy increase appears in the object and how much in the table; we can only find the total. We call friction a *nonconservative* force, but that only means that *macroscopic mechanical* energy is not conserved; total energy is always conserved. Friction merely converts some macroscopic mechanical energy into internal energy of the block and the table. This internal energy increase manifests itself as a slight temperature increase. We often say that mechanical energy is *dissipated* by friction or other nonconservative forces; in other words, energy in an ordered form (translational motion of the block) has been changed into disordered energy (random motion of molecules within the block and table).

Practice Problem 14.1   On the Rebound

If a rubber ball of mass 1.0 kg is dropped from a height of 2.0 m and rebounds on the first bounce to 0.75 of the height from which it was dropped, how much energy is dissipated during the collision with the floor?

   A change in the internal energy of a system does not always cause a temperature change. As we explore further in Section 14.5, the internal energy of a system can change while the temperature of the system remains constant—for instance, when ice melts.

Conceptual Example 14.2

Internal Energy of a Bowling Ball

A bowling ball at rest has a temperature of 18°C. The ball is then rolled down a bowling alley. Ignoring the dissipation of energy by friction and drag forces, is the internal energy of the ball higher, lower, or the same as when the ball was at rest? Is the temperature of the ball higher, lower, or the same as when the ball was at rest?

Strategy, Solution, and Discussion   The only change is that the ball is now rolling—the ball has macroscopic translational and rotational kinetic energy. However, the definition of *internal energy* does *not* include the kinetic energy of

the molecules due to translation, rotation, or vibration *of the system as a whole*. Therefore, the *internal* energy of the ball is the same. Temperature is associated with the average translational kinetic energy due to the *individual random* motions of molecules; the temperature is still 18°C.

Conceptual Practice Problem 14.2
Total Translational KE

Is the *total* translational kinetic energy of the molecules in the ball higher, lower, or the same as when the ball was at rest?

14.2   HEAT

We defined heat in Section 13.1:

> ### Definition of Heat
>
> **Heat** is energy in transit between two objects or systems due to a temperature difference between them.

Many eighteenth-century scientists thought that heat was a fluid, which they called "caloric." The flow of heat into an object was thought to cause the object to expand in volume in order to accommodate the additional fluid; why no mass increase occurred was a mystery. Now we know that heat is not a substance but is a flow of energy. One experiment that led to this conclusion was carried out by Count Rumford (Benjamin Thompson, 1753–1814). While supervising the boring of cannon barrels, he noted that the drill doing the boring became quite hot. At the time it was thought that the grinding up of the cannon metal into little pieces caused caloric to be released because the tiny bits of metal could not hold as much caloric as the large piece from which they came. But Rumford noticed that the drill got hot even when it became so dull that metal was no longer being bored out of the cannon and that he could create a limitless amount of what we now call internal energy. He decided that "heat" must be a form of microscopic motion instead of a material substance.

It was not until later experiments were done by James Prescott Joule (1818–1889) that Rumford's ideas were finally accepted. In his most famous experiment (Fig. 14.2), Joule showed that a temperature increase can be caused by mechanical means. In a series of such experiments, Joule determined the "mechanical equivalent of heat," or the amount of mechanical work required to produce the same effect on a system as a given amount of heat. In those days heat was measured in calories, where one calorie was defined as the heat required to change the temperature of 1 g of water by 1°C (specifically from 14.5 to 15.5°C). Joule's experimental results were within 1% of the currently accepted value, which is

$$1 \text{ cal} = 4.186 \text{ J} \tag{14-1}$$

Equation (14-1) is now the *definition* of the calorie. The Calorie (with an uppercase letter C) used by dietitians and nutritionists is actually a kilocalorie:

$$1 \text{ Calorie} = 1 \text{ kcal} = 10^3 \text{ cal} = 4186 \text{ J}$$

Although the calorie is still used, the SI unit for internal energy and for heat is the same as that used for all forms of energy and all forms of energy transfer: the joule.

Figure 14.2 Joule's experiment. As the two masses fall, they cause paddles to rotate within an insulated container (not to scale) filled with water. The paddles agitate the water and cause its temperature to rise. By measuring the distance through which the masses fell and the temperature change of the known quantity of water, Joule determined the mechanical work done and the internal energy increase of the water.

Heat and Work   Heat and work are similar in that both describe a particular kind of energy *transfer.* Work is an energy transfer due to a force acting through a displacement. Heat is a microscopic form of energy transfer involving large numbers of particles; the exchange of energy occurs due to the individual interactions of the particles. No macroscopic displacement occurs when heat flows and no macroscopic force is exerted by one object on the other.

It does not make sense to say that a system *has* 15 kJ of heat, just as it does not make sense to say that a system *has* 15 kJ of work. Similarly, we cannot say that the heat of a system has changed (nor that the work of a system has changed). A system can possess *energy* in various forms (including internal energy), but it cannot possess heat or work. Heat and work are two ways of *transferring* energy from one system to another. Joule's experiments showed that a quantity of work done on a system or the same quantity of heat flowing into the system causes the same increase in the system's internal energy. If the internal energy increase comes from mechanical work, as from Joule's paddle wheel, no heat flow occurs.

> **CONNECTION:**
>
> Heat, like work, is a kind of energy transfer.

✓ CHECKPOINT 14.2

Take a rubber band and stretch it rapidly several times. Then hold it against your wrist or your lip. In everyday language, you might say the rubber band "heats up." Is the temperature increase caused by heat flow into the rubber band? If not, what has happened?

Direction of Heat Flow   *Heat flows spontaneously from a system at higher temperature to one at lower temperature.* Temperature is associated with the microscopic translational kinetic energy of the molecules; thus, the flow of heat tends to equalize the average microscopic translational kinetic energy of the molecules. When two systems are in thermal contact and no net heat flow occurs, the systems are in thermal equilibrium and have the same temperature.

Example 14.3

A Joule Experiment

In an experiment similar to that done by Joule, an object of mass 12.0 kg descends a distance of 1.25 m at constant speed while causing the rotation of a paddle wheel in an insulated container of water. If the descent is repeated 20.0 times, what is the internal energy increase of the water in joules?

Strategy   Each time the object descends, it converts gravitational potential energy into kinetic energy of the paddle wheel, which in turn agitates the water and converts kinetic energy into internal energy.

Solution   The change in gravitational potential energy during 20.0 downward trips is

$$\Delta U_g = mg\,\Delta h$$
$$= 12.0 \text{ kg} \times 9.80 \text{ N/kg} \times 20.0 \text{ descents} \times 1.25 \text{ m/descent}$$
$$= 2.94 \text{ kJ}$$

If all of this energy goes into the water, the internal energy increase of the water is 2.94 kJ.

Discussion   To perform an experiment like Joule's, we can vary the amount of energy delivered to the water. One way is to change the number of times the object is allowed to descend. Other possibilities include varying the mass of the descending object or raising the apparatus so that the object can descend a greater distance. All of these variations allow a change in the amount of gravitational potential energy converted into internal energy without requiring any changes in the complicated mechanism involving the paddle wheel.

Practice Problem 14.3   Temperature Change of the Water

If the water temperature in the insulated container is found to have increased 2.0°C after 20.0 descents of the falling object, what mass of water is in the container? Assume all of the internal energy increase appears in the water (ignore any internal energy change of the paddle wheel itself). [*Hint:* Recall that the calorie was defined as the heat required to change the temperature of 1 g of water by 1°C.]

The Cause of Thermal Expansion

If not to accommodate additional "caloric," then why do objects generally expand when their temperatures increase? (See Section 13.3.) An object expands when the *average* distance between the atoms (or molecules) increases. The atoms are not at rest; even in a solid, where each atom has a fixed equilibrium position, they *vibrate* to and fro about their equilibrium positions. The energy of vibration is part of the internal energy of the object. When heat flows into the object, raising its temperature, the internal energy increases. Some of the increase goes into vibration, so the average vibrational energy of an atom increases with increasing temperature.

The average distance between atoms usually increases with increasing vibrational energy because the forces between atoms are highly asymmetrical. Two atoms separated by *less* than their equilibrium distance repel one another *strongly*, while two atoms separated by *more* than their equilibrium distance attract one another much less strongly. Therefore, as vibrational energy increases, the maximum distance between the atoms increases more than the minimum distance decreases; the *average* distance between the atoms increases.

The coefficient of expansion varies from material to material because the strength of the interatomic (or intermolecular) bonds varies. As a general rule, the stronger the atomic bond, the smaller the coefficient of expansion. Liquids have much greater coefficients of volume expansion than do solids because the molecules are more loosely bound in a liquid than in a solid.

14.3   HEAT CAPACITY AND SPECIFIC HEAT

Heat Capacity

Suppose we have a system on which no mechanical work is done, but we allow heat to flow into the system by placing it in thermal contact with another system at higher temperature. As the internal energy of the system increases, its temperature increases (provided that no part of the system undergoes a change of phase, such as from solid to liquid). If heat flows *out* of the system rather than into the system, the internal energy of the system decreases. We account for that possibility by making Q negative if heat flows out of the system; since Q is defined as the heat *into* the system, a negative heat represents heat flow *out of* the system.

For a large number of substances, under normal conditions, the temperature change ΔT is approximately proportional to the heat Q. The constant of proportionality is called the **heat capacity** (symbol C):

$$C = \frac{Q}{\Delta T} \qquad\qquad (14\text{-}2)$$

The heat capacity depends both on the substance and on how much of it is present: 1 cal of heat into 1 g of water causes a temperature increase of 1°C, but 1 cal of heat into 2 g of water causes a temperature increase of 0.5°C. The SI unit of heat capacity is J/K. We can write J/K or J/°C interchangeably since only temperature *changes* are involved; a temperature change of 1 K is equivalent to a temperature change of 1°C.

The term *heat capacity* is unfortunate since it has nothing to do with a capacity to *hold* heat, or a limited ability to absorb heat, as the name seems to imply. Instead, it relates the heat into a system to the temperature increase. Think of heat capacity as a measure of how much heat must flow into or out of the system to produce a given temperature change.

Specific Heat

The heat capacity of the water in a drinking glass is much smaller than the heat capacity of the water in Lake Superior. Since the heat capacity of a system is proportional to the

In Chapter 15, we consider cases where both work and heat change the internal energy of a system. We will see that work done on a system can change the system's temperature or cause a change of phase. For now, we assume that the work done is zero and consider changes due to heat flow.

Q is positive for heat flow *into* the system and negative for heat flow *out of* the system.

Table 14.1   Specific Heats of Common Substances at 1 atm and 20°C

Substance	Specific Heat $\left(\dfrac{kJ}{kg \cdot K}\right)$	Substance	Specific Heat $\left(\dfrac{kJ}{kg \cdot K}\right)$
Gold	0.128	Pyrex glass	0.75
Lead	0.13	Granite	0.80
Mercury	0.139	Marble	0.86
Silver	0.235	Aluminum	0.900
Brass	0.384	Air (50°C)	1.05
Copper	0.385	Wood (average)	1.68
Steel	0.45	Steam (110°C)	2.01
Iron	0.44	Ice (0°C)	2.1
Flint glass	0.50	Alcohol (ethyl)	2.4
Crown glass	0.67	Human tissue (average)	3.5
Vycor	0.74	Water (15°C)	4.186

mass of the system, the **specific heat capacity** (symbol c) of a substance is defined as the heat capacity per unit mass:

$$c = \frac{C}{m} = \frac{Q}{m \, \Delta T} \qquad (14\text{-}3)$$

Specific heat capacity is often abbreviated to *specific heat*. The SI units of specific heat are J/(kg·K). In SI units, the specific heat is the number of joules of heat required to produce a 1 K temperature change in 1 kg of the substance. Again, since only temperature changes are involved, we can equivalently write J/(kg·°C).

Table 14.1 lists specific heats for some common substances at 1 atm and 20°C (unless otherwise specified). For the range of temperatures in our examples and problems, assume these specific heat values to be valid. Note that water has a relatively large specific heat compared with most other substances. The relatively large specific heat of water causes the oceans to warm slowly in the spring and to cool slowly as winter approaches, moderating the temperature along the coast.

Rearrangement of Eq. (14-3) leads to an expression for the heat required to produce a known temperature change in a system:

$$Q = mc \, \Delta T \qquad (14\text{-}4)$$

Note that in Eqs. (14-3) and (14-4), the sign convention for Q is consistent: a temperature increase ($\Delta T > 0$) is caused by heat flowing *into* the system ($Q > 0$), while a temperature decrease ($\Delta T < 0$) is caused by heat flowing *out* of the system ($Q < 0$).

Specific heat: heat capacity per unit mass

⚠️ Equations (14-2) through (14-4) apply when no phase change occurs. The value of the specific heat is different for different phases of the same substance. That's why Table 14.1 lists different values for ice, liquid water, and steam.

Example 14.4

Heating Water in a Saucepan

A saucepan containing 5.00 kg of water initially at 20.0°C is heated over a gas burner for 10.0 min. The final temperature of the water is 30.0°C. (a) What is the internal energy increase of the water? (b) What is the expected final temperature if the water were heated for an additional 5.0 min? (c) Is it

possible to estimate the flow of heat from the burner during the first 10.0 min?

Strategy   We are interested in the internal energy and the temperature of the *water*, so we define a system that consists

continued on next page

Example 14.4 continued

of the water in the saucepan. Although the pan is also heated, it is not part of this system. The pan, the burner, and the room are all outside the system.

Since no work is done on the water, the internal energy increase is equal to the heat flowing into the water. The heat can be found from the mass of the water, the specific heat of water, and the temperature change. As long as the burner delivers heat at a constant rate, we can find the additional heat delivered in the additional time. Since the temperature change is proportional to the heat delivered, the temperature changes at a constant rate (a constant number of °C per minute). So, in half the time, half as much energy is delivered and the temperature change is half as much.

Solution   (a) First find the temperature change:

$$\Delta T = T_f - T_i = 30.0°C - 20.0°C = 10.0 \text{ K}$$

(A change of 10.0°C is equivalent to a change of 10.0 K.) The increase in the internal energy of the water is

$$\Delta U = Q = mc \, \Delta T$$

$$= 5.00 \text{ kg} \times 4.186 \text{ kJ/(kg·K)} \times 10.0 \text{ K} = 209 \text{ kJ}$$

(b) We assume that the heat delivered is proportional to the elapsed time. The temperature change is proportional to

the energy delivered, so if the temperature changes 10.0°C in 10.0 min, it changes an additional 5.0°C in an additional 5.0 min. The final temperature is

$$T = 20.0°C + 15.0°C = 35.0°C$$

(c) Not all of the heat flows into the water. Heat also flows from the burner into the saucepan and into the room. All we can say is that *more than* 209 kJ of heat flows from the burner during the 10.0 min.

Discussion   As a check, the heat capacity of the water is 5.00 kg × 4.186 kJ/(kg·K) = 20.9 kJ/K; 20.9 kJ of heat must flow for each 1.0 K change in temperature. Since the temperature change is 10.0 K, the heat required is

$$20.9 \text{ kJ/K} \times 10.0 \text{ K} = 209 \text{ kJ}$$

Practice Problem 14.4   Price of a Bubble Bath

If the cost of electricity is $0.080 per kW·h, what does it cost to heat 160 L of water for a bubble bath from 10.0°C (the temperature of the well water entering the house) to 70.0°C? [*Hint:* 1 L of water has a mass of 1 kg. 1 kW·h = 1000 J/s × 3600 s.]

Heat Flow with More Than Two Objects   Suppose some water is heated in a large iron pot by dropping a hot piece of copper into the pot. We can define the system to be the water, the copper, and the iron pot; the environment is the room containing the system. Heat continues to flow among the three substances (iron pot, water, copper) until thermal equilibrium is reached—that is, until all three substances are at the same temperature. If losses to the environment are negligible, all the heat that flows out of the copper flows into either the iron or the water:

$$Q_{Cu} + Q_{Fe} + Q_{H_2O} = 0$$

In this case, Q_{Cu} is negative since heat flows *out* of the copper; Q_{Fe} and Q_{H_2O} are positive since heat flows into both the iron and the water.

CONNECTION:

Here we apply the principle of energy conservation.

Calorimetry

A calorimeter is an insulated container that enables the careful measurement of heat (Fig. 14.3). The calorimeter is designed to minimize the heat flow to or from the surroundings. A typical constant volume calorimeter, called a *bomb calorimeter*, consists of a hollow aluminum cylinder of known mass containing a known quantity of water; the cylinder is inside a larger aluminum cylinder with insulated walls. An evacuated space separates the two cylinders. An insulated lid fits over the opening of the cylinders; often there are two small holes in the lid, one for a thermometer to be inserted into the contents of the inner cylinder and one for a stirring device to help the contents reach equilibrium faster.

Suppose an object at one temperature is placed in a calorimeter with the water and aluminum cylinder at another temperature. By conservation of energy, all the heat that

Figure 14.3 A calorimeter.

flows out of one substance ($Q < 0$) flows into some other substance ($Q > 0$). If no heat flows to or from the environment, the total heat into the object, water, and aluminum must equal zero:

$$Q_o + Q_w + Q_a = 0$$

Example 14.5 illustrates the use of a calorimeter to measure the specific heat of an unknown substance. The measured specific heat can be compared with a table of known values to help identify the substance.

Example 14.5

Specific Heat of an Unknown Metal

A sample of unknown metal of mass 0.550 kg is heated in a pan of hot water until it is in equilibrium with the water at a temperature of 75.0°C. The metal is then carefully removed from the heat bath and placed into the inner cylinder of an aluminum calorimeter that contains 0.500 kg of water at 15.5°C. The mass of the inner cylinder is 0.100 kg. When the contents of the calorimeter reach equilibrium, the temperature inside is 18.8°C. Find the specific heat of the metal sample and determine whether it could be any of the metals listed in Table 14.1.

Strategy Heat flows from the sample to the water and to the aluminum until thermal equilibrium is reached, at which time all three have the same temperature. We use subscripts to keep track of the three heat flows and three temperature changes. Let T_f be the final temperature of all three. Initially, the water and aluminum are both at 15.5°C while the sample is at 75.0°C. When thermal equilibrium is reached, all three are at 18.8°C. We assume negligible heat flow to the environment—in other words, that no heat flows into or out of the system of aluminum + water + sample.

Solution Heat flows out of the sample ($Q_s < 0$) and into the water and aluminum cylinder ($Q_w > 0$ and $Q_a > 0$). Assuming no heat into or out of the surroundings,

$$Q_s + Q_w + Q_a = 0$$

For each substance, the heat is related to the temperature change. Substituting $Q = mc\,\Delta T$ for each gives

$$m_s c_s\,\Delta T_s + m_w c_w\,\Delta T_w + m_a c_a\,\Delta T_a = 0 \qquad (1)$$

A table helps organize the given information:

	Sample	H$_2$O	Al
Mass (m)	0.550 kg	0.500 kg	0.100 kg
Specific Heat (c)	c_s (unknown)	4.186 kJ/(kg·°C)	0.900 kJ/(kg·°C)
Heat Capacity (mc)	0.550 kg $\times c_s$	2.093 kJ/°C	0.0900 kJ/°C
T_i	75.0°C	15.5°C	15.5°C
T_f	18.8°C	18.8°C	18.8°C
ΔT	−56.2°C	3.3°C	3.3°C

Substituting known values into Eq. (1) yields

$$0.550 \text{ kg} \times c_s \times (-56.2°C) + (2.093 \text{ kJ/°C} + 0.0900 \text{ kJ/°C}) \times 3.3°C = 0$$

Now we solve for c_s.

$$0.550 \text{ kg} \times c_s \times 56.2°C = 7.204 \text{ kJ}$$

$$c_s = \frac{7.204 \text{ kJ}}{0.550 \text{ kg} \times 56.2°C} = 0.233\ \frac{\text{kJ}}{\text{kg·°C}}$$

By comparing this result with the values in Table 14.1, it appears that the unknown sample could be silver.

Discussion As a quick check, the heat capacity of the sample is approximately $\frac{1}{17}$ that of the water since its temperature change is 56.2°C/3.3°C ≈ 17 times as much—ignoring the small heat capacity of the aluminum. Since the masses of the water and sample are about equal, the specific heat of the sample is roughly $\frac{1}{17}$ that of the water:

$$\frac{1}{17} \times 4.186\ \frac{\text{kJ}}{\text{kg·°C}} = 0.25\ \frac{\text{kJ}}{\text{kg·°C}}$$

That is quite close to our answer.

Practice Problem 14.5   Final Temperature

If 0.25 kg of water at 90.0°C is added to 0.35 kg of water at 20.0°C in an aluminum calorimeter with an inner cylinder of mass 0.100 kg, find the final temperature of the mixture.

Table 14.2
Molar Specific Heats
at Constant Volume
of Gases at 25°C

	Gas	$C_V \left(\dfrac{\text{J/K}}{\text{mol}} \right)$
Monatomic	He	12.5
	Ne	12.7
	Ar	12.5
Diatomic	H_2	20.4
	N_2	20.8
	O_2	21.0
Polyatomic	CO_2	28.2
	N_2O	28.4

14.4   SPECIFIC HEAT OF IDEAL GASES

Since the average translational kinetic energy of a molecule in an ideal gas is

$$\langle K_{tr} \rangle = \tfrac{3}{2}kT \qquad \text{(13-20)}$$

the *total* translational kinetic energy of a gas containing N molecules (n moles) is

$$K_{tr} = \tfrac{3}{2}NkT = \tfrac{3}{2}nRT$$

Suppose we allow heat to flow into a *monatomic* ideal gas—one where the gas molecules consist of single atoms—while keeping the volume of the gas constant. Since the volume is constant, no work is done on the gas, so the change in the internal energy is equal to the heat. If we think of the atoms as point particles, the only way for the internal energy to change when heat flows into the gas is for the translational kinetic energy of the atoms to change. The rest of the internal energy is "locked up" in the atoms and does not change unless something else happens, such as a phase transition or a chemical reaction—neither of which can happen in an ideal gas. Then

$$Q = \Delta K_{tr} = \tfrac{3}{2}nR\,\Delta T \qquad \text{(14-5)}$$

From Eq. (14-5), we can find the specific heat of the monatomic ideal gas. However, with gases it is more convenient to define the **molar specific heat** at constant volume (C_V) as

$$C_V = \frac{Q}{n\,\Delta T} \qquad \text{(14-6)}$$

CONNECTION:

Specific heat and molar specific heat can be thought of as the same quantity—heat capacity per amount of substance—expressed in different units.

The subscript "V" is a reminder that the volume of the gas is held constant during the heat flow. The molar specific heat is the heat capacity *per mole* rather than *per unit mass*. In one case, we measure the amount of substance by the number of moles; in the other case, by the mass.

From Eqs. (14-5) and (14-6), we can find the molar specific heat of a monatomic ideal gas:

$$Q = \tfrac{3}{2}nR\,\Delta T = nC_V\,\Delta T$$

$$C_V = \tfrac{3}{2}R = 12.5\,\frac{\text{J/K}}{\text{mol}} \qquad (\textit{monatomic} \text{ ideal gas}) \qquad \text{(14-7)}$$

A glance at Table 14.2 shows that this calculation is remarkably accurate at room temperature for monatomic gases.

Diatomic gases have larger molar specific heats than monatomic gases. Why? We cannot model the diatomic molecule as a point mass; the two atoms in the molecule are separated, giving the molecule a much larger rotational inertia about two perpendicular axes (Fig. 14.4). The molar specific heat is *larger* because not all of the internal energy increase goes into the translational kinetic energy of the molecules; some goes into rotational kinetic energy.

Figure 14.4 Rotation of a model diatomic molecule about three perpendicular axes. The rotational inertia about the *x*-axis (a) is negligible, so we can ignore rotation about this axis. The rotational inertias about the *y*- and *z*-axes (b) and (c) are much larger than for a single atom of the same mass because of the larger distance between the atoms and the axis of rotation.

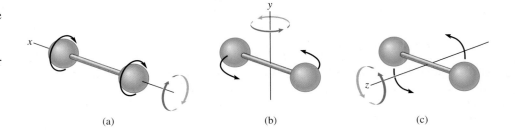

(a)   (b)   (c)

It turns out that the molar specific heat of a diatomic ideal gas at room temperature is approximately

$$C_V = \tfrac{5}{2}R = 20.8 \frac{\text{J/K}}{\text{mol}} \quad \text{(}\textit{diatomic}\text{ ideal gas at room temperature)} \quad \text{(14-8)}$$

Why $\tfrac{5}{2}R$ instead of $\tfrac{3}{2}R$? The diatomic molecule has rotational kinetic energy about two perpendicular axes (Fig. 14.4b and c) in addition to translational kinetic energy associated with motion in three independent directions. Thus, the diatomic molecule has five ways to "store" internal energy while the monatomic molecule has only three. The theorem of **equipartition of energy**—which we cannot prove here—says that internal energy is distributed equally among all the possible ways in which it can be stored (as long as the temperature is sufficiently high). Each independent form of energy has an average of $\tfrac{1}{2}kT$ of energy per molecule and contributes $\tfrac{1}{2}R$ to the molar specific heat at constant volume.

Example 14.6

Heating Some Xenon Gas

A cylinder contains 250 L of xenon gas (Xe) at 20.0°C and a pressure of 5.0 atm. How much heat is required to raise the temperature of this gas to 50.0°C, holding the volume constant? Treat the xenon as an ideal gas.

Strategy The molar heat capacity is the heat required per degree per mole. The number of moles of xenon (n) can be found from the ideal gas law, $PV = nRT$. Xenon is a monatomic gas, so we expect $C_V = \tfrac{3}{2}R$.

Solution First we convert the known quantities into SI units.

$$P = 5.0 \text{ atm} = 5 \times 1.01 \times 10^5 \text{ Pa} = 5.05 \times 10^5 \text{ Pa}$$

$$V = 250 \text{ L} = 250 \times 10^{-3} \text{ m}^3$$

$$T = 20.0°C = 293.15 \text{ K}$$

From the ideal gas law, we find the number of moles,

$$n = \frac{PV}{RT} = \frac{5.05 \times 10^5 \text{ Pa} \times 250 \times 10^{-3} \text{ m}^3}{8.31 \text{ J/(mol·K)} \times 293.15 \text{ K}} = 51.8 \text{ mol}$$

We should check the units. Since $\text{Pa} = \text{N/m}^2$,

$$\frac{\text{Pa} \times \text{m}^3}{\text{J/(mol·K)} \times \text{K}} = \frac{\text{N/m}^2 \times \text{m}^3}{\text{J/mol}} = \frac{\text{N·m}}{\text{J}} \times \text{mol} = \text{mol}$$

For a monatomic gas at constant volume, the energy all goes into increasing the translational kinetic energy of the gas molecules. The molar specific heat is defined by $Q = nC_V\Delta T$, where, for a monatomic gas, $C_V = \tfrac{3}{2}R$. Then,

$$Q = \tfrac{3}{2}nR\,\Delta T$$

where

$$\Delta T = 50.0°C - 20.0°C = 30.0°C$$

Substituting,

$$Q = \tfrac{3}{2} \times 51.8 \text{ mol} \times 8.31 \text{ J/(mol·°C)} \times 30.0°C = 19 \text{ kJ}$$

Discussion Constant volume implies that all the heat is used to increase the internal energy of the gas; if the gas were to expand it could transfer energy by doing work. When we find the number of moles from the ideal gas law, we must remember to convert the Celsius temperature to kelvins. Only when an equation involves a *change* in temperature can we use kelvin or Celsius temperatures interchangeably.

Practice Problem 14.6   Heating Some Helium Gas

A storage cylinder of 330 L of helium gas is at 21°C and is subjected to a pressure of 10.0 atm. How much energy must be added to raise the temperature of the helium in this container to 75°C?

You may wonder why we can ignore rotation for the monatomic molecule—which in reality is not a point particle—or why we can ignore rotation about one axis for the diatomic molecule. The answer comes from quantum mechanics. Energy cannot be added to a molecule in arbitrarily small amounts; energy can only be added in discrete amounts or "steps." At room temperature, there is not enough internal energy to excite the rotational modes with small rotational inertias, so they do not participate in the specific heat. We also ignored the possibility of vibration for the diatomic molecule. That is fine at room temperature, but at higher temperatures vibration becomes significant, adding two more energy modes (one kinetic and one potential). Thus, as temperature increases, the molar specific heat of a diatomic gas increases, approaching $\tfrac{7}{2}R$ at high temperatures.

Table 14.3 Heat to Turn 1 kg of Ice at −25°C to Steam at 125°C	
Phase Transition or Temperature Change	**Q (kJ)**
Ice: −25°C to 0°C	52.3
Melting: ice at 0°C to water at 0°C	333.7
Water: 0°C to 100°C	419
Boiling: water at 100°C to steam at 100°C	2256
Steam: 100°C to 125°C	50

During a phase transition, the temperature of the mixture of two phases does not change.

The *sign* of Q in Eq. (14-9) depends on the direction of the phase transition. For melting or boiling, $Q > 0$ (heat flows *into* the system). For freezing or condensation, $Q < 0$ (heat flows *out of* the system).

14.5   PHASE TRANSITIONS

If heat continually flows into the water in a pot, the water eventually begins to boil; liquid water becomes steam. If heat flows into ice cubes, they eventually melt and turn into liquid water. A **phase transition** occurs whenever a material is changed from one phase, such as the solid phase, to another, such as the liquid phase.

When some ice cubes at 0°C are placed into a glass in a room at 20°C, the ice gradually melts. A thermometer in the water that forms as the ice melts reads 0°C until all the ice is melted. At atmospheric pressure, ice and water can only coexist in equilibrium at 0°C. Once all the ice is melted, the water gradually warms up to room temperature. Similarly, water boiling on a stove remains at 100°C until all the water has boiled away. Suppose we change 1.0 kg of ice at −25°C into steam at 125°C. A graph of the temperature versus heat is shown in Fig. 14.5. During the two phase transitions, *heat flow continues, and the internal energy changes*, *but the temperature of the mixture of two phases does not change.* Table 14.3 shows the heat during each step of the process.

Latent Heat   The heat required *per unit mass* of substance to produce a phase change is called the **latent heat** (*L*). The word "latent" is related to the lack of temperature change during a phase transition.

Definition of latent heat:

$$|Q| = mL \qquad\qquad (14\text{-}9)$$

The heat per unit mass for the solid-liquid phase transition (in either direction) is called the **latent heat of fusion** (L_f). From Table 14.3, it takes 333.7 kJ to change 1 kg of ice to water at 0°C, so for water $L_f = 333.7$ kJ/kg. For the liquid-gas phase transition (in either direction), the heat per unit mass is called the **latent heat of vaporization** (L_v). From Table 14.3, to change 1 kg of water to steam at 100°C takes 2256 kJ, so for water $L_v = 2256$ kJ/kg. Table 14.4 lists latent heats of fusion and vaporization for various materials.

Heat flowing into a substance can cause melting (solid to liquid) or boiling (liquid to gas). Heat flowing out of a substance can cause freezing (liquid to solid) or condensation (gas to liquid). If 2256 kJ must be supplied to turn 1 kg of water into steam, then 2256 kJ of heat is *released* from 1 kg of steam when it condenses to form water.

√ CHECKPOINT 14.5

Why is a burn caused by 100°C steam often much more severe than a burn caused by 100°C water?

How does spraying with water protect the buds?

Figure 14.5 Temperature versus heat for 1 kg of ice that starts at a temperature below 0°C. (Horizontal axis not to scale.) During the two phase transitions— melting and boiling—the temperature does not change.

The large latent heat of fusion of water is partly why spraying fruit trees with water can protect the buds from freezing. Before the buds can freeze, first the water must be cooled to 0°C and then it must freeze. In the process of freezing, the water gives up a large amount of heat and keeps the temperature of the buds from going below 0°C. Even

Table 14.4   Latent Heats of Some Common Substances

Substance	Melting Point (°C)	Heat of Fusion (kJ/kg)	Boiling Point (°C)	Heat of Vaporization (kJ/kg)
Alcohol (ethyl)	−114	104	78	854
Aluminum	660	397	2450	11 400
Copper	1083	205	2340	5070
Gold	1063	66.6	2660	1580
Lead	327	22.9	1620	871
Silver	960.8	88.3	1950	2340
Water	0.0	333.7	100	2256

if the water freezes, then the layer of ice over the buds acts like insulation since ice is not a particularly good conductor of heat.

Microscopic View of a Phase Change   To understand what is happening during a phase change, we must consider the substance on the molecular level. When a substance is in solid form, bonds between the atoms or molecules hold them near fixed equilibrium positions. Energy must be supplied to break the bonds and change the solid into a liquid. When the substance is changed from liquid to gas, energy is used to separate the molecules from the loose bonds holding them together and to move the molecules apart. Temperature does not change during these phase transitions because the *kinetic energy* of the molecules is not changing. Instead, the *potential energy* of the molecules changes as work is done against the forces holding them together.

⚠ Note that energy must be *supplied* to break a bond. Forming a bond *releases* energy.

Example 14.7

Making Silver Charms

A jewelry designer plans to make some specially ordered silver charms for a commemorative bracelet. If the melting point of silver is 960.8°C, how much heat must the jeweler add to 0.500 kg of silver at 20.0°C to be able to pour silver into her charm molds?

Strategy   The solid silver first needs to be heated to its melting point; then more heat has to be added to melt the silver.

Solution   The total heat flow into the silver is the sum of the heat to raise the temperature of the solid and the heat that causes the phase transition:

$$Q = mc\,\Delta T + mL_f$$

The temperature change of the solid is

$$\Delta T = 960.8°C - 20.0°C = 940.8°C$$

We look up the specific heat of solid silver and the latent heat of fusion of silver. Substituting numerical values into the equation for Q yields

$$Q = 0.500\ \text{kg} \times 0.235\ \text{kJ/(kg·°C)} \times 940.8°C + 0.500\ \text{kg} \times 88.3\ \text{kJ/kg}$$

$$= 110.5\ \text{kJ} + 44.15\ \text{kJ} = 155\ \text{kJ}$$

Discussion   An easy mistake to make is to use the wrong latent heat. Here we were dealing with melting, so we needed the latent heat of fusion. Another possible error is to use the specific heat for the wrong phase: here we raised the temperature of *solid* silver, so we needed the specific heat of *solid* silver. With water, we must always be careful to use the specific heat of the correct phase; the specific heats of ice, water, and steam have three different values.

Practice Problem 14.7   Making Gold Medals

Some gold medals are to be made from 750 g of solid gold at 24°C (Fig. 14.6). How much heat is required to melt the gold so that it can be poured into the molds for the medals?

Figure 14.6
A gold medal: the Nobel Prize for physics.

Example 14.8

Turning Water into Ice

Ice cube trays are filled with 0.500 kg of water at 20.0°C and placed into the freezer compartment of a refrigerator. How much energy must be removed from the water to turn it into ice cubes at −5.0°C?

Strategy We can think of this process as three consecutive steps. First, the liquid water is cooled to 0°C. Then the phase change occurs at constant temperature. Now the water is frozen; the ice continues to cool to −5.0°C. The energy that must be removed for the whole process is the sum of the energy removed in each of the three steps.

Solution For liquid water going from 20.0°C to 0.0°C,

$$Q_1 = mc_w \Delta T_1$$

where

$$\Delta T_1 = 0.0°C - 20.0°C = -20.0°C$$

Since ΔT_1 is negative, Q_1 is negative: heat must flow *out of* the water in order for its temperature to decrease. Next the water freezes. The heat is found from the latent heat of fusion:

$$Q_2 = -mL_f$$

Again, heat flows *out* so Q_2 is negative. For phase transitions, we supply the correct sign of Q according to the direction of the phase transition (negative sign for freezing, positive sign for melting). Finally, the ice is cooled to −5.0°C:

$$Q_3 = mc_{ice} \Delta T_2$$

where

$$\Delta T_2 = -5.0°C - 0.0°C = -5.0°C$$

We use subscripts on the specific heats to distinguish the specific heat of ice from that of water. The total heat is

$$Q = m (c_w \Delta T_1 - L_f + c_{ice} \Delta T_2)$$

Now we look up c_w, L_f, and c_{ice} in Tables 14.1 and 14.4 and substitute:

$$Q = 0.500 \text{ kg} \times \left[4.186 \frac{\text{kJ}}{\text{kg·K}} \times (-20.0°C) - 333.7 \frac{\text{kJ}}{\text{kg}} + 2.1 \frac{\text{kJ}}{\text{kg·K}} \times (-5.0°C) \right]$$

$$= -0.500 \text{ kg} \times 427.9 \frac{\text{kJ}}{\text{kg}} = -214 \text{ kJ}$$

So 214 kJ of heat flows out of the water that becomes ice cubes.

Discussion We cannot consider the entire temperature change from +20°C to −5°C in one step. A phase change occurs, so we must include the flow of heat during the phase change. Also, the specific heat of ice is different from the specific heat of liquid water; we must find the heat to cool water 20°C and then the heat to cool ice 5°C.

Practice Problem 14.8   Frozen Popsicles

Nigel pulls a tray of frozen popsicles out of the freezer to share with his friends. If the popsicles are at −4°C and go directly into hungry mouths at 37°C, how much energy is used to bring a popsicle of mass 0.080 kg to body temperature? Assume the frozen popsicles have the same specific heat as ice and the melted popsicle has the specific heat of water.

Example 14.9

Cooling a Drink

Two 50-g ice cubes are placed into 0.200 kg of water in a Styrofoam cup. The water is initially at a temperature of 25.0°C and the ice is initially at a temperature of −15.0°C. What is the final temperature of the drink? The average specific heat for ice between −15°C and 0°C is 2.05 kJ/(kg·°C).

Strategy   We need to raise the temperature of the ice from −15°C to 0°C before the ice can melt, so we first find how much heat this requires. Then we find how much heat is needed to melt all the ice. Once the ice is melted, the water from the melted ice can be raised to the final temperature of the drink. The heat for all three steps (raising temperature of ice, melting ice, raising temperature of water from melted ice) all comes from the water initially at 25°C. That water cools as heat flows out of it. Assuming no heat flow into or out of the room, the quantity of heat that flows out of the water initially at 25°C flows into the ice or melted ice (before, during, and after melting).

Given: $m_{ice} = 0.100$ kg at −15.0°C; $m_w = 0.200$ kg at 25.0°C; $c_{ice} = 2.05$ kJ/(kg·°C)
Look up: L_f for water = 333.7 kJ/kg; $c_w = 4.186$ kJ/(kg·°C)
Find: T_f

Solution   Since heat flows out of the water and into ice, $Q_w < 0$ and $Q_{ice} > 0$. Their sum is zero:

$$Q_{ice} + Q_w = 0$$

The heat flow into the ice is the sum of three terms:

$$Q_{ice} = m_{ice}c_{ice}\Delta T_{ice} + m_{ice}L_f + m_{ice}c_w (T_f - 0.0°C)$$

The heat flow out of the water is

$$Q_w = m_w c_w (T_f - 25.0°C)$$

The heat required to bring the ice from −15.0°C to 0°C is

$$m_{ice}c_{ice}\Delta T_{ice} = 0.100 \text{ kg} \times 2.05 \frac{\text{kJ}}{\text{kg·°C}} \times 15.0°C = 3.075 \text{ kJ}$$

The heat required to melt the ice at 0.0°C is

$$m_{ice}L_f = 0.100 \text{ kg} \times 333.7 \text{ kJ/kg} = 33.37 \text{ kJ}$$

The heat to raise the temperature of the melted ice from 0.0°C to T_f is

$$m_{ice}c_w (T_f - 0.0°C) = 0.100 \text{ kg} \times 4.186 \frac{\text{kJ}}{\text{kg·°C}} \times T_f$$

$$= 0.4186 \frac{\text{kJ}}{°C} \times T_f$$

The heat supplied by the water that was initially at 25.0°C is

$$m_w c_w (T_f - 25.0°C) = 0.200 \text{ kg} \times 4.186 \frac{\text{kJ}}{\text{kg·°C}} \times (T_f - 25.0°C)$$

$$= 0.8372 \frac{\text{kJ}}{°C} \times T_f - 20.93 \text{ kJ}$$

Now we substitute these values back into the original equation, $Q_{ice} + Q_w = 0$.

$$3.075 \text{ kJ} + 33.37 \text{ kJ} + \left(0.4186 \frac{\text{kJ}}{°C} \times T_f\right) + \left(0.8372 \frac{\text{kJ}}{°C} \times T_f - 20.93 \text{ kJ}\right) = 0$$

continued on next page

Example 14.9 continued

Simplifying yields

$$1.2558 \frac{kJ}{°C} \times T_f + 15.515 \text{ kJ} = 0$$

Solving for T_f, we find

$$T_f = -\frac{15.515 \text{ kJ}}{1.2558 \text{ kJ/°C}} = -12.4°C$$

This result does not make sense: we assumed that all of the ice would melt and that the final mixture would be all liquid, but we cannot have liquid water at $-12.4°C$. Let's take another look at the solution.

What if the water initially at 25°C cools all the way to 0°C? From cooling the water, how much heat is available to warm the ice and melt it?

$$Q_w = m_w c_w (0°C - 25.0°C)$$
$$= 0.200 \text{ kg} \times 4.186 \frac{kJ}{kg\cdot°C} \times (-25.0°C) = -20.93 \text{ kJ}$$

Thus, the water can supply 20.93 kJ when it cools to 0°C. But to warm the ice requires 3.075 kJ and to melt all of the ice requires another 33.37 kJ. The ice can be warmed to 0°C, but there is not enough heat available to melt all of the ice. Only some of the ice melts, so the drink ends up as a mixture of water and ice in equilibrium at 0°C.

Discussion   This example shows the value of checking a result to make sure it is reasonable. We started by assuming incorrectly that all of the ice would melt. When we obtained an answer that was impossible, we went back to see if there was enough heat available to melt all of the ice. Since there was not, the final temperature of the drink can only be 0°C—the only temperature at which ice and water can be in thermal equilibrium at atmospheric pressure.

Practice Problem 14.9   Melting Ice

How much of the ice of Example 14.9 melts?

Evaporation

If you leave a cup of water out at room temperature, the water eventually evaporates. Recall that the temperature of the water reflects the average kinetic energy of the water molecules; some have higher than average energies and some have lower. The most energetic molecules have enough energy to break loose from the molecular bonds at the surface of the water. As these highest-energy molecules leave the water, the average energy of those left behind decreases—which is why evaporation is a cooling process. Approximately the same latent heat of vaporization applies to evaporation as to boiling, since the same molecular bonds are being broken. Perspiring basketball players cover up while sitting on the bench for a short time during a game to prevent getting a chill even though the air in the stadium may be warm.

When the humidity is high—meaning there is already a lot of water vapor in the air—evaporation proceeds more slowly. Water molecules in the air can also condense into water; the net evaporation rate is the difference in the rates of evaporation and condensation. A hot, humid day is uncomfortable because our bodies have trouble staying cool when perspiration evaporates slowly.

Application of evaporation: chill caused by perspiration

PHYSICS AT HOME

The effects of evaporation can easily be felt. Rub some water on the inside of your forearm and then blow on your arm. The motion of the air over your arm removes the newly evaporated molecules from the vicinity of your arm and allows other molecules to evaporate more quickly. You can feel the cooling effect. If you have some rubbing alcohol, repeat the experiment. Since the alcohol evaporates faster, the cooling effect is noticeably greater.

Phase Diagrams

A useful tool in the study of phase transitions is the **phase diagram**—a diagram on which pressure is plotted on the vertical axis and temperature on the horizontal axis. Figure 14.7a is a phase diagram for water. A point on the phase diagram represents water in a state determined by the pressure and the temperature at that point. The curves on the phase diagram are the demarcations between the solid, liquid, and gas phases. For most temperatures, there is one pressure at which two particular phases can coexist in equilibrium. Since point P lies on the fusion curve, water can exist as liquid, or as solid, or as a mixture of the two at that temperature and pressure. At point Q, water can only be a solid. Similarly, at A water is a liquid; at B it is a gas.

The one exception is at the **triple point**, where all three phases (solid, liquid, and gas) can coexist in equilibrium. Triple points are used in precise calibrations of thermometers. The triple point of water is precisely 0.01°C at 0.006 atm.

From the vapor pressure curve, we see that as the pressure is lowered, the temperature at which water boils decreases. It takes longer to cook a hard-boiled egg at high elevations because the temperature of the boiling water is less than 100°C; the chemical reactions proceed more slowly at a lower temperature. It might take as long as half an hour to hard-boil an egg on Pike's Peak, where the average pressure is 0.6 atm.

If either the temperature or the pressure or both are changed, the point representing the state of the water moves along some path on the phase diagram. If the path crosses one of the curves, a phase transition occurs and the latent heat for that phase transition is either absorbed or released (depending on direction). Crossing the fusion curve represents freezing or melting; crossing the vapor pressure curve represents condensation or vaporization.

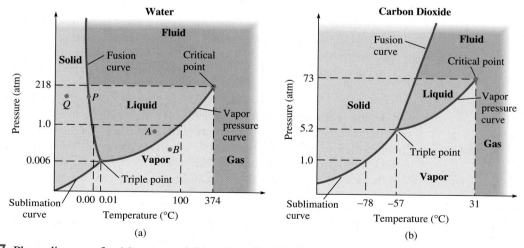

Figure 14.7 Phase diagrams for (a) water and (b) carbon dioxide. The term *vapor* is often used to indicate a substance in the gaseous state below its critical temperature; above the critical temperature it is called gas. (Note that the axes do not use a linear scale.)

Notice that the vapor pressure curve ends at the **critical point**. Thus, if the path for changing a liquid to a gas goes around the critical point without crossing the vapor pressure curve, no phase transition occurs. At temperatures above the critical temperature or pressures above the critical pressure, it is *impossible* to make a clear distinction between the liquid and gas phases.

Sublimation occurs when a solid becomes gas (or vice versa) without passing through the liquid phase. An example occurs when ice on a car windshield becomes water vapor on a cold dry day. Mothballs and dry ice (solid carbon dioxide) also pass directly from solid to gas. At atmospheric pressure, only the solid and gas phases of CO_2 exist (Fig. 14.7b). The liquid phase is not stable below 5.2 atm of pressure, so carbon dioxide does not melt at atmospheric pressure. Instead it sublimates; it goes from solid directly to gas. Solid CO_2 is called *dry ice* because it is cold and looks like ice, but does not melt. Sublimation has its own latent heat; the latent heat for sublimation is not the sum of the latent heats for fusion and vaporization.

The Unusual Phase Diagram of Water   The phase diagram of water has an unusual feature: the slope of the fusion curve is negative. The fusion curve has a negative slope only for substances (such as water, gallium, and bismuth) that expand on freezing. In these substances the molecules are *closer together* in the liquid than they are in the solid! As liquid water starting at room temperature is cooled, it contracts until it reaches 3.98°C. At this temperature water has its highest density (at a pressure of 1 atm); further cooling makes the water *expand*. When water freezes, it expands even more; ice is less dense than water.

One consequence of the expansion of water on freezing is that cell walls might rupture when foods are frozen and thawed. The taste of frozen food suffers as a result. Another consequence is that lakes, rivers, and ponds do not freeze solid in the winter. A layer of ice forms on *top* since ice is less dense than water; underneath the ice, liquid water remains, which permits fish, turtles, and other aquatic life to survive until spring (Fig. 14.8).

Figure 14.8 A Nunavut villager fishing for Arctic char.

14.6   THERMAL CONDUCTION

Until now we have considered the *effects* of heat flow, but not the mechanism of how heat flow occurs. We now turn our attention to three types of heat flow—*conduction, convection,* and *radiation.*

The **conduction** of heat can take place within solids, liquids, and gases. Conduction is due to collisions between atoms (or molecules) in which energy is exchanged. If the average energy is the same everywhere, there is no net flow of heat. If, on the other hand, the temperature is not uniform, then on average the atoms with more energy transfer some energy to those with less. The net result is that heat flows from the higher-temperature region to the lower-temperature region.

Conduction also occurs between objects that are in contact. A teakettle on an electric burner receives heat by conduction since the heating coil of the burner is in contact with the bottom of the kettle. The atoms that are vibrating in the object at higher temperature (the coil) collide with atoms in the object at lower temperature (the bottom of the kettle), resulting in a net transfer of energy to the colder object. If conduction is allowed to proceed, with no heat flow to or from the surroundings, then the objects in contact eventually reach thermal equilibrium when the average translational kinetic energies of the atoms are equal.

(a)

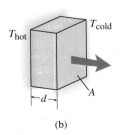

(b)

Figure 14.9 (a) Heat conduction along a cylindrical bar of length *d*. (b) Heat conduction through a slab of material of thickness *d*.

Fourier's Law of Heat Conduction   Suppose we consider a simple geometry such as an object with uniform cross section in which heat flows in a single direction. Examples are a plate of glass, with different temperatures on the inside and outside surfaces, or a cylindrical bar, with its ends at different temperatures (Fig. 14.9). The rate of heat conduction depends on the temperature difference $\Delta T = T_{hot} - T_{cold}$, the length (or thickness) *d*, the cross-sectional area A through which heat flows, and the nature of the material itself. The greater the temperature difference, the greater the heat flow. The thicker the material, the longer it takes for the heat to travel through—since the energy transfer has to be passed along a longer "chain" of atomic collisions—making the rate of heat flow smaller. A larger cross-sectional area allows more heat to flow.

The nature of the material is the final thing that affects the rate of energy transfer. In metals the electrons associated with the atom are free to move about and they carry the heat. When a material has free electrons, the transfer rate is faster; if the electrons are all tightly bound, as in nonmetallic solids, the transfer is slower. Liquids, in turn, conduct heat less readily than solids, because the forces between atoms are weaker. Gases are even less efficient as conductors of heat than solids or liquids since the atoms of a gas are so much farther apart and have to travel a greater distance before collisions occur. The **thermal conductivity** (symbol κ; the Greek letter kappa) of a substance is directly proportional to the rate at which energy is transferred through the substance. Higher values of κ are associated with good conductors of heat, smaller values with *thermal insulators* that tend to prevent the flow of heat. Table 14.5 lists the thermal conductivities for several common substances.

Let $\mathcal{P} = Q/\Delta t$ represent the rate of heat flow (or *power*). (The script $\mathcal{P}$ is used to avoid confusing power with pressure.) The dependence of the *rate* of heat flow through a substance on all the factors mentioned is given by

Fourier's law of heat conduction:

$$\mathcal{P} = \kappa A \frac{\Delta T}{d} \qquad (14\text{-}10)$$

where κ is the thermal conductivity of the material, A is the cross-sectional area, d is the thickness (or length) of the material, and ΔT is the temperature difference between one side and the other. The quantity $\Delta T/d$ is called the *temperature gradient*; it tells how many °C or K the temperature changes per unit of distance moved along the path of heat flow. Inspection of Eq. (14-10) shows that the SI units of κ are W/(m·K).

In Fig. 14.9b, a slab of material is shown that conducts heat because of a temperature difference between the two sides. By rearranging Eq. (14-10) and solving for ΔT,

$$\Delta T = \mathcal{P} \frac{d}{\kappa A} = \mathcal{P} R \qquad (14\text{-}11)$$

The quantity $d/(\kappa A)$ is called the **thermal resistance** R.

$$R = \frac{d}{\kappa A} \qquad (14\text{-}12)$$

Thermal resistance has SI units of K/W (kelvins per watt). Notice that the thermal resistance depends on the nature of the material (through the thermal conductivity κ) and the geometry of the object (d/A). Equation (14-11) is useful for solving problems when heat flows through one material after another.

Conduction Through Two or More Materials in Series Suppose we have two layers of material between two temperature extremes as in Fig. 14.10. These layers are in *series* because the heat flows through one and then through the other. Looking at one layer at a time,

$$T_1 - T_2 = \mathcal{P} R_1 \qquad \text{and} \qquad T_2 - T_3 = \mathcal{P} R_2$$

Then, adding the two together

$$(T_1 - T_2) + (T_2 - T_3) = \mathcal{P} R_1 + \mathcal{P} R_2$$
$$\Delta T = T_1 - T_3 = \mathcal{P}(R_1 + R_2)$$

Table 14.5 Thermal Conductivities at 20°C

Material	$\kappa \left(\dfrac{\text{W}}{\text{m·K}} \right)$
Air	0.023
Rigid panel polyurethane insulation	0.023–0.026
Fiberglass insulation	0.029–0.072
Rock wool insulation	0.038
Cork	0.046
Wood	0.13
Soil (dry)	0.14
Asbestos	0.17
Snow	0.25
Sand	0.39
Water	0.6
Window glass (typical)	0.63
Pyrex glass	1.13
Vycor	1.34
Concrete	1.7
Ice	1.7
Stainless steel	14
Lead	35
Steel	46
Nickel	60
Tin	66.8
Platinum	71.6
Iron	80.2
Brass	122
Zinc	116
Tungsten	173
Aluminum	237
Gold	318
Copper	401
Silver	429

CONNECTION:

Fourier's law says that the rate of heat flow is proportional to the temperature gradient. Closely analogous is Poiseuille's law for viscous fluid flow [Eq. (9-15)], in which the volume flow rate is proportional to the pressure gradient.

Figure 14.10 (a) Conduction of heat through two different layers ($T_1 > T_2 > T_3$). (b) Graph of temperature T as a function of position x. The slope of the graph in either material is the temperature gradient $\Delta T/d$ in that material. The temperature gradients are not the same because the materials have different thermal conductivities.

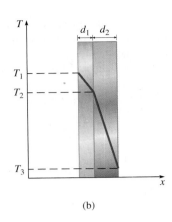

(a)

(b)

The rate of heat flow through the first layer is the same as the rate through the second layer because otherwise the temperatures would be changing. For n layers,

$$\Delta T = \mathcal{P}\sum R_n \qquad n = 1, 2, 3, \ldots \qquad (14\text{-}13)$$

Equation (14-13) shows that the effective thermal resistance for layers in series is the sum of each layer's thermal resistance.

✓ CHECKPOINT 14.6

In Fig. 14.10, which of the two materials has the larger thermal conductivity?

Example 14.10

The Rate of Heat Flow Through Window Glass

A windowpane that measures 20.0 cm by 15.0 cm is set into the front door of a house. The glass is 0.32 cm thick. The temperature outdoors is −15°C and inside is 22°C. At what rate does heat leave the house through that one small window?

Strategy We assume one side of the glass to be at the temperature of the air inside the house and the other to be at the outdoor temperature.

Given: $\Delta T = 22°C - (-15°C) = 37°C$; thickness of windowpane $d = 0.32 \times 10^{-2}$ m; area of windowpane $A = 0.200$ m $\times$ 0.150 m $= 0.0300$ m^2
Look up: thermal conductivity for glass $= 0.63$ W/(m·K)
Find: rate of heat flow, $\mathcal{P}$

Solution The temperature gradient is

$$\frac{\Delta T}{d} = \frac{37°C}{0.32 \times 10^{-2}\text{ m}} = 1.16 \times 10^4\text{ K/m}$$

Now we have all the information we need to find the rate of conductive heat flow:

$$\mathcal{P} = \kappa A \frac{\Delta T}{d}$$
$$= 0.63\text{ W/(m·K)} \times 0.0300\text{ m}^2 \times 1.16 \times 10^4\text{ K/m}$$
$$= 220\text{ W}$$

Discussion A loss of 220 W through one small window is significant. However, our assumption about the temperatures of the two glass surfaces exaggerates the temperature difference across the glass. In reality, the inside surface of the glass is colder than the air inside the house, while the outside surface is warmer than the air outside.

Practice Problem 14.10   An Igloo

A group of children build an igloo in their garden. The snow walls are 0.30 m thick. If the inside of the igloo is at 10.0°C and the outside is at −10.0°C, what is the rate of heat flow through the snow walls of area 14.0 m^2?

Figure 14.11 Temperature variation on either side of a windowpane. A plot of temperature versus position is superimposed on a cross section of the window glass and the air layers on either side.

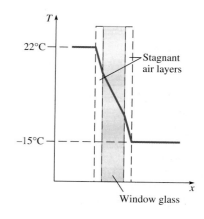

Thermal Conductivity of Air   Air has a low thermal conductivity; it is an excellent thermal insulator *when it is still*. An accurate calculation of the energy loss through a single-paned window *must* take into account the thin layer of stagnant air, due to viscosity, on each side of the glass. If the temperature is measured near a window, the temperature of the air just beside the window is intermediate in value between the temperatures of the room air and the outside air (see Fig. 14.11). Thus, the temperature gradient *across the glass* is considerably smaller than the difference between indoor and outdoor temperatures. In fact, much of the thermal resistance of a window is due to the stagnant air layers rather than to the glass.

Example 14.11

Heat Loss Through a Double-Paned Window

The single-paned window of Example 14.10 is replaced by a double-paned window with an air gap of 0.50 cm between the two panes. The inner surface of the inner pane is at 22°C and the outer surface of the outer pane is at −15°C. What is the new rate of heat loss through the double-paned window?

Strategy   Now there are three layers to consider: two layers of glass and one layer of air. We find the thermal resistance of each layer and then add them together to find the total thermal resistance. Then we find the temperature difference between the inside of the house and the air outdoors and divide by the total thermal resistance to find the rate at which heat is lost through the replacement window.

Solution   For the first layer of glass,

$$R_1 = \frac{d}{\kappa A} = \frac{0.32 \times 10^{-2} \text{ m}}{0.63 \text{ W/(m·K)} \times 0.0300 \text{ m}^2} = 0.169 \text{ K/W}$$

For the air gap,

$$R_2 = \frac{d}{\kappa A} = \frac{0.50 \times 10^{-2} \text{ m}}{0.023 \text{ W/(m·K)} \times 0.0300 \text{ m}^2} = 7.246 \text{ K/W}$$

The second layer of glass has the same thermal resistance as the first:

$$R_3 = R_1$$

The total thermal resistance is

$$\sum R_n = 0.169 + 7.246 + 0.169 = 7.584 \text{ K/W}$$

and the rate of conductive heat flow is

$$\mathscr{P} = \frac{Q}{\Delta t} = \frac{\Delta T}{\sum R_n} = \frac{37 \text{ K}}{7.584 \text{ K/W}} = 4.9 \text{ W}$$

Discussion   The reduction in the rate of heat loss by replacing a single-paned window with a double pane is significant. This example, however, overestimates the reduction since we assume that heat can only be conducted through the air layer. In reality, heat can also flow through air by convection and radiation. A more accurate calculation would have to account for the other methods of heat flow.

Practice Problem 14.11   Two Panes of Glass Without the Air Gap

Repeat Example 14.11 if the two panes of glass are touching one another, without the intervening layer of air.

R-Factors   The U.S. building industry rates materials used in construction with *R-factors*. The R-factor is not quite the same as the thermal resistance; thermal resistance cannot be specified without knowing the cross-sectional area. The R-factor is the thickness divided by the thermal conductivity:

$$\text{R-factor} = \frac{d}{\kappa} = RA$$

$$\frac{\mathscr{P}}{A} = \frac{\Delta T}{\text{R-factor}}$$

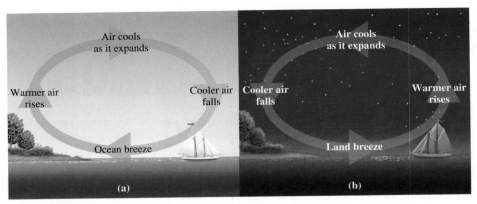

Figure 14.12 (a) During the day, air coming off the ocean is heated as it passes over the warm ground on shore; the heated air rises and expands. The expansion cools the air; it becomes more dense and falls back down. This cycle sets up a convection current that brings cool breezes from the sea to the shore. (b) The reverse circulation occurs at night when the land is cold and the sea is warmer, retaining heat absorbed during the day.

Unfortunately, SI units are not used. The R-factors quoted in the United States are in units of $°F·ft^2/(Btu/h)$! R-factors are added, just as thermal resistances are, when heat flows through several different layers.

14.7   THERMAL CONVECTION

Applications of convection: offshore and onshore breezes, double-paned windows, and down jackets

Applications of forced convection: building heating systems; temperature regulation in the human body.

Figure 14.13 Convection currents in heated water. Heat flows through the bottom surface of the pot by conduction and then heats the layer of water in contact with the pot bottom. The heated water is less dense, so buoyant forces make it rise, setting up convection currents.

Convection involves *fluid currents* that carry heat from one place to another. In conduction, energy flows through a material but the material itself does not move. In convection, *the material itself moves* from one place to another. Thus, convection can occur only in fluids, not in solids. When a wood stove is burning, convection currents in the air carry heat upward to the ceiling. The heated air is less dense than cooler air, so the buoyant force causes it to rise, carrying heat with it. Meanwhile, cooler air that is more dense sinks toward the floor. An example of convection currents at the seashore is shown in Fig. 14.12. Air is a poor *conductor* of heat, but it can easily flow and carry heat by *convection.*

The use of sealed, double-paned windows replaces the large air gap of about 6 or 7 cm between a storm window and regular window with a much smaller gap. The smaller air gap minimizes circulating convection currents between the two panes. Down jackets and quilts are good insulators because air is trapped in many little spaces among the feathers, minimizing heat flow due to convection. Materials such as rock wool, glass wool, or fiberglass are used to insulate walls; much of their insulating value is due to the air trapped around and between the fibers.

Natural and Forced Convection   In *natural convection*, the currents are due to gravity. Fluid with a higher density sinks because the buoyant force is smaller than the weight; less dense fluid rises because the buoyant force exceeds the weight (Figs. 14.13 and 14.14). In *forced convection*, fluid is pushed around by mechanical means such as a fan or pump. In forced-hot-air heating, warm air is blown into rooms by a fan (Fig. 14.15); in hot water baseboard heating, hot water is pumped through baseboard radiators. Another example of forced convection is blood circulation in the body. The heart pumps blood around the body. When our body temperature is too high, the blood vessels near the skin dilate so that more blood can be pushed into them by the heart. The blood carries heat from the interior of the body to the skin; heat then flows from the skin into the cooler surroundings. If the surroundings are *hotter* than the skin, such as in a hot tub, this strategy backfires and can lead to dangerous overheating of the body. The hot water delivers heat to the dilated blood vessels; the blood carries the heat back to the central core of the body, *raising* the core temperature. (For more information on convection, see text website.)

Convection and Global Climate Change

One worry for scientists studying global warming is that northern Europe might be plunged into a deep freeze—a seeming contradiction that results from an interruption of the natural convection cycle. Earth's climate is influenced by convection currents caused by temperature differences between the poles and the tropics (Fig. 14.16). Massive sea currents travel through the Pacific and Atlantic oceans, carrying about half of the heat from the tropics to the poles, where it is dissipated. Storms moving north from the tropics carry much of the rest of the heat. If the polar regions warm at a faster rate than the tropics, the smaller temperature difference between them changes the patterns of the prevailing winds, the tracks followed by storms, the speed of ocean currents, and the amount of precipitation.

For example, the melting of the ice shelves combined with increased precipitation could lead to a layer of fresh water lying on top of the more dense salt water in the North Atlantic. Normally, the cold ocean water at the surface sinks and starts the process of convection. With the buoyancy of the less dense freshwater layer keeping it from sinking, the convection currents slow down or are stopped. Without the pull of the convection current, the usual northward movement of water from the warm Gulf Stream would slow or cease, causing *colder* temperatures in northern Europe.

Such an effect on climate is not without precedent. At the end of the last Ice Age, freshwater from melting glaciers flowed out the St. Lawrence River and into the North Atlantic. A freshwater layer, buoyed up by the more dense salt water, disrupted the usual ocean currents. The Gulf Stream was effectively shut down and Europe experienced a thousand years of deep freeze.

14.8 THERMAL RADIATION

All bodies emit energy through electromagnetic radiation—due to the oscillation of electric charges in the atoms. Thermal radiation consists of electromagnetic waves that travel at the speed of light. Unlike conduction and convection, radiation does not require a material medium; the Sun radiates heat to Earth through the near vacuum of space.

Application of convection: ocean currents and global climate change

Figure 14.14 Birds (and people flying sailplanes) take advantage of thermal updrafts.

Figure 14.15 Household heating systems rely on forced convection.

→ Warm currents → Cool currents

Figure 14.16 Surface convection currents in the oceans. The Gulf Stream is a current of warm water flowing across the Atlantic.

An object emits thermal radiation while absorbing some of the thermal radiation emitted by other objects. The rate of absorption may be less than, equal to, or greater than the rate of emission.

When solar radiation reaches Earth, it is partially absorbed and partially reflected. Earth also emits radiation at nearly the same average rate that it absorbs energy from the Sun. If there were an exact equilibrium between absorption and emission, Earth's average temperature would stay constant. However, increasing concentrations of CO_2 and other "greenhouse gases" in Earth's atmosphere cause energy to be emitted at a slightly lower rate than it is absorbed. As a result, Earth's average temperature is rising. Although the predicted temperature increase may seem small on an absolute scale, it will have dramatic consequences for life on Earth.

Conceptual Example 14.12

An Alligator Lying in the Sun

An alligator crawls out into the Sun to get warm. Solar radiation is incident on the alligator at the rate of 300 W; 70 W of it is reflected. (a) What happens to the other 230 W? (b) If the alligator emits 100 W, does its body temperature rise, fall, or stay the same? Ignore heat flow by conduction and convection.

Solution and Discussion   (a) When radiation falls on an object, some can be absorbed, some can be reflected, and—for a transparent or translucent object—some can be transmitted through the object without being absorbed or reflected. Since the alligator is opaque, no radiation is transmitted through it. All the radiation is either absorbed or reflected, so the other 230 W is absorbed. (b) Since 230 W is absorbed while 100 W is emitted, the alligator absorbs more

radiation than it emits. Absorption increases internal energy while emission decreases it, so the alligator's internal energy is increasing at a rate of 130 W. Thus, we expect the alligator's body temperature to rise. (The actual rate of increase of internal energy would be smaller since conduction and convection carry heat away as well.)

Conceptual Practice Problem 14.12   Maintaining Constant Temperature

After some time elapses, the alligator's body temperature reaches a constant level. The rate of absorption is still 230 W. If the alligator loses heat by conduction and convection at a rate of 90 W, at what rate does it emit radiation?

Stefan's Radiation Law

An idealized body that absorbs all the radiation incident upon it is called a **blackbody**. A blackbody absorbs not only all visible light, but infrared, ultraviolet, and all other wavelengths of electromagnetic radiation. It turns out (see Conceptual Question 23) that a good *absorber* is also a good *emitter* of radiation. A blackbody emits more radiant power per unit surface area than any real object at the same temperature. The rate at which a blackbody emits radiation per unit surface area is proportional to the fourth power of the *absolute* temperature:

Stefan's Law of Radiation (blackbody)

$$\mathscr{P} = \sigma A T^4 \qquad (14\text{-}14)$$

In Eq. (14-14), A is the surface area and T is the surface temperature of the blackbody *in kelvins.* Since Stefan's law involves the absolute temperature and not a temperature difference, °C *cannot* be substituted. The universal constant σ (Greek letter sigma) is called *Stefan's constant*:

$$\sigma = 5.670 \times 10^{-8} \text{ W/(m}^2 \cdot \text{K}^4) \qquad (14\text{-}15)$$

The fourth-power temperature dependence implies that the power emitted is extremely sensitive to temperature changes. If the absolute temperature of a body doubles, the energy emitted increases by a factor of $2^4 = 16$.

Emissivity   Since real bodies are not perfect absorbers and therefore emit less than a blackbody, we define the **emissivity** (e) as the ratio of the emitted power of the body to that of a blackbody at the same temperature. Then Stefan's law becomes

Stefan's Law of Radiation

$$\mathcal{P} = e\sigma A T^4 \tag{14-16}$$

The emissivity ranges from 0 to 1; $e = 1$ for a perfect radiator and absorber (a blackbody) and $e = 0$ for a perfect reflector. The emissivity for polished aluminum, an excellent reflector, is about 0.05; for soot (carbon black) it is about 0.95. Equation (14-16) is a refinement of Stefan's law, but it is still an approximation because it treats the emissivity as a constant. Emissivity is actually a function of the wavelength of the emitted radiation. Equation (14-16) is useful when the emissivity is approximately constant over the range of wavelengths in which most of the power is radiated.

Human skin, no matter what the pigmentation, has an emissivity of about 0.97 in the infrared part of the spectrum. Many objects have high emissivities in the infrared even though they may reflect much of the visible light incident on them and, therefore, have low emissivities in the visible range.

Radiation Spectrum

The electromagnetic radiation we are concerned with falls into three wavelength ranges. Infrared radiation includes wavelengths from about 100 μm down to 0.7 μm. The wavelengths of visible light range from about 0.7 μm to about 0.4 μm. Ultraviolet wavelengths are less than 0.4 μm.

The total power radiated is not the only thing that varies with temperature. Figure 14.17 shows the radiation spectrum—a graph of how much radiation occurs as a function of wavelength—for blackbodies at two different temperatures. The wavelength at which the maximum power is emitted decreases as temperature increases. Objects at ordinary temperatures emit primarily in the infrared—around 10 μm in wavelength for 300 K. The Sun, since it is much hotter, radiates primarily at shorter wavelengths. Its radiation peaks in the visible (no surprise there) but includes plenty of infrared and ultraviolet as well. The wavelength of maximum radiation is inversely proportional to the absolute temperature:

Wien's Law

$$\lambda_{\text{max}} T = 2.898 \times 10^{-3} \text{ m·K} \tag{14-17}$$

where the temperature T is the temperature in kelvins and λ_{max} is the wavelength of maximum radiation in meters.

As the temperature of the blackbody rises to 1000 K and above, the peak intensity shifts toward shorter wavelengths until some of the emitted radiation falls in the visible. Since the longest visible wavelengths are for red light, the heated body glows dull red. As the temperature of the blackbody continues to increase, the red glow becomes brighter red, then orange, then yellow-white, and eventually blue-white as

Figure 14.17 Graphs of blackbody radiation as a function of wavelength at two different temperatures. At the higher temperature, the wavelength of maximum radiation is shorter (Wien's law) and the total power radiated, represented by the area under the graph, increases (Stefan's law).

the blackbody emits more and more visible light. When the body is emitting all the colors of the visible spectrum, the glow appears white to the eye. When something is red-hot, it is not as hot as something that is white-hot.

Example 14.13

Temperature of the Sun

The maximum rate of energy emission from the Sun occurs in the middle of the visible range—at about $\lambda = 0.5$ μm. Estimate the temperature of the Sun's surface.

Strategy   We assume the Sun to be a blackbody. Then the wavelength of maximum emission and the surface temperature are related by Wien's law.

Solution   Given: $\lambda_{max} = 0.5$ μm $= 5 \times 10^{-7}$ m. Then from Wien's law, we know that the product of the wavelength for maximum power emission and the corresponding temperature for the power emission is

$$\lambda_{max} T = 2.898 \times 10^{-3} \text{ m·K}$$

We can solve for the temperature since we know λ_{max}:

$$T = \frac{2.898 \times 10^{-3} \text{ m·K}}{5 \times 10^{-7} \text{ m}}$$
$$= 6000 \text{ K}$$

Discussion   Quick check: an object at 300 K has $\lambda_{max} \approx 10$ μm, which is 20 times the λ_{max} in the radiation from the Sun (0.5 μm). Since λ_{max} and T are inversely proportional, the Sun's surface temperature is 20 times 300 K = 6000 K.

Practice Problem 14.13   Wavelengths of Maximum Power Emission for Skin

The temperature of skin varies from 30°C to 35°C depending on the blood flow near the skin surface. What is the range of wavelengths of maximum power emission from skin?

Simultaneous Emission and Absorption of Thermal Radiation

An object simultaneously emitting and absorbing thermal radiation has a *net* rate of heat flow due to thermal radiation given by $\mathcal{P}_{net} = \mathcal{P}_{emitted} - \mathcal{P}_{absorbed}$. Suppose an object with surface area A and temperature T is bathed in thermal radiation coming from its surroundings in all directions that are at a *uniform* temperature T_s. Then the *net* rate of heat flow due to thermal radiation is

Net rate of energy transfer due to emission and absorption of thermal radiation

$$\mathcal{P}_{net} = e\sigma A T^4 - e\sigma A T_s^4 = e\sigma A(T^4 - T_s^4) \tag{14-18}$$

A body emits energy even if it is at the same temperature as its surroundings; it just emits at the same rate that it absorbs, so $\mathcal{P}_{net} = 0$. If $T > T_s$, the object emits more thermal radiation than it absorbs. If $T < T_s$, the object absorbs more thermal radiation than it emits.

Why is the rate of *absorption* proportional to the *emissivity*? Because a good emitter is also a good absorber. The emissivity e measures not only how much the object emits compared to a blackbody; it also measures how much the object *absorbs* compared with a blackbody. A blackbody at the same temperature as its surroundings would have to absorb radiation at the rate $\mathcal{P}_{absorbed} = \sigma A T_s^4$ to exactly balance the rate of emission. However, emissivity does depend on temperature. Equation (14-18) assumes the emissivity at temperature T is the same as the emissivity at temperature T_s. If T and T_s are very different, we would have to modify Eq. (14-18) to use two different emissivities.

 Do not substitute temperature in Celsius degrees into Eq. (14-18). The quantity inside the parentheses might look like a temperature difference, but it is not. The two kelvin temperatures are raised to the fourth power, *then* subtracted—which is not the same as the corresponding two Celsius temperatures subjected to the same mathematical operations. By the same token, do not subtract the temperatures in kelvins and then raise to the fourth power. The difference of the fourth powers is not equal to the difference raised to the fourth power, as can be readily demonstrated:

$$(2^4 - 1^4) = 15 \quad \text{but} \quad (2 - 1)^4 = 1$$

Medical Applications of Thermal Radiation

Thermal radiation from the body is used as a diagnostic tool in medicine. "Instant-read" thermometers work by measuring the intensity of thermal radiation in the patient's ear. A thermogram shows whether one area is radiating more heat than it should, indicating a higher temperature due to abnormal cellular activity. For example, when a broken bone is healing, heat can be detected at the location of the break just by placing a hand lightly on the area of skin over the break. Infrared detectors, originally developed for military uses (nightscopes, for example), can be used to detect radiation from the skin. The radiation is absorbed and an electrical signal is produced that is then used to produce a visual display (Fig. 14.18). Thermography has been used to screen travelers at airports in Asia for the high fever that accompanies infection with severe acute respiratory syndrome (SARS).

Figure 14.18 Thermography of a backache. The magenta areas are warmer than the surrounding tissue, revealing the location of the source of pain.

Example 14.14

Thermal Radiation from the Human Body

 A person of body surface area 2.0 m² is sitting in a doctor's examining room with no clothing on. The temperature of the room is 22°C and the person's average skin temperature is 34°C. Skin emits about 97% as much as a blackbody at the same temperature for wavelengths in the infrared region, where most of the emission occurs. At what *net* rate is energy radiated away from the body?

Strategy Both radiation and absorption occur in the infrared—the absolute temperatures of the skin and the room are not very different. Therefore, we can assume that 97% of the incident radiation from the room is absorbed. Equation (14-18) therefore applies. We must convert the Celsius temperatures to kelvins.

Given: surface area, $A = 2.0$ m²; $T_{room} = 22°C$; skin temperature, $T = 34°C$; fraction of energy emitted, $e = 0.97$

To find: net rate of energy transfer, $\mathcal{P}_{net}$

Solution The temperature of the skin surface is

$$T = 273 + 34 = 307 \text{ K}$$

and of the room is

$$T_s = 273 + 22 = 295 \text{ K}$$

The net rate of energy transfer between the room and the body is

$$\mathcal{P}_{net} = e\sigma A(T^4 - T_s^4)$$

Substituting,

$$\mathcal{P}_{net} = 0.97 \times 5.67 \times 10^{-8} \text{ W/(m}^2 \cdot \text{K}^4) \times 2.0 \text{ m}^2 \times (307^4 - 295^4) \text{ K}^4$$

$$= 140 \text{ W}$$

Discussion 140 W is a significant heat loss because the body also loses about 10 W by convection and conduction. To stay at a constant body temperature, an inactive person must give off heat at a rate of 90 W to account for basal metabolic activity; if the rate of heat loss exceeds that, the body temperature starts to drop. The patient had better wrap a blanket around his body or start running in place.

We need only the fraction of energy emitted and absorbed by the body; the emissivity of the walls of the room is irrelevant. If the walls are poor emitters, then they also absorb poorly, so they reflect radiation. The amount of radiation incident on the body is the same.

Practice Problem 14.14   The Roller Blader Radiates

Find how much energy per unit time a roller blader loses by radiation from her body. Her skin temperature is 35°C and the air temperature is 30°C. Her surface area is 1.2 m², of which 75% is exposed to the air. Assume skin has $e = 0.97$.

Example 14.15

Radiative Equilibrium of Earth

Radiant energy from the Sun reaches Earth at a rate of 1.7×10^{17} W. An average of about 30% is reflected and the rest is absorbed. Energy is also radiated by the atmosphere. Assuming equal rates of absorption and emission, and that the atmosphere emits as a blackbody in the infrared ($e = 1$), calculate the temperature of the atmosphere. (The Sun's radiation peaks in the visible part of the spectrum, but Earth's radiation peaks in the infrared due to its much lower surface temperature.)

Strategy   Earth must radiate the same power as it absorbs. We use Stefan's law to find the rate at which energy is radiated as a function of temperature and then equate that to the rate of energy absorption.

Solution   Earth absorbs 70% of the incident solar radiation. To have a relatively constant temperature, it must emit radiation at the same rate:

$$\mathcal{P} = 0.70 \times 1.7 \times 10^{17} \text{ W} = 1.2 \times 10^{17} \text{ W}$$

From Stefan's law,

$$\mathcal{P} = e\sigma A T^4$$

where we take $e = 1$ since the atmosphere is assumed to emit as a blackbody. Earth's surface area is

$$A = 4\pi R_E^2$$

Solving Stefan's law for T yields

$$T = \left(\frac{\mathcal{P}}{e\sigma A}\right)^{1/4}$$

Now we substitute numerical values:

$$T = \left(\frac{\mathcal{P}}{e\sigma 4\pi R_E^2}\right)^{1/4}$$

$$= \left[\frac{1.2 \times 10^{17} \text{ W}}{1 \times 5.67 \times 10^{-8} \text{ W/(m}^2\cdot\text{K}^4) \times 4\pi (6.4 \times 10^6 \text{ m})^2}\right]^{1/4}$$

$$= 253 \text{ K} = -20°\text{C}$$

Discussion   Remember that $-20°$C is supposed to be the average temperature of the *atmosphere*, not of Earth's surface. This relatively simple calculation gives impressively accurate results. To find the temperature of Earth's surface, we must take the greenhouse effect into account.

Practice Problem 14.15   Reflecting Less Incident Radiation

If Earth were to reflect 25% of the incident radiation instead of 30%, what would be the average temperature of the atmosphere?

Application of Thermal Radiation: Global Climate Change

Earth receives heat by radiation from the Sun. The atmosphere helps trap some of the radiation, acting rather like the glass in a greenhouse. When sunlight falls on the glass of a greenhouse, most of the visible radiation and short-wavelength infrared (*near-infrared*) travel right on through; the glass is transparent to those wavelengths. The glass absorbs much of the incoming ultraviolet radiation. The radiation that gets through the glass is mostly absorbed inside the greenhouse. Since the inside of the greenhouse is much cooler than the Sun, it emits primarily infrared radiation (IR). The glass is not transparent to this longer-wavelength IR; much of it is absorbed by the glass. The glass itself also emits IR, but in both directions: half of it is emitted back inside the greenhouse. The absorption of IR by the glass keeps the greenhouse warmer than it would otherwise be. (The glass in a greenhouse has a second function not mirrored in Earth's atmosphere—it prevents heat from being carried away by convection.)

Earth is something like a greenhouse, where the atmosphere fulfills the role of the glass. Like glass, the atmosphere is largely transparent to visible and near IR; the ozone layer in the upper atmosphere absorbs some of the ultraviolet. The atmosphere absorbs a great deal of the longer-wavelength IR emitted by Earth's surface. The atmosphere *radiates* IR in two directions: back toward the surface and out toward space (Fig. 14.19). "Greenhouse gases" such as CO_2 and water vapor are particularly good absorbers of IR. The higher the concentration of greenhouse gases in the atmosphere, the more IR is

Figure 14.19 The global greenhouse effect. In this *simplified* diagram, all the UV from the Sun is absorbed by the atmosphere, while all the visible and IR from the Sun is transmitted. Earth absorbs the visible and IR and radiates longer-wavelength IR. The longer-wavelength IR is absorbed by the atmosphere, which itself radiates IR both back toward the surface and out toward space.

absorbed and the warmer Earth's surface becomes. Even small changes in the average surface temperature can have dramatic effects on climate.

In applying Stefan's radiation law to Earth, there are some complications. One is the effect of the cloud cover. Clouds are quite reflective, but they are sometimes there and sometimes not. The heating of the lakes and oceans causes water to evaporate and form clouds. The clouds then serve as a screen and reflect sunlight away from Earth, reducing the temperature again.

Master the Concepts

- The internal energy of a system is the total energy of all of the molecules in the system except for the macroscopic kinetic energy (kinetic energy associated with macroscopic translation or rotation) and the external potential energy (energy due to external interactions).

- Heat is a *flow* of energy that occurs due to a temperature difference.

- The joule is the SI unit for all forms of energy, for heat, and for work. An alternative unit sometimes used for heat and internal energy is the calorie:

$$1 \text{ cal} = 4.186 \text{ J} \qquad (14\text{-}1)$$

- The ratio of heat flow into a system to the temperature change of the system is the heat capacity of the system:

$$C = \frac{Q}{\Delta T} \qquad (14\text{-}2)$$

- The heat capacity per unit mass is the specific heat capacity (or specific heat) of a substance:

$$c = \frac{Q}{m \, \Delta T} \qquad (14\text{-}3)$$

- The *molar specific heat* is the heat capacity per mole:

$$C_V = \frac{Q}{n \, \Delta T} \qquad (14\text{-}6)$$

At room temperature, the molar heat capacity at constant volume for a monatomic ideal gas is approximately $C_V = \frac{3}{2}R$, and for a diatomic ideal gas it is approximately $C_V = \frac{5}{2}R$.

- Phase transitions occur at constant temperature. The heat *per unit mass* that must flow to melt a solid or to freeze a liquid is the latent heat of fusion L_f. The latent heat of vaporization L_v is the heat *per unit mass* that must flow to change the phase from liquid to gas or from gas to liquid.

- *Sublimation* occurs when a solid changes directly to a gas without going into a liquid form.

- A phase diagram is a graph of pressure versus temperature that indicates solid, liquid, and gas regions for a

continued on next page

Master the Concepts continued

substance. The sublimation, fusion, and vapor pressure curves separate the three phases. Crossing one of these curves represents a phase transition.

- Heat flows by three processes: conduction, convection, and radiation.
- Conduction is due to atomic (or molecular) collisions within a substance or from one object to another when they are in contact. The rate of heat flow within a substance is:

$$\mathcal{P} = \kappa A \frac{\Delta T}{d} \qquad \text{(14-10)}$$

where $\mathcal{P}$ is the rate of heat flow (or power delivered), κ is the thermal conductivity of the material, A is the cross-sectional area, d is the thickness (or length) of the material, and ΔT is the temperature difference between one side and the other.

- Convection involves *fluid currents* that carry heat from one place to another. In convection, the material itself moves from one place to another.

- Thermal radiation does not have to travel through a material medium. The energy is carried by electromagnetic waves that travel at the speed of light. All bodies emit energy through electromagnetic radiation. An idealized body that absorbs all the radiation incident on it is called a blackbody. A blackbody emits more radiant power per unit surface area than any real object at the same temperature. Stefan's law of thermal radiation is

$$\mathcal{P} = e\sigma A T^4 \qquad \text{(14-16)}$$

where the emissivity e ranges from 0 to 1, A is the surface area, T is the surface temperature of the blackbody *in kelvins*, and Stefan's constant is $\sigma = 5.670 \times 10^{-8} \ \text{W/(m}^2 \cdot \text{K}^4)$. The wavelength of maximum power emission is inversely proportional to the absolute temperature:

$$\lambda_{\max} T = 2.898 \times 10^{-3} \ \text{m} \cdot \text{K} \qquad \text{(14-17)}$$

The difference between the power emitted by the body and that absorbed by the body from its surroundings is the net power emitted:

$$\mathcal{P}_{\text{net}} = e\sigma A(T^4 - T_s^4) \qquad \text{(14-18)}$$

Conceptual Questions

1. What determines the direction of heat flow when two objects at different temperatures are placed in thermal contact?

2. When an old movie has a scene of someone ironing, the person is often shown testing the heat of a hot flat iron with a moistened finger. Why is this safe to do?

3. Why do lakes and rivers freeze first at their surfaces?

4. Why is drinking water in a camp located near the equator often kept in porous jars?

5. Why are several layers of clothing warmer than one coat of equal weight?

6. Why are vineyards planted along lakeshores or riverbanks in cold climates?

7. A metal plant stand on a wooden deck feels colder than the wood around it. Is it necessarily colder? Explain.

8. Near a large lake, in what direction does a breeze passing over the land tend to blow at night?

9. What is the purpose of having fins on an automobile or motorcycle radiator?

10. Why do roadside signs warn that bridges ice before roadways? Explain.

11. Why do cooking directions on packages advise different timing to be followed for some locations?

12. Explain the theory behind the pressure cooker. How does it speed up cooking times?

13. When you eat a pizza that has just come from the oven, why is it that you are apt to burn the roof of your mouth with the first bite although the crust of the pizza feels only warm to your hand?

14. Explain why the molar specific heat of a diatomic gas such as O_2 is larger than that of a monatomic gas such as Ne.

15. At very low temperatures, the molar specific heat of hydrogen (H_2) is $C_V = 1.5R$. At room temperature, $C_V = 2.5R$. Explain.

16. When the temperature as measured in °C of a radiating body is doubled (such as a change from 20°C to 40°C), is the radiation rate necessarily increased by a factor of 16?

17. A cup of hot coffee has been poured, but the coffee drinker has a little more work to do at the computer before she picks up the cup. She intends to add some milk to the coffee. To keep the coffee hot as long as possible, should she add the milk at once, or wait until just before she takes her first sip?

18. Would heat loss be reduced or increased by increasing the usual air gap, 1 to 2 cm, between commercially made double-paned windows? Explain your reasoning. [*Hint:* Consider convection.]

19. A study of food preservation in Britain discovered that the temperature of meat that is kept in transparent plastic packages and stored in open and lighted freezers can be as much as 12°C above the temperature of the freezer. Why is this? How could this be prevented?

20. Which possesses more total internal energy, the water within a large, partially ice-covered lake in winter or a 6-cup teapot filled with hot tea? Explain.

21. A room in which the air temperature is held constant may feel warm in the summer but cool in the winter. Explain. [*Hint:* The walls are not necessarily at the same temperature as the air.]

22. Many homes are heated with "radiators," which are hollow metal devices filled with hot water or steam and located in each room of the house. They are sometimes painted with metallic, high-gloss silver paint so that they look well polished. Does this make them better radiators of heat? If not, what might be a more efficient finish to use?

23. Two objects with the same surface area are inside an evacuated container. The walls of the container are kept at a constant temperature. Suppose one object absorbs a larger fraction of incident radiation than the other. Explain why that object must emit a correspondingly greater amount of radiation than the other. Thus a good absorber must be a good emitter.

24. Even though heat is not a fluid, Eq. (14-11) has a close analogy in Poiseuille's law, which describes the viscous flow of a fluid through a pipe (see Problem 9.60). (a) Explain the analogy. (b) For two or more thermal conductors in series, the total thermal resistance is just the sum of the thermal resistances [Eq. (14-13)]. Is the total fluid flow resistance for two or more pipes in series equal to the sum of the resistances? Explain.

Multiple-Choice Questions

1. The main loss of heat from Earth is by
   (a) radiation.
   (b) convection.
   (c) conduction.
   (d) All three processes are significant modes of heat loss from Earth.

2. Assume the average temperature of Earth's atmosphere to be 253 K. What would be the eventual average temperature of Earth's atmosphere if the surface temperature of the Sun were to drop by a factor of 2?

   (a) 253 K
   (b) $\dfrac{253 \text{ K}}{2} = 127$ K
   (c) $\dfrac{253 \text{ K}}{4} = 63$ K
   (d) $\dfrac{253 \text{ K}}{2^4} = 16$ K

3. In equilibrium, Mars emits as much radiation as it absorbs. If Mars orbits the Sun with an orbital radius that is 1.5 times the orbital radius of Earth about the Sun, what is the approximate atmospheric temperature of Mars? Assume the atmospheric temperature of Earth to be 253 K.

   (a) $\dfrac{253 \text{ K}}{1.5} = 170$ K
   (b) $\dfrac{253 \text{ K}}{1.5^2} = 112$ K
   (c) $\dfrac{253 \text{ K}}{1.5^4} = 50$ K
   (d) $\dfrac{253 \text{ K}}{\sqrt{1.5}} = 207$ K

4. Which term best represents the relation between a blackbody and radiant energy? A blackbody is an ideal _____ of radiant energy.
   (a) emitter   (b) absorber
   (c) reflector   (d) emitter and absorber

5. A window conducts power P from a house to the cold outdoors. What power is conducted through a window of *half* the area and *half* the thickness?
   (a) $4P$ (b) $2P$ (c) P (d) $P/2$ (e) $P/4$

6. Iron has a specific heat that is about 3.4 times that of gold. A cube of gold and a cube of iron, both of equal mass and at 20°C, are placed in two different Styrofoam cups, each filled with 100 g of water at 40°C. The Styrofoam cups have negligible heat capacities. After equilibrium has been attained,
   (a) the temperature of the gold is lower than that of the iron.
   (b) the temperature of the gold is higher than that of the iron.
   (c) the temperatures of the water in the two cups are the same.
   (d) Either (a) or (b), depending on the mass of the cubes.

7. Sublimation is involved in which of these phase changes?

    (a) liquid to gas
    (b) solid to liquid
    (c) solid to gas
    (d) gas to liquid

8. When a vapor condenses to a liquid,

    (a) its internal energy increases.
    (b) its temperature rises.
    (c) its temperature falls.
    (d) it gives off internal energy.

9. When a substance is at its triple point, it

    (a) is in its solid phase.
    (b) is in its liquid phase.
    (c) is in its vapor phase.
    (d) may be in any or all of these phases.

10. The phase diagram for water is shown in the figure. If the temperature of a certain amount of ice is increased by following the path represented by the dashed line from A to B in the phase diagram, which of the graphs of temperature as a function of heat added is correct?

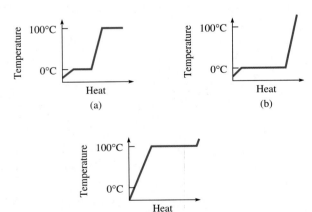

11. Two thin rods are made from the same material and are of lengths L_1 and L_2. The two ends of the rods have the same temperature difference. What should the relation be between their diameters and lengths so that they conduct equal amounts of heat energy in a given time?

    (a) $\dfrac{L_1}{L_2} = \dfrac{d_1}{d_2}$
    (b) $\dfrac{L_1}{L_2} = \dfrac{d_2}{d_1}$
    (c) $\dfrac{L_1}{L_2} = \dfrac{d_1^2}{d_2^2}$
    (d) $\dfrac{L_1}{L_2} = \dfrac{d_2^2}{d_1^2}$

12. If you place your hand underneath, but not touching, a kettle of hot water, you *mainly* feel the presence of heat from

    (a) conduction.
    (b) convection.
    (c) radiation.

Problems

- ☺   Combination conceptual/quantitative problem
- ☤   Biological or medical application
- ✦   Challenging problem
- Blue #   Detailed solution in the Student Solutions Manual
- ① ②   Problems paired by concept
- 🌐   Text website interactive or tutorial

14.1 Internal Energy

☺ 1. A mass of 1.4 kg of water at 22°C is poured from a height of 2.5 m into a vessel containing 5.0 kg of water at 22°C. (a) How much does the internal energy of the 6.4 kg of water increase? (b) Is it likely that the water temperature increases? Explain.

2. The water passing over Victoria Falls, located along the Zambezi River on the border of Zimbabwe and Zambia, drops about 105 m. How much internal energy is produced per kilogram as a result of the fall?

3. How much internal energy is generated when a 20.0-g lead bullet, traveling at 7.00×10^2 m/s, comes to a stop as it strikes a metal plate?

4. Nolan threw a baseball, of mass 147.5 g, at a speed of 162 km/h to a catcher. How much internal energy was generated when the ball struck the catcher's mitt?

☺ 5. A child of mass 15 kg climbs to the top of a slide that is 1.7 m above a horizontal run that extends for 0.50 m at the base of the slide. After sliding down, the child comes to rest just before reaching the very end of the horizontal portion of the slide. (a) How much internal energy was generated during this process? (b) Where did the generated energy go? (To the slide, to the child, to the air, or to all three?)

6. A 64-kg sky diver jumped out of an airplane at an altitude of 0.90 km. She opened her parachute after a while and eventually landed on the ground with a speed of 5.8 m/s. How much energy was dissipated by air resistance during the jump?

✦ 7. During basketball practice Shane made a jump shot, releasing a 0.60-kg basketball from his hands at a height of 2.0 m above the floor with a speed of 7.6 m/s. The ball swooshes through the net at a height of 3.0 m above the floor and with a speed of 4.5 m/s.

How much energy was dissipated by air drag from the time the ball left Shane's hands until it went through the net?

14.2 Heat; 14.3 Heat Capacity and Specific Heat

8. An experiment is conducted with a basic Joule apparatus, where a mass is allowed to descend by 1.25 m and rotate paddles within an insulated container of water. There are several different sizes of descending masses to choose among. If the investigator wishes to deliver 1.00 kJ to the water within the insulated container after 30.0 descents, what descending mass value should be used?

9. Convert 1.00 kJ to kilowatt-hours (kWh).

10. What is the heat capacity of 20.0 kg of silver?

11. What is the heat capacity of a gold ring that has a mass of 5.00 g?

12. If 125.6 kJ of heat are supplied to 5.00×10^2 g of water at 22°C, what is the final temperature of the water?

13. It is a damp, chilly day in a New England seacoast town suffering from a power failure. To warm up the cold, clammy sheets, Jen decides to fill hot water bottles to tuck between the sheets at the foot of the beds. If she wishes to heat 2.0 L of water on the wood stove from 20.0°C to 80.0°C, how much heat must flow into the water?

14. An 83-kg man eats a banana of energy content 1.00×10^2 kcal. If all of the energy from the banana is converted into kinetic energy of the man, how fast is he moving, assuming he starts from rest?

15. A high jumper of mass 60.0 kg consumes a meal of 3.00×10^3 kcal prior to a jump. If 3.3% of the energy from the food could be converted to gravitational potential energy in a single jump, how high could the athlete jump?

16. What is the heat capacity of a 30.0-kg block of ice?

17. What is the heat capacity of 1.00 m^3 of (a) aluminum? (b) iron? See Table 9.1 for density values.

18. What is the heat capacity of a system consisting of (a) a 0.450-kg brass cup filled with 0.050 kg of water? (b) 7.5 kg of water in a 0.75-kg aluminum bucket?

19. A 0.400-kg aluminum teakettle contains 2.00 kg of water at 15.0°C. How much heat is required to raise the temperature of the water (and kettle) to 100.0°C?

20. How much heat is required to raise the body temperature of a 50.0-kg woman from 37.0°C to 38.4°C?

21. It takes 880 J to raise the temperature of 350 g of lead from 0 to 20.0°C. What is the specific heat of lead?

22. A mass of 1.00 kg of water at temperature T is poured from a height of 0.100 km into a vessel containing water of the same temperature T, and a temperature change of 0.100°C is measured. What mass of water was in the vessel? Ignore heat flow into the vessel, the thermometer, etc.

23. A thermometer containing 0.10 g of mercury is cooled from 15.0°C to 8.5°C. How much energy left the mercury in this process?

24. A heating coil inside an electric kettle delivers 2.1 kW of electric power to the water in the kettle. How long will it take to raise the temperature of 0.50 kg of water from 20.0°C to 100.0°C? (tutorial: heating)

14.4 Specific Heat of Ideal Gases

25. A cylinder contains 250 L of hydrogen gas (H_2) at 0.0°C and a pressure of 10.0 atm. How much energy is required to raise the temperature of this gas to 25.0°C?

26. A container of nitrogen gas (N_2) at 23°C contains 425 L at a pressure of 3.5 atm. If 26.6 kJ of heat are added to the container, what will be the new temperature of the gas?

27. Imagine that 501 people are present in a movie theater of volume 8.00×10^3 m^3 that is sealed shut so no air can escape. Each person gives off heat at an average rate of 110 W. By how much will the temperature of the air have increased during a 2.0-h movie? The initial pressure is 1.01×10^5 Pa and the initial temperature is 20.0°C. Assume that all the heat output of the people goes into heating the air (a diatomic gas).

28. A chamber with a fixed volume of 1.0 m^3 contains a monatomic gas at 3.00×10^2 K. The chamber is heated to a temperature of 4.00×10^2 K. This operation requires 10.0 J of heat. (Assume all the energy is transferred to the gas.) How many gas molecules are in the chamber?

14.5 Phase Transitions

29. As heat flows into a substance, its temperature changes according to the graph in the diagram. For what sections of the graph is the substance undergoing a phase change? For the sections you identified, what kind of phase change is occurring? (tutorial: temperature graph)

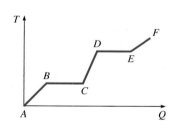

30. Given these data, compute the heat of vaporization of water. The specific heat capacity of water is 4.186 J/(g·K).

Mass of calorimeter = 3.00×10^2 g	Specific heat of calorimeter = 0.380 J/(g·K)
Mass of water = 2.00×10^2 g	Initial temperature of water and calorimeter = 15.0°C
Mass of condensed steam = 18.5 g	Initial temperature of steam = 100.0°C
	Final temperature of calorimeter = 62.0°C

31. Given these data, compute the heat of fusion of water. The specific heat capacity of water is 4.186 J/(g·K).

Mass of calorimeter = 3.00×10^2 g	Specific heat of calorimeter = 0.380 J/(g·K)
Mass of water = 2.00×10^2 g	Initial temperature of water and calorimeter = 20.0°C
Mass of ice = 30.0 g	Initial temperature of ice = 0°C
	Final temperature of calorimeter = 8.5°C

32. In a physics lab, a student accidentally drops a 25.0-g brass washer into an open dewar of liquid nitrogen at 77.2 K. How much liquid nitrogen boils away as the washer cools from 293 K to 77.2 K? The latent heat of vaporization for nitrogen is 199.1 kJ/kg.

33. What mass of water at 25.0°C added to a Styrofoam cup containing two 50.0-g ice cubes from a freezer at −15.0°C will result in a final temperature of 5.0°C for the drink?

34. How much heat is required to change 1.0 kg of ice, originally at −20.0°C, into steam at 110.0°C? Assume 1.0 atm of pressure.

35. Ice at 0.0°C is mixed with 5.00×10^2 mL of water at 25.0°C. How much ice must melt to lower the water temperature to 0.0°C?

36. Tina is going to make iced tea by first brewing hot tea, then adding ice until the tea cools. How much ice, at a temperature of −10.0°C, should be added to a 2.00×10^{-4} m³ glass of tea at 95.0°C to cool the tea to 10.0°C? Ignore the temperature change of the glass. (✦ tutorial: iced tea)

37. Repeat Problem 36 without neglecting the temperature change of the glass. The glass has a mass of 350 g and the specific heat of the glass is 0.837 kJ/(kg·K). By what percentage does the answer change from the answer for Problem 36?

38. The graph shows the change in temperature as heat is supplied to a certain mass of ice initially at −80.0°C. What is the mass of the ice?

39. How many grams of aluminum at 80.0°C would have to be dropped into a hole in a block of ice at 0.0°C to melt 10.0 g of ice?

40. Is it possible to heat the aluminum of Problem 39 to a high enough temperature so that it melts an equal mass of ice? If so, what temperature must the aluminum have?

41. If a leaf is to maintain a temperature of 40°C (reasonable for a leaf), it must lose 250 W/m² by transpiration (evaporative heat loss). Note that the leaf also loses heat by radiation, but we will neglect this. How much water is lost after 1 h through transpiration only? The area of the leaf is 0.005 m².

42. A birch tree loses 618 mg of water per minute through transpiration (evaporation of water through stomatal pores). What is the rate of heat lost through transpiration?

43. You are given 250 g of coffee (same specific heat as water) at 80.0°C (too hot to drink). In order to cool this to 60.0°C, how much ice (at 0.0°C) must be added? Ignore heat content of the cup and heat exchanges with the surroundings.

44. A phase diagram is shown. Starting at point A, follow the dashed line to point E and consider what happens to the substance represented by this diagram as its pressure and temperature are changed. (a) Explain what happens for each line segment, AB, BC, CD, and DE. (b) What is the significance of point a and of point b?

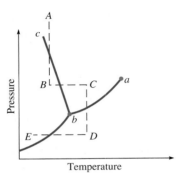

45. Compute the heat of fusion of a substance from these data: 31.15 kJ will change 0.500 kg of the solid at 21°C to liquid at 327°C, the melting point. The specific heat of the solid is 0.129 kJ/(kg·K).

46. A dog loses a lot of heat through panting. The air rushing over the upper respiratory tract causes evaporation and thus heat loss. A dog typically pants at a rate of 670 pants per minute. As a rough calculation, assume that one pant causes 0.010 g of water to be evaporated from the respiratory tract. What is the rate of heat loss for the dog through panting?

14.6 Thermal Conduction

47. (a) What thickness of cork would have the same R-factor as a 1.0-cm thick stagnant air pocket? (b) What thickness of tin would be required for the same R-factor?

48. A metal rod with a diameter of 2.30 cm and length of 1.10 m has one end immersed in ice at 32.0°F and the other end in boiling water at 212°F. If the ice melts at a rate of 1.32 g every 175 s, what is the thermal conductivity of this metal? Identify the metal. Assume there is no heat lost to the surrounding air.

49. Given a slab of material with area 1.0 m² and thickness 2.0×10^{-2} m, (a) what is the thermal resistance if the material is asbestos? (b) What is the thermal resistance if the material is iron? (c) What is the thermal resistance if the material is copper?

50. A copper rod of length 0.50 m and cross-sectional area 6.0×10^{-2} cm² is connected to an iron rod with the same

cross section and length 0.25 m. One end of the copper is immersed in boiling water and the other end is at the junction with the iron. If the far end of the iron rod is in an ice bath at

0°C, find the rate of heat transfer passing from the boiling water to the ice bath. Assume there is no heat loss to the surrounding air. (tutorial: composite rod)

51. For a temperature difference $\Delta T = 20.0°C$, one slab of material conducts 10.0 W/m²; another of the same shape conducts 20.0 W/m². What is the rate of heat flow per m² of surface area when the slabs are placed side by side with $\Delta T_{tot} = 20.0°C$?

10.0 W/m²
for
$\Delta T = 20.0°C$ 20.0 W/m²
for
$\Delta T = 20.0°C$ $\Delta T_{tot} = 20.0°C$

52. A wall consists of a layer of wood and a layer of cork insulation of the same thickness. The temperature inside is 20.0°C and the temperature outside is 0.0°C. (a) What is the temperature at the interface between the wood and cork if the cork is on the inside and the wood on the outside? (b) What is the temperature at the interface if the wood is inside and the cork is outside? (c) Does it matter whether the cork is placed on the inside or the outside of the wooden wall? Explain.

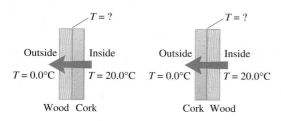

$T = ?$ $T = ?$

Outside Inside   Outside Inside
$T = 0.0°C$ $T = 20.0°C$ $T = 0.0°C$ $T = 20.0°C$

Wood Cork   Cork Wood

53. The thermal conductivity of the fur (including the skin) of a male Husky dog is 0.026 W/(m·K). The dog's heat output is measured to be 51 W, its internal temperature is 38°C, its surface area is 1.31 m², and the thickness of the fur is 5.0 cm. How cold can the outside temperature be before the dog must increase its heat output?

54. The thermal resistance of a seal's fur and blubber combined is 0.33 K/W. If the seal's internal temperature is 37°C and the temperature of the sea is about 0°C, what must be the heat output of the seal in order for it to maintain its internal temperature?

55. A hiker is wearing wool clothing of 0.50-cm thickness to keep warm. Her skin temperature is 35°C and the outside temperature is 4.0°C. Her body surface area is

1.2 m². (a) If the thermal conductivity of wool is 0.040 W/(m·K), what is the rate of heat conduction through her clothing? (b) If the hiker is caught in a rainstorm, the thermal conductivity of the soaked wool increases to 0.60 W/(m·K) (that of water). Now what is the rate of heat conduction?

56. A window whose glass has $\kappa = 1.0$ W/(m·K) is covered completely with a sheet of foam of the same thickness as the glass, but with $\kappa = 0.025$ W/(m·K). How is the rate at which heat is conducted through the window changed by the addition of the foam?

57. A copper bar of thermal conductivity 401 W/(m·K) has one end at 104°C and the other end at 24°C. The length of the bar is 0.10 m and the cross-sectional area is 1.0×10^{-6} m². (a) What is the rate of heat conduction, $\mathcal{P}$, along the bar? (b) What is the temperature gradient in the bar? (c) If two such bars were placed in series (end to end) between the same temperature baths, what would $\mathcal{P}$ be? (d) If two such bars were placed in parallel (side by side) with the ends in the same temperature baths, what would $\mathcal{P}$ be? (e) In the series case, what is the temperature at the junction where the bars meet?

58. One cross-country skier is wearing a down jacket that is 2.0 cm thick. The thermal conductivity of goose down is 0.025 W/(m·K). Her companion on the ski outing is wearing a wool jacket that is 0.50 cm thick. The thermal conductivity of wool is 0.040 W/(m·K). (a) If both jackets have the same surface area and the skiers both have the same body temperature, which one will stay warmer longer? (b) How much longer can the person with the warmer jacket stay outside for the same amount of heat loss?

14.8 Thermal Radiation

59. If a blackbody is radiating at $T = 1650$ K, at what wavelength is the maximum intensity?

60. Wien studied the spectral distribution of many radiating bodies to finally discover a simple relation between wavelength and intensity. Use the limited data shown in Fig. 14.17 to find the constant predicted by Wien for the product of wavelength of maximum emission and temperature.

61. An incandescent lightbulb has a tungsten filament that is heated to a temperature of 3.00×10^3 K when an electric current passes through it. If the surface area of the filament is approximately 1.00×10^{-4} m² and it has an emissivity of 0.32, what is the power radiated by the bulb?

62. A tungsten filament in a lamp is heated to a temperature of 2.6×10^3 K by an electric current. The tungsten has an emissivity of 0.32. What is the surface area of the filament if the lamp delivers 40.0 W of power?

63. A person of surface area 1.80 m² is lying out in the sunlight to get a tan. If the intensity of the incident sunlight is 7.00×10^2 W/m², at what rate must heat be lost by the person in order to maintain a constant body temperature? (Assume the effective area of skin exposed to the

Sun is 42% of the total surface area, 57% of the incident radiation is absorbed, and that internal metabolic processes contribute another 90 W for an inactive person.)

64. A student wants to lose some weight. He knows that rigorous aerobic activity uses about 700 kcal/h (2900 kJ/h) and that it takes about 2000 kcal per day (8400 kJ) just to support necessary biological functions, including keeping the body warm. He decides to burn calories faster simply by sitting naked in a 16°C room and letting his body radiate calories away. His body has a surface area of about 1.7 m² and his skin temperature is 35°C. Assuming an emissivity of 1.0, at what rate (in kcal/h) will this student "burn" calories?

65. An incandescent light bulb radiates at a rate of 60.0 W when the temperature of its filament is 2820 K. During a brownout (temporary drop in line voltage), the power radiated drops to 58.0 W. What is the temperature of the filament? Neglect changes in the filament's length and cross-sectional area due to the temperature change. (⟨W⟩ tutorial: light bulb)

66. If the maximum intensity of radiation for a blackbody is found at 2.65 μm, what is the temperature of the radiating body?

67. A black wood stove has a surface area of 1.20 m² and a surface temperature of 175°C. What is the net rate at which heat is radiated into the room? The room temperature is 20°C.

68. A lizard of mass 3.0 g is warming itself in the bright sunlight. It casts a shadow of 1.6 cm² on a piece of paper held perpendicularly to the Sun's rays. The intensity of sunlight at the Earth is 1.4×10^3 W/m², but only half of this energy penetrates the atmosphere and is absorbed by the lizard. (a) If the lizard has a specific heat of 4.2 J/(g·°C), what is the rate of increase of the lizard's temperature? (b) Assuming that there is no heat loss by the lizard (to simplify), how long must the lizard lie in the Sun in order to raise its temperature by 5.0°C?

69. At a tea party, a coffeepot and a teapot are placed on the serving table. The coffeepot is a shiny silver-plated pot with emissivity of 0.12; the teapot is ceramic and has an emissivity of 0.65. Both pots hold 1.00 L of liquid at 98°C when the party begins. If the room temperature is at 25°C, what is the rate of radiative heat loss from the two pots? [Hint: To find the surface area, approximate the pots with cubes of similar volume.]

70. If the total power per unit area from the Sun incident on a horizontal leaf is 9.00×10^2 W/m², and we assume that 70.0% of this energy goes into heating the leaf, what would be the rate of temperature rise of the leaf? The specific heat of the leaf is 3.70 kJ/(kg·°C), the leaf's area is 5.00×10^{-3} m², and its mass is 0.500 g.

71. Consider the leaf of Problem 70. Assume that the top surface of the leaf absorbs 70.0% of 9.00×10^2 W/m² of radiant energy, while the bottom surface absorbs all of the radiant energy incident on it due to its surroundings at 25.0°C. (a) If the only method of heat loss for the leaf

were thermal radiation, what would be the temperature of the leaf? (Assume that the leaf radiates like a blackbody.) (b) If the leaf is to remain at a temperature of 25.0°C, how much power per unit area must be lost by other methods such as transpiration (evaporative heat loss)?

Comprehensive Problems

72. A hotel room is in thermal equilibrium with the rooms on either side and with the hallway on a third side. The room loses heat primarily through a 1.30-cm-thick glass window that has a height of 76.2 cm and a width of 156 cm. If the temperature inside the room is 75°F and the temperature outside is 32°F, what is the approximate rate (in kJ/s) at which heat must be added to the room to maintain a constant temperature of 75°F? Ignore the stagnant air layers on either side of the glass.

73. While camping, some students decide to make hot chocolate by heating water with a solar heater that focuses sunlight onto a small area. Sunlight falls on their solar heater, of area 1.5 m², with an intensity of 750 W/m². How long will it take 1.0 L of water at 15.0°C to rise to a boiling temperature of 100.0°C?

74. Five ice cubes, each with a mass of 22.0 g and at a temperature of −50.0°C, are placed in an insulating container. How much heat will it take to change the ice cubes completely into steam?

75. A 10.0-g iron bullet with a speed of 4.00×10^2 m/s and a temperature of 20.0°C is stopped in a 0.500-kg block of wood, also at 20.0°C. (a) At first all of the bullet's kinetic energy goes into the internal energy of the bullet. Calculate the temperature increase of the bullet. (b) After a short time the bullet and the block come to the same temperature T. Calculate T, assuming no heat is lost to the environment.

76. If the temperature surrounding the sunbather in Problem 63 is greater than the normal body temperature of 37°C and the air is still, so that radiation, conduction, and convection play no part in cooling the body, how much water (in liters per hour) from perspiration must be given off to maintain the body temperature? The heat of vaporization of water is 2430 J/g at normal skin temperature.

77. If 4.0 g of steam at 100.0°C condenses to water on a burn victim's skin and cools to 45.0°C, (a) how much heat is given up by the steam? (b) If the skin was originally at 37.0°C, how much tissue mass was involved in cooling the steam to water? See Table 14.1 for the specific heat of human tissue.

78. If 4.0 g of boiling water at 100.0°C was splashed onto a burn victim's skin, and if it cooled to 45.0°C on the 37.0°C skin, (a) how much heat is given up by the water? (b) How much tissue mass, originally at 37.0°C, was involved in cooling the water? See Table 14.1. Compare the result with that found in Problem 77.

79. The amount of heat generated during the contraction of muscle in an amphibian's leg is given by

$$Q = 0.544 \text{ mJ} + (1.46 \text{ mJ/cm})\Delta x$$

where Δx is the length shortened. If a muscle of length 3.0 cm and mass 0.10 g is shortened by 1.5 cm during a contraction, what is the temperature rise? Assume that the specific heat of muscle is 4.186 J/(g·°C).

80. Many species cool themselves by sweating, because as the sweat evaporates, heat is given up to the surroundings. A human exercising strenuously has an evaporative heat loss rate of about 650 W. If a person exercises strenuously for 30.0 min, how much water must he drink to replenish his fluid loss? The heat of vaporization of water is 2430 J/g at normal skin temperature.

81. A wall consists of a layer of wood outside and a layer of insulation inside. The temperatures inside and outside the wall are +22°C and −18°C; the temperature at the wood/insulation boundary is −8.0°C. By what factor would the heat loss through the wall increase if the insulation were not present?

82. Two 62-g ice cubes are dropped into 186 g of water in a glass. If the water is initially at a temperature of 24°C and the ice is at −15°C, what is the final temperature of the drink?

83. A 0.500-kg slab of granite is heated so that its temperature increases by 7.40°C. The amount of heat supplied to the granite is 2.93 kJ. Based on this information, what is the specific heat of granite?

84. A spring of force constant $k = 8.4 \times 10^3$ N/m is compressed by 0.10 m. It is placed into a vessel containing 1.0 kg of water and then released. Assuming all the energy from the spring goes into heating the water, find the change in temperature of the water.

85. One end of a cylindrical iron rod of length 1.00 m and of radius 1.30 cm is placed in the blacksmith's fire and reaches a temperature of 327°C. If the other end of the rod is being held in your hand (37°C), what is the rate of heat flow along the rod? The thermal conductivity of iron varies with temperature, but an average value between the two temperatures is 67.5 W/(m·K). (tutorial: conduction)

86. A blacksmith heats a 0.38-kg piece of iron to 498°C in his forge. After shaping it into a decorative design, he places it into a bucket of water to cool. If the available water is at 20.0°C, what minimum amount of water must be in the bucket to cool the iron to 23.0°C? The water in the bucket should remain in the liquid phase.

87. The student from Problem 64 realizes that standing naked in a cold room will not give him the desired weight loss results since it is much less efficient than simply exercising. So he decides to burn calories through conduction. He fills the bathtub with 16°C water and gets in. The water right next to his skin warms up to the same temperature as his skin, 35°C, but the water only 3.0 mm away remains at 16°C. At what rate (in kcal/h) would he "burn" calories?

The thermal conductivity of water at this temperature is 0.58 W/(m·K). [*Warning:* Do not try this. Sitting in water this cold can lead to hypothermia and even death.]

88. A stainless steel saucepan, with a base that is made of 0.350-cm-thick steel [$\kappa = 46.0$ W/(m·K)] fused to a 0.150-cm thickness of copper [$\kappa = 401$ W/(m·K)], sits on a ceramic heating element at 104.00°C. The diameter of the pan is 18.0 cm and it contains boiling water at 100.00°C. (a) If the copper-clad bottom is touching the heat source, what is the temperature at the copper-steel interface? (b) At what rate will the water evaporate from the pan?

89. A 75-kg block of ice at 0.0°C breaks off from a glacier, slides along the frictionless ice to the ground from a height of 2.43 m, and then slides along a horizontal surface consisting of gravel and dirt. Find how much of the mass of the ice is melted by the friction with the rough surface, assuming 75% of the internal energy generated is used to heat the ice.

90. Small animals eat much more food per kg of body mass than do larger animals. The basal metabolic rate (BMR) is the minimal energy intake necessary to sustain life in a state of complete inactivity. The table lists the BMR, mass, and surface area for five animals. (a) Calculate the BMR/kg of body mass for each animal. Is it true that smaller animals must consume much more food per kg of body mass? (b) Calculate the BMR/m² of surface area. (c) Can you explain why the BMR/m² is approximately the same for animals of different sizes? Consider what happens to the food energy metabolized by an animal in a resting state.

Animal	BMR (kcal/day)	Mass (kg)	Surface Area (m²)
Mouse	3.80	0.018	0.0032
Dog	770	15	0.74
Human	2050	64	2.0
Pig	2400	130	2.3
Horse	4900	440	5.1

91. Imagine a person standing naked in a room at 23.0°C. The walls are well insulated, so they also are at 23.0°C. The person's surface area is 2.20 m² and his basal metabolic rate is 2167 kcal/day. His emissivity is 0.97. (a) If the person's skin temperature were 37.0°C (the same as the internal body temperature), at what net rate would heat be lost through radiation? (Ignore losses by conduction and convection.) (b) Clearly the heat loss in (a) is not sustainable—but skin temperature is less than internal body temperature. Calculate the skin temperature such that the net heat loss due to radiation is equal to the basal metabolic rate. (c) Does wearing clothing slow the loss of heat by radiation, or does it only decrease losses by conduction and convection? Explain.

92. Bare, dark-colored basalt has a thermal conductivity of 3.1 W/(m·K), whereas light-colored sandstone's thermal

conductivity is only 2.4 W/(m·K). Even though the same amount of radiation is incident on both and their surface temperatures are the same, the temperature gradient within the two materials will differ. For the same patch of area, what is the ratio of the depth in basalt as compared with the depth in sandstone that gives the same temperature difference?

93. The power expended by a cheetah is 160 kW while running at 110 km/h, but its body temperature cannot exceed 41.0°C. If 70.0% of the energy expended is dissipated within its body, how far can it run before it overheats? Assume that the initial temperature of the cheetah is 38.0°C, its specific heat is 3.5 kJ/(kg·°C), and its mass is 50.0 kg.

94. A scientist working late at night in her low-temperature physics laboratory decides to have a cup of hot tea, but discovers the lab hot plate is broken. Not to be deterred, she puts about 8 oz of water, at 12°C, from the tap into a lab dewar (essentially a large thermos bottle) and begins shaking it up and down. With each shake the water is thrown up and falls back down a distance of 33.3 cm. If she can complete 30 shakes per minute, how long will it take to heat the water to 87°C? Would this really work? If not, why not?

95. A 2.0-kg block of copper at 100.0°C is placed into 1.0 kg of water in a 2.0-kg iron pot. The water and the iron pot are at 25.0°C just before the copper block is placed into the pot. What is the final temperature of the water, assuming negligible heat flow to the environment?

96. A piece of gold of mass 0.250 kg and at a temperature of 75.0°C is placed into a 1.500-kg copper pot containing 0.500 L of water. The pot and water are at 22.0°C before the gold is added. What is the final temperature of the water?

97. For a cheetah, 70.0% of the energy expended during exertion is internal work done on the cheetah's system and is dissipated within his body; for a dog only 5.00% of the energy expended is dissipated within the dog's body. Assume that both animals expend the same total amount of energy during exertion, both have the same heat capacity, and the cheetah is 2.00 times as heavy as the dog. (a) How much higher is the temperature change of the cheetah compared to the temperature change of the dog? (b) If they both start out at an initial temperature of 35.0°C, and the cheetah has a temperature of 40.0°C after the exertion, what is the final temperature of the dog? Which animal probably has more endurance? Explain.

98. A 20.0-g lead bullet leaves a rifle at a temperature of 87.0°C and hits a steel plate. If the bullet melts, what is the minimum speed it must have?

99. The inner vessel of a calorimeter contains 2.50×10^2 g of tetrachloromethane, CCl_4, at 40.00°C. The vessel is surrounded by 2.00 kg of water at 18.00°C. After a time, the CCl_4 and the water reach the equilibrium temperature of 18.54°C. What is the specific heat of CCl_4?

100. On a very hot summer day, Daphne is off to the park for a picnic. She puts 0.10 kg of ice at 0°C in a thermos and then adds a grape-flavored drink, which she has mixed from a powder using room temperature water (25°C). How much grape-flavored drink will just melt all the ice?

101. It requires 17.10 kJ to melt 1.00×10^2 g of urethane $[CO_2(NH_2)C_2H_5]$ at 48.7°C. What is the latent heat of fusion of urethane in kJ/mol?

102. A 20.0-g lead bullet leaves a rifle at a temperature of 47.0°C and travels at a velocity of 5.00×10^2 m/s until it hits a large block of ice at 0°C and comes to rest within it. How much ice will melt?

Answers to Practice Problems

14.1 4.9 J
14.2 Higher. The molecules have the same amount of *random* translational kinetic energy plus the additional kinetic energy associated with the ball's translation and rotation.
14.3 350 g
14.4 at least $0.89
14.5 48°C
14.6 92 kJ
14.7 150 kJ
14.8 40 kJ
14.9 53.5 g
14.10 230 W
14.11 110 W
14.12 To maintain constant temperature, the net heat must be zero. The rate at which energy is emitted is 140 W.
14.13 9.4 µm (at 35°C) to 9.6 µm (at 30°C)
14.14 28 W
14.15 −16°C

Answers to Checkpoints

14.2 No, the temperature increase is not caused by heat flow. When you stretch the rubber band, you do work on it. This increases its internal energy and its temperature. (If you now put the rubber band down, heat does flow *out* of the rubber band, decreasing its internal energy and its temperature until it is in thermal equilibrium with its surroundings.)
14.5 The steam releases a large quantity of heat as it condenses into water on the skin. Much more energy is transferred to the skin than would be the case for the same amount of water at 100°C.
14.6 The rate of heat flow through the two materials is the same, so the material with the larger thermal conductivity has the smaller temperature gradient. Figure 14.10b shows that the temperature gradient is smaller in the material on the left, so it has the larger thermal conductivity.

Thermodynamics

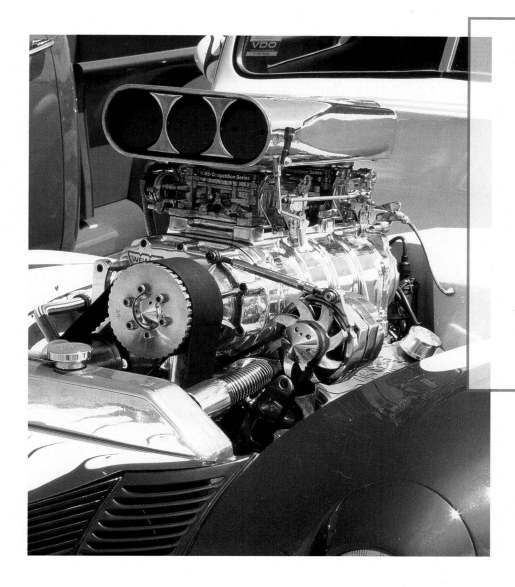

The gasoline engines in cars are terribly inefficient. Of the chemical energy that is released in the burning of gasoline, typically only 20% to 25% is converted into useful mechanical work done on the car to move it forward. Yet scientists and engineers have been working for decades to make a more efficient gasoline engine. Is there some fundamental limit to the efficiency of a gasoline engine? Is it possible to make an engine that converts all—or nearly all—of the chemical energy in the fuel into useful work? (See p. 544 for the answer.)

15.1   THE FIRST LAW OF THERMODYNAMICS

Both work and heat can change the internal energy of a system. Work can be done on a rubber ball by squeezing it, stretching it, or slamming it into a wall. Heat will flow into the ball if it is left out in the Sun or put into a hot oven. These two methods of changing the internal energy of a system lead to the **first law of thermodynamics**:

First Law of Thermodynamics

The change in internal energy of a system is equal to the heat flow into the system plus the work done *on* the system.

The first law is a specialized statement of energy conservation applied to a thermodynamic system, such as a gas inside a cylinder that has a movable piston. The gas can exchange energy with its surroundings in two ways. Heat can flow between the gas and its surroundings when they are at different temperatures and work can be done on the gas when the piston is pushed in.

In equation form, we can write

First Law of Thermodynamics

$$\Delta U = Q + W \qquad (15\text{-}1)$$

In Eq. (15-1), ΔU is the change in internal energy of the system. The internal energy can increase or decrease, so ΔU can be positive or negative. The signs of Q and W have the same meaning we have used in previous chapters. If heat flows into the system, Q is positive, while if heat flows out of the system, Q is negative. W represents the work done *on* the system, which can be positive or negative, depending on the directions of the applied force and the displacement. Using the example of the gas in a cylinder, if the piston is pushed in, then the force on the gas due to the piston and the displacement of the gas are in the same direction (Fig. 15.1a) and W is positive. If the piston moves out, then the force and the displacement are in opposite directions, because the piston still pushes inward on the gas, and W is negative (Fig. 15.1b). Table 15.1 summarizes the meanings of the signs of ΔU, Q, and W.

The choice of a *system* is made in any way convenient for a given problem.

CONNECTION:

The first law is not a new principle—just a specialized form of energy conservation.

The symbol U, previously used for potential energy, is used exclusively for *internal energy* in this chapter. Internal energy was defined in Section 14.1.

CONNECTION:

Our sign conventions for Q and W are consistent with their definitions in previous chapters (Chapter 6 for work and Chapter 14 for heat).

Figure 15.1 (a) When a gas is compressed, the work done *on* the gas is positive. (b) When a gas expands, the work done *on* the gas is *negative*.

(a)   (b)

Table 15.1	Sign Conventions for the First Law of Thermodynamics		
Quantity	**Definition**	**Meaning of + Sign**	**Meaning of − Sign**
Q	Heat flow into the system	Heat flows *into* the system	Heat flows *out of* the system
W	Work done *on* the system	Surroundings do *positive* work on the system	Surroundings do *negative* work on the system (system does positive work on the surroundings)
ΔU	Internal energy change	Internal energy *increases*	Internal energy *decreases*

Example 15.1

Stirring a Can of Paint

A contractor uses a paddle stirrer to mix a can of paint (Fig. 15.2). The paddle turns at 28.0 rad/s and exerts a torque of 16.0 N·m on the paint, doing work at a rate

$$\text{power} = \tau\omega = 16.0 \text{ N·m} \times 28.0 \text{ rad/s} = 448 \text{ W}$$

An internal energy increase of 12.5 kJ causes the temperature of the paint to increase by 1.00 K. (a) If there were no heat flow between the paint and the surroundings, what would be the temperature change of the paint as it is stirred for 5.00 min? (b) If the actual temperature change was 6.3 K, how much heat flowed from the paint to the surroundings?

Strategy   From conservation of energy, the change in the internal energy of the paint is equal to the heat flow into the paint plus the work done on the paint.

Solution   (a) In 5.00 min, the work done by the paddle on the paint is

$$W = 0.448 \text{ kJ/s} \times 5.00 \text{ min} \times 60 \text{ s/min} = 134.4 \text{ kJ}$$

Figure 15.2
An electric paint stirrer does work on the paint as it stirs.

Since we assume no heat flow ($Q = 0$), the internal energy of the paint changes by $\Delta U = Q + W = +134.4$ kJ. The temperature increases 1.00 K for every 12.5 kJ of increased internal energy, so

$$\Delta T = 134.4 \text{ kJ} \times \frac{1.00 \text{ K}}{12.5 \text{ kJ}} = 10.8 \text{ K}$$

(b) To apply the first law, we first find the internal energy change:

$$\Delta U = \frac{12.5 \text{ kJ}}{1.00 \text{ K}} \times 6.3 \text{ K} = 78.75 \text{ kJ}$$

Now we apply the first law:

$$\Delta U = Q + W$$

$$Q = \Delta U - W = 78.75 \text{ kJ} - 134.4 \text{ kJ} = -56 \text{ kJ}$$

Q is negative because 56 kJ of heat flow *out of* the paint.

Discussion   How did we know the work done by the paddle on the paint was *positive*? Think of the force the paddle exerts on the paint as it pushes paint out of its way; the force and the displacement are in the same direction.

The quantity 12.5 kJ/K is the heat capacity of the paint—it tells us how many kJ the internal energy of the paint must increase for its temperature to increase 1 K, *regardless of whether the internal energy increase is caused by heat, work, or a combination of the two.*

Conceptual Practice Problem 15.1
Changing Internal Energy of a Gas

While 14 kJ of heat flows into the gas in a cylinder with a moveable piston, the internal energy of the gas increases by 42 kJ. Was the piston pulled out or pushed in? Explain. [*Hint:* Determine whether the piston does positive or negative work on the gas.]

15.2 THERMODYNAMIC PROCESSES

A thermodynamic process is the method by which a system is changed from one *state* to another. The state of a system is described by a set of **state variables** such as pressure, temperature, volume, number of moles, and internal energy. State variables describe the state of a system at some instant of time but not how the system got to that state. Heat and work are *not* state variables—they describe *how* a system gets from one state to another.

The *PV* Diagram

If a system is changed so that it is always very near equilibrium, the changes in state can be represented by a curve on a plot of pressure versus volume (called a *PV* **diagram**). Each point on the curve represents an equilibrium state of the system. The *PV* diagram is a useful tool for analyzing thermodynamic processes. One of the chief uses of a *PV* diagram is to find the work done on the system.

Work and Area Under a *PV* Curve   Figure 15.3a shows the expansion of a gas, starting with volume V_i and pressure P_i; Fig. 15.3b is the *PV* diagram for the process. In Fig. 15.3, the force exerted by the piston on the gas is downward, while the displacement of the gas is upward, so the piston does negative work on the gas. This work represents a transfer of energy from the gas to its surroundings. (Equivalently, we can say the gas does positive work on the piston.) The piston pushes against the gas with a force of magnitude $F = PA$, where P is the pressure of the gas and A is the cross-sectional area of the piston. This force is not constant since the pressure decreases as the gas expands. As was shown in Section 6.6, the work done by a variable force is the area under a graph of $F_x(x)$.

To see how work is related to the area under the curve, first note that the units of $P \times V$ are those of work:

$$[\text{pressure} \times \text{volume}] = [\text{Pa}] \times [\text{m}^3] = \frac{[\text{N}]}{[\text{m}^2]} \times [\text{m}^3] = [\text{N}] \times [\text{m}] = [\text{J}]$$

So far, so good. Imagine that the piston moves out a *small* distance d—small enough that the pressure change is insignificant. The work done on the gas is

$$W = Fd \cos 180° = -PAd$$

The volume change of the gas is

$$\Delta V = Ad$$

So the work done on the gas is

$$W = -P \, \Delta V \tag{15-2}$$

Figure 15.3 (a) Expansion of a gas from initial pressure P_i and volume V_i to final pressure P_f and volume V_f. During the expansion, *negative* work is done on the gas by the moving piston because the force exerted on the gas and the displacement are in opposite directions. (b) A *PV* diagram for the expansion shows the pressure and volume of the gas starting at the initial values, passing through intermediate values, and ending at the final values.

Piston of cross-sectional area A

Initial state   Final state

(a)

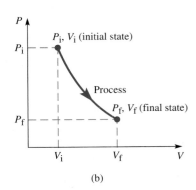

P_i, V_i (initial state)

Process

P_f, V_f (final state)

(b)

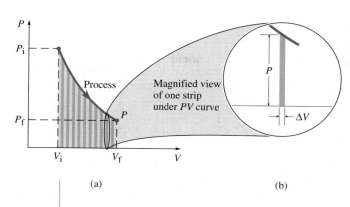

Figure 15.4 (a) The area under the *PV* curve is divided into many narrow strips of width ΔV and of varying heights *P*. The sum of the areas of the strips is the total area under the *PV* curve, which represents the magnitude of the work done on the gas. (b) An enlarged view of one strip under the curve. If the strip is very narrow, we can ignore the change in *P* and approximate its area as $P\Delta V$.

Magnitude of work done *on a system* = area under *PV* curve. $W > 0$ for compression and $W < 0$ for expansion.

To find the *total* work done on the gas, we add up the work done during each small volume change. During each small ΔV, the magnitude of the work done is the area of a thin strip of height *P* and width ΔV under the *PV* curve (Fig. 15.4). Therefore, the magnitude of the total work done on the gas is the area under the *PV* curve. During an increase in volume, ΔV is positive and the work done on the gas is negative. During a decrease in volume, ΔV is negative and the work done on the gas is positive.

The magnitude of the work done on a system depends on the *path* taken on the *PV* curve. Figure 15.5 shows two other possible paths between the same initial and final states as those of Fig. 15.4. In Fig. 15.5a, the pressure is kept constant at the initial value P_i while the volume is increased from V_i to V_f. Then the volume is kept constant while the pressure is reduced from P_i to P_f. The magnitude of the work done is represented by the shaded area under the *PV* curve; it is greater than the magnitude of the work done in Fig. 15.4a. Alternatively, in Fig. 15.5b the pressure is first reduced from P_i to P_f while the volume is held fixed; then the volume is allowed to increase from V_i to V_f while the pressure is kept at P_f. We see by the shaded area that the magnitude of the work done this way is less than the magnitude of the work done in Fig. 15.4a. The work done differs from one process to another, even though the initial and final states are the same in each case.

Work Done During a Closed Cycle Because the work done on a system depends on the path on the *PV* diagram, the net work done on a system during a **closed cycle**—a series of processes that leave the system in the same state it started in—can be nonzero. For example, during the cycle 1→2→3→4→1 in Fig. 15.5c, you can verify that the net work done on the gas is negative. Equivalently, the net work done *by* the gas is positive. A closed cycle during which the system does net work is the essential idea behind the heat engine (Section 15.5).

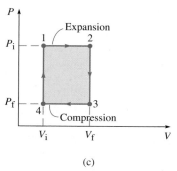

Figure 15.5 (a) and (b) Two different paths between the same initial and final states. (c) A closed cycle. The net work done on the gas during this cycle is the negative of the area inside the rectangle because the negative work done during expansion (1→2) is greater in magnitude than the positive work done during compression (3→4).

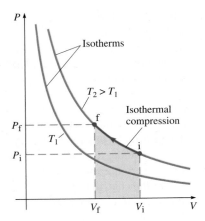

Figure 15.6 Isotherms for an ideal gas at two different temperatures. Each isotherm is a graph of $P = nRT/V$ for a constant temperature. The shaded area represents the work done by the gas during an isothermal compression at temperature T_2, which is positive. (The work done by the gas during an isothermal *expansion* would be *negative*.)

Definition of heat reservoir

Constant Pressure Processes

A process by which the state of a system is changed while the pressure is held constant is called an *isobaric* process. The word *isobaric* comes from the same Greek root as the word "barometer." In Fig. 15.5a, the first change of state from V_i to V_f along the line from 1 to 2 occurs at the constant pressure P_i. A constant pressure process appears as a horizontal line on the *PV* diagram. The work done on the gas is

$$W = -P_i (V_f - V_i) = -P_i \Delta V \quad \text{(constant pressure)} \tag{15-3}$$

Constant Volume Processes

A process by which the state of a system is changed while the *volume* remains constant is called an *isochoric* process. Such a process is illustrated in Fig. 15.5a when the system moves along the line from 2 to 3 as the pressure changes from P_i to P_f at the constant volume V_f. No work is done during a constant volume process; without a displacement, work cannot be done. The area under the *PV* curve—a vertical line—is zero:

$$W = 0 \quad \text{(constant volume)} \tag{15-4}$$

If no work is done, then from the first law of thermodynamics, the change in internal energy is equal to the heat flow into the system:

$$\Delta U = Q \quad \text{(constant volume)} \tag{15-5}$$

Constant Temperature Processes

A process in which the temperature of the system remains constant is called an **isothermal** process. On a *PV* diagram, a path representing a constant temperature process is called an **isotherm** (Fig. 15.6). All the points on an isotherm represent states of the system with the same temperature.

How can we keep the temperature of the system constant? One way is to put the system in thermal contact with a **heat reservoir**—something with a heat capacity so large that it can exchange heat in either direction without changing its temperature significantly. Then as long as the state of the system does not change too rapidly, the heat flow between the system and the reservoir keeps the system's temperature constant.

Adiabatic Processes

A process in which no heat is transferred into or out of the system is called an **adiabatic** process. An adiabatic process is *not* the same as a constant temperature (isothermal) process. In an isothermal process, heat flow into or out of a system is necessary to maintain a constant temperature. In an adiabatic process, *no* heat flow occurs, so if work is done, the temperature of the system may change. One way to perform an adiabatic process is to completely insulate the system so that no heat can flow in or out; another way is to perform the process so quickly that there is no time for heat to flow in or out.

For example, the compressions and rarefactions caused by a sound wave occur so fast that heat flow from one place to another is negligible. Hence, the compressions and rarefactions are adiabatic. Isaac Newton made a now-famous error when he assumed that these processes were isothermal and calculated a speed of sound that was about 20% lower than the measured value.

> **PHYSICS AT HOME**
>
> Hold an elastic band against your lip; it should feel cool. Now grasp the elastic and stretch it back and forth rapidly several times. Hold the stretched region to your lip. Does it feel warm? The elastic's temperature is higher because the work you did in stretching it increased its internal energy. The rapid stretching is approximately adiabatic—it occurs quickly so there is little time for heat to flow out of the elastic.

Table 15.2   Summary of Thermodynamic Processes

Process	Name	Condition	Consequences
Constant temperature	Isothermal	T = constant	(*For an ideal gas*, $\Delta U = 0$)
Constant pressure	Isobaric	P = constant	$W = -P \, \Delta V$
Constant volume	Isochoric	V = constant	$W = 0$; $\Delta U = Q$
No heat flow	Adiabatic	$Q = 0$	$\Delta U = W$

From the first law of thermodynamics

$$\Delta U = Q + W \qquad (15\text{-}1)$$

With $Q = 0$,

$$\Delta U = W \quad \text{(adiabatic)}$$

Table 15.2 summarizes all of the thermodynamic processes discussed. (See also the interactive: thermodynamics.)

✓ CHECKPOINT 15.2

(a) Can an adiabatic process cause a change in temperature? Explain. (b) Can heat flow during an isothermal process? (c) Can the internal energy of a system change during an isothermal process?

Figure 15.7 A PV diagram for a constant volume process for an ideal gas. Every point on an isotherm (red dashed lines) represents a state of the gas at the same temperature.

15.3 THERMODYNAMIC PROCESSES FOR AN IDEAL GAS

Constant Volume

Figure 15.7 is a PV diagram for heat flow into an ideal gas at constant volume. Since the temperature of the gas changes, the initial and final states are shown as points on two different isotherms. (Note that the higher-temperature isotherm is farther from the origin.) The area under the vertical line is zero; no work is done when the volume is constant. With $W = 0$, the heat flow increases the internal energy of the gas, so the temperature increases.

In Section 14.4, we discussed the molar specific heat of an ideal gas at constant volume. The first law of thermodynamics enables us to calculate the internal energy change ΔU. Since no work is done during a constant volume process, $\Delta U = Q$. For a constant volume process, $Q = nC_V \, \Delta T$ and therefore,

$$\Delta U = nC_V \, \Delta T \quad \text{(ideal gas)} \qquad (15\text{-}6)$$

Internal energy is a state variable—its value depends only on the current state of the system, not on the path the system took to get there. Therefore, as long as the number of moles is constant, *the internal energy of an ideal gas changes only when the temperature changes.* Equation (15-6) therefore gives the internal energy change of an ideal gas for *any* thermodynamic process, not just for constant volume processes.

Constant Pressure

Another common situation is when the *pressure* of the gas is constant. In this case, work is done because the volume changes. The first law of thermodynamics enables us to calculate the molar specific heat at constant pressure (C_P), which is different from the molar specific heat at constant volume (C_V).

CONNECTION:

Section 15.2 described some general aspects of various thermodynamic processes. Now we find out what happens when the system undergoing the process is an ideal gas.

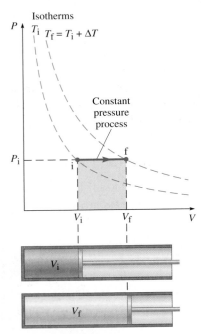

Figure 15.8 A PV diagram of a constant pressure expansion of an ideal gas. Heat flows into the ideal gas ($Q > 0$). The increase in the internal energy ΔU is less than Q because negative work is done on the expanding gas by the piston. The work done by the gas is the negative of the shaded area under the path.

Figure 15.8 shows a PV diagram for the constant pressure expansion of an ideal gas starting and ending at the same temperatures as for the constant volume process of Fig. 15.7. Applying the first law to the constant pressure process requires that

$$\Delta U = Q + W$$

where the work done on the gas is, from the ideal gas law,

$$W = -P\,\Delta V = -nR\,\Delta T$$

The definition of C_P is

$$Q = nC_P\,\Delta T \qquad (15\text{-}7)$$

Substituting Q and W into the first law, we obtain

$$\Delta U = nC_P\,\Delta T - nR\,\Delta T \qquad (15\text{-}8)$$

Since the internal energy of an ideal gas is determined by its temperature, ΔU for this constant pressure process is the same as ΔU for the constant volume process between the same two temperatures:

$$\Delta U = nC_V\,\Delta T \qquad (15\text{-}6)$$

Then

$$nC_V\,\Delta T = nC_P\,\Delta T - nR\,\Delta T$$

Canceling common factors of n and ΔT, this reduces to

$$C_P = C_V + R \qquad \text{(ideal gas)} \qquad (15\text{-}9)$$

Since R is a positive constant, the molar specific heat of an ideal gas at constant pressure is larger than the molar specific heat at constant volume.

Is this result reasonable? When heat flows into the gas at constant pressure, the gas expands, doing work on the surroundings. Thus, not all of the heat goes into increasing the internal energy of the gas. More heat has to flow into the gas at constant pressure for a given temperature increase than at constant volume.

Example 15.2

Warming a Balloon at Constant Pressure

A weather balloon is filled with helium gas at 20.0°C and 1.0 atm of pressure. The volume of the balloon after filling is measured to be 8.50 m³. The helium is heated until its temperature is 55.0°C. During this process, the balloon expands at constant pressure (1.0 atm). What is the heat flow into the helium?

Strategy   We can find how many moles of gas n are present in the balloon by using the ideal gas law. For this problem, we consider the helium to be a system. Helium is a monatomic gas, so its molar specific heat at constant *volume* is $C_V = \frac{3}{2}R$. The molar specific heat at constant *pressure* is then $C_P = C_V + R = \frac{5}{2}R$. Then the heat flow into the gas during its expansion is $Q = nC_P\Delta T$.

Solution   The ideal gas law is

$$PV = nRT$$

We know the pressure, volume, and temperature: $P = 1.0$ atm $= 1.01 \times 10^5$ Pa, $V = 8.50$ m³, and $T = 273$ K $+ 20.0$°C $= 293$ K. Solving for the number of moles yields

$$n = \frac{PV}{RT} = \frac{1.01 \times 10^5 \text{ Pa} \times 8.50 \text{ m}^3}{8.31 \text{ J/(mol·K)} \times 293 \text{ K}} = 352.6 \text{ mol}$$

For an ideal gas at constant pressure, the heat required to change the temperature is

$$Q = nC_P\,\Delta T$$

where $C_P = \frac{5}{2}R$. The temperature change is

$$\Delta T = 55.0°C - 20.0°C = 35.0 \text{ K}$$

Now we have everything we need to find Q:

$$Q = nC_P\,\Delta T = 352.6 \text{ mol} \times \tfrac{5}{2} \times 8.31 \text{ J/(mol·K)} \times 35.0 \text{ K}$$

$$= 260 \text{ kJ}$$

continued on next page

Example 15.2 continued

⚠️ **Discussion** We do not have to find the work done on the gas separately and then subtract it from the change in internal energy to find Q. The work done is *already* accounted for by the molar specific heat at constant pressure. This simplifies the problem since we use the same method for constant pressure as we use for constant volume; the only change is the choice of C_V or C_P.

Practice Problem 15.2   Air Instead of Helium

Suppose the balloon were filled with dry air instead of helium. Find Q for the same temperature change. (Dry air is mostly N_2 and O_2, so assume an ideal diatomic gas.)

Constant Temperature

For an ideal gas, we can plot isotherms using the ideal gas law $PV = nRT$ (Fig. 15.6). Since the change in internal energy of an ideal gas is proportional to the temperature change,

$$\Delta U = 0 \quad \text{(ideal gas, isothermal process)} \qquad (15\text{-}10)$$

From the first law of thermodynamics, $\Delta U = 0$ means that $Q = -W$. Note that Eq. (15-10) is true for an *ideal gas* at constant temperature. Other systems can change internal energy without changing temperature; one example is when the system undergoes a phase change.

It can be shown (using calculus to find the area under the PV curve) that the work done on an ideal gas during a constant temperature expansion or contraction from volume V_i to volume V_f is

$$W = nRT \ln\left(\frac{V_i}{V_f}\right) \quad \text{(ideal gas, isothermal)} \qquad (15\text{-}11)$$

In Eq. (15-11), "ln" stands for the natural (or base-e) logarithm.

Example 15.3

Constant Temperature Compression of an Ideal Gas

An ideal gas is kept in thermal contact with a heat reservoir at 7°C (280 K) while it is compressed from a volume of 20.0 L to a volume of 10.0 L (Fig. 15.9). During the compression, an average force of 33.3 kN is used to move the piston a distance of 0.15 m. How much heat is exchanged between the gas and the reservoir? Does the heat flow into or out of the gas?

Strategy We can find the work done on the gas from the average force applied and the distance moved. For isothermal compression of an ideal gas, $\Delta U = 0$. Then $Q = -W$.

Solution The work done on the gas is

$$W = fd = 33.3 \text{ kN} \times 0.15 \text{ m} = 5.0 \text{ kJ}$$

This work adds 5.0 kJ to the internal energy of the gas. Then 5.0 kJ of heat must flow out of the gas if its internal energy

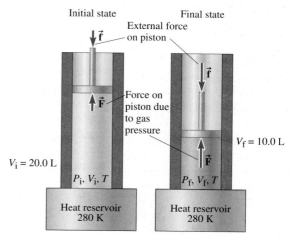

Figure 15.9

Isothermal compression of an ideal gas. Thermal contact with a heat reservoir keeps the gas at a constant temperature.

continued on next page

Example 15.3 continued

does not change. The work done on the gas is positive since the piston is pushed with an inward force as it moves inward.

$$Q = -W = -5.0 \text{ kJ}$$

Since positive Q represents heat flow *into* the gas, the negative sign tells us that heat flows out of the gas into the reservoir.

 Discussion Although the temperature remains constant during the process, it does not mean that no heat flows. To maintain a constant temperature when work is done on the gas, some heat must flow out of the gas. If the

gas were thermally isolated so no heat could flow, then the work done on the gas would increase the internal energy, resulting in an increase in the temperature of the gas.

Practice Problem 15.3   Work Done During Constant Temperature Expansion of a Gas

Suppose 2.0 mol of an ideal gas are kept in thermal contact with a heat reservoir at 57°C (330 K) while the gas expands from a volume of 20.0 L to a volume of 40.0 L. Does heat flow into or out of the gas? How much heat flows? [*Hint:* Use $W = nRT \ln (V_i/V_f)$, which applies to an ideal gas at constant temperature.]

Warm → Cold

Spontaneous heat flow

Warm ⇄✗ Cold

Reverse heat flow does not happen spontaneously

Figure 15.10 Spontaneous heat flow goes from warm to cool; the reverse does not happen spontaneously.

 Irreversible processes do *not* violate energy conservation.

15.4   REVERSIBLE AND IRREVERSIBLE PROCESSES

Have you ever wished you could make time go backward? Perhaps you accidentally broke an irreplaceable treasure in a friend's house, or missed a one-time opportunity to meet your favorite movie star, or said something unforgivable to someone close to you. Why can't the clock be turned around?

Imagine a perfectly elastic collision between two billiard balls. If you were to watch a movie of the collision, you would have a hard time telling whether the movie was being played forward or backward. The laws of physics for an elastic collision are valid even if the direction of time is reversed. Since the total momentum and the total kinetic energy are the same before and after the collision, the reversed collision is physically possible.

The perfectly elastic collision is one example of a **reversible** process. A reversible process is one that does not violate any laws of physics if "played in reverse." Most of the laws of physics do not distinguish forward in time from backward in time. A projectile moving in the absence of air resistance (on the Moon, say) is reversible: if we play the movie backward, the total mechanical energy is still conserved and Newton's second law ($\Sigma \vec{F} = m\vec{a}$) still holds at every instant in the projectile's trajectory.

Notice the caveats in the examples: "perfectly elastic" and "in the absence of air resistance." If friction or air resistance is present, then the process is **irreversible**. If you played *backward* a movie of a projectile with noticeable air resistance, it would be easy to tell that something is wrong. The force of air resistance on the projectile would act in the wrong direction—in the direction of the velocity, instead of opposite to it. The same would be true for sliding friction. Slide a book across the table; friction slows it down and brings it to rest. The macroscopic kinetic energy of the book—due to the orderly motion of the book in one direction—has been converted into disordered energy associated with the random motion of molecules; the table and book will be at slightly higher temperatures. The reversed process certainly would never occur, even though it does not violate the first law of thermodynamics (energy conservation). We would not expect a slightly warmed book placed on a slightly warmed table surface to spontaneously begin to slide across the table, gaining speed and cooling off as it goes, even if the total energy is the same before and after. It is easy to convert ordered energy into disordered energy, but not so easy to do the reverse. *The presence of energy dissipation (sliding friction, air resistance) always makes a process irreversible.*

As another example of an irreversible process, imagine placing a container of warm lemonade into a cooler with some ice (Fig. 15.10). Some of the ice melts and the lemonade gets cold as heat flows out of the lemonade and into the ice. The reverse would never happen: putting cold lemonade into a cooler with some partially melted ice, we would never find that the lemonade gets warmer as the liquid water freezes. *Spontaneous heat flow from a hotter body to a colder body is always irreversible.*

Conceptual Example 15.4

Irreversibility and Energy Conservation

Suppose heat *did* flow spontaneously from the cold ice to the warm lemonade, making the ice colder and the lemonade warmer. Would conservation of energy be violated by this process?

Solution and Discussion   Heat flow from the ice to the lemonade would increase the internal energy of the lemonade by the same amount that the internal energy of the ice would decrease. The total internal energy of the ice and the lemonade would remain unchanged—energy would be conserved. The process would never occur, but *not* because energy conservation would be violated.

Conceptual Practice Problem 15.4   A Campfire

On a camping trip, you gather some twigs and logs and start a fire. Discuss the campfire in terms of irreversible processes.

As we will see later in this chapter, irreversible processes such as the frictional dissipation of energy and the spontaneous heat flow from a hotter to a colder body can be thought of in terms of a change in the amount of order in the system. A system never goes *spontaneously* from a disordered state to a more ordered state. Reversible processes are those that do not change the total amount of disorder in the universe; irreversible processes increase the amount of disorder.

Second Law of Thermodynamics   According to the **second law of thermodynamics**, the total amount of disorder in the universe never decreases. Irreversible processes increase the disorder of the universe. We see in Section 15.8 that the second law is based on the statistics of systems with extremely large numbers of atoms or molecules. For now, we start with an equivalent statement of the second law, phrased in terms of heat flow:

Second Law of Thermodynamics (Clausius Statement)

Heat never flows spontaneously from a colder body to a hotter body.

Spontaneous heat flow from a colder body to a hotter body would decrease the total disorder in the universe.

The second law of thermodynamics determines what we sense as the direction of time—none of the other physical laws we have studied would be violated if the direction of time were reversed.

✓ **CHECKPOINT 15.4**

A perfectly elastic collision is reversible. What about an inelastic collision? Explain.

15.5   HEAT ENGINES

We said in Section 15.4 that it is far *easier* to convert ordered energy into disordered energy than to do the reverse. Converting ordered into disordered energy occurs spontaneously, but the reverse does not. A **heat engine** is a device designed to convert disordered energy into ordered energy. We will see that there is a fundamental limitation on how much ordered energy (mechanical work) can be produced by a heat engine from a given amount of disordered energy (heat).

Application of thermodynamics: heat engines

The development of practical steam engines—heat engines that use steam as the working substance—around the beginning of the eighteenth century was one of the crucial elements in the industrial revolution. These steam engines were the first machines that produced a sustained work output using an energy source other than muscle, wind, or moving water. Steam engines are still used in many electric power plants.

The source of energy in a heat engine is most often the burning of some fuel such as gasoline, coal, oil, natural gas, and the like. A nuclear power plant is a heat engine using energy released by a nuclear reaction instead of a chemical reaction (as in burning). A geothermal engine uses the high temperature found beneath the Earth's crust (which comes to the surface in places such as volcanoes and hot springs).

Cyclical Engines   The engines that we will study operate in cycles. Each cycle consists of several thermodynamic processes that are repeated the same way during each cycle. In order for these processes to repeat the same way, the engine must end the cycle in the same state in which it started. In particular, the internal energy of the engine must be the same at the end of a cycle as it was in the beginning. Then for one complete cycle,

$$\Delta U = 0$$

From the first law of thermodynamics (energy conservation),

$$Q_{\text{net}} + W_{\text{net}} = 0 \qquad \text{or} \qquad |W_{\text{net}}| = |Q_{\text{net}}|$$

Therefore, for a cyclical heat engine,

> The net work done by an engine during one cycle is equal to the net heat flow into the engine during the cycle.

Heat flow into the engine

Heat engine

Work done by the engine

Heat flow out of the engine

Figure 15.11 A heat engine. The engine is represented by a circle and the arrows indicate the direction of the energy flow. The total energy entering the engine during one cycle equals the total energy leaving the engine during the cycle.

We stress that it is the *net* heat flow since an engine not only takes in heat but exhausts some as well. Figure 15.11 shows the energy transfers during one cycle of a heat engine.

Application: the Internal Combustion Engine   One familiar engine is the internal combustion engine found in automobiles. *Internal* combustion refers to the fact that gasoline is burned inside a cylinder; the resulting hot gases push against a piston and do work. A steam engine is an *external* combustion engine. The coal burned, for example, releases heat that is used to make steam; the steam is the working substance of the engine that drives the turbines.

Most automobile engines work in a cyclic thermodynamic process shown in Fig. 15.12. Of the energy released by burning gasoline, only about 20% to 25% is turned into mechanical work used to move the car forward and run other systems. The rest is discarded. The hot exhaust gases carry energy out of the engine, as does the liquid cooling system.

Efficiency of an Engine

To measure how effectively an engine converts heat into mechanical work, we define the engine's **efficiency** *e* as what you get (net useful work) divided by what you supply (heat input):

> **Efficiency of an engine:**
>
> $$e = \frac{\text{net work done by the engine}}{\text{heat input}} = \frac{W_{\text{net}}}{Q_{\text{in}}} \qquad (15\text{-}12)$$

Figure 15.12 The four-stroke automobile engine. Each cycle has four strokes during which the piston moves (steps 1, 2, 4, and 5).

To avoid getting mixed up by algebraic signs, we let the symbols Q_{in}, Q_{out}, and W_{net} stand for the *magnitudes* of the heat flows into and out of the engine and the net work done by the engine *during one or more cycles.* Hence, Q_{in}, Q_{out}, and W_{net} are never negative. We supply minus signs in equations when necessary, based on the direction of energy flow. Doing so helps keep us focused on what is happening physically with the energy flows, rather than on a sign convention. (We will do the same when we discuss refrigerators and heat pumps later in this chapter.)

The efficiency is stated as either a fraction or a percentage. It gives the fraction of the heat input that is turned into useful work. Note that the heat input is *not* the same as the net heat flow into the engine; rather,

$$Q_{net} = Q_{in} - Q_{out} \qquad (15\text{-}13)$$

The efficiency of an engine is less than 100% because some of the heat input is exhausted, instead of being converted into useful work.

If an engine does work at a constant rate and its efficiency does not change, then it also takes in and exhausts heat at constant rates. The work done, heat input, and heat exhausted during any time interval are all proportional to the elapsed time. Therefore, all the same relationships that are true for the amounts of heat flow and work done apply to the *rates* at which heat flows and work is done. For example, the efficiency is

$$e = \frac{\text{net work done}}{\text{heat input}} = \frac{\text{net } \textit{rate} \text{ of doing work}}{\textit{rate} \text{ of taking in heat}} = \frac{W_{net}/\Delta t}{Q_{in}/\Delta t}$$

Example 15.5

Rate at Which Heat Is Exhausted from an Engine

An engine operating at 25% efficiency produces work at a rate of 0.10 MW. At what rate is heat exhausted into the surroundings?

Strategy We are given that the engine does work at a constant *rate*. The efficiency is also constant.

Solution The efficiency is the ratio of $W_{net}/\Delta t$, the rate at which the engine does net work, to $Q_{in}/\Delta t$, the rate of heat flow into the engine:

$$e = \frac{W_{net}}{Q_{in}} = \frac{W_{net}/\Delta t}{Q_{in}/\Delta t}$$

The *net* rate of heat flow $Q_{net}/\Delta t$ is

$$\frac{Q_{net}}{\Delta t} = \frac{Q_{in}}{\Delta t} - \frac{Q_{out}}{\Delta t}$$

Since the internal energy of the engine does not change over a complete cycle, energy conservation (or the first law of thermodynamics) requires that

$$Q_{net} = W_{net} \quad \text{or} \quad Q_{in} - Q_{out} = W_{net}$$

In terms of the rate at which heat is delivered or exhausted and the rate at which work is done,

$$\frac{Q_{in}}{\Delta t} - \frac{Q_{out}}{\Delta t} = \frac{W_{net}}{\Delta t}$$

In other words, the rate at which the engine does work is equal to the *net* rate of heat input. We are asked to find the rate of heat exhausted $Q_{out}/\Delta t$:

$$\frac{Q_{out}}{\Delta t} = \frac{Q_{in}}{\Delta t} - \frac{W_{net}}{\Delta t} = \frac{W_{net}/\Delta t}{e} - \frac{W_{net}}{\Delta t}$$

$$= \frac{W_{net}}{\Delta t}\left(\frac{1}{e} - 1\right) = 0.10 \text{ MW} \times \left(\frac{1}{0.25} - 1\right)$$

$$= 0.30 \text{ MW}$$

Discussion Heat flows *out* of the engine at a rate of 0.30 MW.

As a check: 25% efficiency means that $\frac{1}{4}$ of the heat input does work and $\frac{3}{4}$ of it is exhausted. Therefore, the ratio of work to exhaust is

$$\frac{1/4}{3/4} = \frac{1}{3} = \frac{0.10 \text{ MW}}{0.30 \text{ MW}}$$

For simplicity, we could have let W_{net}, Q_{in}, and Q_{out} refer to *rates* instead of to total amounts—to do this we just cancel common factors of Δt out of the equations for efficiency and energy conservation.

Practice Problem 15.5 **Heat Engine Efficiency**

An engine "wastes" 4.0 J of heat for every joule of work done. What is its efficiency?

Efficiency and the First Law According to the first law of thermodynamics, the efficiency of a heat engine cannot exceed 100%. An efficiency of 100% would mean that all of the heat input is turned into useful work and no "waste" heat is exhausted. It might seem theoretically possible to make a 100% efficient engine by eliminating all of the imperfections in design such as friction and lack of perfect insulation. However, it is not, as we see in Section 15.7.

15.6 REFRIGERATORS AND HEAT PUMPS

Application: refrigerators and heat pumps

The second law of thermodynamics says that heat cannot *spontaneously* flow from a colder body to a hotter body; but machines such as refrigerators and heat pumps can make that happen. In a refrigerator, heat is pumped out of the food compartment into the warmer room. That doesn't happen by itself; it requires the *input* of work. The electricity used by a refrigerator turns the compressor motor, which does the work required to make the refrigerator function (Fig. 15.13). An air conditioner is essentially the same thing: it pumps heat out of the house into the hotter outdoors.

The only difference between a refrigerator (or an air conditioner) and a heat pump is which end is performing the useful task. Refrigerators and air conditioners pump heat out of a compartment that they are designed to keep cool. Heat pumps pump heat from the colder outdoors into the warmer house. The idea is not to cool the outdoors; it is to warm the house.

Notice that the energy transfers in a heat pump are reversed in direction from those in a heat engine (Fig. 15.14). In the heat engine, heat flows from hot to cold, with work

CONNECTION:

A refrigerator or heat pump is like a heat engine with the directions of the energy transfers *reversed*.

Figure 15.13 In a refrigerator, a fluid is compressed, increasing its temperature. Heat is exhausted as the fluid passes through the condenser. Now the fluid is allowed to expand; its temperature falls. Heat flows from the food compartment into the cold fluid. The fluid returns to the compressor to begin the same cycle again.

as the output. In a heat pump, heat flows from cold to hot, with work as the *input*. It will be most convenient to distinguish the heat transfers not by which is input and which output (since that switches in going from an engine to a heat pump), but rather by the temperature at which the exchange is made, using subscripts "H" and "C" for hot and cold. Q_H, Q_C, and W_{net} stand for the *magnitudes* of the energy transfers during one or more cycles and are never negative. We supply minus signs in equations when necessary, based on the directions of the energy transfers, as appropriate for the engine, heat pump, or refrigerator under consideration.

Thus, the efficiency of the heat engine can be rewritten

$$e = \frac{\text{net work output}}{\text{heat input}} = \frac{W_{net}}{Q_H} \qquad (15\text{-}12)$$

The efficiency can also be expressed in terms of the heat flows. Since $W_{net} = Q_H - Q_C$,

$$e = \frac{Q_H - Q_C}{Q_H} = 1 - \frac{Q_C}{Q_H} \qquad (15\text{-}14)$$

The efficiency of an engine is *less* than 1.

Figure 15.14 Energy transfers during one cycle for (a) a heat engine and (b) a refrigerator or heat pump. With our definition of Q_H, Q_C, and W_{net} as positive quantities, in either case conservation of energy requires that $Q_H = W_{net} + Q_C$.

Sign convention for engines, refrigerators, and heat pumps: Q_H, Q_C, and W_{net} are all positive.

Coefficient of Performance To measure the performance of a heat pump or refrigerator, we define a **coefficient of performance** K. Just as for the efficiency of an engine, the coefficients of performance are ratios of what you get divided by what you pay for:

- for a heat pump:

$$K_p = \frac{\text{heat delivered}}{\text{net work input}} = \frac{Q_H}{W_{net}} \qquad (15\text{-}15)$$

- for a refrigerator or air conditioner:

$$K_r = \frac{\text{heat removed}}{\text{net work input}} = \frac{Q_C}{W_{net}} \qquad (15\text{-}16)$$

A higher coefficient of performance means a better heat pump or refrigerator. Unlike the efficiency of an engine, coefficients of performance can be (and usually are) *greater than 1*.

The second law says that heat cannot flow spontaneously from cold to hot—we need to do some work to make that happen. That's equivalent to saying that the coefficient of performance can't be infinite.

Example 15.6

A Heat Pump

A heat pump has a performance coefficient of 2.5. (a) How much heat is delivered to the house for every joule of electrical energy consumed? (b) In an electric heater, for each joule of electric energy consumed, one joule of heat is delivered to the house. Where does the "extra" heat delivered by the heat pump come from? (c) What would its coefficient of performance be when used as an air conditioner instead?

continued on next page

Example 15.6 continued

Strategy   There are two slightly different meanings of coefficient of performance. For a heat pump, whose object is to deliver heat to the house, the coefficient of performance is the heat delivered (Q_H) per unit of net work done to run the pump. With an air conditioner, the object is to *remove* heat from the house. The coefficient of performance is the heat *removed* (Q_C) per unit of work done.

Solution   (a) As a heat pump,

$$K_p = \frac{\text{heat delivered}}{\text{net work input}} = \frac{Q_H}{W_{net}} = 2.5$$

$$Q_H = 2.5 W_{net}$$

For every joule of electric energy (= work input), 2.5 J of heat are delivered to the house.

(b) The 2.5 J of heat delivered include the 1.0 J of work input plus 1.5 J of heat pumped in from the outside. The electric heater just transforms the joule of work into a joule of heat.

(c) From (b), the coefficient is 1.5:

$$K_r = \frac{\text{heat removed}}{\text{net work input}} = \frac{Q_C}{W_{net}} = \frac{1.5 \text{ J}}{1.0 \text{ J}} = 1.5$$

Discussion   One thing that makes a heat pump economical in many situations is that the same machine can function as a heat pump (in winter) and as an air conditioner (in summer). The heat pump delivers heat to the interior of the house, while the air conditioner pumps heat out.

Practice Problem 15.6   Heat Exhausted by Air Conditioner

An air conditioner with a coefficient of performance $K_r = 3.0$ consumes electricity at an average rate of 1.0 kW. During 1.0 h of use, how much heat is exhausted to the outdoors?

15.7   REVERSIBLE ENGINES AND HEAT PUMPS

What limitation does the *second* law of thermodynamics place on the efficiencies of heat engines or on the coefficients of performance of heat pumps and refrigerators? To address that question, we first introduce a simplified model of engines and heat pumps. We assume the existence of two reservoirs, a hot reservoir at absolute temperature T_H and a cold reservoir at absolute temperature T_C (where $T_C < T_H$). In this model, an engine takes its heat input from the hot reservoir and exhausts heat into the cold reservoir (Fig. 15.15). A heat pump takes in heat from the cold reservoir and exhausts heat to the hot reservoir. The cold reservoir stays at temperature T_C and the hot reservoir stays at T_H.

Recall that a *reservoir* is a system with such a large heat capacity that it can exchange heat in either direction with a negligibly small temperature change.

Now imagine a hypothetical **reversible engine** exchanging heat with two reservoirs. In this engine, no irreversible processes occur: there is no friction or other dissipation of energy and heat only flows between systems that have the same temperature. In practice, there would have to be some small temperature difference to make heat flow from one system to another, but we can imagine making the temperature difference smaller and smaller. Hence, the reversible engine is an idealization, not something we can actually build. We can now show that

- the efficiency of this reversible engine depends only on the absolute temperatures of the two reservoirs; and
- the efficiency of a real engine that exchanges heat with two reservoirs cannot be greater than the efficiency of a reversible engine using the same two reservoirs.

A Reversible Engine Has the Maximum Possible Efficiency   We can prove that no real engine can have a higher efficiency than a reversible engine using the same two reservoirs by the following thought experiment. Imagine two engines using the same hot and cold reservoirs that do the same amount of work per cycle (Fig. 15.16a). Suppose engine 1 is reversible and hypothetical engine 2 has a higher efficiency than engine 1 ($e_2 > e_1$). The more efficient engine does the same amount of work per cycle but takes in a smaller quantity of heat from the hot reservoir per cycle ($Q_{H2} < Q_{H1}$). Energy conservation for a cyclical engine requires that $Q_C = Q_H - W_{net}$, so the more efficient engine also exhausts a smaller quantity of heat to the cold reservoir ($Q_{C2} < Q_{C1}$).

Figure 15.15 Simplified model of a heat engine. Heat flows into the engine from a reservoir at temperature T_H, and heat flows out of the engine into a reservoir at T_C.

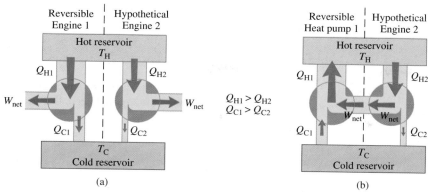

Figure 15.16 (a) Two engines that take in heat from the same hot reservoir and exhaust heat to the same cold reservoir. The two engines do the same amount of net work per cycle. Engine 1 is reversible, while hypothetical engine 2 is assumed to have an efficiency *higher* than that of engine 1, which we will show to be impossible. (b) Engine 1 is reversed, making it into a reversible heat pump. The work output of hypothetical engine 2 is used to run the heat pump. The net effect of the two connected devices is heat flow from the cold reservoir to the hot reservoir without any work input.

Now imagine reversing the energy flow directions for engine 1, turning it into a heat pump. Engine 1 is reversible, so the magnitudes of the energy transfers per cycle do not change. Connect this heat pump to engine 2, using the work output of the engine as the work input for the heat pump (Fig. 15.16b). Since $Q_{C1} > Q_{C2}$ and $Q_{H1} > Q_{H2}$, the net effect of the two devices is a flow of heat from the cold reservoir to the hot reservoir without the input of work, which is impossible—it violates the second law of thermodynamics. The conclusion is that according to the second law, no engine can have an efficiency greater than that of a reversible engine that uses the same two reservoirs.

Furthermore, every reversible engine exchanging heat with the same two reservoirs, no matter what the details of its construction, has the same efficiency. (To see why, use the same thought experiment with two reversible engines such that $e_2 > e_1$.) Therefore, the efficiency of such an engine can depend only on the temperatures of the hot and cold reservoirs. It turns out that e_r is given by the remarkably simple expression:

$$e_r = 1 - \frac{T_C}{T_H} \qquad (15\text{-}17)$$

Efficiency of a Reversible Engine

Equation (15-17) was first derived by Sadi Carnot (see later in this section). The temperatures in Eq. (15-17) must be *absolute* temperatures. [Absolute temperature is also called *thermodynamic temperature* because you can use the efficiency of reversible engines to set a temperature scale. In fact, the definition of the kelvin is based on Eq. (15-17).]

Using Eq. (15-17), the ratio of the heat exhaust to the heat input *for a reversible engine* is

$$\frac{Q_C}{Q_H} = \frac{Q_H - W_{net}}{Q_H} = 1 - \frac{W_{net}}{Q_H} = 1 - e_r = \frac{T_C}{T_H} \qquad (15\text{-}18)$$

For a reversible engine, the ratio of the heat magnitudes is equal to the temperature ratio.

The efficiency of a reversible engine is always less than 100%, assuming that the cold reservoir is not at absolute zero. Even an ideal, perfectly reversible engine must exhaust some heat, so the efficiency can never be 100%, *even in principle*. Efficiencies of real engines cannot be greater than those of reversible engines, so the second law of thermodynamics sets a limit on the theoretical maximum efficiency of an engine ($e < 1 - T_C/T_H$).

Reversible Refrigerators and Heat Pumps   Equation (15-18) also applies to reversible heat pumps and refrigerators because they are just reversible engines with the directions of the energy transfers reversed. Using Eq. (15-18) and the first law, we can find the coefficients of performance for reversible heat pumps and refrigerators (see Problems 42 and 44):

$$K_{p,\,rev} = \frac{1}{1 - T_C/T_H} \quad \text{and} \quad K_{r,\,rev} = \frac{1}{T_H/T_C - 1} = K_{p,\,rev} - 1 \quad \textbf{(15-19)}$$

Real heat pumps and refrigerators cannot have coefficients of performance greater than those of reversible heat pumps and refrigerators operating between the same two reservoirs.

Example 15.7

Efficiency of an Automobile Engine

In an automobile engine, the combustion of the fuel-air mixture can reach temperatures as high as 3000°C and the exhaust gases leave the cylinder at about 1000°C. (a) Find the efficiency of a *reversible* engine operating between reservoirs at those two temperatures. (b) Theoretically, we might be able to have the exhaust gases leave the engine at the temperature of the outside air (20°C). What would be the efficiency of the hypothetical reversible engine in this case?

Strategy First we identify the temperatures of the hot and cold reservoirs in each case. We must convert the reservoir temperatures to kelvins in order to find the efficiency of a reversible engine.

Solution (a) The reservoir temperatures in kelvins are found using

$$T = T_C + 273 \text{ K}$$

Therefore,

$$T_H = 3000°C = 3273 \text{ K}$$

$$T_C = 1000°C = 1273 \text{ K}$$

The efficiency of a reversible engine operating between these temperatures is

$$e_r = 1 - \frac{T_C}{T_H} = 1 - \frac{1273 \text{ K}}{3273 \text{ K}} = 0.61 = 61\%$$

(b) The high-temperature reservoir is still at 3273 K, while the low-temperature reservoir is now

$$T_C = 293 \text{ K}$$

This gives a higher efficiency:

$$e_r = 1 - \frac{T_C}{T_H} = 1 - \frac{293 \text{ K}}{3273 \text{ K}} = 0.910 = 91.0\%$$

 Can an engine be 100% efficient?

Discussion As mentioned in the chapter opener, real gasoline engines achieve efficiencies of only about 20% to 25%. Although improvement is possible, the second law of thermodynamics limits the theoretical maximum efficiency to that of a reversible engine operating between the same temperatures. The *theoretical* maximum efficiency can only be increased by using a hotter hot reservoir or a colder cold reservoir. However, practical considerations may prevent us from using a hotter hot reservoir or colder cold reservoir. Hotter combustion gases might cause engine parts to wear out too fast, or there may be safety concerns. Letting the gases expand to a greater volume would make the exhaust gases colder, leading to an increase in efficiency, but might *reduce* the *power* the engine can deliver. (A reversible engine has the theoretical maximum efficiency, but the *rate* at which it does work is vanishingly small because it takes a long time for heat to flow across a small temperature difference.)

Practice Problem 15.7 **Temperature of Hot Gases**

If the efficiency of a reversible engine is 75% and the temperature of the outdoor world into which the engine sends its exhaust is 27°C, what is the combustion temperature in the engine cylinder? [*Hint:* Think of the combustion temperature as the temperature of the hot reservoir.]

Example 15.8

Coal-Burning Power Plant

A coal-burning electrical power plant burns coal at 706°C. Heat is exhausted into a river near the power plant; the average river temperature is 19°C. What is the minimum possible rate of thermal pollution (heat exhausted into the river) if the station generates 125 MW of electricity?

continued on next page

Example 15.8 continued

Strategy The minimum discharge of heat into the river would occur if the engine generating the electricity were *reversible*. As in Example 15.5, we can take all of the rates to be constant.

Solution First find the absolute temperatures of the reservoirs:

$$T_H = 706°C = 979 \text{ K}$$

$$T_C = 19°C = 292 \text{ K}$$

The efficiency of a reversible engine operating between these temperatures is

$$e_r = 1 - \frac{T_C}{T_H} = 1 - \frac{292 \text{ K}}{979 \text{ K}} = 0.702$$

We want to find the rate at which heat is exhausted, which is $Q_C/\Delta t$. The efficiency is equal to the ratio of the net work output to the heat input from the hot reservoir:

$$e = \frac{W_{net}}{Q_H}$$

Conservation of energy requires that

$$Q_H = Q_C + W_{net}$$

Solving for Q_C,

$$Q_C = Q_H - W_{net} = \frac{W_{net}}{e} - W_{net} = W_{net} \times \left(\frac{1}{e} - 1\right)$$

Assuming that all the rates are constant,

$$\frac{Q_C}{\Delta t} = 125 \text{ MW} \times \left(\frac{1}{0.702} - 1\right) = 53 \text{ MW}$$

The rate at which heat enters the river is 53 MW.

Discussion We expect the actual rate of thermal pollution to be higher. A real, irreversible engine would have a lower efficiency, so more heat would be dumped into the river.

Practice Problem 15.8 Generating Electricity from Coal

What is the minimum possible rate of heat *input* (from the burning of coal) needed to generate 125 MW of electricity in this same plant?

The Carnot Cycle

Sadi Carnot (1796–1832), a French engineer, published a treatise in 1824 that greatly expanded the understanding of how heat engines work. His treatment introduced a hypothetical, ideal engine that uses two heat reservoirs at different temperatures as the source and sink for heat and an ideal gas as the working substance of the engine. We now call this engine a **Carnot engine** and its cycle of operation the **Carnot cycle**. Remember that the Carnot engine is an *ideal* engine, not a real engine.

Carnot was able to calculate the efficiency of an engine operating in this cycle and obtained Eq. (15-17). Since *all* reversible engines operating between the same two reservoirs must have the same efficiency, deriving the efficiency for one particular kind of reversible engine is sufficient to derive it for all of them.

The Carnot engine is a particular kind of reversible engine. (Other reversible engines might use a working substance other than an ideal gas or might exchange heat with three or more reservoirs.) We must assume that all friction has somehow been eliminated—otherwise an irreversible process takes place. We also must avoid heat flow across a finite temperature difference, which would be irreversible. Therefore, whenever the ideal gas takes in or gives off heat, the gas must be at the same temperature as the reservoir with which it exchanges energy.

How can we get heat to flow without a temperature difference? Imagine putting the gas in good thermal contact with a reservoir at the same temperature. Now *slowly* pull a piston so that the gas expands. Since the gas does work, it must lose internal energy—and therefore its temperature drops, since in an ideal gas the internal energy is proportional to absolute temperature. As long as the expansion occurs slowly, heat flows into the gas fast enough to keep its temperature constant.

So, to keep every step reversible, we must exchange heat in *isothermal* processes. To take in heat, we expand the gas; to exhaust heat, we compress it. We also need reversible processes to change the gas temperature from T_H to T_C and back to T_H. These processes must be *adiabatic* (no heat flow) since otherwise an irreversible heat flow would occur. (For more detail on the Carnot cycle, see the text website.)

15.8   ENTROPY

When two systems of different temperatures are in thermal contact, heat flows out of the hotter system and into the colder system. There is no change in the total energy of the two systems; energy just flows out of one and into the other. Why then does heat flow in one direction but not in the other? As we will see, heat flow *into* a system not only increases the system's internal energy, it also increases the *disorder* of the system. Heat flow *out of* a system decreases not only its internal energy but also its disorder.

The **entropy** of a system (symbol S) is a quantitative measure of its disorder. Entropy is a state variable (like U, P, V, and T): a system in equilibrium has a unique entropy that does *not* depend on the past history of the system. (Recall that heat and work are *not* state variables. Heat and work describe *how* a system goes from one state to another.) The word *entropy* was coined by Rudolf Clausius (1822–1888) in 1865; its Greek root means *evolution* or *transformation.*

If an amount of heat Q flows into a system at constant absolute temperature T, the entropy change *of the system* is

$$\Delta S = \frac{Q}{T} \qquad (15\text{-}20)$$

The SI unit for entropy is J/K. Heat flowing into a system increases the system's entropy (both ΔS and Q are positive); heat leaving a system decreases the system's entropy (both ΔS and Q are negative). Equation (15-20) is valid as long as the temperature of the system is constant, which is true if the heat capacity of the system is large (as for a reservoir), so that the heat flow Q causes a negligibly small temperature change in the system.

Note that Eq. (15-20) gives only the *change* in entropy, not the initial and final values of the entropy. As with potential energy, the *change* in entropy is what's important in most situations.

If a small amount of heat Q flows from a hotter system to a colder system ($T_H > T_C$), the *total* entropy change of the systems is

$$\Delta S_{tot} = \Delta S_H + \Delta S_C = \frac{-Q}{T_H} + \frac{Q}{T_C}$$

Since $T_H > T_C$,

$$\frac{Q}{T_H} < \frac{Q}{T_C}$$

The increase in the colder system's entropy is larger than the decrease of the hotter system's entropy and the total entropy increases:

$$\Delta S_{tot} > 0 \quad \text{(irreversible process)} \qquad (15\text{-}21)$$

Thus, the flow of heat from a hotter system to a colder system causes an increase in the total entropy of the two systems. Every irreversible process increases the total entropy of the universe. A process that would decrease the total entropy of the universe is impossible. A reversible process causes no change in the total entropy of the universe. We can restate the second law of thermodynamics in terms of entropy:

> ### Second Law of Thermodynamics (Entropy Statement)
>
> The entropy of the universe never decreases.

For example, a reversible engine removes heat Q_H from a hot reservoir at temperature T_H and exhausts Q_C to a cold reservoir at T_C. The entropy of the engine itself is left unchanged since it operates in a cycle. The entropy of the hot reservoir decreases by an amount Q_H/T_H and that of the cold reservoir increases by Q_C/T_C. Since the entropy of the universe must be unchanged by a reversible engine, it must be true that

$$-\frac{Q_H}{T_H} + \frac{Q_C}{T_C} = 0 \quad \text{or} \quad \frac{Q_C}{Q_H} = \frac{T_C}{T_H}$$

The efficiency of the engine is therefore

$$e_r = \frac{W_{net}}{Q_H} = \frac{Q_H - Q_C}{Q_H} = 1 - \frac{Q_C}{Q_H} = 1 - \frac{T_C}{T_H}$$

as stated in Section 15.7.

Entropy is *not* a conserved quantity like energy. The entropy of the universe is always increasing. It is possible to decrease the entropy of a *system*, but only at the expense of increasing the entropy of the surroundings by at least as much (usually more).

CONNECTION:

Energy is a conserved quantity; entropy is not.

✓ CHECKPOINT 15.8

The entropy of a system increases by 10 J/K. Does this mean the process is necessarily irreversible? Explain.

Example 15.9

Entropy Change of a Freely Expanding Gas

Suppose 1.0 mol of an ideal gas is allowed to freely expand into an evacuated container of equal volume so that the volume of the gas doubles (Fig. 15.17). No work is done on the gas as it expands, since there is nothing pushing against it. The containers are insulated so no heat flows into or out of the gas. What is the entropy change of the gas?

Valve closed

Figure 15.17

Two chambers connected by a valve. One chamber contains a gas and the other has been evacuated. When the valve is opened, the gas expands until it fills both chambers.

Strategy The only way to calculate entropy changes that we've learned so far is for heat flow at a constant temperature. In free expansion, there is no heat flow—but that does not necessarily mean there is no entropy change. Since entropy is a state variable, ΔS depends only on the initial and final states of the gas, not the intermediate states. We can therefore find the entropy change using *any* thermodynamic process with the same initial and final states. The initial and final temperatures of the gas are identical since the internal energy does not change; therefore we find the entropy change for an *isothermal* expansion.

Figure 15.18

As the gas in the cylinder expands, heat flows into it from the reservoir and keeps its temperature constant.

Solution Imagine the gas confined to a cylinder with a moveable piston (Fig. 15.18). In an isothermal expansion, heat flows into the gas from a reservoir at a constant temperature *T*. As the gas

expands, it does work on the piston. If the temperature is to stay constant, the work done must equal the heat flow into the gas:

$$\Delta U = 0 \quad \text{implies} \quad Q + W = 0$$

In Section 15.3, we found the work done by an ideal gas during an isothermal expansion:

$$W = nRT \ln\left(\frac{V_i}{V_f}\right)$$

The volume of the gas doubles, so $V_i/V_f = 0.50$:

$$W = nRT \ln 0.50$$

Since $Q = -W$, the entropy change is

$$\Delta S = \frac{Q}{T} = -nR \ln 0.50$$

$$= -(1.0 \text{ mol}) \times \left(8.31 \frac{J}{mol \cdot K}\right) \times (-0.693) = +5.8 \text{ J/K}$$

Discussion The entropy change is positive, as expected. Free expansion is an irreversible process; the gas molecules do not spontaneously collect back in the original container. The reverse process would cause a decrease in entropy, without a larger increase elsewhere, and so violates the second law.

Practice Problem 15.9 Entropy Change of the Universe When a Lump of Clay Is Dropped

A room-temperature lump of clay of mass 400 g is dropped from a height of 2 m and makes a totally inelastic collision with the floor. Approximately what is the entropy change of the universe due to this collision? [*Hint:* The temperature of the clay rises, but only slightly.]

Application of the Second Law to Evolution

Some have argued that evolution cannot have occurred because it would violate the second law of thermodynamics. The argument views evolution as an increase in order: life spontaneously developed from simple life forms to more complex, more highly ordered organisms.

However, the second law says only that the *total entropy of the universe* cannot decrease. It does not say that the entropy of a particular system cannot decrease. When heat flows from a hot body to a cold body, the entropy of the hot body decreases, but the increase in the cold body's entropy is greater, so the entropy of the universe increases. A living organism is not a closed system and neither is the Earth. An adult human, for instance, requires roughly 10 MJ of chemical energy from food per day. What happens to this energy? Some is turned into useful work by the muscles, some more is used to repair body tissues, but most of it is dissipated and leaves the body as heat. The human body therefore is constantly increasing the entropy of its environment. As evolution progresses from simpler to more complicated organisms, the increase in order within the organisms must be accompanied by a larger increase in disorder in the environment.

Application of the Second Law to the "Energy Crisis"

When people speak of "conserving energy," they usually mean using fuel and electricity sparingly. In the physics sense of the word *conserve*, energy is *always* conserved. Burning natural gas to heat your house does not change the amount of energy around; it just changes it from one form to another.

What we need to be careful not to waste is *high-quality* energy. Our concern is not the total amount of energy, but rather whether the energy is in a form that is useful and convenient. The chemical energy stored in fuel is relatively high-quality (ordered) energy. When fuel is burned, the energy is degraded into lower-quality (disordered) energy.

Statistical Interpretation of Entropy

Thermodynamic systems are collections of huge numbers of atoms or molecules. How these atoms or molecules behave statistically determines the disorder in the system. In other words, the second law of thermodynamics is based on the statistics of systems with extremely large numbers of atoms or molecules.

The **microstate** of a thermodynamic system specifies the state of each constituent particle. For instance, in a monatomic ideal gas with N atoms, a microstate is specified by the position and velocity of each of the N atoms. As the atoms move about and collide, the system changes from one microstate to another. The **macrostate** of a thermodynamic system specifies only the values of the macroscopic state variables (such as pressure, volume, temperature, and internal energy).

Statistical analysis is the microscopic basis for the second law of thermodynamics. It turns out, remarkably, that the number of microstates corresponding to a given macrostate is related to the entropy of that macrostate in a simple way. Letting Ω (the Greek capital omega) stand for the number of microstates, the relationship is

$$S = k \ln \Omega \tag{15-22}$$

where k is Boltzmann's constant. Equation (15-22) is inscribed on the tombstone of Ludwig Boltzmann (1844–1906), the Austrian physicist who made the connection between entropy and statistics in the late nineteenth century. The relationship between S and Ω has to be logarithmic because entropy is additive: if system 1 has entropy S_1 and system 2 has entropy S_2, then the total entropy is $S_1 + S_2$. However, the number of microstates is *multiplicative*. Think of dice: if die 1 has 6 microstates and die 2 also has 6, the total number of microstates when rolling two dice is not 12, but $6 \times 6 = 36$. The entropy is additive since $\ln 6 + \ln 6 = \ln 36$. (For more information on entropy and statistics see text website.)

15.9   THE THIRD LAW OF THERMODYNAMICS

Like the second law, the third law of thermodynamics can be stated in several equivalent ways. We will state just one of them:

Third Law of Thermodynamics

It is impossible to cool a system to absolute zero.

While it is impossible to *reach* absolute zero, there is no limit on how *close* we can get. Scientists who study low-temperature physics have attained equilibrium temperatures as low as 1 μK and have sustained temperatures of 2 mK; transient temperatures in the nano- and picokelvin range have been observed.

Master the Concepts

- The first law of thermodynamics is a statement of energy conservation:

$$\Delta U = Q + W \qquad (15\text{-}1)$$

where Q is the heat flow *into* the system and W is the work done *on* the system.

- Pressure, temperature, volume, number of moles, internal energy, and entropy are state variables; they describe the state of a system at some instant of time but *not* how the system got to that state. Heat and work are *not* state variables—they describe *how* a system gets from one state to another.

- The work done on a system when the pressure is constant—or for a volume change small enough that the pressure change is insignificant—is

$$W = -P\,\Delta V \qquad (15\text{-}2)$$

The magnitude of the work done is the total area under the *PV* curve.

W > 0 for compression

- The change in internal energy of an ideal gas is determined solely by the temperature change. Therefore,

$$\Delta U = 0 \quad \text{(ideal gas, isothermal process)} \qquad (15\text{-}10)$$

- A process in which no heat is transferred into or out of the system is called an adiabatic process.

- The molar specific heats of an ideal gas at constant volume and constant pressure are related by

$$C_P = C_V + R \qquad (15\text{-}9)$$

- Spontaneous heat flow from a hotter body to a colder body is always irreversible.

Warm ⟶ Cold

Spontaneous heat flow

- For one cycle of an engine, heat pump, or refrigerator, conservation of energy requires

$$Q_{\text{net}} = Q_H - Q_C = W_{\text{net}}$$

where Q_H, Q_C, and W_{net} are defined as positive quantities.

- The efficiency of an engine is defined as

$$e = \frac{W_{\text{net}}}{Q_H} \qquad (15\text{-}12)$$

- The coefficient of performance for a heat pump is

$$K_p = \frac{\text{heat delivered}}{\text{net work input}} = \frac{Q_H}{W_{\text{net}}} \qquad (15\text{-}15)$$

- The coefficient of performance for a refrigerator or air conditioner is

$$K_r = \frac{\text{heat removed}}{\text{net work input}} = \frac{Q_C}{W_{\text{net}}} \qquad (15\text{-}16)$$

continued on next page

Master the Concepts continued

- A reservoir is a system with such a large heat capacity that it can exchange heat in either direction with a negligibly small temperature change.

Reverse heat flow does not happen spontaneously

- The second law of thermodynamics can be stated in various equivalent ways. Two of them are: (1) heat never flows spontaneously from a colder body to a hotter body, and (2) the entropy of the universe never decreases.

- The efficiency of a *reversible* engine is determined only by the *absolute* temperatures of the hot and cold reservoirs:

$$e_r = 1 - \frac{T_C}{T_H} \qquad (15\text{-}17)$$

- If an amount of heat Q flows into a system at constant absolute temperature T, the entropy change of the system is

$$\Delta S = \frac{Q}{T} \qquad (15\text{-}20)$$

- The third law of thermodynamics: it is impossible to cool a system to absolute zero.

Conceptual Questions

1. Is it possible to make a heat pump with a coefficient of performance equal to 1? Explain.

2. An electric baseboard heater can convert 100% of the electric energy used into heat that flows into the house. Since a gas furnace might be located in a basement and sends exhaust gases up the chimney, the heat flow into the living space is less than 100% of the chemical energy released by burning. Does this mean that electric heating is better? Which heating method consumes less fuel? In your answer, consider how the electricity might have been generated and the efficiency of that process.

3. A whimsical statement of the laws of thermodynamics—probably not one favored by gamblers—goes like this:

    I. You can never win; you can only lose or break even.

    II. You can only break even at absolute zero.

    III. You can never get to absolute zero.

    What do we mean by "win," "lose," and "break even"? [*Hint:* Think about a heat engine.]

4. Why must all reversible engines (operating between the same reservoirs) have the same efficiency? Try an argument by contradiction: imagine that two reversible engines exist with $e_1 > e_2$. Reverse one of them (into a heat pump) and use the work output from the engine to run the heat pump. What happens? (If it seems fine at first, switch the two.)

5. When supplies of fossil fuels such as petroleum and coal dwindle, people might call the situation an "energy crisis." From the standpoint of physics, why is that not an accurate name? Can you think of a better one?

6. If you leave the refrigerator door open and the refrigerator runs continuously, does the kitchen get colder or warmer? Explain.

7. Most heat pumps incorporate an auxiliary electric heater. For relatively mild outdoor temperatures, the electric heater is not used. However, if the outdoor temperature gets very low, the auxiliary heater is used to supplement the heat pump. Why?

8. Why are heat pumps more often used in mild climates than in areas with severely cold winters?

9. Are entropy changes always caused by the flow of heat? If not, give some other examples of processes that increase entropy. (tutorial: reversibility)

10. Can a heat engine be made to operate without creating any "thermal pollution," that is, without making its cold reservoir get warmer in the long run? The net work output must be greater than zero.

11. A warm pitcher of lemonade is put into an ice chest. Describe what happens to the entropies of lemonade and ice as heat flows from the lemonade to the ice within the chest.

12. A new dormitory is being built at a college in North Carolina. To save costs, it is proposed to not include air conditioning ducts and vents. A member of the board overseeing the construction says that stand-alone air conditioning units can be supplied to each room later. He has seen advertisements that claim these new units do not need to be vented to the outside. Can the claim be true? Explain.

13. After a day at the beach, a child brings home a bucket containing some salt water. Eventually the water evaporates, leaving behind a few salt crystals. The molecular order of the salt crystals is greater than the order of the dissolved salt sloshing around in the sea water. Is this a violation of the entropy principle? Explain.

14. Explain why the molar specific heat at constant volume is not the same as the molar specific heat at constant pressure for gases. Why is the distinction between constant volume and constant pressure usually insignificant for the specific heats of liquids and solids?

Multiple-Choice Questions

1. A heat engine runs between reservoirs at temperatures of 300°C and 30°C. What is its maximum possible efficiency?

   (a) 10%   (b) 47%   (c) 53%
   (d) 90%   (e) 100%

2. If two different systems are put in thermal contact so that heat can flow from one to the other, then heat will flow until the systems have the same

   (a) energy.
   (b) heat capacity.
   (c) entropy.
   (d) temperature.

3. As moisture from the air condenses on the outside of a cold glass of water, the entropy of the condensing moisture

   (a) stays the same.
   (b) increases.
   (c) decreases.
   (d) not enough information

4. As a system undergoes a constant volume process

   (a) the pressure does not change.
   (b) the internal energy does not change.
   (c) the work done on or by the system is zero.
   (d) the entropy stays the same.
   (e) the temperature of the system does not change.

5. Which of these statements are implied by the *second* law of thermodynamics?

   (a) The entropy of an engine (including its fuel and/or heat reservoirs) operating in a cycle never decreases.
   (b) The increase in internal energy of a system in any process is the sum of heat absorbed plus work done on the system.
   (c) A heat engine, operating in a cycle, that rejects no heat to the low-temperature reservoir is impossible.
   (d) Both (a) and (c).
   (e) All three [(a), (b), and (c)].

6. On a summer day, you keep the air conditioner in your room running. From the list numbered 1 to 4, choose the hot reservoir and the cold reservoir.

   1. the air outside
   2. the compartment inside the air conditioner where the air is compressed
   3. the freon gas that is the working substance (expands and compresses in each cycle)
   4. the air in the room

   (a) 1 is the hot reservoir, 2 is the cold reservoir.
   (b) 1 is the hot reservoir, 3 is the cold reservoir.
   (c) 1 is the hot reservoir, 4 is the cold reservoir.
   (d) 2 is the hot reservoir, 3 is the cold reservoir.
   (e) 2 is the hot reservoir, 4 is the cold reservoir.
   (f) 3 is the hot reservoir, 4 is the cold reservoir.

7. The *PV* diagram illustrates several paths to get from an initial to a final state. For which path does the system do the most work?

   (a) path *igf*
   (b) path *if*
   (c) path *ihf*
   (d) All paths represent equal work.

8. An ideal gas is confined to the left chamber of an insulated container. The right chamber is evacuated. A valve is opened between the chambers, allowing gas to flow into the right chamber. After equilibrium is established, the temperature of the gas _____ . [*Hint:* What happens to the internal energy?]

   (a) is lower than the initial temperature
   (b) is higher than the initial temperature
   (c) is the same as the initial temperature
   (d) could be higher than, the same as, or lower than the initial temperature

9. When the first law of thermodynamics ($\Delta U = Q + W$) is applied to a system S, the variables Q and W stand for

   (a) the heat flow *out of S* and the work done *on S*.
   (b) the heat flow *out of S* and the work done *by S*.
   (c) the heat flow *into S* and the work done *by S*.
   (d) the heat flow *into S* and the work done *on S*.

10. As an ideal gas is adiabatically expanding,

    (a) the temperature of the gas does not change.
    (b) the internal energy of the gas does not change.
    (c) work is not done on or by the gas.
    (d) no heat is given off or taken in by the gas.
    (e) both (a) and (d)
    (f) both (a) and (b)

11. As an ideal gas is compressed at constant temperature,

    (a) heat flows out of the gas.
    (b) the internal energy of the gas does not change.
    (c) the work done on the gas is zero.
    (d) none of the above
    (e) both (a) and (b)
    (f) both (a) and (c)

12. Given 1 mole of an ideal gas, in a state characterized by P_A, V_A, a change occurs so that the final pressure and volume are equal to P_B, V_B, where $V_B > V_A$. Which of these is true?

    (a) The heat supplied to the gas during the process is completely determined by the values P_A, V_A, P_B, and V_B.
    (b) The change in the internal energy of the gas during the process is completely determined by the values P_A, V_A, P_B, and V_B.
    (c) The work done by the gas during the process is completely determined by the values P_A, V_A, P_B, and V_B.
    (d) All three are true.
    (e) None of these is true.

13. Which choice correctly identifies the three processes shown in the diagrams?

(I)

(II)

(III)

(a) I = isobaric; II = isochoric; III = adiabatic
(b) I = isothermal; II = isothermal; III = isobaric
(c) I = isochoric; II = adiabatic; III = isobaric
(d) I = isobaric; II = isothermal; III = isochoric

Problems

- ©   Combination conceptual/quantitative problem
- ☤   Biological or medical application
- ✦   Challenging problem
- Blue #   Detailed solution in the Student Solutions Manual
- (1   2)   Problems paired by concept
- Ⓦ   Text website interactive or tutorial

15.1 The First Law of Thermodynamics;

15.2 Thermodynamic Processes;

15.3 Thermodynamic Processes for an Ideal Gas

1. On a cold day, Ming rubs her hands together to warm them up. She presses her hands together with a force of 5.0 N. Each time she rubs them back and forth they move a distance of 16 cm with a coefficient of kinetic friction of 0.45. Assuming no heat flow to the surroundings, after she has rubbed her hands back and forth eight times, by how much has the internal energy of her hands increased?

2. A system takes in 550 J of heat while performing 840 J of work. What is the change in internal energy of the system?

3. The internal energy of a system increases by 400 J while 500 J of work are performed on it. What was the heat flow into or out of the system?

4. A model steam engine of 1.00-kg mass pulls eight cars of 1.00-kg mass each. The cars start at rest and reach a velocity of 3.00 m/s in a time of 3.00 s while moving a distance of 4.50 m. During that time, the engine takes in 135 J of heat. What is the change in the internal energy of the engine?

5. A monatomic ideal gas at 27°C undergoes a constant pressure process from A to B and a constant volume process from B to C. Find the total work done during these two processes.

6. A monatomic ideal gas at 27°C undergoes a constant volume process from A to B and a constant pressure process from B to C. Find the total work done during these two processes.

7. An ideal monatomic gas is taken through the cycle in the PV diagram. (a) If there are 0.0200 mol of this gas, what are the temperature and pressure at point C? (b) What is the change in internal energy of the gas as it is taken from A to B? (c) How much work is done by this gas per cycle? (d) What is the total change in internal energy of this gas in one cycle?

8. An ideal gas is in contact with a heat reservoir so that it remains at a constant temperature of 300.0 K. The gas is compressed from a volume of 24.0 L to a volume of 14.0 L. During the process, the mechanical device pushing the piston to compress the gas is found to expend 5.00 kJ of energy. How much heat flows between the heat reservoir and the gas and in what direction does the heat flow occur?

9. Suppose 1.00 mol of oxygen is heated at constant pressure of 1.00 atm from 10.0°C to 25.0°C. (a) How much heat is absorbed by the gas? (b) Using the ideal gas law, calculate the change of volume of the gas in this process. (c) What is the work done by the gas during this expansion? (d) From the first law, calculate the change of internal energy of the gas in this process.

✦10. Suppose a monatomic ideal gas is changed from state A to state D by one of the processes shown on the PV diagram. (a) Find the total work done on the gas if it follows the constant volume path A–B followed by the constant pressure path B–C–D. (b) Calculate the total change in internal energy of the gas during the entire process and the total heat flow into the gas.

Problems 10–12

✦11. Repeat Problem 10 for the case when the gas follows the constant temperature path A–C followed by the constant pressure path C–D.

✦12. Repeat Problem 10 for the case when the gas follows the constant pressure path A–E followed by the constant temperature path E–D.

15.5 Heat Engines; 15.6 Refrigerators and Heat Pumps

13. A heat engine follows the cycle shown in the figure. (a) How much net work is done by the engine in one cycle? (b) What is the heat flow *into* the engine per cycle? (tutorial: closed cycle)

14. What is the efficiency of an electric generator that produces 1.17 kW·h per kg of coal burned? The heat of combustion of coal is 6.71×10^6 J/kg.

15. A heat pump delivers heat at a rate of 7.81 kW for 10.0 h. If its coefficient of performance is 6.85, how much heat is taken from the cold reservoir during that time?

16. (a) How much heat does an engine with an efficiency of 33.3% absorb in order to deliver 1.00 kJ of work? (b) How much heat is exhausted by the engine?

17. The efficiency of an engine is 0.21. For every 1.00 kJ of heat absorbed by the engine, how much (a) net work is done by it and (b) heat is released by it?

18. A certain engine can propel a 1800-kg car from rest to a speed of 27 m/s in 9.5 s with an efficiency of 27%. What are the rate of heat flow into the engine at the high temperature and the rate of heat flow out of the engine at the low temperature?

19. The United States generates about 5.0×10^{16} J of electric energy a day. This energy is equivalent to work, since it can be converted into work with almost 100% efficiency by an electric motor. (a) If this energy is generated by power plants with an average efficiency of 0.30, how much heat is dumped into the environment each day? (b) How much water would be required to absorb this heat if the water temperature is not to increase more than 2.0°C?

20. The intensity (power per unit area) of the sunlight incident on Earth's surface, averaged over a 24-h period, is about 0.20 kW/m². If a solar power plant is to be built with an output capacity of 1.0×10^9 W, how big must the area of the solar energy collectors be for photocells operating at 20.0% efficiency?

21. An engine releases 0.450 kJ of heat for every 0.100 kJ of work it does. What is the efficiency of the engine?

22. An engine works at 30.0% efficiency. The engine raises a 5.00-kg crate from rest to a vertical height of 10.0 m, at which point the crate has a speed of 4.00 m/s. How much heat input is required for this engine?

23. How much heat does a heat pump with a coefficient of performance of 3.0 deliver when supplied with 1.00 kJ of electricity?

24. An air conditioner whose coefficient of performance is 2.00 removes 1.73×10^8 J of heat from a room per day.

How much does it cost to run the air conditioning unit per day if electricity costs $0.10 per kilowatt-hour? (Note that 1 kilowatt-hour = 3.6×10^6 J.)

15.7 Reversible Engines and Heat Pumps

25. An ideal engine has an efficiency of 0.725 and uses gas from a hot reservoir at a temperature of 622 K. What is the temperature of the cold reservoir to which it exhausts heat?

26. A heat engine takes in 125 kJ of heat from a reservoir at 815 K and exhausts 82 kJ to a reservoir at 293 K. (a) What is the efficiency of the engine? (b) What is the efficiency of an ideal engine operating between the same two reservoirs?

27. In a certain steam engine, the boiler temperature is 127°C and the cold reservoir temperature is 27°C. While this engine does 8.34 kJ of work, what minimum amount of heat must be discharged into the cold reservoir?

28. Calculate the maximum possible efficiency of a heat engine that uses surface lake water at 18.0°C as a source of heat and rejects waste heat to the water 0.100 km below the surface where the temperature is 4.0°C.

29. An ideal refrigerator removes heat at a rate of 0.10 kW from its interior (+2.0°C) and exhausts heat at 40.0°C. How much electrical power is used?

30. A heat pump is used to heat a house with an interior temperature of 20.0°C. On a chilly day with an outdoor temperature of −10.0°C, what is the minimum work that the pump requires in order to deliver 1.0 kJ of heat to the house? (tutorial: heat pump)

31. A coal-fired electrical generating station can use a higher T_H than a nuclear plant; for safety reasons the core of a nuclear reactor is not allowed to get as hot as coal. Suppose that $T_H = 727$°C for a coal station but $T_H = 527$°C for a nuclear station. Both power plants exhaust waste heat into a lake at $T_C = 27$°C. How much waste heat does each plant exhaust into the lake to produce 1.00 MJ of electricity? Assume both operate as reversible engines. (tutorial: power stations)

32. Two engines operate between the same two temperatures of 750 K and 350 K, and have the same rate of heat input. One of the engines is a reversible engine with a power output of 2.3×10^4 W. The second engine has an efficiency of 42%. What is the power output of the second engine?

33. (a) Calculate the efficiency of a reversible engine that operates between the temperatures 600.0°C and 300.0°C. (b) If the engine absorbs 420.0 kJ of heat from the hot reservoir, how much does it exhaust to the cold reservoir?

34. A reversible engine with an efficiency of 30.0% has $T_C = 310.0$ K. (a) What is T_H? (b) How much heat is exhausted for every 0.100 kJ of work done?

35. An electric power station generates steam at 500.0°C and condenses it with river water at 27°C. By how much would its theoretical maximum efficiency decrease if it had to switch to cooling towers that condense the steam at 47°C?

36. An oil-burning electric power plant uses steam at 773 K to drive a turbine, after which the steam is expelled at 373 K. The engine has an efficiency of 0.40. What is the theoretical maximum efficiency possible at those temperatures?

37. An inventor proposes a heat engine to propel a ship, using the temperature difference between the water at the surface and the water 10 m below the surface as the two reservoirs. If these temperatures are 15.0°C and 10.0°C, respectively, what is the maximum possible efficiency of the engine?

38. A heat engine uses the warm air at the ground as the hot reservoir and the cooler air at an altitude of several thousand meters as the cold reservoir. If the warm air is at 37°C and the cold air is at 25°C, what is the maximum possible efficiency for the engine?

39. A reversible refrigerator has a coefficient of performance of 3.0. How much work must be done to freeze 1.0 kg of liquid water initially at 0°C?

40. An engine operates between temperatures of 650 K and 350 K at 65.0% of its maximum possible efficiency. (a) What is the efficiency of this engine? (b) If 6.3×10^3 J is exhausted to the low temperature reservoir, how much work does the engine do?

41. A town is planning on using the water flowing through a river at a rate of 5.0×10^6 kg/s to carry away the heat from a new power plant. Environmental studies indicate that the temperature of the river should only increase by 0.50°C. The maximum design efficiency for this plant is 30.0%. What is the maximum possible power this plant can produce?

42. Show that the coefficient of performance for a reversible heat pump is $1/(1 - T_C/T_H)$.

43. On a hot day, you are in a sealed, insulated room. The room contains a refrigerator, operated by an electric motor. The motor does work at the rate of 250 W when it is running. Assume the motor is ideal (no friction or electrical resistance) and that the refrigerator operates on a reversible cycle. In an effort to cool the room, you turn on the refrigerator and open its door. Let the temperature in the room be 320 K when this process starts, and the temperature in the cold compartment of the refrigerator be 256 K. At what *net* rate is heat added to (+) or subtracted from (−) the room and all of its contents?

44. Show that the coefficient of performance for a reversible refrigerator is $1/[(T_H/T_C) - 1]$.

45. Show that in a reversible engine the amount of heat Q_C exhausted to the cold reservoir is related to the net work done W_{net} by

$$Q_C = \frac{T_C}{T_H - T_C} W_{net}$$

15.8 Entropy

46. List these in order of increasing entropy: (a) 0.01 mol of N_2 gas in a 1-L container at 0°C; (b) 0.01 mol of N_2 gas in a 2-L container at 0°C; (c) 0.01 mol of liquid N_2.

47. List these in order of increasing entropy: (a) 0.5 kg of ice and 0.5 kg of (liquid) water at 0°C; (b) 1 kg of ice at 0°C; (c) 1 kg of (liquid) water at 0°C; (d) 1 kg of water at 20°C.

48. An ice cube at 0.0°C is slowly melting. What is the change in the ice cube's entropy for each 1.00 g of ice that melts?

49. From Table 14.4, we know that approximately 2256 kJ are needed to transform 1.00 kg of water at 100°C to steam at 100°C. What is the change in entropy of 1.00 kg of water evaporating at 100.0°C? (Specify whether the change in entropy is an increase, +, or a decrease, −.)

50. What is the change in entropy of 10 g of steam at 100°C as it condenses to water at 100°C? By how much does the entropy of the universe increase in this process?

51. A large block of copper initially at 20.0°C is placed in a vat of hot water (80.0°C). For the first 1.0 J of heat that flows from the water into the block, find (a) the entropy change of the block, (b) the entropy change of the water, and (c) the entropy change of the universe. Note that the temperatures of the block and water are essentially unchanged by the flow of only 1.0 J of heat.

52. A large, cold (0.0°C) block of iron is immersed in a tub of hot (100.0°C) water. In the first 10.0 s, 41.86 kJ of heat are transferred, although the temperatures of the water and the iron do not change much in this time. Ignoring heat flow between the system (iron + water) and its surroundings, calculate the change in entropy of the system (iron + water) during this time.

53. On a cold winter day, the outside temperature is −15.0°C. Inside the house the temperature is +20.0°C. Heat flows out of the house through a window at a rate of 220.0 W. At what rate is the entropy of the universe changing due to this heat conduction through the window?

54. Within an insulated system, 418.6 kJ of heat is conducted through a copper rod from a hot reservoir at +200.0°C to a cold reservoir at +100.0°C. (The reservoirs are so big that this heat exchange does not change their temperatures appreciably.) What is the net change in entropy of the system, in kJ/K?

55. A student eats 2000 kcal per day. (a) Assuming that all of the food energy is released as heat, what is the rate of heat released (in watts)? (b) What is the rate of change of entropy of the surroundings if all of the heat is released into air at room temperature (20°C)?

56. The motor that drives a reversible refrigerator produces 148 W of useful power. The hot and cold temperatures of the heat reservoirs are 20.0°C and −5.0°C. What is the maximum amount of ice it can produce in 2.0 h from water that is initially at 8.0°C?

57. An engineer designs a ship that gets its power in the following way: The engine draws in warm water from the ocean, and after extracting some of the water's internal energy, returns the water to the ocean at a temperature 14.5°C lower than the ocean temperature. If the ocean is at a uniform temperature of 17°C, is this an efficient engine? Will the engineer's design work?

58. A balloon contains 200.0 L of nitrogen gas at 20.0°C and at atmospheric pressure. How much energy must be added to raise the temperature of the nitrogen to 40.0°C while allowing the balloon to expand at atmospheric pressure?

59. An ideal gas is heated at a constant pressure of 2.0×10^5 Pa from a temperature of −73°C to a temperature of +27°C. The initial volume of the gas is 0.10 m³. The heat energy supplied to the gas in this process is 25 kJ. What is the increase in internal energy of the gas?

60. If the pressure on a fish increases from 1.1 to 1.2 atm, its swim bladder decreases in volume from 8.16 mL to 7.48 mL while the temperature of the air inside remains constant. How much work is done on the air in the bladder?

Comprehensive Problems

61. A monatomic ideal gas follows the cyclic process shown in the figure. The temperature of the point at the bottom left of the triangle is 470.0 K. (a) How much net work does this engine do per cycle? (b) What is the maximum temperature of this engine? (c) How many moles of gas are used in this engine?

62. For a reversible engine, will you obtain a better efficiency by increasing the high-temperature reservoir by an amount ΔT or decreasing the low-temperature reservoir by the same amount ΔT?

63. A 0.50-kg block of iron [$c = 0.44$ kJ/(kg·K)] at 20.0°C is in contact with a 0.50-kg block of aluminum [$c = 0.900$ kJ/(kg·K)] at a temperature of 20.0°C. The system is completely isolated from the rest of the universe. Suppose heat flows from the iron into the aluminum until the temperature of the aluminum is 22.0°C. (a) From the first law, calculate the final temperature of the iron. (b) Estimate the entropy change of the system. (c) Explain how the result of part (b) shows that this process is impossible. [*Hint:* Since the system is isolated, $\Delta S_{\text{System}} = \Delta S_{\text{Universe}}$.]

64. List these in order of increasing entropy: (a) 1 mol of water at 20°C and 1 mol of ethanol at 20°C in separate containers; (b) a mixture of 1 mol of water at 20°C and 1 mol of ethanol at 20°C; (c) 0.5 mol of water at 20°C and 0.5 mol of ethanol at 20°C in separate containers;

(d) a mixture of 1 mol of water at 30°C and 1 mol of ethanol at 30°C.

65. Suppose you mix 4.0 mol of a monatomic gas at 20.0°C and 3.0 mol of another monatomic gas at 30.0°C. If the mixture is allowed to reach equilibrium, what is the final temperature of the mixture? [*Hint:* Use energy conservation.]

66. A balloon contains 160 L of nitrogen gas at 25°C and 1.0 atm. How much energy must be added to raise the temperature of the nitrogen to 45°C while allowing the balloon to expand at atmospheric pressure?

67. The efficiency of a muscle during weight lifting is equal to the work done in lifting the weight divided by the total energy output of the muscle (work done plus internal energy dissipated in the muscle). Determine the efficiency of a muscle that lifts a 161-N weight through a vertical displacement of 0.577 m and dissipates 139 J in the process.

68. (a) What is the entropy change of 1.00 mol of H_2O when it changes from ice to water at 0.0°C? (b) If the ice is in contact with an environment at a temperature of 10.0°C, what is the entropy change of the universe when the ice melts?

69. Estimate the entropy change of 850 g of water when it is heated from 20.0°C to 50.0°C. [*Hint:* Assume that the heat flows into the water at an average temperature.]

70. For a more realistic estimate of the maximum coefficient of performance of a heat pump, assume that a heat pump takes in heat from outdoors at *10°C below* the ambient outdoor temperature, to account for the temperature difference across its heat exchanger. Similarly, assume that the output must be *10°C hotter* than the house (which itself might be kept at 20°C) to make the heat flow into the house. Make a graph of the coefficient of performance of a reversible heat pump under these conditions as a function of outdoor temperature (from −15°C to +15°C in 5°C increments).

71. A 0.500-kg block of iron at 60.0°C is placed in contact with a 0.500-kg block of iron at 20.0°C. (a) The blocks soon come to a common temperature of 40.0°C. *Estimate* the entropy change of the universe when this occurs. [*Hint:* Assume that all the heat flow occurs at an average temperature for each block.] (b) Estimate the entropy change of the universe if, instead, the temperature of the hotter block increased to 80.0°C while the temperature of the colder block decreased to 0.0°C. [*Hint:* The answer is negative, indicating that the process is impossible.]

72. A container holding 1.20 kg of water at 20.0°C is placed in a freezer that is kept at −20.0°C. The water freezes and comes to thermal equilibrium with the interior of the freezer. What is the minimum amount of electrical energy required by the freezer to do this if it operates between reservoirs at temperatures of 20.0°C and −20.0°C?

73. A reversible heat engine has an efficiency of 33.3%, removing heat from a hot reservoir and rejecting heat to a cold reservoir at 0°C. If the engine now operates in reverse, how long would it take to freeze 1.0 kg of water at 0°C, if it operates on a power of 186 W?

74. Consider a heat engine that is *not* reversible. The engine uses 1.000 mol of a diatomic ideal gas. In the first step (A) there is a constant temperature expansion while in contact with a warm reservoir at 373 K from $P_1 = 1.55 \times 10^5$ Pa and $V_1 = 2.00 \times 10^{-2}$ m^3 to $P_2 = 1.24 \times 10^5$ Pa and $V_2 = 2.50 \times 10^{-2}$ m^3. Then (B) a heat reservoir at the cooler temperature of 273 K is used to cool the gas at constant volume to 273 K from P_2 to $P_3 = 0.91 \times 10^5$ Pa. This is followed by (C) a constant temperature compression while still in contact with the cold reservoir at 273 K from P_3, V_2 to $P_4 = 1.01 \times 10^5$ Pa, V_1. The final step (D) is heating the gas at constant volume from 273 K to 373 K by being in contact with the warm reservoir again, to return from P_4, V_1 to P_1, V_1. Find the change in entropy of the cold reservoir in step B. Remember that the gas is always in contact with the cold reservoir. (b) What is the change in entropy of the hot reservoir in step D? (c) Using this information, find the change in entropy of the total system of gas plus reservoirs during the whole cycle.

75. A fish at a pressure of 1.1 atm has its swim bladder inflated to an initial volume of 8.16 mL. If the fish starts swimming horizontally, its temperature increases from 20.0°C to 22.0°C as a result of the exertion. (a) Since the fish is still at the same pressure, how much work is done by the air in the swim bladder? [*Hint:* First find the new volume from the temperature change.] (b) How much heat is gained by the air in the swim bladder? Assume air to be a diatomic ideal gas. (c) If this quantity of heat is lost by the fish, by how much will its temperature decrease? The fish has a mass of 5.00 g and its specific heat is about 3.5 J/(g·°C).

76. Consider the heat engine described in Problem 74. (a) For each step in the cycle, find the work done by the gas, the heat flow into or out of the gas, and the change in internal energy of the gas. (b) Find the efficiency of this engine. (c) Compare to the efficiency of a reversible engine that uses the same two reservoirs.

77. A town is considering using its lake as a source of power. The average temperature difference from the top to the bottom is 15°C, and the average surface temperature is 22°C. (a) Assuming that the town can set up a reversible engine using the surface and bottom of the lake as heat reservoirs, what would be its efficiency? (b) If the town needs about 1.0×10^8 W of power to be supplied by the lake, how many m^3 of water does the heat engine use per second? (c) The surface area of the lake is 8.0×10^7 m^2 and the average incident intensity (over 24 h) of the sunlight is 200 W/m^2. Can the lake supply enough heat to meet the town's energy needs with this method?

78. In a heat engine, 3.00 mol of a monatomic ideal gas, initially at 4.00 atm of pressure, undergoes an isothermal expansion, increasing its volume by a factor of 9.50 at a constant temperature of 650.0 K. The gas is then compressed at a constant pressure to its original volume. Finally, the pressure is increased at constant volume back to the original pressure. (a) Draw a PV diagram of this three-step heat engine. (b) For each step of this process, calculate the work done on the gas, the change in internal energy, and the heat transferred into the gas. (c) What is the efficiency of this engine?

Answers to Practice Problems

15.1 The internal energy increase is greater than the heat flow into the gas, so positive work was done on the gas. Positive work is done by the piston when it moves inward.

15.2 360 kJ

15.3 Heat flows into the gas; $Q = 3.8$ kJ.

15.4 The fire is irreversible: smoke, carbon dioxide, and ash will not come together to form logs and twigs.

15.5 20%

15.6 4.0 kW·h = 14 MJ

15.7 1200 K

15.8 178 MW

15.9 0.03 J/K

Answers to Checkpoints

15.2 (a) Yes. The heat flow during an adiabatic process is zero ($Q = 0$), but work can be done. The work done on the system changes its internal energy, which can cause a temperature change. (b) Yes. If a system is in thermal contact with a heat reservoir, heat flows between the reservoir and the system to keep the temperature constant. (c) Yes. During a phase transition such as freezing or melting, the internal energy of the system changes but the temperature does not.

15.4 An inelastic collision involves the conversion of kinetic energy into internal energy, an irreversible process.

15.8 No, in an irreversible process the *total* entropy of the universe increases. If the entropy of one system increases by 10 J/K while the entropy of its surroundings decreases by 10 J/K, the process would be reversible ($\Delta S_{tot} = 0$).

Review & Synthesis: Chapters 13–15

Review Exercises

1. How much does the internal energy change for 1.00 m³ of water after it has fallen from the top of a waterfall and landed in the river 11.0 m below? Assume no heat flow from the water to the air.

2. At what temperature will nitrogen gas (N_2) have the same rms speed as helium (He) when the helium is at 20.0°C?

3. A bit of space debris penetrates the hull of a spaceship traversing the asteroid belt and comes to rest in a container of water that was at 20.0°C before being hit. The mass of the space rock is 1.0 g and the mass of the water is 1.0 kg. If the space rock traveled at 8.4×10^3 m/s and if all of its kinetic energy is used to heat the water, what is the final temperature of the water?

4. A pot containing 2.00 kg of water is sitting on a hot stove and the water is stirred violently by a mixer that does 6.0 kJ of mechanical work on the water. The temperature of the water rises by 4.00°C. What quantity of heat flowed into the water from the stove during the process?

5. (a) How much ice at −10.0°C must be placed in 0.250 kg of water at 25.0°C to cool the water to 0°C and melt all of the ice? (b) If half that amount of ice is placed in the water, what is the final temperature of the water?

6. A Pyrex container is filled to the very top with 40.0 L of water. Both the container and the water are at a temperature of 90.0°C. When the temperature has cooled to 20.0°C, how much additional water can be added to the container?

7. A 75-g cube of ice at −10.0°C is placed in 0.500 kg of water at 50.0°C in an insulating container so that no heat is lost to the environment. Will the ice melt completely? What will be the final temperature of this system?

8. A hot air balloon with a volume of 12.0 m³ is initially filled with air at a pressure of 1.00 atm and a temperature of 19.0°C. When the balloon air is heated, the volume and the pressure of the balloon remain constant because the balloon is open to the atmosphere at the bottom. How many moles are in the balloon when the air is heated to 40.0°C?

9. A star's spectrum emits more radiation with a wavelength of 700.0 nm than with any other wavelength. (a) What is the surface temperature of the star? (b) If the star's radius is 7.20×10^8 m, what power does it radiate? (c) If the star is 9.78 ly from Earth, what will an Earth-based observer measure for this star's intensity? Stars are nearly perfect blackbodies. [*Note:* ly stands for light-years.]

10. A wall that is 2.74 m high and 3.66 m long has a thickness composed of 1.00 cm of wood plus 3.00 cm of insulation (with the thermal conductivity approximately of wool). The inside of the wall is 23.0°C and the outside of the wall is at −5.00°C. (a) What is the rate of heat flow through the wall? (b) If half the area of the wall is replaced with a single pane of glass that is 0.500 cm thick, how much heat flows out of the wall now?

11. In a refrigerator, 2.00 mol of an ideal monatomic gas are taken through the cycle shown in the figure. The temperature at point A is 800.0 K. (a) What are the temperature and pressure at point D? (b) What is the net work done on the gas as it is taken through four cycles? (c) What is the internal energy of the gas when it is at point A? (d) What is the total change in internal energy of this gas during four complete cycles?

12. Boiling water in an aluminum pan is being converted to steam at a rate of 10.0 g/s. The flat bottom of the pan has an area of 325 cm² and the pan's thickness is 3.00 mm. If 27.0% of all heat that is transferred to the pan from the flame beneath it is lost from the sides of the pan and the remaining 73.0% goes into the water, what is the temperature of the base of the pan?

13. A 2.00-kg block of ice at 0.0°C melts. What is the change in entropy of the ice as a result of this process?

14. A sphere with a diameter of 80 cm is held at a temperature of 250°C and is radiating energy. If the intensity of the radiation detected at a distance of 2.0 m from the sphere's center is 102 W/m², what is the emissivity of the sphere?

15. A 7.30-kg steel ball at 15.2°C is dropped from a height of 10.0 m into an insulated container with 4.50 L of water at 10.1°C. If no water splashes, what is the final temperature of the water and steel?

16. Michael has set the gauge pressure of the tires on his car to 36.0 psi (lb/in²). He draws chalk lines around the edges of the tires where they touch the driveway surface to measure the area of contact between the tires and the ground. Each front tire has a contact area of 24.0 in² and each rear tire has a contact area of 20.0 in². (a) What is the weight (in lb) of the car? (b) The center-to-center distance between front and rear tires is 7.00 ft. Taking the straight line between the centers of the tires on the left side (driver's side) to be the y-axis with the origin at the center of the front left tire (positive direction pointing forward), what is the y-coordinate of the car's CM?

17. Your hot water tank is insulated, but not very well. To reduce heat loss, you wrap some old blankets around it. With the water at 81°C and the room at 21°C, a thermometer inserted between the outside of the original tank and your blanket reads 36°C. By what factor did the blanket reduce the heat loss?

18. An ideal refrigerator keeps its contents at 0.0°C and exhausts heat into the kitchen at 40.0°C. For every 1.0 kJ of work done, (a) how much heat is exhausted? (b) How much heat is removed from the contents?

19. The outdoor temperature on a winter's day is −4°C. If you use 1.0 kJ of electric energy to run a heat pump, how much heat does that put into your house at 21°C? Assume that the heat pump is ideal.

20. A copper rod has one end in ice at a temperature of 0°C, the other in boiling water. The length and diameter of the rod are 1.00 m and 2.00 cm, respectively. At what rate in grams per hour does the ice melt? Assume no heat flows out of the sides of the rod.

21. (a) Why is the coolant fluid in an automobile kept under high pressure? (b) Why do radiator caps have safety valves, allowing you to reduce the pressure before removing the cap? [*Hint:* See Fig. 14.7a, the phase diagram for water.]

22. A steam engine has a piston with a diameter of 15.0 cm and a stroke (the displacement of the piston) of 20.0 cm. The average pressure applied to this piston is 1.3×10^5 Pa. What operating frequency in cycles per second (Hz) would yield an average power output of 27.6 kW?

23. Two aluminum blocks in thermal contact have the same temperature. (a) Under what condition do they have the same internal energy? (b) Is there an energy transfer between the two blocks? (c) Are the blocks necessarily in physical contact?

24. A power plant burns coal to produce pressurized steam at 535 K. The steam then condenses back into water at a temperature of 323 K. (a) What is the maximum possible efficiency of this plant? (b) If the plant operates at 50.0% of its maximum efficiency and its power output is 1.23×10^8 W, at what rate must heat be removed by means of a cooling tower?

25. A heat engine consists of the following four step cyclic process. During step 1, 2.00 mol of a diatomic ideal gas at a temperature of 325 K are compressed isothermally to one-eighth of the original volume. In step 2, the temperature of the gas is increased to 985 K by an isochoric process. During step 3, the gas expands isothermally back to its original volume. Finally, in step 4, an isochoric process takes the gas back to its original temperature. (a) Sketch a qualitative *PV* diagram, showing the four steps in this cycle. (b) Make a table showing the values of *W*, *Q*, and ΔU for each of the four steps and the totals for one cycle of this process. (c) What is the efficiency of this engine? (d) What would be the efficiency of a Carnot engine operating at the same extreme temperatures?

26. On a day when the air temperature is 19°C, a 0.15-kg baseball is dropped from the top of a 24-m tower. After the ball hits the ground, bounces a few times, and comes to rest, by how much has the entropy of the universe increased?

27. In a certain bimetallic strip (see Fig. 13.7) the brass strip is 0.100% longer than the steel strip at a temperature of 275°C. At what temperature do the two strips have the same length?

28. A 0.360-kg piece of solid lead at 20°C is placed into an insulated container holding 0.980 kg of liquid lead at 420°C. The system comes to an equilibrium temperature with no loss of heat to the environment. Ignore the heat capacity of the container. (a) Is there any solid lead remaining in the system? (b) What is the final temperature of the system?

29. (a) Calculate Earth's escape speed—the minimum speed needed for an object near the surface to escape Earth's gravitational pull. [*Hint:* Use conservation of energy and ignore air resistance.] (b) Calculate the average speed of a hydrogen molecule (H_2) at 0°C. (c) Calculate the average speed of an oxygen molecule (O_2) at 0°C. (d) Use your answers from parts (a) through (c) along with what you know about the distribution of molecular speeds to explain why Earth's atmosphere contains plenty of oxygen but almost no hydrogen.

30. A 10.0-cm cylindrical chamber has a 5.00-cm-diameter piston attached to one end. The piston is connected to an ideal spring with a spring constant of 10.0 N/cm, as shown. Initially, the spring is not compressed but is latched in place so that it cannot move. The cylinder is filled with gas to a pressure of 5.00×10^5 Pa. Once the gas in the cylinder is at this pressure, the spring is unlatched. Because of the difference in pressure between the inside of the chamber and the outside, the spring moves a distance Δx. Heat is allowed to flow into the chamber as it expands so that the temperature of the gas remains constant; thus, you may assume *T* to be the same before and after the expansion. Find the compression of the spring, Δx.

Cylinder   Piston   Spring

5.00 cm

⟵10.0 cm⟶ Δx Wall

MCAT Review

The section that follows includes MCAT exam material and is reprinted with permission of the Association of American Medical Colleges (AAMC).

1. Suppose 2 identical copper bars, A and B, with initial temperatures of 25°C and 75°C, respectively, are placed in contact with each other. If the specific heat of copper is independent of temperature, and if A and B do *not* exchange heat or work with the surroundings, is it likely that A and B will reach 24°C and 76°C, respectively?

   A. Yes, because the bars are identical.

   B. Yes, because heat will flow from B to A.

   C. No, because heat will not flow from A to B.

   D. No, because energy will not be conserved.

2. Some ocean currents carry water from the polar regions to warmer seas. What is the approximate temperature of a solution resulting from mixing 1.00 kg of seawater at 0°C with 1.00 kg of seawater at 5°C?

   A. 1.25°C   B. 2.50°C   C. 3.25°C   D. 4.00°C

3. How much energy is gained by 18.0 g of ice if it melts at the polar ice caps?

   A. 4.18 kJ

   B. 5.87 kJ

   C. 6.02 kJ

   D. 6.17 kJ

Read the paragraph and then answer the following questions:

The steam engine pictured here demonstrates principles of thermodynamics. Water boils, creating steam that pushes against a piston. The steam then changes back to water in the condenser, and the water circulates back to the boiler. The efficiency of this engine is

$$e = W/Q_H = 1 - Q_C/Q_H$$

where W is the output work, Q_H is the heat put in, and Q_C is the heat that flows out as exhaust. It is not possible to convert all of the input heat into output work.

A refrigerator works like a heat engine in reverse. Heat is absorbed from a refrigerator when the liquid that circulates through the refrigerator changes to gas. The gas is then changed back to liquid in a compressor, and the refrigerant is then recirculated.

MCAT Review Questions 4–9

4. Making which of the following changes to the steam engine will increase its efficiency?

   A. Increasing the exhaust temperature

   B. Decreasing the exhaust temperature

   C. Increasing the amount of heat input

   D. Decreasing the amount of heat input

5. The amount of heat that a unit of mass of a refrigerant can remove from a refrigerator is primarily dependent on which of the following characteristics of the refrigerant?

   A. Heat of vaporization

   B. Heat of fusion

   C. Specific heat in liquid form

   D. Specific heat in gaseous form

6. Surrounding the condenser with which one of the following would be most effective for changing steam to water?

   A. High-pressure steam

   B. Low-pressure steam

   C. Stationary water

   D. Circulating water

7. The amount of useful work that can be generated from a source of heat can only be

   A. less than the amount of heat.

   B. less than or equal to the amount of heat.

   C. equal to the amount of heat.

   D. equal to or greater than the amount of heat.

8. What energy transformation causes the piston of the steam engine discussed in the passage to move to the right?

   A. Mechanical to internal

   B. Mechanical to chemical

   C. Internal to mechanical

   D. Internal to electrical

9. Which of the following accurately contrasts the boiling or freezing points of water and of a refrigerant used in a household refrigerator?

   A. The boiling point of the refrigerant should be higher than the boiling point of water.

   B. The boiling point of the refrigerant should be lower than the freezing point of water.

   C. The freezing point of the refrigerant should be higher than the boiling point of water.

   D. The freezing point of the refrigerant should be higher than the freezing point of water.

Read the paragraph and then answer the following questions:

An engineer was instructed to design a holding tank for synthetic lubricating oil. Two requirements were that the amount of time necessary to drain the tank and the force needed to lift the drain plug be minimized. In the initial design, the drain plug, which weighed 500 N, rested on the drain hole and was lifted by a thin rod that extended through the top of the tank. The tank was insulated and had 10 electric immersion heaters that each use 5 kW of power. The oil has a boiling point of 220°C, a specific gravity of 0.7, and a specific heat that is 60% that of water. The heat capacity of the tank was negligible compared to the fluids contained in it.

Rod for lifting drain plug

Drain plug
500 N   Immersion heaters

MCAT Review Questions 10 and 11

The tank was built and then tested by filling it with water. The air pressure inside and outside the tank was 1 atm. The force required to lift the plug was found to be 5310 N. In testing the heater capability, the tank was filled to the top with water at 20°C. With all 10 heaters operating, the water temperature reached 100°C 15 h later. The technician who conducted the evaluation reported that the full tank of water was completely discharged approximately 30 s after opening the drain.

10. With the heaters operating, how long would it take to raise the temperature of a full tank of oil from 20°C to 60°C?

A. 3.2 h

B. 6.3 h

C. 7.5 h

D. 9.0 h

11. It is suggested that the air in the tank above the oil be pressurized at 4 atm above normal air pressure. Which of the following is the *least* likely to occur along with this increase in pressure?

A. The time required to heat the oil would be greatly extended.

B. The drain plug would be more difficult to lift.

C. Fluid velocity would be increased when the tank is drained.

D. The time required to drain the tank would decrease.

Mathematics Review

A.1   ALGEBRA

There are two basic kinds of algebraic manipulations.

- The same operation can always be performed on both sides of an equation.
- Substitution is always permissible (if $a = b$, then any occurrence of a in any equation can be replaced with b).

Products distribute over sums

$$a(b + c) = ab + ac \tag{A-1}$$

The reverse—replacing $ab + ac$ with $a(b + c)$—is called *factoring*. Since dividing by c is the same as multiplying by $1/c$,

$$\frac{a + b}{c} = \frac{a}{c} + \frac{b}{c} \tag{A-2}$$

Equation (A-2) is the basis of the procedure for adding fractions. To add fractions, they must be expressed with a *common denominator*.

$$\frac{a}{b} + \frac{c}{d} = \frac{a}{b} \times \frac{d}{d} + \frac{c}{d} \times \frac{b}{b} = \frac{ad}{bd} + \frac{bc}{bd}$$

Now applying Eq. (A-2), we end up with

$$\frac{a}{b} + \frac{c}{d} = \frac{ad + bc}{bd} \tag{A-3}$$

To divide fractions, remember that dividing by c/d is the same as multiplying by d/c:

$$\frac{a}{b} \div \frac{c}{d} = \frac{\dfrac{a}{b}}{\dfrac{c}{d}} = \frac{a}{b} \times \frac{d}{c} = \frac{ad}{bc}$$

A product in a square root can be separated:

$$\sqrt{ab} = \sqrt{a} \times \sqrt{b} \tag{A-4}$$

Pitfalls to Avoid

These are some of the most common *incorrect* algebraic substitutions. Don't fall into any of these traps!

$$\sqrt{a + b} \neq \sqrt{a} + \sqrt{b}$$

$$\frac{a}{b + c} \neq \frac{a}{b} + \frac{a}{c}$$

$$\frac{a}{b} + \frac{c}{d} \neq \frac{a + c}{b + d}$$

$$(a + b)^2 \neq a^2 + b^2$$

In the last one, the cross term is missing: $(a + b)^2 = a^2 + 2ab + b^2$.

Graphs of Linear Functions

If the graph of y as a function of x is a straight line, then y is a *linear function* of x. The relationship can be written in the standard form

$$y = mx + b \tag{A-5}$$

where m is the *slope* and b is the *y-intercept*. The slope measures how steep the line is. It tells how much y changes for a given change in x:

$$m = \frac{\Delta y}{\Delta x} = \frac{y_2 - y_1}{x_2 - x_1} \qquad \text{(A-6)}$$

The y-intercept is the value of y when $x = 0$. On the graph, the line crosses the y-axis at $y = b$.

Example A.1

What is the equation of the line graphed in Fig. A.1?

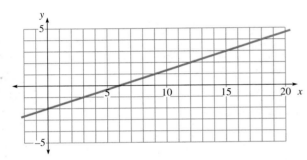

Figure A.1

Solution   The y-intercept is -2. To find the slope, we choose two points on the line and then divide the "rise" (Δy) by the "run" (Δx). Using the points $(0, -2)$ and $(18, 4)$,

$$m = \frac{\text{rise}}{\text{run}} = \frac{y_2 - y_1}{x_2 - x_1} = \frac{4 - (-2)}{18 - 0} = \frac{1}{3}$$

Then $y = mx + b = \frac{1}{3}x - 2$.

A.2   SOLVING EQUATIONS

Solving an equation means using algebraic operations to isolate one variable. Many students tend to substitute numerical values into an equation as soon as possible. In many cases, that's a mistake. Although at first it may seem easier to manipulate numerical quantities than to manipulate algebraic symbols, there are several advantages to working with symbols:

- Symbolic algebra is much easier to follow than a series of numerical calculations. Plugging in numbers tends to obscure the logic behind your solution. If you need to trace back through your work (to find an error or review for an exam), it'll be much clearer if you have worked through the problem symbolically. It will also help your instructor when grading your homework papers or exams. When your work is clear, your instructor is better able to help you understand your mistakes. You may also get more partial credit on exams!

- Symbolic algebra lets you draw conclusions about how one quantity depends on another. For instance, working symbolically you might see that the horizontal range of a projectile is proportional to the *square* of the initial speed. If you had substituted the numerical value of the initial speed, you wouldn't notice that. In particular, when an algebraic symbol cancels out of the equation, you know that the answer doesn't depend on that quantity.

- On the most practical level, it's easy to make arithmetic or calculation errors. The later on in your solution that numbers are substituted, the fewer number of steps you have to check for such errors.

When solving equations that contain square roots, be careful not to assume that a square root is positive. The equation $x^2 = a$ has *two* solutions for x, $x = \pm\sqrt{a}$. (The symbol $\pm$ means *either + or −*.)

Solving Quadratic Equations

An equation is quadratic in x if it contains terms with no powers of x other than a squared term (x^2), a linear term (x^1), and a constant (x^0). Any quadratic equation can be put into the standard form:

$$ax^2 + bx + c = 0 \qquad \text{(A-7)}$$

The quadratic formula gives the solutions to any quadratic equation written in standard form:

$$x = \frac{-b \pm \sqrt{b^2 - 4ac}}{2a} \qquad \text{(A-8)}$$

The symbol "$\pm$" (read "plus or minus") indicates that in general there are two solutions to a quadratic equation; that is, two values of x will satisfy the equation. One solution is found by taking the + sign and the other by taking the − sign in the quadratic formula. If $b^2 - 4ac = 0$, then there is only one solution (or, technically, the two solutions happen to be the same). If $b^2 - 4ac < 0$, then there is no solution to the equation (for x among the real numbers).

The quadratic formula still works if $b = 0$ or $c = 0$, although in such cases the equation can easily be solved without recourse to the quadratic formula.

Example A.2

Solve the equation $5x(3 - x) = 6$.

Solution First put the equation in standard quadratic form:

$$15x - 5x^2 = 6$$

$$-5x^2 + 15x - 6 = 0$$

We identify $a = -5$, $b = 15$, $c = -6$. Then

$$x = \frac{-b \pm \sqrt{b^2 - 4ac}}{2a}$$

$$= \frac{-15 \pm \sqrt{15^2 - 4 \times (-5) \times (-6)}}{-10}$$

$$\approx \frac{-15 \pm 10.25}{-10} = 0.475 \text{ or } 2.525$$

Solving Simultaneous Equations

Simultaneous equations are a set of N equations with N unknown quantities. We wish to solve these equations *simultaneously* to find the values of all of the unknowns. We *must* have at least as many equations as unknowns. It pays to keep track of the number of unknown quantities and the number of equations in solving more challenging problems. If there are more unknowns than equations, then look for some other relationship between the quantities—perhaps some information given in the problem that has not been used.

One way to solve simultaneous equations is by *successive substitution*. Solve one of the equations for one unknown (in terms of the other unknowns). Substitute this expression into each of the other equations. That leaves $N - 1$ equations and $N - 1$ unknowns. Repeat until there is only one equation left with one unknown. Find the value of that unknown quantity, and then work backward to find all the others.

Example A.3

Solve the equations $2x - 4y = 3$ and $x + 3y = -5$ for x and y.

Solution   First solve the second equation for x in terms of y:

$$x = -5 - 3y$$

Substitute $-5 - 3y$ for x in the first equation:

$$2 \times (-5 - 3y) - 4y = 3$$

This can be solved for y:

$$-10 - 10y = 3$$

$$-10y = 13$$

$$y = \frac{13}{-10} = -1.3$$

Now that y is known, use it to find x:

$$x = -5 - 3y = -5 - 3 \times (-1.3) = -1.1$$

It's a good idea to check the results by substituting into the original equations.

A.3   EXPONENTS AND LOGARITHMS

These identities show how to manipulate exponents.

$$a^{-x} = \frac{1}{a^x} \tag{A-9}$$

$$(a^x) \times (a^y) = a^{x+y} \tag{A-10}$$

$$\frac{a^x}{a^y} = (a^x) \times (a^{-y}) = a^{x-y} \tag{A-11}$$

$$(a^x) \times (b^x) = (ab)^x \tag{A-12}$$

$$(a^x)^y = a^{xy} \tag{A-13}$$

$$a^{1/n} = \sqrt[n]{a} \tag{A-14}$$

$$a^0 = 1 \quad \text{(for any } a \neq 0) \tag{A-15}$$

$$0^a = 0 \quad \text{(for any } a \neq 0) \tag{A-16}$$

A common mistake to avoid: $(a^x) \times (a^y) \neq a^{xy}$ [see Eq. (A-10)].

Logarithms

Taking a logarithm is the inverse of exponentiation:

$$x = \log_b y \quad \text{means that} \quad y = b^x \tag{A-17}$$

Thus, one undoes the other:

$$\log_b b^x = x \tag{A-18}$$

$$b^{\log_b x} = x \tag{A-19}$$

The two commonly used bases b are 10 (the *common* logarithm) and $e = 2.71828\ldots$ (the *natural* logarithm). The common logarithm is written "$\log_{10}$," or sometimes just "log" if base 10 is understood. The natural logarithm is usually written "ln" rather than "$\log_e$."
These identities are true for any base logarithm.

$$\log xy = \log x + \log y \tag{A-20}$$

$$\log \frac{x}{y} = \log x - \log y \tag{A-21}$$

$$\log x^a = a \log x \tag{A-22}$$

Here are some common mistakes to avoid:

$$\log (x + y) \neq \log x + \log y$$

$$\log (x + y) \neq \log x \times \log y$$

$$\log xy \neq \log x \times \log y$$

$$\log x^a \neq (\log x)^a$$

Semilog Graphs

A semilog graph uses a logarithmic scale on the vertical axis and a linear scale on the horizontal axis. Semilog graphs are useful when the data plotted is thought to be an exponential function. If

$$y = y_0 e^{ax}$$

then

$$\ln y = ax + \ln y_0$$

so a graph of $\ln y$ versus x will be a straight line with slope a and y-intercept $\ln y_0$.

Rather than calculating $\ln y$ for each data point and plotting on regular graph paper, it is convenient to use special semilog paper. The vertical axis is marked so that the values of y can be plotted directly, but the markings are spaced proportional to the log of y. (If you are using a plotting calculator or a computer to make the graph, log scale should be chosen for one axis from the menu of options.) The slope a on a semilog graph is *not* $\Delta y / \Delta x$ since the logarithm is actually being plotted. The correct way to find the slope is

$$a = \frac{\Delta(\ln y)}{\Delta x} = \frac{\ln y_2 - \ln y_1}{x_2 - x_1}$$

Note that there cannot be a zero on a logarithmic scale.

The two graphs of Figs. A.2 and A.3 are linear and semilog plots, respectively, of the function $y = 3e^{-2x}$.

Log-Log Graphs

A log-log graph uses logarithmic scales for both axes. Log-log graphs are useful when the data plotted is thought to be a power function

$$y = Ax^n$$

For such a function,

$$\log y = n \log x + \log A$$

so a graph of $\log y$ versus $\log x$ will be a straight line with slope n and y-intercept $\log A$. The slope (n) on a log-log graph is found as

$$n = \frac{\Delta(\log y)}{\Delta(\log x)} = \frac{\log y_2 - \log y_1}{\log x_2 - \log x_1}$$

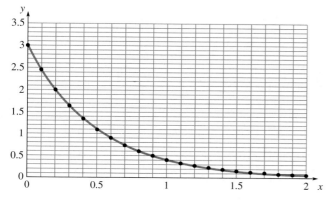

Figure A.2 Graph of the exponential function $y = 3e^{-2x}$ on linear graph paper.

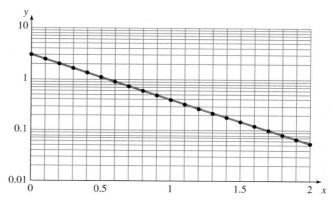

Figure A.3 Graph of the exponential function $y = 3e^{-2x}$ on semilog graph paper.

Figure A.4 Graph of the power function $y = 130x^{3/2}$ on linear graph paper.

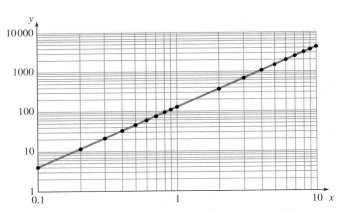

Figure A.5 Graph of the power function $y = 130x^{3/2}$ on log-log graph paper.

The graphs of Figs. A.4 and A.5 are linear and log-log plots, respectively, of the function $y = 130x^{3/2}$.

A.4   PROPORTIONS AND RATIOS

The notation

$$y \propto x$$

means that y is directly proportional to x. A proportionality can be written as an equation

$$y = kx$$

if the constant of proportionality k is written explicitly. Be careful: an equation can *look like* a proportionality without being one. For example, $V = IR$ means that $V \propto I$ *if and only if* R is constant. If R depends on I, then V is not proportional to I.

The notation

$$y \propto \frac{1}{x}$$

means that y is inversely proportional to x. The notation

$$y \propto x^{n}$$

means that y is proportional to the nth power of x.

Writing out proportions as ratios usually simplifies solutions when some common items in an equation are unknown but we do know the values of all but one of the proportional quantities (tutorial: ball toss). For example if $y \propto x^{n}$, we can write

$$\frac{y_1}{y_2} = \left(\frac{x_1}{x_2}\right)^{n}$$

Percentages

Percentages require careful attention. Look at these four examples:

"B is 30% of A" means $B = 0.30A$

"B is 30% larger than A" means $B = (1 + 0.30)A = 1.30A$

"B is 30% smaller than A" means $B = (1 - 0.30)A = 0.70A$

"A increases by 30%" means $\Delta A = +0.30A$

Example A.4

If $P \propto T^4$, and T increases by 10.0%, by what percentage does P increase?

Solution

$$\Delta T = +0.100 T_i$$

$$T_f = T_i + \Delta T = 1.100 T_i$$

$$\frac{P_f}{P_i} = \left(\frac{T_f}{T_i}\right)^4 = 1.100^4 \approx 1.464$$

Therefore, P increases by about 46.4%.

A.5 APPROXIMATIONS

Binomial Approximations

A binomial is the sum of two terms. The general rule for the nth power of an algebraic sum is given by the binomial expansion:

$$(a + b)^n = a^n + na^{n-1}b + \frac{n(n-1)}{1 \times 2} a^{n-2}b^2 + \frac{n(n-1)(n-2)}{1 \times 2 \times 3} a^{n-3}b^3 + \cdots$$

The binomial approximations are used when a binomial in which one term is much smaller than the other is raised to a power n. Only the first two terms of the binomial expansion are of significant value; the other terms are dropped. A common case for physics problems is that in which $a = 1$, or can be made equal to one by factoring. The basic approximation forms are then given by

$$(1 + x)^n \approx 1 + nx \quad \text{when } |x| \ll 1 \quad \text{(A-23)}$$

$$(1 - x)^n \approx 1 - nx \quad \text{when } |x| \ll 1 \quad \text{(A-24)}$$

The power n can be any real number, including negative as well as positive numbers. It does not have to be an integer. (tutorial: small percentage changes) An *estimate* of the error—the difference between the approximation and the exact expression—is given by

$$\text{error} \approx \tfrac{1}{2}n(n-1)x^2 \quad \text{(A-25)}$$

Of course, the larger term in a binomial is not necessarily 1, but the larger term can be factored out and then Eq. (A-23) or Eq. (A-24) applied. For instance, if $A \gg b$, then

$$(A + b)^n = \left[A \times \left(1 + \frac{b}{A}\right)\right]^n = A^n \left(1 + \frac{b}{A}\right)^n$$

Another common expansion is

$$e^x = 1 + x + \frac{x^2}{2!} + \frac{x^3}{3!} + \cdots$$

where, for any integer n, $n! = n \times (n-1) \times (n-2) \times \cdots \times [n - (n-1)]$; for example, $3! = 3 \times 2 \times 1 = 6$.

Small-Angle Approximations

Approximations for small angles appear in Section A.7 on trigonometry.

Table A.1	Properties of Common Geometric Shapes		
Geometric Shape	**Properties**	**Geometric Shape**	**Properties**

Circle	Diameter $d = 2r$ Circumference $C = \pi d = 2\pi r$ Area $A = \pi r^2$	Sphere	Surface area $A = 4\pi r^2$ Volume $V = \frac{4}{3}\pi r^3$
Rectangle	Perimeter $P = 2b + 2h$ Area $A = bh$	Parallelepiped	Surface area $A = 2(ab + bc + ac)$ Volume $V = abc$
Right triangle	Perimeter $P = a + b + c$ Area $A = \frac{1}{2}\text{base} \times \text{height} = \frac{1}{2}ba$ Pythagorean theorem $c^2 = a^2 + b^2$ Hypotenuse $c = \sqrt{a^2 + b^2}$	Right circular cylinder	Surface area $A = 2\pi r^2 + 2\pi rh$ $= 2\pi r(r + h)$ Volume $V = \pi r^2 h$
Triangle	Area $A = \frac{1}{2}bh$		

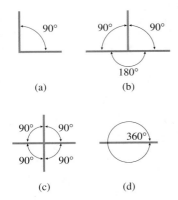

Figure A.6 (a) A right angle; (b) two adjacent right angles, or a straight line; (c) four adjacent right angles; (d) a full circle.

Figure A.7 Acute and obtuse angles.

A.6 GEOMETRY

Geometric Shapes

Table A.1 lists the geometric shapes that commonly appear in physics problems. It is often necessary to determine the area or volume of one of these simple shapes to complete the solution of a problem. The formulae for the properties associated with each geometric form are listed in the column to the right.

Angular Measure

An angle between two straight lines that meet at a single point is specified in degrees. If the two lines are perpendicular to each other, as shown in Fig. A.6a, the angular separation is said to be a right angle or 90°. In Fig. A.6b two such 90° angles are placed side by side; they add to 180°, so a straight line represents an angular separation of 180°. When four right angles are grouped as shown in Fig. A.6c, the angles add to 360° and a full circle contains 360° as shown in Fig. A.6d. An angle that is less than 90° is called an **acute** angle; one greater than 90° is called an **obtuse** angle.

When two lines meet, as shown in Fig. A.7, there are two possible angles that might be specified; one is the acute angle α and the other is the obtuse angle β. The symbol used to indicate an angle is $\angle$. When two angles placed adjacent to each other form a straight line, they are called supplementary angles; angles α and β in Fig. A.7 are supplementary angles. When two angles placed adjacent to each other form a right angle, they are called complementary angles.

Various triangles are shown in Fig. A.8. The sum of the interior angles of any triangle is 180°. An isosceles triangle has two sides of equal length; the angles opposite to the equal sides are equal angles. An equilateral triangle has all three sides of equal length; it is also equiangular. Right triangles have one right angle, 90°, and the sum of the other two angles is 90°, so those angles are acute angles. Commonly used right triangles have sides in the ratio of 3:4:5 and 5:12:13.

Triangles are similar when all three angles of one are equal to the three angles of the other. If two angles of one triangle are equal to two angles of the other, the third angles are necessarily equal and the triangles are similar. The ratio of corresponding sides of similar triangles are equal, as shown in Fig. A.9. Similar triangles of the same size are called congruent triangles.

Figure A.10 shows other useful relations among angles between intersecting lines. When two angles add to 180°, as $\angle\alpha + \angle\beta$ in one of the small figures, the angles are supplementary. Another small figure shows two angles, $\angle\alpha + \angle\beta$ adding to 90°, so in that case the angles are complementary.

For many physics problems it is convenient to use angles measured in radians rather than in degrees; the abbreviation for radians is rad. The arc length s measured along a circle is proportional to the angle between the two radii that define the arc, as shown in Fig. A.11. One radian is defined as the angle subtended when the arc length is equal to the length of the radius.

For θ measured in radians,

$$s = r\theta$$

When the angular displacement is all the way around the circle, 360°, the arc length is equal to the circumference of the circle:

$$s = 2\pi r = r\theta$$

The equivalent to 360° measured in radians is thus $\theta = 2\pi$ radians and the equivalence between radians and degrees is

$$1\ \text{rad} = \frac{360°}{2\pi} \approx 57.3° \qquad \text{or} \qquad 1° = \frac{2\pi}{360°} \approx 0.01745\ \text{rad}$$

Note that the radian has no physical dimensions; it is a ratio of two lengths so it is a pure number. We use the term *rad* to remind us of the angular units being used.

Figure A.8 Triangles.

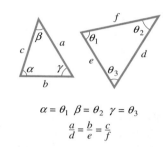

$\alpha = \theta_1 \ \ \beta = \theta_2 \ \ \gamma = \theta_3$

$\dfrac{a}{d} = \dfrac{b}{e} = \dfrac{c}{f}$

Figure A.9 Similar triangles.

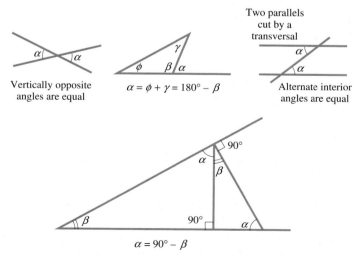

Figure A.10 Angles formed by intersecting lines.

If $s = r$, $\theta = 1$ radian

Figure A.11 Radian measure.

A.7 TRIGONOMETRY

The basic trigonometric functions used in physics are shown in Fig. A.12. Note that in determining the function values, the units of length cancel, so the sine, cosine, and tangent functions are dimensionless.

The side opposite and the side adjacent to either of the acute angles in the right triangle are of lesser length than the hypotenuse, according to the Pythagorean theorem. Therefore, the absolute values of the sine and cosine cannot exceed 1. The absolute value of the tangent can exceed 1.

Figure A.13 shows the signs (positive or negative) associated with the trigonometric functions for an angle θ located in each of the four quadrants. The hypotenuse r is positive, so the sign for the sine or cosine is determined by the signs of x or y as measured along the positive or negative x- and y-axes. The sign of the tangent then depends on the signs of the sine and cosine. The angle θ is measured in a counterclockwise direction starting from the positive x-axis, which represents $0°$. Angles measured from the x-axis going in a clockwise direction (below the x-axis) are negative angles; an angle of $-60°$, which is located in the fourth quadrant, is the same as an angle of $+300°$. Figure A.14 shows graphs of $y = \sin \theta$ and $y = \cos \theta$ as functions of θ in radians. Also graphed

Figure A.12 Trigonometric functions used in physics problems; angles θ and ϕ are complementary angles.

Right triangle

$\phi = 90° - \theta$

$$\sin \theta = \frac{\text{side opposite } \angle \theta}{\text{hypotenuse}} = \frac{b}{c} = \cos \phi$$

$$\cos \theta = \frac{\text{side adjacent } \angle \theta}{\text{hypotenuse}} = \frac{a}{c} = \sin \phi$$

$$\tan \theta = \frac{\text{side opposite } \angle \theta}{\text{side adjacent } \angle \theta} = \frac{b}{a} = \frac{\sin \theta}{\cos \theta} = \frac{1}{\tan \phi}$$

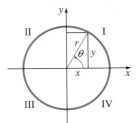

Quadrant I: $0 < \theta < 90°$
$\sin \theta = y/r$ is positive
$\cos \theta = x/r$ is positive
$\tan \theta = y/x$ is positive

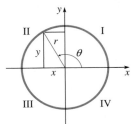

Quadrant II: $90° < \theta < 180°$
$\sin \theta = y/r$ is positive
$\cos \theta = x/r$ is negative
$\tan \theta = y/x$ is negative

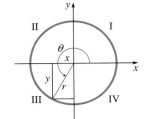

Quadrant III: $180° < \theta < 270°$
$\sin \theta = y/r$ is negative
$\cos \theta = x/r$ is negative
$\tan \theta = y/x$ is positive

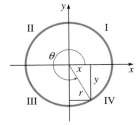

Quadrant IV: $270° < \theta < 360°$
$\sin \theta = y/r$ is negative
$\cos \theta = x/r$ is positive
$\tan \theta = y/x$ is negative

Figure A.13 Signs of trigonometric functions in various quadrants.

(a)

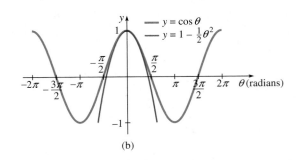

(b)

Figure A.14 (a) Graphs of $y = \sin \theta$ and $y = \theta$. Note that $\sin \theta \approx \theta$ for small θ. (b) Graphs of $y = \cos \theta$ and $y = 1 - \frac{1}{2}\theta^2$. Note that $\cos \theta \approx 1 - \frac{1}{2}\theta^2$ for small θ.

Table A.2   Useful Trigonometric Identities

$\sin^2 \theta + \cos^2 \theta = 1$

$\sin(-\theta) = -\sin \theta$

$\cos(-\theta) = \cos \theta$

$\tan(-\theta) = -\tan \theta$

$\sin(180° \pm \theta) = \mp \sin \theta$

$\cos(180° \pm \theta) = -\cos \theta$

$\tan(180° \pm \theta) = \pm \tan \theta$

$\sin(90° \pm \beta) = \cos \beta$

$\cos(90° \pm \beta) = \mp \sin \beta$

$\sin 2\theta = 2 \sin \theta \cos \theta$

$\cos 2\theta = \cos^2 \theta - \sin^2 \theta$
$\quad\quad = 2 \cos^2 \theta - 1 = 1 - 2 \sin^2 \theta$

$\tan 2\theta = \dfrac{2 \tan \theta}{1 - \tan^2 \theta}$

$\sin(\alpha \pm \beta) = \sin \alpha \cos \beta \pm \cos \alpha \sin \beta$

$\cos(\alpha \pm \beta) = \cos \alpha \cos \beta \mp \sin \alpha \sin \beta$

$\tan(\alpha \pm \beta) = \dfrac{\tan \alpha \pm \tan \beta}{1 \mp \tan \alpha \tan \beta}$

$\sin \alpha + \sin \beta = 2 \sin\left[\tfrac{1}{2}(\alpha + \beta)\right] \cos\left[\tfrac{1}{2}(\alpha - \beta)\right]$

$\sin \alpha - \sin \beta = 2 \cos\left[\tfrac{1}{2}(\alpha + \beta)\right] \sin\left[\tfrac{1}{2}(\alpha - \beta)\right]$

$\cos \alpha + \cos \beta = 2 \cos\left[\tfrac{1}{2}(\alpha + \beta)\right] \cos\left[\tfrac{1}{2}(\alpha - \beta)\right]$

$\cos \alpha - \cos \beta = -2 \sin\left[\tfrac{1}{2}(\alpha + \beta)\right] \sin\left[\tfrac{1}{2}(\alpha - \beta)\right]$

Table A.3   Inverse Trigonometric Functions

Function	Principal Value Range (Quadrants)		To Find Value in a Different Quadrant
$\sin^{-1}$	$-\dfrac{\pi}{2}$ to $\dfrac{\pi}{2}$	(I and IV)	Subtract principal value from π
$\cos^{-1}$	0 to π	(I and II)	Subtract principal value from 2π
$\tan^{-1}$	$-\dfrac{\pi}{2}$ to $\dfrac{\pi}{2}$	(I and IV)	Add principal value to π

are two functions that are useful approximations for the sine and cosine functions when $|\theta|$ is sufficiently small (see the section titled Small-Angle Approximations, p. A-12).

Table A.2 lists some of the most useful trigonometric identities.

Inverse Trigonometric Functions   The inverse trigonometric functions can be written in either of two ways. To use the inverse cosine as an example: $\cos^{-1} x$ or arccos x. Both of these expressions mean *an angle whose cosine is equal to x.* A calculator returns only the *principal value* of an inverse trigonometric function (Table A.3), which may or may not be the correct solution in a given problem.

Law of Sines and Law of Cosines   These two laws apply to any triangle labeled as shown in Fig. A.15:

Law of sines: $\dfrac{\sin \alpha}{a} = \dfrac{\sin \beta}{b} = \dfrac{\sin \gamma}{c}$

Law of cosines: $c^2 = a^2 + b^2 - 2ab \cos \gamma$ (where γ is the interior angle formed by the intersection of sides a and b)

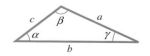

Figure A.15 A general triangle.

Figure A.16 Illustration of the small angle approximations $\sin \theta \approx \theta$ and $\cos \theta \approx 1 - \frac{1}{2}\theta^2$ (for θ in radians) using a right triangle with $\theta \ll 1$ rad.

Small-Angle Approximations

These approximations are written for θ *in radians* and are valid when $\theta \ll 1$ rad.

$$\sin \theta \approx \theta \qquad \text{(A-26)}$$

$$\cos \theta \approx 1 - \frac{1}{2}\theta^2 \qquad \text{(A-27)}$$

$$\tan \theta \approx \theta \qquad \text{(A-28)}$$

The sizes of the errors involved in using these approximations are roughly $\frac{1}{6}\theta^3$, $\frac{1}{24}\theta^4$, and $\frac{2}{3}\theta^3$, respectively. In *some* circumstances it may be all right to ignore the $\frac{1}{2}\theta^2$ term and write

$$\cos \theta \approx 1 \qquad \text{(A-29)}$$

The origin of these approximations can be illustrated using a right triangle of hypotenuse 1 with one very small angle θ (Fig. A.16). If θ is very small, then the adjacent side ($\cos \theta$) will be nearly the same length as the hypotenuse (1). Then we can think of those two sides as radii of a circle that subtend an angle θ. The relationship between the arc length s and the angle subtended is

$$s = \theta r$$

Since $\sin \theta \approx s$ and $r = 1$, we have $\sin \theta \approx \theta$. To find an approximate form for $\cos \theta$ (but one more accurate than $\cos \theta \approx 1$), we can use the Pythagorean theorem:

$$\sin^2 \theta + \cos^2 \theta = 1$$

$$\cos \theta = \sqrt{1 - \sin^2 \theta} \approx \sqrt{1 - \theta^2}$$

Now, using a binomial approximation,

$$\cos \theta \approx (1 - \theta^2)^{1/2} \approx 1 - \frac{1}{2}\theta^2$$

A.8   VECTORS

The distinction between vectors and scalars is discussed in Section 2.1. Scalars have magnitude while vectors have magnitude and direction. A vector is represented graphically by an arrow of length proportional to the magnitude of the vector and aligned in a direction that corresponds to the vector direction.

In print, the symbol for a vector quantity is sometimes written in bold font, or in roman font with an arrow over it, or in bold font with an arrow over it (as done in this book). When writing by hand, a vector is designated by drawing an arrow over the symbol: $\vec{A}$. When we write just plain A, that stands for the *magnitude* of the vector. We also use absolute value bars to stand for the magnitude of a vector, so $A = |\vec{A}|$.

Addition and Subtraction of Vectors

When vectors are added or subtracted, the magnitudes and directions must be taken into account. Details on vector addition and subtraction are found in Sections 2.2 and 2.3. Here we provide a brief summary.

The graphical method for adding vectors involves placing the vectors tip to tail and then drawing from the tail of the first to the tip of the second, as shown in Fig. A.17.

(a)

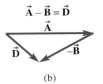

(b)

Figure A.17 Graphical (a) addition and (b) subtraction of two vectors.

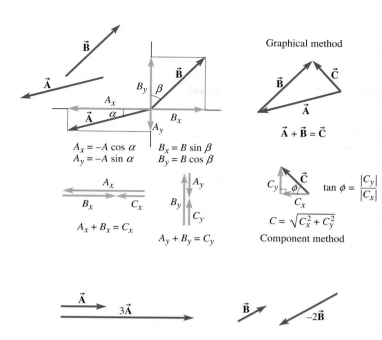

Figure A.18 Adding two arbitrary vectors by two different methods.

Figure A.19 Multiplication of a vector by a scalar.

To subtract a vector, add its opposite. In Fig. A.17, $-\vec{\mathbf{B}}$ has the same magnitude as $\vec{\mathbf{B}}$ but is opposite in direction. Then $\vec{\mathbf{A}} + \vec{\mathbf{B}} = \vec{\mathbf{A}} - (-\vec{\mathbf{B}})$.

Figure A.18 shows both the graphical and component methods of vector addition.

Product of a Vector and a Scalar

When a vector is multiplied by a scalar, the magnitude of the vector is multiplied by the absolute value of the scalar, as shown in Fig. A.19. The direction of the vector does not change unless the scalar factor is negative, in which case the direction is reversed.

Scalar Product of Two Vectors

One type of product of two vectors is the *scalar product* (also called the *dot product*). The notation for it is

$$C = \vec{\mathbf{A}} \cdot \vec{\mathbf{B}}$$

As its name implies, the scalar product of two vectors is a scalar quantity; it can be positive, negative, or zero but has no direction.

The scalar product depends on the magnitudes of the two vectors and on the angle θ between them. To find the angle, draw the two vectors starting *at the same point* (Fig. A.20). Then the scalar product is defined by

$$\vec{\mathbf{A}} \cdot \vec{\mathbf{B}} = AB \cos \theta$$

Reversing the order of the two vectors does not change the scalar product: $\vec{\mathbf{B}} \cdot \vec{\mathbf{A}} = \vec{\mathbf{A}} \cdot \vec{\mathbf{B}}$. The scalar product can be written in terms of the components of the two vectors:

$$\vec{\mathbf{A}} \cdot \vec{\mathbf{B}} = A_x B_x + A_y B_y + A_z B_z$$

Cross Product of Two Vectors

Another type of product of two vectors is the *cross product* (also called the *vector product*), which is introduced in Chapter 19. It is denoted by

$$\vec{\mathbf{A}} \times \vec{\mathbf{B}} = \vec{\mathbf{C}}$$

Figure A.20 Two vectors are drawn starting at the same point. The angle θ between the vectors is used to find the scalar product and the cross product of the vectors.

The cross product is a *vector* quantity; it has magnitude and direction. $\vec{\mathbf{A}} \times \vec{\mathbf{B}}$ is read as "$\vec{\mathbf{A}}$ cross $\vec{\mathbf{B}}$."

For two vectors, $\vec{\mathbf{A}}$ and $\vec{\mathbf{B}}$, separated by an angle θ (with θ chosen to be the *smaller* angle between the two as in Fig. A.20), the magnitude of the cross product $\vec{\mathbf{C}}$ is

$$|\vec{\mathbf{C}}| = |\vec{\mathbf{A}} \times \vec{\mathbf{B}}| = AB \sin \theta$$

The direction of the cross product $\vec{\mathbf{C}}$ is one of the two directions perpendicular to both $\vec{\mathbf{A}}$ and $\vec{\mathbf{B}}$. To choose the correct direction, use the right-hand rule explained in Section 19.2.

The cross product depends on the order of the multiplication.

$$\vec{\mathbf{A}} \times \vec{\mathbf{B}} = -\vec{\mathbf{B}} \times \vec{\mathbf{A}}$$

The magnitude is $AB \sin \theta$ in both cases, but the direction of one cross product is opposite to the direction of the other.

A.9   SELECTED MATHEMATICAL SYMBOLS

$\times$ or $\cdot$	multiplication
Δ	change in, small increment, or uncertainty in
$\approx$	is approximately equal to
$\neq$	is not equal to
$\leq$	is less than or equal to
$\geq$	is greater than or equal to
$\ll$	is much less than
$\gg$	is much greater than
$\propto$	is proportional to
$|Q|$	absolute value of Q
$|\vec{\mathbf{a}}|$	magnitude of vector $\vec{\mathbf{a}}$
$\perp$	perpendicular
$\parallel$	parallel
∞	infinity
$'$	prime (used to distinguish different values of the same variable)
Q_{av}, $\overline{Q}$, or $\langle Q \rangle$	average of Q
Σ	sum
Π	product
$\log_b x$	the logarithm (base b) of x
$\ln x$	the natural (base e) logarithm of x
$\pm$	plus or minus
$\mp$	minus or plus
$\cdots$	ellipsis (indicates continuation of a series or list)
$\angle$	angle
$\Rightarrow$	implies
$\therefore$	therefore

Table of Selected Nuclides

Atomic Number Z	Element	Symbol	Mass Number A	Mass of *neutral atom* (u)	Percentage Abundance (or Decay Mode)	Half-life (if Unstable)
0	(Neutron)	n	1	1.008 664 9	β^-	10.24 min
1	Hydrogen	H	1	1.007 825 0	99.985	
	(Deuterium)	(D)	2	2.014 101 8	0.015	
	(Tritium)	(T)	3	3.016 049 3	β^-	12.32 yr
2	Helium	He	3	3.016 029 3	0.000 137	
			4	4.002 603 2	99.999 863	
3	Lithium	Li	6	6.015 122 3	7.6	
			7	7.016 004 0	92.4	
4	Beryllium	Be	7	7.016 929 2	EC	53.22 d
			8	8.005 305 1	2α	6.8×10^{-17} s
			9	9.012 182 1	100	
5	Boron	B	10	10.012 937 0	19.8	
			11	11.009 305 5	80.2	
6	Carbon	C	11	11.011 433 8	EC	20.334 min
			12	12.000 000 0	98.89	
			13	13.003 354 8	1.11	
			14	14.003 242 0	β^-	5730 yr
			15	15.010 599 3	β^-	2.449 s
7	Nitrogen	N	12	12.018 613 2	EC	11.00 ms
			13	13.005 738 6	EC	9.965 min
			14	14.003 074 0	99.634	
			15	15.000 108 9	0.366	
8	Oxygen	O	15	15.003 065 4	EC	122.24 s
			16	15.994 914 6	99.762	
			17	16.999 131 5	0.038	
			18	17.999 160 4	0.200	
			19	19.003 579 3	β^-	26.88 s
9	Fluorine	F	19	18.998 403 2	100	
10	Neon	Ne	20	19.992 440 2	90.48	
			22	21.991 385 5	9.25	
11	Sodium	Na	22	21.994 436 8	EC	2.6019 yr
			23	22.989 769 7	100	
			24	23.990 963 3	β^-	14.9590 h
12	Magnesium	Mg	24	23.985 041 9	78.99	
13	Aluminum	Al	27	26.981 538 4	100	
14	Silicon	Si	28	27.976 926 5	92.230	
15	Phosphorus	P	31	30.973 761 5	100	
			32	31.973 907 2	β^-	14.262 d
16	Sulfur	S	32	31.972 070 7	95.02	
17	Chlorine	Cl	35	34.968 852 7	75.77	
18	Argon	Ar	40	39.962 383 1	99.6003	
19	Potassium	K	39	38.963 706 9	93.2581	
			40	39.963 998 7	0.0117; β^-	1.248×10^9 yr
20	Calcium	Ca	40	39.962 591 2	96.94	
24	Chromium	Cr	52	51.940 511 9	83.789	
25	Manganese	Mn	54	53.940 363 2	EC	312.0 d
			55	54.938 049 6	100	
26	Iron	Fe	56	55.934 942 1	91.754	

(continued)

Atomic Number Z	Element	Symbol	Mass Number A	Mass of *neutral atom* (u)	Percentage Abundance (or Decay Mode)	Half-life (if Unstable)
27	Cobalt	Co	59	58.933 200 2	100	
			60	59.933 822 2	β^-	5.271 yr
28	Nickel	Ni	58	57.935 347 9	68.077	
			60	59.930 790 6	26.223	
29	Copper	Cu	63	62.929 601 1	69.17	
30	Zinc	Zn	64	63.929 146 6	48.63	
36	Krypton	Kr	84	83.911 507 3	57.0	
			86	85.910 610 3	17.3	
			92	91.926 153 1	β^-	1.840 s
37	Rubidium	Rb	85	84.911 789 3	72.17	
			93	92.922 033 8	β^-	5.84 s
38	Strontium	Sr	88	87.905 614 3	82.58	
			90	89.907 737 6	β^-	28.90 yr
39	Yttrium	Y	89	88.905 847 9	100	
			90	89.907 151 4	β^-	64.00 h
47	Silver	Ag	107	106.905 093 6	51.839	
50	Tin	Sn	120	119.902 196 6	32.58	
53	Iodine	I	131	130.906 124 2	β^-	8.0252 d
55	Cesium	Cs	133	132.905 447 3	100	
			141	140.920 044 1	β^-	24.84 s
56	Barium	Ba	138	137.905 241 3	71.698	
			141	140.914 406 9	β^-	18.27 min
60	Neodymium	Nd	143	142.909 810 3	12.2	
62	Samarium	Sm	147	146.914 893 3	14.99; α	1.06×10^{11} yr
79	Gold	Au	197	196.966 552 3	100	
82	Lead	Pb	204	203.973 029 3	1.4	$\geq 1.4 \times 10^{17}$ yr
			206	205.974 449 3	24.1	
			207	206.975 881 3	22.1	
			208	207.976 636 3	52.4	
			210	209.984 173 3	β^-	22.20 yr
			211	210.988 731 3	β^-	36.1 min
			212	211.991 887 5	β^-	10.64 h
			214	213.999 798 1	β^-	26.8 min
83	Bismuth	Bi	209	208.980 383 3	100	
			211	210.987 258 6	α	2.14 min
			214	213.998 699 1	β^-	19.9 min
84	Polonium	Po	210	209.982 857 3	α	138.376 d
			214	213.995 186 3	α	164.3 μs
			218	218.008 965 8	α	3.10 min
86	Radon	Rn	222	222.017 570 5	α	3.8235 d
88	Radium	Ra	226	226.025 402 6	α	1600 yr
			228	228.031 064 1	β^-	5.75 yr
90	Thorium	Th	228	228.028 731 3	α	1.91 yr
			232	232.038 050 4	100; α	1.405×10^{10} yr
			234	234.043 595 4	β^-	24.10 d
92	Uranium	U	235	235.043 923 1	0.7204; α	7.038×10^8 yr
			236	236.045 561 9	α	2.342×10^7 yr
			238	238.050 782 6	99.2742; α	4.468×10^9 yr
			239	239.054 287 8	β^-	23.45 min
93	Neptunium	Np	237	237.048 167 3	α	2.144×10^6 yr
94	Plutonium	Pu	239	239.052 156 5	α	24 110 yr
			242	242.058 736 8	α	3.75×10^5 yr
			244	244.064 198 5	α	8.00×10^7 yr

EC = electron capture.

Answers to Selected Questions and Problems

CHAPTER 1

Multiple-Choice Questions

1. (b) **2.** (a) **3.** (b) **4.** (c) **5.** (d) **6.** (b) **7.** (d) **8.** (b) **9.** (d) **10.** (c)

Problems

1. 2.5 m **3.** 7.7% **5.** 6/s **7.** 10^{-8} **9.** 11.8 yr **11.** 36.0%
13. (a) 1.29×10^8 kg (b) 1.3×10^8 m/s **15.** (a) 3.63×10^7 g
(b) 1.273×10^2 m **17.** 1.7×10^{-10} m^3 **19.** 459 m/s
21. 2.8×10^{-7} inches **23.** (a) 4.863×10^2 m; 10^2
(b) 1.834×10^3 m; 10^3 **25.** (a) 8.6 m/s (b) 19 mi/h
27. 0.12 or 12% **29.** 13.6 g/cm^3 **31.** 1.7×10^{-10} km^3
33. (a) 2.7×10^{-3} ft/s (b) 1.9×10^{-3} mi/h **35.** kg·m^2·s^{-2}

37. $[T]^2 = \dfrac{[L]^3}{\dfrac{[L]^3}{[M][T]^2} \times [M]} = \dfrac{[L]^3}{[M]} \times \dfrac{[M][T]^2}{[L]^3} = [T]^2$ **39.** (a) $[L^3]$

(b) volume **41.** 30–40 cm **43.** (a) 10 kg (b) 10 m
45. Answers may vary. **47.** 100 m
49.

(a) 101.8°F (b) 0.9°F/h (c) No; the patient would die before 12 hours passed and the temperature reached 113°F.
51. 104.5°F **53.** (a) a (b) $+v_0$
55. (a)

The presentation is useful because the graph is linear.
57. (a) 186.303 (b) 186.297 (c) 0.56 (d) 62 000
(e) Case (a): 0.0016%; Case (b): 0.0016%; For case (c), ignoring 0.0030 causes you to multiply by zero and get a zero result. For case (d), ignoring 0.0030 causes you to divide by zero.
(f) You can neglect small values when they are added to or subtracted from sufficiently large values. The term "sufficiently large" is determined by the number of significant figures required.
59. 4.0 **61.** 434 m/s **63.** (a) 3; 5.74×10^{-3} kg (b) 1; 2 m
(c) 3; 4.50×10^{-3} m (d) 3; 4.50×10^1 kg (e) 4; 1.009×10^5 s
(f) 4; 9.500×10^3 mL **65.** (a) 6 Mm (b) 2 m (c) 1 μm
(d) 3 nm (e) 0.3 nm **67.** (a) 3.3×10^{-8} m (b) 3.3×10^{-2} μm
(c) 1.3×10^{-6} in **69.** 2.2×10^2 m^3 **71.** (a) $a = K\dfrac{v^2}{r}$, where K is a dimensionless constant. (b) 21.0% **73.** 2.24 mi/h = 1 m/s; for a quick, approximate conversion, multiply by 2.
75. 10^{11} gal **77.** $\dfrac{\text{kg} \cdot \text{m}}{\text{s}^2}$ **79.** $59\,000\,000\,000$
81. (a) 2.4×10^5 km/h (b) 10 min **83.** (a) $\sqrt{\dfrac{hG}{c^5}}$
(b) 1.3×10^{-43} s **85.** 0.46 s^{-1}
87. (a)

(b) about 100 g
(c)

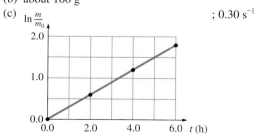

; 0.30 s^{-1}

CHAPTER 2

Multiple-Choice Questions

1. (b)   **2.** (b)   **3.** (a)   **4.** (d)   **5.** (b)   **6.** (c)   **7.** (b)   **8.** (c)
9. (d)   **10.** (b)

Problems

1. the weight of the person   **3.** velocity   **5.** 778 N
7. (a)

(b)

9.

about 1.4 N
11. 70 N at about 5° below the horizontal   **13.** 20 N in the positive x-direction   **15.** 2 N to the east   **17.** (a) 31.0 m/s
(b) 58.1° with the $+x$-axis and 31.9° with the $-y$-axis
19. 8.7 units   **21.** (a) 5.0 m/s^2 (b) 37° CCW from the $+y$-axis
23. (a) 9.4 cm at 32° CCW from the $+y$-axis   (b) 130 N at 27°
CW from the $+x$-axis   (c) 16.3 m/s at 33° CCW from the $-x$-axis
(d) 2.3 m/s^2 at 1.6° CCW from the $+x$-axis   **25.** 806 N
27.

29. s = sailboat; e = Earth; w = wind; l = lake; m = mooring line

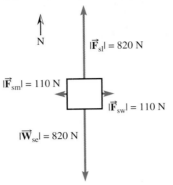

31. (a) 30 N to the right   (b) 0   (c) 18 N downward
33. (a) same direction   (b) perpendicular   (c) opposite directions;
1.0 N   **35.** 13° from the vertical   **37.** (a) and (b) are third-law
pairs; (a) and (c) are equal and opposite due to the first law.
39. One force acting on the fish is an upward force on the fish by
the line; its interaction partner is a downward force on the line by
the fish. A second force acting on the fish is the downward gravitational force on the fish; its interaction partner is the upward
gravitational force on the Earth by the fish.
41. (a) 543 N   (b) contact force of Margie's feet   (c) 588 N
(d) contact force on the Earth due to the scale
43. (a) 50.0 N upward (total for both feet)   (b) 650.0 N upward
(c) s = woman and chair system; e = Earth; f = floor

45. (a) The rock will fall toward the Moon's surface.
(b) 1.6 N toward the Moon   (c) 2.7 mN toward Earth
(d) 1.6 N toward the Moon   **47.** (a) 392 N   (b) 88.1 lb
49. 1.5×10^{-9} N   **51.** 640 N   (a) 240 N   (b) 580 N   (c) 100 N
53. 4 km   **55.** (a) 1.98×10^{20} N   (b) the same   **57.** 3.770
59. b = book; t = table; e = Earth; h = hand

(d) (a) and (b)   (e) 2.0 N opposite the direction of
motion   (f) The FBD would look just like the diagram for part (c). The book would not slow down
because there is no net force on the book.

61.

	$\vec{N}$	$\vec{f}$
(a)	perpendicular to and away from	along the ramp upward
(b)	perpendicular to and away from	along the ramp downward
(c)	perpendicular to and away from	along the ramp upward

63. (a) zero   (b) $\frac{T}{mg}$ **65.** t = table; e = Earth; 1 = block 1; 2 = block 2; 3 = block 3; 4 = block 4; h = horizontal force; 1234 = system of blocks (The blocks are numbered from left to right.)

(a)

(b)

69. (a) 160 N up the slope   (b) 0.19

71. 400 N   **73.** $\frac{W}{2\sin\theta}$ **75.** Both scales read 120 N.

77. Scale B reads 120 N; scale A reads 120 N.   **79.** (a) $\sqrt{2}Mg$ (b) 45°   **81.** $T_{15} = 30$ N; $T_{25} = 18$ N   **83.** electromagnetic and gravitational forces   **85.** the weak force   **87.** (a) 530 N (b) 510 N   (c) no   **89.** 440 N   **91.** (a) zero   (b) 2.6×10^4 N **93.** 90.0% of the Earth-Moon distance   **95.** (a) All 0 (b) A > B > C   (c) A = 16.5 N; B = 11.0 N; C = 5.5 N **97.** (a) $\mu_s > 0.48$ (b) 0.60   (c) 0.48   **99.** (a) 110.0 N (b) $T_A = 115.0$ N = T_C and $T_B = 110.0$ N = T_D.

101. i = ice; e = Earth; s = stone; o = opponent's stone

103. (a) c = computer; d = desk; e = Earth

(b) zero   (c) 52 N   **105.** (a) In both cases the two ropes pull on the scale with forces of 550 N in opposite directions, so the scales give the same reading.   (b) 550 N   **107.** (a) A = 137 N; B = 39 N   (b) A = 147 N; B = 39 N   **109.** 0.49%

111. $\frac{mg}{\cos\theta}$ **113.** 1810 N; 5 times the force with which Yoojin pulls; the oak tree supplies additional force.   **115.** (a) 2.60×10^8 m from Earth   (b) away from

CHAPTER 3

Multiple-Choice Questions

1. (e)   **2.** (d)   **3.** (a)   **4.** (b)   **5.** (e)   **6.** (d)   **7.** (a)   **8.** (b) **9.** (a)   **10.** (a)   **11.** (c)   **12.** (a)   **13.** (a)   **14.** (d)   **15.** (c)

16. (a)   **17.** (a) (b)   (b) (a)   (c) (d)   (d) (c)   **18.** (a) **19.** (c)   **20.** (a) increasing   (b) $+x$ (c) decreasing   (d) $-x$

Problems

1.

about 7.9 cm   **3.** (a) $B_x = 6.9$; $B_y = -1.7$ (b) 6.9 at 15° CW from the $-y$-axis   (c) 10 at 30° CCW from the $-x$-axis (d) x-comp: -8.7; y-comp: -5.0 **5.** 4.92 mi at 24.0° north of east **7.** (a) 45 km   (b) 16 km   **9.** 2.0 km at 20° east of south **11.** 4.4 miles at 58° north of east   **15.** 14.0 m/s north **17.** 91.5 mph   **19.** 30 km/h east   **21.** 32 s **23.** (a)

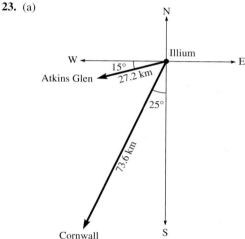

(b) 59.9 km at 85° north of east   (c) 80 km/h at 85° north of east **25.** 16.5 m   **27.** 1.0 m/s   **29.** (a) 8 m   (b) $t = 10$ s to $t = 14$ s **31.** (a) 102 km/h   (b) 90.8 km/h at 16.6° south of west   **33.** 26 km/h at 31° north of east   **35.** 1.05 m/s to the north   **37.** (a) 1.4 m/s² in the $+x$-direction   (b) 220 m in the $+x$-direction   (c) 55 m/s in the $+x$-direction   **39.** 7.0 m/s² in the direction opposite the car's velocity   **41.** 2.5 m/s²   **43.** 4.8 kN   **45.** (a) 9.4 m/s at 45° north of east   (b) 15 m/s² at 45° south of east   (c) Changing the direction of the velocity requires an acceleration.

47. (a)

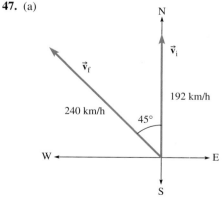

(b) 170 km/h at 7° south of west   (c) 57 km/h² at 7° south of west   **49.** 44.7 m/s at 26.6° south of east   **51.** 28 m/s² toward the paddle   **53.** (a) no   (b) yes   (c) 0.55 m/s²   (d) The force of friction will be less on the Moon; more.   **55.** 22.7 kN upward

57. (a) 3.5 m/s² up   (b) 15 m/s up   **59.** (a) m_1: 2.5 m/s² up; m_2: 2.5 m/s² down   (b) 37 N   **61.** 2.1 m/s² in the direction of motion   **63.** 1.8 m/s²; yes   **65.** 20 N   **67.** (a) 39.0 m/s (b) 7.4° south of west   **69.** 0.42 km/h   **71.** 254 s   **73.** 27° upstream   **75.** (a) 76.37° north of east   (b) 2.717 h **77.** (a) 1.80 mi/h   (b) 48.0 min   (c) 0.800 mi upstream (d) 32.2° upstream

79.

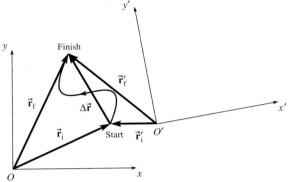

81. 32.0°   **83.** (a) 873 km   (b) 9.90° south of east   (c) 2.250 h (d) 2.18 h   **85.** (a) $g(\sin\theta_2 - \cos\theta_2\tan\theta_1)$ (b) 3.8 m/s² **87.** (a) 16 N   (b) The block will accelerate.   (c) 1.3 m/s² **89.** (a) zero   (b) 18 N in the forward direction   (c) 2.9 m/s²

91. (a) $mg\tan\theta$ (b) $mg\tan\theta$ (c) $mg\tan\theta + \dfrac{ma}{\cos\theta}$

93. (a) 68.5 km/h at 12.5° north of east   (b) 68.5 km/h at 12.5° south of west   **95.** $\vec{a} \neq \vec{a}_{av}$, so the acceleration is not constant. **97.** 2.0×10^5 N west   **99.** (a) 1.8 m/s² down   (b) 8.7 m/s

101. 39 s   **103.** $\dfrac{m_1}{m_1 + m_2}$ **105.** (a) 1.0 mm/s   (b) 20 ms

(c) 100 m/s **107.**   (a) t_3 and t_4 (b) t_0, t_2, t_5, and t_7 (c) t_1 and t_6 (d) t_0, t_3, and t_7 (e) t_6 **109.** (a) $1.10mg$ (b) $1.10mg$

CHAPTER 4

Multiple-Choice Questions

1. (c)   **2.** (c)   **3.** (e)   **4.** (c)   **5.** (a)   **6.** (d)   **7.** (d)   **8.** (a) **9.** (b)   **10.** (d)   **11.** (e)   **12.** (a)   **13.** (b)   **14.** (a)   **15.** (b) **16.** (c)

Problems

1. 1.5 m/s² northeast   **3.** (a) 224 m   (b) 0.99 m/s²   **5.** (a) 23 m/s (b) 0.19   **7.** 4.22 km   **9.** 52.1 m before you stop; the tractor is 11.5 m in front of you; you won't hit the tractor   **11.** (a) 0.34 m/s², where the watermelon moves up and to the left   (b) 1.5 cm (c) 6.8 cm/s   **13.** 2.27 m/s   **15.** 5.0 m/s² in the +x-direction **17.** (a)

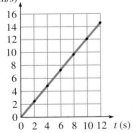

(b) 86.4 m   (c) 14.4 m/s (d)

19. 0.365°;

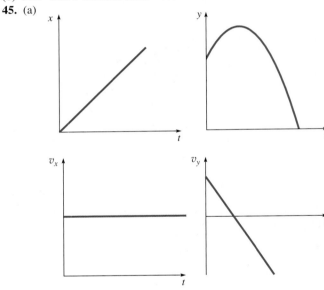

21. 0.50 m   **23.** 5.0 m/s   **25.** (a) 1.6 s   (b) 48 m   **27.** 30.0 m/s **29.** (a) 290 m/s² toward Lois   (b) 270 m/s   **31.** 1.22 s **33.** (a) 55 m   (b) 7.5 s   **35.** 46 m   **37.** The clay is on the ground after 1.32 s, so the horizontal distance along the ground is 26.3 m.   **39.** (a) 5.9 m   (b) 17.0 m/s   **41.** (a) 202 m (b) 51.1° below the horizontal   **43.** 15.8 m **45.** (a)

(b) 27.6 m/s at 25.0° above the horizontal   (c) 37.5 m (d) 44.4 m above the ground   **47.** 37.1 m   **49.** (a) 37 m (b) 170 m   (c) 32 m/s; −27 m/s   **51.** 200 km   **53.** (a) $\dfrac{v_i^2}{g}$ (b) 45°   **55.** (a) 127 m, 127 m   (b) 96.2 m, 96.2 m   (c) 134 m (d) The ranges are the same for each pair of complementary angles. The largest range occurred for an angle of 45.0° above the horizontal.   **57.** 766 N downward   **59.** 0.8 m/s² downward **61.** (a) 567 N   (b) 629 N   **63.** 620 N   **65.** (a) 4.5 s   (b) 81 m **67.** step 4   **69.** (a) 33.1 h   (b) 34.1 h   (c) 33.6 h   **71.** (a) 0.30 s (b) 0.05 s   (c) 0.45 m   (d) 10 m/s² down   (e) 120 m/s² up **73.** 12 m east and 40 m north   **75.** (a) 88 N   (b) 2 s   (c) 70 N (d) 10 kg   **77.** $2v$ **79.** 48 m   **81.** 3260 ft; 25.5 s   **83.** (a) 28.6 cm (b) smaller   (c) larger   (d) $H = 21.3$ cm; $R = 85.1$ cm

89. (a) $a = \dfrac{m_2 - \mu_k m_1}{m_1 + m_2}\,g$; $T = (1 + \mu_k)\dfrac{m_1 m_2}{m_1 + m_2}\,g$

(b) $m_1 \ll m_2$: $a \approx g$ and $T \approx (1 + \mu_k)m_1 g \ll m_2 g$, so the tension is negligible compared to the weight of m_2; it's essentially in free fall. $m_1 \gg m_2$: $a = 0$ and $T = m_2 g$. $m_1 = m_2$: $a = (1 - \mu_k)g/2$ and $T = (1 + \mu_k)mg/2$. (c) $a = 0$ only for $m_2 = 0$; thus, there is no value at which the two masses slide with constant velocity. For $m_2 = 0$, there is no tension in the cord. **91.** No; the flowerpot either fell from 133 m high or, if it came from a lower location (such as the 24th floor), it was thrown downward. The first witness is not credible.

CHAPTER 5

Multiple-Choice Questions

1. (b) **2.** (a) **3.** (f) **4.** (b) **5.** (a) **6.** (b) **7.** (b) **8.** (a) **9.** (e) **10.** (c) **11.** (b) **12.** (b)

Problems

1. 17 m **3.** 0.105 rad/s **5.** 26 rad/s **7.** (a) 3.49 rad/s (b) 0.45 m/s **9.** 3800 ft **11.** (a) 31 m/s (b) 31 rad/s

13. 3.37 cm/s^2 **15.** 5.74 m/s **17.** (a) $\dfrac{mv^2}{L}$

(b) $T = m\sqrt{g^2 + \left(\dfrac{v^2}{L\cos\theta}\right)^2}$ **19.** (a) $\sqrt{\mu_s g R}$

(b) The static frictional force is not large enough to keep the car in a circular path; the car skids toward the outside of the curve. **21.** 7.9 m/s **23.** 59° **25.** (a) 2300 N (b) 19 m/s

27. $\tan^{-1}\dfrac{v^2}{rg}$ **29.** 2.99×10^4 m/s **31.** 130 h

33. $r_{\text{Io}} = 420\,000$ km; $r_{\text{Europa}} = 670\,000$ km **35.** 2.04×10^7 m **37.** 16 h **39.** (a) 13 N (b) The bob has an upward acceleration, so the net F_y must be upward and greater than the weight of the bob. **41.** 23.2 m/s **43.** 4.0 rad/s^2 **47.** $a_t = 2.54$ m/s^2; $a_r = 2.45$ m/s^2; 11.9 N **49.** (a) 1.7 rad/s (b) 0.56 rev **51.** (a) 17.7 m/s (b) 6.28 m/s (c) 6.59 m/s^2 at an angle of 17.7° east of south **53.** (a) 1.3×10^6 s (b) 5.0×10^{10} rev **55.** $16g$ **57.** 7.0 rad/s **59.** (a) 0.034 m/s^2 (b) less (c) 0.34% smaller (d) at the poles **61.** (a) 518.5 N (b) 521.5 N (c) 45 m **63.** 0.40ω **65.** 150 m/s **67.** (a) 3.00 m/s east (b) 3.00 m/s west **69.** 2.9 rotations for A; 5.7 rotations for B **71.** (a) 38 m/s (b) You would need 135 km of tape to record one hour. **73.** (a) $8.0\pi^2$ m/s$^2 = 79$ m/s^2 (b) $4.0\pi^2$ N = 39 N **75.** smallest; 4.1 s **77.** 110 μm/s **79.** 8 cm **81.** 120 km/h **83.** (a) $90g$ (b) 7.9×10^{-11} N (c) 4.4×10^{-18} N (d) $5.0 \times 10^5 g$ **85.** 1.4 rev/s **87.** 42 200 km

REVIEW & SYNTHESIS: CHAPTERS 1–5

Review Exercises

1. N/m = kg/s^2 **3.** (a) 220 markers (b) 221 markers **5.** (a) 1.74 m/s (b) 0.332 m/s in his original direction of motion **7.** (a) 3300 ft or 1000 m **9.** The cart will go off the road toward south. **11.** (a) 19 m (b) 3.6 m/s **13.** 1.7 m/s **15.** (a) 15.1 N (b) 34.3 N **17.** Stefan's plan is superior and thus more likely to work. **19.** 29 km/h at 83° north of west **21.** (a) The rocks will have the same speed when they hit the ground. (b) 19.8 m/s **23.** 2.40 s **25.** (a) 3.6×10^7 m

(b) 55 N **27.** 11.5 m/s **29.** 2.02 s; 1.65 m to the left of B's initial position **31.** 0.98 m/s directed downward

33. (a) $R = \dfrac{2v_i^2 \sin\theta \cos\theta}{g}$ (b) 221 m (c) 4 m **35.** (a) 283 m (b) 84.9 m **37.** (a) 216 billion solar masses (b) 0.46

MCAT Review

1. D **2.** C **3.** D **4.** C **5.** C **6.** D **7.** A

CHAPTER 6

Multiple-Choice Questions

1. (c) **2.** (b) **3.** (b) **4.** (a) **5.** (c) **6.** (c) **7.** (c) **8.** (c) **9.** (b) **10.** (b) **11.** (f)

Problems

1. 75 J **3.** No work is done. **5.** 210 kJ **7.** (a) 0 (b) 8.8 J **9.** 1.3 m **11.** 15.6 J **13.** (a) 0.70 J (b) 0.37 m/s **15.** 0 **17.** −4.17 kJ **19.** 5.8 MJ (meteoroid); 0.46 MJ (car); the meteoroid has more than 12 times the kinetic energy of the car. **21.** (a) 0 (b) 3.4 kJ (c) dissipated as heat **23.** (a) 0 (b) −2.9 J **25.** (a) 2 (b) 1.88 kJ (c) 1.88 kJ (d) 8.00 m **27.** (a) 14.3 m/s (b) Yes; the cart will reach position 4. **29.** 8.42 m/s **31.** −52 kJ **33.** (a) $\sqrt{v^2 + 2gh}$ (b) The final speed is independent of the angle. **35.** (a) 0.286 N/cm (b) 11.0 cm **37.** 2.37 km/s **39.** 13.0 km/s **41.** 2 **43.** 10.0 km/s **45.** 1.6 km/s **47.** 8 J **49.** 5.2 J **51.** (a) 4.9 cm (b) 1.4 N/cm (c) 88 mJ **53.** (a) 1.9 N/cm (b) 0.49 J (c) 2.4 kg **55.** zero **57.** 0.35 m **59.** 13 m **61.** 8.7 cm **63.** (a) 2.2 m/s (b) 0.21 m (c) 0.50 m **67.** 22 W **69.** (a) 20 N (b) 6.7 m/s **71.** 60 kW **73.** 6.2 g; the other 90% of the energy is dissipated as heat. **75.** 930 kW **77.** 4.8 m/s **79.** 16 m/s **83.** (a) $k/2$ (b) $2k$ **85.** 27 N **87.** 0.33 m **89.** 1.6 m/s **91.** (a) 10 kW (b) 5.8° **93.** (a) 2.62 kW (b) 7.85 kW **95.** (a) 2200 kcal/day (b) more than 0.51 lb **97.** (b) 4.9 m/s (c) 1.24 m **99.** $\frac{2}{3}R$ **101.** (a) $k = k_1 + k_2$ (b) 0.16 J **103.** 1.3 cm; 32 J **105.** (a) 26 cm (b) 34 cm **109.** No; because the kinetic energy cannot be negative as would be the case in the region 3 cm $< x <$ 8 cm. The particle must remain in the region $x <$ 3 cm.

CHAPTER 7

Multiple-Choice Questions

1. (c) **2.** (d) **3.** (c) **4.** (b) **5.** (d) **6.** (b) **7.** (f) **8.** (d) **9.** (a) **10.** (e) **11.** (d) **12.** (b)

Problems

1. 0 **5.** 3 kg·m/s north **7.** 20 kg·m/s in the $-x$-direction **9.** 1.0×10^2 kg·m/s downward **11.** 320 s **13.** 6.0×10^3 N opposite the car's direction of motion **15.** (a) 750 kg·m/s upward (b) 990 N·s downward (c) 2500 N downward **17.** (a) 11 m/s

(b) 1300 N **19.** (a) 33 m/s   (b) 0.94 N down   **21.** 2.6×10^5 m/s
23. 0.30 m/s **25.** 0.10 m/s **27.** (8.0 cm, 20 cm) **29.** 4.0 cm
in the positive x-direction **31.** (0.900 m, -2.15 m) **33.** 21 cm
35. (6 m/s, -4 m/s) **37.** (a) (-0.13 m/s, -4.1 m/s)   (b) The center
of mass of the system remains at the origin after the explosion.
39. 270 m/s to the right
41. (a) 0.20 m/s   (b) 0.25 m/s **43.** 5.0 m/s **45.** 2.0 kg·m/s
to the right **47.** 43 m/s **49.** 3.0 m/s **51.** 0.20 kg
53. 0.49 m **55.** 5.0 m/s **57.** 170 m/s
59. (a) $\Delta p_{1x} = -1.00 m_1 v_i$; $\Delta p_{1y} = 0.751 m_1 v_i$ (b) $\Delta p_{2x} = m_1 v_i$;
$\Delta p_{2y} = -0.751 m_1 v_i$; the momentum changes for each mass are
equal and opposite. **61.** $1.73 v_{1f}$ **63.** 8.7 kg·m/s **65.** 6.0 m/s
at 21° south of east **67.** 1.7 m/s at 30° below the x-axis
69. 20 m/s at 18° west of north **71.** 10.2 m/s
73. 5.0×10^9 kg·m/s **75.** 34 N **77.** (2.0, 0.75, 0.25) in
79. Inexperienced: 5000 N; experienced: 500 N **80.** 37 m/s in
the $+x$-direction **81.** (a) 5.3 kg·m/s opposite the ball's direction of motion   (b) 5.3 kg·m/s opposite the ball's direction of
motion   (c) 1.8 kN opposite the ball's direction of motion
83. (a) 148.6° CCW from the electron's direction
(b) 9.60×10^{-19} kg·m/s in the direction found in (a)
85. The lighter car was speeding. **87.** 10^{-18} N **89.** $\frac{1}{9}h$
91. 10 m/s **93.** (a) $\frac{111}{2}$ (b) 1   (c) $\frac{111}{2}$

CHAPTER 8

Multiple-Choice Questions

1. (b) **2.** (d) **3.** (a) **4.** (c) **5.** (e) **6.** (b) **7.** (a) **8.** (f)
9. (e) **10.** (c)

Problems

3. (a) reduced by a factor of 8   (b) reduced by a factor of 32
5. (a) 1.5 kg·m²   (b) 0.75 kg·m²   (c) 1.5 kg·m²
7. $\frac{2}{5}\frac{R_E^2}{R_o^2}$, where R_E is the Earth's radius and R_o is Earth's orbital
radius about the Sun. **9.** (a) no   (b) 0.017 **11.** 4.0 N·m
13. 780 N·m **15.** 25 N·m **19.** 57.4 N·m **21.** 1.2 cm toward
the doorknob as measured from the center of the door
23. 150 J **25.** (a) 5.5 kJ   (b) 29 N·m **27.** 98 N **29.** 17.0°
31. The center of mass = 0.8542 m < 0.8600 m; the system balances. **33.** 180 N toward the wall **35.** $T = 350$ N; $F_x = 290$ N;
$F_y = -2$ N; the magnitude of F_y is small. **37.** 22.3° **39.** palms:
390 N; feet: 270 N **41.** tendon, 2100 N upward and tibia, 2800 N
downward **43.** 130 N **45.** 3.0 kN; about 5.5 times larger
49. 0.0012 N·m **51.** 4.3 N·m **53.** 0.09 N·m
55. (a) 0.11 rad/s²   (b) 0.44 rad/s **59.** 2.9 m/s **61.** 1.79 m
63. 2.75 s **65.** (a) $\frac{5}{2}r$ (b) $\frac{27}{10}r$ **67.** h will decrease. The
smaller the rotational inertia, the less gravitational energy will go
into rotational energy, and the more will go into translational
energy. Problem 66 had a minimum of $h = 3r$. With a solid sphere,
the minimum is $h = 2.7r$, which is a little less than $3r$.
69. 0.0864 kg·m²/s **71.** 1.4×10^7 kg·m²/s **73.** 1.60 s
75. 15.6 rad/s **77.** 0.125 rad/s **79.** (a) 3.0   (b) 1.6
81. 2.10×10^6 N·m **83.** 1.14 **85.** 98 N·m **87.** 5.4 rad/s
89. The objects reach the bottom in the following order from first
to last: cube, solid sphere, solid cylinder, hollow sphere, and hollow
cylinder. **91.** 0.792 m **93.** (a) 16 kg·m²   (b) 8.0×10^7 J

(c) 320   (d) 120 km **97.** 110 N **99.** (a) 1.35×10^{-5} kg·m²
(b) 524 N **101.** 0.19 kg·m²/s **103.** (a) 9.4×10^{-4} kg·m²/s
(b) 1.2×10^{-6} kg·m²/s **105.** 230 N **107.** (a) 735.0 N
(b) 0.88 m   (c) $0.55h$ **109.** 23 N **111.** 1.3 rev/s
113. (a) 9.6 m/s   (b) 3.1 m/s   (c) 21 m/s

REVIEW & SYNTHESIS: CHAPTERS 6–8

Review Exercises

1. (a) 0.20 m   (b) 250 N/m **3.** $2mg$ **5.** (a) 940 J   (b) 0.734
7. 2.3 m **9.** 30 m/s **11.** (a) 0.502 kg·m²   (b) 17 N·m
13. 1.53 m/s **15.** 0.73 m **17.** 10.3 J **19.** $h_A = 0.57$ m; $h_B =$
2.3 m **21.** 1.27 m **23.** 2.0 m/s **25.** 2.06 m/s at 41.6° south
of east

27. (a) $\dfrac{\omega_1}{1 + \dfrac{mr^2}{MR^2}}$

(b) The total angular momentum does not change, since no external
torques act on the system.   (c) Yes; the kinetic energy changes.
29. (a) The Vulcan ship will have the greater kinetic energy. The
ships will have the same momentum.   (b) The ships will have the
same kinetic energy. The Romulan ship will have the greater
momentum.   (c) In part (a), the momenta are the same,
9.5×10^8 kg·m/s, but the kinetic energies differ: Vulcan at
6.9×10^{12} J and Romulan at 3.5×10^{12} J. In part (b), the kinetic
energies are the same, 9.5×10^8 J, but the momenta differ: Vulcan
at 1.1×10^7 kg·m/s and Romulan at 1.6×10^7 kg·m/s.
31. (a) $U = -550$ J; $K = 450$ J   (b) $E = -100$ J; $U = -100$ J;
$K = 0$ (c) 200 J   (d) The particle has a kinetic energy of 450 J
at $t = 0$, and we are told the motion is to the left. The particle will
continue moving left but the kinetic energy will decrease by
450/4.5 J for every cm of travel until it reaches $x = 1$ cm. At this
point $K = 0$, and the particle has stopped instantaneously. It will next
move to the right with an increasing K until it reaches $x = 5.5$ cm.
At this point $K = 450$ J, and this kinetic energy will be maintained
as it continues moving right until it reaches $x = 11$ cm. At this
point, its kinetic energy will decrease by 450/2.5 J for every cm of
travel until it reaches $x = 13.5$ cm. At this point $K = 0$, and the
particle has again stopped instantaneously. It will then turn around
again. **33.** (a) 19.4 m/s   (b) no **35.** 13 m/s

MCAT Review

1. D **2.** D **3.** B **4.** B **5.** D **6.** C **7.** B **8.** B **9.** D
10. A **11.** B **12.** D **13.** B **14.** C **15.** A **16.** D **17.** C

CHAPTER 9

Multiple-Choice Questions

1. (b) **2.** (b) **3.** (d) **4.** (a) **5.** (a) **6.** (b) **7.** (a) **8.** (a)
9. (d) **10.** (c)

Problems

1. 49 atm **3.** 22 kPa **5.** The baby applies 2.0 times as much
pressure as the adult. **7.** 4.0 kN southward **9.** 1.0 m

11. (a) 30 N　(b) 5.8 N·m　13. 2.0 atm　15. $\frac{V_{Pt}}{V_{Al}} = 0.126$
17. 1.0 MN　19. (a) 343 kPa　(b) 410 Pa　21. (a) 2.2×10^5 Pa
(b) 1700 torr　(c) 2.2 atm　23. 114.0 cm Hg　25. (a) 5.6 cm
(b) 0.37 cm　27. 250 kg/m^3　29. (a) 91.7%　(b) 0.917
31. (a) 8.8 N upward　(b) 9.6 N upward　33. 100%　35. 0.78
37. yes　39. (a) 9.8 m/s^2 upward　(b) 3.3 m/s^2 upward
(c) 68.6 m/s^2 upward　41. 50 m/s　43. (a) 39.1 cm/s
(b) 78.5 cm^3/s　(c) 78.5 g/s　45. 1.12×10^5 Pa　47. 1.9×10^5 N
49. 310 kPa　51. 8.6 m　55. (a) 6850 Pa　(b) 0.685 N
57. 0.040 m^3/s　59. (a) 50 Pa　(b) 1100 Pa　(c) approximately
13 kPa　61. 0.4 Pa·s　63. (a) 1.3×10^{-10} N
(b) 2.6×10^{-14} W　65. Since m/v_t is constant, the drag force is
primarily viscous.　67. 3.0 mm/s　69. 5 Pa　71. (a) $\gamma L \Delta s$
(b) $\Delta E = \gamma \Delta A$　73. (a) 1.54 N　(b) 1.54×10^4 N　(c) For
a given depth the pressure is the same everywhere, so the very
tall, narrow column of water is as effective as having a whole
barrel of water filled to the same height and pushing upward on
the barrel top.　75. (a) 7.43%　(b) 1060 kg　77. (a) 5.94 m/s
(b) As long as we can assume Bernoulli's equation applies, it
doesn't matter what fluid is in the vat.　(c) The speed would be
reduced by a factor of 0.40.　79. 230 kg　81. 23.0 m　83. 110 m
85. 1.1 cm　87. 27 kPa　89. (a) 2.2 m/s up　(b) 21 kPa/s
91. (a) 1.4 N　(b) 0.43 N upward　(c) 6.8 m/s^2 downward
93. d is not a linear function of ρ: $d = \dfrac{m}{\pi \rho r^2}$,
95. (a) 26 m/s　(b) 2.6 m/s
97. 0.83 g/cm^3　99. (a) 5.2 kPa = 0.051 atm　(b) 11.8 Pa/m
(c) 8.61 km　(d) A decreasing air density means that the atmosphere extends to a higher altitude.　101. (a) 220%　(b) 0.68

CHAPTER 10

Multiple-Choice Questions

1. (c)　2. (b)　3. (b)　4. (a)　5. (a)　6. (a)　7. (c)　8. (b)
9. (c)　10. (a)　11. (f)　12. (e)　13. (e)　14. (f)　15. (f)
16. (e)　17. (c)　18. (c)　19. (j)　20. (k)

Problems

1. 0.097 mm　3. 2.2 cm　5. 0.80 mm　7. 5.0 mm
9. tension: 1.5×10^{10} N/m^2; compression: 9.0×10^9 N/m^2
11. 8.7×10^{-5} m　13. 630 N　15. human: 3 cm^2; horse: 7.1 cm^2
17. (a) 2.8×10^7 Pa　(b) 4.7×10^{-4}　(c) 9.3×10^{-4} m
(d) 5.0×10^5 N　19. volume: 7.7×10^{-4}; radius: 2.6×10^{-4}
21. The volume of the steel sphere would decrease by
57×10^{-6} cm^3.　23. 7.5×10^5 N　25. 0.30 N　27. 7.9 m/s^2
29. 3.10 m/s; 8560 m/s^2　33. (a) high frequency
(b) 1.3×10^{-6} m/s; 1.6×10^{-4} m/s^2　(c) 0.0013 m/s; 160 m/s^2
35. 5.0 rad/s　37. 2.5 Hz　39. (a) 1.7×10^{-4} m　(b) 0.13 m/s
(c) 510 N　41. (a) 1.4 kN　(b) 0.13 J　43. (a) 0.39 m　(b) 2.0 m/s
45. 0.70 s　47. 0.250 Hz　49. (a) a vertical straight line of
length 24 cm　(b) a positive cosine plot of amplitude 12 cm

51. (a) $\frac{2}{\pi}\omega A$　(b) ωA　(c) $\frac{2}{\pi}$
(d)

If the acceleration were constant so that the speed varied linearly,
the average speed would be 1/2 of the maximum velocity. Since the
actual speed is always larger than what it would be for constant
acceleration, the average speed must be larger.

53. (a)

(b)

(c)

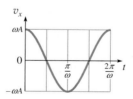

(d) U, K, and E would gradually be reduced to zero.
55. 4.0 s　57. 1.5 s　59. (a) $v_x = \omega A \cos \omega t$

(b) $\frac{1}{2} m \omega^2 A^2$

61. 1.11　63. 1st method: 3.14 cm/s; 2nd method: 3.14 cm/s
65. 11 mJ　67. (a) 6.1 mJ　(b) 1.1%　69. −9.75%　71. 2.5 s
73. (a) more　(b) 56 N　75. (a) The frequency and period don't
vary with amplitude, they only vary with m and k. Since these two
values remain constant, so do the frequency and period.
(b) The total energy for an amplitude of $2D$ is four times that for
an amplitude of D.　(c) The frequency and period are still the
same.　(d) The energy is greater when given an initial push, since
it has an amplitude $> 2D$. The increase in energy is $\frac{1}{2} m v_i^2$.

77.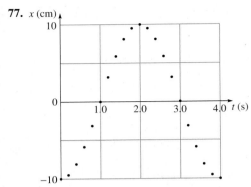

The distance between adjacent dots should be the least at the endpoints and greatest at the center, so its speed is lowest at the endpoints and fastest at its equilibrium position.   **81.** $y = (1.6 \text{ cm}) \cos[(25 \text{ rad/s})t]$
83. (a) 0.395 m   (b) 1.11 m/s   (c) 0.960 m/s
85. 8.0×10^8 Pa; it is just under the elastic limit.   **87.** 0.63 Hz
89. (a) $\rho g h$ (b) 7.6 km   (c) no   **91.** (a) 42.2°   (b) 48 g
(c) 9.1 cm   **93.** (a) $\sqrt{2gL}$ (b) $\frac{\pi}{2}\sqrt{gL}$; larger

95. (a) $2\pi \sqrt{\dfrac{L\left(\dfrac{m_1}{3} + m_2\right)}{g\left(\dfrac{m_1}{2} + m_2\right)}} = 2\pi \sqrt{\dfrac{2L(m_1 + 3m_2)}{3g(m_1 + 2m_2)}}$

(b) For $m_1 \gg m_2$, $T = 2\pi\sqrt{\dfrac{2L}{3g}}$, and for $m_1 \ll m_2$, $T = 2\pi\sqrt{\dfrac{L}{g}}$.

CHAPTER 11

Multiple-Choice Questions

1. (b)   **2.** (c)   **3.** (d)   **4.** (f)   **5.** (a)   **6.** (b)   **7.** (d)   **8.** (a)
9. (b)   **10.** (d)

Problems

1. 52 W/m²   **3.** 170 mW/m²   **5.** 4.0×10^{26} W   **7.** (a) 6.0 m
(b) 1.7 s   **9.** 168 m/s   **11.** 16 ms   **13.** 0.375 m   **15.** (a) 340 Hz
(b) 3.0×10^8 Hz   **17.** 0.33 Hz   **19.** 0.83 cm/s   **21.** (a) 4.0 mm
(b) 1.0 m   (c) 0.010 s   (d) 100 m/s   (e) in the +x-direction (to
the right)   **23.** $y(x, t) = (0.120 \text{ m}) \sin [(134 \text{ s}^{-1})t + (20.9 \text{ m}^{-1})x]$
25. (a) 2.6 cm   (b) 14 m   (c) 20 m/s   (d) 1.4 Hz   (e) 0.70 s
27. $v_m = 0.063$ m/s; $a_m = 0.79$ m/s²

29. (a)

(b)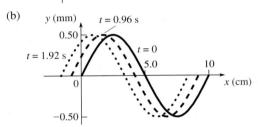

(c) $y(x, t) = (0.80 \text{ mm}) \sin (kx - \omega t)$ represents a wave traveling in the +x-direction.
$y(x, t) = (0.50 \text{ mm}) \sin (kx + \omega t)$ represents a wave traveling in the −x-direction.

31.

33. (a)   ; 6.9 cm

(b) 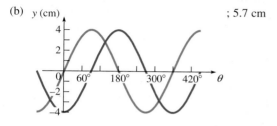   ; 5.7 cm

35. 96.0° **37.** 1.7 s **39.** (a) 0°; 8.0 cm (b) 180°; 2.0 cm
(c) 4:1 **41.** 79 mW/m^2 **43.** (a) 0.25 W/m^2 (b) 0.010 W/m^2
(c) 0.130 W/m^2 **45.** 7.8% **47.** 0.016 m **49.** (a) 33 Hz
(b) 300 N **51.** 4.5×10^{-4} kg/m **53.** (a) 260 Hz (b) 2.8 g
55. 0.050 kg **57.** 190 m **59.** 3.3 m **61.** 80 km **63.** 3.64 cm,
7.07 cm, 10.32 cm **65.** 470 Hz **67.** (a) Hooke's law:

$$T = k(x - x_0) \approx kx \text{ for } x \gg x_0. \quad \text{(b) } 4.00 \text{ s} \quad \textbf{69.} \ v \propto \sqrt{\frac{\gamma}{\lambda\rho}}; \text{ dis-}$$

persive **71.** (a) upward (b) downward (c) A **73.** 12

77.

CHAPTER 12

Multiple-Choice Questions

1. (c) **2.** (a) **3.** (b) **4.** (c) **5.** (b) **6.** (c) **7.** (b) **8.** (c)
9. (b) **10.** (d)

Problems

1. 3.4 mm **3.** 173 ms **5.** 4.7 s $\approx$ 5 s **7.** 1.4 km/s **11.** 1.1 µJ
13. 95 dB; this is not much different than with only one machine
running. **15.** (a) 28.7 N/m^2 (b) 1.58 mN **19.** 8.58 mm
21. (a) 65.6 cm (b) 252.4 Hz **23.** 43.3 cm **25.** 34°C
27. 3/4 **29.** (a) There is a displacement node (pressure antinode) at the center of the rod and displacement antinodes (pressure
nodes) at the ends. (b) 5100 m/s (c) 13.1 cm (d) The ends
move in opposite directions and, thus, they are out of phase.
31. (a) 290.0 Hz (b) 1.4% **33.** (a) 85.6 N (b) 432 m/s
(c) 335 Hz (d) 0.256 m
35. 580 Hz **37.** 6.35 Hz **39.** (a) 1.5 kHz (b) 500 Hz
41. (a) 3.0 kHz (b) 330 Hz (c) 1.0 kHz **45.** (a) 670 m
(b) 2.8 s **47.** 403 m **49.** 83.6 kHz **51.** 640 Hz
53. (a) 319 Hz (b) 319 Hz; 1.1 m **55.** 17.9 Hz; 53.6 Hz; 89.3 Hz;
125 Hz **57.** (b) First object: 110%; second object: 46%
59. 2.3 kHz **61.** 0.0955 s **63.** (a) 5.05 m (b) 16.35 Hz
65. 196 Hz **67.** 0.019 **69.** 29.0 dB

REVIEW & SYNTHESIS: CHAPTERS 9–12

Review Exercises

1. (a) Aluminum, since it is less dense it occupies more volume.
(b) Wood, since it displaces more water than the steel. (c) Lead:
0.87 N; aluminum: 3.6 N; steel: 1.2 N; wood: 9.8 N **3.** 0.116 m/s
5. 0.88 m/s **7.** (a) Eq. I; 1.50 cm/s (b) Eq. II; 2.09 cm
(c) Eq. II; 13.5 cm/s (d) Eq. II **9.** (a) 58 N (b) 49 cm
11. 21.4 cm **13.** 1500 Hz; 22.9 cm **15.** about 1 min
17. 346 Hz **19.** (a) 41.7 cm/s; 118 kPa (b) 5.98 cm
21. (a) 1.28 m (b) 141 m/s (c) 4.48×10^{-4} kg/m
(d) 1.60 m/s (e) 110.0 Hz (f) 3.12 m **23.** (a) 5.13×10^{-2} N
(b) 2.69 s **25.** (a) 6.17×10^{-4} m (b) 8.61 J (c) 0.536 s

MCAT Review

1. A **2.** A **3.** D **4.** C **5.** C **6.** B **7.** D **8.** B **9.** B
10. A **11.** B **12.** D **13.** C **14.** C

CHAPTER 13

Multiple-Choice Questions

1. (e) **2.** (d) **3.** (b) **4.** (c) **5.** (b) **6.** (d) **7.** (a) **8.** (c)
9. (c) **10.** (e)

Problems

1. (a) 29°C (b) 302 K **3.** (a) −40 (b) 575
5. $T_J = (0.750°\text{J}/°\text{C})T_C + 85.5\text{J}$ **7.** 2.0 mm **9.** (a) 3.6 mm
(b) 10.8 mm **11.** 3.8×10^{-4} mm^2 **13.** (b) 2.4×10^{-3}
15. 1.67 mL **17.** 75°C **19.** 1.3 m **21.** 150°C **23.** 24.98 cm
29. 7.31×10^{-26} kg **31.** 1.7×10^{27} **33.** 2.650×10^{25} atoms
35. 8.9985 mol **37.** 2.5×10^{19} molecules **39.** 10^{18} atoms
41. 400°C **45.** 135 kPa
47. (a) 1.3 kg/m^3 (b) 1.2 kg/m^3 **49.** 1.3×10^3 m^3 **51.** 1.50
53. 1.3×10^{26} **55.** 2.1 mm **57.** (a) 28 min (b) 11 min
59. (b) 3410×10^{-6} K^{-1} **61.** 152 J **65.** 3.4 kJ **67.** $\frac{1}{\sqrt{2}}$
69. (a) 493 m/s (b) 461 m/s (c) 393 m/s **71.** yes
73. 2220 K **77.** 0.14°C **79.** (a) 100 nm (b) 200 nm
(c) 8 µm **81.** 2.5×10^4 s **83.** 140 atm **85.** 165°C **87.** HNO$_3$
89. (a) 6.42×10^{-21} J (b) 0.25% **91.** (a) The number of
moles decreases by 25%. (b) −48°C
93. average: 78.1; rms: 78.6; 83 **95.** (a) 0.400 mm Hg/°C
(b) 3.21×10^{-3} mol **97.** 4 nm **99.** (a) 5.2×10^{24} m^{-3}
(b) 1.9% **101.** 630°C **103.** 1.9×10^{14} molecules **105.** 25 m/s
107. 3.05 mm **109.** 7.4×10^3 N/m

CHAPTER 14

Multiple-Choice Questions

1. (a) **2.** (b) **3.** (d) **4.** (d) **5.** (c) **6.** (b) **7.** (c) **8.** (d)
9. (d) **10.** (b) **11.** (c) **12.** (c)

Problems

1. (a) 34 J   (b) Yes; the increase in internal energy causes a slight temperature increase.   **3.** 4.90 kJ   **5.** (a) 250 J   (b) all three   **7.** 5.4 J   **9.** 2.78×10^{-4} kW·h   **11.** 6.40×10^{-4} kJ/K   **13.** 0.50 MJ   **15.** 700 m   **17.** (a) 2430 kJ/K   (b) 3500 kJ/K   **19.** 742 kJ   **21.** 0.13 kJ/(kg·K)   **23.** 0.090 J   **25.** 57 kJ   **27.** 58°C   **29.** (a) B to C, solid to liquid; D to E, liquid to gas   (b) B   (c) D   **31.** 330 J/g   **33.** 461 g   **35.** 157 g   **37.** 242 g; 35%   **39.** 46.3 g   **41.** 2 g   **43.** 36 g   **45.** 22.8 kJ/kg   **47.** (a) 2.0 cm   (b) 29 m   **49.** (a) 0.12 K/W   (b) 2.5×10^{-4} K/W   (c) 5.0×10^{-5} K/W   **51.** 6.67 W/m^2 **53.** −37°C   **55.** (a) 300 W   (b) 4500 W   **57.** (a) 0.32 W   (b) 800 K/m   (c) 0.16 W   (d) 0.64 W   (e) 64°C   **59.** 1.76 µm   **61.** 150 W   **63.** 390 W   **65.** 2800 K   **67.** 2.24 kW   **69.** Coffeepot: 4.5 W; teapot: 24 W   **71.** (a) 39°C   (b) 182 W/m^2 **73.** 320 s   **75.** (a) 180°C   (b) 20.9°C   **77.** (a) 9.9 kJ   (b) 360 g   **79.** 0.0065°C   **81.** 4.0 times higher   **83.** 0.792 kJ/(kg·K)   **85.** 10.4 W   **87.** 5400 kcal/h   **89.** 4.0 g   **91.** (a) 190 W   (b) 31°C   (c) Wearing clothing slows heat loss by radiation because air layers trapped between clothing layers act as insulation.   **93.** 140 m   **95.** 35°C   **97.** (a) 7.00 times higher   (b) 35.7°C; the dog is a much better regulator of temperature and, as a result, has more endurance.   **99.** 0.84 kJ/(kg·K)   **101.** 15.2 kJ/mol

CHAPTER 15

Multiple-Choice Questions

1. (b)   **2.** (d)   **3.** (c)   **4.** (c)   **5.** (d)   **6.** (c)   **7.** (a)   **8.** (c)   **9.** (d)   **10.** (d)   **11.** (e)   **12.** (b)   **13.** (d)

Problems

1. 2.9 J   **3.** 100 J of heat flows out of the system.   **5.** 202.6 J   **7.** (a) 98.0 kPa; 1180 K   (b) −200 J   (c) 66 J   (d) $\Delta U = 0$ because $\Delta T = 0$ in a cycle.   **9.** (a) 436 J   (b) 1.23 L   (c) 125 J   (d) 312 J   **11.** (a) −1372 J   (b) $\Delta U = 1216$ J; $Q = 2588$ J   **13.** (a) 182 kJ   (b) 182 kJ   **15.** 240 MJ   **17.** (a) 210 J   (b) 790 J   **19.** (a) 1.2×10^{17} J   (b) 1.4×10^{13} kg   **21.** 0.182   **23.** 3.0 kJ   **25.** 171 K   **27.** 25.0 kJ   **29.** 14 W   **31.** The coal-fired plant and the nuclear plant exhaust 0.43 MJ and 0.60 MJ of heat, respectively.   **33.** (a) 0.3436   (b) 275.7 kJ   **35.** 4.2%   **37.** 0.0174   **39.** 110 kJ   **41.** 4.5 GW   **43.** +250 W   **47.** (b), (a), (c), (d)   **49.** +6.05 kJ/K   **51.** (a) 3.4×10^{-3} J/K   (b) -2.8×10^{-3} J/K   (c) 6×10^{-4} J/K   **53.** 0.102 J/(K·s)   **55.** (a) 97 W   (b) 0.33 W/K   **57.** The engine will not work.   **59.** 15 kJ   **61.** (a) 304 kJ   (b) 2350 K   (c) 13.0 mol   **63.** (a) 15.9°C   (b) −0.03 J/K   (c) The entropy of the universe never decreases.   **65.** 24°C   **67.** 0.401 or 40.1%   **69.** 350 J/K   **71.** (a) 0.90 J/K   (b) −2.7 J/K   **73.** 15 min   **75.** (a) 6.2 mJ   (b) 22 mJ   (c) 1.2 mK   **77.** (a) 0.051   (b) 31 m^3 (c) yes

REVIEW & SYNTHESIS: CHAPTERS 13–15

Review Exercises

1. 108 kJ   **3.** 28.4°C   **5.** (a) 74 g   (b) 11°C   **5.** 467 mol   **7.** The ice will melt completely; 32°C   **9.** (a) 4140 K   (b) 1.09×10^{26} W   (c) 1.01×10^{-9} W/m^2 **11.** (a) 8.87 kPa; 1200 K   (b) 23 kJ   (c) 20.0 kJ   (d) 0   **13.** 2.44 kJ/K   **15.** 10.9°C   **17.** reduced to 75% of the original   **19.** 12 kJ   **21.** (a) The boiling temperature of water varies with pressure. If the pressure is high, the water molecules are pushed close together, making it harder for them to form a gas. (Gas molecules are farther apart from each other than are liquid molecules.) A higher pressure raises the temperature at which the coolant fluid will boil.   (b) If you were to remove the cap on your radiator without first bringing the radiator pressure down to atmospheric pressure, the fluid would suddenly boil, sending out a jet of hot steam that could burn you.   **23.** (a) if they have the same mass   (b) Since they are at the same temperature, there is no net energy transfer between the two blocks.   (c) The blocks need not touch each other in order to be in thermal contact. They can be in thermal contact due to convection and radiation.   **25.** (a)

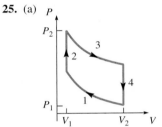

(b)

Process	W (kJ)	ΔU (kJ)	Q (kJ)
Step 1	11.2	0	−11.2
Step 2	0	27.4	27.4
Step 3	−34.1	0	34.1
Step 4	0	−27.4	−27.4
Total	−22.8	0	22.8

(c) 0.371 or 37.1%   (d) 0.670 or 67.0%   **27.** 132°C   **29.** (a) 11 200 m/s   (b) 1850 m/s   (c) 461 m/s   (d) The atoms in the high end of the distribution are much faster than the average. Some of the hydrogen atoms have speeds greater than the escape speed, thus they can escape. This is not the case for oxygen, which is much more massive and, thus, much slower.

MCAT Review

1. C   **2.** B   **3.** C   **4.** B   **5.** A   **6.** D   **7.** A   **8.** C   **9.** B   **10.** A   **11.** A

Student Solutions Manual
to accompany
College Physics

Chapters 1-15

Chapter 1

INTRODUCTION

Conceptual Questions

1. Knowledge of physics is important for a full understanding of many scientific disciplines, such as chemistry, biology, and geology. Furthermore, much of our current technology can only be understood with knowledge of the underlying laws of physics. In the search for more efficient and environmentally safe sources of energy, for example, physics is essential. Also, many study physics for the sense of fulfillment that comes with learning about the world we inhabit.

5. Scientific notation eliminates the need to write many zeros in very large or small numbers. Also, the appropriate number of significant digits is unambiguous when written this way.

9. The kilogram, meter, and second are three of the base units used in the SI system.

13. Trends in a set of data are often the most interesting aspect of the outcome of an experiment. Such trends are more apparent when data is plotted graphically rather than listed in numerical tables.

Problems

1. **Strategy** The new fence will be $100\% + 37\% = 137\%$ of the height of the old fence.

   Solution Find the height of the new fence.
   $1.37 \times 1.8 \text{ m} = \boxed{2.5 \text{ m}}$

3. **Strategy** Relate the surface area S to the radius r using $S = 4\pi r^2$.

   Solution Find the ratio of the new radius to the old.
   $S_1 = 4\pi r_1^2$ and $S_2 = 4\pi r_2^2 = 1.160 S_1 = 1.160(4\pi r_1^2)$.
   $$4\pi r_2^2 = 1.160(4\pi r_1^2)$$
   $$r_2^2 = 1.160 r_1^2$$
   $$\left(\frac{r_2}{r_1}\right)^2 = 1.160$$
   $$\frac{r_2}{r_1} = \sqrt{1.160} = 1.077$$
   The radius of the balloon increases by $\boxed{7.7\%}$.

5. **Strategy** The surface area S and the volume V are given by $S = 6s^2$ and $V = s^3$, respectively.

   Solution Find the ratio of the surface area to the volume.
   $$\frac{S}{V} = \frac{6s^2}{s^3} = \boxed{\frac{6}{s}}$$

9. **Strategy** Use a proportion.

   Solution Find Jupiter's orbital period.
   $T^2 \propto R^3$, so $\dfrac{T_J^2}{T_E^2} = \dfrac{R_J^3}{R_E^3} = 5.19^3$. Thus, $T_J = 5.19^{3/2} T_E = \boxed{11.8 \text{ yr}}$.

11. **Strategy** The area of the poster is given by $A = \ell w$. Let the original and final areas be $A_1 = \ell_1 w_1$ and $A_2 = \ell_2 w_2$, respectively.

    Solution Calculate the percentage reduction of the area.
    $$A_2 = \ell_2 w_2 = (0.800\ell_1)(0.800 w_1) = 0.640\ell_1 w_1 = 0.640 A_1$$
    $$\frac{A_1 - A_2}{A_1} \times 100\% = \frac{A_1 - 0.640 A_1}{A_1} \times 100\% = \boxed{36.0\%}$$

13. **(a) Strategy** Rewrite the numbers so that the power of 10 is the same for each. Then add and give the answer with the number of significant figures determined by the less precise of the two numbers.

    Solution Perform the operation with the appropriate number of significant figures.
    $$3.783 \times 10^6 \text{ kg} + 1.25 \times 10^8 \text{ kg} = 0.03783 \times 10^8 \text{ kg} + 1.25 \times 10^8 \text{ kg} = \boxed{1.29 \times 10^8 \text{ kg}}$$

    (b) Strategy Find the quotient and give the answer with the number of significant figures determined by the number with the fewest significant figures.

    Solution Perform the operation with the appropriate number of significant figures.
    $$(3.783 \times 10^6 \text{ m}) \div (3.0 \times 10^{-2} \text{ s}) = \boxed{1.3 \times 10^8 \text{ m/s}}$$

17. **Strategy** Multiply and give the answer in scientific notation with the number of significant figures determined by the number with the fewest significant figures.

    Solution Solve the problem.
    $$(3.2 \text{ m}) \times (4.0 \times 10^{-3} \text{ m}) \times (1.3 \times 10^{-8} \text{ m}) = \boxed{1.7 \times 10^{-10} \text{ m}^3}$$

21. **Strategy** There are approximately 39.37 inches per meter.

    Solution Find the thickness of the cell membrane in inches.
    $$7.0 \times 10^{-9} \text{ m} \times 39.37 \text{ inches/m} = \boxed{2.8 \times 10^{-7} \text{ inches}}$$

25. **(a) Strategy** There are 60 seconds in one minute, 5280 feet in one mile, and 3.28 feet in one meter.

    Solution Express 0.32 miles per minute in meters per second.
    $$\frac{0.32 \text{ mi}}{1 \text{ min}} \times \frac{1 \text{ min}}{60 \text{ s}} \times \frac{5280 \text{ ft}}{1 \text{ mi}} \times \frac{1 \text{ m}}{3.28 \text{ ft}} = \boxed{8.6 \text{ m/s}}$$

    (b) Strategy There are 60 minutes in one hour.

    Solution Express 0.32 miles per minute in miles per hour.
    $$\frac{0.32 \text{ mi}}{1 \text{ min}} \times \frac{60 \text{ min}}{1 \text{ h}} = \boxed{19 \text{ mi/h}}$$

29. Strategy There are 1000 grams in one kilogram and 100 centimeters in one meter.

Solution Find the density of mercury in units of g/cm^3.

$$\frac{1.36 \times 10^4 \text{ kg}}{1 \text{ m}^3} \times \frac{1000 \text{ g}}{1 \text{ kg}} \times \left(\frac{1 \text{ m}}{100 \text{ cm}}\right)^3 = \boxed{13.6 \ g/cm^3}$$

33. (a) Strategy There are 12 inches in one foot, 2.54 centimeters in one inch, and 60 seconds in one minute.

Solution Express the snail's speed in feet per second.

$$\frac{5.0 \text{ cm}}{1 \text{ min}} \times \frac{1 \text{ min}}{60 \text{ s}} \times \frac{1 \text{ in}}{2.54 \text{ cm}} \times \frac{1 \text{ ft}}{12 \text{ in}} = \boxed{2.7 \times 10^{-3} \text{ ft/s}}$$

(b) Strategy There are 5280 feet in one mile, 12 inches in one foot, 2.54 centimeters in one inch, and 60 minutes in one hour.

Solution Express the snail's speed in miles per hour.

$$\frac{5.0 \text{ cm}}{1 \text{ min}} \times \frac{60 \text{ min}}{1 \text{ h}} \times \frac{1 \text{ in}}{2.54 \text{ cm}} \times \frac{1 \text{ ft}}{12 \text{ in}} \times \frac{1 \text{ mi}}{5280 \text{ ft}} = \boxed{1.9 \times 10^{-3} \text{ mi/h}}$$

37. Strategy Replace each quantity in $T^2 = 4\pi^2 r^3/(GM)$ with its dimensions.

Solution Show that the equation is dimensionally correct.

T^2 has dimensions $[T]^2$ and $\dfrac{4\pi^2 r^3}{GM}$ has dimensions $\dfrac{[L]^3}{\dfrac{[L]^3}{[M][T]^2} \times [M]} = \dfrac{[L]^3}{[M]} \times \dfrac{[M][T]^2}{[L]^3} = [T]^2$.

Since $\boxed{[T]^2 = [T]^2}$, the equation is dimensionally correct.

41. Strategy Approximate the distance from your eyes to a book held at your normal reading distance.

Solution The normal reading distance is about 30-40 cm, so the approximate distance from your eyes to a book you are reading is $\boxed{30\text{-}40 \text{ cm}}$.

45. Strategy (Answers will vary.) In this case, we use San Francisco, CA for the city. The population of San Francisco is approximately 750,000. Assume that there is one automobile for every two residents of San Francisco, that an average automobile needs three repairs or services per year, and that the average shop can service 10 automobiles per day.

Solution Estimate the number of automobile repair shops in San Francisco.

If an automobile needs three repairs or services per year, then it needs $\dfrac{3 \text{ repairs}}{\text{auto} \cdot \text{y}} \times \dfrac{1 \text{ y}}{365 \text{ d}} \approx \dfrac{0.01 \text{ repairs}}{\text{auto} \cdot \text{d}}$.

If there is one auto for every two residents, then there are $\dfrac{1 \text{ auto}}{2 \text{ residents}} \times 750{,}000 \text{ residents} \approx 4 \times 10^5 \text{ autos}$.

If a shop requires one day to service 10 autos, then the number of shops-days per repair is

$1 \text{ shop} \times \dfrac{1 \text{ d}}{10 \text{ repairs}} = \dfrac{0.1 \text{ shop} \cdot \text{d}}{\text{repair}}$.

The estimated number of auto shops is $4 \times 10^5 \text{ autos} \times \dfrac{0.01 \text{ repairs}}{\text{auto} \cdot \text{d}} \times \dfrac{0.1 \text{ shop} \cdot \text{d}}{\text{repair}} = \boxed{400 \text{ shops}}$.

Checking the phone directory, we find that there are approximately 463 automobile repair and service shops in San Francisco. The estimate is off by $\dfrac{400 - 463}{400} \times 100\% = \boxed{-16\%}$. The estimate was 16% too low, but in the ball park!

47. Strategy One story is about 3 m high.

Solution Find the order of magnitude of the height in meters of a 40-story building.

$(3 \text{ m})(40) \sim \boxed{100 \text{ m}}$

49. Strategy The plot of temperature versus elapsed time is shown. Use the graph to answer the questions.

Solution

(a) By inspection of the graph, it appears that the temperature at noon was $\boxed{101.8°\text{F}}$.

(b) Estimate the slope of the line.

$m = \dfrac{102.6°\text{F} - 100.0°\text{F}}{1{:}00 \text{ P.M.} - 10{:}00 \text{ A.M.}} = \dfrac{2.6°\text{F}}{3 \text{ h}} = \boxed{0.9°\text{F/h}}$

(c) In twelve hours, the temperature would, according to the trend, be approximately
$T = (0.9 \text{ °F/h})(12 \text{ h}) + 102.5°\text{F} = 113°\text{F}$.

The patient would be dead before the temperature reached this level. So, the answer is $\boxed{\text{no}}$.

53. Strategy Put the equation that describes the line in slope-intercept form, $y = mx + b$.

$$at = v - v_0$$
$$v = at + v_0$$

Solution

(a) v is the dependent variable and t is the independent variable, so $\boxed{a}$ is the slope of the line.

(b) The slope-intercept form is $y = mx + b$. Find the vertical-axis intercept.
$v \leftrightarrow y$, $t \leftrightarrow x$, $a \leftrightarrow m$, so $v_0 \leftrightarrow b$.

Thus, $\boxed{+v_0}$ is the vertical-axis intercept of the line.

57. Strategy For parts (a) through (d), perform the calculations.

Solution

(a) $186.300 + 0.0030 = \boxed{186.303}$

(b) $186.300 - 0.0030 = \boxed{186.297}$

(c) $186.300 \times 0.0030 = \boxed{0.56}$

(d) $186.300 / 0.0030 = \boxed{62,000}$

(e) **Strategy** For cases (a) and (b), the percent error is given by $\dfrac{0.0030}{Actual\ Value} \times 100\%$.

Solution Find the percent error.

Case (a): $\dfrac{0.0030}{186.303} \times 100\% = \boxed{0.0016\%}$

Case (b): $\dfrac{0.0030}{186.297} \times 100\% = \boxed{0.0016\%}$

For case (c), ignoring 0.0030 causes you to multiply by zero and get a zero result. For case (d), ignoring 0.0030 causes you to divide by zero.

(f) **Strategy** Make a rule about neglecting small values using the results obtained above.

Solution

You can neglect small values when they are added to or subtracted from sufficiently large values. The term "sufficiently large" is determined by the number of significant figures required.

59. Strategy Assuming that the cross section of the artery is a circle, we use the area of a circle, $A = \pi r^2$.

Solution

$A_1 = \pi r_1^2$ and $A_2 = \pi r_2^2 = \pi (2.0 r_1)^2 = 4.0 \pi r_1^2$.
Form a proportion.

$$\frac{A_2}{A_1} = \frac{4.0 \pi r_1^2}{\pi r_1^2} = 4.0$$

The cross-sectional area of the artery increases by a factor of $\boxed{4.0}$.

61. Strategy If s is the speed of the molecule, then $s \propto \sqrt{T}$ where T is the temperature.

Solution Form a proportion.

$$\frac{s_{\text{cold}}}{s_{\text{warm}}} = \frac{\sqrt{T_{\text{cold}}}}{\sqrt{T_{\text{warm}}}}$$

Find s_{cold}.

$$s_{\text{cold}} = s_{\text{warm}} \sqrt{\frac{T_{\text{cold}}}{T_{\text{warm}}}} = (475 \text{ m/s}) \sqrt{\frac{250.0 \text{ K}}{300.0 \text{ K}}} = \boxed{434 \text{ m/s}}$$

65. Strategy Use the metric prefixes n (10^{-9}), μ (10^{-6}), m (10^{-3}), or M (10^6).

Solution

(a) M (or mega) is equal to 10^6, so $6 \times 10^6 \text{ m} = \boxed{6 \text{ Mm}}$.

(b) There are approximately 3.28 feet in one meter, so $6 \text{ ft} \times \dfrac{1 \text{ m}}{3.28 \text{ ft}} = \boxed{2 \text{ m}}$.

(c) μ (or micro) is equal to 10^{-6}, so $10^{-6} \text{ m} = \boxed{1 \ \mu\text{m}}$.

(d) n (or nano) is equal to 10^{-9}, so $3 \times 10^{-9} \text{ m} = \boxed{3 \text{ nm}}$.

(e) n (or nano) is equal to 10^{-9}, so $3 \times 10^{-10} \text{ m} = \boxed{0.3 \text{ nm}}$.

67. Strategy The circumference of a viroid is approximately 300 times 0.35 nm. The diameter is given by $C = \pi d$, or $d = C/\pi$.

Solution Find the diameter of the viroid in the required units.

(a) $d = \dfrac{300(0.35 \text{ nm})}{\pi} \times \dfrac{10^{-9} \text{ m}}{1 \text{ nm}} = \boxed{3.3 \times 10^{-8} \text{ m}}$

(b) $d = \dfrac{300(0.35 \text{ nm})}{\pi} \times \dfrac{10^{-3} \ \mu\text{m}}{1 \text{ nm}} = \boxed{3.3 \times 10^{-2} \ \mu\text{m}}$

(c) $d = \dfrac{300(0.35 \text{ nm})}{\pi} \times \dfrac{10^{-7} \text{ cm}}{1 \text{ nm}} \times \dfrac{1 \text{ in}}{2.54 \text{ cm}} = \boxed{1.3 \times 10^{-6} \text{ in}}$

69. **Strategy** The volume of the blue whale can be found by dividing the mass of the whale by its average density.

Solution Find the volume of the blue whale in cubic meters.
$$V = \frac{m}{\rho} = \frac{1.9 \times 10^5 \, \text{kg}}{0.85 \, \text{g/cm}^3} \times \frac{1000 \, \text{g}}{1 \, \text{kg}} \times \left(\frac{1 \, \text{m}}{100 \, \text{cm}}\right)^3 = \boxed{2.2 \times 10^2 \, \text{m}^3}$$

73. **Strategy** There are 2.54 cm in one inch and 3600 seconds in one hour.

Solution Find the conversion factor for changing meters per second to miles per hour.
$$\frac{1 \, \text{m}}{1 \, \text{s}} \times \frac{100 \, \text{cm}}{1 \, \text{m}} \times \frac{1 \, \text{in}}{2.54 \, \text{cm}} \times \frac{1 \, \text{ft}}{12 \, \text{in}} \times \frac{1 \, \text{mi}}{5280 \, \text{ft}} \times \frac{3600 \, \text{s}}{1 \, \text{h}} = \boxed{2.24 \, \text{mi/h} = 1 \, \text{m/s}}$$
So, $\boxed{\text{for a quick, approximate conversion, multiply by 2}}$.

77. **Strategy** The SI base unit for mass is kg. Replace each quantity in $W = mg$ with its SI base units.

Solution Find the SI unit for weight.
$$\text{kg} \cdot \frac{\text{m}}{\text{s}^2} = \boxed{\frac{\text{kg} \cdot \text{m}}{\text{s}^2}}$$

81. **(a) Strategy** There are 7.0 leagues in one pace and 4.8 kilometers in one league.

Solution Find your speed in kilometers per hour.
$$\frac{120 \, \text{paces}}{1 \, \text{min}} \times \frac{7.0 \, \text{leagues}}{1 \, \text{pace}} \times \frac{4.8 \, \text{km}}{1 \, \text{league}} \times \frac{60 \, \text{min}}{1 \, \text{h}} = \boxed{2.4 \times 10^5 \, \text{km/h}}$$

(b) Strategy The circumference of the earth is approximately 40,000 km. The time it takes to march around the Earth is found by dividing the distance by the speed.

Solution Find the time of travel.
$$40{,}000 \, \text{km} \times \frac{1 \, \text{h}}{2.4 \times 10^5 \, \text{km}} \times \frac{60 \, \text{min}}{1 \, \text{h}} = \boxed{10 \, \text{min}}$$

85. **Strategy** The dimensions of k and m are mass per time squared and mass, respectively. Dividing either quantity by the other will eliminate the mass dimension.

Solution The square root of k/m has dimensions of inverse time, which is correct for frequency.
So, $f = \sqrt{k/m}$. Find k.
$$f_1 = \sqrt{\frac{k}{m_1}}, \text{ so } f_1^2 = \frac{k}{m_1}, \text{ or } k = m_1 f_1^2.$$
Find the frequency of the chair with the 75-kg astronaut.
$$f_2 = \sqrt{\frac{k}{m_2}} = \sqrt{\frac{m_1 f_1^2}{m_2}} = f_1 \sqrt{\frac{m_1}{m_2}} = (0.50 \, \text{s}^{-1}) \sqrt{\frac{62 \, \text{kg} + 10.0 \, \text{kg}}{75 \, \text{kg} + 10.0 \, \text{kg}}} = \boxed{0.46 \, \text{s}^{-1}}$$

Chapter 2

FORCE

Conceptual Questions

1. In an automobile accident the force due to the collision changes the motion of the car, but the driver and passengers continue to move in accordance with Newton's first law. Seat belts supply the force necessary to change their motion and slow them down. Without seat belts people would collide with the steering wheel or windshield, for example, and stand a greater risk of injury.

5. When the handle hits the board and stops abruptly, Newton's first law says that the steel head will continue to move for a short distance, resisting changes in velocity, until the force of friction between the head and the handle has brought it to rest. It will have then moved down some to where the handle is a little wider, resulting in a tightening of the head onto the handle.

9. (a) The reading of the scale is the magnitude of the normal force pushing up on you. This equals your weight as long as the normal force and the force of gravity are the only forces acting on you, and you are at rest or moving with a constant velocity.

   (b) If you were standing on the scale in a swimming pool for example, there would be a buoyant force from the water pushing up on you, and the scale would read a smaller apparent weight. Also, the scale would not read your weight if you were accelerating—for example standing on the scale in an elevator as it was moving upward with increasing speed.

13. The key is that the equal and opposite forces of Newton's third law are acting on two different objects—one on the wagon and the other on you. The wagon can therefore experience a non-zero net force, which causes it to accelerate forward.

17. Newton's third law tells us that if the person on the raft walks away from the pier, the raft will in turn move toward the pier. Thus, after walking the length of the raft, it should be possible for the person with the hook on the pier to grab the raft and reel it in. Without the person on the pier to hold the raft, this technique would be of no use, as the raft would move back away from the pier on the return walk.

21. Yes, as long as the y-axis is perpendicular to the chosen x-axis. This will often simplify a problem.

Problems

1. **Strategy** Determine the forces *not* acting on the scale.

   Solution The scale is in contact with the floor, so a contact force due to the floor is exerted on the scale. The scale is in contact with the person's feet, so a contact force due to the person's feet is exerted on the scale. The scale is in the proximity of a very large mass (Earth), so the weight of the scale is a force exerted on the scale. The weight of the person is a force exerted on the person due to the very large mass, so it is not a force exerted on the scale.

5. **Strategy** There are 0.2248 pounds per newton.

   Solution Find the weight of the astronaut in newtons.

   $$175 \text{ lb} \times \frac{1 \text{ N}}{0.2248 \text{ lb}} = \boxed{778 \text{ N}}$$

9. **Strategy** Use the fact that $|\vec{A}| = |\vec{B}|$ and symmetry to determine the direction of $\vec{C}$; then sketch $\vec{C}$.

Solution By symmetry, we find that $\vec{C}$ points downward; the horizontal components cancel when $\vec{A}$ and $\vec{B}$ are added. The downward components of each vector have the same magnitude, about 0.7 N. So, the magnitude of $\vec{C}$ is about 1.4 N. The sketch is shown:

13. **Strategy** Use graph paper to draw a diagram.

Solution Find the vector sum of the vectors.

Because of symmetry, the y-components of the vectors cancel. The x-components look to be about 10 N, so the vector sum is $10\text{ N} + 10\text{ N} = 20\text{ N}$, or 20 N in the positive x-direction.

15. **Strategy** Graph the vectors and their sum. Use the graph and the grid to estimate the components of the vectors. Then use the component method to find the vector sum.

Solution Find the vector sum.

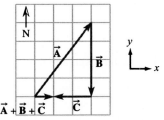

x-comp: $A_x + B_x + C_x = 3(2\text{ N}) + 0(2\text{ N}) - 2(2\text{ N}) = 2\text{ N}$
y-comp: $A_y + B_y + C_y = 4(2\text{ N}) - 4(2\text{ N}) + 0(2\text{ N}) = 0$

The vector sum of the forces is 2 N in the positive x-direction or 2 N to the east.

17. **Strategy** The components of $\vec{v}$ are given. Since the x-component is positive and the y-component is negative, the vector lies in the fourth quadrant. Give the angle with respect to the axes.

Solution Find the magnitude and direction of $\vec{v}$.

(a) $v = \sqrt{v_x^2 + v_y^2} = \sqrt{(16.4\text{ m/s})^2 + (-26.3\text{ m/s})^2} = 31.0\text{ m/s}$

(b) $\theta = \tan^{-1}\dfrac{-26.3}{16.4} = $ 58.1° with the $+x$-axis and 31.9° with the $-y$-axis

21. **Strategy** The components of $\vec{\mathbf{a}}$ are given. Since the *x*-component is negative and the *y*-component is positive, the vector lies in the second quadrant. Give the angle with respect to the axis to which it lies closest.

    Solution Find the magnitude and direction of $\vec{\mathbf{a}}$.

    (a) $a = \sqrt{a_x{}^2 + a_y{}^2} = \sqrt{(-3.0 \ \text{m/s}^2)^2 + (4.0 \ \text{m/s}^2)^2} = \boxed{5.0 \ \text{m/s}^2}$

    (b) $\theta = \tan^{-1} \dfrac{4.0}{-3.0} = \boxed{37° \ \text{CCW from the } +y\text{-axis}}$

25. **Strategy** Since the man and mattress are neither moving upward nor downward, the net force must be zero in the vertical direction.

    Solution So that the net force is zero, the upward force of the water must be equal to the combined weight of the man and the air mattress, or $\boxed{806 \ \text{N}}$.

29. **Strategy** The force of the lake on the boat must be equal in magnitude and opposite in direction to the weight of the boat. The force of the wind on the boat must be equal in magnitude and opposite in direction to that of the line. Let the subscripts be the following:
    s = sailboat   e = Earth   w = wind   l = lake   m = mooring line

    Solution The free-body diagram is shown.

    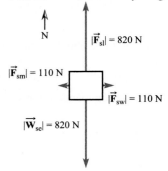

31. **Strategy** For each object, add the forces to find the net force.

    Solution

    (a) 10 N left + 40 N right = -10 N right + 40 N right = $\boxed{30 \ \text{N to the right}}$

    (b) The forces balance, so the net force is $\boxed{0}$.

    (c) The horizontal forces balance, so the net force is due only to the downward force. The net force is $\boxed{18 \ \text{N downward}}$.

33. **Strategy** Use the properties of vectors to answer the questions.

    Solution

    (a) The only way for the net force to have a magnitude of 7.0 N is if the two forces are in the $\boxed{\text{same direction}}$.

    (b) Recognizing that the three vectors form a 3-4-5 right triangle, we know that the vectors are $\boxed{\text{perpendicular}}$.

    (c) The smallest magnitude net force can only be obtained if the two vectors are in $\boxed{\text{opposite directions}}$; the magnitude of the smallest net force is $\boxed{1.0 \ \text{N}}$.

37. Strategy We are concerned with the interactions of pairs of objects that exert forces on each other. Analyze the given forces in light of Newton's first and third laws.

Solution Forces (a) and (b) are third law pairs. This is an interaction between two objects, the bike and the Earth. Each body exerts a gravitational force on the other body; and these forces are equal in magnitude and opposite in direction. Forces (a) and (c) are equal and opposite due to the first law. They act not on each other, but on the same body.

41. Strategy Use Newton's first and third laws.

Solution

(a) Margie exerts a downward force on the scale equal to her weight, 543 N. According to the third law, the scale exerts an upward force on Margie equal in magnitude to the magnitude of the force exerted by Margie on it, or 543 N.

(b) Refer to part (a). The interaction partner of the force exerted on Margie by the scale is the contact force of Margie's feet on the scale.

(c) The Earth must hold up both the scale and (indirectly) Margie, since Margie is standing on the scale. So, the Earth must push up on the scale with a force equal to the combined weight of Margie and the scale, or $543 \text{ N} + 45 \text{ N} = 588 \text{ N}$.

(d) Refer to part (c). The interaction partner of the force exerted on the scale by the Earth is the contact force on the Earth due to the scale.

45. (a) Strategy Compare the strengths of the forces at the location of the rock.

Solution The gravitational force between to bodies is inversely proportional to the square of the distance between them. The Moon is much closer to the rock than is the Earth, so (even though the Earth is much more massive than the Moon) the rock will fall toward the Moon's surface.

(b) Strategy The Moon's gravitational field strength is 1.62 N/kg. The force of the Moon on the rock is equal to the weight of the rock on the Moon.

Solution Find the weight of the rock to find the gravitational force exerted by the Moon on it.
$F = W = mg = (1.0 \text{ kg})(1.62 \text{ N/kg}) = 1.6 \text{ N}$
The force on the rock due to the Moon is 1.6 N toward the Moon.

(c) Strategy Use Newton's law of universal gravitation. The average Earth-Moon distance is 3.845×10^8 m. The mass of the Earth is 5.974×10^{24} kg.

Solution Find the gravitational force exerted by the Earth on the rock.
$$F = \frac{Gm_1m_2}{r^2} = \frac{(6.674 \times 10^{-11} \text{ N} \cdot \text{m}^2/\text{kg}^2)(1.0 \text{ kg})(5.974 \times 10^{24} \text{ kg})}{(3.845 \times 10^8 \text{ m})^2} = 2.7 \text{ mN}$$
Since gravitational force is attractive, the force exerted by the Earth on the rock is 2.7 mN toward Earth.

(d) Strategy Recognize that the force due to the Moon is much greater than that due to the Earth.

Solution Find the net gravitational force.
1.6 N toward the Moon + 0.0027 N toward Earth = 1.6 N toward the Moon − 0.0027 N toward the Moon
$$= \boxed{1.6 \text{ N toward the Moon}}$$

47. Strategy Use the conversion factor for pounds to newtons, $0.2248\ \text{lb} = 1\ \text{N}$.

Solution

(a) Find the weight of the girl in newtons.
$$W = mg = (40.0\ \text{kg})(9.80\ \text{N/kg}) = \boxed{392\ \text{N}}$$

(b) Find the weight of the girl in pounds.
$$(392\ \text{N})(0.2248\ \text{lb/N}) = \boxed{88.1\ \text{lb}}$$

49. Strategy Use Newton's universal law of gravitation. The Voyager spacecraft are approximately 15 billion kilometers from the Sun. Use this value for the distance between the Earth and the spacecraft.

Solution Find the approximate magnitude of the gravitational force between Earth and the spacecraft.
$$F = \frac{Gm_1m_2}{r^2} = \frac{(6.674\times10^{-11}\ \text{N}\cdot\text{m}^2/\text{kg}^2)(825\ \text{kg})(5.974\times10^{24}\ \text{kg})}{(15\times10^{12}\ \text{m})^2} = \boxed{1.5\times10^{-9}\ \text{N}}$$

53. Strategy Gravitational field strength is given by $g = GM/R^2$. Find $H = R_2 - R_1$, where R_1 and R_2 are the distances from the center of the Earth to the surface of the Earth and the location of the balloon, respectively.

Solution Find the height above sea level of the balloon, H.
$$H = R_2 - R_1 = \sqrt{\frac{GM}{g_2}} - \sqrt{\frac{GM}{g_1}} = \sqrt{GM}\left(g_2^{-1/2} - g_1^{-1/2}\right)$$
$$= \sqrt{(6.674\times10^{-11}\ \text{N}\cdot\text{m}^2/\text{kg}^2)(5.974\times10^{24}\ \text{kg})}\left[(9.792\ \text{N/kg})^{-1/2} - (9.803\ \text{N/kg})^{-1/2}\right] = \boxed{4\ \text{km}}$$

57. Strategy Use Newton's universal law of gravitation.

Solution Find the ratio.
$$\frac{F_1}{F_2} = \frac{Gm_1m_2}{r_1^2} \div \frac{Gm_1m_2}{r_2^2} = \left(\frac{r_2}{r_1}\right)^2 = \left(\frac{r_1 + 6.00\times10^6\ \text{m}}{r_1}\right)^2 = \left(\frac{6.371\times10^6\ \text{m} + 6.00\times10^6\ \text{m}}{6.371\times10^6\ \text{m}}\right)^2 = \boxed{3.770}$$

61. Strategy The direction of the normal force is always perpendicular to the surface of the ramp. The friction force is in whatever direction necessary to oppose the motion of the object.

Solution The results are shown in the table.

	$\vec{\mathbf{N}}$	$\vec{\mathbf{f}}$
(a)	perpendicular to and away from	along the ramp upward
(b)	perpendicular to and away from	along the ramp downward
(c)	perpendicular to and away from	along the ramp upward

63. **(a) Strategy** Use Newton's first law of motion.

    Solution Since the sleigh is moving with constant speed, the net force acting on the sleigh is $\boxed{\text{zero}}$.

    (b) Strategy Since $F_{net} = 0$, the force of magnitude T must be equal to the force of kinetic friction.

    Solution Find the coefficient of kinetic friction.

    $T = f_k = \mu_k mg$, so $\mu_k = \boxed{\dfrac{T}{mg}}$.

65. **Strategy** Let the subscripts be the following:
    t = table   e = Earth   1 = block 1   2 = block 2   3 = block 3   4 = block 4
    h = horizontal force   1234 = system of blocks   (The blocks are numbered from left to right.)

    Solution The diagrams are shown.

    (a)   **(b)**

69. **(a) Strategy** Draw a diagram and use Newton's laws of motion.

    Solution According to the first law, since the skier is moving with constant velocity, the net force on the skier is zero. Calculate the force of kinetic friction.
    $\sum F_x = f_k - mg\sin\theta = 0$, so
    $f_k = mg\sin\theta = (85\ \text{kg})(9.80\ \text{N/kg})\sin 11° = 160\ \text{N}.$
    The force of kinetic friction is $\boxed{160\ \text{N up the slope}}$.

    (b) Strategy Use the diagram and results from part (a).

    Solution Find the normal force.
    $\sum F_y = N - mg\cos\theta = 0$, so $N = mg\cos\theta$. Since $f_k = \mu_k N$,

    $\mu_k = \dfrac{f_k}{N} = \dfrac{mg\sin\theta}{mg\cos\theta} = \tan\theta = \tan 11° = \boxed{0.19}$.

73. **Strategy** Use Newton's laws of motion. Draw a diagram.

    Solution Find the tension.
    $\sum F_x = T\cos\theta - T\cos\theta = 0$ and

    $\sum F_y = T\sin\theta + T\sin\theta - W = 0$. So, $2T\sin\theta = W$, or $T = \boxed{\dfrac{W}{2\sin\theta}}$.

75. **Strategy** Recall that the tension in the rope is the same along its length.

    Solution The tension is equal to the weight at the end of the rope, 120 N. Therefore, $\boxed{\text{both scales read 120 N}}$.

77. **Strategy** Use Newton's laws of motion and analyze each scale separately.

   Solution Scale B reads 120 N due to the apples hanging from it. According to Newton's third law, scale A also reads 120 N, since B is attached directly below it, which is attached to the weight.

81. **Strategy** Use Newton's laws of motion. Draw a free-body diagram.

   Solution Find the tension in each wire.

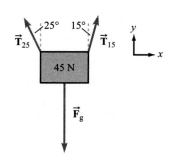

   $$\sum F_x = T_{25} \sin 25° - T_{15} \sin 15° = 0, \text{ so } T_{25} \sin 25° = T_{15} \sin 15°, \text{ or}$$

   $$T_{25} = \frac{\sin 15°}{\sin 25°} T_{15}.$$

   $$\sum F_y = T_{25} \cos 25° + T_{15} \cos 15° - F = 0, \text{ so } T_{15} \cos 15° + T_{25} \cos 25° = F.$$

   Substitute for T_{25}.

   $$T_{15} \cos 15° + \left(\frac{\sin 15°}{\sin 25°} T_{15} \right) \cos 25° = F$$

   $$T_{15} \left(\cos 15° + \frac{\sin 15°}{\tan 25°} \right) = F$$

   $$T_{15} = \frac{45 \text{ N}}{\cos 15° + \sin 15°/\tan 25°} = \boxed{30 \text{ N}}$$

   $$T_{25} = \frac{\sin 15°}{\sin 25°} (30 \text{ N}) = \boxed{18 \text{ N}}$$

85. **Strategy** Consider the ranges and natures of the fundamental forces.

   Solution Of all of the fundamental forces, the weak force has the shortest range (about 10^{-17} m). In the Sun, the weak interaction enables thermonuclear reactions to occur, without which there would be no sunlight.

89. **Strategy** Draw a diagram and use Newton's laws of motion.

   Solution According to the first law, for the box to move with constant speed, the net force on the box must by zero. Calculate the magnitude of the force of the push required.

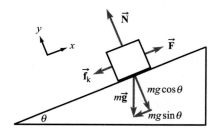

   $$\sum F_y = N - mg \cos \theta = 0, \text{ so } N = mg \cos \theta.$$

   $$\sum F_x = F - f_k - mg \sin \theta = 0, \text{ so}$$

   $$F = f_k + mg \sin \theta = \mu_k N + mg \sin \theta$$

   $$= \mu_k mg \cos \theta + mg \sin \theta = mg(\mu_k \cos \theta + \sin \theta)$$

   $$= (65 \text{ kg})(9.80 \text{ N/kg})(0.30 \cos 25° + \sin 25°) = \boxed{440 \text{ N}}.$$

93. Strategy Set the magnitudes of the forces on the spaceship due to the Earth and the Moon equal. (The forces are along the same line.)

Solution Find the distance from the Earth expressed as a percentage of the distance between the centers of the Earth and the Moon.

$$F_{sE} = \frac{GM_E m}{r_E^2} = F_{sM} = \frac{GM_M m}{r_M^2}, \text{ so } r_E = r_M\sqrt{\frac{M_E}{0.0123M_E}} = 9.02r_M.$$

Find the percentage.

$$\frac{r_E}{r_E + r_M} = \frac{9.02r_M}{9.02r_M + r_M} = \frac{9.02}{10.02} = 0.900$$

The distance from the Earth is 90.0% of the Earth-Moon distance.

97. (a) Strategy The force of static friction is greater than the applied force. Draw a diagram.

Solution Find the possible values for the coefficient of static friction.

$$f_s = \mu_s N > F, \text{ so } \mu_s > \frac{F}{N} = \frac{120 \text{ N}}{250 \text{ N}} = 0.48.$$

Therefore, $\mu_s > 0.48$.

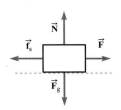

(b) Strategy Refer to part (a).

Solution Compute the coefficient of static friction.

$$\mu_s = F/N = (150 \text{ N})/(250 \text{ N}) = 0.60$$

(c) Strategy Refer to part (a), but with the coefficient of kinetic friction instead of that for static friction.

Solution Compute the coefficient of kinetic friction.

$$\mu_k = F/N = (120 \text{ N})/(250 \text{ N}) = 0.48$$

101. Strategy Let the subscripts be the following:
i = ice   e = Earth   s = stone   o = opponent's stone

Solution

(a) The only forces on the stone are gravity due to the Earth and the normal force due to the ice.

(b) As the stone slides down the rink, it experiences a force of kinetic friction opposite to its motion.

(c) The additional force is that due to the opponent's stone.

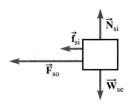

103. (a) Strategy Let the subscripts be the following:
c = computer   d = desk   e = Earth

Solution The only forces on the computer are gravity due to the
Earth and the normal force due to the desk. The free-body diagram
is shown.

(b) Strategy Consider the nature of friction forces.

Solution Since the only forces acting on the computer are in the vertical direction, the friction force is boxed{zero}.

(c) Strategy Find the maximum force of static friction on the computer due to the desk; this is the horizontal
force necessary to make it begin to slide.

Solution $F = f_s = \mu_s N = \mu_s W = 0.60(87 \text{ N}) = \boxed{52 \text{ N}}$

105. Strategy Use Newton's laws of motion. Draw diagrams.

Solution

(a) Below are two diagrams for each of the two cases.

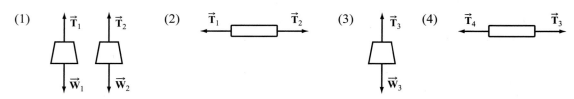

Sum the forces in (1).
Left weight: $\sum F_y = T_1 - W_1 = 0$, so $T_1 = W_1 = 550 \text{ N}$.

Right weight: $\sum F_y = T_2 - W_2 = 0$, so $T_2 = W_2 = 550 \text{ N}$.

Since $W_1 = W_2$, $T_1 = T_2 = 550$ N; the tensions are the same, and the scale in (2) has forces exerted on it of
magnitude 550 N, which are opposite in direction

Sum the forces in (3).
Single weight: $\sum F_y = T_3 - W_3 = 0$, so $T_3 = W_3 = 550$ N. The scale in (4) is in equilibrium, so
$T_4 = T_3 = 550$ N.
Both scales are in equilibrium and each has two forces which are equal in magnitude and opposite in direction
exerted on it. The magnitudes of the forces are equal, so boxed{in each case, the two ropes pull on the scale with
forces of 550 N in opposite directions, so the scales give the same reading}.

(b) The reading on each scale is equal to the tension in the rope, boxed{550 N}.

109. Strategy The gravitational field strengths at sea level at the equator and at the North Pole are 9.784 N/kg and 9.832 N/kg, respectively. Weight is directly proportional to *g*.

Solution Find the percentage by which the weight of an object changes when moved from the equator to the North Pole.

$(9.832 - 9.784)/9.784 \times 100\% = \boxed{0.49\%}$

113. Strategy Let the +*y*-direction be in the direction of the 360.0-N force (*F*). Draw a diagram and use Newton's laws of motion.

Solution Find the force exerted on the poplar tree.

$\sum F_y = F - 2T \sin\theta = 0$ before the poplar is cut through.

So, $F = 2T \sin\theta$. The force exerted on the poplar is the tension *T*, so $T = \dfrac{F}{2\sin\theta}$.

Refer to the figure in the text to find $\sin\theta$.

$\sin\theta = \dfrac{\text{displacement}}{\text{half length of rope}} = \dfrac{2.00 \text{ m}}{\sqrt{(20.0 \text{ m})^2 + (2.00 \text{ m})^2}} = 0.0995$

Thus, $T = \dfrac{360.0 \text{ N}}{2(0.0995)} = \boxed{1810 \text{ N}}$. Compare the forces.

$\dfrac{1810 \text{ N}}{360.0 \text{ N}} \approx \boxed{5 \text{ times the force with which Yoojin pulls}}$

The values for the two situations are different because $\boxed{\text{the oak tree supplies additional force}}$.

Chapter 3

ACCELERATION AND NEWTON'S SECOND LAW OF MOTION

Conceptual Questions

1. Distance traveled is a scalar quantity equal to the total length of the path taken in moving from one point to another. Displacement is a vector quantity directed from the initial point towards the final point with a magnitude equal to the straight line distance between the two points. The magnitude of the displacement is always less than or equal to the total distance traveled.

5. The area under the curve of an a_x versus time graph is equal to the change in the x-component of the velocity.

9. The average speed and the magnitude of the average velocity of an object are equal if and only if the object travels along a straight line path without changing direction. In all other cases, the average speed is greater than the magnitude of the average velocity because the total distance traveled must be greater than the straight-line distance between the starting and ending points.

13. Newton's second law states that the vector sum of all external forces acting on an object is equal to the product of the mass of the object and its acceleration. From this law, we conclude that objects connected to opposite ends of a negligibly massive spring must exert a negligible net force—the second law would otherwise predict an infinite acceleration. The forces acting on each side of the spring must therefore be equal in magnitude and opposite in direction—and from Newton's third law, the forces exerted on the objects by the spring must also be equal in magnitude.

17. **(a)** $a_x > 0$ and $v_x < 0$ means you are moving south and slowing down.

    (b) $a_x = 0$ and $v_x < 0$ means you are moving south at a constant speed.

    (c) $a_x < 0$ and $v_x = 0$ means you are momentarily at rest but speeding up in a southward direction.

    (d) $a_x < 0$ and $v_x < 0$ means you are moving south and speeding up.

    (e) As can be seen from our answers above, it is not a good idea to use the term "negative acceleration" to mean slowing down. In parts (c) and (d), the acceleration is negative, but the bicycle is speeding up. Also, in part (a), the acceleration is positive, but the bicycle is slowing down.

Problems

1. **Strategy** Use the fact that $|\vec{A}| = |\vec{B}|$ and symmetry to determine the direction of $\vec{D}$.

   Solution The vertical components cancel when $\vec{B}$ is subtracted from $\vec{A}$. The direction of the horizontal component of $\vec{B}$ is reversed due to the subtraction, and so the vector resulting from the subtraction is in the direction of the horizontal component of $\vec{A}$; that is, to the left. The horizontal components of each vector have the same magnitude, which is about 3.9 cm; so the magnitude of $\vec{D}$ is about 7.9 cm. The sketch is shown:

5. **Strategy** Add the displacement from Jerry's dorm to the fitness center to the displacement from Cindy's apartment to Jerry's dorm to find the total displacement from Cindy's apartment to the fitness center.

Solution Add the displacements.

1.50 mi east + 2.00 mi north + 3.00 mi east = 4.50 mi east + 2.00 mi north
Let north be along the $+y$-axis and east be along the $+x$-axis. Then, the components of the total displacement are $\Delta x = 4.50$ mi and $\Delta y = 2.00$ mi.
Find the magnitude.

$$\Delta r = \sqrt{(\Delta x)^2 + (\Delta y)^2} = \sqrt{(4.50 \text{ mi})^2 + (2.00 \text{ mi})^2} = \boxed{4.92 \text{ mi}}$$

Find the direction.

$$\theta = \tan^{-1}\frac{2.00}{4.50} = \boxed{24.0° \text{ north of east}}$$

9. **Strategy** Let east be the $+x$-direction and north be the $+y$-direction.

Solution Compute the direction of travel and the distance walked.

$\Delta r_{1x} = 1.2$ km
$\Delta r_{1y} = 0$
$\Delta r_{2x} = (2.7 \text{ km})\cos 135° = -1.9$ km
$\Delta r_{2y} = (2.7 \text{ km})\sin 135° = 1.9$ km
$\Delta r_x = \Delta r_{1x} + \Delta r_{2x} = 1.2 \text{ km} - 1.9 \text{ km} = -0.7$ km
$\Delta r_y = \Delta r_{1y} + \Delta r_{2y} = 1.9$ km

$$|\Delta \vec{r}| = \sqrt{(\Delta r_x)^2 + (\Delta r_y)^2} = \sqrt{(-0.7 \text{ km})^2 + (1.9 \text{ km})^2} = 2.0 \text{ km}$$

The direction of the return trip is opposite the displacement vector found.
$\Delta r_x' = 0.7$ km and $\Delta r_y' = -1.9$ km.

$$\theta = \tan^{-1}\frac{-1.9}{0.7} = 20° \text{ east of south}$$

So, they must travel $\boxed{2.0 \text{ km at } 20° \text{ east of south.}}$

13. **Strategy** Write an expression for each displacement as the difference of two position vectors and then add them.

Solution Prove that the total displacement of a trip is equal to the sum of the displacements of each leg.
We have, $\Delta \vec{r} = (\vec{r}_2 - \vec{r}_1) + (\vec{r}_3 - \vec{r}_2) + (\vec{r}_4 - \vec{r}_3) + \cdots + (\vec{r}_n - \vec{r}_{n-1})$, so $\boxed{\Delta \vec{r} = \vec{r}_n - \vec{r}_1}$, since all position vectors are added and subtracted exactly once except for the first, $\vec{r}_1$, which is only subtracted, and the last, $\vec{r}_n$, which is only added.

15. **Strategy** Use the definition of average velocity.

Solution Find the average velocity of the shot put.

$$\vec{v}_{av} = \frac{\Delta \vec{r}}{\Delta t} = \frac{23.12 \text{ m north}}{1.65 \text{ s}} = \boxed{14.0 \text{ m/s north}}$$

17. **Strategy** Set up ratios of speeds to distances.

Solution Find the speed of the baseball v.

$$\frac{v}{60.5 \text{ ft}} = \frac{65.0 \text{ mph}}{43.0 \text{ ft}}, \text{ so } v = \frac{65.0 \text{ mph}}{43.0 \text{ ft}}(60.5 \text{ ft}) = \boxed{91.5 \text{ mph}}.$$

21. Strategy When the Boxster catches the Scion, the displacement of the Boxster will be $\Delta r + 186$ m and the displacement for the Scion will be Δr. Δt for both cars will be the same.

Solution Find the time it takes for the Boxster to catch the Scion.

$v_{av} = \dfrac{\Delta r_{car}}{\Delta t}$, so for the Boxster, $v_{av,B} = \dfrac{\Delta r + 186 \text{ m}}{\Delta t}$ or $\Delta r = v_{av,B}\Delta t - 186$ m.

For the Scion,

$v_{av,S} = \dfrac{\Delta r}{\Delta t}$, so $\Delta r = v_{av,S}\Delta t$.

Equate the two expressions for Δr.

$$v_{av,S}\Delta t = v_{av,B}\Delta t - 186 \text{ m}$$

$$(v_{av,S} - v_{av,B})\Delta t = -186 \text{ m}$$

$$\Delta t = \frac{186 \text{ m}}{v_{av,B} - v_{av,S}} = \frac{186 \text{ m}}{24.4 \text{ m/s} - 18.6 \text{ m/s}} = \frac{186 \text{ m}}{5.8 \text{ m/s}} = \boxed{32 \text{ s}}$$

25. Strategy Use the area under the curve to find the displacement of the skateboard.

Solution The displacement of the skateboard is given by the area under the v vs. t curve. Under the curve for $t = 3.00$ s to $t = 8.00$ s, there are 16.5 squares and each square represents $(1.0 \text{ m/s})(1.0 \text{ s}) = 1.0$ m; so the board moves $\boxed{16.5 \text{ m}}$.

27. Strategy The slope of the x vs. t curve is equal to v_x. Use the definition of average speed.

Solution Compute the average speed at $t = 2.0$ s.

$$v_x = \frac{6.0 \text{ m} - 4.0 \text{ m}}{3.0 \text{ s} - 1.0 \text{ s}} = \boxed{1.0 \text{ m/s}}$$

29. (a) Strategy Use the area between the v_y vs. t curve and the x-axis to find the displacement of the elevator.

Solution From $t = 0$ s to $t = 10$ s, there are 8 squares. From $t = 14$ s to $t = 20$ s, there are 4 squares. Each square represents $(1 \text{ m/s})(2 \text{ s}) = 2$ m. The displacement from $t = 14$ s to $t = 20$ s is negative ($v_y < 0$). So, the total displacement is $\Delta y = 8(2 \text{ m}) + (-4)(2 \text{ m}) = 8$ m, and the elevator is $\boxed{8 \text{ m}}$ above its starting point.

(b) Strategy Use the slope of the curve to determine when the elevator reaches its highest point.

Solution The vertical velocity is positive for $t = 0$ s to $t = 10$ s. It is negative for $t = 14$ s to $t = 20$ s. It is zero for $t = 10$ s to $t = 14$ s. So, the elevator reaches its highest location at $t = 10$ s and remains there until $t = 14$ s before it goes down. Thus, the elevator is at its highest location from $\boxed{t = 10 \text{ s to } t = 14 \text{ s}}$.

33. Strategy Use the definition of average velocity. Draw a diagram.

Solution Let east be in the $+x$-direction and north be in the $+y$-direction.
Find the magnitude of $\Delta \vec{r}$.

$$\left| \Delta \vec{r} \right| = \sqrt{[3.2 \text{ km} + (4.8 \text{ km})\cos 75.0^\circ + 3.2 \text{ km}]^2 + [(4.8 \text{ km})\sin 75.0^\circ]^2} = 8.9 \text{ km}$$

Find the direction of $\Delta \vec{r}$.

$$\theta = \tan^{-1} \frac{4.6 \text{ km}}{7.6 \text{ km}} = 31^\circ \text{ north of east}$$

So, $\left| \vec{v}_{av} \right| = \dfrac{\Delta r}{\Delta t} = \dfrac{8.94 \text{ km}}{0.10 \text{ h} + 0.15 \text{ h} + 0.10 \text{ h}} = 26 \text{ km/h}$ and $\vec{v}_{av} = \dfrac{\Delta \vec{r}}{\Delta t} = \boxed{26 \text{ km/h at } 31^\circ \text{ north of east}}$.

37. Strategy Use the definitions of instantaneous acceleration, displacement, and average velocity.

Solution

(a) We draw a line tangent to the point at $(14.0 \text{ s}, 55.0 \text{ m/s})$.

It looks as if the tangent line passes through the point $(7.0 \text{ s}, 45.0 \text{ m/s})$.

$$\vec{a}_x = \frac{\Delta \vec{v}_x}{\Delta t} = \frac{(55.0 \text{ m/s} - 45.0 \text{ m/s}) \text{ in the } +x\text{-direction}}{14.0 \text{ s} - 7.0 \text{ s}} = \boxed{1.4 \text{ m/s}^2 \text{ in the } +x\text{-direction}}$$

(b) The area under the v_x vs. t curve from $t = 12.0$ s to $t = 16.0$ s represents the displacement of the body. Each grid square represents $(10.0 \text{ m/s})(1.0 \text{ s}) = 1.0 \times 10^1$ m, and there are approximately 22 squares under the curve for $t = 12.0$ s to $t = 16.0$ s, so the car travels $\boxed{220 \text{ m in the } +x\text{-direction}}$.

(c) $\vec{v}_{av} = \dfrac{\Delta \vec{r}}{\Delta t} = \dfrac{220 \text{ m in the } +x\text{-direction}}{4.0 \text{ s}} = \boxed{55 \text{ m/s in the } +x\text{-direction}}$

41. Strategy The magnitude of the acceleration is the absolute value of the slope of the graph at $t = 7.0$ s.

Solution

$$a_x = \left| \frac{\Delta v_x}{\Delta t} \right| = \left| \frac{0 - 20.0 \text{ m/s}}{12.0 \text{ s} - 4.0 \text{ s}} \right| = \boxed{2.5 \text{ m/s}^2}$$

45. **(a) Strategy** Use the definition of average velocity. Draw a diagram.

Solution Let the center of the circle be the origin, then
$\Delta \vec{r} = \vec{r}_f - \vec{r}_i = 20.0$ m east $- 20.0$ m south.

$|\Delta \vec{r}| = \sqrt{(20.0 \text{ m})^2 + (-20.0 \text{ m})^2} = 28.3$ m

Let east be the $+x$-direction and north the $+y$-direction.

$\theta = \tan^{-1} \dfrac{20.0}{20.0} = 45.0°$ north of east

So, $|\vec{v}_{av}| = \dfrac{\Delta r}{\Delta t} = \dfrac{28.3 \text{ m}}{3.0 \text{ s}} = 9.4$ m/s and $\vec{v}_{av} = \dfrac{\Delta \vec{r}}{\Delta t} = \boxed{9.4 \text{ m/s at } 45° \text{ north of east}}$.

(b) Strategy Use the definition of average acceleration and the fact that $C = 2\pi r$.

Solution Find the average acceleration of the car.

$|\vec{v}_f| = |\vec{v}_i| = \dfrac{2\pi r(3/4)}{\Delta t} = \dfrac{3\pi r}{2\Delta t}$, so $\vec{a}_{av} = \dfrac{3\pi r}{2(\Delta t)^2}$ (south $-$ west).

$|\vec{a}_{av}| = \dfrac{3\pi r}{2(\Delta t)^2}\sqrt{1^2 + (-1)^2} = \dfrac{3\pi r}{\sqrt{2}(\Delta t)^2}$

$\theta = \tan^{-1} \dfrac{-1}{1} = 45°$ south of east

$\vec{a}_{av} = \dfrac{\Delta \vec{v}}{\Delta t} = \dfrac{3\pi(20.0 \text{ m})}{\sqrt{2}(3.0 \text{ s})^2}$ at $45°$ south of east $= \boxed{15 \text{ m/s}^2 \text{ at } 45° \text{ south of east}}$

(c) Strategy Consider Newton's first law of motion.

Solution Although the magnitude of the velocity is constant, its direction must change continuously for the car to travel in a circle; $\boxed{\text{changing the direction of the velocity requires an acceleration}}$.

49. **Strategy** Since the particle is moving to the east and is accelerated to the south, its velocity in 8.00 s will be between east and south. Use the component method. Let north be in the $+y$-direction and east be in the $+x$-direction.

Solution

$v_x = 40.0$ m/s and $v_y = a_y \Delta t = (-2.50 \text{ m/s}^2)(8.00 \text{ s}) = -20.0$ m/s.

$|\vec{v}| = \sqrt{v_x^2 + v_y^2} = \sqrt{(40.0 \text{ m/s})^2 + (-20.0 \text{ m/s})^2} = 44.7$ m/s

$\theta = \tan^{-1} \dfrac{v_y}{v_x} = \tan^{-1} \dfrac{-20.0 \text{ m/s}}{40.0 \text{ m/s}} = 26.6°$ south of east

So, $\vec{v} = \boxed{44.7 \text{ m/s at } 26.6° \text{ south of east}}$.

53. (a) Strategy Determine the maximum force of static friction and compare it to the force of the push, 5.0 N.

Solution Find the maximum force of static friction.

$$f_{s,\text{max}} = \mu_s N = \mu_s mg_{\text{Moon}} = 0.35(2.0 \text{ kg})(9.80 \text{ m/s}^2) = 6.9 \text{ N} > 5.0 \text{ N}$$

No, the puck does not move, since the maximum force of static friction is greater than the force of the push.

(b) Strategy and Solution Since 7.5 N > 6.9 N, the maximum force of static friction, yes, the puck does move.

(c) Strategy Use Newton's second law.

Solution Find the acceleration of the puck.

$$\Sigma F = F_{\text{push}} - f_k = F_{\text{push}} - \mu_k mg = ma, \text{ so}$$

$$a = \frac{F_{\text{push}}}{m} - \mu_k g = \frac{6.0 \text{ N}}{2.0 \text{ kg}} - 0.25(9.80 \text{ m/s}^2) = \boxed{0.55 \text{ m/s}^2}.$$

(d) Strategy Use Newton's second law and the fact that gravity is weaker on the Moon.

Solution The acceleration of the puck is

$$a = \frac{F_{\text{push}}}{m} - \mu_k g.$$

Since gravity is weaker on the Moon, the second term on the right side of the equation is smaller than it would be for Earth. This is the same thing as saying that the force of friction will be less on the Moon. Therefore, the acceleration of the puck is more on the Moon than on Earth.

55. Strategy Use Newton's second law for the vertical direction.

Solution Draw a free-body diagram. Find the tension.

$$\Sigma F_y = T - mg = ma_y, \text{ so}$$

$$T = m(a_y + g) = (2010 \text{ kg})(1.50 \text{ m/s}^2 + 9.80 \text{ m/s}^2) = 22.7 \text{ kN}.$$

The tension in the cable is 22.7 kN upward.

57. (a) Strategy Use Newton's second law for the vertical direction. Let $+y$ be in the upward direction.

Solution Draw a free-body diagram.

$$\Sigma F_y = T - mg = ma_y, \text{ so } a_y = \frac{T - mg}{m} = \frac{33.6 \text{ kN} - 24.8 \text{ kN}}{2530 \text{ kg}} = +3.5 \text{ m/s}^2.$$

So, the acceleration of the elevator is $\boxed{3.5 \text{ m/s}^2 \text{ up}}$.

(b) Strategy Use the definition of average acceleration and solve for the final speed.

Solution

$$a_y = \frac{\Delta v}{\Delta t}, \text{ so } \Delta v = v_f - v_i = a_y \Delta t, \text{ or } v_f = v_i + a_y \Delta t = 1.20 \text{ m/s} + (3.5 \text{ m/s}^2)(4.00 \text{ s}) = 15 \text{ m/s}.$$

So, the velocity of the elevator 4.00 s later will be $\boxed{15 \text{ m/s up}}$.

61. **Strategy** Use Newton's second law.

Solution Draw a free-body diagram.

$$\sum F_y = T\cos\theta - mg = 0, \text{ so } T = \frac{mg}{\cos\theta}.$$

$$\sum F_x = T\sin\theta = ma_x, \text{ so } a_x = \frac{T\sin\theta}{m}.$$

$$a_x = \frac{mg}{\cos\theta}\left(\frac{\sin\theta}{m}\right) = g\tan\theta = (9.80 \text{ m/s}^2)\tan 12° = 2.1 \text{ m/s}^2$$

The acceleration of the airplane is $\boxed{2.1 \text{ m/s}^2 \text{ in the direction of motion}}$.

65. **Strategy** Use Newton's laws of motion.

Solution The stone is lifted with constant velocity, so the net force on the stone in the vertical direction is zero. The force is equal and opposite to the force of gravity on the stone, which is *mg* downward.

$$F = mg = (2.0 \text{ kg})(9.80 \text{ m/s}^2) = 20 \text{ N}$$

The force exerted by the stone on the man's hand is equal in magnitude to the force of gravity on the stone. So, the magnitude of the total force is $\boxed{20 \text{ N}}$.

69. **Strategy** Consider the relative motion of the ship and the water.

Solution The relative speeds are:

$$v_{\text{upstream}} = v_{\text{ship}} - v_{\text{water}} = v_{\text{up}} = v_s - v_w$$

$$v_{\text{downstream}} = v_{\text{ship}} + v_{\text{water}} = v_d = v_s + v_w$$

Find the speed of the current, v_w.

$$\Delta x = v_{\text{up}}\Delta t_{\text{up}} = (v_s - v_w)\Delta t_{\text{up}}, \text{ so } \frac{\Delta x}{\Delta t_{\text{up}}} = v_s - v_w \quad (1). \quad \Delta x = v_d\Delta t_d = (v_s + v_w)\Delta t_d, \text{ so } \frac{\Delta x}{\Delta t_d} = v_s + v_w \quad (2).$$

Subtract (1) from (2).

$$\frac{\Delta x}{\Delta t_d} - \frac{\Delta x}{\Delta t_{\text{up}}} = 2v_w, \text{ so } v_w = \frac{\Delta x}{2}\left(\frac{1}{\Delta t_d} - \frac{1}{\Delta t_{\text{up}}}\right) = \frac{208 \text{ km}}{2}\left(\frac{1}{19.2 \text{ h}} - \frac{1}{20.8 \text{ h}}\right) = \boxed{0.42 \text{ km/h}}.$$

71. **Strategy** Consider the relative motion of the two vehicles. Find $\vec{v}_{BV}$ = the velocity of the BMW relative to the VW.

Solution Let north be in the +x-direction.

v_{BRx} = the velocity of the BMW relative to the road = 100.0 km/h

v_{RVx} = the velocity of the road relative to the VW = $-v_{VR}$ = 42 km/h

$v_{BVx} = v_{BRx} + v_{RVx} = 100.0 \text{ km/h} + 42 \text{ km/h}$

Find Δt.

$$\Delta t = \frac{\Delta x}{v_{BVx}} = \frac{10.0 \text{ km}}{100.0 \text{ km/h} + 42 \text{ km/h}}\left(\frac{3600 \text{ s}}{1 \text{ h}}\right) = \boxed{254 \text{ s}}$$

73. Strategy The upstream component of the velocity of the boat must be equal in magnitude to that of the current.

Solution Let $+y$-direction be toward the opposite shore.
$(4.0 \text{ km/h})\sin\theta = 1.8 \text{ km/h}$, so $\theta = \sin^{-1}\dfrac{1.8}{4.0} = 27°$.
The direction of the velocity of the boat relative to the water is $\boxed{27° \text{ upstream.}}$

75. (a) Strategy The east-west components of the airplane's and the wind's velocities must be equal in magnitude for the plane to travel north.

Solution Let the $+y$-direction be north and the $+x$-direction be east.
$v_{px} = v_p \cos\theta = v_{air, x} = v_{air} \cos 45.00°$, so
$$\theta = \cos^{-1}\frac{v_{air}}{v_p\sqrt{2}} = \cos^{-1}\frac{100.0 \text{ km/h}}{(300.0 \text{ km/h})\sqrt{2}} = \boxed{76.37° \text{ north of east}}.$$

(b) Strategy The northern or y-component of the plane's velocity relative to the ground is the y-component of its velocity relative to the air minus the y-component of the air's velocity relative to the ground.

Solution Find the time.
$$\Delta t = \frac{\Delta y}{v_y} = \frac{\Delta y}{v_p \sin\theta - v_{air} \sin 45.00°}$$
$$= \frac{600.0 \text{ km}}{(300.0 \text{ km/h})\sin\left[\cos^{-1}\dfrac{100.0 \text{ km/h}}{(300.0 \text{ km/h})\sqrt{2}}\right] - (100.0 \text{ km/h})\sin 45.00°} = \boxed{2.717 \text{ h}}$$

77. Strategy Consider the relative motion of the water (w) and Sheena (s). Let the $+y$-direction be upstream and the $+x$-direction be toward the opposite bank (b).

Solution

(a) Find the x-component.
$$v_x = (3.00 \text{ mi/h})\cos 60.0° = 1.50 \text{ mi/h}$$
The y-component is $v_y = v_{Sby} = v_{Swy} + v_{wby}$.
$$v_y = (3.00 \text{ mi/h})\sin 60.0° - 1.60 \text{ mi/h} = 1.00 \text{ mi/h}$$
Use the Pythagorean theorem.
$$v_{Sb} = \sqrt{(1.50 \text{ mi/h})^2 + (1.00 \text{ mi/h})^2} = \boxed{1.80 \text{ mi/h}}$$

(b) $\Delta t = \dfrac{\Delta x}{v_x} = \dfrac{1.20 \text{ mi}}{1.50 \text{ mi/h}} = (0.800 \text{ h})\left(\dfrac{60 \text{ min}}{h}\right) = \boxed{48.0 \text{ min}}$

(c) $\Delta y = v_y \Delta t = (1.00 \text{ mi/h})(0.800 \text{ h}) = \boxed{0.800 \text{ mi upstream}}$

(d) The upstream component of her velocity relative to the water must be equal in magnitude to the velocity of the current relative to the bank, or $v_y = 0$.

$(3.00 \text{ mi/h})\sin\theta - 1.60 \text{ mi/h} = 0$, so $\theta = \sin^{-1}\dfrac{1.60}{3.00} = \boxed{32.2° \text{ upstream}}$.

81. **Strategy** The cutter must move with the moving glass to cut perpendicularly to the direction of motion of the conveyor belt. Thus, the cutter must be set at some angle with respect to the width of the belt and toward the direction of motion of the belt. Draw a diagram.

    Solution Let d be the distance that the sheet of glass travels in the time t that it takes the cutter to cut it. Then, $d = (15.0 \text{ cm/s})t$. Since the cutter moves across the width at a speed of 24.0 cm/s and the width is 72.0 cm, the time t is given by

    $$t = \frac{72.0 \text{ cm}}{24.0 \text{ cm/s}} = 3.00 \text{ s. Solve for } \theta.$$

    $$\tan \theta = \frac{d}{72.0 \text{ cm}} = \frac{(15.0 \text{ cm/s})t}{72.0 \text{ cm}} = \frac{(15.0 \text{ cm/s})(3.00 \text{ s})}{72.0 \text{ cm}} = 0.625, \text{ so}$$

    $$\theta = \tan^{-1} 0.625 = \boxed{32.0°}.$$

85. **Strategy** For each slide, the $+x$-direction is up the slide, and the $+y$-direction is away from the slides' top surfaces. Use Newton's second law.

    Solution

    (a) Slide 1:
    $$\Sigma F_x = f - mg \sin \theta_1 = 0, \text{ so } f = mg \sin \theta_1 \text{ and } \Sigma F_y = N - mg \cos \theta_1 = 0, \text{ so } N = mg \cos \theta_1.$$
    Thus, $f = \mu N = \mu mg \cos \theta_1 = mg \sin \theta_1$ and $\mu = \tan \theta_1$.

    Slide 2:
    $$\Sigma F_x = f - mg \sin \theta_2 = -ma, \text{ so } f = -ma + mg \sin \theta_2 \text{ and } \Sigma F_y = N - mg \cos \theta_2 = 0, \text{ so } N = mg \cos \theta_2.$$
    Thus, $f = \mu N = \mu mg \cos \theta_2 = -ma + mg \sin \theta_2$ and $\mu = -\dfrac{a}{g \cos \theta_2} + \tan \theta_2.$

    Set the two expressions for μ equal and solve for a.
    $$-\frac{a}{g \cos \theta_2} + \tan \theta_2 = \tan \theta_1, \text{ so } a = -g(\cos \theta_2 \tan \theta_1 - \cos \theta_2 \tan \theta_2) = \boxed{g(\sin \theta_2 - \cos \theta_2 \tan \theta_1)}.$$

    (b) Compute the magnitude of the acceleration.
    $$a = (9.80 \text{ m/s}^2)(\sin 61° - \cos 61° \tan 45°) = \boxed{3.8 \text{ m/s}^2}$$

89. (a) Strategy and Solution Since the speed is constant, the acceleration is zero; therefore, the force of friction is zero.

(b) Strategy The force of friction must be in the same direction as the motion of the truck, otherwise the crate would slide off. The crate's acceleration is the same as the truck's.

Solution

$$f = F_{ct} = ma = \frac{W}{g}a = (180 \text{ N})\frac{1.0 \text{ m/s}^2}{9.80 \text{ m/s}^2} = 18 \text{ N}$$

The force of friction is 18 N in the forward direction.

(c) Strategy Set $f_{max} = ma$ and solve for a.

Solution

$$a = \frac{f_{max}}{m} = \frac{\mu_s N}{m} = \frac{\mu_s mg}{m} = \mu_s g = 0.30(9.80 \text{ m/s}^2) = 2.9 \text{ m/s}^2$$

91. Strategy Let the $+x$-direction be up the incline. Use Newton's second law.

Solution

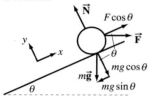

(a) Let F be the horizontal force.

$$\sum F_x = F\cos\theta - mg\sin\theta = 0, \text{ so } F = \boxed{mg\tan\theta}.$$

(b) To roll the crate up at constant speed, the net force is zero, so the force is that from part (a), $\boxed{mg\tan\theta}$.

(c) $\sum F_x = F\cos\theta - mg\sin\theta = ma$, so $F = \boxed{mg\tan\theta + \dfrac{ma}{\cos\theta}}$.

93. **(a) Strategy** Compute the displacements. Use the definition of average velocity. East is the positive x-direction.

Solution The first displacement is $(80.0 \text{ km/h})(45.0 \text{ min})(1 \text{ h}/60 \text{ min})$
$= 60.0$ km east, and the second is $(60.0 \text{ km/h})(30.0 \text{ min})(1 \text{ h}/60 \text{ min})$
$= 30.0$ km at $38.0°$ north of east. Find the average velocity.

$$|\Delta \vec{r}| = \sqrt{(\Delta r_x)^2 + (\Delta r_y)^2}$$
$$= \sqrt{[60.0 \text{ km} + (30.0 \text{ km})\cos 38.0°]^2 + [(30.0 \text{ km})\sin 38.0°]^2} = 85.7 \text{ km}$$

$$\theta = \tan^{-1} \frac{(30.0 \text{ km})\sin 38.0°}{60.0 \text{ km} + (30.0 \text{ km})\cos 38.0°} = 12.5° \text{ north of east}$$

$$\vec{v}_{av} = \frac{\Delta \vec{r}}{\Delta t} = \frac{85.66 \text{ km}}{45.0 \text{ min} + 30.0 \text{ min}} \left(\frac{60 \text{ min}}{1 \text{ h}}\right) \text{ at } 12.5° \text{ north of east}$$
$$= \boxed{68.5 \text{ km/h at } 12.5° \text{ north of east}}$$

(b) **Strategy and Solution** The return trip is the exact opposite journey, so the average velocity has the same magnitude but the opposite direction. The average velocity is $\boxed{68.5 \text{ km/h at } 12.5° \text{ south of west}}$.

97. **Strategy and Solution** Since the 10 cars are identical, each contributes one tenth of the force opposing the force of the locomotive. The first pulls with nine tenths of the force, the second pulls with eight tenths, etc. So, the last car pulls with one tenth of the magnitude of the force of the locomotive and is opposite the force's direction.

$$-\frac{2.0 \times 10^6 \text{ N east}}{10} = \boxed{2.0 \times 10^5 \text{ N west}}$$

101. **Strategy** Consider the motion of the person relative to the escalator.

Solution
$v_w = $ the speed of the person walking on the stalled escalator
$v_r = $ the speed of the person riding on the escalator without walking
$v_{wr} = $ the speed of the person walking while riding $= v_w + v_r$ and $x = $ the distance traveled $= v_w t_w = v_r t_r = v_{wr} t$,

$$\text{so } t = \frac{x}{v_{wr}} = \frac{x}{v_w + v_r} = \frac{v_w t_w}{v_w + v_w \frac{t_w}{t_r}} = \frac{94 \text{ s}}{1 + \frac{94 \text{ s}}{66 \text{ s}}} = \boxed{39 \text{ s}}.$$

105. (a) Strategy Use the definition of average speed.

Solution

$$v_{av} = \frac{\Delta x}{\Delta t} = \frac{100 \times 10^{-9} \text{ m}}{0.10 \times 10^{-3} \text{ s}} = \boxed{1.0 \text{ mm/s}}$$

(b) Strategy Find the time it takes the pain signal to travel the length of a 1.0-m long neuron. Then, add the times of travel across synapses and neurons.

Solution

$$t_n = \frac{x}{v} = \frac{1.0 \text{ m}}{100 \text{ m/s}} = 10 \text{ ms}$$

Find the total time to reach the brain.

$$t_n + t_{syn} + t_n + t_{syn} = 2t_n + 2t_{syn} = 2(t_n + t_{syn}) = 2(10 \text{ ms} + 0.10 \text{ ms}) = \boxed{20 \text{ ms}}$$

(c) Strategy Use the definition of average speed.

Solution

$$v_{av} = \frac{\Delta x}{\Delta t} = \frac{2.0 \text{ m} + 2(100 \times 10^{-9} \text{ m})}{20 \times 10^{-3} \text{ s}} = \boxed{100 \text{ m/s}}$$

109. (a) Strategy Since the downward speed is decreasing at a rate of 0.10g, the acceleration of the truck is 0.10g upwards. Use Newton's second law.

Solution

$$\Sigma F_x = 0 \text{ and } \Sigma F_y = T - mg = ma_y = m(0.10g), \text{ so } T = \boxed{1.10mg}.$$

(b) Strategy and Solution Although the motion of the helicopter has changed, the acceleration of the truck is the same as in part (a), so the tension is the same, $\boxed{1.10mg}$.

Chapter 4

MOTION WITH CONSTANT ACCELERATION

Conceptual Questions

1. Neglecting air resistance, the trajectory of a bullet that has exited the muzzle of a rifle is solely influenced by gravity. The force due to gravity causes the bullet to accelerate downward toward the Earth but does not influence its horizontal motion. Thus, to hit a target, the muzzle must be aimed above the target by a distance equal to the amount that the bullet will fall in the course of its travel. If aimed at the target instead of above it, the bullet will miss low.

5. The terminal velocity of an object depends linearly on its mass and inversely on a parameter determined by its size and shape. The mass of a feather and brick differ by several orders of magnitude. Therefore, if the difference in the drag parameters of the two objects is much smaller than their mass differences, the brick must have a higher terminal velocity. Because the brick is traveling at a higher velocity for the majority of its journey, it arrives at the ground first. The density of the atmosphere on the surface of the Moon is much less than the density of the atmosphere on Earth. Thus, the effects of drag are reduced on the Moon and both objects will hit the ground at nearly the same instant—however, only in a perfect vacuum would the objects fall at exactly identical rates.

9. The forces of gravity and air resistance act upon the parachutist. Descending to Earth with a constant velocity, the parachutist has zero acceleration.

13. The trajectory is sometimes parabolic in another reference frame that moves with a constant velocity with respect to the first. The only possibility other than parabolic is a straight-line trajectory.

17. The two balls will cross at a height greater than half h. Prior to crossing, the bottom ball will be moving faster than the top ball, and so will cover more distance.

Problems

1. **Strategy** Relate the acceleration, speed, and distance using Eq. (4-5). Let southwest be the positive direction.

   Solution Find the constant acceleration required to stop the airplane. The acceleration must be opposite to the direction of motion of the airplane, so the direction of the acceleration is −southwest = northeast.

   $$v_{fx}{}^2 - v_{ix}{}^2 = 2a_x\Delta x, \text{ so } a_x = \frac{v_{fx}{}^2 - v_{ix}{}^2}{2\Delta x} = \frac{0-(55 \text{ m/s})^2}{2(1.0\times10^3 \text{ m})} = -1.5 \text{ m/s}^2.$$

   Thus, the acceleration is $\boxed{1.5 \text{ m/s}^2 \text{ northeast}}$.

5. **(a) Strategy** Draw a diagram and use Newton's second law to find the acceleration of the skier. Then, relate the acceleration, speed, and distance using Eq. (4-5).

   Solution Find the acceleration.
   $\sum F_x = mg\sin\theta = ma_x$, so $a_x = g\sin\theta$.
   Find the speed at the bottom of the slope.
   $$v_{fx}^2 - v_{ix}^2 = 2a_x\Delta x$$
   $$v_{fx}^2 - 0 = 2g\sin\theta\Delta x$$
   $$v_{fx} = \sqrt{2g\sin\theta\Delta x} = \sqrt{2(9.80 \text{ m/s}^2)(\sin 32°)(50 \text{ m})} = \boxed{23 \text{ m/s}}$$

(b) Strategy Find the acceleration using Eq. (4-5). Then, use Newton's second law.

Solution Find a_x.

$v_{fx}^2 - v_{ix}^2 = 2a_x \Delta x$, so

$$a_x = \frac{v_{fx}^2 - v_{ix}^2}{2\Delta x} = \frac{0 - \left(\sqrt{2g\sin\theta\Delta x_{slope}}\right)^2}{2\Delta x} = -\frac{2g\sin\theta\Delta x_{slope}}{2\Delta x} = -\frac{g\sin\theta\Delta x_{slope}}{\Delta x}.$$

Find μ_k.

$\sum F_x = -f_k = ma_x$, so $f_k = \mu_k N = -ma_x$ and $\mu_k = -\dfrac{ma_x}{N}$.

$\sum F_y = N - mg = 0$, so $N = mg$. Thus, we have

$$\mu_k = -\frac{ma_x}{N} = -\frac{ma_x}{mg} = -\frac{a_x}{g} = \frac{\sin\theta\Delta x_{slope}}{\Delta x} = \frac{(\sin 32°)(50\text{ m})}{140\text{ m}} = \boxed{0.19}.$$

9. **Strategy** Find the time it takes for the car to collide with the tractor (assuming it does) by setting the distance the car travels equal to that of the tractor plus the distance between them and solving for t. Use Eq. (4-4). Then, use the essential relationships for constant acceleration to answer the remaining questions.

Solution Solve for the time.

$(27.0\text{ m/s})\Delta t + \dfrac{1}{2}(-7.00\text{ m/s}^2)(\Delta t)^2 = (10.0\text{ m/s})\Delta t + 25.0\text{ m}$, so $0 = (3.50\text{ m/s}^2)(\Delta t)^2 - (17.0\text{ m/s})\Delta t + 25.0\text{ m}$

and solving for t we get an imaginary value for the time. Therefore, $\boxed{\text{you won't hit the tractor}}$.
Find the distance the car requires to stop.

$\Delta x_c = \dfrac{v_{fc}^2 - v_{ic}^2}{2a} = \dfrac{0 - (27.0\text{ m/s})^2}{2(-7.00\text{ m/s}^2)} = \boxed{52.1\text{ m}}$. Since the acceleration of the car is constant, the average speed of

the car as it attempts to stop is $v_{c,av} = (v_{fc} + v_{ic})/2 = (0 + 27.0\text{ m/s})/2 = 13.5\text{ m/s}$. Thus, the time required for the

car to stop is $\Delta t = \Delta x_c / v_{c,av} = (52.1\text{ m})/(13.5\text{ m/s}) = 3.86\text{ s}$. The distance the tractor travels in this time is

$\Delta x_t = v_t \Delta t = (10.0\text{ m/s})(3.86\text{ s}) = 38.6\text{ m}$. Now, $38.6\text{ m} + 25.0\text{ m} = 63.6\text{ m}$, which is $63.6\text{ m} - 52.1\text{ m} = \boxed{11.5\text{ m}}$
beyond the stopping point of the car.

13. **Strategy** Find the net force on the elevator; and from it determine the acceleration. Then use Eq. (4-5) to find the speed.

Solution Find the net force on the elevator.

$$\sum F_y = T - mg = ma_y, \text{ so } a_y = \frac{T - mg}{m} = \frac{7730\text{ N} - (832\text{ kg})(9.80\text{ m/s}^2)}{832\text{ kg}} = -0.5091\text{ m/s}^2.$$

Find the speed.

$v_{fx}^2 - v_{ix}^2 = v_{fx}^2 - 0 = 2a_x\Delta x$, so $v_{fx} = \sqrt{2a_x\Delta x} = \sqrt{2(-0.5091\text{ m/s}^2)(-5.00\text{ m})} = \boxed{2.26\text{ m/s}}$.

15. **Strategy** Refer to the figure. Analyze graphically and algebraically.

   Solution Graphical analysis: Find the slope of the graph.
   $$a_{av,x} = \frac{40 \text{ m/s} - 20 \text{ m/s}}{9.0 \text{ s} - 5.0 \text{ s}} = 5.0 \text{ m/s}^2$$

   Algebraic solution: $v_{fx} - v_{ix} = a_{av,x}\Delta t$, so $a_{av,x} = \dfrac{v_{fx} - v_{ix}}{\Delta t} = \dfrac{40 \text{ m/s} - 20 \text{ m/s}}{9.0 \text{ s} - 5.0 \text{ s}} = 5.0 \text{ m/s}^2$.

   The average acceleration is $\boxed{5.0 \text{ m/s}^2 \text{ in the } +x\text{-direction}}$.

17. **(a) Strategy** The graph will be a line with a slope of 1.20 m/s^2.

   Solution $v_x = 0$ when $t = 0$. The graph is shown.

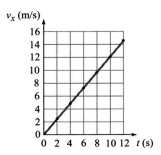

   (b) Strategy Use Eq. (4-4).

   Solution Find the distance the train traveled.
   $$\Delta x = v_{ix}\Delta t + \frac{1}{2}a_x(\Delta t)^2 = (0)\Delta t + \frac{1}{2}a_x(\Delta t)^2 = \frac{1}{2}a_x(\Delta t)^2$$
   $$= \frac{1}{2}(1.20 \text{ m/s}^2)(12.0 \text{ s})^2 = \boxed{86.4 \text{ m}}$$

   (c) Strategy Use Eq. (4-1).

   Solution Find the final speed of the train.
   $$v_{fx} - v_{ix} = v_{fx} - 0 = a_x\Delta t, \text{ so } v_{fx} = a_x\Delta t = (1.20 \text{ m/s}^2)(12.0 \text{ s}) = \boxed{14.4 \text{ m/s}}.$$

   (d) Strategy Refer to Figure 4.10, which shows a motion diagram.

   Solution The motion diagram is shown.

19. **Strategy** Let the $+x$-direction be down the incline. Use Newton's second law and Eq. (4-5).

   Solution Find the acceleration of the glider.
   $\Sigma F_x = mg\sin\theta = ma_x$, so $a_x = g\sin\theta$.
   Find the angle of inclination.
   $$v_{fx}^2 - v_{ix}^2 = v_{fx}^2 - 0 = 2a_x\Delta x = 2g\sin\theta\Delta x, \text{ so}$$

   $$\theta = \sin^{-1}\frac{v_{fx}^2}{2g\Delta x} = \sin^{-1}\frac{(0.250 \text{ m/s})^2}{2(9.80 \text{ m/s}^2)(0.500 \text{ m})} = \boxed{0.365°}.$$

   The slope is $a_x = g\sin\theta = 0.0625 \text{ m/s}^2 = 6.25 \text{ cm/s}^2$.
   The positions and times are shown in the graph.

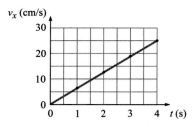

21. Strategy Use Eq. (4-5) to find the distance of the block from the top of the incline.

Solution

$$v_f^2 - v_i^2 = v_f^2 - 0 = v_f^2 = 2ad \text{ and } (0.50v_f)^2 = 2a\Delta x = 0.25v_f^2.$$

Form a proportion.

$$\frac{v_f^2}{0.25v_f^2} = \frac{2ad}{2a\Delta x}, \text{ so } \Delta x = \frac{d}{4.0} = \frac{2.0 \text{ m}}{4.0} = \boxed{0.50 \text{ m}}.$$

25. Strategy Ignoring air resistance, the golf ball is in free fall. Use Eq. (4-9).

Solution

(a) Find the time it takes the golf ball to fall 12.0 m.

$$v_{iy} = 0, \text{ so } \Delta y = -\frac{1}{2}g(\Delta t)^2 \text{ and } \Delta t = \sqrt{-\frac{2\Delta y}{g}} = \sqrt{\frac{-2(0-12.0 \text{ m})}{9.80 \text{ m/s}^2}} = \boxed{1.6 \text{ s}}.$$

(b) Find how far the golf ball would fall in $2\sqrt{\dfrac{-2(0-12.0 \text{ m})}{9.80 \text{ m/s}^2}} = 3.13 \text{ s}.$

$$\Delta y = -\frac{1}{2}g(\Delta t)^2 = -\frac{1}{2}(9.80 \text{ m/s}^2)(3.13 \text{ s})^2 = -48 \text{ m}$$

The golf ball would fall $\boxed{48 \text{ m}}$.

27. Strategy Use Eq. (4-10).

Solution Find the sandbag's speed when it hits the ground.

$$v_{fy}^2 - v_{iy}^2 = -2g\Delta y, \text{ so } v_{fy} = \sqrt{v_{iy}^2 - 2g\Delta y} = \sqrt{(10.0 \text{ m/s})^2 - 2(9.80 \text{ m/s}^2)(-40.8 \text{ m})} = \boxed{30.0 \text{ m/s}}.$$

29. (a) Strategy Use Eq. (4-9) to find the time it takes the rock to reach Lois. Then, use Eq. (4-4) to find Superman's required constant acceleration.

Solution

$$\Delta y = v_{iy}\Delta t + \frac{1}{2}a_y(\Delta t)^2 = 0 + \frac{1}{2}a_y(\Delta t)^2, \text{ so } \Delta t = \sqrt{\frac{2\Delta y}{a_y}}.$$

$$\Delta x = v_{ix}\Delta t + \frac{1}{2}a_x(\Delta t)^2 = 0 + \frac{1}{2}a_x(\Delta t)^2 = \frac{1}{2}a_x\left(\sqrt{\frac{2\Delta y}{a_y}}\right)^2 = \frac{a_x\Delta y}{a_y}, \text{ so }$$

$$a_x = \frac{a_y\Delta x}{\Delta y} = \frac{(-9.80 \text{ m/s}^2)(120 \text{ m})}{-4.0 \text{ m}} = 290 \text{ m/s}^2.$$

Superman must accelerate at $\boxed{290 \text{ m/s}^2 \text{ toward Lois}}$ to save her.

(b) Strategy Use Eq. (4-1).

Solution Find Superman's speed when he reaches Lois.

$$v_x = a_x\Delta t = \frac{a_y\Delta x}{\Delta y}\sqrt{\frac{2\Delta y}{a_y}} = \Delta x\sqrt{\frac{2a_y}{\Delta y}} = (120 \text{ m})\sqrt{\frac{2(-9.80 \text{ m/s}^2)}{-4.0 \text{ m}}} = \boxed{270 \text{ m/s}}$$

33. (a) Strategy Use Eq. (4-9) to find the height and Eq. (4-7) to find the speed of the rocket when it runs out of fuel. Then, use Eq. (4-10) to find the maximum height of the rocket, where the height and speed of the rocket when it runs out of fuel are the initial conditions and its final speed is zero.

Solution Find the height h_1 and speed v_1 of the rocket when it runs out of fuel.

$$\Delta y = v_{iy}\Delta t + \frac{1}{2}a_y(\Delta t)^2 = 0 + \frac{1}{2}a_y(\Delta t)^2 = \frac{1}{2}a_y(\Delta t)^2 = h_1 \text{ and } \Delta v_y = a_y\Delta t = v_1.$$

Find the maximum height.

$$v_{fy}^2 - v_{iy}^2 = -2g\Delta y = 0 - v_{iy}^2 = -2g(y_f - y_i), \text{ so}$$

$$y_f = y_i + \frac{v_{iy}^2}{2g} = h_1 + \frac{v_1^2}{2g} = \frac{1}{2}a_y(\Delta t)^2 + \frac{(a_y\Delta t)^2}{2g} = \frac{1}{2}(17.5 \text{ m/s}^2)(1.5 \text{ s})^2 + \frac{[(17.5 \text{ m/s}^2)(1.5 \text{ s})]^2}{2(9.80 \text{ m/s}^2)} = \boxed{55 \text{ m}}.$$

(b) Strategy The rocket runs out of fuel after $\Delta t_1 = 1.5$ s. Then it travels for a time Δt_2 before it reaches its maximum height. Finally, it falls freely (from rest) for a time Δt_3 until it reaches the ground.

Solution Find Δt_2 using Eq. (4-7) and Δt_3 using Eq. (4-9).

$$v_{fy} - v_{iy} = a_y\Delta t = -g\Delta t_2 = 0 - v_1, \text{ so } \Delta t_2 = \frac{v_1}{g} = \frac{a_y\Delta t_1}{g}. \quad y_f = \frac{1}{2}g(\Delta t_3)^2, \text{ so } \Delta t_3 = \sqrt{\frac{2y_f}{g}}.$$

Find the total time of flight.

$$\Delta t_1 + \Delta t_2 + \Delta t_3 = \Delta t_1 + \frac{a_y\Delta t_1}{g} + \sqrt{\frac{2y_f}{g}} = 1.5 \text{ s} + \frac{(17.5 \text{ m/s}^2)(1.5 \text{ s})}{9.80 \text{ m/s}^2} + \sqrt{\frac{2(55 \text{ m})}{9.80 \text{ m/s}^2}} = \boxed{7.5 \text{ s}}$$

37. Strategy Use equations of motion with constant acceleration to determine the vertical and horizontal positions of the clay after 1.50 s have elapsed.

Solution Find the position of the clay.

$$x_f = v_{ix}\Delta t = (20.0 \text{ m/s})(1.50 \text{ s}) = 30.0 \text{ m}$$

$$y_f = y_i + v_{iy}\Delta t - \frac{1}{2}g(\Delta t)^2 = 8.50 \text{ m} + 0 - \frac{1}{2}(9.80 \text{ m/s}^2)(1.50 \text{ s})^2 = -2.53 \text{ m}$$

The clay cannot pass through the ground, so it hit and stuck prior to 1.50 s. Find the time it took for the clay to land.

$$y_f = 0 = y_i + v_{iy}\Delta t - \frac{1}{2}g(\Delta t)^2 = y_i - \frac{1}{2}g(\Delta t)^2, \text{ so}$$

$$\Delta t = \sqrt{\frac{2y_i}{g}} = \sqrt{\frac{2(8.50 \text{ m})}{9.80 \text{ m/s}^2}} = 1.317 \text{ s, and } x_f = v_{ix}\Delta t = (20.0 \text{ m/s})(1.317 \text{ s}) = 26.3 \text{ m}.$$

The clay hits and it is on the ground after 1.32 s, so the horizontal distance along the ground is 26.3 m.

41. (a) Strategy Ignoring air resistance, the bomb will travel a distance equal to the speed of the plane times the time is takes the bomb to reach ground level.

Solution Use Eq. (4-9) to find the time it takes for the bomb to reach ground level.

$$\Delta y = v_{iy}\Delta t + \frac{1}{2}a_y(\Delta t)^2 = 0 - \frac{1}{2}g(\Delta t)^2, \text{ so } \Delta t = \sqrt{\frac{-2\Delta y}{g}}. \text{ So, the bomb should be released}$$

$$\Delta x = v_x\Delta t = v_x\sqrt{\frac{-2\Delta y}{g}} = (40.0 \text{ m/s})\sqrt{\frac{-2(-125 \text{ m})}{9.80 \text{ m/s}^2}} = \boxed{202 \text{ m}} \text{ horizontally from the target.}$$

(b) **Strategy** The horizontal component of the velocity of the bomb is 40.0 m/s. Find the vertical component of the velocity and use the components to find the direction the bomb is traveling just before it hits the target.

Solution Use Eq. (4-10) to find the vertical component of the bomb's velocity.

$v_{fy}^2 - v_{iy}^2 = 2a_y \Delta y = -2g\Delta y = v_{fy}^2 - 0$, so $v_{fy} = \sqrt{-2g\Delta y}$. Find the angle.

$$\theta = \tan^{-1}\frac{v_{fy}}{v_{fx}} = \tan^{-1}\frac{\sqrt{-2g\Delta y}}{v_{fx}} = \tan^{-1}\frac{\sqrt{-2(9.80\ \text{m/s}^2)(-125\ \text{m})}}{40.0\ \text{m/s}}$$

$= \boxed{51.1° \text{ below the horizontal}}$

45. (a) **Strategy** Consider each quantity's dependence on time.

Solution

$\Delta x = v_x \Delta t$, so x increases linearly with time.

According to Eq. (4-9), y is parabolic.

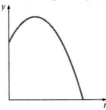

Since the net acceleration of the stone in the horizontal direction is zero, v_x is constant.

v_y starts positive and decreases linearly.

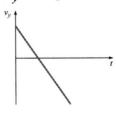

(b) **Strategy** Find v_i in terms of Δx, Δt, and θ.

Solution Solve for the initial speed.

$\Delta x = (v_i \cos\theta)\Delta t$, so $v_i = \dfrac{\Delta x}{\Delta t \cos\theta} = \dfrac{105\ \text{m}}{(4.20\ \text{s})\cos 25.0°} = 27.6\ \text{m/s}.$

So, the initial velocity is $\boxed{27.6 \text{ m/s at } 25.0° \text{ above the horizontal}}$.

(c) **Strategy** Find h using the result for v_i found in part (b).

Solution Use Eq. (4-9).

$$\Delta y = v_{iy}\Delta t + \frac{1}{2}a_y(\Delta t)^2 = (v_i \sin\theta)\Delta t - \frac{1}{2}g(\Delta t)^2 = \left(\frac{\Delta x}{\Delta t \cos\theta}\sin\theta\right)\Delta t - \frac{1}{2}g(\Delta t)^2 = \Delta x \tan\theta - \frac{1}{2}g(\Delta t)^2$$

$$= (105\ \text{m})\tan 25.0° - \frac{1}{2}(9.80\ \text{m/s}^2)(4.20\ \text{s})^2 = -37.5\ \text{m}$$

So, $h = \boxed{37.5\ \text{m}}$.

(d) Strategy Set $v_y = 0$ to find the time when the stone reaches its maximum height.

Solution Use Eq. (4-7) to find the time.

$$v_{fy} - v_{iy} = a_y \Delta t = -g\Delta t, \text{ so } v_{fy} = v_i \sin\theta - g\Delta t = 0, \text{ or } \Delta t = \frac{v_i \sin\theta}{g}.$$

Find H.

$$H = h + (v_i \sin\theta)\Delta t - \frac{1}{2}g(\Delta t)^2 = h + v_i \sin\theta\left(\frac{v_i \sin\theta}{g}\right) - \frac{1}{2}g\left(\frac{v_i \sin\theta}{g}\right)^2 = h + \frac{v_i^2 \sin^2\theta}{g} - \frac{v_i^2 \sin^2\theta}{2g}$$

$$= h + \frac{v_i^2 \sin^2\theta}{2g} = 37.5 \text{ m} + \frac{(27.6 \text{ m/s})^2 \sin^2 25.0°}{2(9.80 \text{ m/s}^2)} = \boxed{44.4 \text{ m above the ground}}$$

49. (a) Strategy At the maximum height of the cannonball's trajectory, $v_{fy} = 0$. Use Eq. (4-10).

Solution Find the maximum height reached by the cannonball.

$$v_{fy}^2 - v_{iy}^2 = 0 - (v_i \sin\theta)^2 = 2a_y \Delta y = -2g(y_f - y_i), \text{ so}$$

$$y_f = y_i + \frac{v_i^2 \sin^2\theta}{2g} = 7.0 \text{ m} + \frac{(40 \text{ m/s})^2 \sin^2 37°}{2(9.80 \text{ m/s}^2)} = \boxed{37 \text{ m}}.$$

(b) Strategy Solve $\Delta x = v_x \Delta t$ for the time and substitute the result into Eq. (4-9). Then, solve for Δx to find the horizontal distance from the release point.

Solution When the cannonball hits the ground, $\Delta y = -7.0$ m.

$$\Delta x = v_x \Delta t = (v_i \cos\theta)\Delta t, \text{ so } \Delta t = \frac{\Delta x}{v_i \cos\theta}. \text{ Substitute.}$$

$$\Delta y = y_f - y_i = v_{iy}\Delta t + \frac{1}{2}a_y(\Delta t)^2 = (v_i \sin\theta)\frac{\Delta x}{v_i \cos\theta} - \frac{1}{2}g\frac{(\Delta x)^2}{v_i^2 \cos^2\theta} = \Delta x \tan\theta - \frac{g(\Delta x)^2}{2v_i^2 \cos^2\theta}, \text{ so}$$

$$0 = \frac{g}{2v_i^2 \cos^2\theta}(\Delta x)^2 - (\tan\theta)\Delta x + \Delta y. \text{ Use the quadratic formula.}$$

$$\Delta x = \frac{\tan\theta \pm \sqrt{\tan^2\theta - \dfrac{4g\Delta y}{2v_i^2 \cos^2\theta}}}{\dfrac{2g}{2v_i^2 \cos^2\theta}} = \frac{\tan 37° \pm \sqrt{\tan^2 37° - \dfrac{2(9.80 \text{ m/s}^2)(-7.0 \text{ m})}{(40 \text{ m/s})^2 \cos^2 37°}}}{\dfrac{9.80 \text{ m/s}^2}{(40 \text{ m/s})^2 \cos^2 37°}} = 170 \text{ m or } -9 \text{ m}$$

Since the catapult doesn't fire backward, -9 m is extraneous. So, the cannonball lands $\boxed{170 \text{ m}}$ from its release point.

(c) Strategy The x-component is the same as the initial value. Find the y-component using Eq. (4-10).

Solution The x-component of the velocity is $v_{fx} = v_{ix} = v_i \cos\theta = (40 \text{ m/s})\cos 37° = \boxed{32 \text{ m/s}}$.
Find the y-component of the velocity.

$$v_{fy}^2 - v_{iy}^2 = v_{fy}^2 - v_i^2 \sin^2\theta = 2a_y\Delta y = -2g\Delta y, \text{ so}$$

$$v_{fy} = \pm\sqrt{v_i^2 \sin^2\theta - 2g\Delta y} = \pm\sqrt{(40 \text{ m/s})^2 \sin^2 37° - 2(9.80 \text{ m/s}^2)(-7.0 \text{ m})} = \boxed{-27 \text{ m/s}},$$

where the negative sign was chosen because the cannonball is on its way down.

53. Strategy Use the expression for the range.

Solution

(a) The maximum value of $\sin 2\theta$ occurs when $2\theta = 90°$.

Therefore, $R_{\max} = v_i^2 \sin 90°/g = v_i^2 (1)/g = \boxed{v_i^2/g}$.

(b) The maximum value of $\sin 2\theta$ occurs when $2\theta = 90°$ or $\theta = \boxed{45°}$.

57. Strategy Draw a free-body diagram and use Newton's second law.

Solution The force Yolanda exerts on the floor of the elevator is equal and opposite to the normal force exerted on her feet by the floor of the elevator.
$\Sigma F_y = N - W = N - mg = ma_y$, so $N = m(g + a_y)$. Therefore, the magnitude of the force

she exerts is $F = m(g + a_y) = (64.2 \text{ kg})(9.80 \text{ m/s}^2 + 2.13 \text{ m/s}^2) = 766 \text{ N}$. The force is
$\boxed{766 \text{ N downward}}$.

61. Strategy Refer to Example 4.12.

Solution

(a) The elevator is accelerating downward, so $a_y = -0.50 \text{ m/s}^2$.

$$W' = \frac{W}{g}(g + a_y) = W\left(1 + \frac{a_y}{g}\right) = (598 \text{ N})\left(1 + \frac{-0.50 \text{ m/s}^2}{9.80 \text{ m/s}^2}\right) = \boxed{567 \text{ N}}$$

(b) Since the elevator is moving downward and slowing down, it is accelerating upward, so $a_y = 0.50 \text{ m/s}^2$.

$$W' = W\left(1 + \frac{a_y}{g}\right) = (598 \text{ N})\left(1 + \frac{0.50 \text{ m/s}^2}{9.80 \text{ m/s}^2}\right) = \boxed{629 \text{ N}}$$

63. Strategy The apparent weight is given by $W' = W(1 + a_y/g)$.

Solution Up is the positive direction. Find Felipe's actual weight.

$$W' = W\left(1 + \frac{a_y}{g}\right), \text{ so } W = \frac{W'}{1 + \frac{a_y}{g}} = \frac{750 \text{ N}}{1 + \frac{2.0 \text{ m/s}^2}{9.80 \text{ m/s}^2}} = \boxed{620 \text{ N}}.$$

65. (a) Strategy Find the time it takes the coconut to strike the ground using Eq. (4-9).

Solution Solve for Δt. The initial velocity in the vertical direction is zero.

$$\Delta y = v_{iy}\Delta t + \frac{1}{2}a_y(\Delta t)^2 = (0)\Delta t - \frac{1}{2}g(\Delta t)^2, \text{ so}$$

$$\Delta t = \sqrt{-\frac{2\Delta y}{g}} = \sqrt{-\frac{2(-100 \text{ m})}{9.80 \text{ m/s}^2}} = \boxed{4.5 \text{ s}}.$$

(b) Strategy Use the result of part (a) and $\Delta x = v_x \Delta t$ to find the horizontal distance the coconut travels, Δx.

Solution The horizontal distance the coconut travels from the release point is
$\Delta x = v_x \Delta t = (18 \text{ m/s})(4.5 \text{ s}) = \boxed{81 \text{ m}}$.

67. **Strategy** Let $+y$ be downward. $v_{ix} = v_x = v_i$ and $v_{iy} = 0$, so $\Delta x = v_i \Delta t$ and $\Delta y = \frac{1}{2} g (\Delta t)^2$.

Let the step number $n = \frac{x}{0.30 \text{ m}} = \frac{y}{0.18 \text{ m}}$, such that $n = 0$ to 1 represents step 1, $n = 1$ to 2 represents step 2, etc.

Solution Find the step the marble strikes first.

$$n = \frac{v_i \Delta t}{0.30 \text{ m}} = \frac{g(\Delta t)^2}{2(0.18 \text{ m})}, \text{ so } \Delta t = \frac{2(0.18 \text{ m}) v_i}{(0.30 \text{ m}) g} = 1.2 \frac{v_i}{g}.$$

Therefore,

$$n = \frac{v_i}{0.30 \text{ m}} \left(1.2 \frac{v_i}{g} \right) = (4.0 \text{ m}^{-1}) \frac{v_i^2}{g} = (4.0 \text{ m}^{-1}) \frac{(3.0 \text{ m/s})^2}{9.80 \text{ m/s}^2} = 3.7.$$

The value of n is between 3 and 4, so the marble first strikes $\boxed{\text{step 4}}$.

69. **(a) Strategy** The time required for the round-trip is equal to the round-trip distance divided by the cruising speed.

Solution

$$\Delta t = \frac{\text{round-trip distance}}{\text{cruising speed}} = \frac{2(5.80 \times 10^3 \text{ km})}{350.0 \text{ km/h}} = \boxed{33.1 \text{ h}}$$

(b) Strategy Consider the relative motion of the plane, air, and the ground.

Solution Subscripts: airplane = p; air = a; ground = g.

$\Delta t = \Delta t_{\text{tailwind}} + \Delta t_{\text{headwind}}$

$$= \frac{d}{v_{pa} + v_{ag}} + \frac{d}{v_{pa} - v_{ag}} = \frac{5.80 \times 10^3 \text{ km}}{350.0 \text{ km/h} + 60.0 \text{ km/h}} + \frac{5.80 \times 10^3 \text{ km}}{350.0 \text{ km/h} - 60.0 \text{ km/h}} = \boxed{34.1 \text{ h}}$$

(c) Strategy Let $+y$ be antiparallel to the crosswind. Set $v_{pgy} = 0$, so the plane can travel in a straight line.

$v_{pax} = v_{pa} \cos \theta$ is the speed of the plane along the straight line between the cities.

Solution

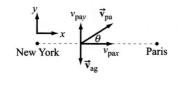

$$v_{pgy} = v_{pay} + v_{agy} = v_{pa} \sin \theta - v_{ag} = 0, \text{ so } \theta = \sin^{-1} \frac{v_{ag}}{v_{pa}} = \sin^{-1} \frac{60.0}{350.0} = 9.87°.$$

Thus, $\Delta t = \dfrac{2 \Delta x}{v_{pa} \cos \theta} = \dfrac{2(5.80 \times 10^3 \text{ km})}{(350.0 \text{ km/h}) \cos 9.87°} = \boxed{33.6 \text{ h}}$.

73. **Strategy** Use Eqs. (4-4) and (4-9). Let $+x$ be east and $+y$ be north.

Solution Find the components of the position vector $\vec{\mathbf{r}}$.

$$x_f = x_i + v_{ix} \Delta t + \frac{1}{2} a_x (\Delta t)^2 = 2.0 \text{ m} + (0)(2.0 \text{ s}) + \frac{1}{2} (5.0 \text{ m/s}^2)(2.0 \text{ s})^2 = 12 \text{ m}$$

and

$$y_f = y_i + v_{iy} \Delta t + \frac{1}{2} a_y (\Delta t)^2 = 0 + (20 \text{ m/s})(2.0 \text{ s}) + \frac{1}{2} (0)(2.0 \text{ s})^2 = 40 \text{ m}.$$

So, $\vec{\mathbf{r}} = \boxed{12 \text{ m east and 40 m north}}$.

77. Strategy Each car has traveled the same distance Δx in the same time Δt when they meet.

Solution Using Eq. (4-4), we have

$\Delta x = v_i \Delta t + \dfrac{1}{2}a(\Delta t)^2 = 0 + \dfrac{1}{2}a(\Delta t)^2 = v\Delta t$, so $\Delta t = \dfrac{2v}{a}$. The speed of the police car is $v_p = a\Delta t = a(2v/a) = \boxed{2v}$.

81. Strategy $v_{1fx}^2 - v_{1ix}^2 = 2a_1 d_1$, where $a_1 = 10.0 \text{ ft/s}^2$ and d_1 is the distance to the point of no return.

$v_{2fx}^2 - v_{2ix}^2 = 2a_2 d_2$, where $a_2 = -7.00 \text{ ft/s}^2$ and d_2 is the distance from the point of no return to the end of the runway. The initial speed v_{1ix} and the final speed v_{2fx} are zero. The speed at the point of no return is $v_{1fx} = v_{2ix}$. Let $v_{1fx} = v_{2ix} = v$ for simplicity. Also, $d = d_1 + d_2$ is the length of the runway.

Solution From the setup, we have $v^2 = 2a_1 d_1$ and $-v^2 = 2a_2 d_2 = 2a_2(d - d_1)$.

Eliminate v^2.

$$2a_1 d_1 = 2a_2(d_1 - d)$$
$$a_1 d_1 = a_2 d_1 - a_2 d$$
$$(a_1 - a_2)d_1 = -a_2 d$$

$$d_1 = \frac{a_2}{a_2 - a_1}d = \frac{-7.00 \text{ ft/s}^2}{-7.00 \text{ ft/s}^2 - 10.0 \text{ ft/s}^2}(1.50 \text{ mi})\left(\frac{5280 \text{ ft}}{1 \text{ mi}}\right) = \boxed{3260 \text{ ft}}$$

Find the time to d_1 using Eq. (4-4).

$$d_1 = \frac{1}{2}a_1(\Delta t)^2, \text{ so } \Delta t = \sqrt{\frac{2d_1}{a_1}} = \sqrt{\frac{2(3260 \text{ ft})}{10.0 \text{ ft/s}^2}} = \boxed{25.5 \text{ s}}.$$

85. Strategy $v_{fy} = 0$ at the maximum height. Use Eqs. (4-7) and (4-9).

Solution

$v_{fy} = v_i \sin\theta - g\Delta t = v_i \sin 45° - g\Delta t = \dfrac{v_i}{\sqrt{2}} - g\Delta t = 0$. Thus, $\Delta t = \dfrac{v_i}{g\sqrt{2}}$.

Find H_{max}, the maximum height of the projectile's trajectory.

$$H_{max} = (v_i \sin\theta)\Delta t - \frac{1}{2}g(\Delta t)^2 = \frac{v_i}{\sqrt{2}}\left(\frac{v_i}{g\sqrt{2}}\right) - \frac{1}{2}g\left(\frac{v_i}{g\sqrt{2}}\right)^2 = \frac{v_i^2}{2g} - \frac{v_i^2}{4g} = \frac{v_i^2}{4g}$$

Find R, the range of the projectile.

$\Delta y = (v_i \sin\theta)\Delta t - \dfrac{1}{2}g(\Delta t)^2$ and $\Delta x = (v_i \cos\theta)\Delta t$.

When the projectile returns to its original height, $\Delta y = 0$.

$\Delta y = (v_i \sin\theta)\Delta t - \dfrac{1}{2}g(\Delta t)^2 = v_i \sin\theta - \dfrac{1}{2}g\Delta t = 0$, so $\Delta t = \dfrac{2v_i \sin\theta}{g}$.

Substitute this value for Δt into $R = \Delta x = (v_i \cos\theta)\Delta t$.

$$R = (v_i \cos\theta)\Delta t = v_i \cos\theta\left(\frac{2v_i \sin\theta}{g}\right) = \frac{2v_i^2 \sin\theta\cos\theta}{g}$$

Substitute for θ.

$$R = \frac{2v_i^2 \sin 45° \cos 45°}{g} = \frac{v_i^2}{g}; \text{ therefore, } H_{max} = \frac{1}{4}\left(\frac{v_i^2}{g}\right) = \frac{R}{4}.$$

89. Strategy Choose the +x-axis to the right and +y-axis up. Use Newton's second law.

Solution

(a) For m_1:

$\sum F_{1y} = N - W_1 = N - m_1 g = 0$, so $N = m_1 g$.

$\sum F_{1x} = T - f_k = T - \mu_k N = T - \mu_k m_1 g = m_1 a_{1x}$

For m_2:

$\sum F_{2x} = 0$ and $\sum F_{2y} = T - W_2 = T - m_2 g = m_2 a_{2y}$.

Now, a_{1x} and a_{2y} must be equal in magnitude, otherwise the cord will
compress or expand. a_{1x} is in the +x-direction and a_{2y} is in the $-y$-direction.

So, let $a = a_{1x} = -a_{2y}$. Then, $T - \mu_k m_1 g = m_1 a$ and $T - m_2 g = -m_2 a$.

Subtract the second equation from the first and solve for a.

$-\mu_k m_1 g + m_2 g = m_1 a + m_2 a$

$g(m_2 - \mu_k m_1) = a(m_1 + m_2)$

$$\boxed{a = \frac{m_2 - \mu_k m_1}{m_1 + m_2} g}$$

Find T.

$T - m_2 g = -m_2 a$

$$T = m_2 g - m_2 \frac{m_2 - \mu_k m_1}{m_1 + m_2} g = \frac{m_2(m_1 + m_2) - m_2(m_2 - \mu_k m_1)}{m_1 + m_2} g = \frac{m_1 m_2 + m_2^2 - m_2^2 + m_1 m_2 \mu_k}{m_1 + m_2} g$$

$$\boxed{T = (1 + \mu_k) \frac{m_1 m_2}{m_1 + m_2} g}$$

(b) For $m_1 \ll m_2$,

$a \approx \dfrac{m_2 - \mu_k(0)}{0 + m_2} g = \boxed{g}$ and

$T \approx (1 + \mu_k) \dfrac{m_1 m_2}{0 + m_2} g = \boxed{\begin{array}{l}(1 + \mu_k) m_1 g \ll m_2 g, \text{ so the tension is negligible compared to the weight of } m_2; \\ \text{it's essentially in free fall.}\end{array}}$.

If $m_1 \gg m_2$, the force of friction between the table and m_1 is so large that m_1 will not slide, so $a = \boxed{0}$ and

$T - m_2 g = -m_2 a = 0$, or $T = \boxed{m_2 g}$.

For $m_1 = m_2 = m$,

$a = \dfrac{m - \mu_k m}{m + m} g = \dfrac{m(1 - \mu_k)}{2m} g = \boxed{\dfrac{1}{2}(1 - \mu_k)g}$ and $T = (1 + \mu_k) \dfrac{m^2}{2m} g = \boxed{\dfrac{1}{2}(1 + \mu_k)mg}$.

(c) $\boxed{\begin{array}{l} a = 0 \text{ only for } m_2 = 0; \text{ thus, there is no value at which the two masses slide with constant velocity. For} \\ m_2 = 0, \text{ there is no tension in the cord.}\end{array}}$

Chapter 5

CIRCULAR MOTION

Conceptual Questions

1. Depressing the gas pedal is not the only way to make the car accelerate. The driver can also apply the brakes or turn the car to make it accelerate.

5. In uniform circular motion, the acceleration always points toward the center of the circle. Hence it remains perpendicular to the velocity the whole time. When a projectile is launched horizontally, the acceleration is initially perpendicular to the velocity, but does not remain so.

9. When the roller coaster turns hard to the right, the inertia of a rider's upper body keeps it moving in a straight line until it runs into the wall of the car. The wall exerts a normal force on the upper body that causes it to accelerate radially with the car. Thus, no force pushes the rider to the left as they enter a turn—the rider's inertia simply carries them forward while the car moves to the right.

Problems

1. **Strategy** Find the arc length swept out by the carnival swing.

   Solution Use Eq. (5-4).
   $$s = r\theta = (8.0 \text{ m})(120°)\left(\frac{2\pi \text{ rad}}{360°}\right) = \boxed{17 \text{ m}}$$

5. **Strategy** Use Eq. (5-9) to find the angular speed of the bicycle's tires.

   Solution
   $$|\omega| = \frac{v}{r} = \frac{9.0 \text{ m/s}}{0.35 \text{ m}} = \boxed{26 \text{ rad/s}}$$

7. (a) **Strategy and Solution** There are 2π radians per revolution and 60 seconds per minute, so
   $$\left(\frac{33.3 \text{ rev}}{\text{min}}\right)\left(\frac{2\pi \text{ rad}}{\text{rev}}\right)\left(\frac{1 \text{ min}}{60 \text{ s}}\right) = \boxed{3.49 \text{ rad/s}}.$$

   (b) **Strategy** Use the relationship between linear speed and angular speed.

   Solution Find the speed of the doll.
   $$v = r|\omega| = (0.13 \text{ m})(3.49 \text{ rad/s}) = \boxed{0.45 \text{ m/s}}$$

9. **Strategy** Use the conversion factor between degrees and radians and $s = r\theta$, where $s = 100.0$ ft, $\theta = 1.5°$, and r is the radius of curvature.

   Solution Find the radius of curvature of a "1.5° curve".
   $$r = \frac{s}{\theta} = \frac{100.0 \text{ ft}}{1.5°}\left(\frac{360°}{2\pi \text{ rad}}\right) = \boxed{3800 \text{ ft}}$$

13. **Strategy** Use the relationship between angular speed and radial acceleration.

   Solution The number of seconds in one day is 86,400, so the angular speed of the Earth (and baobab) is $|\omega| = 2\pi \text{ rad}/86,400 \text{ s}$. Compute the radial acceleration.

   $$a_r = \omega^2 r = \omega^2 R_{\text{Earth}} = \left(\frac{2\pi \text{ rad}}{86,400 \text{ s}}\right)^2 (6.371 \times 10^6 \text{ m}) = \boxed{3.37 \text{ cm/s}^2}$$

17. **(a) Strategy** Use Newton's second law and the relationship between linear speed and radial acceleration.

   Solution According to Newton's second law,

   $$\Sigma F_r = T = ma_r = m\frac{v^2}{r} = m\frac{v^2}{L}, \text{ thus, } T = \boxed{\frac{mv^2}{L}}.$$

   (b) Strategy Draw a free-body diagram for the rock. Use Newton's second law.

   Solution Decompose the force into vertical (y) and radial (r) components.

   $$\Sigma F_r = T_r = \frac{mv^2}{r} = \frac{mv^2}{L\cos\theta} \text{ and } \Sigma F_y = T_y - mg = 0.$$

   Find the magnitude of the tension.

   $$T = \sqrt{T_r^2 + T_y^2} = \sqrt{\left(\frac{mv^2}{L\cos\theta}\right)^2 + (mg)^2}$$

   $$= \boxed{m\sqrt{g^2 + \left(\frac{v^2}{L\cos\theta}\right)^2}}$$

21. **Strategy** Let the x-axis point toward the center of curvature and the y-axis point upward. Draw a free-body diagram. Use Newton's second law and the relationship between radial acceleration and linear speed.

   Solution

   $$\Sigma F_y = N\cos\theta - mg = 0, \text{ so } N\cos\theta = mg, \text{ and } \Sigma F_x = N\sin\theta = ma_r = m\frac{v^2}{r}.$$

   Solve for v.

   $$\frac{N\sin\theta}{N\cos\theta} = \frac{m\frac{v^2}{r}}{mg}, \text{ so } v^2 = rg\tan\theta, \text{ or}$$

   $$v = \sqrt{rg\tan\theta} = \sqrt{(120 \text{ m})(9.80 \text{ m/s}^2)\tan 3.0°} = \boxed{7.9 \text{ m/s}}.$$

25. Strategy Let the x-axis point toward the center of curvature and the y-axis point upward. Draw a free-body diagram. Use Newton's second law and the relationship between radial acceleration and linear speed.

Solution

(a) $\Sigma F_y = N\cos\theta - mg - f\sin\theta = 0$ and $\Sigma F_x = N\sin\theta + f\cos\theta = mv^2/r$.

Solve for N in the first equation and substitute into the second.

$N = \dfrac{f\sin\theta + mg}{\cos\theta}$, so

$\dfrac{f\sin\theta + mg}{\cos\theta}\sin\theta + f\cos\theta = m\dfrac{v^2}{r}$

$f\sin^2\theta + mg\sin\theta + f\cos^2\theta = m\dfrac{v^2}{r}\cos\theta$

$f(\sin^2\theta + \cos^2\theta) = m\dfrac{v^2}{r}\cos\theta - mg\sin\theta$

$f(1) = m\left(\dfrac{v^2}{r}\cos\theta - g\sin\theta\right)$

$f = (1400\ \text{kg})\left[\dfrac{(32\ \text{m/s})^2}{410\ \text{m}}\cos 5.0° - (9.80\ \text{m/s}^2)\sin 5.0°\right] = \boxed{2300\ \text{N}}$

(b) Set the expression found for the force of friction equal to zero.

$f = 0 = m\left(\dfrac{v^2}{r}\cos\theta - g\sin\theta\right)$, so $\dfrac{v^2}{r}\cos\theta = g\sin\theta$, or

$v = \sqrt{gr\tan\theta} = \sqrt{(9.80\ \text{m/s}^2)(410\ \text{m})\tan 5.0°} = \boxed{19\ \text{m/s}}$.

29. Strategy Use $v = r\omega$ and $\omega = 2\pi/T$, where the radius is the average Earth-Sun distance and the period is one year.

Solution

$v = r\omega = r\left(\dfrac{2\pi}{T}\right) = \dfrac{2\pi r}{T} = \dfrac{2\pi(1.50\times 10^{11}\ \text{m})}{1\ \text{y}}\left(\dfrac{1\ \text{y}}{3.156\times 10^7\ \text{s}}\right) = \boxed{2.99\times 10^4\ \text{m/s}}$

31. Strategy According to Kepler's third law, $r^3 \propto T^2$. Form a proportion.

Solution Find the orbital period of the second satellite.

$\left(\dfrac{4.0r}{r}\right)^3 = 64 = \left(\dfrac{T_{4.0}}{T}\right)^2 = \dfrac{T_{4.0}{}^2}{T^2}$, so $T_{4.0}{}^2 = 64T^2$, or $T_{4.0} = 8.0T = 8.0(16\ \text{h}) = \boxed{130\ \text{h}}$.

33. Strategy Use Eq. (5-14) with the mass of Jupiter in place of the mass of the Sun.

Solution Solve for r.

$$\frac{4\pi^2}{GM_J}r^3 = T^2 \text{, so } r^3 = \frac{GM_J}{4\pi^2}T^2 \text{, or } r = \sqrt[3]{\frac{GM_J}{4\pi^2}T^2}\,.$$

Compute the distance from the center of Jupiter for each satellite.

$$r_{Io} = \sqrt[3]{\frac{GM_J}{4\pi^2}T_{Io}^{\,2}} = \sqrt[3]{\frac{(6.674\times10^{-11}\ \text{N}\cdot\text{m}^2/\text{kg}^2)(1.9\times10^{27}\ \text{kg})}{4\pi^2}(1.77\ \text{d})^2\left(\frac{86,400\ \text{s}}{1\ \text{d}}\right)^2} = \boxed{420,000\ \text{km}}$$

$$r_{Europa} = \sqrt[3]{\frac{GM_J}{4\pi^2}T_{Europa}^{\,2}} = \sqrt[3]{\frac{(6.674\times10^{-11}\ \text{N}\cdot\text{m}^2/\text{kg}^2)(1.9\times10^{27}\ \text{kg})}{4\pi^2}(3.54\ \text{d})^2\left(\frac{86,400\ \text{s}}{1\ \text{d}}\right)^2} = \boxed{670,000\ \text{km}}$$

37. Strategy Use Newton's second law and law of universal gravitation, as well as the relationship between radial acceleration and linear speed.

Solution

$$\Sigma F_r = \frac{GmM_J}{(3.0\,R_J)^2} = \frac{mv^2}{3.0R_J}$$

Now, the gravitational field strength of Jupiter is given by $g_J = \dfrac{GM_J}{R_J^{\,2}}$. Find the period of the spacecraft's orbit.

$$\frac{mv^2}{3.0R_J} = \frac{mg_J}{9.0}\text{, so } v^2 = \frac{g_J R_J}{3.0} = \left(\frac{2\pi r}{T}\right)^2 = \frac{4\pi^2(3.0R_J)^2}{T^2}\text{. Solving for } T\text{, we have}$$

$$T = 2\pi\sqrt{\frac{27R_J}{g_J}} = 2\pi\sqrt{\frac{27(71,500\times10^3\ \text{m})}{23\ \text{N/kg}}}\left(\frac{1\ \text{h}}{3600\ \text{s}}\right) = \boxed{16\ \text{h}}\,.$$

41. Strategy Use Newton's second law and the relationship between radial acceleration and linear speed.

Solution The only forces acting on the car are gravity and the normal force of the ground pushing on the car. The radial acceleration is downward, or toward the center of the radius of curvature. Let up be positive.

$$\Sigma F_r = N - mg = ma_r = m\left(-\frac{v^2}{r}\right)$$

When the car is just in contact with the ground, the normal force must be zero. If the car goes any faster it will lose contact with the road. Solve for the speed.

$$-\frac{mv^2}{r} = N - mg = 0 - mg\text{, so } v^2 = gr\text{, or } v = \sqrt{gr} = \sqrt{(9.80\ \text{m/s}^2)(55.0\ \text{m})} = \boxed{23.2\ \text{m/s}}\,.$$

43. Strategy Use Eq. (5-20) to find the constant angular acceleration.

Solution Since the cyclist starts from rest, the initial angular velocity is zero.

$$\Delta\theta = \omega_i\Delta t + \frac{1}{2}\alpha(\Delta t)^2 = (0)\Delta t + \frac{1}{2}\alpha(\Delta t)^2 = \frac{1}{2}\alpha(\Delta t)^2\text{, so } \alpha = \frac{2\Delta\theta}{(\Delta t)^2} = \frac{2(8.0\ \text{rev})\left(\frac{2\pi\ \text{rad}}{\text{rev}}\right)}{(5.0\ \text{s})^2} = \boxed{4.0\ \text{rad/s}^2}\,.$$

45. **Strategy** Equations (5-18) and (5-19) are $\Delta\omega = \omega_f - \omega_i = \alpha\Delta t$ and $\Delta\theta = \frac{1}{2}(\omega_f + \omega_i)\Delta t$, respectively.

Solution Solve for ω_f in Eq. (5-18), then substitute the result into Eq. (5-19) and simplify.

$\Delta\omega = \omega_f - \omega_i = \alpha\Delta t$, so $\omega_f = \omega_i + \alpha\Delta t$. Substitute.

$$\Delta\theta = \frac{1}{2}(\omega_f + \omega_i)\Delta t = \frac{1}{2}(\omega_i + \alpha\Delta t + \omega_i)\Delta t = \frac{1}{2}(2\omega_i + \alpha\Delta t)\Delta t = \omega_i\Delta t + \frac{1}{2}\alpha(\Delta t)^2 = \Delta\theta, \text{ which is Eq. (5-20).}$$

47. **Strategy** Draw a free-body diagram for the bob. Use Newton's second law and the relationship between radial acceleration and linear speed.

Solution Refer to the figure.

$\Sigma F_y = T - mg\cos\theta = ma_r$ and $\Sigma F_x = mg\sin\theta = ma_t$, so

$a_t = g\sin\theta = (9.80 \text{ m/s}^2)\sin 15.0° = \boxed{2.54 \text{ m/s}^2}$ and

$a_r = \frac{v^2}{r} = \frac{(1.40 \text{ m/s})^2}{0.800 \text{ m}} = \boxed{2.45 \text{ m/s}^2}$. The tension is

$T = m(a_r + g\cos\theta) = (1.00 \text{ kg})\left[2.45 \text{ m/s}^2 + (9.80 \text{ m/s}^2)\cos 15.0°\right] = \boxed{11.9 \text{ N}}$.

49. (a) **Strategy** Use Eq. (5-18) to find the magnitude of the constant angular acceleration.

Solution

$$|\Delta\omega| = |\alpha|\Delta t, \text{ so } |\alpha| = \frac{|\Delta\omega|}{\Delta t} = \frac{(33.3 \text{ rpm})\left(\frac{2\pi \text{ rad}}{\text{rev}}\right)\left(\frac{1 \text{ min}}{60 \text{ s}}\right)}{2.0 \text{ s}} = \boxed{1.7 \text{ rad/s}^2}.$$

(b) **Strategy** Use Eq. (5-20) to find the number of revolutions.

Solution

$$\Delta\theta = \omega_i\Delta t + \frac{1}{2}\alpha(\Delta t)^2 = (0)\Delta t + \frac{1}{2}\alpha(\Delta t)^2$$

$$\Delta\theta = \frac{1}{2}\alpha(\Delta t)^2$$

$$\left(\frac{1 \text{ rev}}{2\pi \text{ rad}}\right)\Delta\theta = \frac{1}{2}\left(1.744 \text{ rad/s}^2\right)(2.0 \text{ s})^2\left(\frac{1 \text{ rev}}{2\pi \text{ rad}}\right) = \boxed{0.56 \text{ rev}}$$

53. (a) **Strategy** Use Eq. (5-18) to find the time it takes for the rotor to come to rest.

Solution The acceleration is opposite the rotation of the rotor, so it is negative.

$$\Delta t = \frac{\omega_f - \omega_i}{\alpha} = \frac{0 - 5.0\times10^5 \text{ rad/s}}{-0.40 \text{ rad/s}^2} = \boxed{1.3\times10^6 \text{ s}}$$

(b) **Strategy** Use Eq. (5-21) to find the number of revolutions the rotor spun before it stopped.

Solution

$$\Delta\theta = \frac{\omega_f^2 - \omega_i^2}{2\alpha}$$

$$\left(\frac{1 \text{ rev}}{2\pi \text{ rad}}\right)\Delta\theta = \frac{0 - (5.0\times10^5 \text{ rad/s})^2}{2(-0.40 \text{ rad/s}^2)}\left(\frac{1 \text{ rev}}{2\pi \text{ rad}}\right) = \boxed{5.0\times10^{10} \text{ rev}}$$

57. **Strategy** Use $a_r = \omega^2 r$ to find the angular speed required.

Solution The magnitude of the radial acceleration must be the same as the magnitude of the gravitational field strength.

$$a_r = \omega^2 r = g, \text{ so } \omega = \sqrt{\frac{g}{r}} = \sqrt{\frac{9.80 \text{ m/s}^2}{0.20 \text{ m}}} = \boxed{7.0 \text{ rad/s}}.$$

61. **(a) Strategy** At the top, $\vec{g}$ and $\vec{a}$ are both directed downward. Draw a free-body diagram. Use Newton's second law.

Solution

$$\Sigma F_r = N - mg = ma_r = m(-a_y), \text{ so } W' = N = mg - ma_y.$$

The apparent weight is less than the true weight by ma_y. Thus, the lower weight,
$\boxed{518.5 \text{ N}}$, is measured at the top.

(b) Strategy At the bottom, $\vec{g}$ is directed downward and $\vec{a}$ is directed upward. Draw a free-body diagram.

Solution

$$\Sigma F_r = N - mg = ma_r = m(a_y), \text{ so } W' = N = mg + ma_y.$$

The apparent weight is greater than the true weight by ma_y. Thus, the higher weight,
$\boxed{521.5 \text{ N}}$, is measured at the bottom.

(c) Strategy The apparent weight at the top is given by $W'_{top} = W(1 - a_y/g)$, where $W = mg$. Use
$a_r = \omega^2 r = a_y$ to find the radius.

Solution Solve for the radius r.

$$W'_{top} = W\left(1 - \frac{a_y}{g}\right) = W\left(1 - \frac{\omega^2 r}{g}\right), \text{ so } r = \frac{g}{\omega^2}\left(1 - \frac{W'_{top}}{W}\right) = \frac{9.80 \text{ m/s}^2}{(0.025 \text{ rad/s})^2}\left(1 - \frac{518.5 \text{ N}}{520.0 \text{ N}}\right) = \boxed{45 \text{ m}}.$$

65. **Strategy** Use the relationship between linear speed and angular speed.

Solution Compute the linear speed of the tip of the nylon cord.

$$v = \omega r = (660 \text{ rad/s})(0.23 \text{ m}) = \boxed{150 \text{ m/s}}$$

69. **Strategy** Use Eq. (5-20) to find the number of rotations each gear goes through in 2.0 s. Refer to Problem 68.

Solution

$$\Delta\theta_A = \omega_i \Delta t + \frac{1}{2}\alpha(\Delta t)^2$$

$$\left(\frac{1 \text{ rotation}}{2\pi \text{ rad}}\right)\Delta\theta_A = \left(\frac{1 \text{ rotation}}{2\pi \text{ rad}}\right)\left[2\pi(0.955 \text{ Hz})(2.0 \text{ s}) + \frac{1}{2}(3.0 \text{ rad/s}^2)(2.0 \text{ s})^2\right] = \boxed{2.9 \text{ rotations}}$$

From Problem 68, we know that gear B has an angular speed that is twice that of gear A. Thus, gear B rotates twice for each rotation of gear A. Therefore,

$$\left(\frac{1 \text{ rotation}}{2\pi \text{ rad}}\right)\Delta\theta_B = 2\left(\frac{1 \text{ rotation}}{2\pi \text{ rad}}\right)\left[2\pi(0.955 \text{ Hz})(2.0 \text{ s}) + \frac{1}{2}(3.0 \text{ rad/s}^2)(2.0 \text{ s})^2\right] = \boxed{5.7 \text{ rotations}}.$$

73. (a) Strategy Use the relationship between radial acceleration and linear speed.

Solution

$$a_{\mathrm{r}} = \frac{v^2}{r} = \frac{(2.0\pi \ \mathrm{m/s})^2}{0.50 \ \mathrm{m}} = \boxed{8.0\pi^2 \ \mathrm{m/s^2} = 79 \ \mathrm{m/s^2}}$$

(b) Strategy Use Newton's second law.

Solution

$$\Sigma F_{\mathrm{r}} = T = ma_{\mathrm{r}}, \ \text{so} \ T = (0.50 \ \mathrm{kg})(8.0\pi^2 \ \mathrm{m/s^2}) = \boxed{4.0\pi^2 \ \mathrm{N} = 39 \ \mathrm{N}}.$$

77. Strategy For each revolution of the flagellum, the bacterium moves the distance of the pitch.

Solution Compute the speed of the bacterium.

$$v = (1.0 \ \mu\mathrm{m/rev})(110 \ \mathrm{rev/s}) = \boxed{110 \ \mu\mathrm{m/s}}$$

81. Strategy Use the relationship between linear speed and angular speed.

Solution

$$v = r|\omega| = \left(\frac{0.65 \ \mathrm{m}}{2}\right)(101 \ \mathrm{rad/s})\left(\frac{1 \ \mathrm{km}}{1000 \ \mathrm{m}}\right)\left(\frac{3600 \ \mathrm{s}}{\mathrm{h}}\right) = \boxed{120 \ \mathrm{km/h}}$$

85. Strategy and Solution The cutting tool moves one inch in the time $\Delta t = \dfrac{d}{v} = \dfrac{1 \ \mathrm{in}}{0.080 \ \mathrm{in/s}}$. The lathe chuck must

complete 18 revolutions in the time Δt. Thus, the rotational speed must be $\dfrac{18 \ \mathrm{rev}}{\frac{1 \ \mathrm{in}}{0.080 \ \mathrm{in/s}}} = \boxed{1.4 \ \mathrm{rev/s}}$.

REVIEW AND SYNTHESIS: CHAPTERS 1–5

Review Exercises

1. **Strategy** Replace the quantities with their units.

   Solution Find the units of the spring constant k.

   $F = kx$, so $k = \dfrac{F}{x}$, and the units of k are $\boxed{\text{N/m}} = \dfrac{\text{kg} \cdot \text{m/s}^2}{\text{m}} = \boxed{\text{kg/s}^2}$.

5. **(a) Strategy** Find the total distance traveled and the time of travel. Then divide the distance by the time to obtain the average speed.

   Solution Find Mike's average speed.

   $\Delta x = 50.0 \text{ m} + 34.0 \text{ m} = 84.0 \text{ m}$ and $\Delta t = \dfrac{50.0 \text{ m}}{1.84 \text{ m/s}} + \dfrac{34.0 \text{ m}}{1.62 \text{ m/s}} = 48.2 \text{ s}$, so the average speed is

   $v_{\text{av}} = \dfrac{\Delta x}{\Delta t} = \dfrac{84.0 \text{ m}}{48.2 \text{ s}} = \boxed{1.74 \text{ m/s}}$.

   (b) Strategy Find Mike's total displacement and divide it by the time found in part (a) to obtain his average velocity. Let his initial direction be positive.

   Solution Mike's total displacement is $\Delta \vec{\mathbf{r}} = 50.0 \text{ m forward} - 34.0 \text{ m back} = 16.0 \text{ m forward}$. So, his average

   velocity is $\vec{\mathbf{v}}_{\text{av}} = \dfrac{\Delta \vec{\mathbf{r}}}{\Delta t} = \dfrac{16.0 \text{ m forward}}{48.2 \text{ s}} = 0.332 \text{ m/s forward}$, or

   $\boxed{0.332 \text{ m/s in his original direction of motion}}$.

9. **Strategy** Let north be up. Using a ruler and a protractor, draw the force vectors to scale; then, find the sum of the force vectors graphically.

   Solution Draw the diagram and measure the length and angle of the sum of the force vectors.

   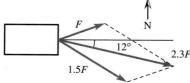

   The net force has a magnitude of about 2.3F, where F is the magnitude of the force with which Sandy pulls. The net force is at an angle of about 12° south of east. So, $\boxed{\text{the cart will go off the road toward south}}$.

13. **Strategy** Use Newton's second law to find the acceleration due to friction. Then use the acceleration and distance the plate must travel to determine the necessary initial speed.

Solution According to Newton's second law, $\Sigma F_y = N - mg = 0$ and $\Sigma F_x = -f_k = ma$.

So, $a = -\dfrac{f_k}{m} = -\dfrac{\mu_k N}{m} = -\dfrac{\mu_k mg}{m} = -\mu_k g$. Find the initial speed.

$v_f^2 - v_i^2 = 0 - v_i^2 = 2a\Delta x = -2\mu_k g \Delta x$, so

$v_i = \sqrt{2\mu_k g \Delta x} = \sqrt{2(0.32)(9.80 \text{ m/s}^2)(0.44 \text{ m})} = \boxed{1.7 \text{ m/s}}$.

17. **Strategy and Solution** Consider a cord attached to a wall at one end and pulled by one of the boys at the other end. The cord does not accelerate when the boy pulls it; thus, the force on the cord from the wall must be equal in magnitude to the pulling force. This situation is identical to the one in which the two boys pull from opposite ends of the cord—the tension in the cord is the same as the case when only one boy is pulling. However, if both pull from one end, the tension is doubled, so $\boxed{\text{Stefan's plan is superior and thus more likely to work}}$.

21. **(a) Strategy** Use Eq. (4-10). Let the $+y$-direction be down and neglect air resistance.

Solution Let the initial speed for all three rocks be v_i and the vertical distance from the cliff to the ground be h. For the first rock (thrown straight down):

$v_{fy}^2 - v_{iy}^2 = v_f^2 - v_i^2 = 2gh$, so $v_f = \sqrt{v_i^2 + 2gh}$.

For the second rock (thrown straight up):

$v_{fy}^2 - v_{iy}^2 = v_f^2 - v_i^2 = 2gh$, so $v_f = \sqrt{v_i^2 + 2gh}$.

For the third rock (thrown horizontally):

$v_{fy}^2 - v_{iy}^2 = v_{fy}^2 - 0 = v_{fy}^2 = 2gh$ and $v_{fx} = v_{ix} = v_i$, so $v_f = \sqrt{v_{fx}^2 + v_{fy}^2} = \sqrt{v_i^2 + 2gh}$.

Therefore, just before the rocks hit the ground at the bottom of the cliff, $\boxed{\text{all three have the same final speed}}$.

(b) Strategy Use the result obtained for the final speed in part (a).

Solution Compute the final speed.

$v_f = \sqrt{v_i^2 + 2gh} = \sqrt{(10.0 \text{ m/s})^2 + 2(9.80 \text{ m/s}^2)(15.00 \text{ m})} = \boxed{19.8 \text{ m/s}}$

25. **(a) Strategy** Use Kepler's third law. Ignore the mass of the cable.

Solution Find the height H.

$$R = \left(\frac{Gm_E T^2}{4\pi^2}\right)^{1/3} = R_E + H, \text{ so}$$

$$H = \left(\frac{Gm_E T^2}{4\pi^2}\right)^{1/3} - R_E = \left(\frac{[6.674\times10^{-11} \text{ m}^3/(\text{kg}\cdot\text{s}^2)](5.974\times10^{24} \text{ kg})(86,400 \text{ s})^2}{4\pi^2}\right)^{1/3} - 6.371\times10^6 \text{ m}$$

$$\cong \boxed{3.6\times10^7 \text{ m}}$$

(b) Strategy Use Newton's second law and law of universal gravitation.

Solution Find the tension in the cable.

$$R = R_E + \frac{H}{2} = 6.371 \times 10^6 \text{ m} + \frac{3.5874 \times 10^7 \text{ m}}{2} = 2.4308 \times 10^7 \text{ m}$$

$$\Sigma F_y = F_g - T = ma = \frac{mv^2}{R} = m\omega^2 R, \text{ so } T = \frac{Gm_E m}{R^2} - m\left(\frac{4\pi^2}{T^2}\right)R.$$

$$T = \frac{[6.674 \times 10^{-11} \text{ m}^3/(\text{kg} \cdot \text{s}^2)](5.974 \times 10^{24} \text{ kg})(100 \text{ kg})}{(2.4308 \times 10^7 \text{ m})^2} - \frac{4\pi^2 (100 \text{ kg})(2.4308 \times 10^7 \text{ m})}{(86,400 \text{ s})^2} = \boxed{55 \text{ N}}$$

29. **Strategy** Use Newton's second law to determine the acceleration of each block. Then, use the accelerations to describe the motion of each block.

Solution Let the positive x-direction be to the right.

The accelerations of each block are $a_A = \dfrac{F_A}{m_A}$ and $a_B = \dfrac{F_B}{m_B}$. In the time Δt, the blocks are displaced by

$\Delta x_{A1} = \dfrac{1}{2}a_A(\Delta t)^2 = \dfrac{1}{2}\left(\dfrac{F_A}{m_A}\right)(\Delta t)^2$ and $\Delta x_{B1} = \dfrac{1}{2}a_B(\Delta t)^2 = \dfrac{1}{2}\left(\dfrac{F_B}{m_B}\right)(\Delta t)^2$. At the end of Δt, the blocks move

with constant velocities until they meet. These velocities are $v_A = a_A\Delta t = \dfrac{F_A}{m_A}\Delta t$ and $v_B = a_B\Delta t = \dfrac{F_B}{m_B}\Delta t$. Let the

time between Δt and the moment when the two blocks meet be Δt_2. Then, the displacements of each block

during Δt_2 are $\Delta x_{A2} = v_A\Delta t_2 = \dfrac{F_A}{m_A}\Delta t \Delta t_2$ and $\Delta x_{B2} = v_B\Delta t_2 = \dfrac{F_B}{m_B}\Delta t \Delta t_2$. Let $d = 3.40$ m. Then, we have the

equation $d = \dfrac{1}{2}\left(\dfrac{F_A}{m_A}\right)(\Delta t)^2 + \dfrac{F_A}{m_A}\Delta t \Delta t_2 - \dfrac{1}{2}\left(\dfrac{F_B}{m_B}\right)(\Delta t)^2 - \dfrac{F_B}{m_B}\Delta t \Delta t_2$, where the displacements of block B are

subtracted because they are negative. Solving this equation for Δt_2 gives

$$\Delta t_2 = \frac{d - \dfrac{(\Delta t)^2}{2}\left(\dfrac{F_A}{m_A} - \dfrac{F_B}{m_B}\right)}{\left(\dfrac{F_A}{m_A} - \dfrac{F_B}{m_B}\right)\Delta t} = \frac{3.40 \text{ m} - \dfrac{(0.100 \text{ s})^2}{2}\left(\dfrac{2.00 \text{ N}}{0.225 \text{ kg}} - \dfrac{-5.00 \text{ N}}{0.600 \text{ kg}}\right)}{\left(\dfrac{2.00 \text{ N}}{0.225 \text{ kg}} - \dfrac{-5.00 \text{ N}}{0.600 \text{ kg}}\right)(0.100 \text{ s})} = 1.92 \text{ s}. \text{ So, the elapsed time from } t = 0 \text{ until}$$

the blocks meet is $\Delta t + \Delta t_2 = 0.100 \text{ s} + 1.92 \text{ s} = \boxed{2.02 \text{ s}}$. The distance from block B's initial position to where

the two blocks meet is negative the displacement of B.

$$-\frac{1}{2}\left(\frac{F_B}{m_B}\right)(\Delta t)^2 - \frac{F_B}{m_B}\Delta t \Delta t_2 = -\frac{1}{2}\left(\frac{-5.00 \text{ N}}{0.600 \text{ kg}}\right)(0.100 \text{ s})^2 - \frac{-5.00 \text{ N}}{0.600 \text{ kg}}(0.100 \text{ s})(1.924 \text{ s}) = 1.65 \text{ m}$$

The blocks meet at $\boxed{1.65 \text{ m to the left of } B\text{'s initial position}}$.

33. **Strategy** Use Eq. (4-8) for x and (4-9) for y.

Solution

(a) The vertical and horizontal components of the projectile are given by

$$\Delta y = (v_i \sin\theta)\Delta t - \frac{1}{2}g(\Delta t)^2 \text{ and } \Delta x = (v_i \cos\theta)\Delta t.$$

When a projectile returns to its original height, $\Delta y = 0$.

$$0 = (v_i \sin\theta)\Delta t - \frac{1}{2}g(\Delta t)^2 = v_i \sin\theta - \frac{1}{2}g\Delta t, \text{ so } \Delta t = \frac{2v_i \sin\theta}{g}.$$

Substitute this value for Δt into $R = \Delta x = (v_i \cos\theta)\Delta t$ to find the range.

$$R = (v_i \cos\theta)\Delta t = v_i \cos\theta\left(\frac{2v_i \sin\theta}{g}\right) = \boxed{\frac{2v_i^2 \sin\theta\cos\theta}{g}}$$

(b) Using the equation for the range found in part (a), we find that the range of the projectile if it is not intercepted by the wall is $R = \dfrac{2(50.0 \text{ m/s})^2 \sin 30.0° \cos 30.0°}{9.80 \text{ m/s}^2} = \boxed{221 \text{ m}}$.

(c) Find the time of flight in terms of v_i, Δx, and θ.

$$\Delta x = (v_i \cos\theta)\Delta t, \text{ so } \Delta t = \frac{\Delta x}{v_i \cos\theta}.$$

Find the height at which the cannonball strikes.

$$y = y_i + (v_i \sin\theta)\Delta t - \frac{1}{2}g(\Delta t)^2 = y_i + (v_i \sin\theta)\left(\frac{\Delta x}{v_i \cos\theta}\right) - \frac{1}{2}g\left(\frac{\Delta x}{v_i \cos\theta}\right)^2 = y_i + \Delta x \tan\theta - \frac{g(\Delta x)^2}{2v_i^2 \cos^2\theta}$$

$$= 1.10 \text{ m} + (215 \text{ m})\tan 30.0° - \frac{(9.80 \text{ m/s}^2)(215 \text{ m})^2}{2(50.0 \text{ m/s})^2 \cos^2 30.0°} = \boxed{4 \text{ m}}$$

37. (a) **Strategy** Use Newton's law of universal gravitation. Assume the mass of the galaxy is concentrated at its center.

Solution Estimate the mass of the galaxy.

$$\frac{GMm}{R^2} = \frac{mv^2}{R}, \text{ so}$$

$$M = \frac{v^2 R}{G} = \frac{(2.75\times10^5 \text{ m/s})^2 (40{,}000 \text{ ly})}{6.674\times10^{-11} \text{ m}^3/(\text{kg}\cdot\text{s}^2)}\left(\frac{9.461\times10^{15} \text{ m}}{1 \text{ ly}}\right)$$

$$= 4.3\times10^{41} \text{ kg or about } \boxed{216 \text{ billion solar masses}}.$$

(b) **Strategy** Compute the ratio of the visible mass to the estimated mass.

Solution

$$\frac{10^{11}}{2.16\times10^{11}} = \boxed{0.46}$$

MCAT Review

1. **Strategy and Solution** Gravity contributes an acceleration of $-g$. Air resistance is always opposite an object's direction of motion, so the vertical component of the acceleration contributed by air resistance is negative as well. According to Newton's second law, $F = ma$, so the magnitude of the acceleration due to air resistance is $a_R = F_R/m = bv^2/m$. Since we want the vertical component of acceleration, the correct answer is $\boxed{D}$, $-g - (bvv_y)/(0.5 \text{ kg})$.

2. **Strategy** Use the result for the range derived in Problem 4.48b.

   Solution Assuming air resistance is negligible, the horizontal distance the projectile travels before returning to the elevation from which it was launched is $R = \dfrac{v_i^2 \sin 2\theta}{g} = \dfrac{(30 \text{ m/s})^2 \sin[2(40°)]}{9.80 \text{ m/s}^2} = 90 \text{ m}$. Thus, the correct answer is $\boxed{C}$.

3. **Strategy and Solution** The magnitude of the horizontal component of air resistance is $F_R \cos\theta = bv^2 \cos\theta = bv(v\cos\theta) = bvv_x$. Thus, the correct answer is $\boxed{D}$.

4. **Strategy** Use Newton's second law to analyze each case. For simplicity, consider only vertical motion.

   Solution Let the positive y-direction be up.
   On the way up:

   $$\Sigma F_y = -mg - bv^2 = ma_y, \text{ so } a_y = -g - \frac{bv^2}{m}.$$

   On the way down:

   $$\Sigma F_y = -mg + bv^2 = ma_y, \text{ so } a_y = -g + \frac{bv^2}{m}.$$

   The magnitude of the acceleration is greater on the way up than on the way down. On the way up, the magnitude of the acceleration is never less than g. On the way down, it may be as small as zero. The projectile must travel the same distance in each case. So, when a projectile is rising, it begins with an initial speed which is reduced to zero relatively quickly due to the relatively large negative acceleration it experiences. When a projectile is falling, it begins with zero speed and is accelerated toward the ground by a smaller acceleration relative to when it is rising. Thus, it must take the projectile longer to reach the ground than to reach its maximum height; therefore, the correct answer is $\boxed{C}$.

5. **Strategy** Find the time it takes to cross the river. Use this time and the speed of the river to find how far downstream the raft travels while crossing. Then use the Pythagorean theorem to find the total distance traveled.

   Solution Let x be the width of the river and y be the distance traveled down the river during the crossing. The raft takes the time $\Delta t = x/v_{\text{raft}}$ to cross the river. During this time, the raft travels the distance $y = v_{\text{river}}\Delta t = v_{\text{river}}(x/v_{\text{raft}})$ down the river. Compute the distance traveled.

   $$\sqrt{x^2 + y^2} = \sqrt{x^2 + \left(\frac{v_{\text{river}}}{v_{\text{raft}}}x\right)^2} = x\sqrt{1 + \left(\frac{v_{\text{river}}}{v_{\text{raft}}}\right)^2} = (200 \text{ m})\sqrt{1 + \left(\frac{2 \text{ m/s}}{2 \text{ m/s}}\right)^2} = 283 \text{ m}$$

   The correct answer is $\boxed{C}$.

6. **Strategy** To row directly across the river, the component of the raft's velocity that is antiparallel to the current of the river must equal the speed of the current, 2 m/s.

   Solution Since the angle is relative to the shore, the antiparallel component of the raft's velocity is $(3 \text{ m/s})\cos\theta$. Set this equal to the speed of the current and solve for θ.

   $(3 \text{ m/s})\cos\theta = 2 \text{ m/s}$, so $\cos\theta = \dfrac{2}{3}$, or $\theta = \cos^{-1}\dfrac{2}{3}$. The correct answer is $\boxed{\text{D}}$.

7. **Strategy** Use Eq. (4-9).

   Solution Find the time it takes the rock to reach the ground.

   $$\Delta y = v_{iy}\Delta t + \frac{1}{2}a_y(\Delta t)^2 = (0)\Delta t - \frac{1}{2}g(\Delta t)^2, \text{ so } \Delta t = \sqrt{-\frac{2\Delta y}{g}} = \sqrt{-\frac{2(0-100 \text{ m})}{10 \text{ m/s}^2}} = 4.5 \text{ s}.$$

   The correct answer is $\boxed{\text{A}}$.

Chapter 6

CONSERVATION OF ENERGY

Conceptual Questions

1. Assuming the object can be treated as a point particle, the total work done on it by external forces is equal to the change in its kinetic energy. An object moving in a circle may be changing its speed as it goes around, so the total work done on it is not necessarily zero.

5. Yes, static friction can do work. As an example, imagine a book on a conveyor belt that carries it up an incline. The force of static friction on the book is directed upward along the surface of the belt and has a component that is parallel to the book's displacement. Thus, the force of static friction does positive work on the book. (At the same time, the work done on the book by gravity is negative and the total work done on the book is zero.)

9. The bicyclist requires a minimum amount of energy to climb the hill. This quantity is independent of the means that the bicyclist employs to acquire the energy and is solely a function of the height of the hill (the energy required is also affected by the work done by frictional and drag forces—the magnitude of this effect is approximately equal for any method used by the bicyclist to climb the hill and therefore doesn't affect our reasoning). After beginning the ascent, a component of the gravitational force acts in the direction opposite to the displacement thereby increasing the amount of negative work done on the rider with respect to the amount done while riding on flat land. Therefore, the rate at which the rider must do work to acquire the necessary energy is greater when pedaling uphill than when on flat land. It is thus advantageous to acquire as much energy as possible before the ascent when the amount of kinetic energy gained per amount of work done by the rider is greatest.

13. Zorba is correct. You get to a top speed sooner on the first slide, so it takes less time to get to the bottom, but the final speeds are the same from $mgh = \frac{1}{2}mv^2$.

Problems

1. **Strategy** Use Eq. (6-1).

   Solution Find the work done by Denise dragging her basket of laundry.
   $$W = F\Delta r \cos\theta = (30.0 \text{ N})(5.0 \text{ m})\cos 60.0° = \boxed{75 \text{ J}}$$

3. **Strategy and Solution** Since the book undergoes no displacement, $\boxed{\text{no work is done}}$ *on the book* by Hilda.

5. **Strategy** Use Newton's second law and Eq. (6-2).

   Solution Find the net force on the barge.
   $$\Sigma F_y = T\sin\theta - T\sin\theta = 0 \text{ and } \Sigma F_x = T\cos\theta + T\cos\theta = F_x.$$
   Find the work done on the barge.
   $$W = F_x\Delta x = (2T\cos\theta)\Delta x = 2(1.0 \text{ kN})\cos 45°(150 \text{ m}) = \boxed{210 \text{ kJ}}$$

9. **Strategy** Use Eq. (6-2). Let the x-axis point in the direction of motion.

   Solution The force of friction is opposite the motion of the box, and according to Newton's second law, it is equal to $f_k = \mu_k N = \mu_k mg$. Juana's horizontal force is in the direction of motion. Solve for the displacement. $W = F_x \Delta x$, so

   $$\Delta x = \frac{W}{F_x} = \frac{W}{F - f_k} = \frac{W}{F - \mu_k mg} = \frac{74.4 \text{ J}}{124 \text{ N} - 0.120(56.8 \text{ kg})(9.80 \text{ m/s}^2)} = \boxed{1.3 \text{ m}}.$$

11. **Strategy** The work done on the briefcase by the executive is equal to the change in kinetic energy of the briefcase. Use Eqs. (6-6) and (6-7).

    Solution Find the work done by the executive on the briefcase.

    $$W = \Delta K = \frac{1}{2} m(v_f^2 - v_i^2) = \frac{1}{2}(5.00 \text{ kg})\left[(2.50 \text{ m/s})^2 - 0\right] = \boxed{15.6 \text{ J}}$$

13. **Strategy** The kinetic energy of the sack is equal to the work done on it by Sam. Use Eqs. (6-2), (6-6), and (6-7).

    Solution

    (a) Compute the kinetic energy of the sack.

    $$\Delta K = \frac{1}{2} m(v_f^2 - v_i^2) = \frac{1}{2} mv^2 - 0 = K = W = F_x \Delta x, \text{ so } K = (2.0 \text{ N})(0.35 \text{ m}) = \boxed{0.70 \text{ J}}.$$

    (b) Solve for the speed of the sack.

    $$K = \frac{1}{2} mv^2, \text{ so } v = \sqrt{\frac{2K}{m}} = \sqrt{\frac{2(0.70 \text{ J})}{10.0 \text{ kg}}} = \boxed{0.37 \text{ m/s}}.$$

17. **Strategy** Use Eqs. (6-6) and (6-7).

    Solution Compute the work done by the wall on the skater.

    $$W_{\text{total}} = \Delta K = K_f - K_i = 0 - \frac{1}{2} mv^2 = -\frac{1}{2}(69.0 \text{ kg})(11.0 \text{ m/s})^2 = \boxed{-4.17 \text{ kJ}}$$

21. (a) **Strategy and Solution** Since the floor is level, the motion of the desk is perpendicular to the force due to gravity; therefore, the change in the desk's gravitational potential energy is $\boxed{\text{zero}}$.

    (b) **Strategy** The motion of the desk is in the direction of the applied constant force. Use Eq. (6-2).

    Solution Compute the work done by Justin.
    $$W = F_x \Delta x = (340 \text{ N})(10.0 \text{ m}) = \boxed{3.4 \text{ kJ}}$$

    (c) **Strategy and Solution** Justin did work against friction, not gravity, so the energy has been $\boxed{\text{dissipated as heat}}$ by friction between the bottom of the desk and the floor.

23. **Strategy** Use Eq. (6-9).

    Solution

    (a) Since the orange returns to its original position $(\Delta y = 0)$ and air resistance is ignored, the change in its potential energy is $\boxed{0}$.

    (b) Let the y-axis point upward and the initial position be $y = 0$.
    $$\Delta U_{\text{grav}} = mg\Delta y = (0.30 \text{ kg})(9.80 \text{ m/s}^2)(-1.0 \text{ m} - 0) = \boxed{-2.9 \text{ J}}$$

25. (a) **Strategy and Solution** Since there are two pulleys, only half the force is required to move the mass (but twice the length of rope must be pulled), so the pulley system multiplies the force exerted by a factor of $\boxed{2}$.

    (b) **Strategy** Use $\Delta U = mg\Delta h$.

    Solution Find the change in potential energy of the weight.
    $$\Delta U = mg\Delta h = (48.0 \text{ kg})(9.80 \text{ m/s}^2)(4.00 \text{ m}) = \boxed{1.88 \text{ kJ}}$$

    (c) **Strategy and Solution** By conservation of energy, the work done to lift the mass is equal to its change in potential energy, so $W = \Delta U = \boxed{1.88 \text{ kJ}}$.

    (d) **Strategy and Solution** Twice the length of rope must be pulled to do a given amount of work while applying half the force, so the length of rope pulled is $\boxed{8.00 \text{ m}}$.

27. (a) **Strategy** Use conservation of energy.

    Solution Find the speed of the cart as it passes point 3.
    $$E_1 = \frac{1}{2}mv_1^2 \text{ if } y_1 = 0 \text{ and } E_3 = \frac{1}{2}mv_3^2 + mgy_3. \quad E_f = E_3 = \frac{1}{2}mv_3^2 + mgy_3 = E_i = E_1 = \frac{1}{2}mv_1^2, \text{ so}$$
    $$v_3 = \sqrt{v_1^2 - 2gy_3} = \sqrt{(20.0 \text{ m/s})^2 - 2(9.81 \text{ m/s}^2)(10.0 \text{ m})} = \boxed{14.3 \text{ m/s}}.$$

    (b) **Strategy** Use the result of part (a), replacing 3 with 4. If the result is real—the argument of the square root is nonnegative—the cart will reach position 4.

    Solution Compute the speed of the cart at position 4.
    $$v_4 = \sqrt{v_1^2 - 2gy_4} = \sqrt{(20.0 \text{ m/s})^2 - 2(9.81 \text{ m/s}^2)(20.0 \text{ m})} = 3 \text{ m/s}$$
    The answer is $\boxed{\text{yes; the cart will reach position 4}}$.

29. **Strategy** The initial height of the rope is $l\cos\theta$ where l is the length of the rope and θ is the angle it makes with the vertical. Then $\Delta y = l\cos\theta - l = l(\cos\theta - 1)$. Use conservation of energy.

    Solution Find Bruce's speed at the bottom of the swing.
    $$\Delta K = \frac{1}{2}mv^2 - 0 = \frac{1}{2}mv^2 = -\Delta U = -mg\Delta y = mgl(1 - \cos\theta), \text{ so}$$
    $$v = \sqrt{2gl(1 - \cos\theta)} = \sqrt{2(9.80 \text{ m/s}^2)(20.0 \text{ m})(1 - \cos 35.0°)} = \boxed{8.42 \text{ m/s}}.$$

33. Strategy Use conservation of energy.

Solution

(a) Solve for the final speed of the ball.

$$\Delta K = \frac{1}{2}mv_{\mathrm{f}}^2 - \frac{1}{2}mv^2 = -\Delta U = mgh, \text{ so } v_{\mathrm{f}} = \boxed{\sqrt{v^2 + 2gh}}.$$

(b) By inspection of the equation found in part (a), we find that $\boxed{\text{the final speed is independent of the angle}}$.

37. Strategy Use the result for escape speed found in Example 6.8.

Solution Replace the values for Earth with those for the Moon.

$$v = \sqrt{\frac{2GM_{\mathrm{Moon}}}{R_{\mathrm{Moon}}}} = \frac{\sqrt{2(6.674\times10^{-11}\ \mathrm{N\cdot m^2/kg^2})(7.35\times10^{22}\ \mathrm{kg})}}{1.74\times10^6\ \mathrm{m}} = \boxed{2.37\ \mathrm{km/s}}$$

39. Strategy Use conservation of energy and the result for escape speed found in Example 6.8.

Solution Replacing the values for Earth with those for the Zoroaster, we find that the escape speed for Zoroaster is given by $v_{\mathrm{esc}} = \sqrt{2GM_{\mathrm{Z}}/R_{\mathrm{Z}}}$. Find the speed of the meteor when it hits the surface of the planet.

$$\Delta K = \frac{1}{2}mv_{\mathrm{f}}^2 - \frac{1}{2}mv_{\mathrm{i}}^2 = -\Delta U = \frac{GM_{\mathrm{Z}}m}{R_{\mathrm{Z}}}, \text{ so}$$

$$v_{\mathrm{f}} = \sqrt{v_{\mathrm{i}}^2 + \frac{2GM_{\mathrm{Z}}}{R_{\mathrm{Z}}}} = \sqrt{v_{\mathrm{i}}^2 + v_{\mathrm{esc}}^2} = \sqrt{(5.0\ \mathrm{km/s})^2 + (12.0\ \mathrm{km/s})^2} = \boxed{13.0\ \mathrm{km/s}}.$$

41. Strategy Use Eq. (6-14) and form a ratio.

Solution Find the ratio of the potential energies at perigee and apogee.

$$\frac{U_{\mathrm{perigee}}}{U_{\mathrm{apogee}}} = \frac{-\dfrac{GmM_{\mathrm{E}}}{2R_{\mathrm{E}}}}{-\dfrac{GmM_{\mathrm{E}}}{4R_{\mathrm{E}}}} = \frac{4}{2} = \boxed{2}$$

45. Strategy Use Newton's second law and law of universal gravitation.

Solution Calculate the orbital speed.

$$\Sigma F_{\mathrm{r}} = \frac{GM_{\mathrm{E}}m}{(4.0R_{\mathrm{E}})^2} = ma_{\mathrm{r}} = m\frac{v_{\mathrm{orb}}^2}{4.0R_{\mathrm{E}}}, \text{ so } v_{\mathrm{orb}} = \sqrt{\frac{GM_{\mathrm{E}}}{4.0R_{\mathrm{E}}}}.$$

Calculate the escape speed.

$$K_{\mathrm{i}} + U_{\mathrm{i}} = \frac{1}{2}mv_{\mathrm{esc}}^2 - \frac{GM_{\mathrm{E}}m}{4.0R_{\mathrm{E}}} = K_{\mathrm{f}} + U_{\mathrm{f}} = 0 + 0, \text{ so } v_{\mathrm{esc}} = \sqrt{\frac{GM_{\mathrm{E}}}{2.0R_{\mathrm{E}}}}.$$

Find the change in speed.

$$\Delta v = v_{\mathrm{esc}} - v_{\mathrm{orb}} = \sqrt{\frac{GM_{\mathrm{E}}}{2.0R_{\mathrm{E}}}} - \sqrt{\frac{GM_{\mathrm{E}}}{4.0R_{\mathrm{E}}}} = \left(\frac{1}{\sqrt{2.0}} - \frac{1}{2.0}\right)\sqrt{\frac{GM_{\mathrm{E}}}{R_{\mathrm{E}}}}$$

$$= \left(\frac{1}{\sqrt{2.0}} - \frac{1}{2.0}\right)\sqrt{\frac{(6.674\times10^{-11}\ \mathrm{N\cdot m^2/kg^2})(5.974\times10^{24}\ \mathrm{kg})}{6.371\times10^6\ \mathrm{m}}} = \boxed{1.6\ \mathrm{km/s}}$$

49. **Strategy** The work done by the hammer on the object is represented by the area between the curve and the x-axis.

   Solution Compute the work done in driving the nail.
   $$W = (50 \text{ N})(0.012 \text{ m}) + (120 \text{ N})(0.050 \text{ m} - 0.012 \text{ m}) = \boxed{5.2 \text{ J}}$$

51. **(a) Strategy** Use Hooke's law and form a proportion.

   Solution Form the proportion.
   $$k = \frac{F_1}{x_1} = \frac{F_2}{x_2}$$
   Solve for x_2 to find the amount that the spring stretches.
   $$x_2 = \frac{F_2}{F_1} x_1 = \frac{7.0 \text{ N}}{5.0 \text{ N}} (3.5 \text{ cm}) = \boxed{4.9 \text{ cm}}$$

   (b) Strategy Substitute known values for F_1 and x_1 to find k.

   Solution Compute the spring constant.
   $$k = \frac{F_1}{x_1} = \frac{5.0 \text{ N}}{3.5 \text{ cm}} = \boxed{1.4 \text{ N/cm}}$$

   (c) Strategy The triangular area under a forces on the spring vs. the stretch of the spring graph is equal to the work done by the forces.

   Solution Compute the work done by the forces on the spring.
   $$W = \frac{1}{2} Fx = \frac{1}{2} (5.0 \text{ N})(0.035 \text{ m}) = \boxed{88 \text{ mJ}}$$

53. **(a) Strategy** Set the weight of the mass equal to the force in Hooke's law.

   Solution Compute the spring constant.
   $$W = mg = F = kx, \text{ so } k = \frac{mg}{x} = \frac{(1.4 \text{ kg})(9.80 \text{ N/kg})}{7.2 \text{ cm}} = \boxed{1.9 \text{ N/cm}}.$$

   (b) Strategy Use Eq. (6-24).

   Solution Compute the elastic potential energy stored in the spring.
   $$U_{\text{elastic}} = \frac{1}{2} kx^2 = \frac{1}{2} \left[\frac{(1.4 \text{ kg})(9.80 \text{ N/kg})}{0.072 \text{ m}} \right] (0.072 \text{ m})^2 = \boxed{0.49 \text{ J}}$$

   (c) Strategy Solve for m in the equation for k found in part (a).

   Solution Compute the second mass.
   $$m_2 = \frac{kx_2}{g} = \left(\frac{m_1 g}{x_1} \right) \frac{x_2}{g} = \frac{x_2}{x_1} m_1 = \frac{12.2 \text{ cm}}{7.2 \text{ cm}} (1.4 \text{ kg}) = \boxed{2.4 \text{ kg}}$$

57. **Strategy and Solution** Let E be the elastic energy stored in the legs. This energy is converted into gravitational potential energy, mgh, when the kangaroo jumps. Since only one leg is used, and since $h \propto E$, the kangaroo can only jump half as high, or $(0.70 \text{ m})/2 = \boxed{0.35 \text{ m}}$.

61. Strategy Take the surface of the unstretched trampoline to be $y = 0$. Use conservation of energy and Newton's second law.

Solution Find the spring constant from the gravitational potential energy.

$mgh = \dfrac{1}{2}ky_{min}^2$, so $k = \dfrac{2mgh}{y_{min}^2}$.

Use Newton's second law for the situation where the gymnast is at rest.

$\Sigma F = ky - mg = 0$, so

$$y = \frac{mg}{k} = mg\left(\frac{y_{min}^2}{2mgh}\right) = \frac{y_{min}^2}{2h} = \frac{(-0.75 \text{ m})^2}{2(2.5 \text{ m} + 0.75 \text{ m})} = \boxed{8.7 \text{ cm}}.$$

65. Strategy Watts are joules per second and there are 3600 seconds in 1 hour.

Solution Show that $1 \text{ kW} \cdot \text{h} = 3.6 \text{ MJ}$.

$$1 \text{ kW} \cdot \text{h} = 10^3 \ \frac{\text{J}}{\text{s}} \cdot \text{h} \cdot \frac{3600 \text{ s}}{1 \text{ h}} = 3.6 \times 10^6 \text{ J} = 3.6 \text{ MJ}$$

69. Strategy Use Eq. (6-27).

Solution

(a) Find the force exerted on the cyclist by the air.

$P_a + P_c = 0$ since $\dfrac{\Delta U}{\Delta t} = 0$. $\vec{\mathbf{v}}$ is antiparallel to $\vec{\mathbf{F}}_a$.

$$P_a = F_a v \cos\theta, \text{ so } F_a = \frac{P_a}{v\cos\theta} = \frac{-120 \text{ W}}{(6.0 \text{ m/s})\cos 180°} = \boxed{20 \text{ N}}.$$

(b) Find the speed of the cyclist.

$$v = \frac{P_c}{F_c \cos\theta} = \frac{120 \text{ W}}{(-18 \text{ N})\cos 180°} = \boxed{6.7 \text{ m/s}}$$

73. Strategy Relate the change in gravitational potential energy of the person to the energy provided by the carbohydrate.

Solution Find the mass of carbohydrate required for the person to climb the stairs.

$$\frac{\text{energy}}{\text{energy available per gram}} = \frac{mgh}{0.100(\text{energy per gram})} = \frac{(74 \text{ kg})(9.80 \text{ m/s}^2)(15 \text{ m})}{0.100(17.6 \times 10^3 \text{ J/g})} = \boxed{6.2 \text{ g}}$$

The other 90% of the energy is dissipated as heat.

77. Strategy Use conservation of energy.

Solution Compute the required speed of the high jumper.

$$K_i + U_i = \frac{1}{2}mv^2 + 0 = \frac{1}{2}mv^2 = K_f + U_f = 0 + mgh = mgh, \text{ so}$$

$$v = \sqrt{2gh} = \sqrt{2(9.80 \text{ m/s}^2)(1.2 \text{ m})} = \boxed{4.8 \text{ m/s}}.$$

81. Strategy Use Newton's second law and law of universal gravitation.

Solution Prove that $U = -2K$ for any gravitational circular orbit.

$$\Sigma F_r = \frac{GMm}{r^2} = ma_r = \frac{mv^2}{r}, \text{ so}$$

$$m\frac{v^2}{r} = \frac{GMm}{r^2}$$

$$mv^2 = \frac{GMm}{r}$$

$$\frac{1}{2}mv^2 = \frac{1}{2}\left(\frac{GMm}{r}\right)$$

$$K = -\frac{1}{2}U$$

$$U = -2K$$

85. Strategy Use Eqs. (6-10) and (6-11) for the work and energy solution. Use Newton's second law and Eq. (4-5) for the force solution. Let $d = 8.0$ m, $d_1 = 5.0$ m, and $d_2 = 8.0$ m $- 5.0$ m $= 3.0$ m.

Solution First method: Find the constant tension using work and energy.
$W_{\text{total}} = W_c + W_{\text{nc}} = \Delta K = 0$, since the speeds at the top and bottom of the incline are zero. Also, $W_c = -\Delta U$ and $W_{\text{nc}} = Td_2$.

$W_{\text{nc}} = Td_2 = -W_c = \Delta U$, so

$$T = \frac{\Delta U}{d_2} = \frac{mg\Delta y}{d_2} = \frac{mg(0 - d\sin\theta)}{d_2} = -\frac{mgd\sin\theta}{d_2} = -\frac{(4.0 \text{ kg})(9.80 \text{ m/s}^2)(8.0 \text{ m})\sin 15°}{3.0 \text{ m}} = -27 \text{ N}.$$

The sign is negative because the work done by the tension is opposite the box's motion. So, the magnitude of the tension is $\boxed{27 \text{ N}}$.

Second method: Find the speed of the block just before the person grasps the cord using Newton's second law.
$\Sigma F_y = N - mg\cos\theta = 0$ and $\Sigma F_x = mg\sin\theta = ma.$

$$v_f^2 - v_i^2 = v_f^2 - 0 = 2g\sin\theta d_1$$

Let $v_f = v.$

Find the tension.

$$\Sigma F_x = -T + mg\sin\theta = ma_x, \text{ so } a_x = -\frac{T}{m} + g\sin\theta.$$

$$v_f^2 - v_i^2 = 0 - v^2 = -2g\sin\theta d_1 = 2a_x\Delta x = 2\left(-\frac{T}{m} + g\sin\theta\right)d_2, \text{ so}$$

$$T = mg\sin\theta\left(\frac{d_1 + d_2}{d_2}\right) = mg\sin\theta\frac{d}{d_2} = (4.0 \text{ kg})(9.80 \text{ m/s}^2)\sin 15°\left(\frac{8.0 \text{ m}}{3.0 \text{ m}}\right) = 27 \text{ N}.$$

89. **Strategy** Use conservation of energy and Newton's second law.

    Solution Find k.

    $$\Sigma F_y = kx_1 - mg = 0, \text{ so } k = \frac{mg}{x_1}. \text{ Find } v_{max}.$$

    $$K_i + K_f = 0 + \frac{1}{2}mv_{max}^2 = U_i + U_f = \frac{1}{2}kx_{max}^2 + 0, \text{ so}$$

    $$v_{max} = x_{max}\sqrt{\frac{k}{m}} = x_{max}\sqrt{\frac{g}{x_1}} = (0.100 \text{ m} - 0.050 \text{ m})\sqrt{\frac{9.80 \text{ m/s}^2}{0.060 \text{ m} - 0.050 \text{ m}}} = \boxed{1.6 \text{ m/s}}.$$

    $F = kx_1$

    0.20 kg

    mg

93. (a) **Strategy** Use the definition of average power. The change in energy is equal to the gravitational potential energy.

    Solution Find the average power the motor must deliver.

    $$P_{av} = \frac{\Delta E}{\Delta t} = \frac{mgh}{\Delta t} = \frac{(1202 \text{ kg} - 801 \text{ kg})(9.80 \text{ m/s}^2)(40.0 \text{ m})}{60.0 \text{ s}} = \boxed{2.62 \text{ kW}}$$

    (b) **Strategy** Without the counterweight, the motor must deliver more power.

    Solution Find the average power the motor must deliver.

    $$P_{av} = \frac{(1202 \text{ kg})(9.80 \text{ m/s}^2)(40.0 \text{ m})}{60.0 \text{ s}} = \boxed{7.85 \text{ kW}}$$

    The answer is significantly larger.

95. **Strategy** The basal metabolic rate is equal to the number of kilocalories per day required by a person resting under standard conditions.

    Solution

    (a) Compute Jermaine's basal metabolic rate.

    $$BMR = \left(\frac{1 \text{ kcal}}{0.010 \text{ mol}}\right)\left(\frac{0.015 \text{ mol}}{\text{min}}\right)\left(\frac{1440 \text{ min}}{\text{day}}\right) = \boxed{2200 \text{ kcal/day}}$$

    (b) Find the mass of fat lost.

    $$\frac{2160 \text{ kcal/day}}{9.3 \text{ kcal/g}}\left(\frac{2.2 \text{ lb}}{10^3 \text{ g}}\right) = 0.51 \text{ lb/day}$$

    Since Jermaine is not resting the entire time, he loses $\boxed{\text{more than } 0.51 \text{ lb}}$.

97. (a) Strategy Draw a diagram and use trigonometry.

Solution Referring to the diagram, we see that when Jane is at the lowest point of her swing, $L = h + L\cos 20°$. Solving for h, we find that $h = L - L\cos 20°$.

(b) Strategy We assume that no nonconservative forces act (significantly) on Jane. Thus, $\Delta E = 0$.

Solution Use conservation of energy to find Jane's speed at the lowest point of her swing.

$$\Delta E = 0 = \Delta K + \Delta U = \frac{1}{2}mv_f^2 - \frac{1}{2}mv_i^2 + mg\Delta y = \frac{1}{2}mv_f^2 - \frac{1}{2}mv_i^2 + mg(0 - h), \text{ so } \frac{1}{2}v_f^2 = \frac{1}{2}v_i^2 + gh, \text{ or}$$

$$v_f = \sqrt{v_i^2 + 2gh} = \sqrt{v_i^2 + 2gL(1 - \cos 20°)} = \sqrt{(4.0 \text{ m/s})^2 + 2(9.80 \text{ m/s}^2)(7.0 \text{ m})(1 - \cos 20°)} = \boxed{4.9 \text{ m/s}}.$$

(c) Strategy When Jane's entire initial kinetic energy is converted into gravitational potential energy, she will have reached her maximum height.

Solution Use conservation of energy to find how high Jane can swing (with respect to her lowest point).

$$\Delta E = 0 = \Delta K + \Delta U = 0 - \frac{1}{2}mv_i^2 + mg\Delta y = -\frac{1}{2}mv_i^2 + mg(h_{max} - h_{min}), \text{ so}$$

$$h_{max} = \frac{v_i^2}{2g} + L(1 - \cos 20°) = \frac{(4.0 \text{ m/s})^2}{2(9.80 \text{ m/s}^2)} + (7.0 \text{ m})(1 - \cos 20°) = \boxed{1.24 \text{ m}}.$$

101. (a) Strategy Use Hooke's law and Newton's laws of motion.

Solution According to Hooke's law, $F_1 = k_1 x_1$ and $F_2 = k_2 x_2$.

Imagine that the springs are suspended from a ceiling such that the bottom of each is at the same height. Then a mass m is attached to the bottom of both, the springs stretch, and the system comes to equilibrium. Assume that the masses of the springs are negligible. Sum the vertical forces.
$F_1 + F_2 - W = 0$, so $W = F_1 + F_2 = k_1 x_1 + k_2 x_2$.

Assuming the springs are attached to the same point on the top of the mass, $x_1 = x_2 = x$.

$W = k_1 x_1 + k_2 x_2 = k_1 x + k_2 x = (k_1 + k_2)x = kx = W$

So, in response to a force that stretches the springs (W, in this case), the springs act like one spring with a spring constant $\boxed{k = k_1 + k_2}$.

(b) Strategy Use the result from part (a) and Eq. (6-24).

Solution Compute the potential energy stored in the spring.

$$U = \frac{1}{2}kx^2 = \frac{1}{2}(k_1 + k_2)x^2 = \frac{1}{2}(500 \text{ N/m} + 300 \text{ N/m})(0.020 \text{ m})^2 = \boxed{0.16 \text{ J}}$$

105. (a) Strategy Use Newton's second law and Eq. (6-10).

Solution Find the speed at the bottom of the incline.

$$\Delta K = \frac{1}{2}mv^2 - 0 = W_c + W_{nc} = mgh - fd \text{ so } v = \sqrt{2gh - \frac{2fd}{m}}.$$

Use Newton's second law with $+y$ perpendicular to the incline and $+x$ down the incline.

$$\Sigma F_y = N - mg\cos\theta = 0, \text{ so } N = mg\cos\theta.$$

Now, $d = 0.85$ m, $h = d\sin\theta$, and $f = \mu N = \mu mg\cos\theta$.

Substitute.

$$v = \sqrt{2gd\sin\theta - \frac{2\mu mgd\cos\theta}{m}} = \sqrt{2gd(\sin\theta - \mu\cos\theta)}$$

Find the maximum compression.

$$K_f + U_f = 0 + \frac{1}{2}kx^2 = K_i + U_i = \frac{1}{2}mv^2 + 0, \text{ so}$$

$$x = v\sqrt{\frac{m}{k}} = \sqrt{\frac{2mgd}{k}(\sin\theta - \mu\cos\theta)} = \sqrt{\frac{2(0.50 \text{ kg})(9.80 \text{ m/s}^2)(0.85 \text{ m})}{35 \text{ N/m}}(\sin 30.0° - 0.25\cos 30.0°)}$$

$$= \boxed{26 \text{ cm}}.$$

(b) Strategy When the block is accelerated by the spring, it attains its previous kinetic energy and speed.

Solution Find the distance along the incline, d'.

$$\Delta K = 0 - \frac{1}{2}mv^2 = W_c + W_{nc} = -mgh - fd' = -mgd'\sin\theta - \mu mgd'\cos\theta = -d'[mg(\sin\theta + \mu\cos\theta)], \text{ so}$$

$$d' = \frac{v^2}{2g(\sin\theta + \mu\cos\theta)} = \frac{2gd(\sin\theta - \mu\cos\theta)}{2g(\sin\theta + \mu\cos\theta)} = (85 \text{ cm})\frac{\sin 30.0° - 0.25\cos 30.0°}{\sin 30.0° + 0.25\cos 30.0°} = \boxed{34 \text{ cm}}.$$

109. Strategy Use conservation of energy.

Solution According to the graph, the potential energy in the region under consideration is 300 J. So, $U_f = 300$ J. Initially, the kinetic energy is 200 J and the potential energy is 0, so $K_i = 200$ J and $U_i = 0$. Compute the final kinetic energy; that is, the kinetic energy in the region under consideration.

$E = \Delta K + \Delta U = K_f - K_i + U_f - U_i = K_f - 200 \text{ J} + 300 \text{ J} - 0 = K_f + 100 \text{ J} = 0$, so $K_f = -100$ J, which is impossible, since $\boxed{\text{kinetic energy cannot be negative}}$. Therefore, the answer is $\boxed{\text{no}}$, the particle cannot enter the region $3 \text{ cm} < x < 8 \text{ cm}$. Since the particle cannot enter the region, $\boxed{\text{it must remain in the region } x < 3 \text{ cm}}$.

Chapter 7

LINEAR MOMENTUM

Conceptual Questions

1. The likelihood of injury resulting from jumping from a second floor window is primarily determined by the average force acting to decelerate the body.

   (a) The deceleration time interval for a person landing stiff legged on pavement is very short. The impulse-momentum theorem tells us that the average force acting on the person's feet must therefore be very large—such a person is likely to incur injuries.

   (b) Jumping into a privet hedge increases the time interval over which the body decelerates. This decreases the average force on the person's limbs and therefore decreases the likelihood of injury.

   (c) Jumping into a firefighter's net is the best option of the three. The net stretches downward, gradually bringing the person to rest. Additionally, the firefighters lower the net with their hands as the person lands to further lengthen the time interval during which the person is brought to rest.

5. The law of the conservation of linear momentum states that in the absence of external interactions, the linear momentum of a closed system is constant. Floating in free space, the astronaut and the wrench form a closed system free from interactions with other bodies. If the astronaut throws the wrench in the direction opposite the ship, conservation of momentum dictates that he must in turn move toward the ship.

9. First law: The momentum of an object is constant unless acted upon by an external force. Second law: The net force acting on an object is equal to the rate of change of the object's momentum. Third law: When two objects interact, the changes in momentum that each imparts to the other are equal in magnitude and opposite in direction.

13. An impulse must be supplied to the egg to change its momentum and bring it to rest. A good strategy is to make the time interval over which the stopping force is applied as large as possible. This will reduce the magnitude of the force required to stop the egg. One should therefore attempt to catch the egg with a swinging motion, moving the hand backwards as it is being caught, to bring it to rest as slowly and gently as possible.

17. Daryl has done his homework. If he falls when rock climbing, his rope will stretch and stop him more gradually than the rope Mary wants to buy. In a fall, the climber's momentum must go from some initial value to zero. If the time over which the momentum is decreased to zero is longer, the average force delivered by the rope is smaller.

Problems

1. **Strategy** Use the definition of linear momentum.

   Solution Find the magnitude of the total momentum of the system.
   $$\vec{\mathbf{p}}_{\text{total}} = \vec{\mathbf{p}}_1 + \vec{\mathbf{p}}_2 = m\vec{\mathbf{v}}_1 + m\vec{\mathbf{v}}_2 = m(\vec{\mathbf{v}}_1 + \vec{\mathbf{v}}_2) = m[\vec{\mathbf{v}}_1 + (-\vec{\mathbf{v}}_1)] = 0, \text{ so the magnitude is } \boxed{0}.$$

5. **Strategy** Add the momenta of the three particles.

   Solution Find the total momentum of the system.
   $$\vec{\mathbf{p}}_{\text{tot}} = \vec{\mathbf{p}}_1 + \vec{\mathbf{p}}_2 + \vec{\mathbf{p}}_3 = m_1\vec{\mathbf{v}}_1 + m_2\vec{\mathbf{v}}_2 + m_3\vec{\mathbf{v}}_3 = m_1 v_1 \text{ north} + m_2 v_2 \text{ south} + m_3 v_3 \text{ north}$$
   $$= (m_1 v_1 - m_2 v_2 + m_3 v_3) \text{ north} = [(3.0 \text{ kg})(3.0 \text{ m/s}) - (4.0 \text{ kg})(5.0 \text{ m/s}) + (7.0 \text{ kg})(2.0 \text{ m/s})] \text{ north}$$
   $$= \boxed{3 \text{ kg} \cdot \text{m/s north}}$$

7. **Strategy** The initial momentum is toward the wall and the final momentum is away from the wall.

   Solution Find the change in momentum.
   $\Delta p = p_f - p_i = mv_f - mv_i = m(v_f - v_i) = (5.0 \text{ kg})(-2.0 \text{ m/s} - 2.0 \text{ m/s}) = -20 \text{ kg} \cdot \text{m/s}$, so
   $\Delta \vec{p} = \boxed{20 \text{ kg} \cdot \text{m/s in the } -x\text{-direction}}$.

9. **Strategy** Use the definition of linear momentum and Eq. (4-7). Let up be the positive direction.

   Solution $v_f = v_{fy} = v_{iy} - g\Delta t = -g\Delta t$, since the object starts from rest.
   Find Δp.
   $\Delta p = p_f - p_i = m(v_f - v_i) = m(-g\Delta t - 0) = -mg\Delta t = -(3.0 \text{ kg})(9.80 \text{ m/s}^2)(3.4 \text{ s}) = -1.0 \times 10^2 \text{ kg} \cdot \text{m/s}$, so
   $\Delta \vec{p} = \boxed{1.0 \times 10^2 \text{ kg} \cdot \text{m/s downward}}$.

13. **Strategy** Use the impulse-momentum theorem. Let the positive direction be in the direction of motion.

    Solution Find the average horizontal force exerted on the automobile during breaking.
    $F_{av} = \dfrac{\Delta p}{\Delta t} = \dfrac{m(v_f - v_i)}{\Delta t} = \dfrac{(1.0 \times 10^3 \text{ kg})(0 - 30.0 \text{ m/s})}{5.0 \text{ s}} = -6.0 \times 10^3 \text{ N}$
    So, $\vec{F}_{av} = \boxed{6.0 \times 10^3 \text{ N opposite the car's direction of motion}}$.

17. **(a) Strategy** Use conservation of energy.

    Solution Find the speed with which the pole-vaulter lands.
    $\Delta K = \dfrac{1}{2}mv^2 = -\Delta U = mgh$, so $v = \sqrt{2gh} = \sqrt{2(9.80 \text{ m/s}^2)(6.0 \text{ m})} = \boxed{11 \text{ m/s}}$.

    (b) Strategy Use the impulse-momentum theorem.

    Solution Find the average force on the pole-vaulter's body.
    $\Delta p = F_{av}\Delta t$, so
    $F_{av} = \dfrac{\Delta p}{\Delta t} = \dfrac{m(v_f - v_i)}{\Delta t} = \dfrac{m[0 - (-v)]}{\Delta t} = \dfrac{mv}{\Delta t} = \dfrac{m}{\Delta t}\sqrt{2gh} = \dfrac{60.0 \text{ kg}}{0.50 \text{ s}}\sqrt{2(9.80 \text{ m/s}^2)(6.0 \text{ m})} = \boxed{1300 \text{ N}}$.

21. **Strategy** Use conservation of momentum.

    Solution Find the recoil speed of the thorium nucleus.
    $\vec{p}_i = 0 = -\vec{p}_f$, so if n = nucleus and p = particle,
    $\vec{p}_n + \vec{p}_p = m_n\vec{v}_n + m_p\vec{v}_p = 0$, so $|\vec{v}_n| = \dfrac{m_p}{m_n}|-\vec{v}_p| = \dfrac{4.0 \text{ u}}{234 \text{ u}}[0.050(2.998 \times 10^8 \text{ m/s})] = \boxed{2.6 \times 10^5 \text{ m/s}}$.

25. **Strategy** Use conservation of momentum.

    Solution Find the recoil speed of the railroad car.
    $\vec{p}_i = 0 = -\vec{p}_f$, and since we are only concerned with the horizontal direction, we have:
    $m_c v_{cx} = m_s v_{sx}$, so $v_{cx} = \dfrac{m_s}{m_c}v_{sx} = \dfrac{98 \text{ kg}}{5.0 \times 10^4 \text{ kg}}(105 \text{ m/s})\cos 60.0° = \boxed{0.10 \text{ m/s}}$.

27. **Strategy** Use the component form of the definition of center of mass.

Solution Find the location of particle B.

Find x_{CM}.

$$x_{CM} = \frac{m_A x_A + m_B x_B}{m_A + m_B} = \frac{0 + m_B x_B}{m_A + m_B}, \text{ so}$$

$$x_B = \frac{m_A + m_B}{m_B} x_{CM} = \frac{30.0 \text{ g} + 10.0 \text{ g}}{10.0 \text{ g}} (2.0 \text{ cm}) = 8.0 \text{ cm}.$$

Similarly,

$$y_B = \frac{30.0 \text{ g} + 10.0 \text{ g}}{10.0 \text{ g}} (5.0 \text{ cm}) = 20 \text{ cm}.$$

The coordinates of particle B are $(x_B, y_B) = \boxed{(8.0 \text{ cm, } 20 \text{ cm})}$.

29. **Strategy** Since no y-components of the positions have changed, the center of mass moves only in the x-direction. Use the component form of the definition of center of mass.

Solution Find the displacement of the center of mass of the three bodies.

$$x_i = \frac{mx_{1i} + mx_{2i} + mx_{3i}}{m + m + m} = \frac{x_{1i} + x_{2i} + x_{3i}}{3} = \frac{1 \text{ m} + 2 \text{ m} + 3 \text{ m}}{3} = 2 \text{ m}$$

$$x_f = \frac{x_{1f} + x_{2f} + x_{3f}}{3} = \frac{x_{1i} + x_{2i} + x_{3i} + 0.12 \text{ m}}{3} = \frac{6 \text{ m} + 0.12 \text{ m}}{3}$$

$$\Delta x = x_f - x_i = \frac{6 \text{ m} + 0.12 \text{ m}}{3} - 2 \text{ m} = \frac{0.12 \text{ m}}{3} = 4.0 \text{ cm}$$

The center of mass moves $\boxed{4.0 \text{ cm in the positive } x\text{-direction}}$.

33. **Strategy** The x-coordinate of each three-dimensional shape is midway along its horizontal dimension.

Solution Find the x-component of the center of mass of the composite object.

$$x_{CM} = \frac{m_s x_s + m_c x_c + m_r x_r}{m_s + m_c + m_r} = \frac{(200 \text{ g})(5.0 \text{ cm}) + (450 \text{ g})(10 \text{ cm} + 17/2 \text{ cm}) + (325 \text{ g})(10 \text{ cm} + 17 \text{ cm} + 16/2 \text{ cm})}{200 \text{ g} + 450 \text{ g} + 325 \text{ g}}$$

$$= \boxed{21 \text{ cm}}$$

35. **Strategy** The total momentum of the system is equal to the total mass of the system times the velocity of the center of mass.

Solution Find the total momentum.

$$\vec{p} = M\vec{v}_{CM} = m_A \vec{v}_A + m_B \vec{v}_B \text{ since } \vec{p} = \vec{p}_A + \vec{p}_B. \text{ Thus, } \vec{v}_{CM} = \frac{m_A \vec{v}_A + m_B \vec{v}_B}{m_A + m_B}.$$

Find the components of $\vec{v}_{CM}$.

$$v_{CMx} = \frac{m_A v_{Ax} + m_B v_{Bx}}{m_A + m_B} = \frac{(3 \text{ kg})(14 \text{ m/s}) + (4 \text{ kg})(0)}{3 \text{ kg} + 4 \text{ kg}} = 6 \text{ m/s}$$

$$v_{CMy} = \frac{(3 \text{ kg})(0) + (4 \text{ kg})(-7 \text{ m/s})}{3 \text{ kg} + 4 \text{ kg}} = -4 \text{ m/s}$$

So, the components are $(v_{CMx}, v_{CMy}) = \boxed{(6 \text{ m/s, } -4 \text{ m/s})}$.

37. **(a) Strategy** Draw a diagram and use conservation of linear momentum.

    Solution

    $$\vec{\mathbf{p}} = M\vec{\mathbf{v}}_{CM} = \frac{M}{4}\vec{\mathbf{v}}_1 + \frac{M}{3}\vec{\mathbf{v}}_2 + \frac{5M}{12}\vec{\mathbf{v}}_3 = 0 \;\;\text{Use components.}$$

    $$\frac{M}{4}v_{1x} + \frac{M}{3}v_{2x} + \frac{5M}{12}v_{3x} = 3v_{1x} + 4v_{2x} + 5v_{3x} = 0, \text{ so}$$

    $$v_{3x} = -\frac{3v_{1x} + 4v_{2x}}{5} = -\frac{3(5.0\ \text{m/s})\cos 37° + 4(4.0\ \text{m/s})\cos 135°}{5} = -0.13\ \text{m/s}.$$

    $$\frac{M}{4}v_{1y} + \frac{M}{3}v_{2y} + \frac{5M}{12}v_{3y} = 3v_{1y} + 4v_{2y} + 5v_{3y} = 0, \text{ so}$$

    $$v_{3y} = -\frac{3v_{1y} + 4v_{2y}}{5} = -\frac{3(5.0\ \text{m/s})\sin 37° + 4(4.0\ \text{m/s})\sin 135°}{5} = -4.1\ \text{m/s}.$$

    The velocity components are $\boxed{(-0.13\ \text{m/s}, -4.1\ \text{m/s})}$.

    (b) Strategy and Solution Due to the law of conservation of linear momentum, $\boxed{\text{the center of mass of the system remains at the origin after the explosion}}$.

41. **Strategy** Use conservation of momentum.

    Solution

    (a) The collision is perfectly inelastic, so $v_{1f} = v_{2f} = v_f$. Find the speed of the two cars after the collision.
    $$m_1 v_{1i} + m_2 v_{2i} = mv_{1i} + 4.0m(0) = m_1 v_{1f} + m_2 v_{2f} = mv_f + 4.0mv_f, \text{ so } v_f = \frac{v_{1i}}{5.0} = \frac{1.0\ \text{m/s}}{5.0} = \boxed{0.20\ \text{m/s}}.$$

    (b) The cars are at rest after the collision, so $v_{1f} = v_{2f} = 0$.
    $$mv_{1i} + 4.0mv_{2i} = 0, \text{ so } v_{2i} = -\frac{v_{1i}}{4.0} = -\frac{1.0\ \text{m/s}}{4.0} = -0.25\ \text{m/s}. \text{ The initial speed was } \boxed{0.25\ \text{m/s}}.$$

43. **Strategy** Use conservation of momentum. The collision is perfectly inelastic, so $v_{1f} = v_{2f} = v_f$. Also, the block is initially at rest, so $v_{2i} = 0$.

    Solution Find the speed of the block of wood and the bullet just after the collision.
    $$m_1 v_{1f} + m_2 v_{2f} = (m_1 + m_2)v_f = m_1 v_{1i} + m_2 v_{2i} = m_1 v_{1i} + m_2(0), \text{ so}$$
    $$v_f = \frac{m_1}{m_1 + m_2}v_{1i} = \frac{0.050\ \text{kg}}{0.050\ \text{kg} + 0.95\ \text{kg}}(100.0\ \text{m/s}) = \boxed{5.0\ \text{m/s}}.$$

45. **Strategy** Use conservation of momentum.

    Solution Find the total momentum of the two blocks after the collision.
    $$\Delta p_2 = -\Delta p_1$$
    $$p_{2f} - p_{2i} = p_{1i} - p_{1f}$$
    $$p_{1f} + p_{2f} = p_{1i} + p_{2i}$$
    $$(m_1 + m_2)v_f = m_1 v_{1i} + m_2 v_{2i}$$
    $$p_f = (2.0\ \text{kg})(1.0\ \text{m/s}) + (1.0\ \text{kg})(0) = 2.0\ \text{kg}\cdot\text{m/s} = p_{1i}$$

    Since p_{1i} was directed to the right, and $p_f = p_{1i}$, the total momentum of the two blocks after the collision is
    $\boxed{2.0\ \text{kg}\cdot\text{m/s to the right}}$.

49. Strategy Use conservation of momentum. Let the positive direction be the initial direction of motion.

Solution Find the speed of the 5.0-kg body after the collision.

$m_1 v_{1f} + m_2 v_{2f} = m_1 v_{1i} + m_2 v_{2i}$, so

$$v_{2f} = \frac{m_1(v_{1i} - v_{1f}) + m_2 v_{2i}}{m_2} = \frac{(1.0 \text{ kg})[10.0 \text{ m/s} - (-5.0 \text{ m/s})] + (5.0 \text{ kg})(0)}{5.0 \text{ kg}} = \boxed{3.0 \text{ m/s}}.$$

51. Strategy The spring imparts the same (in magnitude) impulse to each block. (The same magnitude force is exerted on each block by the ends of the spring for the same amount of time.) So, each block has the same final magnitude of momentum. (The initial momentum is zero.)

Solution Find the mass of block B.

$m_B v_B = m_A v_A$, so

$$m_B = \frac{v_A}{v_B} m_A = \frac{d_A / \Delta t}{d_B / \Delta t} m_A = \frac{d_A}{d_B} m_A = \frac{1.0 \text{ m}}{3.0 \text{ m}} (0.60 \text{ kg}) = \boxed{0.20 \text{ kg}}.$$

53. Strategy The collision is perfectly inelastic, so $v_{1f} = v_{2f} = v$. The block is initially at rest, so $v_{2i} = 0$ and $v_{1i} = v_i$. Use conservation of momentum and Eq. (4-9).

Solution Find the speed of the bullet and block system.

$$(m_{\text{bul}} + m_{\text{blk}})v = m_{\text{bul}} v_i + m_{\text{blk}}(0), \text{ so } v = \frac{m_{\text{bul}}}{m_{\text{bul}} + m_{\text{blk}}} v_i.$$

Determine the time it takes the system to hit the floor.

$$\Delta y = -h = v_{iy}\Delta t - \frac{1}{2} g(\Delta t)^2 = 0 - \frac{1}{2} g(\Delta t)^2, \text{ so } \Delta t = \sqrt{\frac{2h}{g}}.$$

Find the horizontal distance traveled.

$$\Delta x = v_{ix}\Delta t = v\Delta t = \frac{m_{\text{bul}}}{m_{\text{bul}} + m_{\text{blk}}} v_i \sqrt{\frac{2h}{g}} = \frac{0.010 \text{ kg}}{0.010 \text{ kg} + 4.0 \text{ kg}} (400.0 \text{ m/s}) \sqrt{\frac{2(1.2 \text{ m})}{9.80 \text{ m/s}^2}} = \boxed{0.49 \text{ m}}$$

57. Strategy Use conservation of momentum. Let each of the first two pieces be 45° from the positive x-axis (one CW, one CCW).

Solution Find the speed of the third piece.
Find v_{3x}.

$$p_{1x} + p_{2x} + p_{3x} = mv_{1x} + mv_{2x} + mv_{3x} = 0, \text{ so } v_{3x} = -v_{1x} - v_{2x} = -v\cos 45° - v\cos(-45°) = -\frac{v}{\sqrt{2}} - \frac{v}{\sqrt{2}} = -v\sqrt{2}.$$

Similarly,

$$v_{3y} = -v_{1y} - v_{2y} = -v\sin 45° - v\sin(-45°) = -\frac{v}{\sqrt{2}} + \frac{v}{\sqrt{2}} = 0, \text{ so } v_3 = |v_{3x}| = v\sqrt{2} = (120 \text{ m/s})\sqrt{2} = \boxed{170 \text{ m/s}}.$$

59. Strategy Use conservation of momentum. Refer to Practice Problem 7.11.

Solution

(a) Find the momentum change of the ball of mass m_1.

$$\Delta p_{1x} = -\Delta p_{2x} = m_2 v_{2ix} - m_2 v_{2fx} = m_2(0 - v_{2fx}) = -m_2 v_{2fx} = -5m_1 \left[\frac{1}{4} v_i \cos(-36.9°)\right] = \boxed{-1.00 m_1 v_i}$$

$$\Delta p_{1y} = -\Delta p_{2y} = m_2 v_{2iy} - m_2 v_{2fy} = 5m_1(0 - v_{2fy}) = -5m_1 v_{2fy} = -5m_1\left[\frac{1}{4}v_i \sin(-36.9°)\right] = \boxed{0.751 m_1 v_i}$$

(b) Find the momentum change of the ball of mass m_2.

$$\Delta p_{2x} = -\Delta p_{1x} = m_1(v_{1ix} - v_{1fx}) = m_1(v_i - 0) = \boxed{m_1 v_i}$$

$$\Delta p_{2y} = -\Delta p_{1y} = m_1(v_{1iy} - v_{1fy}) = m_1(0 - v_1) = -m_1 v_1 = -m_1(0.751 v_i) = \boxed{-0.751 m_1 v_i}$$

$\boxed{\text{The momentum changes for each mass are equal and opposite.}}$

61. Strategy Use conservation of momentum.

Solution Find v_{2f} in terms of v_{1f}.

$$m v_{1fy} + m v_{2fy} = m v_{1f} \sin\theta_1 + m v_{2f} \sin\theta_2 = m v_{1iy} + m v_{2iy} = 0 + 0, \text{ so}$$

$$v_{2f} = \frac{-\sin\theta_1}{\sin\theta_2} v_{1f} = \frac{-\sin 60.0°}{\sin(-30.0°)} v_{1f} = \boxed{1.73 v_{1f}}.$$

65. Strategy The collision is perfectly inelastic, so the final velocities of the cars are identical. Use conservation of momentum.

Solution Let the 1700-kg car be (1) and the 1300-kg car be (2).

$$p_{ix} = m_1 v_{1ix} + m_2 v_{2ix} = m_1 v_{1ix} + 0 = p_{fx} = (m_1 + m_2)v_{fx}, \text{ so } v_{fx} = \frac{m_1}{m_1 + m_2} v_{1ix}.$$

$$p_{iy} = m_1 v_{1iy} + m_2 v_{2iy} = p_{fy} = (m_1 + m_2)v_{fy}, \text{ so } v_{fy} = \frac{m_1 v_{1iy} + m_2 v_{2iy}}{m_1 + m_2}.$$

Compute the final speed and the direction.

$$v_f = \sqrt{v_{fx}^2 + v_{fy}^2} = \sqrt{\left(\frac{m_1 v_{1ix}}{m_1 + m_2}\right)^2 + \left(\frac{m_1 v_{1iy} + m_2 v_{2iy}}{m_1 + m_2}\right)^2}$$

$$= \frac{\sqrt{[(1700 \text{ kg})(14 \text{ m/s})\cos 45°]^2 + [(1700 \text{ kg})(14 \text{ m/s})\sin 45° + (1300 \text{ kg})(-18 \text{ m/s})]^2}}{1700 \text{ kg} + 1300 \text{ kg}} = 6.0 \text{ m/s}$$

$$\theta = \tan^{-1}\frac{v_{fy}}{v_{fx}} = \tan^{-1}\frac{(1700 \text{ kg})(14 \text{ m/s})\sin 45° + (1300 \text{ kg})(-18 \text{ m/s})}{(1700 \text{ kg})(14 \text{ m/s})\cos 45°} = -21°$$

Thus, the final velocity of the cars is $\boxed{6.0 \text{ m/s at } 21° \text{ S of E}}$.

69. **Strategy** Use conservation of momentum.

Solution Let swallow 1 and its coconut be (1) and swallow 2 and its coconut be (2) (before the collision). After the collision, let swallow 1's coconut be (3), swallow 2's coconut be (4), and the tangled-up swallows be (5).

$$p_{ix} = m_1 v_{1x} + m_2 v_{2x} = 0 + 0 = p_{fx} = m_3 v_{3x} + m_4 v_{4x} + m_5 v_{5x}, \text{ so } v_{5x} = -\frac{m_3 v_{3x} + m_4 v_{4x}}{m_5}.$$

$$p_{iy} = m_1 v_{1y} + m_2 v_{2y} = m_1 v_1 + m_2 v_2 = p_{fy} = m_3 v_{3y} + m_4 v_{4y} + m_5 v_{5y}, \text{ so}$$

$$v_{5y} = \frac{m_1 v_1 + m_2 v_2 - m_3 v_{3y} - m_4 v_{4y}}{m_5}.$$

Compute the final speed of the tangled swallows, v_5.

$$v_5 = \sqrt{v_{5x}^2 + v_{5y}^2} = \frac{1}{m_5} \sqrt{[-(m_3 v_{3x} + m_4 v_{4x})]^2 + (m_1 v_1 + m_2 v_2 - m_3 v_{3y} - m_4 v_{4y})^2}$$

$$= \frac{\sqrt{\begin{array}{l}[(0.80 \text{ kg})(13 \text{ m/s})\cos 260° + (0.70 \text{ kg})(14 \text{ m/s})\cos 60°]^2 \\ +[(1.07 \text{ kg})(20 \text{ m/s}) + (0.92 \text{ kg})(-15 \text{ m/s}) - (0.80 \text{ kg})(13 \text{ m/s})\sin 260° - (0.70 \text{ kg})(14 \text{ m/s})\sin 60°]^2\end{array}}}{0.270 \text{ kg} + 0.220 \text{ kg}}$$

$$= 20 \text{ m/s}$$

Compute the direction.

$$\theta = \tan^{-1} \frac{v_{5y}}{v_{5x}}$$

$$= \tan^{-1} \frac{(1.07 \text{ kg})(20 \text{ m/s}) + (0.92 \text{ kg})(-15 \text{ m/s}) - (0.80 \text{ kg})(13 \text{ m/s})\sin 260° - (0.70 \text{ kg})(14 \text{ m/s})\sin 60°}{-(0.80 \text{ kg})(13 \text{ m/s})\cos 260° - (0.70 \text{ kg})(14 \text{ m/s})\cos 60°}$$

$$= -72°$$

Since $v_{5x} < 0$ and $v_{5y} > 0$, the velocity vector is located in the second quadrant, so the angle is $180° - 72° = 108°$ from the positive x-axis or 18° west of north. Thus, the velocity of the birds immediately after the collision is $\boxed{20 \text{ m/s at } 18° \text{ W of N}}$.

71. **Strategy** Use conservation of momentum. The collision is perfectly inelastic, so $v_{1f} = v_{2f} = v_f$.

Solution Find the speed of the cars just after the collision.
$$m_1 v_{1f} + m_2 v_{2f} = (m_1 + m_2) v_f = m_1 v_{1i} + m_2 v_{2i} = m_1 v_i + 0, \text{ so}$$

$$v_f = \frac{m_1 g}{(m_1 + m_2)g} v_i = \frac{13.6 \text{ kN}}{13.6 \text{ kN} + 9.0 \text{ kN}} (17.0 \text{ m/s}) = \boxed{10.2 \text{ m/s}}.$$

73. **Strategy** Use the definition of linear momentum.

Solution Find the magnitude of the total momentum of the ship and the crew.
$$p_{tot} = m_{tot} v = (2.0 \times 10^3 \text{ kg} + 4.8 \times 10^4 \text{ kg})(1.0 \times 10^5 \text{ m/s}) = \boxed{5.0 \times 10^9 \text{ kg} \cdot \text{m/s}}$$

75. Strategy Use the impulse-momentum theorem.

Solution Find the average force exerted by the ground on the ball.

$$F_{av} = \frac{\Delta p}{\Delta t}$$

$$= \frac{m\sqrt{(\Delta v_x)^2 + (\Delta v_y)^2}}{\Delta t}$$

$$= \frac{0.060\ \text{kg}}{0.065\ \text{s}}\sqrt{\left[(53\ \text{m/s})\cos 18° - (54\ \text{m/s})\cos(-22°)\right]^2 + \left[(53\ \text{m/s})\sin 18° - (54\ \text{m/s})\sin(-22°)\right]^2} = \boxed{34\ \text{N}}$$

(diagram: y, x axes; 54 m/s and 53 m/s; angles 22° and 18°)

77. Strategy The center of mass of each block is its center. Add up the individual center of mass components to find the components of the center of mass of the block structure.

Solution

$$x_{CM} = \frac{mx_1 + 2mx_2 + 5mx_3 + 4mx_4}{12m} = \frac{x_1 + 2x_2 + 5x_3 + 4x_4}{12} = \frac{0 + 2(1.0\ \text{in}) + 5(2.0\ \text{in}) + 4(3.0\ \text{in})}{12} = 2.0\ \text{in}$$

$$y_{CM} = \frac{6my_1 + 4my_2 + my_3 + my_4}{12m} = \frac{6y_1 + 4y_2 + y_3 + y_4}{12} = \frac{6(0) + 4(1.0\ \text{in}) + 2.0\ \text{in} + 3.0\ \text{in}}{12} = 0.75\ \text{in}$$

$$z_{CM} = \frac{9mz_1 + 3mz_2}{12m} = \frac{9z_1 + 3z_2}{12} = \frac{9(0) + 3(1.0\ \text{in})}{12} = 0.25\ \text{in}$$

The center of mass of the block structure is located at $\boxed{(2.0\ \text{in}, 0.75\ \text{in}, 0.25\ \text{in})}$.

81. (a) Strategy The initial momentum of the baseball is $p_i = mv_i$. The final momentum is zero.

Solution Compute the change in momentum.
$$\Delta p = p_f - p_i = 0 - mv_i = -mv_i = -(0.15\ \text{kg})(35\ \text{m/s}) = -5.3\ \text{kg} \cdot \text{m/s}$$

Thus, the change in momentum was $\boxed{5.3\ \text{kg} \cdot \text{m/s}\ \text{opposite the ball's direction of motion}}$.

(b) Strategy and Solution According to the impulse-momentum theorem, the impulse applied to the ball is equal to the change in the momentum of the ball, or $\boxed{5.3\ \text{kg} \cdot \text{m/s}\ \text{opposite the ball's direction of motion}}$.

(c) Strategy Use the impulse momentum theorem.

Solution Since the acceleration is assumed constant, the time it takes for the ball to come to a complete stop is $\Delta t = \Delta x / v_{av}$. Compute the average force applied to the ball by the catcher's glove.

$$\vec{\mathbf{F}}_{av} = \frac{\Delta \vec{\mathbf{p}}}{\Delta t} = v_{av}\frac{\Delta \vec{\mathbf{p}}}{\Delta x} = \left(\frac{35\ \text{m/s}}{2}\right)\frac{5.25\ \text{kg} \cdot \text{m/s}\ \text{opposite the direction of motion}}{0.050\ \text{m}}$$

$$= \boxed{1.8\ \text{kN}\ \text{opposite the ball's direction of motion}}$$

85. **Strategy** We must determine the initial speeds of the two cars. The collision is perfectly inelastic, so the final velocities of the cars are identical. Use conservation of momentum and the work-kinetic energy theorem.

Solution Let the 1100-kg car be (1) and the 1300-kg car be (2). Use the work-kinetic energy theorem to determine the kinetic energy and, thus, the initial speed of the wrecked cars, which is the final speed of the collision.

$$W = F\Delta r = f_k \Delta r = -\mu_k mg\Delta r = \Delta K = 0 - \frac{1}{2}mv_i^2, \text{ so } v_i = \sqrt{2\mu_k g\Delta r}.$$

Thus, the final speed of the collision is $v_f = \sqrt{2\mu_k g\Delta r}$.

Find the initial speeds.

$$P_{ix} = m_1 v_{1ix} + m_2 v_{2ix} = m_1 v_{1i} + 0 = p_{fx} = (m_1 + m_2)v_{fx}, \text{ so}$$

$$v_{1i} = \frac{m_1 + m_2}{m_1}v_{fx} = \frac{m_1 + m_2}{m_1}\sqrt{2\mu_k g\Delta r}\cos 150° = \frac{2400\text{ kg}}{1100\text{ kg}}\sqrt{2(0.80)(9.80\text{ m/s}^2)(17\text{ m})}\cos 150°\left(\frac{1\text{ km/h}}{0.2778\text{ m/s}}\right)$$

$$= -110\text{ km/h}.$$

$$P_{iy} = m_1 v_{1iy} + m_2 v_{2iy} = 0 + m_2 v_{2i} = p_{fy} = (m_1 + m_2)v_{fy}, \text{ so}$$

$$v_{2i} = \frac{m_1 + m_2}{m_2}v_{fy} = \frac{m_1 + m_2}{m_2}\sqrt{2\mu_k g\Delta r}\sin 150° = \frac{2400\text{ kg}}{1300\text{ kg}}\sqrt{2(0.80)(9.80\text{ m/s}^2)(17\text{ m})}\sin 150°\left(\frac{1\text{ km/h}}{0.2778\text{ m/s}}\right)$$

$$= 54\text{ km/h}.$$

Since $110 > 70$, the lighter car was speeding .

89. **Strategy** Use conservation of energy and momentum. Let $2m = m_B = 2m_A$.

Solution Find the maximum kinetic energy of A alone and, thus, its speed just before it strikes B.

$$\Delta K = \frac{1}{2}mv_1^2 - 0 = -\Delta U = mgh - 0, \text{ so } v_1 = \sqrt{2gh}.$$

Use conservation of momentum to find the speed of the combined bobs just after impact. The collision is perfectly inelastic, so $v_{Af} = v_{Bf} = v_2$.

$$m_A v_{Af} + m_B v_{Bf} = (m + 2m)v_2 = m_A v_{Ai} + m_B v_{Bi} = mv_1 + 0, \text{ so } v_2 = \frac{1}{3}v_1.$$

Find the maximum height.

$$\Delta K = 0 - \frac{1}{2}mv_2^2 = -\frac{1}{2}m\left(\frac{1}{3}\sqrt{2gh}\right)^2 = -\Delta U = 0 - mgh_2, \text{ so } h_2 = \boxed{\frac{1}{9}h}.$$

93. Strategy Use conservation of momentum and Eq. (6-6) for the kinetic energies. Since the radium nucleus is at rest, $\vec{p}_i = \vec{p}_{Ra} = 0$.

Solution

(a) Find the ratio of the speed of the alpha particle to the speed of the radon nucleus.

$p_f = m_{Rn}v_{Rn} + m_\alpha v_\alpha = p_i = 0$, so $m_\alpha v_\alpha = -m_{Rn}v_{Rn}$. Therefore,

$$\frac{v_\alpha}{v_{Rn}} = \frac{m_{Rn}}{m_\alpha} = \frac{222\ u}{4\ u} = \frac{222}{4} = \boxed{\frac{111}{2}}, \text{ where the negative was dropped because speed is nonnegative.}$$

(b) Since the initial momentum is zero, $\vec{p}_{Rn} = -\vec{p}_\alpha$; therefore, $\dfrac{|\vec{p}_\alpha|}{|\vec{p}_{Rn}|} = \dfrac{p_\alpha}{p_{Rn}} = \boxed{1}$.

(c) Find the ratio of the kinetic energies.

$$\frac{K_\alpha}{K_{Rn}} = \frac{\frac{1}{2}m_\alpha v_\alpha^2}{\frac{1}{2}m_{Rn}v_{Rn}^2} = \frac{m_\alpha}{m_{Rn}}\left(\frac{v_\alpha}{v_{Rn}}\right)^2 = \frac{4\ u}{222\ u}\left(\frac{111}{2}\right)^2 = \boxed{\frac{111}{2}}$$

Chapter 8

TORQUE AND ANGULAR MOMENTUM

Conceptual Questions

1. To maximize the torque, locate it as far as possible from the rotation axis: along the lower edge.

5. For a body to be in equilibrium, both the net force and the net torque acting on it must equal zero. To satisfy the first requirement, the two forces must be equal in magnitude and opposite in direction. To satisfy the second requirement, the two forces must act along the same line—a net torque would otherwise act to rotate the object.

9. An object's moment of inertia depends on how its mass is distributed with respect to the axis of rotation. The farther the mass is from the axis, the greater the object's moment of inertia. When animals have leg muscles that are concentrated close to the hip joint, their legs have relatively small moments of inertia. This makes it easier for them to rotate their legs, allowing them to run faster.

13. The vertical component of the angular momentum of the system (merry-go-round and child) is conserved throughout this process, since there are no external torques about the vertical axis of the merry-go-round. When the child moves out to the rim, the rotational inertia of the system increases, because the child is located farther from the axis. To conserve angular momentum, the angular velocity must therefore decrease. Noting that the rotational kinetic energy can be written as $L^2/(2I)$ and that L remains constant while I increases, we see that the rotational kinetic energy of the system decreases.

17. The astronaut and satellite constitute an isolated system. The initial angular momentum of the system is zero. When the astronaut tries to remove the bolt, both he and the satellite will rotate. They will rotate in opposite directions so that the total angular momentum of the system remains zero. To put it another way, when the astronaut applies a torque to a part of the satellite, the satellite applies an equal and opposite torque to him. The astronaut must anchor the satellite and himself somehow before trying to remove the bolt.

21. The melting of Earth's polar ice caps would distribute some of its mass from locations near its rotation axis to locations that are on average farther from its rotation axis. The rotational inertia of a sphere is greater if its mass is distributed farther from its axis of rotation—the Earth's moment of inertia would therefore increase. Angular momentum conservation requires that the product of the Earth's rotational inertia and its angular velocity be constant. A larger moment of inertia must be accompanied by a smaller angular velocity—the melting of the caps would therefore increase the length of the day.

Problems

1. **Strategy and Solution** I has units $\text{kg} \cdot \text{m}^2$. ω^2 has units $(\text{rad/s})^2$. So, $\frac{1}{2}I\omega^2$ has units
   $\text{kg} \cdot \text{m}^2 \cdot \text{rad}^2/\text{s}^2 = \text{kg} \cdot \text{m}^2/\text{s}^2 = \text{J}$, which is a unit of energy.

3. **Strategy** $I = \frac{2}{5}MR^2$ for a solid sphere and mass density is $\rho = M/V$.

   Solution

   (a) $M = \rho V = \rho \frac{4}{3}\pi R^3$ for a solid sphere. Form a proportion.

   $$\frac{M_{\text{child}}}{M_{\text{adult}}} = \left(\frac{R_{\text{child}}}{R_{\text{adult}}}\right)^3 = \left(\frac{1}{2}\right)^3 = \frac{1}{8}, \text{ so the mass is } \boxed{\text{reduced by a factor of 8}}.$$

   (b) Form a proportion.

   $$\frac{I_{\text{child}}}{I_{\text{adult}}} = \frac{1}{8}\left(\frac{R_{\text{child}}}{R_{\text{adult}}}\right)^2 = \frac{1}{8}\left(\frac{1}{2}\right)^2 = \frac{1}{32}$$

   The rotational inertia is $\boxed{\text{reduced by a factor of 32}}$.

5. **Strategy** Find the rotational inertia in each case by using Eq. (8-2).

   Solution

   (a) $I = m(r^2 + 0^2 + 0^2 + r^2) = 2mr^2 = 2(3.0 \text{ kg})(0.50 \text{ m})^2 = \boxed{1.5 \text{ kg} \cdot \text{m}^2}$

   (b) $I = m(0^2 + r^2 + 0^2 + r^2) = 2mr^2 = 2(3.0 \text{ kg})(0.50 \text{ m}/\sqrt{2})^2 = \boxed{0.75 \text{ kg} \cdot \text{m}^2}$

   (c) $I = m(r^2 + r^2 + r^2 + r^2) = 4mr^2 = 4(3.0 \text{ kg})(0.50 \text{ m}/\sqrt{2})^2 = \boxed{1.5 \text{ kg} \cdot \text{m}^2}$

9. (a) **Strategy and Solution** Since a significant fraction of the wheel's kinetic energy is rotational, to model it as if it were sliding without friction would be unjustified. So, the answer is $\boxed{\text{no}}$.

   (b) **Strategy** Use Eq. (8-1) and form a proportion.

   Solution Find the fraction of the total kinetic energy that is rotational.

   $$\frac{K_{\text{rot}}}{K_{\text{total}}} = \frac{4\left(\frac{1}{2}I\omega^2\right)}{\frac{1}{2}Mv^2 + 4\left(\frac{1}{2}I\omega^2\right)} = \frac{1}{\frac{Mv^2}{4I\omega^2}+1} = \frac{1}{1+\frac{Mv^2}{4I(v^2/R^2)}} = \frac{1}{1+\frac{MR^2}{4I}} = \frac{1}{1+\frac{(1300 \text{ kg})(0.35 \text{ m})^2}{4(0.705 \text{ kg·m}^2)}} = \boxed{0.017}$$

13. **Strategy** Use Eq. (8-3).

    Solution Find the magnitude of the torque.
    $$|\tau| = F_\perp r = mgr = (40.0 \text{ kg})(9.80 \text{ N/kg})(2.0 \text{ m}) = \boxed{780 \text{ N} \cdot \text{m}}$$

17. Strategy Use Eq. (8-4).

Solution Find the net torque in each case.

(a) $\Sigma\tau = F(r_{2\perp} - r_{1\perp}) = Fx_2 - Fx_1 = F(x_2 - x_1) = Fd$, since $d = x_2 - x_1$.

(b) $\Sigma\tau = F(r_{2\perp} - r_{1\perp}) = F(r_2 \sin\theta_2) - F(r_1 \sin\theta_1) = Fx_2 - Fx_1 = F(x_2 - x_1) = Fd$

21. Strategy The center of gravity is located at the center of mass. Let the origin be at the center of the door.

Solution Due to symmetry, $y_{CM} = 0$.
$$x_{CM} = \frac{m_1 x_1 + m_2 x_2}{M} = \frac{m_1(0) + m_2(x)}{M} = \frac{W_2 x}{W} = \frac{(5.0\ \text{N})(-0.75\ \text{m})}{5.0\ \text{N} + 300.0\ \text{N}} = -0.012\ \text{m}$$
The center of gravity is located $\boxed{1.2\ \text{cm toward the doorknob as measured from the center of the door.}}$

25. (a) Strategy Use the work-kinetic energy theorem.

Solution Find the work done spinning up the wheel.
$$W = \Delta K = \frac{1}{2}I\omega_f^2 = \frac{1}{2}(MR^2)\omega_f^2$$
$$= \frac{1}{2}(182\ \text{kg})(0.62\ \text{m})^2[(120\ \text{rev/min})(1/60\ \text{min/s})(2\pi\ \text{rad/rev})]^2 = \boxed{5.5\ \text{kJ}}$$

$\omega_f = 120$ rpm
0.62 m

(b) Strategy Use the equations for rotational motion with constant acceleration and the relationship between work, torque, and angular displacement.

Solution Find the torque.
$$W = \tau\Delta\theta = \tau(\omega_{av}\Delta t), \text{ so } \tau = \frac{W}{\omega_{av}\Delta t} = \frac{5.5\times10^3\ \text{J}}{(120\ \text{rev/min})(1/60\ \text{min/s})(2\pi\ \text{rad/rev})(30.0\ \text{s})/2} = \boxed{29\ \text{N}\cdot\text{m}}.$$

27. Strategy Choose the axis of rotation at the fulcrum. Use Eqs. (8-8).

Solution Find the force required to lift the load.
$\Sigma\tau = 0 = -F_A \cos\theta(2.4\ \text{m}) + F_{load} \cos\theta(1.2\ \text{m})$, so
$$F_A = \frac{1.2\ \text{m}}{2.4\ \text{m}}F_{load} = 0.50mg = 0.50(20.0\ \text{kg})(9.80\ \text{N/kg}) = \boxed{98\ \text{N}}.$$

29. Strategy Choose the rotation axis at the edge of the base of the sculpture that is in contact with the floor as it is tipped. The angle that the base makes with the floor is the same angle that the force due to gravity makes with the vertical axis of the sculpture.

Solution Set the net torque equal to zero at the equilibrium point to find the maximum angle.
$\Sigma\tau = 0 = -mgb\sin\theta + mga\cos\theta$, where $b = 1.80\ \text{m}$ and $a = (1.10\ \text{m})/2 = 0.550\ \text{m}$.
Solve for the angle.
$$b\sin\theta = a\cos\theta, \text{ so } \theta = \tan^{-1}\frac{a}{b} = \tan^{-1}\frac{0.550\ \text{m}}{1.80\ \text{m}} = \boxed{17.0°}.$$

33. Strategy Use Eqs. (8-8).

Solution Choose the axis of rotation at the point of contact between the driveway and the ladder.
$\Sigma F_x = 0 = f - N_w$, so $f = N_w$.

$\Sigma \tau = 0 = N_w(4.7 \text{ m}) - W_1(2.5 \text{ m})\cos\theta - W_p\left(\dfrac{3.0 \text{ m}}{4.7 \text{ m}}\right)(5.0 \text{ m})\cos\theta$, so $N_w = \dfrac{\cos\theta}{4.7 \text{ m}}\left[W_1(2.5 \text{ m}) + W_p\left(\dfrac{15 \text{ m}}{4.7}\right)\right]$.

Find θ.

$4.7 \text{ m} = (5.0 \text{ m})\sin\theta$, so $\theta = \sin^{-1}\dfrac{4.7}{5.0}$.

Calculate f.

$f = N_w = \dfrac{\cos\sin^{-1}\frac{4.7}{5.0}}{4.7 \text{ m}}\left[(120 \text{ N})(2.5 \text{ m}) + (680 \text{ N})\left(\dfrac{15 \text{ m}}{4.7}\right)\right] = 180 \text{ N}$

So, the force of friction is $\boxed{180 \text{ N toward the wall}}$.

35. Strategy Use Eqs. (8-8).

Solution Choose the axis of rotation at the hinge.
$\Sigma \tau = 0 = T(2.38 \text{ m})\sin 35° - (80.0 \text{ N})(1.50 \text{ m}) - (120.0 \text{ N})(3.00 \text{ m})$, so

$T = \dfrac{(80.0 \text{ N})(1.50 \text{ m}) + (120.0 \text{ N})(3.00 \text{ m})}{(2.38 \text{ m})\sin 35°} = \boxed{350 \text{ N}}$.

Find F_x and F_y.
$\Sigma F_x = 0 = -T\cos 35° + F_x$ and $\Sigma F_y = 0 = F_y + T\sin 35° - 80.0 \text{ N} - 120.0 \text{ N}$, so

$F_x = T\cos 35° = (350 \text{ N})\cos 35° = \boxed{290 \text{ N}}$ and $F_y = -(351.6 \text{ N})\sin 35° + 80.0 \text{ N} + 120.0 \text{ N} = \boxed{-2 \text{ N}}$.

$\boxed{\text{The magnitude of } F_y \text{ is small}}$ compared to that of F_x and T.

37. Strategy Use Eqs. (8-8). Choose the axis of rotation at the point where the beam meets the store.

Solution The tension in the cable cannot exceed 417 N. Sum the torques.
$\Sigma \tau = 0 = T\sin\theta(1.50 \text{ m}) - (50.0 \text{ N})(0.75 \text{ m}) - (200.0 \text{ N})(1.00 \text{ m})$
Solve for θ and substitute 417 N (the breaking strength) for T.

$\theta = \sin^{-1}\dfrac{(50.0 \text{ N})(0.75 \text{ m}) + (200.0 \text{ N})(1.00 \text{ m})}{(417 \text{ N})(1.50 \text{ m})} = 22.3°$

The minimum angle is $\boxed{22.3°}$.

41. Strategy Use Eqs. (8-8). Choose the axis of rotation at the point of contact of the normal force.

Solution Find the tension in the Achilles tendon, F_A.
$\Sigma \tau = 0 = -F_A(4.60 \text{ cm} + 12.8 \text{ cm}) + F_T(12.8 \text{ cm})$ and $\Sigma F_y = 0 = N + F_A - F_T$, or $F_T = N + F_A$, so

$-F_A(17.4 \text{ cm}) + (N + F_A)(12.8 \text{ cm}) = 0$, or $F_A = \dfrac{(12.8 \text{ cm})(750 \text{ N})}{4.6 \text{ cm}} = 2100 \text{ N}$.

Find the force that the tibia exerts on the ankle joint, F_T.

$F_T = N + F_A = 750 \text{ N} + \dfrac{12.8}{4.6}(750 \text{ N}) = 2800 \text{ N}$

The forces are: $\boxed{\text{tendon, 2100 N upward and tibia, 2800 N downward}}$.

43. **Strategy** Use Eqs. (8-8). Choose the axis of rotation at the elbow.

Solution Find the force exerted by the biceps muscle.
$\Sigma \tau = 0 = -W_m(35.0 \text{ cm}) - W_a(16.5 \text{ cm}) + F_b(5.00 \text{ cm})\sin\theta$, so

$$F_b = \frac{W_m(35.0 \text{ cm}) + W_a(16.5 \text{ cm})}{(5.00 \text{ cm})\sin\theta} = \frac{(9.9 \text{ N})(35.0 \text{ cm}) + (18.0 \text{ N})(16.5 \text{ cm})}{(5.00 \text{ cm})\dfrac{30.0 \text{ cm}}{\sqrt{(30.0 \text{ cm})^2 + (5.00 \text{ cm})^2}}} = \boxed{130 \text{ N}}.$$

45. **Strategy** Refer to Figure 8.32. First find the magnitude of the force exerted by the back F_b by analyzing the torques about an axis at the sacrum; then, find the horizontal component of the extreme force on the sacrum F_s. Use Eqs. (8-8).

Solution Sum the torques to find F_b.

$\Sigma \tau = 0 = F_b(44 \text{ cm})\sin 12° - (10 \text{ kg})(9.80 \text{ m/s}^2)(76 \text{ cm}) - (55 \text{ kg})(9.80 \text{ m/s}^2)(38 \text{ cm})$, so

$$F_b = \frac{(10 \text{ kg})(9.80 \text{ m/s}^2)(76 \text{ cm}) + (55 \text{ kg})(9.80 \text{ m/s}^2)(38 \text{ cm})}{(44 \text{ cm})\sin 12°} = 3053 \text{ N}.$$

The only forces with components in the horizontal direction are those due to the back and the sacrum. Find the horizontal component of the extreme force, F_{sx}.

$\Sigma F_x = 0 = F_{sx} - F_b \cos 12°$, so $F_{sx} = F_b \cos 12° = (3053 \text{ N})\cos 12° = \boxed{3.0 \text{ kN}}$.

$\dfrac{(3053 \text{ N})\cos 12°}{540 \text{ N}} = 5.5$, so the force is $\boxed{\text{about 5.5 times larger}}$ than that from his torso alone!

49. **Strategy** Use the rotational form of Newton's second law and Eq. (5-21).

Solution Find the torque that the motor must deliver.

$I = \frac{1}{2}MR^2$ for a uniform disk, so

$$\Sigma \tau = I\alpha = \frac{1}{2}MR^2\left(\frac{\omega_f^2 - \omega_i^2}{2\Delta\theta}\right) = \frac{MR^2\omega_f^2}{4\Delta\theta} = \frac{(0.22 \text{ kg})\left(\frac{0.305 \text{ m}}{2}\right)^2(3.49 \text{ rad/s})^2}{4(2.0 \text{ rev})(2\pi \text{ rad/rev})} = \boxed{0.0012 \text{ N}\cdot\text{m}}.$$

53. **Strategy** The rotational inertia of the wheel is $I = MR^2$. Use the rotational form of Newton's second law.

Solution Find the magnitude of the average torque.

$$|\Sigma \tau_{av}| = I\alpha = MR^2\left|\frac{\Delta\omega}{\Delta t}\right| = (2 \text{ kg})(0.30 \text{ m})^2\left(\frac{4.00 \text{ rev/s}}{50 \text{ s}}\right)\left(\frac{2\pi \text{ rad}}{\text{rev}}\right) = \boxed{0.09 \text{ N}\cdot\text{m}}$$

55. **Strategy** The rotational inertia is $I = \frac{1}{2}MR^2$. Use the rotational form of Newton's second law and Eq. (5-18).

Solution

(a) $\alpha = \dfrac{\Sigma \tau}{I} = \dfrac{FR + FR}{\frac{1}{2}MR^2} = \dfrac{4F}{MR} = \dfrac{4(10.0 \text{ N})}{(180 \text{ kg})(2.0 \text{ m})} = \boxed{0.11 \text{ rad/s}^2}$

(b) $\omega_f = \omega_i + \alpha\Delta t = 0 + (0.11 \text{ rad/s}^2)(4.0 \text{ s}) = \boxed{0.44 \text{ rad/s}}$

57. Strategy Follow the steps to derive the rotational from of Newton's second law.

Solution

(a) According to Newton's second law, $F_i = m_i a_i$, so $a_i = F_i / m_i$.

(b) The torque is the product of the perpendicular component of the force and the shortest distance between the rotation axis and the point of application of the force, so $\tau_i = F_i r_i = m_i a_i r_i$.

(c) The tangential acceleration is related to the angular acceleration by $a_i = r_i \alpha$, so $\tau_i = m_i (r_i \alpha) r_i = m_i r_i^2 \alpha$.

(d) Summing the torques and using the definition of rotational inertia, we have

$$\sum_{i=1}^{N} \tau_i = \sum_{i=1}^{N} m_i r_i^2 \alpha = \left(\sum_{i=1}^{N} m_i r_i^2 \right) \alpha = I\alpha.$$

61. Strategy The sphere is rolling on a horizontal surface, so its total energy is equal to its total kinetic energy. Use conservation of energy.

Solution Compute the total energy.

$$E_{\text{total}} = K_{\text{tr}} + K_{\text{rot}} = \frac{1}{2}mv^2 + \frac{1}{2}I\omega^2 = \frac{1}{2}mv^2 + \frac{1}{2}\left(\frac{2}{5}mr^2\right)\left(\frac{v}{r}\right)^2 = \frac{1}{2}mv^2 + \frac{1}{5}mv^2 = \frac{7}{10}mv^2$$

$$= \frac{7}{10}(0.600 \text{ kg})(5.00 \text{ m/s})^2 = 10.5 \text{ J}$$

Find the height achieved by the sphere.

$$\Delta U = mgh = -\Delta K = K, \text{ so } h = \frac{K}{mg} = \frac{10.5 \text{ J}}{(0.600 \text{ kg})(9.80 \text{ N/kg})} = \boxed{1.79 \text{ m}}.$$

63. Strategy Let $h = 17.0$ m, m be the mass of the bucket, and M be the mass of the cylinder. The tangential speed of the cylinder is the same as the linear speed of the bucket, since they are attached by a rope. Use conservation of energy and Eq. (4-8). The rotational inertia of a uniform solid cylinder is $\frac{1}{2}MR^2$.

Solution Find the speed of the bucket when it reaches the bottom of the well.

$$\Delta K = \frac{1}{2}mv^2 + \frac{1}{2}I\omega^2 = \frac{1}{2}mv^2 + \frac{1}{2}\left(\frac{1}{2}MR^2\right)\left(\frac{v}{R}\right)^2 = \frac{1}{2}mv^2 + \frac{1}{4}Mv^2 = -\Delta U = mgh, \text{ so } v = \sqrt{\frac{4mgh}{2m+M}}.$$

Compute how long it will take for the bucket to fall to the bottom of the well.

$$\Delta y = h = \frac{1}{2}(v_{\text{f}y} + v_{\text{i}y})\Delta t, \text{ so}$$

$$\Delta t = \frac{2h}{v_{\text{f}y} + v_{\text{i}y}} = \frac{2h}{\sqrt{\frac{4mgh}{2m+M}} + 0} = \sqrt{\frac{h(2m+M)}{mg}} = \sqrt{\frac{(17.0 \text{ m})[2(1.10 \text{ kg}) + 2.60 \text{ kg}]}{(1.10 \text{ kg})(9.80 \text{ m/s}^2)}} = \boxed{2.75 \text{ s}}.$$

65. (a) Strategy Use conservation of energy and the relationship between speed and radial acceleration.

Solution At the top of the loop, the sphere's speed must be at least the speed that results in a radial acceleration of g.

$$\frac{v^2}{r} = g, \text{ so } v^2 = gr.$$

The sphere's kinetic energy is $\frac{1}{2}mv^2 = \frac{1}{2}mgr$, and it must equal the potential energy difference

$mgh - mg(2r)$. Thus, $\frac{1}{2}r = h - 2r$ or $h = \boxed{\dfrac{5}{2}r}$.

(b) Strategy The rotational inertia of a uniform solid sphere is $\frac{2}{5}mr^2$. Use conservation of energy.

Solution Find the kinetic energy of the sphere.

$$K = \frac{1}{2}mv^2 + \frac{1}{2}\left(\frac{2}{5}mr^2\right)\left(\frac{v^2}{r^2}\right) = \frac{7}{10}mv^2 = \frac{7}{10}mgr$$

Find h.

$$\Delta K = \frac{7}{10}mgr = -\Delta U = mgh - mg(2r), \text{ so } h = \boxed{\dfrac{27}{10}r}.$$

69. Strategy The rotational inertia of a uniform disk is $I = \frac{1}{2}MR^2$. Use Eq. (8-14).

Solution Find the magnitude of the angular momentum of the turntable.

$$L = I\omega = \frac{1}{2}MR^2\omega = \frac{1}{2}(5.00 \text{ kg})(0.100 \text{ m})^2(0.550 \text{ rev/s})(2\pi \text{ rad/rev}) = \boxed{0.0864 \text{ kg}\cdot\text{m}^2/\text{s}}$$

73. Strategy Since the torque is constant, it is equal to the change in angular momentum divided by the time interval.

Solution Find the time to stop the spinning wheel

$$\tau = \frac{\Delta L}{\Delta t}, \text{ so } \Delta t = \frac{\Delta L}{\tau} = \frac{-6.40 \text{ kg}\cdot\text{m}^2/\text{s}}{-4.00 \text{ N}\cdot\text{m}} = \boxed{1.60 \text{ s}}.$$

75. Strategy Use conservation of angular momentum and Eq. (8-14).

Solution Find the skater's final angular velocity.

$$L_i = I_i\omega_i = L_f = I_f\omega_f, \text{ so } \omega_f = \frac{I_i}{I_f}\omega_i = \frac{2.50}{1.60}(10.0 \text{ rad/s}) = \boxed{15.6 \text{ rad/s}}.$$

77. Strategy The rotational inertias of the wheel and guinea pig are $I_w = MR^2$ and $I_g = mR^2$, respectively, where M is the mass of the wheel, m is the mass of the guinea pig, and R is the radius of the wheel. Use conservation of angular momentum and $v = r\omega$.

Solution Find the angular velocity of the wheel.

$$L_w = L_g, \text{ so } I_w\omega_w = MR^2\omega_w = I_g\omega_g = mR^2\omega_g = mRv_g.$$

Thus, $\omega_w = \dfrac{mv_g}{MR} = \dfrac{(0.500 \text{ kg})(0.200 \text{ m/s})}{(2.00 \text{ kg})(0.400 \text{ m})} = \boxed{0.125 \text{ rad/s}}.$

81. Strategy The average torque is equal to the magnitude of the change in angular momentum divided by the time interval.

Solution Let $\vec{L}_i = L$ in the $+y$-direction. Then $\Delta\vec{L}$ has components $\Delta L_x = L\sin\theta$ and $\Delta L_y = L\cos\theta - L = L(\cos\theta - 1)$. So,

$$|\Delta\vec{L}| = \sqrt{(L\sin\theta)^2 + [L(\cos\theta - 1)]^2} = L\sqrt{\sin^2 60.0° + (\cos 60.0° - 1)^2} = 1.00L.$$

Compute the magnitude of the required torque.

$$\tau = \left|\frac{\Delta\vec{L}}{\Delta t}\right| = \frac{1.00L}{\Delta t} = \frac{1.00I\omega}{\Delta t} = \frac{\frac{1}{2}mr^2\omega}{\Delta t}$$

$$= \frac{(1.00\times10^5 \text{ kg})(2.00 \text{ m})^2(300.0 \text{ rpm})}{2(3.00 \text{ s})}\left(\frac{2\pi \text{ rad}}{\text{rev}}\right)\left(\frac{1 \text{ min}}{60 \text{ s}}\right) = \boxed{2.10\times10^6 \text{ N}\cdot\text{m}}$$

85. Strategy Use Eq. (8-3). The force due to the weight is mg.

Solution Find the torque.

$$\tau = F_\perp r = mgr = (10.0 \text{ kg})(9.80 \text{ N/kg})(1.0 \text{ m}) = \boxed{98 \text{ N}\cdot\text{m}}$$

87. Strategy The rotational inertia of the gymnast is $\frac{1}{3}m(2r)^2$, where $r = 1.0$ m. Use conservation of energy.

Solution Find the angular speed at the bottom of the swing.

$$\Delta K = \frac{1}{2}I\omega^2 = \frac{1}{2}\left[\frac{1}{3}m(2r)^2\right]\omega^2 = \frac{2}{3}mr^2\omega^2 = -\Delta U = mg(2r) = 2rmg, \text{ so}$$

$$\omega = \sqrt{\frac{3g}{r}} = \sqrt{\frac{3(9.80 \text{ m/s}^2)}{1.0 \text{ m}}} = \boxed{5.4 \text{ rad/s}}.$$

89. Strategy Use conservation of energy.

Solution Find the final speeds of each object.
Solid sphere:

$$\Delta K = K_{tr} + K_{rot} = \frac{1}{2}mv^2 + \frac{1}{2}I\omega^2 = \frac{1}{2}mv^2 + \frac{1}{2}\left(\frac{2}{5}mr^2\right)\left(\frac{v}{r}\right)^2 = \frac{1}{2}mv^2 + \frac{1}{5}mv^2 = \frac{7}{10}mv^2 = -\Delta U = U_i - U_f = mgh,$$

so $v = \sqrt{\dfrac{10gh}{7}}$.

Hollow sphere:

$$\frac{1}{2}mv^2 + \frac{1}{2}\left(\frac{2}{3}mr^2\right)\left(\frac{v}{r}\right)^2 = \frac{1}{2}mv^2 + \frac{1}{3}mv^2 = \frac{5}{6}mv^2 = mgh, \text{ so } v = \sqrt{\frac{6gh}{5}}.$$

Solid cylinder:

$$\frac{1}{2}mv^2 + \frac{1}{2}\left(\frac{1}{2}mr^2\right)\left(\frac{v}{r}\right)^2 = \frac{1}{2}mv^2 + \frac{1}{4}mv^2 = \frac{3}{4}mv^2 = mgh, \text{ so } v = \sqrt{\frac{4gh}{3}}.$$

Hollow cylinder:

$$\frac{1}{2}mv^2 + \frac{1}{2}(mr^2)\left(\frac{v}{r}\right)^2 = \frac{1}{2}mv^2 + \frac{1}{2}mv^2 = mv^2 = mgh, \text{ so } v = \sqrt{gh}.$$

Cube:

$\frac{1}{2}mv^2 = mgh$, so $v = \sqrt{2gh}$.

So, $v_{\text{cube}} > v_{\text{solid sphere}} > v_{\text{solid cylinder}} > v_{\text{hollow sphere}} > v_{\text{hollow cylinder}}$.

The objects reach the bottom in the following order from first to last: cube, solid sphere, solid cylinder, hollow sphere, and hollow cylinder.

93. **(a) Strategy** The rotational inertia of a uniform solid disk is $I = \frac{1}{2}MR^2$.

Solution Compute the rotational inertia.

$$I = \frac{1}{2}MR^2 = \frac{1}{2}(200.0 \text{ kg})(0.40 \text{ m})^2 = \boxed{16 \text{ kg} \cdot \text{m}^2}$$

(b) Strategy Use Eq. (8-1).

Solution Compute the initial rotational kinetic energy.

$$K_{\text{rot}} = \frac{1}{2}I\omega^2 = \frac{1}{2}(16 \text{ kg} \cdot \text{m}^2)(3160 \text{ rad/s})^2 = \boxed{8.0 \times 10^7 \text{ J}}$$

(c) Strategy and Solution The ratio of the rotational to the translational kinetic energies is

$$\frac{K_{\text{rot}}}{K_{\text{tr}}} = \frac{K_{\text{rot}}}{\frac{1}{2}mv^2} = \frac{2(8.0 \times 10^7 \text{ J})}{(1000.0 \text{ kg})(22.4 \text{ m/s})^2} = \boxed{320}.$$

(d) Strategy Set the work done by air resistance equal to the stored energy in the flywheel.

Solution Find the distance d the car can travel.

$$Fd = K_{\text{rot}}, \text{ so } d = \frac{K_{\text{rot}}}{F} = \frac{8.0 \times 10^7 \text{ J}}{670.0 \text{ N}} = \boxed{120 \text{ km}}.$$

97. **Strategy** The system is in equilibrium. Use Eqs. (8-8).

Solution Find h.

$$\frac{h}{(1.26 \text{ m})/2} = \tan 75°, \text{ so } h = [(1.26 \text{ m})/2]\tan 75° = (0.630 \text{ m})\tan 75°.$$

At the top of the ladder, each leg exerts a horizontal force on the other. These forces are equal in magnitude and opposite in direction, since the system is in equilibrium. Let the magnitude of this force be F. The tension T in the rope is directed to the left at the connection point on the right leg, so for the right leg, we have $\Sigma F_x = F - T = 0$ or $T = F$.

Calculate the torque about the contact point of the right leg of the ladder and the ground.

$$\Sigma \tau = (0.630 \text{ m})mg - Fh = 0, \text{ so } T = F = \frac{(0.630 \text{ m})mg}{h} = \frac{(0.630 \text{ m})mg}{(0.630 \text{ m})\tan 75°} = \frac{mg}{\tan 75°}.$$

The tension in the rope is the same along its length, so

$$T_{\text{rope}} = \frac{mg}{\tan 75°} = \frac{(42 \text{ kg})(9.80 \text{ N/kg})}{\tan 75°} = \boxed{110 \text{ N}}.$$

101. Strategy The rotational inertial of a uniform disk is $I = \frac{1}{2}MR^2$. Use Eq. (8-14).

Solution Find the magnitude of the angular momentum of the disk.
$$L = I\omega = \frac{1}{2}MR^2\omega = \frac{1}{2}(2.0 \text{ kg})(0.100 \text{ m})^2(3.0 \text{ rev/s})(2\pi \text{ rad/rev}) = \boxed{0.19 \text{ kg} \cdot \text{m}^2/\text{s}}$$

105. Strategy The system is in equilibrium. Choose the axis of rotation at the ankle.

Solution Find the force that each calf muscle needs to exert while the woman is standing.
$\Sigma\tau = 0 = 2F(4.4 \text{ cm})\sin 81° - mg(3.0 \text{ cm})$, so
$$F = \frac{mg(3.0 \text{ cm})}{2(4.4 \text{ cm})\sin 81°} = \frac{(68 \text{ kg})(9.80 \text{ N/kg})(3.0 \text{ cm})}{2(4.4 \text{ cm})\sin 81°} = \boxed{230 \text{ N}}.$$

109. Strategy Since the bike travels with constant velocity, the acceleration is zero and $\Sigma\tau = 0$.

Solution Find the magnitude of the force with which the chain pulls.
$\Sigma\tau = 0 = fr_2 - F_C r_1$, so $F_C = \frac{r_2}{r_1}f = 6.0(3.8 \text{ N}) = \boxed{23 \text{ N}}$.

113. Strategy Choose the axis of rotation at the contact point between the horizontal surface and the tip of the left leg.

Solution Find the maximum wind speeds in which the blowfly and dog can stand.

(a) $\tau_{\text{net}} = 0 = F_{\text{wind}}r\sin\theta - mgr\cos\theta$, so
$$\frac{mg}{\tan\theta} = F_{\text{wind}} = cAv^2 \text{ or } v = \sqrt{\frac{mg}{cA\tan\theta}} = \sqrt{\frac{(0.070\times10^{-3} \text{ kg})(9.80 \text{ m/s}^2)}{(1.3 \text{ N}\cdot\text{s}^2/\text{m}^4)(0.10\times10^{-4} \text{ m}^2)\tan 30.0°}} = \boxed{9.6 \text{ m/s}}.$$

(b) $v = \sqrt{\frac{(0.070\times10^{-3} \text{ kg})(9.80 \text{ m/s}^2)}{(1.3 \text{ N}\cdot\text{s}^2/\text{m}^4)(0.10\times10^{-4} \text{ m}^2)\tan 80.0°}} = \boxed{3.1 \text{ m/s}}$

(c) $v = \sqrt{\frac{(10.0 \text{ kg})(9.80 \text{ m/s}^2)}{(1.3 \text{ N}\cdot\text{s}^2/\text{m}^4)(0.030 \text{ m}^2)\tan 80.0°}} = \boxed{21 \text{ m/s}}$

REVIEW AND SYNTHESIS: CHAPTERS 6–8

Review Exercises

1. **(a) Strategy** Multiply the extension per mass by the mass to find the maximum extension required.

   Solution
   $$\left(\frac{1.0 \text{ mm}}{25 \text{ g}}\right)(5.0 \text{ kg})\left(\frac{1000 \text{ g}}{1 \text{ kg}}\right)\left(\frac{1 \text{ m}}{1000 \text{ mm}}\right) = \boxed{0.20 \text{ m}}$$

   (b) Strategy Set the weight of the mass equal to the magnitude of the force due to the spring scale. Use Hooke's law.

   Solution
   $$\text{Weight} = mg = kx, \text{ so } k = \frac{mg}{x} = \frac{(5.0 \text{ kg})(9.80 \text{ N/kg})}{0.20 \text{ m}} = \boxed{250 \text{ N/m}}.$$

5. **(a) Strategy** Use the conservation of energy.

   Solution Find the work done by friction.
   $$W_{\text{total}} = W_{\text{friction}} + W_{\text{grav}} = W_{\text{friction}} + mgd \sin\theta = \Delta K = 0 - \frac{1}{2}mv_i^2, \text{ so}$$

   $$W_{\text{friction}} = -\frac{1}{2}mv_i^2 - mgd\sin\theta = -m\left(\frac{1}{2}v_i^2 + gd\sin\theta\right)$$

   $$= -(100 \text{ kg})\left[\frac{1}{2}(2.00 \text{ m/s})^2 + (9.80 \text{ m/s}^2)(1.50 \text{ m})\sin 30.0°\right]$$

   $$= -940 \text{ J}.$$

   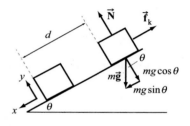

   Thus, the energy dissipated by friction was $\boxed{940 \text{ J}}$.

   (b) Strategy Use Newton's second law.

   Solution Find the normal force on the crate.
   $$\Sigma F_y = N - mg\cos\theta = 0, \text{ so } N = mg\cos\theta.$$

   Since $v_{fx}^2 - v_{ix}^2 = 0 - v_i^2 = 2a_x\Delta x = 2a_x d,$ the acceleration of the crate is $-v_i^2/(2d).$
   Find the force of sliding friction.

   $$\Sigma F_x = -f_k + mg\sin\theta = -\mu_k mg\cos\theta + mg\sin\theta = ma_x = -m\frac{v_i^2}{2d}, \text{ so}$$

   $$\mu_k = \tan\theta + \frac{v_i^2}{2dg\cos\theta} = \tan 30.0° + \frac{(2.00 \text{ m/s})^2}{2(1.50 \text{ m})(9.80 \text{ m/s}^2)\cos 30.0°} = \boxed{0.734}.$$

9. Strategy The collision is inelastic. Use conservation of momentum and energy.

Solution Write equations using conservation of momentum and energy.

momentum: $mv_i = (m+M)v_f$

energy: $\frac{1}{2}(m+M)v_f^2 = (m+M)g\Delta y$

Find the initial speed of the putty.

$$\frac{1}{2}(m+M)\left(\frac{mv_i}{m+M}\right)^2 = (m+M)g\Delta y$$

$$\left(\frac{m}{m+M}\right)^2 v_i^2 = 2g\Delta y$$

$$v_i = \sqrt{2g\Delta y\left(\frac{m+M}{m}\right)^2} = \sqrt{2(9.8 \text{ m/s}^2)(1.50 \text{ m})\left(\frac{0.50 \text{ kg}+2.30 \text{ kg}}{0.50 \text{ kg}}\right)^2} = \boxed{30 \text{ m/s}}$$

13. Strategy Use conservation of energy. Let $d = 2.05$ m. Then, the ramp rises $h = d\sin 5.00°$. The rotational inertia of a uniform sphere is $\frac{2}{5}mr^2$.

Solution Find the speed of the ball when it reaches the top of the ramp.

$$0 = \Delta K + \Delta U = \frac{1}{2}mv_f^2 + \frac{1}{2}I\omega_f^2 - \frac{1}{2}mv_i^2 - \frac{1}{2}I\omega_i^2 + mgh$$

$$= \frac{1}{2}mv_f^2 + \frac{1}{2}\left(\frac{2}{5}mr^2\right)\left(\frac{v_f}{r}\right)^2 - \frac{1}{2}mv_i^2 - \frac{1}{2}\left(\frac{2}{5}mr^2\right)\left(\frac{v_i}{r}\right)^2 + mgh$$

$$= \frac{7}{10}mv_f^2 - \frac{7}{10}mv_i^2 + mgh, \text{ so}$$

$$v_f = \sqrt{v_i^2 - \frac{10}{7}gh} = \sqrt{(2.20 \text{ m/s})^2 - \frac{10}{7}(9.80 \text{ m/s}^2)(2.05 \text{ m})\sin 5.00°} = \boxed{1.53 \text{ m/s}}.$$

17. Strategy Use conservation of energy. The energy delivered to the fluid in the beaker plus the kinetic energies of the pulley, spool, axle, paddles, and the block are equal to the work done by gravity on the block, which is negative the change in the block's gravitational potential energy. The rotational inertia of the pulley (uniform solid disk) is $\frac{1}{2}m_p r^2$.

Solution Let the energy delivered to the fluid be E, the distance the block falls be h, and the rotational inertia of the spool, axle, and paddles be $I_s = 0.00140$ kg·m². Since the radii of the pulley and the spool are the same (r), their tangential speeds are the same, so let $v_p = v_s = v$.

$$m_b gh = \frac{1}{2}m_b v_b^2 + \frac{1}{2}I_p\omega_p^2 + \frac{1}{2}I_s\omega_s^2 + E = \frac{1}{2}m_b v_b^2 + \frac{1}{2}\left(\frac{1}{2}m_p r^2\right)\left(\frac{v}{r}\right)^2 + \frac{1}{2}I_s\left(\frac{v}{r}\right)^2 + E$$

The tangential speeds of the pulley and spool are equal to the speed of the block.

$$m_b gh = \frac{1}{2}m_b v_b^2 + \frac{1}{4}m_p v^2 + \frac{1}{2}I_s\frac{v^2}{r^2} + E = \frac{1}{2}m_b v^2 + \frac{1}{4}m_p v^2 + \frac{1}{2}I_s\frac{v^2}{r^2} + E, \text{ so}$$

$$E = m_b gh - \frac{v^2(2m_b + m_p + 2I_s/r^2)}{4}$$

$$= (0.870 \text{ kg})(9.80 \text{ m/s}^2)(2.50 \text{ m}) - \frac{(3.00 \text{ m/s})^2[2(0.870 \text{ kg}) + 0.0600 \text{ kg} + 2(0.00140 \text{ kg·m}^2)/(0.0300 \text{ m})^2]}{4}$$

$$= \boxed{10.3 \text{ J}}.$$

21. **Strategy** Use energy conservation to find the speed of Jones just before he grabs Smith. Then, use momentum conservation to find the speed of both just after. Finally, again use energy conservation to find the final height.

Solution Find Jones's speed, v_J.

$$\frac{1}{2}m_J v_J^2 = m_J gh_J, \text{ so } v_J = \sqrt{2gh_J}.$$

Find the speed of both, v.

$$p_i = m_J v_J = p_f = (m_J + m_S)v, \text{ so } v = \frac{m_J v_J}{m_J + m_S} = \frac{m_J \sqrt{2gh_J}}{m_J + m_S}.$$

Find the final height, h.

$$(m_J + m_S)gh = \frac{1}{2}(m_J + m_S)\left(\frac{m_J \sqrt{2gh_J}}{m_J + m_S}\right)^2, \text{ so } h = \frac{m_J^2 h_J}{(m_J + m_S)^2} = \frac{(78.0 \text{ kg})^2 (3.70 \text{ m})}{(78.0 \text{ kg} + 55.0 \text{ kg})^2} = \boxed{1.27 \text{ m}}.$$

25. **Strategy** Use conservation of linear momentum.

Solution

$$p_{ix} = m_b v_b = p_{fx} = (m_b + m_c)v_{fx}, \text{ so } v_{fx} = \frac{m_b v_b}{m_b + m_c}.$$

$$p_{iy} = m_c v_c = p_{fy} = (m_b + m_c)v_{fy}, \text{ so } v_{fy} = \frac{m_c v_c}{m_b + m_c}.$$

Compute the magnitude of the final velocity.

$$v = \sqrt{v_{fx}^2 + v_{fy}^2} = \sqrt{\left(\frac{m_b v_b}{m_b + m_c}\right)^2 + \left(\frac{m_c v_c}{m_b + m_c}\right)^2} = \frac{\sqrt{(m_b v_b)^2 + (m_c v_c)^2}}{m_b + m_c}$$

$$= \frac{\sqrt{[(2.00 \text{ kg})(2.70 \text{ m/s})]^2 + [(1.50 \text{ kg})(-3.20 \text{ m/s})]^2}}{2.00 \text{ kg} + 1.50 \text{ kg}} = 2.06 \text{ m/s}$$

Compute the angle.

$$\theta = \tan^{-1}\frac{v_{fy}}{v_{fx}} = \tan^{-1}\frac{\frac{m_c v_c}{m_b + m_c}}{\frac{m_b v_b}{m_b + m_c}} = \tan^{-1}\frac{m_c v_c}{m_b v_b} = \tan^{-1}\frac{(1.50 \text{ kg})(-3.20 \text{ m/s})}{(2.00 \text{ kg})(2.70 \text{ m/s})} = -41.6°$$

The velocity of the block and the clay after the collision is $\boxed{2.06 \text{ m/s at } 41.6° \text{ S of E}}$.

29. (a) Strategy Consider the work-kinetic energy theorem and the impulse momentum theorem.

Solution Since the Romulan ship is twice as massive as the Vulcan ship, the Romulan ship will not travel as far as the Vulcan ship for the same engine force, since $\Delta x = (1/2)a(\Delta t)^2 = (1/2)(F/m)(\Delta t)^2$. Since $W = F\Delta x = \Delta K$, $\boxed{\text{the Vulcan ship will have the greater kinetic energy}}$. Since $\Delta p = F\Delta t$, $\boxed{\text{the ships will have the same momentum}}$.

(b) Strategy Consider the work-kinetic energy theorem and the impulse momentum theorem.

Solution Since the distances and the forces are the same, and since $W = F\Delta x = \Delta K$, $\boxed{\text{the ships will have the same kinetic energy}}$. Since $\Delta x = (1/2)a(\Delta t)^2 = (1/2)(F/m)(\Delta t)^2$, the more massive Romulan ship will have to fire its engines longer than the Vulcan ship to travel the same distance. Since $\Delta p = F\Delta t$ and the forces are the same, $\boxed{\text{the Romulan ship will have the greater momentum}}$.

(c) Strategy Refer to parts (a) and (b).

Solution For part (a), we have the following:
Vulcan:

$$\Delta K = W = F\Delta x = F\left[\frac{F}{2m}(\Delta t)^2\right] = \frac{(9.5\times10^6 \text{ N})^2(100 \text{ s})^2}{2(65,000 \text{ kg})} = 6.9\times10^{12} \text{ J}$$

$$\Delta p = F\Delta t = (9.5\times10^6 \text{ N})(100 \text{ s}) = 9.5\times10^8 \text{ kg}\cdot\text{m/s}$$

Romulan:

$$\Delta K = W = F\Delta x = F\left[\frac{F}{2m}(\Delta t)^2\right] = \frac{(9.5\times10^6 \text{ N})^2(100 \text{ s})^2}{2(130,000 \text{ kg})} = 3.5\times10^{12} \text{ J}$$

$$\Delta p = F\Delta t = (9.5\times10^6 \text{ N})(100 \text{ s}) = 9.5\times10^8 \text{ kg}\cdot\text{m/s}$$

$\boxed{\text{In part (a), the momenta are the same, } 9.5\times10^8 \text{ kg}\cdot\text{m/s, but the kinetic energies differ: Vulcan at } 6.9\times10^{12} \text{ J and Romulan at } 3.5\times10^{12} \text{ J.}}$

For part (b), we have the following:
Vulcan:

$$\Delta K = W = F\Delta x = (9.5\times10^6 \text{ N})(100 \text{ m}) = 9.5\times10^8 \text{ J}$$

Since $K = \frac{1}{2}mv^2 = \frac{p^2}{2m}$, $p = \sqrt{2mK} = \sqrt{2(65,000 \text{ kg})(9.5\times10^8 \text{ J})} = 1.1\times10^7 \text{ kg}\cdot\text{m/s}$.

Romulan:

$$\Delta K = W = F\Delta x = (9.5\times10^6 \text{ N})(100 \text{ m}) = 9.5\times10^8 \text{ J}$$

$$p = \sqrt{2mK} = \sqrt{2(2\times65,000 \text{ kg})(9.5\times10^8 \text{ J})} = 1.6\times10^7 \text{ kg}\cdot\text{m/s}.$$

$\boxed{\text{In part (b), the kinetic energies are the same, } 9.5\times10^8 \text{ J, but the momenta differ: Vulcan at } 1.1\times10^7 \text{ kg}\cdot\text{m/s and Romulan at } 1.6\times10^7 \text{ kg}\cdot\text{m/s.}}$

33. **Strategy** Use conservation of energy. m is the mass of one wheel. M is the total mass of the system. v is the speed of the center of mass of the system (which is the same as the speed of a point on either wheel).

Solution

(a) $K_{rot} = \dfrac{1}{2}I\omega^2 = \dfrac{1}{2}mv^2 = K_{trans}$ for one wheel. $K_{rot,total} = 2 \cdot \dfrac{1}{2}mv^2 = mv^2$ and $K_{trans,total} = \dfrac{1}{2}Mv^2$.

$$K_{total} = U_i$$
$$mv^2 + \dfrac{1}{2}Mv^2 = MgH$$
$$v^2(2m + M) = 2MgH$$
$$v = \sqrt{\dfrac{2MgH}{2m + M}} = \sqrt{\dfrac{2(80.0\ \text{kg})(9.8\ \text{m/s}^2)(20.0\ \text{m})}{2(1.5\ \text{kg}) + 80.0\ \text{kg}}} = \boxed{19\ \text{m/s}}$$

(b) Since the speed depends upon the combined total mass of the system, the speed at the bottom would not be the same for a less massive rider. The answer is $\boxed{\text{no}}$.

MCAT Review

1. **Strategy** Use conservation of momentum.

   Solution
   $p_i = mv_i = p_f = mv_f + p_{wall}$, so $p_{wall} = m(v_i - v_f) = (0.2\ \text{kg})[2.0\ \text{m/s} - (-1.0\ \text{m/s})] = 0.6\ \text{kg} \cdot \text{m/s}$.
   The correct answer is $\boxed{D}$.

2. **Strategy** Use Hooke's law.

   Solution Let up be the positive direction. The gravitational force on the mass is
   $F = mg = (0.10\ \text{kg})(-9.80\ \text{m/s}^2) = -0.98\ \text{N}$. Solving for the spring constant in Hooke's law, we have
   $k = -\dfrac{F}{x} = -\dfrac{-0.98\ \text{N}}{0.15\ \text{m}} = 6.5\ \text{N/m}$. Thus, the correct answer is $\boxed{D}$.

3. **Strategy** The net torque is zero.

   Solution
   $\Sigma\tau = 0 = F(0.60\ \text{m}) - (1.0 \times 10^{-7}\ \text{kg})(9.80\ \text{m/s}^2)(0.40\ \text{m})$, so
   $F = \dfrac{(1.0 \times 10^{-7}\ \text{kg})(9.80\ \text{m/s}^2)(0.40\ \text{m})}{0.60\ \text{m}} = 6.5 \times 10^{-7}\ \text{N}$.
   The correct answer is $\boxed{B}$.

4. **Strategy** Determine the speed of the first ball just before in collides with the second. The collision is completely inelastic; that is, the balls stick together. Use conservation of momentum to find the speed of the balls after the collision.

   Solution Find the speed of the first ball just before the collision.

   $v_{fx} - v_{ix} = v_1 - 0 = a_x \Delta t$, so $v_1 = (10 \text{ m/s}^2)(2.0 \text{ s}) = 20 \text{ m/s}$.

   Find the speed v of the balls just after the collision.

   $$p_i = m_1 v_1 = p_f = (m_1 + m_2)v, \text{ so } v = \frac{m_1 v_1}{m_1 + m_2} = \frac{(0.50 \text{ kg})(20 \text{ m/s})}{0.50 \text{ kg} + 1.0 \text{ kg}} = 6.7 \text{ m/s}.$$

   The correct answer is $\boxed{\text{B}}$.

5. **Strategy** Use Newton's second law and Eq. (6-27).

   Solution The gravitational force working against the motion of the car as it climbs the hill is $mg \sin 10°$, so the additional power required is

   $$P_{car} = -P_{grav} = -Fv\cos 180° = (mg \sin 10°)v = (1000 \text{ kg})(10 \text{ m/s}^2)\sin 10°(15 \text{ m/s})$$
   $$= 1.5 \times 10^5 \times \sin 10° \text{ W}.$$

   The correct answer is $\boxed{\text{D}}$.

6. **Strategy** Find the vertical distance the patient would have climbed had the treadmill been stationary (and very long). Then, find the work done by the patient on the treadmill.

   Solution The "distance" walked along the incline is $(2 \text{ m/s})(600 \text{ s}) = 1200 \text{ m}$.

   Thus, the vertical distance climbed is $(1200 \text{ m})\sin 30° = 600 \text{ m}$. The work done is

   $$W = Fd = mgd = (90 \text{ kg})(10 \text{ m/s}^2)(600 \text{ m}) = 0.54 \text{ MJ}.$$

   The correct answer is $\boxed{\text{C}}$.

7. **Strategy** Find the angle between the force exerted by the patient and the patient's velocity. Use Eq. (6-27).

   Solution The force due to gravity is down, so the force exerted by the patient is up. The velocity is directed at the angle of the incline, or 30° above the horizontal, so the angle between the force and the velocity is 60°. Compute the mechanical power output of the patient.

   $$P = Fv\cos\theta = mgv\cos\theta = (100 \text{ kg})(10 \text{ m/s}^2)(3 \text{ m/s})\cos 60° = 1500 \text{ W}$$

   The correct answer is $\boxed{\text{B}}$.

8. **Strategy and Solution** The force pushing each friction pad is normal to the wheel; that is, it is the normal force in $f_k = \mu_k N$. Solve for the normal force.

   $$N = \frac{f_k}{\mu_k} = \frac{20 \text{ N}}{0.4} = 50 \text{ N}$$

   This is the total force. The force pushing each friction pad is half this, or 25 N. The correct answer is $\boxed{\text{B}}$.

9. **Strategy** Find the average tangential speed at the friction pads. Then, use the relationship between tangential speed and radial acceleration.

Solution

The average tangential speed is $v = \dfrac{4800 \text{ m}}{20 \text{ min}} \times \dfrac{1 \text{ min}}{60 \text{ s}} = 4.0$ m/s. The radial acceleration is

$a_r = \dfrac{v^2}{r} = \dfrac{(4.0 \text{ m/s})^2}{0.3 \text{ m}} = 50$ m/s^2. The correct answer is $\boxed{D}$.

10. **Strategy** Use the work-kinetic energy theorem.

Solution The work done by friction on the wheel is $W = -f_k d$, where d is the linear distance the wheel passes between the pads before it stops. Relate d to the kinetic energy of the wheel.

$W_{total} = -f_k d = \Delta K = 0 - K_i$, so $d = \dfrac{K_i}{f_k}$.

Divide d by the circumference of a circle with radius 0.3 m to find the number of rotations.

$\dfrac{d}{2\pi r} = \dfrac{K_i}{2\pi r f_k} = \dfrac{30 \text{ J}}{2\pi (0.3 \text{ m})(20 \text{ N})} = 0.8$ rotations

Since $0.8 < 1$, the correct answer is $\boxed{A}$.

11. **Strategy** Compute the average mechanical power output of the cyclist and compare it to the power consumed by the wheel at the friction pads.

Solution The metabolic power available for work is $535 \text{ W} - 85 \text{ W} = 450$ W. Since the efficiency is 20%, the average mechanical power output of the cyclist is $0.20 \times 450 \text{ W} = 90$ W. The average tangential speed of the wheel is $v = \dfrac{4800 \text{ m}}{20 \text{ min}} \times \dfrac{1 \text{ min}}{60 \text{ s}} = 4.0$ m/s. Therefore, the power consumed by the friction pads is $P = f_k v = (20 \text{ N})(4.0 \text{ m/s}) = 80$ W. Thus, the difference between the average mechanical power output of the cyclist and the power consumed by the wheel at the friction pads is $90 \text{ W} - 80 \text{ W} = 10$ W.
The correct answer is $\boxed{B}$.

12. **Strategy and Solution** Increasing the force on the friction pads would increase the power consumed by the wheel at the friction pads (because $P = Fv$). So, if the cyclist is pedaling at the same rate and the power consumed by the friction pads increases, the difference between the two decreases and the fraction of mechanical power output of the cyclist consumed by the wheel at the friction pad increases. Thus, the correct answer is $\boxed{D}$.

13. **Strategy** Relate the cyclist's average metabolic rate to the energy released per volume of oxygen consumed, the time on the bike, and volume of oxygen consumed.

Solution The cyclist's average metabolic rate while riding is 535 W. The total energy used during 20 minutes is $(535 \text{ W})(20 \text{ min})\dfrac{60 \text{ s}}{1 \text{ min}} = 642{,}000$ J. The total energy released by the consumption of oxygen is $(20{,}000 \text{ J/L})V$, where V is the volume of oxygen consumed. Equating these two expressions and solving for V gives the number of liters of oxygen the cyclist consumes.

$(20{,}000 \text{ J/L})V = 642{,}000$ J, so $V = \dfrac{642{,}000 \text{ J}}{20{,}000 \text{ J/L}} = 32 \text{ L} \approx 30$ L. The correct answer is $\boxed{B}$.

14. **Strategy and Solution** Since the force has been reduced by 50% and the distance has been doubled, the cyclist does the same amount of work $[W = 0.50F(2\Delta x) = F\Delta x]$. So, the energy transmitted in the second workout is equal to the energy transmitted in the first. The correct answer is $\boxed{C}$.

15. **Strategy** The circumference of a circle is $C = 2\pi r$. A wheel moves a distance equal to its circumference during each rotation. The wheel rotates twice during each rotation of the pedals.

    Solution The circumference of a circle with a radius of 0.15 m is $2\pi(0.15 \text{ m})$. The circumference of a circle with a radius of 0.3 m is $2\pi(0.3 \text{ m})$. During each rotation of the pedals, a point on the wheel at a radius of 0.3 m moves a distance $2[2\pi(0.3 \text{ m})]$. The ratio of the distance moved by a pedal to the distance moved by a point on the wheel located at a radius of 0.3 m in the same amount of time is $\dfrac{2\pi(0.15 \text{ m})}{2[2\pi(0.3 \text{ m})]} = 0.25$.

    The correct answer is $\boxed{A}$.

16. **Strategy** Use the definition of power.

    Solution
    $$P = \frac{\Delta E}{\Delta t}, \text{ so } \Delta t = \frac{\Delta E}{P} = \left(\frac{300 \text{ kcal}}{500 \text{ W}}\right)\left(\frac{4186 \text{ J}}{1 \text{ kcal}}\right)\left(\frac{1 \text{ min}}{60 \text{ s}}\right) = 41.9 \text{ min. The correct answer is } \boxed{D}.$$

17. **Strategy** Consider the distance a point on the wheel travels for each situation.

    Solution The circumference of a circle with a radius of 0.3 m is $2\pi(0.3 \text{ m})$. The circumference of a circle with a radius of 0.4 m is $2\pi(0.4 \text{ m})$. During each rotation, a point on a wheel travels a distance equal to the circumference. The force on the wheel is the same in each case, but the distance traveled by a point on the wheel is greater for a greater radius. In this case, the distance is $0.4 \text{ m}/(0.3 \text{ m}) = 1.33$ times farther or 33%. Since work is equal to the product of force times distance, the work done on the wheel per revolution is 33% more. Thus, the correct answer is $\boxed{C}$.

Chapter 9

FLUIDS

Conceptual Questions

1. A manometer (with one side open) measures gauge pressure. A barometer measures absolute pressure. A tire pressure gauge and a sphygmomanometer both measure gauge pressure.

5. There is practically no atmosphere on the Moon and hence practically zero pressure. Drinking from a glass with a straw would be impossible, since a pressure difference is required to push the liquid up the straw. With a sealed juice box, the astronaut could supply the necessary pressure by squeezing the box.

9. The pressure of the atmosphere decreases with altitude. Therefore, the balloon gradually expands as it rises.

13. The rate at which air moves up a chimney is determined by the size of the pressure change along the chimney's length. Bernoulli's equation tells us that on a windless day, the pressure difference between the two ends of the chimney is proportional to the height of the chimney. On a windy day, the velocity difference between the two ends causes an additional pressure difference—resulting in an increased draft.

17. To get optimal use from hydraulic systems, the fluid used in mediating the operation of the system must be very nearly incompressible. Liquids meet this requirement, but gases like air are compressible. Thus, proper operation of a hydraulic device requires that gases be "bled" from the system.

Problems

1. **Strategy** Use the definition of average pressure.

   Solution Compute the average pressure.

   $$P_{av} = \frac{F}{A} = \frac{500 \text{ N}}{1.0 \text{ cm}^2}\left(\frac{100 \text{ cm}}{1 \text{ m}}\right)^2\left(\frac{1 \text{ atm}}{101.3 \times 10^3 \text{ Pa}}\right) = \boxed{49 \text{ atm}}$$

5. **Strategy** The average pressure is the force applied to the floor divided by the contact area.

   Solution

   The baby applies a pressure of $P_b = \dfrac{F}{A} = \dfrac{m_b g}{3\left(\frac{1}{4}\pi d_s^2\right)} = \dfrac{4m_b g}{3\pi d_s^2}$.

   The adult applies a pressure of $P_a = \dfrac{F}{A} = \dfrac{m_a g}{4\left(\frac{1}{4}\pi d_c^2\right)} = \dfrac{m_a g}{\pi d_c^2}$.

   The ratio of these two pressures is $\dfrac{P_b}{P_a} = \dfrac{4m_b g}{3\pi d_s^2}\left(\dfrac{m_a g}{\pi d_c^2}\right)^{-1} = \dfrac{4m_b d_c^2}{3m_a d_s^2} = \dfrac{4(10 \text{ kg})(0.060 \text{ m})^2}{3(60 \text{ kg})(0.020 \text{ m})^2} = 2.0.$

   $\boxed{\text{The baby applies 2.0 times as much pressure as the adult.}}$

9. Strategy The work done by the small piston must equal that done on the car.

Solution Find the distance that the small piston must be pushed downward to raise the car 1.0 cm.
$F_c/F_p = A/a$ since $\Delta P = F_c/A = F_p/a$.

$$W_p = F_p d_p = W_c = F_c d_c, \text{ so } d_p = \frac{F_c}{F_p} d_c = \frac{A}{a} d_c = 100.0(0.010 \text{ m}) = \boxed{1.0 \text{ m}}.$$

13. Strategy Use Eq. (9-4).

Solution Compute the pressure on the fish.

$$P = P_{atm} + \rho g d = 1.0 \text{ atm} + (1025 \text{ kg/m}^3)(9.80 \text{ m/s}^2)(10 \text{ m})\left(\frac{1 \text{ atm}}{1.013 \times 10^5 \text{ Pa}}\right) = \boxed{2.0 \text{ atm}}$$

17. Strategy Use the definition of average pressure and Eq. (9-4).

Solution Find the magnitude of the force exerted by the water on the bottom of the container.
$$P = P_{atm} + \rho g d = \frac{F}{A}, \text{ so}$$
$$F = (P_{atm} + \rho g d)A = \left[1.013 \times 10^5 \text{ Pa} + (1.0 \times 10^3 \text{ kg/m}^3)(9.80 \text{ m/s}^2)(11.0 \text{ m})\right](5.00 \text{ m}^2) = \boxed{1.0 \text{ MN}}.$$

19. (a) Strategy Use Eq. (9-4).

Solution Compute the pressure increase.
$$\Delta P = \rho_{water} g d = (1.00 \times 10^3 \text{ kg/m}^3)(9.80 \text{ m/s}^2)(35.0 \text{ m}) = \boxed{343 \text{ kPa}}$$

(b) Strategy Use Eq. (9-3).

Solution Compute the pressure decrease.
$$\Delta P = -\rho_{air} g h = -(1.20 \text{ kg/m}^3)(9.80 \text{ m/s}^2)(35 \text{ m}) = -410 \text{ Pa}$$
The pressure decreases by $\boxed{410 \text{ Pa}}$.

21. Strategy Use the appropriate conversion factors to convert the gauge pressure into the various pressure units.

Solution

(a) $(32 \text{ lb/in}^2)\left(\dfrac{1.013 \times 10^5 \text{ Pa}}{14.7 \text{ lb/in}^2}\right) = \boxed{2.2 \times 10^5 \text{ Pa}}$

(b) $(32 \text{ lb/in}^2)\left(\dfrac{760.0 \text{ torr}}{14.7 \text{ lb/in}^2}\right) = \boxed{1700 \text{ torr}}$

(c) $(32 \text{ lb/in}^2)\left(\dfrac{1 \text{ atm}}{14.7 \text{ lb/in}^2}\right) = \boxed{2.2 \text{ atm}}$

25. **Strategy** The amount the fluid rises is one-half the difference of levels, or $\Delta h_{oil}/2$. Use Eq. (9-5).

    Solution

    (a) Find the amount that the fluid level rises.

    $$\Delta P = \rho_{Hg}g\Delta h_{Hg} = \rho_{oil}g\Delta h_{oil}, \text{ so } \frac{\Delta h_{oil}}{2} = \frac{\rho_{Hg}}{2\rho_{oil}}\Delta h_{Hg} = \frac{13.6 \text{ g/cm}^3}{2(0.90 \text{ g/cm}^3)}(0.74 \text{ cm Hg}) = \boxed{5.6 \text{ cm}}.$$

    (b) $\dfrac{\Delta h_{oil}}{2}\left(\dfrac{\rho_{oil}}{\rho_{Hg}}\right) = (5.6 \text{ cm})\dfrac{0.90 \text{ g/cm}^3}{13.6 \text{ g/cm}^3} = \boxed{0.37 \text{ cm}}$

27. **Strategy and Solution** Since the goose has 25% of its volume submerged, its density is 25% of water's, or about $\boxed{250 \text{ kg/m}^3}$.

29. **(a) Strategy** The relationship between the fraction of a floating object's volume that is submerged to the ratio of the object's density to the fluid in which it floats is $V_f/V_o = \rho_o/\rho_f$. Since the water contains ice, use the density of water at $0°C$.

    Solution Find the percent of the volume of ice that is submerged when it floats in water.
    $$\frac{V_{submerged}}{V_{ice}} = \frac{\rho_{ice}}{\rho_{water}} = \frac{917 \text{ kg/m}^3}{999.87 \text{ kg/m}^3} = 0.917, \text{ or } \boxed{91.7\%}$$

    (b) Strategy and Solution The specific gravity and the fraction of the object submerged in water are the same for objects that float, so the specific gravity of ice is $\boxed{0.917}$.

33. **Strategy** Compare the densities of a block of ebony and ethanol.

    Solution The density of a block of ebony is between 1000 and 1300 kg/m^3. The density of ethanol is 790 kg/m^3. Since the density of ebony is more than that of ethanol, the block will sink; therefore, $\boxed{100\%}$ of the volume of the block of ebony is submerged.

37. **Strategy** Find the volume of the coin using the density of water and the mass of the displaced water. Then find its density using its mass as measured in air and compare this to the density of gold.

    Solution The mass of water displaced is $49.7 \text{ g} - 47.1 \text{ g} = 2.6 \text{ g}$. Since the density of water is about 1.00 g/cm^3, the volume of the coin is $2.6 \text{ cm}^3 = 2.6\times10^{-6} \text{ m}^3$. So, the density of the coin is

    $\rho = \dfrac{m}{V} = \dfrac{49.7\times10^{-3} \text{ kg}}{2.6\times10^{-6} \text{ m}^3} = 19,000 \text{ kg/m}^3$. The density of gold is 19,300 kg/m^3, so $\boxed{\text{yes}}$, you should get excited, since the coin may be genuine.

39. Strategy Let the $+y$-direction be upward. Use Newton's second law and Eq. (9-7).

Solution

(a) $\Sigma F_y = F_B - mg = ma$, so

$$a = \frac{F_B}{m} - g = \frac{\rho_w gV}{m} - g = g\left(\frac{\rho_w V}{\rho V} - 1\right) = (9.80 \text{ m/s}^2)\left(\frac{1.00 \text{ g/cm}^3}{0.50 \text{ g/cm}^3} - 1\right) = 9.8 \text{ m/s}^2.$$

Thus, $\vec{a} = \boxed{9.8 \text{ m/s}^2 \text{ upward}}$.

(b) $a = (9.80 \text{ m/s}^2)\left(\frac{1.00 \text{ g/cm}^3}{0.750 \text{ g/cm}^3} - 1\right) = 3.3 \text{ m/s}^2$, so $\vec{a} = \boxed{3.3 \text{ m/s}^2 \text{ upward}}$.

(c) $a = (9.80 \text{ m/s}^2)\left(\frac{1.00 \text{ g/cm}^3}{0.125 \text{ g/cm}^3} - 1\right) = 68.6 \text{ m/s}^2$, so $\vec{a} = \boxed{68.6 \text{ m/s}^2 \text{ upward}}$.

41. Strategy Use Eq. (9-13).

Solution Find the speed of the water as it passes through the nozzle.

$$A_2 v_2 = A_1 v_1, \text{ so } v_2 = \frac{A_1}{A_2}v_1 = \frac{\pi r_1^2}{\pi r_2^2}v_1 = \left(\frac{1.0 \text{ cm}}{0.20 \text{ cm}}\right)^2 (2.0 \text{ m/s}) = \boxed{50 \text{ m/s}}.$$

43. (a) Strategy Use Eq. (9-13).

Solution Find the speed of the water in the hose.

$$v_2 = \frac{A_1}{A_2}v_1 = \frac{\pi r_1^2}{\pi r_2^2}v_1 = \left(\frac{r_1}{r_2}\right)^2 v_1 = \left(\frac{1.00 \text{ mm}}{8.00 \text{ mm}}\right)^2 (25.0 \text{ m/s}) = \boxed{39.1 \text{ cm/s}}$$

(b) Strategy Use Eq. (9-12).

Solution Compute the volume flow rate.

$$\frac{\Delta V}{\Delta t} = A_1 v_1 = \pi (1.00 \times 10^{-3} \text{ m})^2 (25.0 \text{ m/s}) = \boxed{78.5 \text{ cm}^3/\text{s}}$$

(c) Strategy Use Eq. (9-11).

Solution Compute the mass flow rate.

$$\frac{\Delta m}{\Delta t} = \rho A_1 v_1 = (1.00 \text{ g/cm}^3)(78.5 \text{ cm}^3/\text{s}) = \boxed{78.5 \text{ g/s}}$$

45. Strategy Use Eqs. (9-13) and (9-14). Since the pipe is horizontal, $y_1 = y_2$.

Solution Let the larger end be labeled 2. Find the speed of the water at the narrow end in terms of the speed at the larger end.

$A_1 v_1 = A_2 v_2$, so $v_1 = \dfrac{A_2}{A_1} v_2$.

Find the pressure at the narrow end of the segment of pipe.

$$P_1 + \frac{1}{2}\rho v_1^2 = P_2 + \frac{1}{2}\rho v_2^2, \text{ so } P_1 = P_2 + \frac{1}{2}\rho\left[v_2^2 - \left(\frac{A_2}{A_1}v_2\right)^2 \right]$$

$$= 1.20\times10^5 \text{ Pa} + \frac{1}{2}(1.00\times10^3 \text{ kg/m}^3)(0.040 \text{ m/s})^2\left[1 - \left(\frac{50.0 \text{ cm}^2}{0.500 \text{ cm}^2}\right)^2 \right] = \boxed{1.12\times10^5 \text{ Pa}}.$$

47. Strategy Use Eq. (9-14).

Solution The potential energy difference is relatively small, so Bernoulli's equation becomes

$P_1 + \frac{1}{2}\rho v_1^2 = P_2 + \frac{1}{2}\rho v_2^2$, or $P_1 - P_2 = \frac{1}{2}\rho v_2^2 - \frac{1}{2}\rho v_1^2$.

Estimate the force.

$$F = \Delta P A = (P_1 - P_2)A = \left(\frac{1}{2}\rho v_2^2 - \frac{1}{2}\rho v_1^2\right)A = \frac{1}{2}A\rho(v_2^2 - v_1^2)$$

$$= \frac{1}{2}(28 \text{ m}^2)(1.3 \text{ kg/m}^3)[(190 \text{ m/s})^2 - (160 \text{ m/s})^2] = \boxed{1.9\times10^5 \text{ N}}$$

49. Strategy Use Eqs. (9-13) and (9-14).

Solution $y_1 = y_2$ and $v_1 \gg v_2$ since $A_2 \gg A_1$ ($d_2 \gg d_1$), so Bernoulli's equation gives

$$\Delta P = \frac{1}{2}\rho v_1^2 = \frac{1}{2}(1.0\times10^3 \text{ kg/m}^3)(25 \text{ m/s})^2 = \boxed{310 \text{ kPa}}.$$

53. Strategy Use Eq. (9-15).

Solution Show that viscosity has SI units of pascal-seconds.
Solve for η.

$\dfrac{\Delta V}{\Delta t} = \dfrac{\pi}{8}\dfrac{\frac{\Delta P}{L}}{\eta}r^4$, so $\eta = \dfrac{\pi}{8}\dfrac{\Delta P}{L}\dfrac{\Delta t}{\Delta V}r^4$. Thus, the units of η are $\dfrac{\text{Pa}}{\text{m}}\cdot\dfrac{\text{s}}{\text{m}^3}\cdot\text{m}^4 = \text{Pa}\cdot\text{s}$.

57. Strategy Use Eq. (9-15). Form a ratio of the volume flow rates.

Solution Find the total flow rate in system C.

$$\dfrac{\frac{\Delta V}{\Delta t}\text{ C}}{\frac{\Delta V}{\Delta t}\text{ B}} = \dfrac{4\left[\frac{\pi\Delta P_C r^4}{8\eta\left(\frac{L}{2}\right)}\right]}{2\left(\frac{\pi\Delta P_B r^4}{8\eta L}\right)} = \dfrac{4\Delta P_C}{\Delta P_B}, \text{ so } \dfrac{\Delta V}{\Delta t}\text{ C} = \dfrac{4\Delta P_C}{\Delta P_B}\left(\dfrac{\Delta V}{\Delta t}\text{ B}\right) = 4\left(\dfrac{2.0\times10^5 \text{ Pa}}{4.0\times10^5 \text{ Pa}}\right)(0.020 \text{ m}^3/\text{s}) = \boxed{0.040 \text{ m}^3/\text{s}}.$$

61. **Strategy** Use Eq. (9-16) and Newton's second law.

Solution Find the viscosity of the second liquid.

$$\Sigma F_y = F_D + F_B - m_s g = 6\pi\eta rv + m_l g - m_s g = 6\pi\eta rv + (m_l - m_s)g = 6\pi\eta rv - \frac{4}{3}\pi r^3(\rho_s - \rho_l)g = 0,$$

so $\eta = \dfrac{\frac{4}{3}\pi r^3(\rho_s - \rho_l)g}{6\pi rv} = \dfrac{2r^2(\rho_s - \rho_l)g}{9v}$.

Find the viscosity of the second liquid by forming a proportion.

$$\frac{\eta_2}{\eta_1} = \frac{\frac{2r^2(\rho_s-\rho_l)g}{9v_2}}{\frac{2r^2(\rho_s-\rho_l)g}{9v_1}} = \frac{v_1}{v_2}, \text{ so } \eta_2 = \frac{v_1}{1.2v_1}\eta_1 = \frac{\eta_1}{1.2} = \frac{0.5 \text{ Pa}\cdot\text{s}}{1.2} = \boxed{0.4 \text{ Pa}\cdot\text{s}}.$$

65. **Strategy** For a viscous drag force, $v_t \propto m$. For a turbulent drag force, $v_t \propto \sqrt{m}$. For the data in the table, compute m/v_t and m/v_t^2.

Solution The data, m/v_t, and m/v_t^2 are organized in the table.

m (g)	8	12	16	20	24	28
v_t (cm/s)	1.0	1.5	2.0	2.5	3.0	3.5
$\frac{m}{v_t}$ (g·s/cm)	8	8.0	8.0	8.0	8.0	8.0
$\frac{m}{v_t^2}$ (g·s^2/cm^2)	8	5.3	4.0	3.2	2.7	2.3

Since m/v_t is constant, the drag force is primarily viscous.

69. **Strategy** Use Eq. (9-17).

Solution Form a proportion to find the pressure inside the air bubble.

$$\frac{\Delta P_2}{\Delta P_1} = \frac{\frac{2\gamma}{r_2}}{\frac{2\gamma}{r_1}}, \text{ so } \Delta P_2 = \Delta P_1 \frac{r_1}{r_2} = (10 \text{ Pa})\frac{r_1}{2r_1} = \boxed{5 \text{ Pa}}.$$

73. **(a) Strategy** The mass of the water is equal to its density times its volume.

Solution The weight of the water in the straw is
$$mg = (\rho V)g = \rho(\pi r^2 h)g = (1.00 \times 10^3 \text{ kg/m}^3)\pi(0.00250 \text{ m})^2(8.00 \text{ m})(9.80 \text{ m/s}^2) = \boxed{1.54 \text{ N}}.$$

(b) Strategy Equate the pressures and solve for the force on the top of the barrel. Use the definition of pressure.

Solution Find the force with which the water in the barrel pushes up on the top of the barrel.
$$F_b = \frac{A_b}{A_s}F_s = \frac{r_b^2}{r_s^2}F_s = \frac{(25.0 \text{ cm})^2}{(0.250 \text{ cm})^2}(1.54 \text{ N}) = \boxed{1.54 \times 10^4 \text{ N}}.$$

(c) Strategy Consider the nature of pressure in a column of fluid.

Solution For a given depth, the pressure is the same everywhere, so the very tall, narrow column of water is as effective as having a whole barrel of water filled to the same height and pushing upward on the barrel top.

77. **(a) Strategy** Assume that the change in the height of the water level in the vat is negligible and that the pressures at the top of the vat and at the outlet are the same. Use Bernoulli's equation.

Solution Let the top of the vat be labeled 1. With the above assumptions, Bernoulli's equation becomes
$$\rho g y_1 = \rho g y_2 + \frac{1}{2}\rho v_2^2, \text{ so } v_2 = \sqrt{2g(y_1 - y_2)} = \sqrt{2(9.80 \text{ m/s}^2)(1.80 \text{ m})} = \boxed{5.94 \text{ m/s}}.$$

(b) Strategy and Solution The density "falls out" of Bernoulli's equation in our calculation of the speed, so as long as we can assume Bernoulli's equation applies, it doesn't matter what fluid is in the vat.

(c) Strategy and Solution Since the speed is directly proportional to the square root of the gravitational field strength, $\sqrt{1.6/9.80} = 0.40$, the speed would be reduced by a factor of 0.40.

81. **Strategy** Use Eq. (9-14) with $v_1 = v_2 = 0$.

Solution Find the height between the basement and the seventh floor.
$$P_1 + \rho g y_1 = P_2 + \rho g y_2, \text{ so } y_1 - y_2 = \frac{P_2 - P_1}{\rho g} = \frac{4.10 \times 10^5 \text{ Pa} - 1.85 \times 10^5 \text{ Pa}}{(1.00 \times 10^3 \text{ kg/m}^3)(9.80 \text{ m/s}^2)} = \boxed{23.0 \text{ m}}.$$

85. **Strategy** Use the continuity equation. The speed of an object that has fallen a distance h from rest is $v = \sqrt{2gh}$.

Solution Find the diameter of the water flow after the water has fallen 30 cm.
$$A_1 v_1 = \frac{1}{4}\pi d_1^2 v_1 = A_2 v_2 = \frac{1}{4}\pi d_2^2 v_2, \text{ so } d_2 = d_1\sqrt{\frac{v_1}{\sqrt{2gh}}} = (2.2 \text{ cm})\sqrt{\frac{0.62 \text{ m/s}}{\sqrt{2(9.80 \text{ m/s}^2)(0.30 \text{ m})}}} = \boxed{1.1 \text{ cm}}.$$

89. (a) Strategy Use Eqs. (9-7), (9-16), and Newton's second law.

Solution Find the terminal velocity of the bubbles.

$$\Sigma F_y = F_B - F_D - m_a g = \rho_w gV - 6\pi\eta r v_t - \rho_a gV = -6\pi\eta r v_t + (\rho_w - \rho_a)\tfrac{4}{3}\pi r^3 g = 0, \text{ so}$$

$$v_t = \frac{(\rho_w - \rho_a)\tfrac{4}{3}\pi r^3 g}{6\pi\eta r} = \frac{2r^2 g(\rho_w - \rho_a)}{9\eta}$$

$$= \frac{2(1.0\times10^{-3}\ \text{m})^2(9.80\ \text{m/s}^2)(1.00\times10^3\ \text{kg/m}^3 - 1.20\ \text{kg/m}^3)}{9(1.0\times10^{-3}\ \text{Pa}\cdot\text{s})} = 2.2\ \text{m/s}.$$

Thus, $\vec{v}_t = \boxed{2.2\ \text{m/s up}}$.

(b) Strategy Divide the change in pressure by the change in time and use the result from part (a).

Solution

$$\Delta P = \rho g\Delta y, \text{ so } \frac{\Delta P}{\Delta t} = \rho g\frac{\Delta y}{\Delta t} = \rho g v_t = (1.00\times10^3\ \text{kg/m}^3)(9.80\ \text{m/s}^2)(2.175\ \text{m/s}) = \boxed{21\ \text{kPa/s}}.$$

93. Strategy Use Eq. (9-7) and Newton's second law.

Solution Find an expression for d.

$$\Sigma F_y = F_B - mg = \rho gV - mg = \rho gAd - mg = \rho g(\pi r^2)d - mg = 0, \text{ so } d = \frac{m}{\pi\rho r^2}.$$

$$\boxed{d \text{ is not a linear function of } \rho: d = \frac{m}{\pi\rho r^2}.}$$

97. Strategy Use the relationships between pressure, density, force, area, and height.

Solution Find the density of the liquid.

$$\Delta P = \frac{W_l}{A} = \frac{\rho_l gV_l}{A} = \rho_w g\Delta y_w, \text{ so}$$

$$\rho_l = \frac{\rho_w \Delta y_w A}{V_l} = \frac{\rho_w \Delta y_w \pi r^2}{\pi r^2 h} = \frac{\rho_w \Delta y_w}{h} = \frac{(1.0\ \text{g/cm}^3)[0.45\ \text{m} - (0.50\ \text{m} - 0.30\ \text{m})]}{0.30\ \text{m}} = \boxed{0.83\ \text{g/cm}^3}.$$

101. (a) Strategy Use Eq. (9-15).

Solution Find the percentage that the blood pressure difference between the ends of the artery increased.

$$\frac{\Delta P_a - \Delta P_u}{\Delta P_u}\times100\% = \frac{\left(\dfrac{8\eta L}{\pi r_a^4}\right)\dfrac{\Delta V}{\Delta t} - \left(\dfrac{8\eta L}{\pi r_u^4}\right)\dfrac{\Delta V}{\Delta t}}{\left(\dfrac{8\eta L}{\pi r_u^4}\right)\dfrac{\Delta V}{\Delta t}}\times100\% = \frac{\dfrac{1}{r_a^4} - \dfrac{1}{r_u^4}}{\dfrac{1}{r_u^4}}\times100\% = \left[\left(\frac{r_u}{r_a}\right)^4 - 1\right]\times100\%$$

$$= \left[\left(\frac{1}{0.75}\right)^4 - 1\right]\times100\% = \boxed{220\%}$$

(b) Strategy Divide the absolute value of the change in flow rate by the original flow rate.

Solution Compute the factor of blood flow decrease.

$$\left|\frac{\text{change in flow rate}}{\text{original flow rate}}\right| = \frac{\dfrac{\Delta V}{\Delta t}_u - \dfrac{\Delta V}{\Delta t}_a}{\dfrac{\Delta V}{\Delta t}_u} = 1 - \frac{\dfrac{\Delta V}{\Delta t}_a}{\dfrac{\Delta V}{\Delta t}_u} = 1 - \frac{\dfrac{\pi\Delta P r_a^4}{8\eta L}}{\dfrac{\pi\Delta P r_u^4}{8\eta L}} = 1 - \left(\frac{r_a}{r_u}\right)^4 = 1 - (0.75)^4 = \boxed{0.68}$$

Chapter 10

ELASTICITY AND OSCILLATIONS

Conceptual Questions

1. Young's modulus does not tell us which is stronger. Instead, it tells us which is more resistant to deformation for a given stress. The ultimate strength would tell us which is stronger—i.e., which can withstand the greatest stress.

5. The compressive force experienced by the columns is greater at the bottom than at the top, because the bottom must support the weight of the column itself in addition to whatever the column is holding up. By increasing the cross-sectional area of the bottom of the column, the stress it experiences is reduced. Tapering columns so that they are thicker at the base prevents the stress at the bottom from being too large.

9. The tension in the bungee cord at the lowest point would be greater than the person's weight, because there is an upward acceleration. In fact, the tension would have its maximum value at the bottom, because that is where the upward acceleration is the greatest.

13. To produce the same strain, the ratio of the force to the cross-sectional area must remain unchanged. The total cross-sectional area of the two wires together is twice the original area. Thus, the force applied to the two wires must be doubled as well. Modeling a thick wire as a bundle of thin wires, the preceding argument explains why the force to produce a given strain must be proportional to the cross-sectional area—and thus why the strain depends on the stress.

17. In the mass-spring system, the restoring force supplied by the spring is independent of the object's mass. Thus, the larger inertia of a more massive object produces a longer period. The restoring force for small amplitude oscillations of the pendulum is the horizontal component of the tension in the string. In this case, the magnitude of the tension is approximately equal to the weight of the bob. Although a more massive bob has more inertia, it also has a proportionally larger restoring force. Thus, the period of oscillation of the pendulum is independent of the mass.

Problems

1. **Strategy** The stress is proportional to the strain. Use Eq. (10-4).

   Solution Find the vertical compression of the beam.

   $$Y\frac{\Delta L}{L} = \frac{F}{A}, \text{ so } \Delta L = \frac{FL}{YA} = \frac{(5.8 \times 10^4 \text{ N})(2.5 \text{ m})}{(200 \times 10^9 \text{ Pa})(7.5 \times 10^{-3} \text{ m}^2)} = \boxed{0.097 \text{ mm}}.$$

3. **Strategy** The stress is proportional to the strain. Use Eq. (10-4).

   Solution Find how much the wire stretches.

   $$\Delta L = \frac{FL}{YA} = \frac{(5.0 \times 10^3 \text{ N})(2.0 \text{ m})}{(9.2 \times 10^{10} \text{ Pa})(5.0 \text{ mm}^2)(10^{-3} \text{ m/mm})^2} = \boxed{2.2 \text{ cm}}$$

5. **Strategy** Form a proportion of the elongations of the left and right wires. Use Eq. (10-4).

   Solution Find how far the midpoint moves.

   $$\frac{\Delta L_L}{\Delta L_R} = \frac{\frac{FL}{YA_L}}{\frac{FL}{YA_R}} = \frac{A_R}{A_L} = \frac{\pi(2r)^2}{\pi r^2} = 4, \text{ so } \Delta L_L = 4\Delta L_R \text{ and } \Delta L = \Delta L_L + \Delta L_R \text{ is the total elongation, 1.0 mm.}$$

   $$\Delta L = \Delta L_L + \Delta L_R = \Delta L_L + \frac{1}{4}\Delta L_L = \frac{5}{4}\Delta L_L, \text{ so } \Delta L_L = \frac{4}{5}\Delta L = \frac{4}{5}(1.0 \text{ mm}) = \boxed{0.80 \text{ mm}}.$$

9. **Strategy** Refer to Fig. 10.4c. The stress is proportional to the strain.

   Solution Calculate Young's moduli for tension and compression of bone.
   Tension:
   For tensile stress and strain, the graph is far from being linear, but for relatively small values of stress and strain, it is approximately linear. So, for small values of tensile stress and strain, Young's Modulus is

   $$Y = \frac{\text{stress}}{\text{strain}} = \frac{5.0 \times 10^7 \text{ N/m}^2}{0.0033} = \boxed{1.5 \times 10^{10} \text{ N/m}^2}.$$

   Compression:

   Similarly, for small values of compressive stress and strain, $Y = \frac{-4.5 \times 10^7 \text{ N/m}^2}{-0.0050} = \boxed{9.0 \times 10^9 \text{ N/m}^2}$.

11. **Strategy** Set the stress equal to the tensile strength of the hair to find the diameter of the hair.

    Solution Find the diameter of the hair.

    $$\text{tensile strength} = \frac{F}{A} = \frac{F}{\frac{1}{4}\pi d^2}, \text{ so } d = \sqrt{\frac{4F}{\pi(\text{tensile strength})}} = \sqrt{\frac{4(1.2 \text{ N})}{\pi(2.0 \times 10^8 \text{ Pa})}} = \boxed{8.7 \times 10^{-5} \text{ m}}.$$

13. **Strategy** The stress on the copper wire must be less than its elastic limit.

    Solution Find the maximum load that can be suspended from the copper wire.

    $$\frac{F}{A} < \text{elastic limit, so } F < \pi r^2(\text{elastic limit}) = \pi(0.0010 \text{ m})^2(2.0 \times 10^8 \text{ Pa}) = \boxed{630 \text{ N}}.$$

17. **Strategy** Use Eqs. (10-1), (10-2), and (10-4).

    Solution

    (a) $\text{stress} = \frac{F}{A} = \frac{7.0 \times 10^4 \text{ N}}{25 \times 10^{-4} \text{ m}^2} = \boxed{2.8 \times 10^7 \text{ Pa}}$

    (b) $\text{strain} = \frac{\Delta L}{L} = \frac{F}{YA} = \frac{7.0 \times 10^4 \text{ N}}{(6.0 \times 10^{10} \text{ Pa})(25 \times 10^{-4} \text{ m}^2)} = \boxed{4.7 \times 10^{-4}}$

    (c) $\Delta L = \frac{FL}{YA} = \frac{(7.0 \times 10^4 \text{ N})(2.0 \text{ m})}{(6.0 \times 10^{10} \text{ Pa})(25 \times 10^{-4} \text{ m}^2)} = \boxed{9.3 \times 10^{-4} \text{ m}}$

    (d) Set the compressive strength equal to the stress to find the maximum weight the column can support.
    $$\frac{F}{A} = \text{compressive strength, so } F = (\text{compressive strength})A = (2.0 \times 10^8 \text{ Pa})(25 \times 10^{-4} \text{ m}^2) = \boxed{5.0 \times 10^5 \text{ N}}.$$

21. Strategy Use Hooke's law for volume deformations.

Solution Find the change in volume of the sphere.

$$\Delta P = -B\frac{\Delta V}{V}, \text{ so } \Delta V = -\frac{V\Delta P}{B} = -\frac{(1.00 \text{ cm}^3)(9.12\times10^6 \text{ Pa})}{160\times10^9 \text{ Pa}} = -57\times10^{-6} \text{ cm}^3.$$

The volume of the steel sphere would decrease by 57×10^{-6} cm^3.

25. Strategy Use Hooke's law for shear deformations.

Solution Find the magnitude of the tangential force.

$$\frac{F}{A} = \frac{F}{L^2} = S\frac{\Delta x}{L}, \text{ so } F = S\Delta xL = (940 \text{ Pa})(0.64\times10^{-2} \text{ m})(0.050 \text{ m}) = \boxed{0.30 \text{ N}}.$$

29. Strategy The amplitude is half the maximum distance. Use Eqs. (10-21) and (10-22).

Solution Find the maximum velocity and maximum acceleration of the prong.

$$v_m = \omega A = 2\pi fA = 2\pi(440.0 \text{ Hz})\left(\frac{2.24}{2}\times10^{-3} \text{ m}\right) = \boxed{3.10 \text{ m/s}}$$

$$a_m = \omega^2 A = 4\pi^2 f^2 A = 4\pi^2(440.0 \text{ Hz})^2\left(\frac{2.24}{2}\times10^{-3} \text{ m}\right) = \boxed{8560 \text{ m/s}^2}$$

33. Strategy Use Eqs. (10-21) and (10-22).

Solution

(a) Find v_m and a_m in terms of f. Then compare high- and low-frequency sounds.

$$v_m = \omega A = 2\pi fA \propto f \text{ and } a_m = \omega^2 A = 4\pi^2 f^2 A \propto f^2, \text{ so } v_m \text{ and } a_m \text{ are greatest for } \boxed{\text{high frequency}}.$$

(b) $v_m = 2\pi(20.0 \text{ Hz})(1.0\times10^{-8} \text{ m}) = \boxed{1.3\times10^{-6} \text{ m/s}}$

$a_m = 4\pi^2(20.0 \text{ Hz})^2(1.0\times10^{-8} \text{ m}) = \boxed{1.6\times10^{-4} \text{ m/s}^2}$

(c) $v_m = 2\pi(20.0\times10^3 \text{ Hz})(1.0\times10^{-8} \text{ m}) = \boxed{0.0013 \text{ m/s}}$

$a_m = 4\pi^2(20.0\times10^3 \text{ Hz})^2(1.0\times10^{-8} \text{ m}) = \boxed{160 \text{ m/s}^2}$

35. Strategy The angular frequency of oscillation is inversely proportional to the square root of the mass. Form a proportion.

Solution Find the new value of ω.

$$\omega \propto \sqrt{\frac{1}{m}}, \text{ so } \frac{\omega_f}{\omega_i} = \frac{\sqrt{1/m_f}}{\sqrt{1/m_i}} = \sqrt{\frac{m_i}{m_f}} = \sqrt{\frac{1}{4.0}} = \frac{1}{2.0}. \text{ Therefore, } \omega_f = \frac{\omega_i}{2.0} = \frac{10.0 \text{ rad/s}}{2.0} = \boxed{5.0 \text{ rad/s}}.$$

37. **Strategy** Use Eqs. (10-20a) and (10-20b) and Newton's second law.

   Solution Find the spring constant.

   $$\Sigma F_y = kx - m_{child}g = 0, \text{ so } k = \frac{m_{child}g}{x} = \frac{(24 \text{ kg})(9.80 \text{ m/s}^2)}{0.28 \text{ m}} = 840 \text{ N/m}.$$

   Find the mass of the wooden horse.

   $$\omega_{child} = \sqrt{\frac{k}{m_{child} + m_{horse}}}, \text{ so } m_{horse} = \frac{k}{\omega_{child}^2} - m_{child}.$$

   Find the oscillation frequency of the spring when no one is sitting on the horse.

   $$f_{horse} = \frac{\omega_{horse}}{2\pi} = \frac{1}{2\pi}\sqrt{\frac{k}{m_{horse}}} = \frac{1}{2\pi}\sqrt{\frac{k}{\frac{k}{\omega_{child}^2} - m_{child}}} = \frac{1}{2\pi}\sqrt{\frac{840 \text{ N/m}}{\frac{840 \text{ N/m}}{(0.88 \text{ Hz})^2(2\pi \text{ rad/cycle})^2} - 24 \text{ kg}}} = \boxed{2.5 \text{ Hz}}$$

39. **Strategy** Use Eqs. (10-21) and (10-22) and Newton's second law.

   Solution Find the radio's maximum displacement and maximum speed, and the maximum net force exerted on it.

   (a) $a_m = \omega^2 A$, so $A = \dfrac{a_m}{\omega^2} = \dfrac{98 \text{ m/s}^2}{4\pi^2(120 \text{ Hz})^2} = \boxed{1.7 \times 10^{-4} \text{ m}}$.

   (b) $v_m = \omega A = \omega\dfrac{a_m}{\omega^2} = \dfrac{a_m}{\omega} = \dfrac{98 \text{ m/s}^2}{2\pi(120 \text{ Hz})} = \boxed{0.13 \text{ m/s}}$

   (c) According to Newton's second law, $F_m = ma_m = (5.24 \text{ kg})(98 \text{ m/s}^2) = \boxed{510 \text{ N}}$.

41. (a) **Strategy** Use Newton's second law and Eq. (10-22).

   Solution Find the maximum force acting on the diaphragm.
   $$F_m = ma_m = m\omega^2 A = 4\pi^2(0.0500 \text{ kg})(2.0 \times 10^3 \text{ Hz})^2(1.8 \times 10^{-4} \text{ m}) = \boxed{1.4 \text{ kN}}.$$

   (b) **Strategy** The maximum elastic potential energy of the diaphragm is equal to the total mechanical energy.

   Solution Find the mechanical energy of the diaphragm.
   $$E = U = \frac{1}{2}m\omega^2 A^2 = 2\pi^2(0.0500 \text{ kg})(2.0 \times 10^3 \text{ Hz})^2(1.8 \times 10^{-4} \text{ m})^2 = \boxed{0.13 \text{ J}}.$$

43. (a) **Strategy** The speed is maximum when the spring and mass system is at its equilibrium point. Use Newton's second law.

   Solution Find the extension of the spring.
   $$\Sigma F_y = kx - mg = 0, \text{ so } x = \frac{mg}{k} = \frac{(0.60 \text{ kg})(9.80 \text{ N/kg})}{15 \text{ N/m}} = \boxed{0.39 \text{ m}}.$$

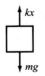

   (b) **Strategy** Use Eqs. (10-20a) and (10-21).

   Solution Find the maximum speed of the body.
   $$v_m = \omega A = \sqrt{\frac{k}{m}}x = \sqrt{\frac{15 \text{ N/m}}{0.60 \text{ kg}}}(0.39 \text{ m}) = \boxed{2.0 \text{ m/s}}$$

45. Strategy Use Hooke's law, Newton's second law, and Eq. (10-20c).

Solution Find the "spring constant" of the boat. At equilibrium,

$\Sigma F_y = kx - m_{\text{person}}g = 0$, so $k = \dfrac{m_{\text{person}}g}{x}$.

Compute the period of oscillation.

$$T = 2\pi\sqrt{\frac{m_{\text{total}}}{k}} = 2\pi\sqrt{\frac{m_{\text{total}}}{m_{\text{person}}g/x}} = 2\pi\sqrt{\frac{m_{\text{total}}x}{m_{\text{person}}g}} = 2\pi\sqrt{\frac{(47 \text{ kg} + 92 \text{ kg})(0.080 \text{ m})}{(92 \text{ kg})(9.80 \text{ m/s}^2)}} = \boxed{0.70 \text{ s}}$$

49. (a) Strategy The object will oscillate up and down with an amplitude determined by the spring constant and the mass of the spring.

Solution Find the amplitude of the motion. At the equilibrium point, the net force on the object is zero.

$\Sigma F_y = kA - mg = 0$, so $A = mg/k = (0.306 \text{ kg})(9.80 \text{ m/s}^2)/(25 \text{ N/m}) = 12$ cm.

The object will move up and down a total vertical distance of $2A = 24$ cm. Thus, the

pattern traced on the paper by the pen is $\boxed{\text{a vertical straight line of length 24 cm}}$.

(b) Strategy and Solution As the paper moves to the left at constant speed while the pen oscillates vertically in SHM, the pen traces a pattern of

$\boxed{\text{a positive cosine plot of amplitude 12 cm}}$.

51. Strategy Use the definition of average speed and Eq. (10-21). In (d), graph v_x on the vertical axis and t on the horizontal axis.

Solution

(a) The average speed is the total distance traveled divided by the time of travel.

$$v_{\text{av}} = \frac{\Delta x}{\Delta t} = \frac{4A}{T} = \frac{4A}{2\pi/\omega} = \boxed{\frac{2}{\pi}\omega A}$$

(b) The maximum speed for SHM is $v_{\text{m}} = \boxed{\omega A}$.

(c) $\dfrac{v_{\text{av}}}{v_{\text{m}}} = \dfrac{\frac{2}{\pi}\omega A}{\omega A} = \boxed{\dfrac{2}{\pi}}$

(d) Graph $v_x(t)$ and a line from the origin to v_{m}.

If the acceleration were constant so that the speed varied linearly, the average speed would be 1/2 of the maximum velocity. Since the actual speed is always larger than what it would be for constant acceleration, the average speed must be larger.

53. **(a)** **Strategy** Use Eq. (10-20a) to find the spring constant. Then, find the elastic potential energy using $\frac{1}{2}kx^2$.

Solution Find the spring constant.

$\omega = \sqrt{\dfrac{k}{m}}$, so $k = \omega^2 m = (2.00\ \text{Hz})^2(2\pi\ \text{rad/cycle})^2(0.2300\ \text{kg}) = 36.3\ \text{N/m}$.

The equation for the elastic potential energy is

$$U(t) = \frac{1}{2}(36.3\ \text{N/m})(0.0800\ \text{m})^2 \sin^2\left[(2.00\ \text{Hz})(2\pi\ \text{rad/cycle})t\right] = (116\ \text{mJ})\sin^2\left[(4.00\pi\ \text{s}^{-1})t\right].$$

Since the sine function is squared, the period of $U(t)$ is half that of a sine function or

$$T = \frac{\pi}{\omega} = \frac{\pi}{4.00\pi\ \text{s}^{-1}} = 250\ \text{ms}. \text{ Graph } U(t).$$

(b) **Strategy** Find the kinetic energy using $\frac{1}{2}mv_x^2$.

Solution The equation for the kinetic energy is

$$K(t) = \frac{1}{2}(0.2300\ \text{kg})(2.00\ \text{Hz})^2\left(\frac{2\pi\ \text{rad}}{\text{cycle}}\right)^2(0.0800\ \text{m})^2\cos^2\left[(2.00\ \text{Hz})\left(\frac{2\pi\ \text{rad}}{\text{cycle}}\right)t\right]$$
$$= (116\ \text{mJ})\cos^2\left[(4.00\pi\ \text{s}^{-1})t\right].$$

Since the cosine function is squared, the period of $K(t)$ is half that of a cosine function or

$$T = \pi/\omega = \pi/(4.00\pi\ \text{s}^{-1}) = 250\ \text{ms}, \text{ which is the same as } U(t). \text{ Graph } K(t).$$

(c) **Strategy** Add $U(t)$ and $K(t)$ and graph the result.

Solution

$$E(t) = U(t) + K(t) = (116\ \text{mJ})\sin^2\left[(4.00\pi\ \text{s}^{-1})t\right] + (116\ \text{mJ})\cos^2\left[(4.00\pi\ \text{s}^{-1})t\right]$$
$$= (116\ \text{mJ})\left\{\sin^2\left[(4.00\pi\ \text{s}^{-1})t\right] + \cos^2\left[(4.00\pi\ \text{s}^{-1})t\right]\right\} = (116\ \text{mJ})(1) = 116\ \text{mJ}$$

Graph $E(t) = U(t) + K(t)$.

(d) **Strategy and Solution** Friction does nonconservative work on the object, thus,

$\boxed{U,\ K,\ \text{and}\ E\ \text{would gradually be reduced to zero}}$.

57. **Strategy and Solution** According to Eq. (10-26b), $T = 2\pi\sqrt{\dfrac{L}{g}}$, which does not depend upon the mass.

Therefore, $T = \boxed{1.5 \text{ s}}$.

61. **Strategy** Use Eq. (10-26b) to find the length of the pendulum. Then, form a ratio of the lengths.

Solution Solve for L.

$T = 2\pi\sqrt{\dfrac{L}{g}}$, so $L = \dfrac{gT^2}{4\pi^2}$.

Form a proportion.

$\dfrac{L_2}{L_1} = \dfrac{T_2^2}{T_1^2} = \left(\dfrac{1.00 \text{ s}}{0.950 \text{ s}}\right)^2 = \boxed{1.11}$

65. **Strategy** The total mechanical energy of a pendulum is $E = \frac{1}{2}m\omega^2 A^2$. Form a proportion.

Solution Find the mechanical energy of the pendulum.

$\dfrac{E_2}{E_1} = \dfrac{A_2^2}{A_1^2}$, so $E_2 = \left(\dfrac{A_2}{A_1}\right)^2 E_1 = \left(\dfrac{3.0 \text{ cm}}{2.0 \text{ cm}}\right)^2 (5.0 \text{ mJ}) = \boxed{11 \text{ mJ}}$.

69. **Strategy** $E = \frac{1}{2}m\omega^2 A^2 \propto A^2$ for a pendulum.

Solution Find the percent decrease of the oscillator's energy in ten cycles.

$\dfrac{\Delta E}{E} \times 100\% = \dfrac{\Delta A^2}{A^2} \times 100\% = \dfrac{(1-0.0500)^2 - 1^2}{1^2} \times 100\% = \dfrac{0.9500^2 - 1^2}{1^2} \times 100\% = \boxed{-9.75\%}$

73. **Strategy** Use Eq. (10-20c).

Solution

(a) The period is directly proportional to the square root of the mass, and the period for the fish is longer than that for the weight, so the fish weighs $\boxed{\text{more}}$ than the weight.

(b) Form a proportion. Let f = fish and w = weight.

$T = 2\pi\sqrt{\dfrac{m}{k}}$, so $\dfrac{T_f}{T_w} = \sqrt{\dfrac{m_f}{m_w}} = \sqrt{\dfrac{W_f}{W_w}}$. Thus, $W_f = \left(\dfrac{T_f}{T_w}\right)^2 W_w = \left(\dfrac{220}{65}\right)^2 (4.90 \text{ N}) = \boxed{56 \text{ N}}$.

77. **Strategy** Graph x on the vertical axis and t on the horizontal axis. Analyze the slope of the graph (the magnitude of which is the speed) in terms of the distance between the dots to determine the fastest and slowest speeds of the mass.

Solution Graph $x(t) = -(10 \text{ cm}) \cos[(1.57 \text{ s}^{-1})t]$.

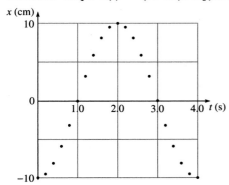

The distance between adjacent dots should be the least at the endpoints and greatest at the center, so its speed is lowest at the endpoints and fastest at its equilibrium position.

81. **Strategy** Since the body begins with its maximum amplitude at $t = 0$, the body oscillates according to a cosine function ($\cos 0 = 1$). Use Newton's second law, Hooke's law, and Eq. (10-20a).

Solution Find the amplitude A.

$$\Sigma F_y = kA - mg = 0, \text{ so } A = \frac{mg}{k} = \frac{4.0 \text{ N}}{250 \text{ N/m}} = 1.6 \text{ cm}.$$

Find the angular frequency ω.

$$\omega = \sqrt{\frac{k}{m}} = \sqrt{\frac{kg}{mg}} = \sqrt{\frac{(250 \text{ N/m})(9.80 \text{ m/s}^2)}{4.0 \text{ N}}} = 25 \text{ rad/s}$$

Thus, the equation describing the motion of the body is $\boxed{y = (1.6 \text{ cm}) \cos[(25 \text{ rad/s})t]}$.

85. **Strategy** Use Eq. (10-2) to find the tensile stress. Then compare the tensile stress to the elastic limit of steel piano wire.

Solution Find the tensile stress in the piano wire in Problem 90.

$$\text{tensile stress} = \frac{F}{A} = \frac{T}{\frac{1}{4}\pi d^2} = \frac{4T}{\pi d^2} = \frac{4(402 \text{ N})}{\pi(0.80 \times 10^{-3} \text{ m})^2} = 8.0 \times 10^8 \text{ Pa} < 8.26 \times 10^8 \text{ Pa}$$

The tensile stress is $\boxed{8.0 \times 10^8 \text{ Pa}}$; it is just under the elastic limit.

89. **Strategy** The force on the column is its weight. Use Eq. (10-2) and the relationship between density, mass, and volume.

    Solution

    (a) Calculate the compressive stress at the bottom of the column.

    $$\text{compressive stress} = \frac{F}{A} = \frac{mg}{A} = \frac{\rho V g}{A} = \frac{\rho h A g}{A} = \boxed{\rho g h}$$

    (b) Find the absolute limit to the height of a cylindrical column, regardless of how wide it is.

    $$h_{\text{m}} = \frac{\text{compressive strength}}{\rho g} = \frac{2.0 \times 10^8 \text{ Pa}}{(2.7 \times 10^3 \text{ kg/m}^3)(9.80 \text{ m/s}^2)} = \boxed{7.6 \text{ km}}$$

    (c) It is unlikely that someone would want to build a marble column taller than 7.6 km. So, the answer is $\boxed{\text{no}}$; this limit is of little practical concern. No beanstalk could ever reach a height of 7.6 km; its height is limited by other means.

93. (a) **Strategy** Use conservation of energy. Do *not* assume SHM.

    Solution Find the speed of the pendulum bob at the bottom of its swing.

    $$\Delta K = \frac{1}{2} mv^2 = -\Delta U = mgL, \text{ so } v = \boxed{\sqrt{2gL}}.$$

    (b) **Strategy** Assume (incorrectly, for such a large amplitude) that the motion *is* SHM. Use Eqs. (10-21) and (10-26a).

    Solution Find the speed of the pendulum bob at the bottom of its swing.

    The amplitude A is a quarter of the circumference of a circle with radius L, or $\dfrac{2\pi L}{4} = \dfrac{\pi}{2} L$.

    Assuming SHM, $v_{\text{m}} = \omega A = \sqrt{\dfrac{g}{L}} \left(\dfrac{\pi}{2} L \right) = \boxed{\dfrac{\pi}{2} \sqrt{gL}}$. Since $v \propto \omega \propto \dfrac{1}{T}$, a smaller speed implies a larger

    period. Since $\dfrac{v_{\text{m}}}{v} = \dfrac{\frac{\pi}{2}\sqrt{gL}}{\sqrt{2gL}} = \dfrac{\pi}{2\sqrt{2}} > 1,$ the period of a pendulum for large amplitudes is $\boxed{\text{larger}}$ than that

    given by Eq. (10-26b).

Chapter 11

WAVES

Conceptual Questions

1. Wrapping a thick coil of copper wire around a piano string increases the string's mass density and therefore decreases the speed of waves traveling along it. The fundamental wavelength is fixed by the length of the string—the decreased wave velocity must therefore be accompanied by a decrease in the frequency at which the string vibrates.

5. Words spoken by two people at the same time are comprehensible because sound waves travel through each other—interfering while superimposed, but returning to their original waveform as they again separate.

9. Since transverse waves do not travel through the core while longitudinal waves do, some part of the core is a molten, viscous liquid that cannot support the transmission of a transverse wave. A longitudinal wave can create compressions and rarefactions in the liquid and travel on through.

Problems

1. **Strategy** Form a proportion with the intensities, treating the Sun as an isotropic source. Use Eq. (11-1).

   Solution Find the intensity of the sunlight that reaches Jupiter.
   $$\frac{I_J}{I_E} = \frac{\frac{P}{4\pi r_J^2}}{\frac{P}{4\pi r_E^2}} = \frac{r_E^2}{r_J^2}, \text{ so } I_J = \left(\frac{r_E}{r_J}\right)^2 I_E = \left(\frac{1}{5.2}\right)^2 (1400 \ \text{W/m}^2) = \boxed{52 \ \text{W/m}^2}.$$

3. **Strategy** Form a proportion with the intensities, treating the jet airplane as an isotropic source. Use Eq. (11-1).

   Solution Find the intensity of the sound waves at the ears of the person.
   $$\frac{I_2}{I_1} = \frac{P/(4\pi r_2^2)}{P/(4\pi r_1^2)} = \left(\frac{r_1}{r_2}\right)^2, \text{ so } I_2 = \left(\frac{r_1}{r_2}\right)^2 I_1 = \left(\frac{5.0 \ \text{m}}{120 \ \text{m}}\right)^2 (1.0\times10^2 \ \text{W/m}^2) = \boxed{170 \ \text{mW/m}^2}.$$

5. **Strategy** The power equals the intensity times the area.

   Solution Find the rate at which the Sun emits electromagnetic waves.
   $$P = IA = I(4\pi R_E^2) = 4\pi(1.4\times10^3 \ \text{W/m}^2)(1.50\times10^{11} \ \text{m})^2 = \boxed{4.0\times10^{26} \ \text{W}}$$

7. **Strategy** Refer to the figure. Use the definition of average speed.

   Solution

   (a) Find the speed.
   $$v_x = \frac{\Delta x}{\Delta t} = \frac{1.80 \ \text{m} - 1.50 \ \text{m}}{0.20 \ \text{s}} = 1.5 \ \text{m/s}$$
   Find the position.
   $$x_f = x_i + v\Delta t = 1.80 \ \text{m} + (1.5 \ \text{m/s})(3.00 \ \text{s} - 0.20 \ \text{s}) = \boxed{6.0 \ \text{m}}$$

(b) $t_f = \dfrac{x_f - x_i}{v_x} + t_i = \dfrac{4.00\ \text{m} - 1.80\ \text{m}}{1.5\ \text{m/s}} + 0.20\ \text{s} = \boxed{1.7\ \text{s}}$

9. **Strategy** Use Eq. (11-4).

   Solution Find the speed of the transverse waves on the string.

   $v = \sqrt{\dfrac{F}{\mu}} = \sqrt{\dfrac{90.0\ \text{N}}{3.20\times10^{-3}\ \text{kg/m}}} = \boxed{168\ \text{m/s}}$

13. **Strategy** Use Eq. (11-5).

   Solution Find the wavelength.

   $\lambda = vT = (75.0\ \text{m/s})(5.00\times10^{-3}\ \text{s}) = \boxed{0.375\ \text{m}}$

15. **Strategy** Use Eq. (11-6).

   Solution Find the frequencies.

   (a) $f = \dfrac{v}{\lambda} = \dfrac{340\ \text{m/s}}{1.0\ \text{m}} = \boxed{340\ \text{Hz}}$

   (b) $f = \dfrac{v}{\lambda} = \dfrac{3.0\times10^8\ \text{m/s}}{1.0\ \text{m}} = \boxed{3.0\times10^8\ \text{Hz}}$

17. **Strategy** Use Eq. (11-6).

   Solution Find the frequency with which the buoy bobs up and down.

   $f = \dfrac{v}{\lambda} = \dfrac{2.5\ \text{m/s}}{7.5\ \text{m}} = \boxed{0.33\ \text{Hz}}$

21. **Strategy** The wave on the string is of the form $y(x, t) = A\sin(\omega t - kx)$. Use the equation, the given information, Eq. (11-7), and the relationship between period and angular frequency to find the amplitude, wavelength, period, and wave speed.

   Solution

   (a) $A = \boxed{4.0\ \text{mm}}$

   (b) $\lambda = \dfrac{2\pi}{k} = \dfrac{2\pi}{6.0\ \text{m}^{-1}} = \boxed{1.0\ \text{m}}$

   (c) $T = \dfrac{2\pi}{\omega} = \dfrac{2\pi}{6.0\times10^2\ \text{s}^{-1}} = \boxed{0.010\ \text{s}}$

   (d) $v = \dfrac{\omega}{k} = \dfrac{6.0\times10^2\ \text{s}^{-1}}{6.0\ \text{m}^{-1}} = \boxed{100\ \text{m/s}}$

   (e) Since the signs of ωt and kx are opposite, the wave travels $\boxed{\text{in the } +x\text{-direction (to the right)}}$.

23. **Strategy** The equation for a transverse sinusoidal wave moving in the negative x-direction can be written in the form $y(x, t) = A\sin(kx + \omega t)$. Use Eq. (11-7) to find the angular frequency and the wavenumber.

    Solution $A = 0.120$ m, $\lambda = 0.300$ m, $v = 6.40$ m/s, and $y(x, t) = A\sin(\omega t + kx)$.

    $$\omega = \frac{2\pi v}{\lambda} = \frac{2\pi(6.40 \text{ m/s})}{0.300 \text{ m}} = 134 \text{ s}^{-1} \text{ and } k = \frac{2\pi}{\lambda} = \frac{2\pi}{0.300 \text{ m}} = 20.9 \text{ m}^{-1}.$$

    Thus, the equation is $\boxed{y(x, t) = (0.120 \text{ m})\sin[(134 \text{ s}^{-1})t + (20.9 \text{ m}^{-1})x]}$.

25. **Strategy** The maximum y-value is the amplitude. Find the horizontal distance for which the wave repeats to find the wavelength. The wave speed is the distance the wave travels divided by the time interval it took to travel that distance. Use Eq. (11-6) to find the frequency of the wave. The period is the reciprocal of the frequency.

    Solution

    (a) $y_{max} = 2.6$ cm, so $A = \boxed{2.6 \text{ cm}}$.

    (b) $\lambda = \Delta x = 16 \text{ m} - 2 \text{ m} = \boxed{14 \text{ m}}$

    (c) $v = \dfrac{\Delta x}{\Delta t} = \dfrac{7.5 \text{ m} - 5.5 \text{ m}}{0.10 \text{ s}} = \boxed{20 \text{ m/s}}$

    (d) $f = \dfrac{v}{\lambda} = \dfrac{20 \text{ m/s}}{14 \text{ m}} = \boxed{1.4 \text{ Hz}}$

    (e) $T = \dfrac{1}{f} = \dfrac{14 \text{ m}}{20 \text{ m/s}} = \boxed{0.70 \text{ s}}$

29. (a) **Strategy** Substitute $t = 0$, 0.96 s, and 1.92 s into $y(x, t) = (0.80 \text{ mm})\sin[(\pi/5.0 \text{ cm}^{-1})x - (\pi/6.0 \text{ s}^{-1})t]$ and graph the resulting equations.

    Solution The three equations are:

    $y(x, 0) = (0.80 \text{ mm})\sin[(\pi/5.0 \text{ cm}^{-1})x]$, $y(x, 0.96 \text{ s}) = (0.80 \text{ mm})\sin[(\pi/5.0 \text{ cm}^{-1})x - 0.50]$, and

    $y(x, 1.92 \text{ s}) = (0.80 \text{ mm})\sin[(\pi/5.0 \text{ cm}^{-1})x - 1.0]$.

    Find the wavelength.

    $$\lambda = \frac{2\pi}{k} = \frac{2\pi}{\pi/(5.0 \text{ cm})} = 10 \text{ cm}$$

    The amplitude of the wave is $A = 0.80$ mm. The first graph (solid) begins at the origin. The second graph (dashed) is shifted to the right by $(5.0 \text{ cm} \times 0.50)/\pi = 0.80$ cm. The third graph (dotted) is shifted to the right twice as far as the second graph, or 1.6 cm.

    The graphs are shown:

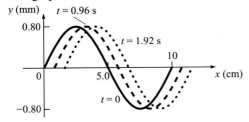

(b) Strategy Substitute $t = 0$, 0.96 s, and 1.96 s into $y(x, t) = (0.50 \text{ mm})\sin[(\pi/5.0 \text{ cm}^{-1})x + (\pi/6.0 \text{ s}^{-1})t]$ and graph the resulting equations.

Solution The three equations are:

$y(x, 0) = (0.50 \text{ mm})\sin[(\pi/5.0 \text{ cm}^{-1})x]$, $y(x, 0.96 \text{ s}) = (0.50 \text{ mm})\sin[(\pi/5.0 \text{ cm}^{-1})x + 0.50]$, and

$y(x, 1.92 \text{ s}) = (0.50 \text{ mm})\sin[(\pi/5.0 \text{ cm}^{-1})x + 1.0]$.

Find the wavelength.

$$\lambda = \frac{2\pi}{k} = \frac{2\pi}{\pi/(5.0 \text{ cm})} = 10 \text{ cm}$$

The amplitude of the wave is $A = 0.50$ mm. The first graph (solid) begins at the origin. The second graph (dashed) is shifted to the left by $(5.0 \text{ cm} \times 0.50)/\pi = 0.80$ cm. The third graph (dotted) is shifted to the left twice as far as the second graph, or 1.6 cm. The graphs are shown:

(c) Strategy Refer to the results of parts (a) and (b).

Solution The graphs obtained in part (a) move to the right as time progresses, so $\boxed{y(x, t) = (0.80 \text{ mm})\sin(kx - \omega t) \text{ represents a wave traveling in the } +x\text{-direction}}$. The graphs obtained in part (b) move to the left as time progresses, so $\boxed{y(x, t) = (0.50 \text{ mm})\sin(kx + \omega t) \text{ represents a wave traveling in the } -x\text{-direction}}$.

31. Strategy Compute the positions of the peaks of each pulse for the given times. Then use the principle of superposition to graph the shape of the cord for each time.

Solution

t (s)	Short Pulse Position	Tall Pulse Position
0.15	$10 \text{ cm} + (40 \text{ cm/s})(0.15 \text{ s}) = 16 \text{ cm}$	$30 \text{ cm} - (40 \text{ cm/s})(0.15 \text{ s}) = 24 \text{ cm}$
0.25	$10 \text{ cm} + (40 \text{ cm/s})(0.25 \text{ s}) = 20 \text{ cm}$	$30 \text{ cm} - (40 \text{ cm/s})(0.25 \text{ s}) = 20 \text{ cm}$
0.30	$10 \text{ cm} + (40 \text{ cm/s})(0.30 \text{ s}) = 22 \text{ cm}$	$30 \text{ cm} - (40 \text{ cm/s})(0.30 \text{ s}) = 18 \text{ cm}$

33. **Strategy** Sketch the sine waves. Use the principle of superposition to find the amplitudes. Let $y_1 = A\sin(\omega t + kx)$ and $y_2 = A\sin(\omega t + kx - \phi)$ and use the trigonometric identity $\sin\alpha + \sin\beta = 2\sin\left(\dfrac{\alpha+\beta}{2}\right)\cos\left(\dfrac{\alpha-\beta}{2}\right)$.

Solution

(a)

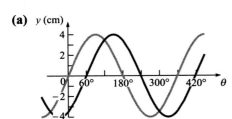

Use the principle of superposition.

$$y = y_1 + y_2 = A\sin(\omega t + kx) + A\sin(\omega t + kx - \phi) = 2A\sin\left(\omega t + kx - \frac{\phi}{2}\right)\cos\frac{\phi}{2} = A'\sin\left(\omega t + kx - \frac{\phi}{2}\right)$$

where $A' = 2A\cos\dfrac{\phi}{2} = 2(4.0 \text{ cm})\cos\dfrac{60.0°}{2} = \boxed{6.9 \text{ cm}}$.

(b)

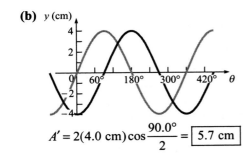

$$A' = 2(4.0 \text{ cm})\cos\frac{90.0°}{2} = \boxed{5.7 \text{ cm}}$$

35. **Strategy** Use the principle of superposition and the trigonometric identity
$$\sin\alpha + \sin\beta = 2\sin\left(\frac{\alpha+\beta}{2}\right)\cos\left(\frac{\alpha-\beta}{2}\right).$$

Solution Find the traveling sine wave.
$$y = y_1 + y_2 = A\sin(\omega t + kx) + A\sin(\omega t + kx - \phi) = 2A\sin\left(\omega t + kx - \frac{\phi}{2}\right)\cos\frac{\phi}{2} = A'\sin\left(\omega t + kx - \frac{\phi}{2}\right)$$

where $A' = 2A\cos\dfrac{\phi}{2} = 6.69$ cm. Find ϕ.

$$\cos\frac{\phi}{2} = \frac{A'}{2A}, \text{ so } \phi = 2\cos^{-1}\frac{A'}{2A} = 2\cos^{-1}\frac{6.69 \text{ cm}}{2(5.00 \text{ cm})} = \boxed{96.0°}.$$

37. **Strategy** Refer to the figure. Use $\Delta x = v_x \Delta t$ and the principle of superposition.

    Solution The pulse moves 1.80 m − 1.50 m = 0.30 m in 0.20 s. So, the speed of the wave is

    $v = \dfrac{0.30 \text{ m}}{0.20 \text{ s}} = 1.5$ m/s. When the pulse reaches the right endpoint, it is reflected and inverted. When exactly half of the pulse has been reflected and inverted, the superposition of the incident and reflected waves results in the cancellation of the waves ($y_1 + y_2 = 0$). Thus, the string looks flat at $t = \dfrac{x}{v} = \dfrac{4.0 \text{ m} - 1.5 \text{ m}}{1.5 \text{ m/s}} = \boxed{1.7 \text{ s}}$.

39. **Strategy** The waves are coherent. Use the principle of superposition.

    Solution

    (a) The resulting wave will have its largest amplitude if the waves interfere constructively. The phase difference is $\boxed{0°}$, and the amplitude is $A_1 + A_2 = 5.0 \text{ cm} + 3.0 \text{ cm} = \boxed{8.0 \text{ cm}}$.

    (b) The resulting wave will have its smallest amplitude if the waves interfere destructively. The phase difference is $\boxed{180°}$, and the amplitude is $|A_1 - A_2| = |5.0 \text{ cm} - 3.0 \text{ cm}| = \boxed{2.0 \text{ cm}}$.

    (c) $8.0 \text{ cm} : 2.0 \text{ cm} = \boxed{4:1}$

41. **Strategy** Intensity is proportional to the amplitude squared. For constructive interference, the amplitude of the superposition is the sum of the original amplitudes.

    Solution Find A_1/A_2.

    $$\frac{A_1}{A_2} = \sqrt{\frac{I_1}{I_2}} = \sqrt{\frac{25}{15}} = \sqrt{\frac{5.0}{3.0}}$$

    Find the amplitude of the superposition.

    $$A = A_1 + A_2 = A_2\sqrt{\frac{5.0}{3.0}} + A_2 = A_2\left(1 + \sqrt{\frac{5.0}{3.0}}\right)$$

    Find the intensity of the superposition.

    $$\sqrt{\frac{I}{I_2}} = \frac{A}{A_2} = 1 + \sqrt{\frac{5.0}{3.0}}, \text{ so } I = \left(1 + \sqrt{\frac{5.0}{3.0}}\right)^2 I_2 = \left(1 + \sqrt{\frac{5.0}{3.0}}\right)^2 (15 \text{ mW/m}^2) = \boxed{79 \text{ mW/m}^2}.$$

45. **Strategy** Use Eqs. (11-2) and (11-13).

    Solution

    $$f_1 = \frac{v}{2L} \text{ and } v = \sqrt{\frac{TL}{m}}. \quad f_1 = \frac{1}{2L}\sqrt{\frac{T_1 L}{m}} = \sqrt{\frac{T_1}{4Lm}}, \text{ so } \left(\frac{f_2}{f_1}\right)^2 = \frac{T_2}{T_1}.$$

    Calculate the percentage reduction in the tension.

    $$\frac{T_1 - T_2}{T_1} \times 100\% = \frac{T_1 - \left(\frac{f_2}{f_1}\right)^2 T_1}{T_1} \times 100\% = \left[1 - \left(\frac{f_2}{f_1}\right)^2\right] \times 100\% = \left[1 - \left(\frac{1 - 0.040}{1}\right)^2\right] \times 100\% = \boxed{7.8\%}$$

49. **Strategy** The frequencies are given by $f_n = nv/(2L)$. The speed of the transverse waves is related to the tension by $v = \sqrt{T/\mu}$.

Solution

(a) Find the frequency of the fundamental oscillation.

$$f_1 = \frac{v}{2L} = \frac{1}{2L}\sqrt{\frac{T}{\mu}} = \frac{1}{2(1.5\text{ m})}\sqrt{\frac{12\text{ N}}{1.2\times10^{-3}\text{ kg/m}}} = \boxed{33\text{ Hz}}$$

(b) Find the tension.

$$f_3 = \frac{3v}{2L} = \frac{3}{2L}\sqrt{\frac{T}{\mu}},\text{ so }T = \frac{4\mu L^2 f_3^2}{9} = \frac{4(1.2\times10^{-3}\text{ kg/m})(1.5\text{ m})^2(0.50\times10^3\text{ Hz})^2}{9} = \boxed{300\text{ N}}.$$

53. **(a) Strategy and Solution** All frequencies higher than the fundamental are integral multiples of the fundamental. Since there are no other frequencies between the two given, the fundamental is the difference between those two. Thus, the fundamental frequency is $1040\text{ Hz} - 780\text{ Hz} = \boxed{260\text{ Hz}}$.

(b) Strategy Use Eqs. (11-2) and (11-13).

Solution Find the total mass of the string.

$$f_1 = \frac{v}{2L} = \frac{1}{2L}\sqrt{\frac{FL}{m}} = \sqrt{\frac{F}{4mL}},\text{ so }m = \frac{F}{4f_1^2 L} = \frac{1200\text{ N}}{4(260\text{ Hz})^2(1.6\text{ m})} = \boxed{2.8\text{ g}}.$$

57. **Strategy** The wave speed for the 1.0-Hz waves is twice that for the 2.0-Hz waves, so it takes the 1.0-Hz waves 120 s to reach you. (120 s + 120 s = 240 s is the time it takes the 2.0-Hz waves to reach you; twice as long.)

Solution Compute the distance to the boat.

$$\Delta x = v\Delta t = (1.56\text{ m/s})(120\text{ s}) = \boxed{190\text{ m}}$$

61. **Strategy** Speed is inversely proportional to the time of travel. Form a proportion and use $\Delta x = v\Delta t$.

Solution Relate the speeds to the times of travel.

$$\frac{v_P}{v_S} = \frac{10.0\text{ km/s}}{8.0\text{ km/s}} = \frac{5.00}{4.0} = \frac{t_S}{t_P}$$

Find the time for the S wave to travel from the source to the detector.

$$\Delta t = t_S - t_P = t_S - t_S\left(\frac{4.0}{5.00}\right) = t_S(1 - 0.80),\text{ so }t_S = \frac{2.0\text{ s}}{0.20} = 10\text{ s}.$$

Calculate the distance between the source and the detector.

$$d = v_S t_S = (8.0\text{ km/s})(10\text{ s}) = \boxed{80\text{ km}}$$

65. **Strategy** Even though the wire is cut in two, the linear mass density does not change (half the length and half the mass). According to Eq. (11-4), the speed of waves on a wire is directly proportional to the square root of the tension. According to Eq. (11-13), the frequency of the waves on a wire is directly proportional to the speed of the waves. Therefore, the frequency is directly proportional to the square root of the tension in a wire. Use Newton's second law.

Solution For the single wire:
$\Sigma F_y = T_1 - mg = 0$, so $T_1 = mg$.

For the two wires:
$\Sigma F_y = 2T_2 - mg = 0$, so $T_2 = mg/2$.

Therefore, $T_1 = 2T_2$. Form a proportion.

$$\frac{f_2}{f_1} = \sqrt{\frac{T_2}{T_1}} = \sqrt{\frac{T_2}{2T_2}} = \frac{1}{\sqrt{2}}, \text{ so } f_2 = \frac{f_1}{\sqrt{2}}.$$

Thus, the new fundamental frequency of each wire is $660 \text{ Hz}/\sqrt{2} = \boxed{470 \text{ Hz}}$.

69. **Strategy** Use dimensional analysis.

    Solution γ has units $N/m = kg/s^2$. ρ has units kg/m^3. λ has units m. $\gamma/(\lambda \cdot \rho)$ has units

    $$\frac{kg/s^2}{m \cdot kg/m^3} = \frac{m^2}{s^2}. \; [\gamma/(\lambda \cdot \rho)]^{1/2} \text{ has units m/s. So, } \boxed{v \propto \sqrt{\frac{\gamma}{\lambda\rho}}}. \text{ Since } v \text{ depends upon } \lambda, \text{ surface waves are}$$

    $\boxed{\text{dispersive}}$.

73. **Strategy** Destructive interference occurs when the path length difference of the two sound waves is an odd multiple of half of the wavelength.

    Solution The wavelength is $\lambda = v / f = (340 \text{ m/s})/(680 \text{ Hz}) = 0.50 \text{ m}$. The largest possible path length difference is equal to the distance between the speakers, 1.5 m. $\lambda / 2 = 0.25 \text{ m}$, so the path length differences that cause destructive interference are 0.25 m, 0.75 m, and 1.25 m. Let the speakers lie along the x-axis at $x = \pm 0.75 \text{ m}$. Then the path length difference is zero along the y-axis and 1.5 m along the x-axis. As the listener walks along the circle of radius 1 m, the path length difference varies from 0 to 1.5 m. The path length difference equals 0.25 m, 0.75 m, and 1.25 m once for each quadrant of the circle (three occurrences of destructive interference). There are four quadrants, so the listener observes destructive interference at $\boxed{12}$ points along the circle.

77. **Strategy** Use the principle of superposition.

    Solution $\Delta x = 1.80 \text{ m} - 1.50 \text{ m} = 0.30 \text{ m}$ in $\Delta t = 0.20 \text{ s}$, so $v = 0.30 \text{ m}/(0.20 \text{ s}) = 1.5 \text{ m/s}$.
    Find the position of the peak at $t = 1.6$ s.
    $x_{\text{peak}} = x_i + vt = 1.5 \text{ m} + (1.5 \text{ m/s})(1.6 \text{ s}) = 3.9 \text{ m}$
    The peak of the pulse is nearly to the end of the string. The reflected pulse is below the string, so most of the height of the original pulse is cancelled.

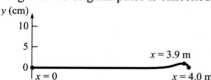

Chapter 12

SOUND

Conceptual Questions

1. The wavelength of the standing waves inside a bassoon is determined by the length of its air chamber. With a fixed fundamental wavelength, the frequency of these waves depends only upon the speed of sound in air, which itself depends significantly upon the air temperature. As a result of thermal contraction and expansion, changes in air temperature also affect the frequency of waves generated on a cello string—albeit much less significantly than for the bassoon.

5. For high-frequency sounds the wavelength is relatively small. The phase difference of the sounds arriving at each ear is then very sensitive to small variations in head position, wind speed, and several other factors. This makes the phase difference method unreliable for high-frequency sounds.

9. The maximum loudness of a stereo is proportional to the maximum intensity level that it can produce. Doubling the power of the stereo's amplifier also doubles its intensity, but it increases the intensity level by only 3 dB.

13. Doubling the pressure amplitude of a sound wave doubles the displacement amplitude, quadruples the intensity, and increases the intensity level by 6 dB.

17. Although the fundamental frequency of the highest note on a piano is approximately 4 kHz, the harmonics of that note occur at higher frequencies. An instrument's timbre is determined by the presence or absence of these harmonics. High quality audio equipment must therefore be able to reproduce frequencies up to the limit of the human audible range in order to faithfully reproduce the sound of an instrument.

Problems

1. **Strategy** Use Eqs. (11-6) and (12-3).

   Solution Find the wavelength of the ultrasonic waves.
   $$\lambda = \frac{v}{f} \text{ and } v = v_0\sqrt{\frac{T}{T_0}}, \text{ so } \lambda = \frac{v}{f} = \frac{v_0}{f}\sqrt{\frac{T}{T_0}} = \frac{331 \text{ m/s}}{1.0\times10^5 \text{ Hz}}\sqrt{\frac{273.15 \text{ K} + 15 \text{ K}}{273.15}} = \boxed{3.4 \text{ mm}}.$$

5. **Strategy** Use $\Delta x = v_x \Delta t$ and the speeds of light and sound. For $T = 20.0°C$, $v = 343$ m/s.

   Solution Verify the rule of thumb.
   $$\Delta t_{\text{light}} = \frac{\Delta x}{c} = \frac{1.6\times10^3 \text{ m}}{3\times10^8 \text{ m/s}} = 5 \text{ μs is negligible;} \quad \Delta t_{\text{sound}} = \frac{\Delta x}{v} = \frac{1.6\times10^3 \text{ m}}{343 \text{ m/s}} = \boxed{4.7 \text{ s}}.$$
   4.7 s = 5 s to one significant figure. The rule of thumb is approximately correct.

7. **Strategy** Use Eq. (12-1).

   Solution Find the speed of sound in mercury.
   $$v = \sqrt{\frac{B}{\rho}} = \sqrt{\frac{2.8\times10^{10} \text{ Pa}}{1.36\times10^4 \text{ kg/m}^3}} = \boxed{1.4 \text{ km/s}}$$

9. **Strategy** Replace each quantity with its SI units and simplify. In (a), use Eq. (12-1). In (b), analyze each combination of ρ and B.

Solution

(a) Show that Eq. (12-1) gives the speed of sound in m/s.

$$v = \sqrt{\frac{B}{\rho}}, \text{ so } \sqrt{\frac{N/m^2}{kg/m^3}} = \sqrt{\frac{(kg \cdot m/s^2)/m^2}{kg/m^3}} = \sqrt{\frac{1/(m \cdot s^2)}{1/m^3}} = \sqrt{\frac{m^2}{s^2}} = m/s.$$

(b) Show that no other combination of B and ρ of than $\sqrt{B/\rho}$ can give dimensions of speed.

$$\frac{\rho}{B} \text{ has units } \frac{kg}{m^3} \cdot \frac{m^2}{N} = \frac{kg}{m \cdot kg \cdot m/s^2} = \frac{s^2}{m^2}; \quad \rho B \text{ has units } \frac{kg}{m^3} \cdot \frac{N}{m^2} = \frac{kg^2 \cdot m/s^2}{m^5} = \frac{kg^2}{m^4 \cdot s^2}; \text{ and}$$

$$\frac{1}{\rho B} \text{ has units } \frac{m^4 \cdot s^2}{kg^2}.$$

No power of the above three combinations (other than $-1/2$, which gives $\sqrt{B/\rho}$) will give the dimensions of speed; therefore, Eq. (12-1) must be correct except for the possibility of a dimensionless constant.

13. **Strategy** Solve for the intensity in Eq. (12-8). The sound is incoherent, so add the three intensities; then solve for the combined intensity level of the three machines.

Solution Solve for the intensity.

$$\beta = (10 \text{ dB})\log_{10}\frac{I}{I_0}, \text{ so } 10^{\frac{\beta}{10 \text{ dB}}} = \frac{I}{I_0} \text{ and } I = I_0 10^{\frac{\beta}{10 \text{ dB}}}.$$

Find the combined intensity level.

$$I_{total} = I_1 + I_2 + I_3 = I_0 10^{\frac{\beta_1}{10 \text{ dB}}} + I_0 10^{\frac{\beta_2}{10 \text{ dB}}} + I_0 10^{\frac{\beta_3}{10 \text{ dB}}}, \text{ so } \frac{I_{total}}{I_0} = 10^{\frac{\beta_1}{10 \text{ dB}}} + 10^{\frac{\beta_2}{10 \text{ dB}}} + 10^{\frac{\beta_3}{10 \text{ dB}}}. \text{ Thus,}$$

$$\beta_{total} = (10 \text{ dB})\log_{10}\frac{I_{total}}{I_0} = (10 \text{ dB})\log_{10}\left(10^{\frac{\beta_1}{10 \text{ dB}}} + 10^{\frac{\beta_2}{10 \text{ dB}}} + 10^{\frac{\beta_3}{10 \text{ dB}}}\right) = (10 \text{ dB})\log_{10}\left(10^{\frac{85 \text{ dB}}{10 \text{ dB}}} + 10^{\frac{90 \text{ dB}}{10 \text{ dB}}} + 10^{\frac{93 \text{ dB}}{10 \text{ dB}}}\right)$$

$$= \boxed{95 \text{ dB}}.$$

Since 95 dB is comparable to 93 dB, the intensity level of all three machines running is not much different than with only one machine running.

17. **Strategy** Use Eq. (12-8) to find an expression for the intensity. Then use each relationship given for the intensities to obtain the relationships for the intensity levels.

Solution Solve for the intensity.

$$\beta = (10 \text{ dB}) \log \frac{I}{I_0}$$

$$10^{\frac{\beta}{10 \text{ dB}}} = \frac{I}{I_0}$$

$$I = I_0 10^{\frac{\beta}{10 \text{ dB}}}$$

(a) Show that if $I_2 = 10.0 I_1$, $\beta_2 = \beta_1 + 10.0$ dB.

$$I_2 = 10.0 I_1$$

$$I_0 10^{\frac{\beta_2}{10 \text{ dB}}} = 10.0 I_0 10^{\frac{\beta_1}{10 \text{ dB}}}$$

$$10^{\frac{\beta_2}{10 \text{ dB}}} = (10.0) 10^{\frac{\beta_1}{10 \text{ dB}}}$$

$$\log 10^{\frac{\beta_2}{10 \text{ dB}}} = \log \left[(10.0) 10^{\frac{\beta_1}{10 \text{ dB}}} \right] = \log 10.0 + \log 10^{\frac{\beta_1}{10 \text{ dB}}}$$

$$\frac{\beta_2}{10 \text{ dB}} = 1.00 + \frac{\beta_1}{10 \text{ dB}}$$

$$\beta_2 = \beta_1 + 10.0 \text{ dB}$$

(b) Show that if $I_2 = 2.0 I_1$, $\beta_2 = \beta_1 + 3.0$ dB.

$$I_2 = 2.0 I_1$$

$$I_0 10^{\frac{\beta_2}{10 \text{ dB}}} = 2.0 I_0 10^{\frac{\beta_1}{10 \text{ dB}}}$$

$$10^{\frac{\beta_2}{10 \text{ dB}}} = (2.0) 10^{\frac{\beta_1}{10 \text{ dB}}}$$

$$\log 10^{\frac{\beta_2}{10 \text{ dB}}} = \log \left[(2.0) 10^{\frac{\beta_1}{10 \text{ dB}}} \right] = \log 2.0 + \log 10^{\frac{\beta_1}{10 \text{ dB}}}$$

$$\frac{\beta_2}{10 \text{ dB}} = 0.30 + \frac{\beta_1}{10 \text{ dB}}$$

$$\beta_2 = \beta_1 + 3.0 \text{ dB}$$

21. (a) **Strategy** $f_n = nv/(2L)$ for a pipe open at both ends and $v = 343$ m/s for $T = 20.0°C$.

Solution Find the length of the organ pipe.

$$f_1 = \frac{v}{2L}, \text{ so } L = \frac{v}{2f_1} = \frac{343 \text{ m/s}}{2(261.5 \text{ Hz})} = \boxed{65.6 \text{ cm}}$$

(b) **Strategy** The frequency of the organ pipe is proportional to the speed of the waves and the speed is proportional to the square root of temperature, so $f \propto v \propto \sqrt{T}$.

Solution Find the fundamental frequency after the temperature drop.

$$f_{0.0°} = f_{20°} \sqrt{\frac{T_{0.0°}}{T_{20°}}} = (261.5 \text{ Hz}) \sqrt{\frac{273.15 \text{ K} + 0.0 \text{ K}}{273.15 \text{ K} + 20.0 \text{ K}}} = \boxed{252.4 \text{ Hz}}$$

23. Strategy $f_n = nv/(2L)$ for a pipe open at both ends.

Solution Find the length of the organ pipe.

$$f_1 = \frac{v}{2L}, \text{ so } L = \frac{v}{2f_1} = \frac{331 \text{ m/s}}{2(382 \text{ Hz})} = \boxed{43.3 \text{ cm}}.$$

25. Strategy $f_n = nv/(2L)$ for a pipe open at both ends and $v = v_0\sqrt{T/T_0}$.

Solution Find an expression for the temperature in terms of n.

$$f_n = \frac{nv}{2L} = \frac{nv_0}{2L}\sqrt{\frac{T}{T_0}}, \text{ so } T = T_0\left(\frac{2Lf_n}{nv_0}\right)^2 = \frac{273.15 \text{ K}}{n^2}\left[\frac{2(2.0 \text{ m})(702 \text{ Hz})}{331 \text{ m/s}}\right]^2 = \frac{19{,}658 \text{ K}}{n^2}.$$

The assumed temperature range is 293 K (20°C) to 308 K (35°C). We need to find n such that T falls within this range. By trial and error, n is found to be 8. So, $T = 19{,}658 \text{ K}/8^2 = 307 \text{ K} = \boxed{34°\text{C}}$.

29. (a) Strategy The rod is analogous to a pipe open at both ends.

Solution $\boxed{\text{There is a displacement node (pressure antinode) at the center of the rod and displacement antinodes (pressure nodes) at the ends}}$.

(b) Strategy For a pipe open at both ends, $\lambda_1 = 2L$. Use Eq. (11-6).

Solution Calculate the speed of sound in aluminum.

$$v = \lambda_1 f_1 = 2Lf_1 = 2(1.0 \text{ m})(2.55\times10^3 \text{ Hz}) = \boxed{5100 \text{ m/s}}.$$

(c) Strategy The frequency of the sound wave in the rod is the same as the frequency of the sound wave in the air. Use Eq. (11-6).

Solution Find the wavelength of the sound wave in the air.

$$\lambda = \frac{v}{f} = \frac{334 \text{ m/s}}{2.55\times10^3 \text{ Hz}} = \boxed{13.1 \text{ cm}}$$

(d) Strategy and Solution The longitudinal motion of the rod is symmetrical about a central axis, so $\boxed{\text{the ends move in opposite directions and, thus, they are out of phase}}$.

33. (a) Strategy Use Eqs. (11-2) and (11-13).

Solution Solve for the tension in the string.

$$v = \sqrt{FL/m} \text{ and } f_1 = v/(2L), \text{ so } F = 4mLf_1^2 = 4(0.300\times10^{-3} \text{ kg})(0.655 \text{ m})(330.0 \text{ Hz})^2 = \boxed{85.6 \text{ N}}.$$

(b) Strategy and Solution The waves travel on the string with a speed of

$$v = 2Lf_1 = 2(0.655 \text{ m})(330.0 \text{ Hz}) = \boxed{432 \text{ m/s}}.$$

(c) Strategy and Solution Since the other musician is lowering the frequency of the whistle, the frequency being played is 330.0 Hz + 5 Hz = $\boxed{335 \text{ Hz}}$ when beats are first heard.

(d) Strategy Use Eq. (12-10b) for a pipe closed at one end.

Solution Find the length of the slide whistle.

$$f = \frac{v}{4L}, \text{ so } L = \frac{v}{4f} = \frac{343 \text{ m/s}}{4(335 \text{ Hz})} = \boxed{0.256 \text{ m}}.$$

37. Strategy Since the observer is moving and the source is stationary, use Eq. (12-13).

Solution As Mandy walks toward one siren (1), $v_o < 0$. As she recedes from the other siren (2), $v_o > 0$. Find the beat frequency heard by Mandy.

$$f_1 - f_2 = \left(1 + \frac{|v_o|}{v}\right)f_s - \left(1 - \frac{|v_o|}{v}\right)f_s = \frac{2|v_o|f_s}{v} = \frac{2(1.56 \text{ m/s})(698 \text{ Hz})}{343 \text{ m/s}} = \boxed{6.35 \text{ Hz}}$$

39. Strategy Since the observer is moving and the source is stationary, use Eq. (12-13).

Solution Compute the frequencies of the sound observed by the moving observer.

(a) The observer is moving toward a stationary source ($v_o < 0$).

$$f_o = \left(1 - \frac{v_o}{v}\right)f_s = [1 - (-0.50)](1.0 \text{ kHz}) = \boxed{1.5 \text{ kHz}}$$

(b) The observer is now moving away from the source ($v_o > 0$).

$$f_o = (1 - 0.50)(1.0 \text{ kHz}) = \boxed{500 \text{ Hz}}$$

41. Strategy Since both source and observer are moving, use Eq. (12-14).

Solution Compute the frequencies of the sound observed by the moving observer.

(a) A source and an observer are traveling toward each other ($v_s > 0$, $v_o < 0$).

$$f_o = \frac{1 - \frac{v_o}{v}}{1 - \frac{v_s}{v}} f_s = \frac{1 - (-0.50)}{1 - 0.50}(1.0 \text{ kHz}) = \boxed{3.0 \text{ kHz}}$$

(b) A source and an observer are traveling away from each other ($v_s < 0$, $v_o > 0$).

$$f_o = \frac{1 - 0.50}{1 + 0.50}(1.0 \text{ kHz}) = \boxed{330 \text{ Hz}}$$

(c) A source and an observer are traveling in the same direction ($v_s < 0$, $v_o < 0$).

$$f_o = \frac{1 + 0.50}{1 + 0.50}(1.0 \text{ kHz}) = \boxed{1.0 \text{ kHz}}$$

45. (a) Strategy The distance traveled (round trip) by the sound of the firing pistol in time Δt is $v\Delta t$. The distance between the ship and one side of the fjord is half this distance. Use Eq. (12-3).

Solution Find the distance between the ship and one side of the fjord.

$$d = \frac{1}{2}v\Delta t = \frac{1}{2}\Delta t v_0 \sqrt{\frac{T}{T_0}} = \frac{1}{2}(4.0 \text{ s})(331 \text{ m/s})\sqrt{\frac{273.15 \text{ K} + 5.0 \text{ K}}{273.15 \text{ K}}} = \boxed{670 \text{ m}}$$

(b) Strategy Let the distance to the closer side of the fjord be $d_1 = \frac{1}{2}vt_1$; then the distance to the other side of the fjord is $d_2 = \frac{1}{2}vt_2$.

Solution Find the time interval between the two echoes.

$$\Delta t = t_2 - t_1 = \frac{2d_2}{v} - t_1 = \frac{2d_2}{2d_1/t_1} - t_1 = \frac{d_2}{d_1}t_1 - t_1 = \left(\frac{1.80 \text{ km} - 0.668 \text{ km}}{0.668 \text{ km}} - 1\right)(4.0 \text{ s}) = \boxed{2.8 \text{ s}}$$

47. **Strategy** The distance traveled (round trip) by the sound wave in time Δt is $v\Delta t$. The depth d of the lake is half this distance.

Solution Find the depth of the lake.

$$d = \frac{1}{2}v\Delta t = \frac{1}{2}(0.540 \text{ s})(1493 \text{ m/s}) = \boxed{403 \text{ m}}$$

49. **Strategy** First treat the moth as a receiver moving away from the source (the bat); then treat the moth as the source moving away from an observer (the bat). Use Eqs. (12-3) and (12-14).

Solution Moth as receiver (v_m and $v_b > 0$; in the direction of propagation):

$$f_1 = \frac{1 - \frac{v_m}{v}}{1 - \frac{v_b}{v}}f_s$$

Moth as source (v_m and $v_b < 0$; opposite the direction of propagation):

$$f_2 = \frac{1 + \frac{v_b}{v}}{1 + \frac{v_m}{v}}f_1 = \frac{\left(1 + \frac{v_b}{v}\right)\left(1 - \frac{v_m}{v}\right)}{\left(1 + \frac{v_m}{v}\right)\left(1 - \frac{v_b}{v}\right)}f_s = \frac{(v + v_b)(v - v_m)}{(v + v_m)(v - v_b)}f_s$$

Find v at 10.0°C.

$$v = v_0\sqrt{\frac{T}{T_0}} = (331 \text{ m/s})\sqrt{\frac{273.15 \text{ K} + 10.0 \text{ K}}{273.15 \text{ K}}} = 337 \text{ m/s}$$

Calculate the frequency, f_2.

$$f_2 = \frac{(337 \text{ m/s} + 4.40 \text{ m/s})(337 \text{ m/s} - 1.20 \text{ m/s})}{(337 \text{ m/s} + 1.20 \text{ m/s})(337 \text{ m/s} - 4.40 \text{ m/s})}(82.0 \text{ kHz}) = \boxed{83.6 \text{ kHz}}$$

53. **(a) Strategy** Use Eqs. (11-2) and (11-13).

Solution Find f_2.

$$v = \sqrt{\frac{FL}{m}} \text{ and } f_2 = \frac{v}{L}, \text{ so } f_2 = \sqrt{\frac{F}{mL}} = \sqrt{\frac{7.00 \text{ N}}{(0.230 \times 10^{-3} \text{ kg})(0.300 \text{ m})}} = \boxed{319 \text{ Hz}}.$$

(b) Strategy The frequency in air is the same as the frequency for the string. Use Eq. (11-6).

Solution The frequency of the sound in the surrounding air is $\boxed{319 \text{ Hz}}$. The wavelength of the sound in the surrounding air is $\lambda = \dfrac{v}{f_2} = \dfrac{350 \text{ m/s}}{319 \text{ Hz}} = \boxed{1.1 \text{ m}}$.

57. (a) Strategy and Solution The intensity is inversely proportional to distance, so $I_1 \propto I_0 / d^2$, where I_1 and I_0 are the intensity at the object causing the reflection and the original intensity, respectively, and d is the distance between the bat and the object. Similarly, for the intensity of the echo, $I_2 \propto I_1 / d^2$ where I_2 is the intensity of the echo at the bat. Therefore, $I_2 \propto \dfrac{I_1}{d^2} \propto \dfrac{I_0/d^2}{d^2} \propto \dfrac{1}{d^4}$.

(b) Strategy Use the result of part (a).

Solution Find the percent increase in the intensity of the echo in terms of the distances.

$$\frac{\Delta I}{I_0} \times 100\% = \frac{I - I_0}{I_0} \times 100\% = \frac{\frac{1}{d^4} - \frac{1}{d_0^4}}{\frac{1}{d_0^4}} \times 100\% = \left[\left(\frac{d_0}{d} \right)^4 - 1 \right] \times 100\%$$

Compute the percent increase for each object.

First object: $\left[\left(\dfrac{0.60}{0.50} \right)^4 - 1 \right] \times 100\% = \boxed{110\%}$; second object: $\left[\left(\dfrac{1.10}{1.00} \right)^4 - 1 \right] \times 100\% = \boxed{46\%}$

61. Strategy The distance traveled (round trip) by the sound pulse in time Δt is $v \Delta t$. The distance to the ocean floor is half this distance.

Solution Find the elapsed time between an emitted pulse and the return of its echo at the correct depth d.

$2d = v \Delta t$, so $\Delta t = \dfrac{2d}{v} = \dfrac{2(40.0 \text{ fathoms}) \left(1.83 \frac{\text{m}}{\text{fathom}} \right)}{1533 \text{ m/s}} = \boxed{0.0955 \text{ s}}$.

65. Strategy The greatest common factor of the frequencies is the fundamental. Compute ratios of the frequencies and use these ratios to determine the greatest common factor of the frequencies.

Solution Compute the ratios.

$\dfrac{588}{392} = \dfrac{3}{2}$ and $\dfrac{980}{392} = \dfrac{5}{2}$, so $\dfrac{392}{2} = 196 \times 1$, $196 \times 3 = 588$, and $196 \times 5 = 980$.

The fundamental frequency is $\boxed{196 \text{ Hz}}$.

69. Strategy Since the combined sound intensity is incoherent, the sound intensity of one of the violins is 1/8 of the combined total ($I_2 = I_1 / 8$). Use Eq. (12-9).

Solution Find the sound intensity level for one violin.

$\beta_2 - \beta_1 = (10 \text{ dB}) \log \dfrac{I_2}{I_1} = (10 \text{ dB}) \log \dfrac{1}{8} = -(10 \text{ dB}) \log 8$, so

$\beta_2 = \beta_1 - (10 \text{ dB}) \log 8 = 38.0 \text{ dB} - (10 \text{ dB}) \log 8 = \boxed{29.0 \text{ dB}}$.

REVIEW AND SYNTHESIS: CHAPTERS 9–12

Review Exercises

1. **Strategy** The magnitude of the buoyant force on an object in water is equal to the weight of the water displaced by the object.

   Solution

   (a) Lead is much denser than aluminum, so for the same mass, its volume is much less. Therefore, $\boxed{\text{aluminum}}$ has the larger buoyant force acting on it; $\boxed{\text{since it is less dense it occupies more volume}}$.

   (b) Steel is denser than wood. Even though the wood is floating, it displaces more water than does the steel. Therefore, $\boxed{\text{wood}}$ has the larger buoyant force acting on it; $\boxed{\text{since it displaces more water than the steel}}$.

   (c) Lead: $\rho_w g V_{Pb} = \rho_w g \dfrac{m_{Pb}}{\rho_{Pb}} = (1.00 \times 10^3 \ \text{kg/m}^3)(9.80 \ \text{m/s}^2)\dfrac{1.0 \ \text{kg}}{11{,}300 \ \text{kg/m}^3} = \boxed{0.87 \ \text{N}}$

   Aluminum: $\rho_w g V_{Al} = \rho_w g \dfrac{m_{Al}}{\rho_{Al}} = (1.00 \times 10^3 \ \text{kg/m}^3)(9.80 \ \text{m/s}^2)\dfrac{1.0 \ \text{kg}}{2702 \ \text{kg/m}^3} = \boxed{3.6 \ \text{N}}$

   Steel: $\rho_w g V_{Steel} = \rho_w g \dfrac{m_{Steel}}{\rho_{Steel}} = (1.00 \times 10^3 \ \text{kg/m}^3)(9.80 \ \text{m/s}^2)\dfrac{1.0 \ \text{kg}}{7860 \ \text{kg/m}^3} = \boxed{1.2 \ \text{N}}$

   Wood: $mg = (1.0 \ \text{kg})(9.80 \ \text{m/s}^2) = \boxed{9.8 \ \text{N}}$ (Since the wood is floating, the buoyant force is equal to its weight.)

5. **Strategy** Use Eqs. (10-20a), (10-21), and (10-22), and Newton's second law.

   Solution The normal force on the 1.0-kg block m_1 is $N = m_1 g$. So, the force of friction on m_1 is $f = \mu N = \mu m_1 g$.

   Find the maximum acceleration that the top block can experience before it starts to slip.

   $\Sigma F = f = m_1 a$, so $a = \dfrac{f}{m_1} = \dfrac{\mu m_1 g}{m_1} = \mu g$.

   For SHM, the maximum acceleration is $a_m = \omega^2 A = \dfrac{k}{m} A$, which in this case is equal to

   $\dfrac{kA}{m_1 + m_2}$. Equate the accelerations and solve for A.

   $\dfrac{kA}{m_1 + m_2} = \mu g$, so $A = \dfrac{\mu(m_1 + m_2)g}{k}$.

   The maximum speed is $v_m = \omega A$. Compute the maximum speed that this set of blocks can have without the top block slipping.

   $v_m = \omega A = \sqrt{\dfrac{k}{m_1 + m_2}}\left[\dfrac{\mu(m_1 + m_2)g}{k}\right] = \mu g \sqrt{\dfrac{m_1 + m_2}{k}} = 0.45(9.80 \ \text{m/s}^2)\sqrt{\dfrac{1.0 \ \text{kg} + 5.0 \ \text{kg}}{150 \ \text{N/m}}} = \boxed{0.88 \ \text{m/s}}$

9. **(a) Strategy** Use Eqs. (11-2) and (11-13).

   Solution Find the tension in the guitar string.

   $$f_1 = \frac{v}{2L} = \frac{1}{2L}\sqrt{\frac{FL}{m}} = \sqrt{\frac{F}{4Lm}}, \text{ so } F = 4Lmf_1^2 = 4(0.655 \text{ m})(0.00331 \text{ kg})(82 \text{ Hz})^2 = \boxed{58 \text{ N}}.$$

   (b) Strategy Use Eqs. (11-4) and (11-13).

   Solution Find the length of the lowest frequency string when it is fingered at the fifth fret.

   $$f_1 = \frac{v}{2L} = \frac{1}{2L}\sqrt{\frac{F}{\mu}}, \text{ so } L = \frac{1}{2f_1}\sqrt{\frac{F}{\mu}} = \frac{1}{2(110 \text{ Hz})}\sqrt{\frac{58 \text{ N}}{0.00331 \text{ kg}/(0.655 \text{ m})}} = \boxed{49 \text{ cm}}.$$

13. **Strategy** The frequency of the sound is increased by a factor equal to the number of holes in the disk. Use Eq. (11-6).

    Solution The frequency of the sound is

    $f = 25(60.0 \text{ Hz}) = \boxed{1500 \text{ Hz}}.$

    Compute the wavelength that corresponds to this frequency.

    $$\lambda = \frac{v}{f} = \frac{343 \text{ m/s}}{1.50 \times 10^3 \text{ Hz}} = \boxed{22.9 \text{ cm}}$$

17. **Strategy** The source is moving in the direction of propagation of the sound, so $v_s > 0$. The observer is moving in the direction opposite the propagation of the sound, so $v_o < 0$. Use Eq. (12-14).

    Solution Find the frequency heard by the passenger in the oncoming boat.

    $$f_o = \frac{v - v_o}{v - v_s} f_s = \frac{343 \text{ m/s} - (-15.6 \text{ m/s})}{343 \text{ m/s} - 20.1 \text{ m/s}}(312 \text{ Hz}) = \boxed{346 \text{ Hz}}$$

21. **Strategy** Use the equations describing waves on a string fixed at both ends.

    Solution

    (a) The wavelength of the fundamental mode is $\lambda = 2L = 2(0.640 \text{ m}) = \boxed{1.28 \text{ m}}$.

    (b) The wave speed on the string is $v = \lambda f = (1.28 \text{ m})(110.0 \text{ Hz}) = \boxed{141 \text{ m/s}}$.

    (c) Find the linear mass density of the string.

    $$v = \sqrt{\frac{F}{\mu}}, \text{ so } \mu = \frac{F}{v^2} = \frac{133 \text{ N}}{(140.8 \text{ m/s})^2} = \boxed{6.71 \text{ g/m}}.$$

    (d) Find the maximum speed of a point on the string.

    $$v = \omega A = 2\pi f A = 2\pi(110.0 \text{ Hz})(0.00230 \text{ m}) = \boxed{0.253 \text{ m/s}}$$

    (e) The frequency in air is that same as that in the bridge and body of the guitar, which is the same as the frequency of the string: $\boxed{110.0 \text{ Hz}}$.

    (f) The speed of sound in air is $v = 331 \text{ m/s} + (0.60 \text{ m/s})(20) = 343 \text{ m/s}$.

    The wavelength of the sound wave in air is $\lambda = \dfrac{v}{f} = \dfrac{343 \text{ m/s}}{110.0 \text{ Hz}} = \boxed{3.12 \text{ m}}$.

25. Strategy Use Newton's second law and Hooke's law.

Solution

(a) Find the tension in the string when hanging straight down.

$\Sigma F = T_1 - mg = 0$, so $T_1 = mg$.

Find the tension in the string while it is swinging.

$\Sigma F_y = T_2 \cos\theta - mg = 0$, so $T_2 = \dfrac{mg}{\cos\theta}$.

Find the stretch of the string.

$Y = \dfrac{\Delta T / A}{\Delta L / L}$, so

$$\Delta L = \frac{L\Delta T}{AY} = \frac{Lmg}{AY}\left(\frac{1}{\cos\theta} - 1\right) = \frac{(2.200 \text{ m})(0.411 \text{ kg})(9.8 \text{ m/s}^2)}{\pi(0.00125 \text{ m})^2(4.00\times10^9 \text{ Pa})}\left(\frac{1}{\cos 65.0°} - 1\right) = \boxed{6.17\times10^{-4} \text{ m}}.$$

(b) Find the kinetic energy.

$$\Sigma F_x = T_2 \sin\theta = ma_x = \frac{mv^2}{r} = \frac{2K}{r}, \text{ so}$$

$$K = \frac{rT_2 \sin\theta}{2} = \frac{L\sin\theta \frac{mg}{\cos\theta}\sin\theta}{2} = \frac{mgL\tan\theta\sin\theta}{2} = \frac{(0.411 \text{ kg})(9.80 \text{ m/s}^2)(2.200 \text{ m})\tan 65.0°\sin 65.0°}{2}$$

$$= \boxed{8.61 \text{ J}}$$

(c) Find the time it takes a transverse wave pulse to travel the length of the string. Neglect the small change due to the stretch when finding the linear mass density.

$$v = \sqrt{\frac{T_2}{\mu}} = \sqrt{\frac{T_2}{\rho A}} \text{ and } L = vt, \text{ so}$$

$$t = \frac{L + \Delta L}{v} = (L + \Delta L)\sqrt{\frac{\rho A}{T_2}} = (L + \Delta L)\sqrt{\frac{\rho A\cos\theta}{mg}} = (2.2006 \text{ m})\sqrt{\frac{(1150 \text{ kg/m}^3)\pi(0.00125 \text{ m})^2\cos 65.0°}{(0.411 \text{ kg})(9.80 \text{ m/s}^2)}}$$

$$= \boxed{0.0536 \text{ s}}$$

MCAT Review

1. **Strategy** The buoyant force on the brick is equal in magnitude to the weight of the volume of water it displaces.

   Solution The brick is completely submerged, so its volume is equal to that of the displaced water. The weight of the displaced water is $30\text{ N} - 20\text{ N} = 10\text{ N}$. Find the volume of the brick.

   $$\rho_w g V_w = \rho_w g V_{brick} = 10\text{ N, so } V_{brick} = \frac{10\text{ N}}{\rho_w g} = \frac{10\text{ N}}{(1000\text{ kg/m}^3)(10\text{ m/s}^2)} = 1 \times 10^{-3}\text{ m}^3$$

   The correct answer is $\boxed{\text{A}}$.

2. **Strategy** The expansion of the cable obeys $F = k\Delta L$.

   Solution Compute the expansion of the cable.

   $$\Delta L = \frac{F}{k} = \frac{5000\text{ N}}{5.0 \times 10^6\text{ N/m}} = 10^{-3}\text{ m}$$

   The correct answer is $\boxed{\text{A}}$.

3. **Strategy** Solve for the intensity in the definition of sound level.

   Solution Find the intensity of the fire siren.

   $$\text{SL} = 10\log_{10}\frac{I}{I_0},\text{ so } I = I_0 10^{\text{SL}/10} = (1.0 \times 10^{-12}\text{ W/m}^2)10^{100/10} = 1.0 \times 10^{-2}\text{ W/m}^2.$$

   The correct answer is $\boxed{\text{D}}$.

4. **Strategy and Solution** The two centimeters of liquid with a specific gravity of 0.5 are equivalent to one centimeter of water; that is, the 6-cm column of liquid is equivalent to a 5-cm column of water. Therefore, the new gauge pressure at the base of the column is five-fourths the original. The correct answer is $\boxed{\text{C}}$.

5. **Strategy** The wavelength is inversely proportional to the index n. Let $\lambda_n = 8$ m and $\lambda_{n+2} = 4.8$ m.

   Solution Find n.

   $$L = \frac{n\lambda_n}{4} = \frac{(n+2)\lambda_{n+2}}{4},\text{ so } \frac{\lambda_n}{\lambda_{n+2}} = \frac{n+2}{n} = 1 + \frac{2}{n},\text{ or } n = 2\left(\frac{\lambda_n}{\lambda_{n+2}} - 1\right)^{-1}.$$

   Compute L.

   $$L = \frac{n\lambda_n}{4} = 2\left(\frac{\lambda_n}{\lambda_{n+2}} - 1\right)^{-1}\frac{\lambda_n}{4} = \frac{1}{2}\left(\frac{8\text{ m}}{4.8\text{ m}} - 1\right)^{-1}(8\text{ m}) = 6\text{ m}$$

   The correct answer is $\boxed{\text{C}}$.

6. **Strategy** The wave may interfere within the range of possibility of totally constructive or totally destructive interference.

   Solution For totally constructive interference, the amplitude of the combined waves is $5 + 3 = 8$ units. For totally destructive interference, the amplitude of the combined waves is $5 - 3 = 2$ units. The correct answer is $\boxed{\text{B}}$.

7. **Strategy and Solution** As the bob repeatedly swings to and fro, it speeds up and slows down, as well as changes direction. Therefore, its linear acceleration must change in both magnitude and direction.

   The correct answer is $\boxed{D}$.

8. **Strategy** Since $K \propto v^2$ and $v \propto r^{-4}$, $K \propto r^{-8}$.

   Solution Compute the ratio of kinetic energies.
   $$\frac{K_2}{K_1} = \left(\frac{2}{1}\right)^{-8} = \frac{1}{256} = \frac{1}{4^4} \text{ or } K_2 : K_1 = 1 : 4^4.$$
   The correct answer is $\boxed{B}$.

9. **Strategy** The buoyant force on a ball is equal to the weight of the volume of water displaced by that ball.

   Solution Since B_1 is not fully submerged and B_2 and B_3 are, the buoyant force on B_1 is less than the buoyant forces on the other two. Since B_2 and B_3 are fully submerged, the buoyant forces on each are the same.

   The correct answer is $\boxed{B}$.

10. **Strategy and Solution** Ball 1 is floating, so its density is less than that of the water. Since Ball 2 is submerged within the water, its density is the same as that of the water. Ball 3 is sitting on the bottom of the tank, so its density is greater than that of the water. The correct answer is $\boxed{A}$.

11. **Strategy** The supporting force of the bottom of the tank is equal to the weight of Ball 3 less the buoyant force of the water.

    Solution Compute the supporting force on Ball 3.
    $$\rho_{\text{Ball 3}} g V_{\text{Ball 3}} - \rho_{\text{water}} g V_{\text{Ball 3}} = g V_{\text{Ball 3}} (\rho_{\text{Ball 3}} - \rho_{\text{water}})$$
    $$= (9.80 \text{ m/s}^2)(1.0 \times 10^{-6} \text{ m}^3)(7.8 \times 10^3 \text{ kg/m}^3 - 1.0 \times 10^3 \text{ kg/m}^3) = 6.7 \times 10^{-2} \text{ N}$$
    The correct answer is $\boxed{B}$.

12. **Strategy** The relationship between the fraction of a floating object's volume that is submerged to the ratio of the object's density to the fluid in which it floats is $V_f / V_o = \rho_o / \rho_f$. So, the fraction of the object that is not submerged is $V_{ns} = 1 - V_f / V_o = 1 - \rho_o / \rho_f$.

    Solution Find the fraction of the volume of Ball 1 that is above the surface of the water.
    $$1 - \frac{\rho_{\text{Ball 1}}}{\rho_{\text{water}}} = 1 - \frac{8.0 \times 10^2 \text{ kg/m}^3}{1.0 \times 10^3 \text{ kg/m}^3} = \frac{1}{5}$$
    The correct answer is $\boxed{D}$.

13. **Strategy** The pressure difference at a depth d in water is given by $\rho_{water} g d$.

Solution Compute the approximate difference in pressure between the two balls.
$$\rho_{water} g d = (1.0 \times 10^3 \text{ kg/m}^3)(9.80 \text{ m/s}^2)(0.20 \text{ m}) = 2.0 \times 10^3 \text{ N/m}^2$$
The correct answer is $\boxed{C}$.

14. **Strategy** For the force exerted on Ball 3 by the bottom of the tank to be zero, Ball 3 must have the same density as the water.

Solution Find the volume of the hollow portion of Ball 3, V_H.

$$\rho_{Ball\ 3} = \frac{m_{Ball\ 3}}{V_{Ball\ 3}} = \frac{\rho_{Fe} V_{Fe}}{V_{Ball\ 3}} = \rho_{water} \text{ and } V_H = V_{Ball\ 3} - V_{Fe}, \text{ so}$$

$$V_H = V_{Ball\ 3} - \frac{\rho_{water}}{\rho_{Fe}} V_{Ball\ 3} = V_{Ball\ 3}\left(1 - \frac{\rho_{water}}{\rho_{Fe}}\right) = (1.0 \times 10^{-6} \text{ m}^3)\left(1 - \frac{1.0 \times 10^3 \text{ kg/m}^3}{7.8 \times 10^3 \text{ kg/m}^3}\right) = 0.87 \times 10^{-6} \text{ m}^3.$$

The correct answer is $\boxed{C}$.

Chapter 13

TEMPERATURE AND THE IDEAL GAS

Conceptual Questions

1. The development of standard temperature scales requires use of the zeroth law of thermodynamics. This law tells us that if a thermometer is in thermodynamic equilibrium with both a test object and an object used to define a standard, then the test and standard objects must be in thermodynamic equilibrium with each other. If this law did not hold, the temperature scale on a thermometer would have no relation to the actual temperature of the test object, and therefore, no standard could be defined.

5. The thermal expansion coefficients of silver and brass only differ by about 5%. Thus, a bimetallic strip made from these materials would bend only slightly during expansion, contrary to its intended purpose.

9. The SI units of mass density and number density are kg/m^3 and m^{-3}, respectively. An equal number density does not imply an equal mass density because the mass of an individual atom may be different in each gas.

13. The pressure of the air outside the balloon decreases as its distance above the Earth increases. The balloon expands until the pressures inside and outside are equal.

17. We could use any two of the quantities to decide whether the gas is dilute. The gas is dilute if the number density is low enough, or equivalently if the average intermolecular distance is large enough compared to the molecular diameter. For example, if the mean free path is much larger than the diameter, then we know that the intermolecular distance is large enough and the number density small enough so that the gas is dilute.

Problems

1. **Strategy** Use Eqs. (13-2b) and (13-3).

   Solution Convert the temperature.

   (a) $T_C = \dfrac{T_F - 32°F}{1.8°F/°C} = \dfrac{84°F - 32°F}{1.8°F/°C} = \boxed{29°C}$

   (b) $T = 29 \text{ K} + 273.15 \text{ K} = \boxed{302 \text{ K}}$

5. **Strategy and Solution** There are $78 + 114 = 192$ degrees C and 144 degrees J between the freezing and boiling points of ethyl alcohol. Thus, the conversion factor is $144/192 = 0.750$. So, $T_J = (0.750°J/°C)T_C + A$, where A is the offset to be determined. Find A by setting both temperatures equal to their respective boiling temperatures. $144°J = (0.750°J/°C)(78°C) + A$, so $A = 144°J - (0.750°J/°C)(78°C) = 85.5°J$.

   Thus, the conversion from °J to °C is given by $\boxed{T_J = (0.750°J/°C)T_C + 85.5°J}$.

9. **Strategy** Since each concrete slab expands along its entire length, only half of the expansion is considered for a particular gap. Two sections meet at a gap, so the gap should be as wide as the expansion of one concrete slab. Use Eq. (13-4).

   Solution Find the sizes of the expansion gaps.

   (a) $\Delta L = L_0 \alpha \Delta T = (15 \text{ m})(12 \times 10^{-6} \text{ K}^{-1})(40.0°C - 20.0°C) = \boxed{3.6 \text{ mm}}$

(b) $\Delta L = L_0 \alpha \Delta T = (15 \text{ m})(12 \times 10^{-6} \text{ K}^{-1})(-20.0°C - 20.0°C) = -7.2 \text{ mm}$

gap width $= 7.2 \text{ mm} + 3.6 \text{ mm} = \boxed{10.8 \text{ mm}}$

11. **Strategy** The hole expands just as if it were a solid brass disk. Use Eq. (13-6).

Solution Find the increase in area of the hole.

$\Delta A = 2\alpha A_0 \Delta T = 2(1.9 \times 10^{-5} \text{ °C}^{-1})(1.00 \text{ mm}^2)(30.0°C - 20.0°C) = \boxed{3.8 \times 10^{-4} \text{ mm}^2}$

13. **Strategy** A decrease in volume for a fixed mass increases the density, and vice versa. Use Eq. (13-7).

Solution

(a) $\dfrac{\Delta V}{V_0} = \beta \Delta T$ and $\dfrac{\Delta \rho}{\rho} = -\dfrac{\Delta V}{V_0}$. Thus, $\dfrac{\Delta \rho}{\rho} = -\beta \Delta T$, so $\Delta \rho = -\beta \rho \Delta T$.

(b) Compute the fractional change in density.

$\dfrac{\Delta \rho}{\rho} = -\beta \Delta T = -(57 \times 10^{-6} \text{ K}^{-1})(-10.0°C - 32°C) = \boxed{2.4 \times 10^{-3}}$

17. **Strategy** Use Eq. (13-4). The internal radius of the ring expands as if it were a solid piece of brass.

Solution Find the temperature at which the internal radius of the ring is 1.0010 cm.

$\dfrac{\Delta L}{L_0} = \alpha \Delta T$, so $\dfrac{\Delta L}{\alpha L_0} = T - T_0$. Compute the temperature.

$T = \dfrac{\Delta L}{\alpha L_0} + T_0 = \dfrac{1.0010 \text{ cm} - 1.0000 \text{ cm}}{(19 \times 10^{-6} \text{ K}^{-1})(1.0000 \text{ cm})} + 22.0°C = \boxed{75°C}$

21. **Strategy** The diameter of the hole expands as if it were a solid piece of copper. Use Eq. (13-4).

Solution Find the temperature at which the diameter of the hole is 1.0000 cm.

$\dfrac{\Delta L}{L_0} = \alpha \Delta T = \alpha(T - T_0)$, so $T = \dfrac{\Delta L}{\alpha L_0} + T_0 = \dfrac{1.0000 \text{ cm} - 0.9980 \text{ cm}}{(16 \times 10^{-6} \text{ K}^{-1})(0.9980 \text{ cm})} + 20.0°C = \boxed{150°C}$.

25. **Strategy** Use Eqs. (13-4) and (13-6) and the given initial and final areas.

Solution Find the fractional change.

$\dfrac{\Delta A}{A_0} = \dfrac{A - A_0}{A_0} = \dfrac{(s_0 + \Delta s)^2 - s_0^2}{s_0^2} = \dfrac{s_0^2 + 2s_0\Delta s + (\Delta s)^2 - s_0^2}{s_0^2} = \dfrac{2s_0\Delta s + (\Delta s)^2}{s_0^2} = \dfrac{\Delta s(2s_0 + \Delta s)}{s_0^2}$

Now, since $s_0 \gg \Delta s$, we have

$\dfrac{\Delta A}{A_0} \approx \dfrac{\Delta s(2s_0 + 0)}{s_0^2} = \dfrac{2s_0\Delta s}{s_0^2} = \dfrac{2\Delta s}{s_0} = 2\alpha\Delta T$ since $\dfrac{\Delta s}{s_0} = \alpha\Delta T$.

29. **Strategy** Add the molecular masses of each element in carbon dioxide.

Solution Find the mass of carbon dioxide in kg.

mass of CO_2 in kg $= m_C + 2m_O = [12.011 \text{ u} + 2(15.9994 \text{ u})](1.6605 \times 10^{-27} \text{ kg/u}) = \boxed{7.31 \times 10^{-26} \text{ kg}}$

33. **Strategy** Divide the total mass by the molar mass of sucrose to find the number of moles. Then use Eq. (13-11) to find the number of hydrogen atoms.

   Solution $m_{C_{12}H_{22}O_{11}} = 12(12.011 \text{ g/mol}) + 22(1.00794 \text{ g/mol}) + 11(15.9994 \text{ g/mol}) = 342.30 \text{ g/mol}$

   There are 342.30 grams of sucrose per mole, so there are $\dfrac{684.6 \text{ g}}{342.30 \text{ g/mol}} = 2.000$ mol of sucrose.

   There are $2.000(22) = 44.00$ moles of hydrogen. Find the number of hydrogen atoms.

   $N = nN_A = (44.00 \text{ mol})(6.022 \times 10^{23} \text{ mol}^{-1}) = \boxed{2.650 \times 10^{25} \text{ atoms}}$

35. **Strategy** Divide the total mass of methane by its molar mass.

   Solution Find the number of moles.

   $n_{CH_4} = \dfrac{\text{mass of CH}_4}{\text{molar mass of CH}_4} = \dfrac{144.36 \text{ g}}{12.011 \text{ g/mol} + 4(1.00794 \text{ g/mol})} = \boxed{8.9985 \text{ mol}}$

37. **Strategy** Use Eq. (13-10).

   Solution Find the number of air molecules.

   $N = \dfrac{\rho V}{m} = (1.2 \text{ kg/m}^3)(1.0 \text{ cm}^3) \left(\dfrac{1 \text{ m}^3}{10^6 \text{ cm}^3} \right) \left(\dfrac{1}{29.0 \text{ u}} \right) \left(\dfrac{1 \text{ u}}{1.66 \times 10^{-27} \text{ kg}} \right) = \boxed{2.5 \times 10^{19} \text{ molecules}}$

41. **Strategy** Use the macroscopic form of the ideal gas law, Eq. (13-16).

   Solution Find the new temperature of the air.

   $PV = nRT$, so $\dfrac{T_f}{T_i} = \dfrac{\frac{P_f V_f}{nR}}{\frac{P_i V_i}{nR}} = \dfrac{P_f V_f}{P_i V_i}$, or

   $T_f = \dfrac{P_f V_f T_i}{P_i V_i} = \dfrac{20.0 P_i (0.111 V_i) T_i}{P_i V_i} = 20.0(0.111)(30 \text{ K} + 273.15 \text{ K}) = 673 \text{ K} = \boxed{400^\circ C}$.

45. **Strategy** The volume and moles of the gas are constant. Use Gay-Lussac's law.

   Solution Find the pressure at the higher temperature.

   $P \propto T$, so $P_f = \dfrac{T_f}{T_i} P_i = \dfrac{70.0 \text{ K} + 273.15 \text{ K}}{20.0 \text{ K} + 273.15 \text{ K}}(115 \text{ kPa}) = \boxed{135 \text{ kPa}}$.

49. **Strategy** The number of moles of the gas is constant. Use the ideal gas law.

   Solution Find the volume of the hydrogen.

   $\dfrac{P_f V_f}{T_f} = \dfrac{P_i V_i}{T_i}$, so $V_f = \dfrac{P_i V_i T_f}{P_f T_i} = \dfrac{(1.00 \times 10^5 \text{ N/m}^2)(5.0 \text{ m}^3)(273.15 \text{ K} - 13 \text{ K})}{(0.33 \times 10^3 \text{ N/m}^2)(273.15 \text{ K} + 27 \text{ K})} = \boxed{1.3 \times 10^3 \text{ m}^3}$.

53. **Strategy** Use the microscopic form of the ideal gas law, Eq. (13-13).

   Solution Find the number of air molecules released.

   $N = \dfrac{PV}{kT}$, and V, k, and T are constant, so

$$\Delta N = \frac{V\Delta P}{kT} = \frac{(1.0 \text{ m}^3)(15.0 \text{ atm} - 20.0 \text{ atm})(1.013\times10^5 \text{ Pa/atm})}{(1.38\times10^{-23} \text{ J/K})(273 \text{ K})} = -1.3\times10^{26}.$$

$\boxed{1.3\times10^{26}}$ air molecules were released.

55. **Strategy** The number of moles of the gas is constant and $V = \frac{1}{6}\pi d^3$. Use the ideal gas law and Eq. (9-3).

Solution Find the diameter of the bubble when it reaches the surface.

$$\frac{P_f V_f}{T_f} = \frac{P_i V_i}{T_i}, \text{ so } V_f = \frac{1}{6}\pi d_f^3 = \frac{P_i T_f}{P_f T_i}V_i = \frac{(P_f + \rho gh)T_f}{P_f T_i}\left(\frac{1}{6}\pi d_i^3\right). \text{ Solve for } d_f.$$

$$d_f = d_i \sqrt[3]{\frac{(P_f + \rho gh)T_f}{P_f T_i}}$$

$$= (1.00 \text{ mm})\sqrt[3]{\frac{[(1.0 \text{ atm})(1.013\times10^5 \text{ Pa/atm}) + (1.0\times10^3 \text{ kg/m}^3)(9.80 \text{ m/s}^2)(80.0 \text{ m})](273.15 \text{ K} + 18 \text{ K})}{(1.0 \text{ atm})(1.013\times10^5 \text{ Pa/atm})(273.15 \text{ K} + 4 \text{ K})}}$$

$$= \boxed{2.1 \text{ mm}}$$

57. **Strategy** The number of moles of air is constant. Assume that the temperature is constant.
$V_f = \frac{\Delta V}{\Delta t}\Delta t$ where $\frac{\Delta V}{\Delta t} = 0.500 \text{ L/s} = 5.00\times10^2 \text{ cm}^3/\text{s}$ and $P_f = P_i + \rho gd$. Use Boyle's law.

Solution Find how long the tank of air will last for each depth.

(a) $\dfrac{V_f}{V_i} = \dfrac{\frac{\Delta V}{\Delta t}\Delta t}{V_i} = \dfrac{P_{\text{tank}}}{P_f} = \dfrac{P_{\text{tank}}}{P_{\text{atm}} + \rho gd}$, so

$$\Delta t = \frac{P_{\text{tank}}V_i}{\frac{\Delta V}{\Delta t}(P_{\text{atm}} + \rho gd)}$$

$$= \frac{(1.0\times10^7 \text{ Pa})(0.010 \text{ m}^3)}{(5.00\times10^2 \text{ cm}^3/\text{s})(10^{-6} \text{ m}^3/\text{cm}^3)(60 \text{ s/min})\left[1.013\times10^5 \text{ Pa} + (1.0\times10^3 \text{ kg/m}^3)(9.80 \text{ m/s}^2)(2.0 \text{ m})\right]}$$

$$= \boxed{28 \text{ min}}$$

(b) $\Delta t = \dfrac{(1.0\times10^7 \text{ Pa})(0.010 \text{ m}^3)}{(5.00\times10^2 \text{ cm}^3/\text{s})(10^{-6} \text{ m}^3/\text{cm}^3)(60 \text{ s/min})\left[1.013\times10^5 \text{ Pa} + (1.0\times10^3 \text{ kg/m}^3)(9.80 \text{ m/s}^2)(20.0 \text{ m})\right]}$

$$= \boxed{11 \text{ min}}$$

61. **Strategy** The total translational kinetic energy of the gas molecules is equal to the number of molecules times the average translational kinetic energy per molecule. Use Eqs. (13-13) and (13-20).

Solution Find the total translational kinetic energy of the gas molecules.

$$K_{\text{total}} = N\langle K_{\text{tr}}\rangle = N\left(\frac{3}{2}kT\right) = \frac{3}{2}PV = \frac{3}{2}(1.013\times10^5 \text{ Pa})(0.00100 \text{ m}^3) = \boxed{152 \text{ J}}$$

65. **Strategy** The total internal kinetic energy of the ideal gas is equal to the number of molecules times the average kinetic energy per molecule. Use Eq. (13-20).

Solution Find the total internal kinetic energy of the ideal gas.

$$K_{\text{total}} = N\langle K_{\text{tr}}\rangle = N\left\langle\frac{3}{2}kT\right\rangle = \frac{3}{2}nRT = \frac{3}{2}(1.0\ \text{mol})[8.314\ \text{J/(mol}\cdot\text{K)}](273.15\ \text{K} + 0.0\ \text{K}) = \boxed{3.4\ \text{kJ}}$$

69. **Strategy** Use Eq. (13-22).

Solution Find the rms speeds of the molecules.

(a) $v_{\text{rms}} = \sqrt{\dfrac{3kT}{m}} = \sqrt{\dfrac{3(1.38\times10^{-23}\ \text{J/K})(273.15\ \text{K} + 0.0\ \text{K})}{2(14.00674\ \text{u})(1.66\times10^{-27}\ \text{kg/u})}} = \boxed{493\ \text{m/s}}$

(b) $v_{\text{rms}} = \sqrt{\dfrac{3(1.38\times10^{-23}\ \text{J/K})(273.15\ \text{K} + 0.0\ \text{K})}{2(15.9994\ \text{u})(1.66\times10^{-27}\ \text{kg/u})}} = \boxed{461\ \text{m/s}}$

(c) $v_{\text{rms}} = \sqrt{\dfrac{3(1.38\times10^{-23}\ \text{J/K})(273.15\ \text{K} + 0.0\ \text{K})}{[12.011\ \text{u} + 2(15.9994\ \text{u})](1.66\times10^{-27}\ \text{kg/u})}} = \boxed{393\ \text{m/s}}$

73. **Strategy** Use Eq. (13-20).

Solution Find the temperature of the ideal gas.

$$\langle K_{\text{tr}}\rangle = \frac{3}{2}kT,\ \text{so}\ T = \frac{2\langle K_{\text{tr}}\rangle}{3k} = \frac{2(4.60\times10^{-20}\ \text{J})}{3(1.38\times10^{-23}\ \text{J/K})} = \boxed{2220\ \text{K}}.$$

75. **Strategy and Solution** The average translational energy of a molecule in an ideal gas is $\langle K_{\text{tr}}\rangle = \frac{1}{2}m\langle v^2\rangle$. The rms speed is $v_{\text{rms}} = \sqrt{\langle v^2\rangle}$, so $\frac{1}{2}mv_{\text{rms}}^2 = \langle K_{\text{tr}}\rangle$. From Eq. (13-19), we know that $\langle K_{\text{tr}}\rangle = \dfrac{3PV}{2N}$, and using the ideal gas law, $PV = nRT$, we have $\frac{1}{2}mv_{\text{rms}}^2 = \frac{3}{2}\left(\dfrac{PV}{N}\right) = \frac{3}{2}\left(\dfrac{nRT}{N}\right)$, so $v_{\text{rms}} = \sqrt{3\left(\dfrac{n}{mN}\right)RT} = \sqrt{\dfrac{3RT}{M}}$.

77. **Strategy** Form a proportion with the two reaction rates and solve for the temperature increase. Use Eq. (13-24).

Solution Find the temperature increase.

$$\frac{1.035}{1} = \frac{e^{-\frac{E_a}{kT_2}}}{e^{-\frac{E_a}{kT_1}}} = e^{\frac{E_a}{k}\left(\frac{1}{T_1} - \frac{1}{T_2}\right)}$$

$$\ln 1.035 = \frac{E_a}{k}\left(\frac{1}{T_1} - \frac{1}{T_2}\right)$$

$$\frac{k \ln 1.035}{E_a} = \frac{1}{T_1} - \frac{1}{T_2}$$

$$\frac{1}{T_2} = \frac{1}{T_1} - \frac{k \ln 1.035}{E_a}$$

$$T_2 = \left(\frac{1}{T_1} - \frac{k \ln 1.035}{E_a}\right)^{-1}$$

$$\Delta T = \left(\frac{1}{T_1} - \frac{k \ln 1.035}{E_a}\right)^{-1} - T_1$$

$$= \left[\frac{1}{273.15 \text{ K} + 10.00 \text{ K}} - \frac{(1.38 \times 10^{-23} \text{ J/K}) \ln 1.035}{2.81 \times 10^{-19} \text{ J}}\right]^{-1} - (273.15 \text{ K} + 10.00 \text{ K}) = \boxed{0.14°\text{C}}$$

81. Strategy Use Eq. (13-26).

Solution Estimate the time it takes a sucrose molecule to move 5.00 mm in one direction.

$$x_{\text{rms}} = \sqrt{2Dt}, \text{ so } t = \frac{x_{\text{rms}}^2}{2D} = \frac{(5.00 \times 10^{-3} \text{ m})^2}{2(5.0 \times 10^{-10} \text{ m}^2/\text{s})} = \boxed{2.5 \times 10^4 \text{ s}}.$$

85. Strategy Find the temperature at which the radius of the steel sphere and the internal radius of the brass ring are the same. Use Eq. (13-5).

Solution Set the final lengths of the radii equal and solve for the final temperature.

$$L_{b0} + L_{b0}\alpha_b\Delta T = L_{s0} + L_{s0}\alpha_s\Delta T$$

$$L_{b0}\alpha_b(T_f - T_i) = L_{s0} - L_{b0} + L_{s0}\alpha_s(T_f - T_i)$$

$$T_f(L_{b0}\alpha_b - L_{s0}\alpha_s) = L_{s0} - L_{b0} + T_i(L_{b0}\alpha_b - L_{s0}\alpha_s)$$

$$T_f = \frac{L_{s0} - L_{b0}}{L_{b0}\alpha_b - L_{s0}\alpha_s} + T_i$$

$$T_f = \frac{1.0010 \text{ cm} - 1.0000 \text{ cm}}{(1.0000 \text{ cm})(19 \times 10^{-6} \text{ K}^{-1}) - (1.0010 \text{ cm})(12 \times 10^{-6} \text{ K}^{-1})} + 22.0°\text{C} = \boxed{165°\text{C}}$$

89. (a) Strategy Use Eq. (13-20).

Solution Compute the average kinetic energy of the air molecules.

$$\langle K_{\text{tr}} \rangle = \frac{3}{2}kT = \frac{3}{2}(1.38 \times 10^{-23} \text{ J/K})\left[\frac{5}{9}(98.6 - 32.0) \text{ K} + 273.15 \text{ K}\right] = \boxed{6.42 \times 10^{-21} \text{ J}}$$

(b) Strategy Since the average kinetic energy is directly proportional to the absolute temperature, find the percent change in the absolute temperature.

Solution Find the percentage by which the kinetic energy of the molecules increased.

$$\frac{\Delta K}{K_0}\times100\% = \frac{\Delta T}{T_0}\times100\% = \frac{\frac{5}{9}(100.0-98.6)\text{ K}}{\frac{5}{9}(98.6-32.0)\text{ K}+273.15\text{ K}}\times100\% = \boxed{0.25\%}$$

93. Strategy and Solution The average of the test scores is $\dfrac{83+62+81+77+68+92+88+83+72+75}{10} = \boxed{78.1}$.

The rms value is $\sqrt{\dfrac{83^2+62^2+81^2+77^2+68^2+92^2+88^2+83^2+72^2+75^2}{10}} = \boxed{78.6}$. The most probable value

is $\boxed{83}$, since it appears twice as often as any other score.

97. Strategy Assume that each air molecule is at the center of a sphere (with volume V/N) of diameter d. Then the average distance between air molecules is approximately d. Use the microscopic form of the ideal gas law, Eq. (13-13).

Solution Estimate the average distance between air molecules.

$$PV = P\left(N\frac{1}{6}\pi d^3\right) = NkT,\text{ so } d = \left(\frac{6kT}{\pi P}\right)^{1/3} = \left[\frac{6(1.38\times10^{-23}\text{ J/K})(273.15\text{ K}+0.0\text{ K})}{\pi(1.00\text{ atm})(1.013\times10^5\text{ Pa/atm})}\right]^{1/3} \approx \boxed{4\text{ nm}}.$$

101. Strategy Use Eq. (13-4).

Solution Find the approximate temperature for the SR-71 while it is in flight.

$$\frac{\Delta L}{L_0} = \alpha\Delta T,\text{ so } T_f = T_i + \frac{\Delta L}{\alpha L_0} = 20°C + \frac{0.20\text{ m}}{(10.1\times10^{-6}\text{ K}^{-1})(32.70\text{ m})} = \boxed{630°C}.$$

105. Strategy Use Eq. (13-22).

Solution Find the decrease in the rms speed of the air molecules.

$$\Delta v_{rms} = \sqrt{\frac{3kT_f}{m}} - \sqrt{\frac{3kT_i}{m}}$$

$$= \sqrt{\frac{3(1.38\times10^{-23}\text{ J/K})(10.0\text{ K}+273.15\text{ K})}{[0.750(2)(14.00674\text{ u})+0.250(2)(15.9994\text{ u})](1.66\times10^{-27}\text{ kg/u})}}$$

$$- \sqrt{\frac{3(1.38\times10^{-23}\text{ J/K})(40.0\text{ K}+273.15\text{ K})}{[0.750(2)(14.00674\text{ u})+0.250(2)(15.9994\text{ u})](1.66\times10^{-27}\text{ kg/u})}}$$

$$= -25\text{ m/s}$$

The rms speed will have decreased by $\boxed{25\text{ m/s}}$.

109. Strategy Use ideal gas law and Hooke's law.

Solution Find the pressure of the gas.

$PV = nRT$, so $P_{gas} = \dfrac{nRT}{V}$. The force with which the piston pushes on the spring is equal to

$F = (P_{gas} - P_{atm})A_{piston}$. Set this equal to $F = k\Delta x$ to find the spring constant.

$k\Delta x = (P_{gas} - P_{atm})A_{piston} = \left(\frac{nRT}{V} - P_{atm}\right)A_{piston}$, so

$$k = \left[\frac{(6.50\times10^{-2}\text{ mol})[8.314\text{ J/(mol·K)}](20.0\text{ K}+273.15\text{ K})}{(0.120\text{ m}+0.0540\text{ m})\pi(0.0800/2\text{ m})^2} - 1.013\times10^5\text{ Pa}\right]\frac{\pi(0.0800/2\text{ m})^2}{0.0540\text{ m}} = \boxed{7.4\times10^3\text{ N/m}}.$$

Chapter 14

HEAT

Conceptual Questions

1. Heat flows from the hotter to the colder object.

5. The air between the layers acts as very good thermal insulation.

9. The fins increase the area of the surface responsible for radiating heat from the engine to the air so that the engine cools more efficiently.

13. Water contained in the sauce and cheese of a pizza has a higher specific heat and thermal conductivity than the crust. Thus, for a given time interval, the amount of heat energy transferred to the roof of the mouth by the sauce and cheese is greater than that which is transferred to the hand by the crust.

17. The rate at which heat flows via conduction, convection, and radiation depends upon the temperature difference between the hot and cold bodies. By adding the milk to the coffee immediately, the temperature difference between the coffee and the surrounding air is minimized, so the rate of heat flow is smaller. Additionally, when the color of the coffee is lighter, the radiative heat loss will be further reduced.

21. In winter, the walls of a room are at a lower temperature than the air within the room. In summer, the walls are warmer than the inside air. The amount of heat lost from a person standing within the room via conduction and convection is constant throughout the year since the temperature of the air is held fixed. The temperature difference between the body and the walls is greatest in winter. As a result, more heat is lost via radiative transfer in winter and the room therefore feels cooler.

Problems

1. (a) **Strategy** The gravitational potential energy of the 1.4 kg of water is converted to internal energy in the 6.4-kg system.

   Solution Compute the increase in internal energy.
   $$U = mgh = (1.4 \text{ kg})(9.80 \text{ m/s}^2)(2.5 \text{ m}) = \boxed{34 \text{ J}}$$

   (b) **Strategy and Solution** $\boxed{\text{Yes; the increase in internal energy increases the average kinetic energy of the water molecules, thus the temperature is slightly increased.}}$

3. **Strategy** The amount of internal energy generated is equal to the decrease in kinetic energy of the bullet.

   Solution Compute the amount of internal energy generated.
   $$|\Delta K| = \frac{1}{2}mv_i^2 = \frac{1}{2}(0.0200 \text{ kg})(7.00 \times 10^2 \text{ m/s})^2 = \boxed{4.90 \text{ kJ}}$$

5. **(a) Strategy** The decrease in gravitational potential energy of the child is equal to the amount of internal energy generated.

   Solution Compute the amount of internal energy generated.
   $$U = mgh = (15 \text{ kg})(9.80 \text{ m/s}^2)(1.7 \text{ m}) = \boxed{250 \text{ J}}$$

   (b) Strategy and Solution Friction warms the slide and the child, and the air molecules are deflected by the child's body. The energy goes into $\boxed{\text{all three}}$.

9. **Strategy** The conversion factor is $1 \text{ kW} \cdot \text{h} = 3.600 \text{ MJ}$.

   Solution Convert 1.00 kJ to kilowatt-hours.
   $$(1.00 \times 10^3 \text{ J}) \frac{1 \text{ kW} \cdot \text{h}}{3.600 \times 10^6 \text{ J}} = \boxed{2.78 \times 10^{-4} \text{ kW} \cdot \text{h}}$$

11. **Strategy** The heat capacity of an object is equal to its mass times its specific heat.

    Solution Find the heat capacity of the 5.00-g gold ring.
    $$C = mc = (0.00500 \text{ kg})[0.128 \text{ kJ/(kg} \cdot \text{K})] = \boxed{6.40 \times 10^{-4} \text{ kJ/K}}$$

13. **Strategy** Use Eq. (14-4).

    Solution Find the amount of heat that must flow into the water.
    $$Q = mc\Delta T = (2.0 \times 10^{-3} \text{ m}^3)(1.0 \times 10^3 \text{ kg/m}^3)[4186 \text{ J/(kg} \cdot \text{K})](80.0 - 20.0) \text{ K} = \boxed{0.50 \text{ MJ}}$$

15. **Strategy** The 3.3% of the energy from the food is converted to gravitational potential energy of the high jumper.

    Solution Find the height the athlete could jump.
    $$U = mgh, \text{ so } h = \frac{U}{mg} = \frac{(3.00 \times 10^6 \text{ cal})(4.186 \text{ J/cal})(0.033)}{(60.0 \text{ kg})(9.80 \text{ m/s}^2)} = \boxed{700 \text{ m}}.$$

17. **Strategy** The heat capacity of an object is equal to its mass times its specific heat. The mass of an object is equal to its density times its volume.

    Solution Find the heat capacities.

    (a) $C = mc = \rho Vc = (2702 \text{ kg/m}^3)(1.00 \text{ m}^3)[0.900 \text{ kJ/(kg} \cdot \text{K})] = \boxed{2430 \text{ kJ/K}}$

    (b) $C = mc = \rho Vc = (7860 \text{ kg/m}^3)(1.00 \text{ m}^3)[0.44 \text{ kJ/(kg} \cdot \text{K})] = \boxed{3500 \text{ kJ/K}}$

19. **Strategy** Use Eq. (14-4) to find the heat required.

    Solution The heat capacity of the system is $C = m_{\text{Al}} c_{\text{Al}} + m_{\text{w}} c_{\text{w}}$.
    $$Q = mc\Delta T = \{(0.400 \text{ kg})[0.900 \text{ kJ/(kg} \cdot \text{K})] + (2.00 \text{ kg})[4.186 \text{ kJ/(kg} \cdot \text{K})]\}(100.0°\text{C} - 15.0°\text{C}) = \boxed{742 \text{ kJ}}$$

21. **Strategy** Use Eq. (14-4).

    Solution Find the specific heat of lead.
    $$c = \frac{Q}{m\Delta T} = \frac{0.88 \text{ kJ}}{(0.35 \text{ kg})(20.0 \text{ K})} = \boxed{0.13 \text{ kJ/(kg} \cdot \text{K)}}$$

25. **Strategy** The energy required to increase the internal energy of the gas is equal to $nC_V\Delta T$ where $C_V = 20.4 \text{ J/(mol} \cdot \text{K)}$ for H_2. Use the ideal gas law to find the number of moles of H_2.

    Solution Find the energy required.
    $$\Delta U = nC_V\Delta T = \frac{PV}{RT}C_V\Delta T = \frac{(10.0 \text{ atm})(1.013 \times 10^5 \text{ Pa/atm})(250 \text{ L})(10^{-3} \text{ m}^3/\text{L})[20.4 \text{ J/(mol} \cdot \text{K)}](25.0 \text{ K})}{[8.314 \text{ J/(mol} \cdot \text{K)}](273.15 \text{ K} + 0.0 \text{ K})}$$
    $$= \boxed{57 \text{ kJ}}$$

29. **(a) Strategy** Phase changes are indicated by the graph where the temperature is constant while heat is added.

    Solution Initially, the substance is solid. As the temperature increases, the substance changes from the solid to the liquid phase, then from the liquid phase to the gas phase. There are two phase changes shown by the graph: from $\boxed{\text{B to C, solid to liquid}}$; and from $\boxed{\text{D to E, liquid to gas}}$.

    (b) Strategy and Solution The beginning of the phase change from solid to liquid indicates the melting point of the substance. That point is labeled by the letter $\boxed{\text{B}}$.

    (c) Strategy and Solution The beginning of the phase change from liquid to gas indicates the boiling point of the substance. That point is labeled by the letter $\boxed{\text{D}}$.

31. **Strategy** The sum of the heat flows is zero. Use Eqs. (14-4) and (14-9).

    Solution Find the heat of fusion of water.
    $$0 = Q_{ice} + Q_w + Q_c = m_{ice}L_f + m_{ice}c_w\Delta T_{ice} + m_w c_w \Delta T_w + m_c c_c \Delta T_c, \text{ so}$$
    $$L_f = -\frac{c_w(m_{ice}\Delta T_{ice} + m_w\Delta T_w) + m_c c_c \Delta T_c}{m_{ice}}$$
    $$= -\frac{[4.186 \text{ J/(g} \cdot \text{K)}][(30.0 \text{ g})(8.5 \text{ K}) + (2.00 \times 10^2 \text{ g})(-11.5 \text{ K})] + (3.00 \times 10^2 \text{ g})[0.380 \text{ J/(g} \cdot \text{K)}](-11.5 \text{ K})}{30.0 \text{ g}}$$
    $$= \boxed{330 \text{ J/g}}$$

33. **Strategy** The sum of the heat flows is zero. Find the mass of the water required to melt the ice and leave the temperature of the drink at 5.0°C. Use Eqs. (14-4) and (14-9).

    Solution Find the mass of water to be added to the cup.
    $$0 = Q_w + Q_{ice}$$
    $$0 = m_w c_w \Delta T_w + m_{ice}L_f + m_{ice}c_{ice}\Delta T_1 + m_{ice}c_w\Delta T_2$$
    $$-m_w c_w \Delta T_w = m_{ice}(L_f + c_{ice}\Delta T_1 + c_w\Delta T_2)$$
    $$m_w = \frac{m_{ice}(L_f + c_{ice}\Delta T_1 + c_w\Delta T_2)}{-c_w\Delta T_w}$$
    $$m_w = -\frac{(50.0 \text{ g} + 50.0 \text{ g})\{333.7 \text{ J/g} + [2.1 \text{ J/(g} \cdot \text{K)}](15.0 \text{ K}) + [4.186 \text{ J/(g} \cdot \text{K)}](5.0 \text{ K})\}}{[4.186 \text{ J/(g} \cdot \text{K)}](-20.0 \text{ K})} = \boxed{461 \text{ g}}$$

35. **Strategy** Heat flows from the water to the ice, melting some of it. Find the mass of ice required to lower the temperature of the water to 0.0°C. Use Eqs. (14-4) and (14-9).

   Solution Find the required mass of ice.
   $0 = Q_{ice} + Q_w = m_{ice}L_f + m_w c_w \Delta T_w$, so
   $$m_{ice} = -\frac{m_w c_w \Delta T_w}{L_f} = -\frac{(5.00 \times 10^2 \text{ mL})(1.00 \text{ g/mL})[4.186 \text{ J/(g·K)}](-25.0 \text{ K})}{333.7 \text{ J/g}} = \boxed{157 \text{ g}}.$$

37. **Strategy** The sum of the heat flows is zero. The tea is basically water. The mass of the tea is found by multiplying the density of water by the volume of the tea. Do not neglect the temperature change of the glass. Use Eqs. (14-4) and (14-9).

   Solution Find the mass of the ice required to cool the tea to 10.0°C. Let ΔT be the temperature change of the tea and the glass.
   $$0 = Q_t + Q_{ice} + Q_g$$
   $$0 = \rho_w V_t c_w \Delta T + m_{ice}L_f + m_{ice}c_{ice}\Delta T_1 + m_{ice}c_w \Delta T_2 + m_g c_g \Delta T$$
   $$0 = (\rho_w V_t c_w + m_g c_g)\Delta T + m_{ice}(L_f + c_{ice}\Delta T_1 + c_w \Delta T_2)$$
   $$m_{ice} = \frac{-(\rho_w V_t c_w + m_g c_g)\Delta T}{L_f + c_{ice}\Delta T_1 + c_w \Delta T_2}$$
   $$= \frac{-\{(1.00 \times 10^3 \text{ kg/m}^3)(2.00 \times 10^{-4} \text{ m}^3)[4.186 \text{ kJ/(kg·K)}] + (0.35 \text{ kg})[0.837 \text{ kJ/(kg·K)}]\}(-85.0 \text{ K})}{333.7 \text{ kJ/kg} + [2.1 \text{ kJ/(kg·K)}](10.0 \text{ K}) + [4.186 \text{ kJ/(kg·K)}](10.0 \text{ K})}$$
   $$= \boxed{242 \text{ g}}$$

   The percentage change from the answer for Problem 40 is $\dfrac{242 \text{ g} - 179 \text{ g}}{179 \text{ g}} \times 100\% = \boxed{35\%}$.

39. **Strategy** Heat flows from the aluminum into the ice. Use Eqs. (14-4) and (14-9).

   Solution Find the mass of aluminum required to melt 10.0 g of ice.
   $Q_{Al} + Q_{ice} = m_{Al}c_{Al}\Delta T_{Al} + m_{ice}L_f = 0$, so
   $$m_{Al} = -\frac{m_{ice}L_f}{c_{Al}\Delta T_{Al}} = -\frac{(10.0 \text{ g})(333.7 \text{ J/g})}{[0.900 \text{ J/(g·K)}](0.0°C - 80.0°C)} = \boxed{46.3 \text{ g}}.$$

41. **Strategy** Use Eq. (14-4) for vaporization. Q is equal to the rate of heat loss per square meter times the area times the time (1 h = 3600 s).

   Solution Find the mass of water lost through transpiration.
   $$m = \frac{Q}{L_v} = \frac{(250 \text{ W/m}^2)(0.005 \text{ m}^2)(3600 \text{ s})}{2256 \text{ J/g}} = \boxed{2 \text{ g}}$$

45. **Strategy** The heat supplied heats the substance to its melting point, melts it, then raises the temperature of the resulting liquid to 327°C. Use Eqs. (14-4) and (14-9).

   Solution Compute the heat of fusion.
   $$Q = mL_f + mc\Delta T, \text{ so } L_f = -c\Delta T + \frac{Q}{m} = -[0.129 \text{ kJ/(kg·K)}](327 - 21) \text{ K} + \frac{31.15 \text{ kJ}}{0.500 \text{ kg}} = \boxed{22.8 \text{ kJ/kg}}.$$

49. Strategy Use Eq. (14-12).

Solution Compute the thermal resistance for each material.

(a) $R = \dfrac{d}{\kappa A} = \dfrac{2.0 \times 10^{-2} \text{ m}}{[0.17 \text{ W/(m} \cdot \text{K)}](1.0 \text{ m}^2)} = \boxed{0.12 \text{ K/W}}$

(b) $R = \dfrac{2.0 \times 10^{-2} \text{ m}}{[80.2 \text{ W/(m} \cdot \text{K)}](1.0 \text{ m}^2)} = \boxed{2.5 \times 10^{-4} \text{ K/W}}$

(c) $R = \dfrac{2.0 \times 10^{-2} \text{ m}}{[401 \text{ W/(m} \cdot \text{K)}](1.0 \text{ m}^2)} = \boxed{5.0 \times 10^{-5} \text{ K/W}}$

51. Strategy From the given information, $\Delta T = \mathscr{P}_1 R_1 = \mathscr{P}_2 R_2 = \mathscr{P}(R_1 + R_2)$.

Solution Find the rate of heat flow per unit area.

$\dfrac{R_1}{R_2} = \dfrac{\mathscr{P}_2}{\mathscr{P}_1}$ and $\mathscr{P} = \dfrac{\mathscr{P}_2 R_2}{R_1 + R_2}$. Thus, $\mathscr{P} = \dfrac{\mathscr{P}_2}{\frac{R_1}{R_2} + 1} = \dfrac{\mathscr{P}_2}{\frac{\mathscr{P}_2}{\mathscr{P}_1} + 1} = \dfrac{20.0 \text{ W/m}^2}{\frac{20.0}{10.0} + 1} = \boxed{6.67 \text{ W/m}^2}$.

53. Strategy Use Fourier's law of heat conduction, Eq. (14-10).

Solution Find the lowest temperature the dog can withstand without increasing its heat output.

$\mathscr{P} = \kappa A \dfrac{\Delta T}{d} = \kappa A \dfrac{T_i - T_o}{d}$, so $T_o = T_i - \dfrac{d\mathscr{P}}{\kappa A} = 38°C - \dfrac{(0.050 \text{ m})(51 \text{ W})}{[0.026 \text{ W/(m} \cdot \text{K)}](1.31 \text{ m}^2)} = \boxed{-37°C}$.

57. Strategy Use Fourier's law of heat conduction, Eq. (14-10).

Solution

(a) $\mathscr{P} = \kappa A \dfrac{\Delta T}{d} = [401 \text{ W/(m} \cdot \text{K)}](1.0 \times 10^{-6} \text{ m}^2) \dfrac{104°C - 24°C}{0.10 \text{ m}} = \boxed{0.32 \text{ W}}$

(b) $\dfrac{\Delta T}{d} = \dfrac{104°C - 24°C}{0.10 \text{ m}} = \boxed{800 \text{ K/m}}$

(c) The effective length has doubled.

$\mathscr{P} = [401 \text{ W/(m} \cdot \text{K)}](1.0 \times 10^{-6} \text{ m}^2) \dfrac{104°C - 24°C}{0.20 \text{ m}} = \boxed{0.16 \text{ W}}$

(d) The effective area has doubled.

$\mathscr{P} = [401 \text{ W/(m} \cdot \text{K)}](2.0 \times 10^{-6} \text{ m}^2) \dfrac{104°C - 24°C}{0.10 \text{ m}} = \boxed{0.64 \text{ W}}$

(e) Since the bars are identical, the temperature at the junction will be midway between the temperatures of the baths.

$\dfrac{104°C + 24°C}{2} = \boxed{64°C}$

61. **Strategy** Use Stefan's law of radiation, Eq. (14-16).

Solution Compute the power radiated by the bulb.
$$\mathcal{P} = e\sigma A T^4 = 0.32[5.670 \times 10^{-8} \text{ W}/(\text{m}^2 \cdot \text{K}^4)](1.00 \times 10^{-4} \text{ m}^2)(3.00 \times 10^3 \text{ K})^4 = \boxed{150 \text{ W}}$$

65. **Strategy** Use Stefan's law of radiation, Eq. (14-16). Form a proportion. Assume the cross-sectional area A is constant.

Solution Find the temperature of the filament.
$$\mathcal{P} = e\sigma A T^4, \text{ so } \frac{\mathcal{P}_{58}}{\mathcal{P}_{60}} = \frac{T_{58}^4}{T_{60}^4} \text{ and } T_{58} = \left(\frac{\mathcal{P}_{58}}{\mathcal{P}_{60}}\right)^{1/4} T_{60} = \left(\frac{58.0}{60.0}\right)^{1/4} (2820 \text{ K}) = \boxed{2800 \text{ K}}.$$

69. **Strategy** Approximate the pots as cubes of similar volume. Use Eq. (14-18).

Solution Find the net rate of radiative heat loss from the two pots.
$$s^3 = V, \text{ so } s = V^{1/3} \text{ and } 6s^2 = A = 6V^{2/3}.$$
Coffeepot:
$$\mathcal{P}_{\text{net}} = e\sigma A (T^4 - T_s^4)$$
$$= 0.12[5.670 \times 10^{-8} \text{ W}/(\text{m}^2 \cdot \text{K}^4)][6(1.00 \text{ L})^{2/3}(10^{-3} \text{ m}^3/\text{L})^{2/3}][(98 \text{ K} + 273.15 \text{ K})^4 - (25 \text{ K} + 273.15 \text{ K})^4]$$
$$= \boxed{4.5 \text{ W}}$$
Teapot:
$$\mathcal{P}_{\text{net}} = 0.65[5.670 \times 10^{-8} \text{ W}/(\text{m}^2 \cdot \text{K}^4)][6(1.00 \text{ L})^{2/3}(10^{-3} \text{ m}^3/\text{L})^{2/3}][(98 \text{ K} + 273.15 \text{ K})^4 - (25 \text{ K} + 273.15 \text{ K})^4]$$
$$= \boxed{24 \text{ W}}$$

71. **(a) Strategy** The power absorbed by the leaf must equal that radiated away. Power is equal to intensity times area. Use Stefan's law of radiation, Eq. (14-16).

Solution Absorbed:
$$I_{\text{top}} A + e\sigma A T_s^4 = 0.700(9.00 \times 10^2 \text{ W}/\text{m}^2)(5.00 \times 10^{-3} \text{ m}^2) +$$
$$(1)[5.670 \times 10^{-8} \text{ W}/(\text{m}^2 \cdot \text{K}^4)](5.00 \times 10^{-3} \text{ m}^2)(273.15 \text{ K} + 25.0 \text{ K})^4$$
$$= 5.39 \text{ W}$$

Find the temperature of the leaf. The area is now $2(5.00 \times 10^{-3} \text{ m}^2) = 10.0 \times 10^{-3} \text{ m}^2$ (both sides of the leaf).
$$\mathcal{P} = e\sigma A T^4, \text{ so}$$
$$T = \left(\frac{\mathcal{P}}{e\sigma A}\right)^{1/4} = \left[\frac{5.39 \text{ W}}{(1)[5.670 \times 10^{-8} \text{ W}/(\text{m}^2 \cdot \text{K}^4)](10.0 \times 10^{-3} \text{ m}^2)}\right]^{1/4} = 312 \text{ K} - 273 \text{ K} = \boxed{39°\text{C}}.$$

(b) Strategy Since the bottom of the leaf absorbs and emits at the same rate, it can be ignored.

Solution Find the power per unit area that must be lost by other methods.
$$\frac{\mathcal{P}_{\text{abs,Sun}}}{A} = \frac{\mathcal{P}_{\text{rad}}}{A} + \frac{\mathcal{P}_{\text{other}}}{A} = e\sigma T^4 + \frac{\mathcal{P}_{\text{other}}}{A}, \text{ so}$$
$$\frac{\mathcal{P}_{\text{other}}}{A} = \frac{\mathcal{P}_{\text{abs,Sun}}}{A} - e\sigma T^4 = 0.700(9.00 \times 10^2 \text{ W}/\text{m}^2) - (1)[5.670 \times 10^{-8} \text{ W}/(\text{m}^2 \cdot \text{K}^4)](273.15 \text{ K} + 25.0 \text{ K})^4$$
$$= 182 \text{ W}/\text{m}^2$$

Thus, the power per unit area that must be lost by other methods is $\boxed{182 \text{ W}/\text{m}^2}$.

73. Strategy Use Eq. (14-4) and the relationship between power and intensity.

Solution The energy provided by the sunlight is converted to heat in the water. The energy provided is $\mathscr{P}\Delta t = IA\Delta t$. Compute the time to heat the water.

$$Q = mc\Delta T = IA\Delta t, \text{ so } \Delta t = \frac{mc\Delta T}{IA} = \frac{(1.0 \text{ L})(1000 \text{ g/L})[4.186 \text{ J/(g·K)}](100.0-15.0) \text{ K}}{(750 \text{ W/m}^2)(1.5 \text{ m}^2)} = \boxed{320 \text{ s}}.$$

77. (a) Strategy Use Eqs. (14-4) and (14-9).

Solution Find the heat given up by the steam.

$$Q = -mc_w\Delta T + mL_v = (4.0 \text{ g})\{-[4.186 \text{ J/(g·K)}](45.0-100.0) \text{ K} + 2256 \text{ J/g}\} = \boxed{9.9 \text{ kJ}}$$

(b) Strategy Use Eq. (14-4).

Solution Compute the mass of the tissue.

$$m = \frac{Q}{c\Delta T} = \frac{9945 \text{ J}}{[3.5 \text{ J/(g·K)}](45.0-37.0) \text{ K}} = \boxed{360 \text{ g}}$$

81. Strategy The heat loss is proportional to the temperature difference.

Solution Compute the increase in heat loss.

$$\mathscr{P}_2 = \frac{\Delta T_2}{\Delta T_1}\mathscr{P}_1 = \frac{-8.0°C-(-18°C)}{22°C-(-18°C)}\mathscr{P}_1 = 0.25\mathscr{P}_1$$

Therefore, $\mathscr{P}_1 = 4.0\mathscr{P}_2$; thus, the heat loss would be $\boxed{4.0 \text{ times higher}}$ without the insulation.

85. Strategy Use Fourier's law of heat conduction, Eq. (14-10).

Solution Determine the rate of heat flow.

$$\mathscr{P} = \kappa A\frac{\Delta T}{d} = [67.5 \text{ W/(m·K)}]\pi(0.0130 \text{ m})^2\frac{327 \text{ K}-37 \text{ K}}{1.00 \text{ m}} = \boxed{10.4 \text{ W}}$$

89. Strategy Gravitational potential energy is converted into internal energy. Use Eq. (14-9) and $U = mgh$.

Solution Find the mass of the ice melted by friction.

$$Q = m_mL_f = 0.75U = 0.75mgh, \text{ so } m_m = \frac{0.75mgh}{L_f} = \frac{0.75(75 \text{ kg})(9.80 \text{ m/s}^2)(2.43 \text{ m})}{333,700 \text{ J/kg}} = \boxed{4.0 \text{ g}}.$$

93. Strategy $W = Fd$ (work) and $P = Fv$ (power) so $W = Pd/v$. Use Eq. (14-4).

Solution Find the distance that the cheetah can run before it overheats.
$$0.700W = Q$$
$$\frac{0.700Pd}{v} = mc\Delta T$$
$$d = \frac{vmc\Delta T}{0.700P} = \frac{(110\times10^3 \text{ m/h})\left(\frac{1 \text{ h}}{3600 \text{ s}}\right)(50.0 \text{ kg})[3500 \text{ J/(kg·°C)}](41.0°C-38.0°C)}{0.700(160,000 \text{ W})} = \boxed{140 \text{ m}}$$

95. Strategy Heat flows from the copper block to the water and iron pot. Use Eq. (14-4).

Solution Find the final temperature of the system.
$$0 = Q_w + Q_{Cu} + Q_{Fe}$$
$$Q_w = -Q_{Cu} - Q_{Fe}$$
$$m_w c_w (T_f - T_i) = -m_{Cu} c_{Cu} (T_f - T_{Cu}) - m_{Fe} c_{Fe} (T_f - T_i)$$
$$T_f (m_w c_w + m_{Cu} c_{Cu} + m_{Fe} c_{Fe}) = m_{Cu} c_{Cu} T_{Cu} + (m_{Fe} c_{Fe} + m_w c_w) T_i$$
Solve for T_f.

$$
\begin{aligned}
T_f &= \frac{m_{Cu} c_{Cu} T_{Cu} + (m_{Fe} c_{Fe} + m_w c_w) T_i}{m_w c_w + m_{Cu} c_{Cu} + m_{Fe} c_{Fe}} \\
&= \frac{(2.0 \text{ kg})[385 \text{ J/(kg} \cdot \text{K)}](100.0°\text{C}) + \{(2.0 \text{ kg})[440 \text{ J/(kg} \cdot \text{K)}] + (1.0 \text{ kg})[4186 \text{ J/(kg} \cdot \text{K)}]\}(25.0°\text{C})}{(1.0 \text{ kg})[4186 \text{ J/(kg} \cdot \text{K)}] + (2.0 \text{ kg})[385 \text{ J/(kg} \cdot \text{K)}] + (2.0 \text{ kg})[440 \text{ J/(kg} \cdot \text{K)}]} = \boxed{35°\text{C}}
\end{aligned}
$$

97. (a) Strategy The work done by each animal is proportional to the heat generated. Use Eq. (14-4). Form a proportion.

Solution Compare the temperature changes.
$$\frac{Q_c}{Q_d} = \frac{2.00 m c \Delta T_c}{m c \Delta T_d} = \frac{0.700}{0.0500} = 14.0, \text{ so } \Delta T_c = 7.00 \Delta T_d.$$

The temperature change of the cheetah is $\boxed{7.00 \text{ times higher}}$ than that of the dog.

(b) Strategy Use the result from part (a).

Solution Find the final temperature of the dog.
$$T_c - T_i = 7.00(T_d - T_i)$$
$$T_c + 6.00 T_i = 7.00 T_d$$
$$T_d = \frac{T_c + 6.00 T_i}{7.00} = \frac{40.0°\text{C} + 6.00(35.0°\text{C})}{7.00} = \boxed{35.7°\text{C}}$$

$\boxed{\text{The dog is a much better regulator of temperature and, as a result, has more endurance.}}$

101. Strategy Multiply the energy required to melt the urethane by the molar mass and divide by the total mass to find the latent heat.

Solution Find the latent heat of fusion of urethane.
$$\frac{(17.10 \text{ kJ})[3(12.011) + 7(1.00794) + 2(15.9994) + 14.00674] \text{ g/mol}}{1.00 \times 10^2 \text{ g}} = \boxed{15.2 \text{ kJ/mol}}$$

Chapter 15

THERMODYNAMICS

Conceptual Questions

1. Yes, but it wouldn't be a very good heat pump. Like an electric heater, the heat output would be equal to the work input, with no heat being taken from the cold reservoir.

5. Energy is always conserved, so there would be just as much energy as before when the fossil fuels are exhausted. There wouldn't be as much high quality or useful energy though, so it would be better to call it something like a "high quality energy crisis."

9. No, entropy changes don't require a flow of heat. For example, when a gas expands freely into a vacuum, its entropy increases but there is no heat flow. Beating an egg is another example of a process that increases entropy with no flow of heat.

13. This is not a violation. Although the salt crystals are in a more ordered state, the surroundings of the bucket are in a more disordered state. The gaseous state of the evaporated sea water is less ordered than the water.

Problems

1. **Strategy** The work done by Ming is equal to the magnitude of the force of friction $f = \mu N$ times the total "rubbing" distance. Use the first law of thermodynamics.

   Solution Find the change in internal energy.
   $$\Delta U = Q + W = 0 + \mu N d = 0.45(5.0 \text{ N})[8(0.16 \text{ m})] = \boxed{2.9 \text{ J}}$$

3. **Strategy** Use the first law of thermodynamics. $\Delta U > 0$ and $W > 0$.

   Solution Find the heat flow.
   $$Q = \Delta U - W = 400 \text{ J} - 500 \text{ J} = -100 \text{ J}$$
   $$\boxed{100 \text{ J of heat flows out of the system.}}$$

5. **Strategy** No work is done during the constant volume process, but work is done during the constant pressure process. Use Eq. (15-3).

   Solution Compute the total work done by the gas.
   $$W = P_i \Delta V = (2.000 \text{ atm})(1.013 \times 10^5 \text{ Pa/atm})(2.000 \text{ L} - 1.000 \text{ L})(10^{-3} \text{ m}^3/\text{L}) = \boxed{202.6 \text{ J}}$$

9. **(a) Strategy** Oxygen gas is diatomic. Use Eqs. (15-7) and (15-9).

　　Solution Find the heat absorbed by the gas.

$$Q = nC_p\Delta T = n(C_v + R)\Delta T = n\left(\frac{5}{2}R + R\right)\Delta T = \frac{7}{2}nR\Delta T = \frac{7}{2}(1.00\ \text{mol})[8.314\ \text{J/(mol·K)}](25.0°C - 10.0°C)$$
$$= \boxed{436\ \text{J}}$$

　(b) Strategy Use the ideal gas law.

　　Solution Find the change in volume of the gas.

$$\Delta V = \frac{nR\Delta T}{P} = \frac{(1.00\ \text{mol})[8.314\ \text{J/(mol·K)}](25.0°C - 10.0°C)}{(1.00\ \text{atm})(1.013\times10^5\ \text{Pa/atm})}\left(10^3\ \frac{\text{L}}{\text{m}^3}\right) = \boxed{1.23\ \text{L}}$$

　(c) Strategy Use Eq. (15-2).

　　Solution Find the work done by the gas.

$$W = P\Delta V = (1.00\ \text{atm})(1.013\times10^5\ \text{Pa/atm})(1.23\times10^{-3}\ \text{m}^3) = \boxed{125\ \text{J}}$$

　(d) Strategy Use the first law of thermodynamics.

　　Solution Calculate the change in internal energy of the gas.

$$\Delta U = Q + W = 436.5\ \text{J} - 124.7\ \text{J} = \boxed{312\ \text{J}}$$

11. **(a) Strategy** For A–C (constant temperature), $W = nRT\ln V_i/V_f$, and for C–D (constant pressure), $W = -P_i\Delta V$. Use the ideal gas law to find T.

　　Solution

$$W_{\text{total}} = nRT\ln\frac{V_i}{V_f} - P\Delta V = nR\left(\frac{P_A V_A}{nR}\right)\ln\frac{V_A}{V_C} - P_i\Delta V$$
$$= \left[(2.000\ \text{atm})(4.000\ \text{L})\ln\frac{4.000\ \text{L}}{8.000\ \text{L}} - (1.000\ \text{atm})(16.000\ \text{L} - 8.000\ \text{L})\right](1.013\times10^5\ \text{Pa/atm})(10^{-3}\ \text{m}^3/\text{L})$$
$$= \boxed{-1372\ \text{J}}$$

　(b) Strategy For constant temperature, $\Delta U = 0$. For constant pressure,

$$\Delta U = Q + W = nC_p\Delta T - P_i\Delta V = \frac{5}{2}nR\left(\frac{P_i\Delta V}{nR}\right) - P_i\Delta V = \frac{3}{2}P_i\Delta V.$$

　　Solution

$$\Delta U = \frac{3}{2}(1.000\ \text{atm})(16.000\ \text{L} - 8.000\ \text{L})(1.013\times10^5\ \text{Pa/atm})(10^{-3}\ \text{m}^3/\text{L}) = \boxed{1216\ \text{J}}.$$

　　The total heat flow is $Q = \Delta U - W = 1216\ \text{J} + 1372\ \text{J} = \boxed{2588\ \text{J}}$.

13. (a) **Strategy** The net work done in one cycle is equal to the area inside the graph.

   Solution Compute the net work done per cycle.
   $$W = (4.00 \text{ atm} - 1.00 \text{ atm})(1.013 \times 10^5 \text{ Pa/atm})(0.800 \text{ m}^3 - 0.200 \text{ m}^3) = \boxed{182 \text{ kJ}}$$

   (b) **Strategy and Solution** The net heat flow into the engine is equal to the work done per cycle, so
   $$Q_{net} = \boxed{182 \text{ kJ}}.$$

17. (a) **Strategy** Use Eq. (15-12).

   Solution Find the net work done by the engine.
   $$W_{net} = eQ_H = 0.21(1.00 \text{ kJ}) = \boxed{210 \text{ J}}$$

   (b) **Strategy** The net work done by an engine during one cycle is equal to the net heat flow into the engine during the cycle.

   Solution Find the heat released by the engine.
   $$W_{net} = Q_H - Q_C, \text{ so } Q_C = Q_H - W_{net} = 1.00 \times 10^3 \text{ J} - 210 \text{ J} = \boxed{790 \text{ J}}.$$

21. **Strategy** Use Eq. (15-12). The net work done by an engine during one cycle is equal to the net heat flow into the engine during the cycle.

   Solution Find the efficiency of the engine.
   $$e = \frac{W_{net}}{Q_{in}} = \frac{W_{net}}{W_{net} + Q_{out}} = \frac{1}{1 + \frac{Q_{out}}{W_{net}}} = \frac{1}{1 + \frac{0.450 \text{ kJ}}{0.100 \text{ kJ}}} = \boxed{0.182}$$

25. **Strategy** Use Eq. (15-17).

   Solution Find the temperature of the cold reservoir.
   $$e_r = 1 - \frac{T_C}{T_H}, \text{ so } T_C = T_H(1 - e_r) = (622 \text{ K})(1 - 0.725) = \boxed{171 \text{ K}}.$$

27. **Strategy** The minimum amount of heat is discharged when the steam engine is reversible. Use Eqs. (15-12) and (15-17), and $W_{net} = Q_H - Q_C$.

   Solution Compute the efficiency of a reversible engine.
   $$e_r = 1 - \frac{T_C}{T_H} = 1 - \frac{273.15 \text{ K} + 27 \text{ K}}{273.15 \text{ K} + 127 \text{ K}} = 0.250$$
   Compute the minimum amount of heat discharged.
   $$Q_C = Q_H - W_{net} = \frac{W_{net}}{e_r} - W_{net} = W_{net}\left(\frac{1}{e_r} - 1\right) = (8.34 \text{ kJ})\left(\frac{1}{0.250} - 1\right) = \boxed{25.0 \text{ kJ}}$$

29. Strategy Assume constant rates and reversibility. Use Eq. (15-17) and conservation of energy. $P = W_{net}/\Delta t$.

Solution Compute the efficiency.
$$e_r = 1 - \frac{T_C}{T_H} = 1 - \frac{273.15 \text{ K} + 2.0 \text{ K}}{273.15 \text{ K} + 40.0 \text{ K}} = 0.1213$$
Find the power used.
$$Q_C = Q_H - W_{net} = \frac{W_{net}}{e} - W_{net} = W_{net}\left(\frac{1}{e} - 1\right), \text{ so } \frac{Q_C}{\Delta t} = \frac{W_{net}}{\Delta t}\left(\frac{1}{e} - 1\right), \text{ and } P = \frac{Q_C/\Delta t}{\frac{1}{e} - 1} = \frac{0.10 \times 10^3 \text{ W}}{\frac{1}{0.1213} - 1} = \boxed{14 \text{ W}}.$$

33. (a) Strategy Use Eq. (15-17).

Solution Find the efficiency of the reversible engine.
$$e_r = 1 - \frac{T_C}{T_H} = 1 - \frac{273.15 \text{ K} + 300.0 \text{ K}}{273.15 \text{ K} + 600.0 \text{ K}} = \boxed{0.3436}$$

(b) Strategy Use Eq. (15-18).

Solution Find the amount of heat exhausted to the cold reservoir.
$$\frac{Q_C}{Q_H} = \frac{T_C}{T_H}, \text{ so } Q_C = \frac{T_C}{T_H}Q_H = \frac{273.15 \text{ K} + 300.0 \text{ K}}{273.15 \text{ K} + 600.0 \text{ K}}(420.0 \text{ kJ}) = \boxed{275.7 \text{ kJ}}.$$

37. Strategy The maximum possible efficiency occurs if the engine is reversible. Use Eq. (15-17).

Solution Find the maximum possible efficiency.
$$e_r = 1 - \frac{T_C}{T_H} = 1 - \frac{273.15 \text{ K} + 10.0 \text{ K}}{273.15 \text{ K} + 15.0 \text{ K}} = \boxed{0.0174}$$

41. Strategy The maximum rate at which the river can carry away heat is $Q_C/\Delta t = mc\Delta T/\Delta t$. Use energy conservation and the definition of efficiency of an engine.

Solution Find the maximum possible power the plant can produce.
$$\frac{W_{net}}{\Delta t} = \frac{Q_H - Q_C}{\Delta t} = \frac{W_{net}}{e\Delta t} - \frac{mc\Delta T}{\Delta t}, \text{ so}$$
$$\frac{W_{net}}{\Delta t} = \left(\frac{1}{e} - 1\right)^{-1}\frac{m}{\Delta t}c\Delta T = \left(\frac{1}{0.300} - 1\right)^{-1}(5.0 \times 10^6 \text{ kg/s})[4186 \text{ J/(kg} \cdot \text{K)}](0.50 \text{ K}) = \boxed{4.5 \text{ GW}}.$$

45. Strategy Use $W_{net} = Q_H - Q_C$, Eq. (15-17), and the definition of efficiency of an engine.

Solution
$$Q_C = Q_H - W_{net} = \frac{W_{net}}{e_r} - W_{net} = W_{net}\left(\frac{1}{e_r} - 1\right) = W_{net}\left(\frac{1}{1 - T_C/T_H} - 1\right) = W_{net}\left(\frac{T_H}{T_H - T_C} - \frac{T_H - T_C}{T_H - T_C}\right) = \frac{T_C}{T_H - T_C}W_{net}$$

47. Strategy and Solution The mass is the same for each case. For equal masses, water has more entropy than ice, and warmer water has more entropy than cooler water, so the order is $\boxed{\text{(b), (a), (c), (d)}}$.

49. Strategy The temperature is constant and the heat entering the system is $Q = mL_v$. Use Eq. (15-20).

Solution Find the change in the entropy of the water.

$$\Delta S = \frac{Q}{T} = \frac{mL_v}{T} = \frac{(1.00 \text{ kg})(2256 \text{ kJ/kg})}{273.15 \text{ K} + 100.0 \text{ K}} = \boxed{+6.05 \text{ kJ/K}}$$

Gas is more disordered than liquid, so the entropy increases.

51. Strategy Use Eq. (15-20).

Solution

(a) Compute the change in entropy of the block.

$$\Delta S_C = \frac{Q}{T_C} = \frac{1.0 \text{ J}}{273.15 \text{ K} + 20.0 \text{ K}} = \boxed{3.4 \times 10^{-3} \text{ J/K}}$$

(b) Compute the change in entropy for the water.

$$\Delta S_H = \frac{Q}{T_H} = \frac{-1.0 \text{ J}}{273.15 \text{ K} + 80.0 \text{ K}} = \boxed{-2.8 \times 10^{-3} \text{ J/K}}$$

(c) Calculate the change in entropy of the universe.

$$\Delta S_{tot} = \Delta S_H + \Delta S_C = \frac{Q}{T_H} + \frac{Q}{T_C} = -2.8 \times 10^{-3} \text{ J/K} + 3.4 \times 10^{-3} \text{ J/K} = \boxed{6 \times 10^{-4} \text{ J/K}}$$

53. Strategy The rate at which the entropy of the universe is changing is equal to the total change in entropy per unit time. Use Eq. (15-20).

Solution

$$\frac{\Delta S}{\Delta t} = \frac{Q}{\Delta t}\left(\frac{1}{T_C} - \frac{1}{T_H}\right) = (220.0 \text{ W})\left(\frac{1}{273.15 \text{ K} - 15.0 \text{ K}} - \frac{1}{273.15 \text{ K} + 20.0 \text{ K}}\right) = \boxed{0.102 \text{ J/(K} \cdot \text{s)}}$$

57. Strategy and Solution $\boxed{\text{The engine will not work.}}$ There is no energy available to do the work necessary to extract the water's internal energy.

61. (a) **Strategy** The work done per cycle is equal to the area contained within the curve.

Solution Compute the work done per cycle.

$$W = \frac{1}{2}(5.00 \text{ atm} - 1.00 \text{ atm})(1.013 \times 10^5 \text{ Pa/atm})(2.00 \text{ m}^3 - 0.500 \text{ m}^3) = \boxed{304 \text{ kJ}}$$

(b) **Strategy** Use the ideal gas law to compute the temperatures at the upper left and lower right points on the curve.

Solution Compute the temperatures.

$$PV = nRT, \text{ so } \frac{P_2 V_2}{P_1 V_1} = \frac{T_2}{T_1}.$$

$$T_{ul} = \frac{P_2 V_2 T_1}{P_1 V_1} = \frac{(5.00)(0.500)(470.0 \text{ K})}{(1.00)(0.500)} = 2350 \text{ K}$$

$$T_{lr} = \frac{P_2 V_2 T_1}{P_1 V_1} = \frac{(1.00)(2.00)(470.0 \text{ K})}{(1.00)(0.500)} = 1880 \text{ K}$$

The maximum temperature is $\boxed{2350 \text{ K}}$.

(c) **Strategy** Use the ideal gas law at the lower-left corner of the diagram.

Solution Find the number of moles of gas used in the engine.

$$n = \frac{PV}{RT} = \frac{(1.00 \text{ atm})(1.013 \times 10^5 \text{ Pa/atm})(0.500 \text{ m}^3)}{[8.314 \text{ J/(mol} \cdot \text{K)}](470.0 \text{ K})} = \boxed{13.0 \text{ mol}}$$

65. **Strategy** The energy of the mixed state, U, must equal the sum of the original (unmixed) states, U_1 and U_2. The energy for a monatomic ideal gas is related to the temperature by $U = \frac{3}{2} NkT$.

Solution Find the final temperature T of the mixture.
$$U = U_1 + U_2$$
$$\frac{3}{2}(N_1 + N_2)kT = \frac{3}{2} N_1 kT_1 + \frac{3}{2} N_2 kT_2$$
$$\frac{3}{2}(n_1 + n_2)RT = \frac{3}{2} n_1 RT_1 + \frac{3}{2} n_2 RT_2$$
$$T = \frac{n_1 T_1 + n_2 T_2}{n_1 + n_2} = \frac{(4.0 \text{ mol})(20.0°C) + (3.0 \text{ mol})(30.0°C)}{4.0 \text{ mol} + 3.0 \text{ mol}} = \boxed{24°C}$$

69. **Strategy** The amount of heat that flows into the water is given by $Q = mc\Delta T$. Assuming the heat flows at an average temperature gives $T = (20.0°C + 50.0°C)/2 = 35.0°C$. Use Eq. (15-20).

Solution Estimate the entropy change.
$$\Delta S = \frac{Q}{T} = \frac{mc\Delta T}{T} \approx \frac{(0.85 \text{ kg})[4186 \text{ J/(kg} \cdot \text{K)}](50.0 - 20.0) \text{ K}}{273.15 \text{ K} + 35.0 \text{ K}} = \boxed{350 \text{ J/K}}$$

73. Strategy Use Eqs. (14-9) and (15-12), and $W_{net} = Q_H - Q_C$.

Solution Find the time required to freeze the water.

$$W_{net} = Q_H - Q_C, \text{ so } Q_C = Q_H - W_{net} = \frac{W_{net}}{e} - W_{net} = W_{net}\left(\frac{1}{e} - 1\right).$$

Therefore, $\dfrac{1}{e} - 1 = \dfrac{Q_C}{W_{net}} = \dfrac{\text{heat removed}}{\text{net work input}} = \dfrac{\text{rate of heat removed}}{\text{power input}} = \dfrac{\Delta Q / \Delta t}{P}$, so

$$\Delta t = \frac{\Delta Q}{P\left(\frac{1}{e} - 1\right)} = \frac{mL_f}{P\left(\frac{1}{e} - 1\right)} = \frac{(1.0 \text{ kg})(333{,}700 \text{ J/kg})}{(186 \text{ W})\left(\frac{1}{0.333} - 1\right)}\left(\frac{1 \text{ min}}{60 \text{ s}}\right) = \boxed{15 \text{ min}}.$$

77. (a) Strategy Use Eq. (15-17).

Solution Compute the efficiency.

$$e_r = 1 - \frac{T_C}{T_H} = 1 - \frac{273.15 \text{ K} + 22 \text{ K} - 15 \text{ K}}{273.15 \text{ K} + 22 \text{ K}} = \boxed{0.051}$$

(b) Strategy The power supplied to the town is equal to the efficiency times the rate at which heat is supplied by the lake. Use Eq. (14-4) and the relationship between mass, density, and volume.

Solution Find the volume of water used each second.

$$P = e\frac{\Delta Q}{\Delta t} = \frac{emc\Delta T}{\Delta t} = \frac{e\rho Vc\Delta T}{\Delta t}, \text{ so}$$

$$V = \frac{P\Delta t}{e\rho c\Delta T} = \frac{(1.0 \times 10^8 \text{ W})(1.0 \text{ s})}{0.051(1.00 \times 10^3 \text{ kg/m}^3)[4186 \text{ J/(kg} \cdot \text{K)}](15 \text{ K})} = \boxed{31 \text{ m}^3}.$$

(c) Strategy The incident power of the Sun must be greater than the power required to run the engine. Power is equal to intensity times area.

Solution Compare the power supplied to the power required by the town.

$$P_{Sun} = IA = (200 \text{ W/m}^2)(8.0 \times 10^7 \text{ m}^2) = 1.6 \times 10^{10} \text{ W}$$

$$P_{engine} = \frac{P_{town}}{e} = \frac{1.0 \times 10^8 \text{ W}}{0.051} = 2.0 \times 10^9 \text{ W}$$

$1.6 \times 10^{10} \text{ W} > 2.0 \times 10^9 \text{ W}$, so $P_{sun} > P_{engine}$, and $\boxed{\text{yes}}$, the lake can supply enough heat to meet the town's needs.

REVIEW AND SYNTHESIS: CHAPTERS 13–15

Review Exercises

1. **Strategy** Assume no heat is lost to the air. The potential energy of the water is converted into heating of the water. The internal energy of the water increases by an amount equal to the initial potential energy.

   Solution Find the change in internal energy.

   $$\Delta U = mgh = (1.00 \text{ m}^3)(1.00 \times 10^3 \text{ kg/m}^3)(9.80 \text{ m/s}^2)(11.0 \text{ m}) = \boxed{108 \text{ kJ}}$$

5. **Strategy** Set the sum of the heat flows equal to zero. Use Eqs. (14-4) and (14-9).

   Solution

   (a) Find the mass of ice required.

   $$0 = Q_w + Q_{ice} = m_w c_w \Delta T_w + m_{ice} L_f + m_{ice} c_{ice} \Delta T_{ice} = m_w c_w \Delta T_w + m_{ice}(L_f + c_{ice} \Delta T_{ice}), \text{ so}$$

   $$m_{ice} = -\frac{m_w c_w \Delta T_w}{L_f + c_{ice} \Delta T_{ice}} = -\frac{(0.250 \text{ kg})[4.186 \text{ kJ/(kg} \cdot \text{K)}](-25.0 \text{ K})}{333.7 \text{ kJ/kg} + [2.1 \text{ kJ/(kg} \cdot \text{K)}](10.0 \text{ K})} = \boxed{74 \text{ g}}.$$

   (b) Find the final temperature of the water, T, which includes the melted ice.

   $$0 = Q_w + Q_{ice}$$
   $$0 = m_w c_w \Delta T_w + m_{ice} L_f + m_{ice} c_{ice} \Delta T_1 + m_{ice} c_w \Delta T_2$$
   $$0 = m_w c_w (T - T_w) + m_{ice} L_f + m_{ice} c_{ice} \Delta T_{ice} + m_{ice} c_w (T - 273.15 \text{ K})$$
   $$0 = (m_w + m_{ice}) c_w T + m_{ice}(L_f + c_{ice} \Delta T_{ice}) - c_w [m_w T_w + m_{ice}(273.15 \text{ K})]$$
   $$T = \frac{c_w [m_w T_w + m_{ice}(273.15 \text{ K})] - m_{ice}(L_f + c_{ice} \Delta T_{ice})}{(m_w + m_{ice}) c_w}$$
   $$T = \frac{\begin{matrix}[4.186 \text{ kJ/(kg} \cdot \text{K)}][(0.250 \text{ kg})(273.15 \text{ K} + 25.0 \text{ K}) + (0.037 \text{ kg})(273.15 \text{ K})] \\ - (0.037 \text{ kg})\{333.7 \text{ kJ/kg} + [2.1 \text{ kJ/(kg} \cdot \text{K)}](10.0 \text{ K})\}\end{matrix}}{(0.250 \text{ kg} + 0.037 \text{ kg})[4.186 \text{ kJ/(kg} \cdot \text{K)}]} - 273.15 \text{ K} = \boxed{11^\circ\text{C}}$$

9. **(a) Strategy** The maximum power emission is inversely proportional to the absolute temperature. Use Wien's law.

   Solution Compute the surface temperature of the star.

   $$T = \frac{2.898 \times 10^{-3} \text{ m} \cdot \text{K}}{\lambda_{max}} = \frac{2.898 \times 10^{-3} \text{ m} \cdot \text{K}}{700.0 \times 10^{-9} \text{ m}} = \boxed{4140 \text{ K}}$$

   (b) Strategy Use Stefan's law of blackbody radiation.

   Solution Compute the power radiated.

   $$\mathcal{P} = \sigma A T^4 = [5.670 \times 10^{-8} \text{ W/(m}^2 \cdot \text{K}^4)][4\pi(7.20 \times 10^8 \text{ m})^2](4140 \text{ K})^4 = \boxed{1.09 \times 10^{26} \text{ W}}$$

   (c) Strategy Intensity is power radiated per unit area.

   Solution Compute the intensity measured by the Earth-based observer.

   $$I = \frac{\mathcal{P}}{A} = \frac{1.085 \times 10^{26} \text{ W}}{4\pi(9.78 \text{ ly})^2(9.461 \times 10^{15} \text{ m/ly})^2} = \boxed{1.01 \times 10^{-9} \text{ W/m}^2}$$

13. Strategy The temperature is constant and the heat entering the system is $Q = mL_f$.

Solution Find the change in entropy of the ice.

$$\Delta S = \frac{Q}{T} = \frac{mL_f}{T} = \frac{(2.00 \text{ kg})(333.7 \text{ kJ/kg})}{273.15 \text{ K} + 0.0 \text{ K}} = \boxed{2.44 \text{ kJ/K}}$$

17. Strategy The heat loss is proportional to the temperature difference.

Solution Compute the reduction in heat loss.

$$\mathcal{P}_2 = \frac{\Delta T_2}{\Delta T_1}\mathcal{P}_1 = \frac{81°C - 36°C}{81°C - 21°C}\mathcal{P}_1 = 0.75\mathcal{P}_1$$

The heat loss was $\boxed{\text{reduced to 75\% of the original}}$.

21. (a) Strategy and Solution

> The boiling temperature of water varies with pressure. If the pressure is high, the water molecules are pushed close together, making it harder for them to form a gas. (Gas molecules are farther apart from each other than are liquid molecules.) A higher pressure raises the temperature at which the coolant fluid will boil.

(b) Strategy and Solution

> If you were to remove the cap on your radiator without first bringing the radiator pressure down to atmospheric pressure, the fluid would suddenly boil, sending out a jet of hot steam that could burn you.

25. (a) Strategy Use the ideal gas law, $PV = nRT$. Draw a qualitative diagram.

Solution First, the temperature is constant, so $P \propto V^{-1}$. Since the volume is reduced to one-eighth of its initial size, the pressure increases by a factor of eight. Next, the volume is constant, while the temperature and pressure increases. Then, the temperature is again constant. Finally, the volume is constant as the temperature and pressure decreases. The P-V diagram is shown.

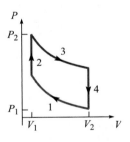

(b) Strategy Refer to the diagram in part (a). Calculate the quantities for each step in the cycle. Note that the gas is diatomic.

Solution Step 1, isothermal process:

The work done on the gas is $W = nRT \ln\dfrac{V_i}{V_f} = (2.00 \text{ mol})[8.314 \text{ J/(mol·K)}](325 \text{ K})\ln 8 = 11.2 \text{ kJ}$.

The change in the internal energy of the gas is 0 for an isothermal process.
The heat transferred is $Q = -W = -11.2 \text{ kJ}$.

Step 2, isochoric process:
Without a displacement, work cannot be done, so $W = 0$.
The change in the internal energy of the gas is equal to the heat that enters the system, so the change in internal energy and the heat transferred are

$$\Delta U = Q = nC_v\Delta T = n\left(\frac{5}{2}R\right)\Delta T = \frac{5}{2}(2.00 \text{ mol})[8.314 \text{ J/(mol·K)}](985 \text{ K} - 325 \text{ K}) = 27.4 \text{ kJ}.$$

Step 3, isothermal process:

The work done on the gas is $W = nRT \ln \dfrac{V_i}{V_f} = (2.00 \text{ mol})[8.314 \text{ J/(mol·K)}](985 \text{ K}) \ln \dfrac{1}{8} = -34.1 \text{ kJ}$.

The change in the internal energy of the gas is 0 for an isothermal process.
The heat transferred is $Q = -W = 34.1 \text{ kJ}$.

Step 4, isochoric process:
Without a displacement, work cannot be done, so $W = 0$.
The change in the internal energy of the gas is equal to the heat that enters the system, so the change in internal energy and the heat transferred are

$$\Delta U = Q = nC_v\Delta T = n\left(\dfrac{5}{2}R\right)\Delta T = \dfrac{5}{2}(2.00 \text{ mol})[8.314 \text{ J/(mol·K)}](325 \text{ K} - 985 \text{ K}) = -27.4 \text{ kJ}.$$

The results of the processes and the totals are shown in the table. (Note that the totals for work and heat differ slightly from the sums of the values for each step due to round-off error.)

Process	W (kJ)	ΔU (kJ)	Q (kJ)
Step 1	11.2	0	−11.2
Step 2	0	27.4	27.4
Step 3	−34.1	0	34.1
Step 4	0	−27.4	−27.4
Total	−22.8	0	22.8

(c) Strategy The efficiency is equal to the ratio of the net work done by the gas to the heat transferred into the gas.

Solution The work done by the gas is negative the work done on the gas.
$W_{net} = -(-22.8 \text{ kJ}) = 22.8 \text{ kJ}$ and the heat transferred into the gas is $Q_{in} = 27.4 \text{ kJ} + 34.1 \text{ kJ} = 61.5 \text{ kJ}$.

The efficiency of the engine is $e = \dfrac{W_{net}}{Q_{in}} = \dfrac{22.8 \text{ kJ}}{61.5 \text{ kJ}} = \boxed{0.371 \text{ or } 37.1\%}$.

(d) Strategy Use Eq. (15-17).

Solution Compute the efficiency of a Carnot engine operating at the same extreme temperatures.
$$e_r = 1 - \dfrac{T_C}{T_H} = 1 - \dfrac{325 \text{ K}}{985 \text{ K}} = \boxed{0.670 \text{ or } 67.0\%}$$

29. (a) Strategy Use conservation of energy. Ignore air resistance.

Solution Find the escape speed.

$$K_i + U_i = K_f + U_f$$

$$\frac{1}{2}mv^2 - \frac{GMm}{R_E} = 0 + 0$$

$$v = \sqrt{\frac{2GM}{R_E}} = \sqrt{\frac{2(6.674\times10^{-11}\ \text{N·m}^2/\text{kg}^2)(5.974\times10^{24}\ \text{kg})}{6.37\times10^6\ \text{m}}} = \boxed{11.2\ \text{km/s}}$$

(b) Strategy Use Eq. (13-22).

Solution Calculate the average speed.

$$v = \sqrt{\frac{3kT}{m}} = \sqrt{\frac{3(1.381\times10^{-23}\ \text{J/K})(273.15\ \text{K})}{(2.00\ \text{u})(1.6605\times10^{-27}\ \text{kg/u})]}} = \boxed{1850\ \text{m/s}}$$

(b) Strategy Use Eq. (13-22).

Solution Calculate the average speed.

$$v = \sqrt{\frac{3kT}{m}} = \sqrt{\frac{3(1.381\times10^{-23}\ \text{J/K})(273.15\ \text{K})}{(32.0\ \text{u})(1.6605\times10^{-27}\ \text{kg/u})]}} = \boxed{461\ \text{m/s}}$$

(d) Strategy and Solution

The atoms in the high end of the distribution are much faster than the average. Some of the hydrogen atoms have speeds greater than the escape speed, thus they can escape. This is not the case for oxygen, which is much more massive and, thus, much slower.

MCAT Review

1. Strategy and Solution According to the second law of thermodynamics, heat never flows spontaneously from a colder body to a hotter body, therefore, heat will not flow from bar A to bar B. The correct answer is $\boxed{C}$.

2. Strategy Assume that the specific heat capacity of seawater is approximately the same at 0°C and 5°C.

Solution Find the approximate temperature T.
$0 = Q_0 + Q_5 = mc(T - 0°C) + mc(T - 5°C)$, so $2T = 5°C$ or $T = 2.50°C$.
The correct answer is $\boxed{B}$.

3. Strategy Use the latent heat of fusion for water.

Solution The heat gained by the ice when melting is $Q = mL_f = (0.0180\ \text{kg})(333.7\ \text{kJ/kg}) = 6.01\ \text{kJ}$.
The correct answer is $\boxed{C}$.

4. Strategy and Solution Since $e = 1 - Q_C/Q_H = 1 - T_C/T_H$, decreasing the exhaust temperature will increase the steam engine's efficiency. The correct answer is $\boxed{B}$.

5. **Strategy and Solution** Since refrigerators remove heat by transferring it to a liquid that vaporizes, refrigerators are primarily dependent upon the heat of vaporization of the refrigerant liquid. The correct answer is $\boxed{A}$.

6. **Strategy and Solution** Steam is generally at a higher temperature than water and the specific heat of steam is lower than that of water, so water would be more effective than steam for changing steam to water. Circulating water brings more mass of water in contact with the condenser than stationary water, so it can carry away heat at a faster rate, therefore, it would be more effective for changing steam to water. The correct answer is $\boxed{D}$.

7. **Strategy and Solution** Since it is not possible to convert all of the input heat into output work, the amount of useful work that can be generated from a source of heat can only be less than the amount of heat. The correct answer is $\boxed{A}$.

8. **Strategy and Solution** The internal energy of the steam is converted into mechanical energy as it expands and moves the piston of the steam engine to the right, therefore, the correct answer is $\boxed{C}$.

9. **Strategy and Solution** The refrigerant must be able to vaporize (boil) at temperatures lower than the freezing point of water so that it can carry away heat (as a gas) from the contents of the refrigerator (which contain water) to cool and possibly freeze the contents. The correct answer is $\boxed{B}$.

10. **Strategy** The heat transferred to the water by the heaters was $Q_w = m_w c_w \Delta T_w$. The heat required for the oil is $Q_o = m_o c_o \Delta T_o$.

    Solution Form a proportion and use the temperature changes of the oil and water and the specific heat and the specific gravity of the oil to obtain a ratio of heat required for the oil to that transferred to the water.
    $$\frac{Q_o}{Q_w} = \frac{m_o c_o \Delta T_o}{m_w c_w \Delta T_w} = \frac{(0.7m_w)(0.60c_w)(60-20)}{m_w c_w (100-20)} = 0.21$$
    So, 21% of the amount of heat transferred to the water is required to heat the oil to 60°C. Assuming the heaters work at the same rate for both the water and the oil, the time required to raise the temperature of the oil from 20°C to 60°C is $0.21(15\text{ h}) = 3.2\text{ h}$. The correct answer is $\boxed{A}$.

11. **Strategy and Solution** The high pressure would increase the pressure on the plug, making it more difficult to lift. The pressure difference between the air in the tank and the air outside of the tank would increase the fluid velocity when the tank is drained, thus, decreasing the time required to drain the tank. The time required to heat the oil would be the least likely affected, since the oil is fairly incompressible. The correct answer is $\boxed{A}$.